ADDISON-WESLEY **MATHEMATICS 12**

Brendan Kelly
Professor of Mathematics
Faculty of Education
University of Toronto
Ontario

Bob Alexander
Formerly Assistant Co-ordinator of Mathematics
Toronto Board of Education
Toronto, Ontario

Paul Atkinson
Superintendent of Instruction
Waterloo County Board of Education
Kitchener, Ontario

Addison-Wesley Publishers Limited

Don Mills, Ontario
Reading, Massachusetts
Menlo Park, California
New York
Wokingham, England
Amsterdam • Bonn
Sydney • Singapore
Tokyo • Madrid
Bogotá • Santiago
San Juan

Design
John Zehethofer
Assembly and Technical Art
Frank Zsigo
Illustrative Art
Pronk & Associates
Editorial
Lesley Haynes
Photo Research
Ifi Zafiriadis
Typesetting
Q Composition
Printer
Friesen Printers

Photographic Credits

The publisher wishes to thank the following sources for photographs and other illustrative materials used in this book. We will gladly receive information enabling us to rectify any errors or references in credits.
Cover, Richard Simpson; 1, Metropolitan Police; 2, Allsport/Masterfile; 2, N. Serba/Miller Comstock Inc.; 2, Bob Alexander; 18, Bob Alexander; 22, Lesley Haynes; 29, J.A. Kraulis/Masterfile; 36, Masterfile; 39, Fraser Day Photography; 73, © Daily Telegraph/Masterfile; 74, Bob Alexander; 79, B. Brooks/Masterfile; 83, Toronto Blue Jays Baseball Club; 107, B. Brooks/Masterfile; 115, Miller Comstock Inc.; 134, Miller Comstock Inc., CP Photos; 173, Ministry Of Natural Resources; 188, J.A. Kraulis/Masterfile; 198, Miller Comstock Inc.; 203, Addison-Wesley Photo Library; 209, Addison-Wesley Photo Library; 210, N. Schmidt/Masterfile; 255, Swiss National Tourist Office; 260, D. Clemson/Miller Comstock Inc.; 271, Addison-Wesley Photo Library; 303, Nova-Scotia Power Corporation; 306, Roberts/Miller Comstock Inc.; 328, Addison-Wesley Photo Library; 332, Lambert/Miller Comstock Inc.; 339, Addison-Wesley Photo Library; 344 Palomar Observatory Photograph; 373; Roberts/Miller Comstock Inc.; 374, Bob Alexander; 381, University of Toronto; 425, Vincent Van Gogh Foundation/National Museum, Vincent Van Gogh, Amsterdam; 449, Roberts/Miller Comstock Inc.; 459, Canapress Photo Service; 486, Vera Lentz/Visions; 495, Addison-Wesley Photo Library; 509, Paul Atkinson; 510, © R. Kinne/Science Source/Masterfile; 512, Roberts/Miller Comstock Inc.; 515, Global Television Network; 518, J.A. Kraulis/Masterfile; 522, Allsport/Masterfile; 530, Ontario Department of Transportation and Communications; 536, Allsport/Masterfile; 546, A. McKim/Masterfile; 547, A. Smith/Masterfile; 548, Canapress Photo Service

Written, printed, and bound in Canada

ISBN 0-201-18606-3

G —FP— 97

Features of Mathematics 12

CONCEPT DEVELOPMENT

Mathematics 12 is carefully sequenced to develop concepts in mathematics. Concepts are explained with several examples, each of which has a detailed solution.

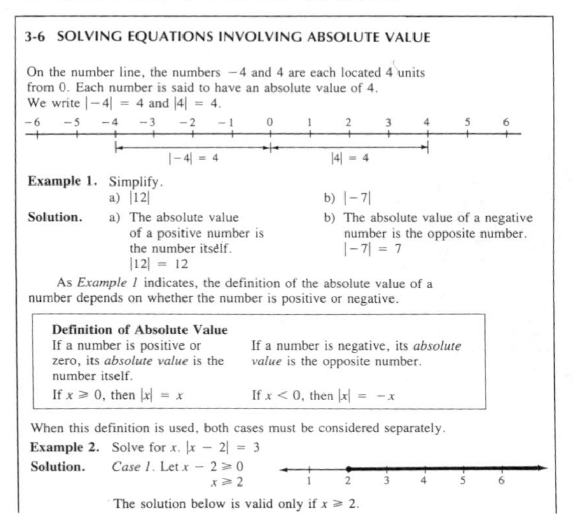

3-6 SOLVING EQUATIONS INVOLVING ABSOLUTE VALUE

On the number line, the numbers -4 and 4 are each located 4 units from 0. Each number is said to have an absolute value of 4.
We write $|-4| = 4$ and $|4| = 4$.

Example 1. Simplify.
a) $|12|$ b) $|-7|$

Solution. a) The absolute value of a positive number is the number itself.
$|12| = 12$
b) The absolute value of a negative number is the opposite number.
$|-7| = 7$

As *Example 1* indicates, the definition of the absolute value of a number depends on whether the number is positive or negative.

Definition of Absolute Value
If a number is positive or zero, its *absolute value* is the number itself.
If $x \geq 0$, then $|x| = x$
If a number is negative, its *absolute value* is the opposite number.
If $x < 0$, then $|x| = -x$

When this definition is used, both cases must be considered separately.

Example 2. Solve for x. $|x - 2| = 3$

Solution. *Case 1.* Let $x - 2 \geq 0$
$x \geq 2$

The solution below is valid only if $x \geq 2$.

REINFORCEMENT

An abundance of exercises is provided to reinforce skills and concepts. These exercises are graded by difficulty with an appropriate balance of A, B, and C exercises. The A exercises may sometimes be completed mentally and the answers given orally, or the questions may be discussed with the students. The B exercises are intended for the students to consolidate their learning of the concepts that were taught. The C exercises present a challenge and usually involve extensions of the concepts taught in that section.

Review Exercises and *Cumulative Reviews* provide additional practice. Answers to all questions are included in the text.

TECHNOLOGY

A contemporary mathematics program must reflect the impact of calculators and computers on society.

$\csc\theta = \frac{\text{hypotenuse}}{\text{opposite}}$ $\sec\theta = \frac{\text{hypotenuse}}{\text{adjacent}}$ $\cot\theta = \frac{\text{adjacent}}{\text{opposite}}$

It follows from these definitions that:

$\csc\theta = \frac{1}{\sin\theta}$ $\sec\theta = \frac{1}{\cos\theta}$ $\cot\theta = \frac{1}{\tan\theta}$.

Since we can readily compute the value of a reciprocal ratio by taking the reciprocal of a primary ratio, most scientific calculators have keys for only the primary trigonometric ratios. For example, to obtain csc 36° on a calculator, we find sin 36° and press the reciprocal key [1/x].

Example 1. Find the values of the six trigonometric ratios for 47°

Solution. Use a calculator.
For sin 47°, key in: 47 [sin] to display 0.7313537
For csc 47°, continue and key in: [1/x] to display 1.3673275
For cos 47°, key in: 47 [cos] to display 0.6819984
For sec 47°, continue and key in: [1/x] to display 1.4662792

Mathematics 12 assumes that students will use scientific calculators, as needed.

General keying sequences are given for scientific calculators where appropriate. Since different calculators have different keying sequences for the same computation, it is up to the students to familiarize themselves with their calculators.

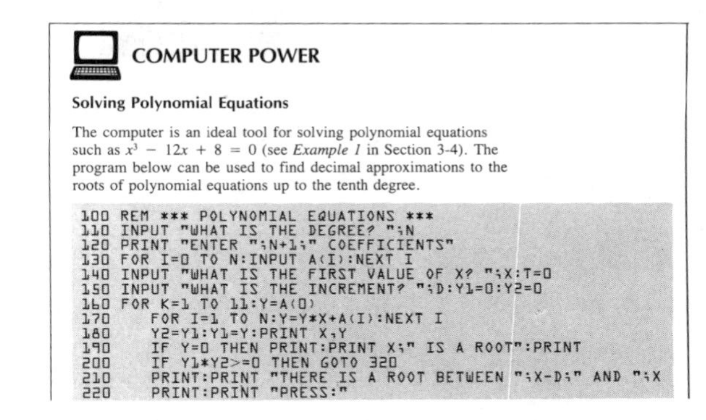

COMPUTER POWER

Solving Polynomial Equations

The computer is an ideal tool for solving polynomial equations such as $x^3 - 12x + 8 = 0$ (see *Example 1* in Section 3-4). The program below can be used to find decimal approximations to the roots of polynomial equations up to the tenth degree.

```
100 REM *** POLYNOMIAL EQUATIONS ***
110 INPUT "WHAT IS THE DEGREE? ";N
120 PRINT "ENTER ";N+1;" COEFFICIENTS"
130 FOR I=0 TO N:INPUT A(I):NEXT I
140 INPUT "WHAT IS THE FIRST VALUE OF X? ";X:T=0
150 INPUT "WHAT IS THE INCREMENT? ";D:Y1=0:Y2=0
160 FOR K=1 TO 11:Y=A(0)
170     FOR I=1 TO N:Y=Y*X+A(I):NEXT I
180     Y2=Y1:Y1=Y:PRINT X,Y
190     IF Y=0 THEN PRINT:PRINT X;" IS A ROOT":PRINT
200     IF Y1*Y2>=0 THEN GOTO 320
210     PRINT:PRINT "THERE IS A ROOT BETWEEN ";X-D;" AND ";X
220     PRINT:PRINT "PRESS:"
```

COMPUTER POWER features provide opportunities for students to explore mathematical problems using a computer. It is assumed that students know how to enter a program in BASIC, but is not necessary for them to understand the program.

APPLICATIONS OF MATHEMATICS

Students can better understand mathematical principles when they are related to their applications. For this reason, applications are integrated throughout *Mathematics 12*.

Every chapter begins with an applied problem that is solved as an example in the chapter.

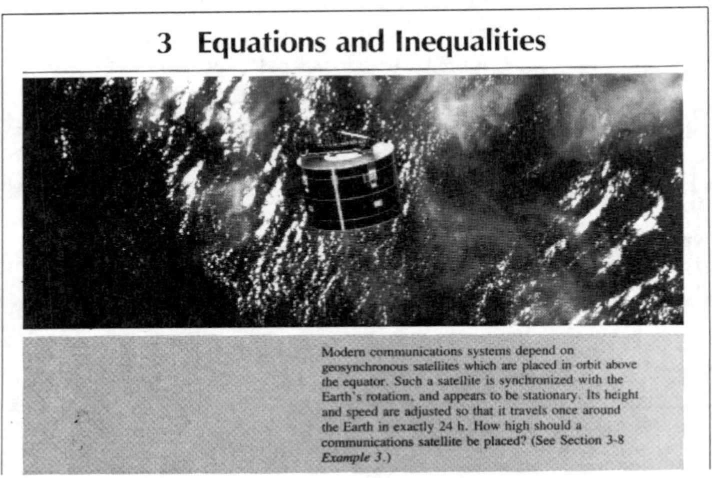

3 Equations and Inequalities

Modern communications systems depend on geosynchronous satellites which are placed in orbit above the equator. Such a satellite is synchronized with the Earth's rotation, and appears to be stationary. Its height and speed are adjusted so that it travels once around the Earth in exactly 24 h. How high should a communications satellite be placed? (See Section 3-8 *Example 3*.)

Many sections begin with an application which illustrates the necessity for the mathematics that follows.

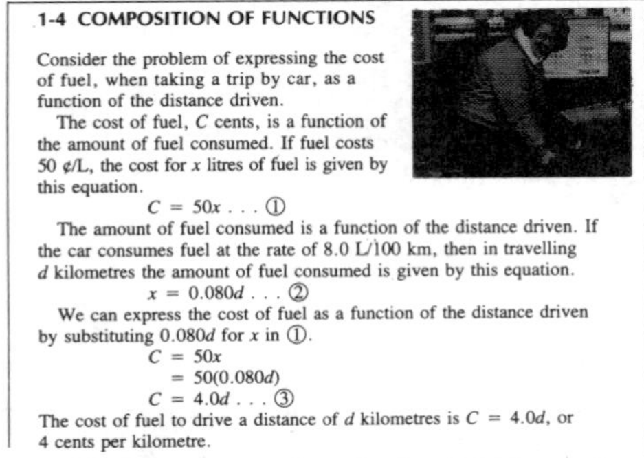

1-4 COMPOSITION OF FUNCTIONS

Consider the problem of expressing the cost of fuel, when taking a trip by car, as a function of the distance driven.

The cost of fuel, C cents, is a function of the amount of fuel consumed. If fuel costs 50 ¢/L, the cost for x litres of fuel is given by this equation.

$C = 50x \ldots ①$

The amount of fuel consumed is a function of the distance driven. If the car consumes fuel at the rate of 8.0 L/100 km, then in travelling d kilometres the amount of fuel consumed is given by this equation.

$x = 0.080d \ldots ②$

We can express the cost of fuel as a function of the distance driven by substituting $0.080d$ for x in ①.

$$\begin{aligned} C &= 50x \\ &= 50(0.080d) \\ C &= 4.0d \ldots ③ \end{aligned}$$

The cost of fuel to drive a distance of d kilometres is $C = 4.0d$, or 4 cents per kilometre.

Applications are also included throughout the exercises.

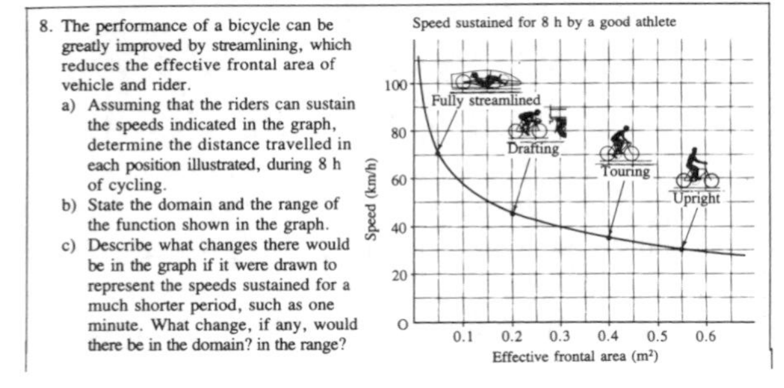

8. The performance of a bicycle can be greatly improved by streamlining, which reduces the effective frontal area of vehicle and rider.
   a) Assuming that the riders can sustain the speeds indicated in the graph, determine the distance travelled in each position illustrated, during 8 h of cycling.
   b) State the domain and the range of the function shown in the graph.
   c) Describe what changes there would be in the graph if it were drawn to represent the speeds sustained for a much shorter period, such as one minute. What change, if any, would there be in the domain? in the range?

PROBLEM SOLVING

Problem solving is integrated throughout the program in the text sections and special features.

Many of the exercises provide challenging problems for the students to solve.

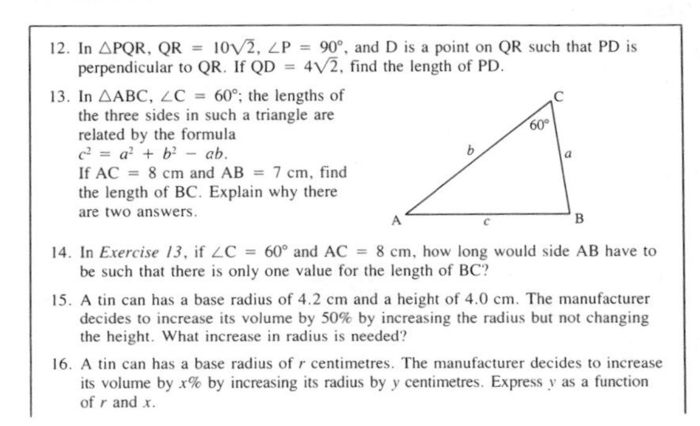

12. In $\triangle$PQR, QR = $10\sqrt{2}$, $\angle$P = 90°, and D is a point on QR such that PD is perpendicular to QR. If QD = $4\sqrt{2}$, find the length of PD.
13. In $\triangle$ABC, $\angle$C = 60°; the lengths of the three sides in such a triangle are related by the formula $c^2 = a^2 + b^2 - ab$. If AC = 8 cm and AB = 7 cm, find the length of BC. Explain why there are two answers.
14. In *Exercise 13*, if $\angle$C = 60° and AC = 8 cm, how long would side AB have to be such that there is only one value for the length of BC?
15. A tin can has a base radius of 4.2 cm and a height of 4.0 cm. The manufacturer decides to increase its volume by 50% by increasing the radius but not changing the height. What increase in radius is needed?
16. A tin can has a base radius of r centimetres. The manufacturer decides to increase its volume by x% by increasing its radius by y centimetres. Express y as a function of r and x.

Frequent *INVESTIGATE* features are starting points for mathematical investigations to help the students develop analytic skills. These features always relate to the concepts that are developed in the sections in which they occur.

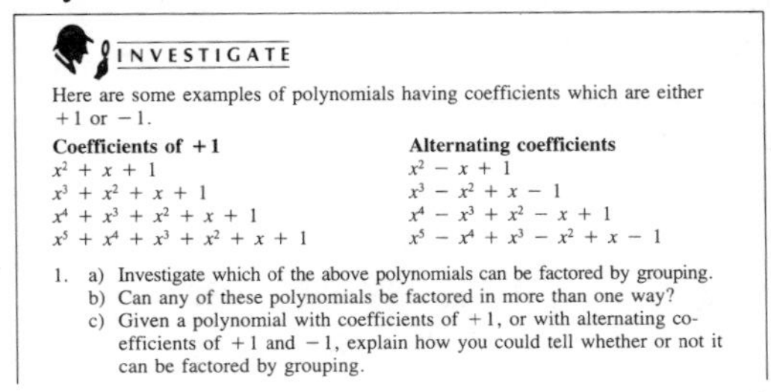

INVESTIGATE

Here are some examples of polynomials having coefficients which are either +1 or −1.

Coefficients of +1	Alternating coefficients
$x^2 + x + 1$	$x^2 - x + 1$
$x^3 + x^2 + x + 1$	$x^3 - x^2 + x - 1$
$x^4 + x^3 + x^2 + x + 1$	$x^4 - x^3 + x^2 - x + 1$
$x^5 + x^4 + x^3 + x^2 + x + 1$	$x^5 - x^4 + x^3 - x^2 + x - 1$

1. a) Investigate which of the above polynomials can be factored by grouping.
   b) Can any of these polynomials be factored in more than one way?
   c) Given a polynomial with coefficients of +1, or with alternating coefficients of +1 and −1, explain how you could tell whether or not it can be factored by grouping.

The *MATHEMATICS PROJECT* features are longer investigations which challenge students and extend mathematical concepts.

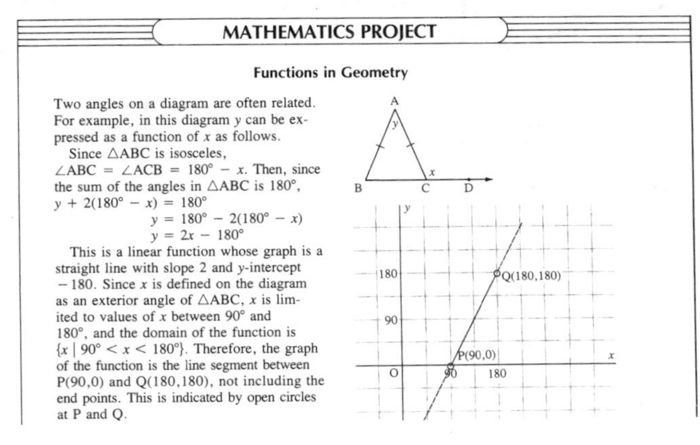

MATHEMATICS PROJECT

Functions in Geometry

Two angles on a diagram are often related. For example, in this diagram y can be expressed as a function of x as follows.

Since $\triangle$ABC is isosceles, $\angle$ABC = $\angle$ACB = 180° − x. Then, since the sum of the angles in $\triangle$ABC is 180°,

$$y + 2(180° - x) = 180°$$
$$y = 180° - 2(180° - x)$$
$$y = 2x - 180°$$

This is a linear function whose graph is a straight line with slope 2 and y-intercept −180. Since x is defined on the diagram as an exterior angle of $\triangle$ABC, x is limited to values of x between 90° and 180°, and the domain of the function is $\{x \mid 90° < x < 180°\}$. Therefore, the graph of the function is the line segment between P(90,0) and Q(180,180), not including the end points. This is indicated by open circles at P and Q.

The *MATHEMATICS AROUND US* features outline applications of mathematics in the sciences, the arts, business, and industry.

MATHEMATICS AROUND US

The Waggle Dance of Honeybees

In 1973, Karl von Frisch received a Nobel Prize for his research in animal behaviour. One of his discoveries concerns a method used by honeybees to communicate the location of a food source to other bees inside a hive. Von Frisch observed bees returning to the hive when they had discovered a food source. Shortly after a bee returned, hundreds of bees left the hive, and went directly to the food source, although the bee which had found the food remained inside the hive. Somehow, the bee had informed the others where the food was located.

By marking the bees with paint, and using glass-walled hives, von Frisch learned how they do this. The bee which found the food performs a dance on the honeycomb inside the hive. It follows a figure-8 pattern and wags its body in the central part. Von Frisch observed that:

- the orientation of the central portion indicates the direction of the food source,
- the speed of the dance indicates the distance to the food.

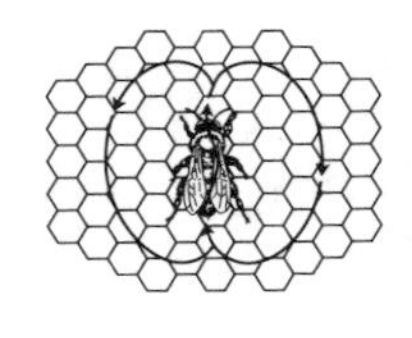

Von Frisch made thousands of observations, comparing the speeds of the bees' dances with the distances to the food, and summarized his results on a graph like the one shown.

Honeybees' Waggle Dance

15 s

THE MATHEMATICAL MIND features offer insights into the work of mathematicians and the historical development of mathematics. Anecdotes of human interest that are part of history are included. In this feature, problems related to the topic are presented for the student to solve.

THE MATHEMATICAL MIND

The Origin of the Function Concept

The concept of a function originated in the seventeenth century, when scientists and mathematicians became interested in the study of motion.

- Galileo showed that the path of a projectile fired into the air is a parabola.

- The moon's motion was studied because knowledge of its position was used to determine longitude at sea.

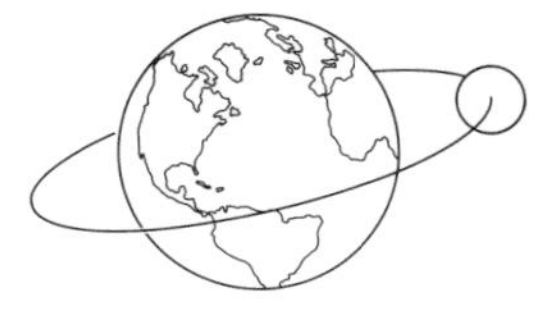

Since moving objects follow a single line or a curve, mathematicians thought that a function was defined by a single equation.

Leonhard Euler 1707–1783

As late as 1734, Leonhard Euler defined a function as any expression formed in any manner from a variable quantity and constants. He also introduced the $f(x)$ notation.

By 1750, scientists studying vibrating strings had encountered an example of a function that could not be defined by a single equation. This caused a controversy over the question of what a function was. Euler extended the definition to include cases where there were different expressions in different intervals of the domain. For example, Euler would have considered the following expression to be a single function.

$$f(x) = \begin{cases} x + 6, & \text{if } x \leq -2 \\ x^2, & \text{if } -2 \leq x \leq 2 \\ x + 2, & \text{if } x \geq 2 \end{cases}$$

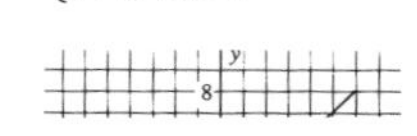

Contents

1 Functions

The distance a car travels after the driver decides to stop consists of two parts. The *reaction-time distance* is the distance the car travels before the brakes are applied. The *braking distance* is the distance the car travels after the brakes are applied. Suppose you have a graph which shows the stopping distance for cars at different speeds, and another graph which shows the reaction-time distance at different speeds. How could you draw a graph which shows the braking distance at different speeds? (See Section 1-6 *Example* 2.)

1-1 FUNCTIONS

In everyday language, we use the word "function" to express the idea that one thing depends on another.

The time to complete the course is a function of the skipper's skill.

The time of free fall is a function of the plane's altitude.

The number appearing on the tape counter of a videocassette recorder is a function of the time of playing. The operator's manual for one machine contains the following table. Both the table and the graph show how the counter number is related to the playing time.

Time (h)	Counter Number
0	0
1	2250
2	3182
3	3897
4	4500
5	5031
6	5511

Graph of counter number against playing time

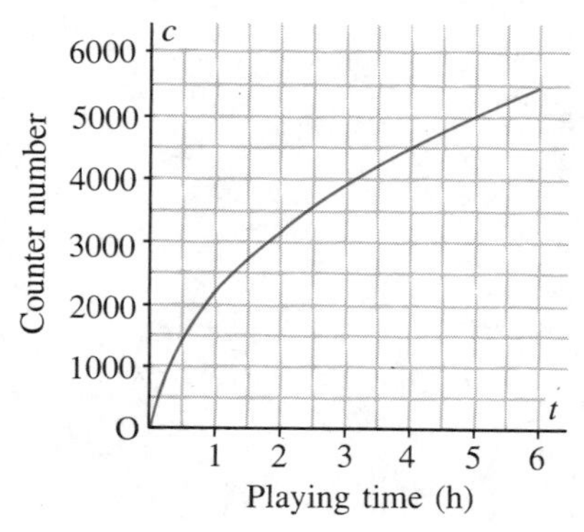

The relation between the counter number and the playing time in hours can be expressed as a set of ordered pairs.

{(0,0), (1,2250), (2,3182), (3,3897), (4,4500), (5,5031), (6,5511)}

This relation can also be expressed with an equation. The equation relating the counter number c with the playing time t hours, is $c = 2250\sqrt{t}$. You can verify that this equation is correct by substituting values for t from the table and using a calculator to calculate the values for c.

On the graph, a smooth curve was drawn through the plotted points. This curve represents the times and the corresponding counter numbers between those given. It is impossible to include all the points in the table of values or the set of ordered pairs because there are infinitely many of them. We can represent these points in a set, using a notation called *set-builder notation*, as follows.

$$\{(x,y) \mid y = 2250\sqrt{x},\ 0 \leqslant x \leqslant 6,\ x \in R\}$$

The set of . . . all ordered pairs (x,y) . . . such that . . . $y = 2250\sqrt{x}$ where x is between 0 and 6 . . . and x is a real number.

Since there cannot be two different counter numbers for the same playing time, this set of ordered pairs has a special property. No two ordered pairs have the same first coordinate. A set of ordered pairs with this property is called a function.

> A *function* is a set of ordered pairs in which no two ordered pairs have the same first coordinate.

A function can be represented in different ways. The requirement that the ordered pairs must have different first coordinates can be seen in each.

- A table of values

x	y
0	0
1	2250
2	3182
3	3897
4	4500
5	5031
6	5511

All the entries in the first column are different.

- A graph

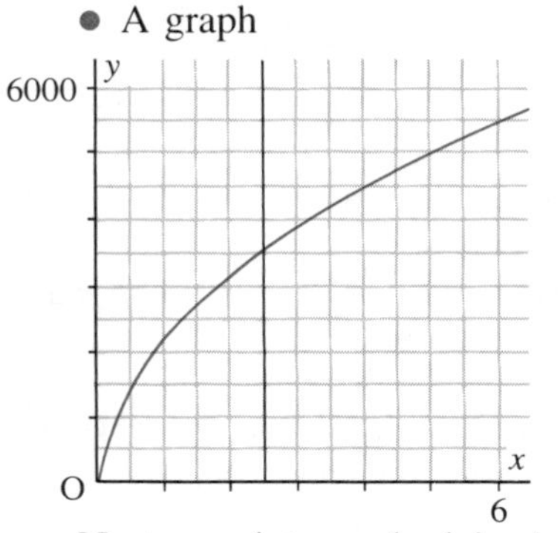

No two points can be joined by a vertical line.

- An equation

$$y = 2250\sqrt{x}$$

For any value of x, there is only one value of y.

> **Tests for a Function** (Either of these tests is sufficient.)
>
> *Vertical-Line Test.* If no two points on a graph can be joined by a vertical line, then the graph represents a function.
>
> *Equation Test.* If a value of x can be found which produces more than one value of y when substituted in an equation, then the equation *does not* represent a function. If there is no such value of x, then the equation *does* represent a function.

Example 1. Given the equations $y = (x - 2)^2$ and $y^2 = x$

a) Graph the equations and use the graphs to determine which represents a function.

b) Use the equations to determine which represents a function.

Solution. a) $y = (x - 2)^2$

x	y
−1	9
0	4
1	1
2	0
3	1
4	4
5	9

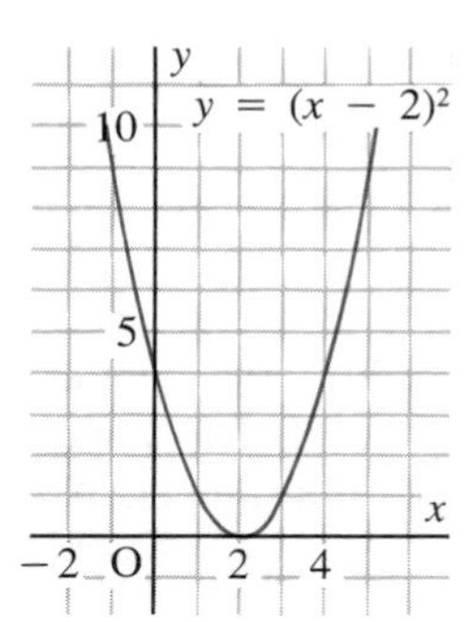

$y^2 = x$

x	y
0	0
1	±1
4	±2
9	±3

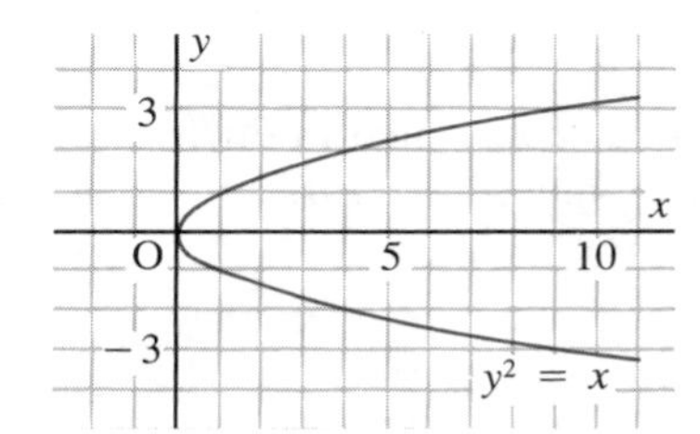

The vertical-line test shows that $y = (x - 2)^2$ is a function, and that $y^2 = x$ is not a function.

b) For the equation $y = (x - 2)^2$, only one value of y can be calculated for any value of x. Therefore, $y = (x - 2)^2$ is a function.
For the equation $y^2 = x$, there are values of x for which more than one value of y can be calculated; for example, when $x = 4$, $y = 2$ or $y = -2$. Since there is more than one value of y when $x = 4$, $y^2 = x$ is not a function.

Example 2. Determine which equations define functions.

a) $x^2 + y^2 = 10$ b) $y = 2^x$ c) $y = \dfrac{x}{x^2 - 1}$

Solution. a) $x^2 + y^2 = 10$

When $x = 0$, $y^2 = 10$

$$y = \pm\sqrt{10}$$

Since there are two values of y when $x = 0$, $x^2 + y^2 = 10$ is not a function.

b) For the equation $y = 2^x$, only one value of y can be calculated for any value of x. Therefore, $y = 2^x$ is a function.

c) The expression $\frac{x}{x^2 - 1}$ is not defined when $x = 1$ or when $x = -1$. For any other value of x, there is only one value of y. Therefore, there is no value of x which produces more than one value of y when substituted in the equation. Therefore, $y = \frac{x}{x^2 - 1}$ defines a function if $x \neq 1$ or $x \neq -1$.

Consider again the example of the tape counter on a videocassette recorder, discussed earlier.

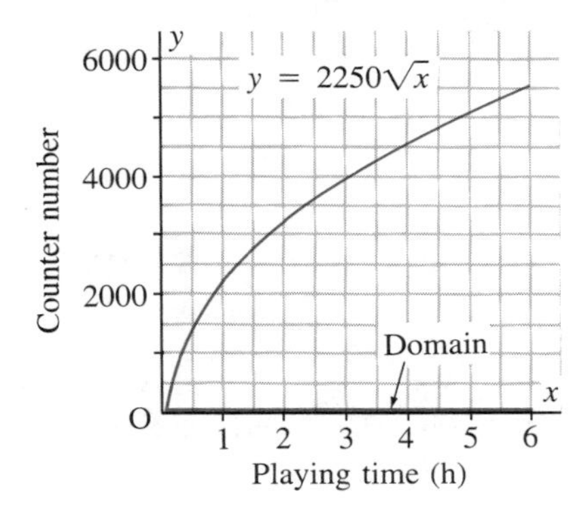

The set of first coordinates is $\{x \mid 0 \leq x \leq 6, x \in R\}$.
This is the set of possible playing times in hours, and is called the domain of the function.

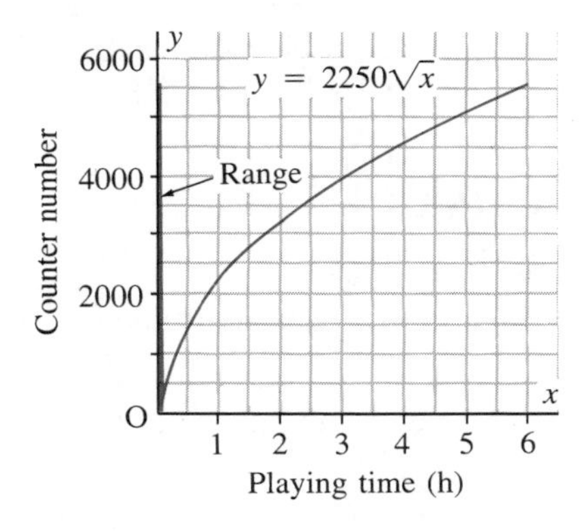

The set of second coordinates is $\{y \mid 0 \leq y \leq 5511, y \in R\}$.
This is the set of counter numbers (for playing times up to 6 h), and is called the range of the function.

Given the *graph* of a function

The *domain* is the set of x-values represented by the graph.

The *range* is the set of y-values represented by the graph.

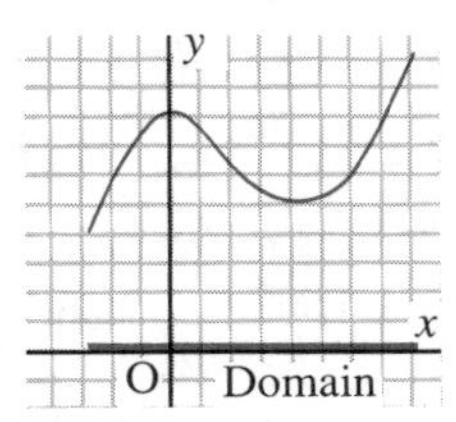

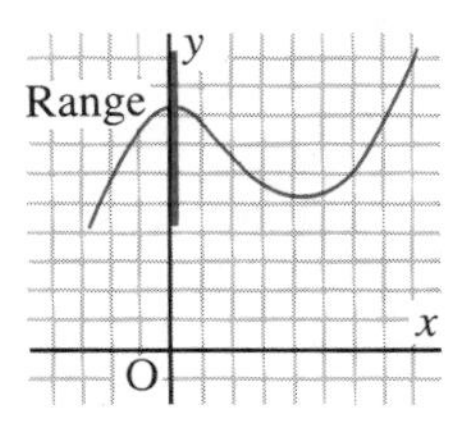

Given the *equation* of a function

The *domain* is the set of all values of x for which the equation is defined.

The *range* is the set of all values of y which are defined for values of x in the domain.

Example 3. Find the domain and the range of the function $y = \sqrt{x^2 - 1}$.

Solution. Since square roots of negative numbers are not real numbers,

$$x^2 - 1 \geqslant 0$$
$$x^2 \geqslant 1$$
$$x \geqslant 1 \text{ or } x \leqslant -1$$

The domain is the set of all real numbers greater than or equal to 1, or less than or equal to -1. In set-builder notation, the domain is $\{x \mid x \geqslant 1 \text{ or } x \leqslant -1, x \in \mathrm{R}\}$.

Since the radical sign indicates a positive square root, the expression $\sqrt{x^2 - 1}$ is never negative. That is, $y \geqslant 0$. Therefore, the range is the set of all non-negative real numbers. In set-builder notation, the range is $\{y \mid y \geqslant 0, y \in \mathrm{R}\}$.

EXERCISES 1-1

Ⓐ

1. Which graphs represent functions?

a)

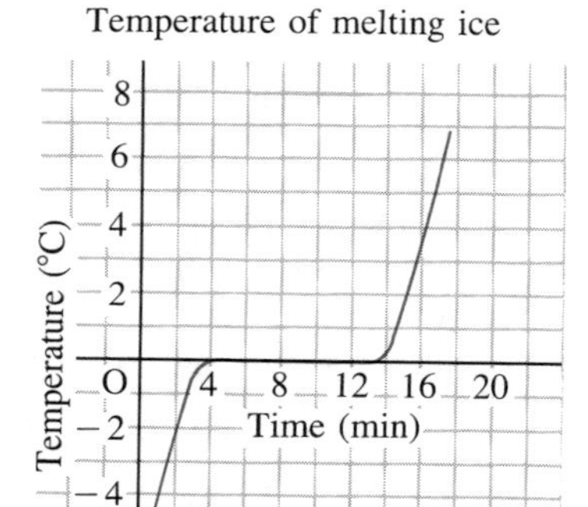

b)

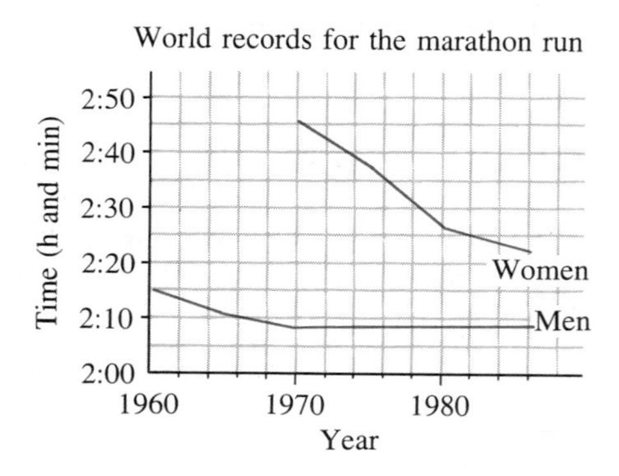

2. State the domain and the range for each function.

a)

Value of
Canadian dollar in U.S. cents
Value (U.S. ¢)
80
78
76
74
M A M J J A S O
Months in 1984

b)

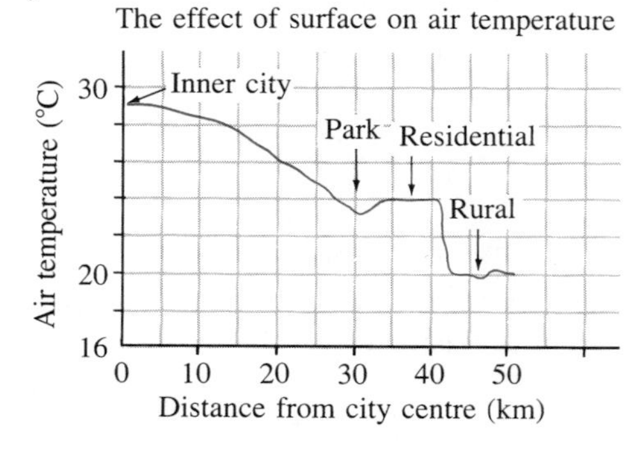

3. Determine if each graph represents a function.

a)

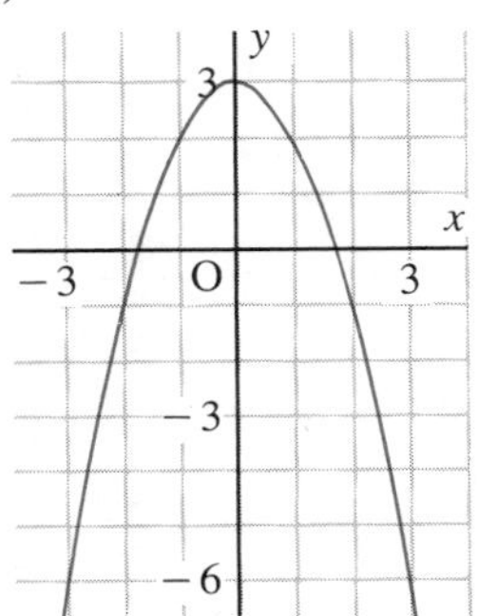

b)

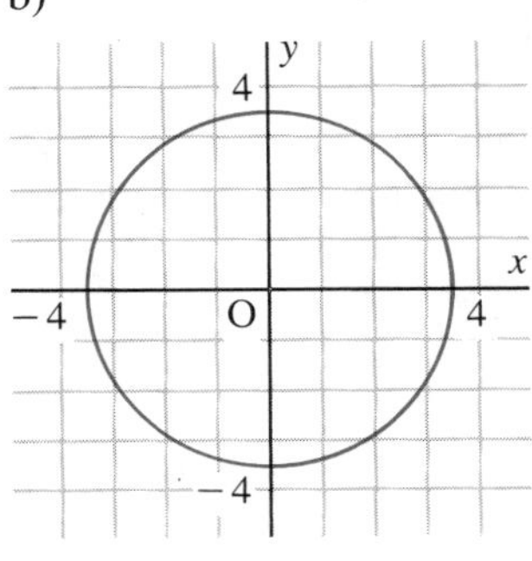

c)

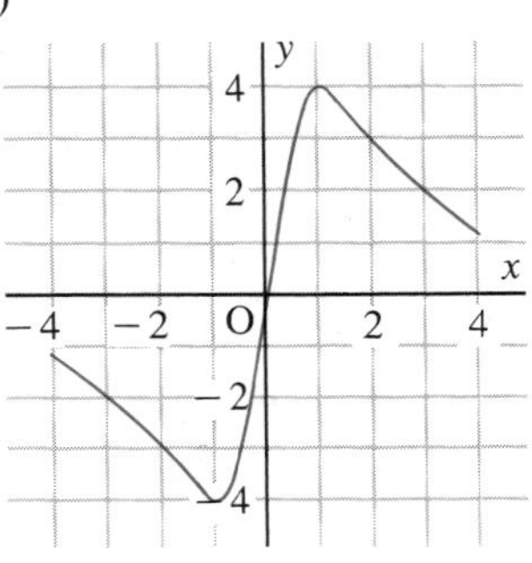

B

4. Determine if each equation represents a function. If it does, state the domain and the range.
   a) $y = 2x - 4$ b) $y = x^2$ c) $y = \sqrt{x + 1}$
   d) $y^2 = x$ e) $y = 10^x$ f) $x^2 - y^2 = 4$

5. State the domain and the range for each function.
   a) $y = 2 - 3x$ b) $y = x^3$ c) $y = \sqrt{1 - x}$
   d) $y = \frac{1}{x}$ e) $y = \frac{1}{x^2 - 1}$ f) $y = \frac{x^2}{x^2 - 4}$

6. Graph each function.
   a) $y = 2x + 3$ b) $y = 5 - 2x$ c) $y = x^2$
   d) $y = (x + 2)^2$ e) $y = \sqrt{x}$ f) $y = \sqrt{x + 3}$

7. Air pressure is a function of altitude.
   a) Use the graph to find the air pressure at each location.

	Location	Altitude (m)
i)	Sea level	0
ii)	Banff, Alberta	1 383
iii)	Mexico City	2 240
iv)	Peak of Mount Everest	8 848
v)	Jet liner	12 000

   b) At what altitude is the air pressure 50% of the pressure at sea level?
   c) State the domain and the range of the function, as graphed.

Pressure variations with altitude

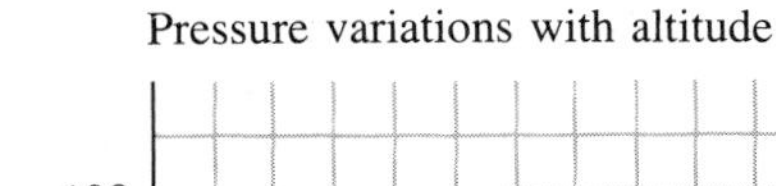

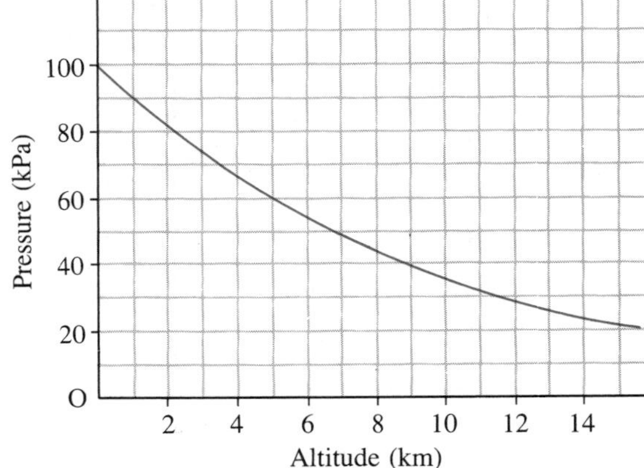

8. The performance of a bicycle can be greatly improved by streamlining, which reduces the effective frontal area of vehicle and rider.
   a) Assuming that the riders can sustain the speeds indicated in the graph, determine the distance travelled in each position illustrated, during 8 h of cycling.
   b) State the domain and the range of the function shown in the graph.
   c) Describe what changes there would be in the graph if it were drawn to represent the speeds sustained for a much shorter period, such as one minute. What change, if any, would there be in the domain? in the range?

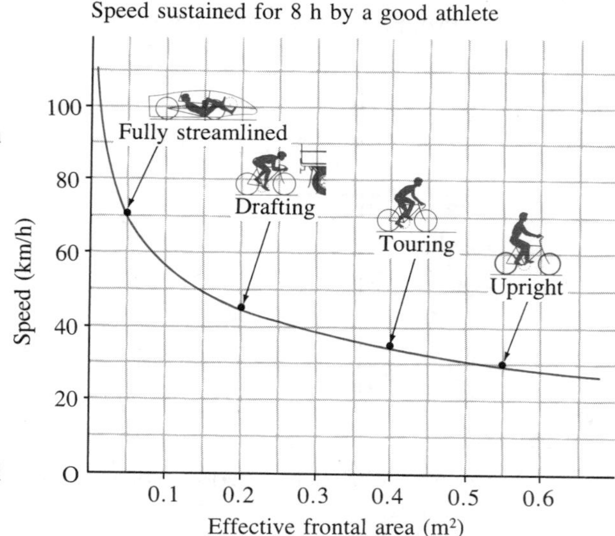

9. Graph each function.
   a) $y = 3x - 5$
   b) $y = (x + 3)^2$
   c) $y = \sqrt{2x - 4}$
   d) $y = \frac{1}{x}$
   e) $y = \frac{5}{x^2 + 1}$
   f) $y = \frac{5x}{x^2 + 1}$

(C)

10. High-speed photographs have shown that the hand of a karate expert can reach speeds of 12 m/s or greater during certain karate manoeuvres.
    a) For each graph shown
       i) Find the speed of the hand after 0.05 s; after 0.10 s.
       ii) Find the hand's greatest speed.
    b) What happens to the speed of the hand during the forward karate punch between 0.12 s and 0.14 s? Why does this not happen during the hammer-fist strike?

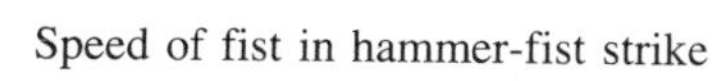

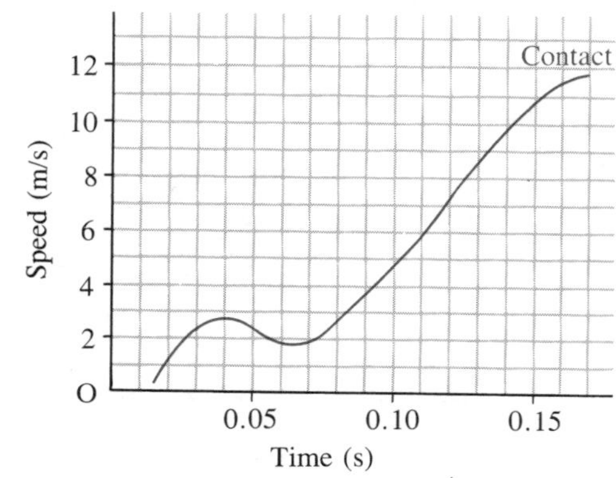

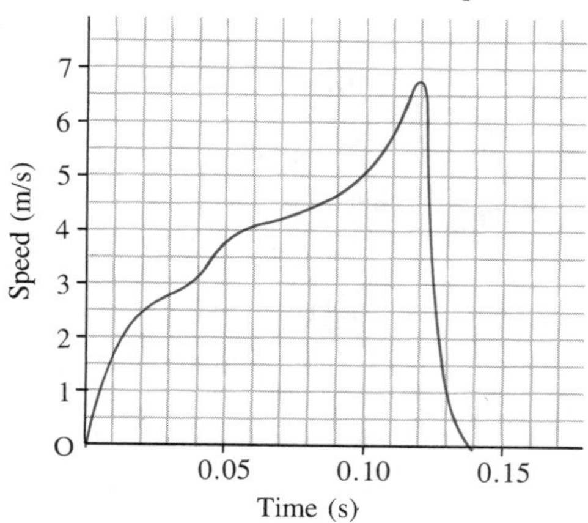

1-2 FUNCTION NOTATION

In the preceding section we saw that a function can be represented by a set of ordered pairs, a table of values, a graph, and an equation. A function can also be represented using a special notation, called *function notation*. For example, we may write:
$f(x) = 5x^2 - 6x + 1$. We say, "f of x equals $5x^2 - 6x + 1$."
This notation simplifies recording the values of the function for several values of x. For example, $f(-3)$ is the value of $f(x)$ when we substitute -3 for x everywhere x occurs in the expression.

$$f(x) = 5x^2 - 6x + 1$$

$$\begin{aligned} f(-3) &= 5(-3)^2 - 6(-3) + 1 \\ &= 45 + 18 + 1 \\ &= 64 \end{aligned}$$

Example 1. If $f(x) = 3x + \frac{1}{x}$, find:

a) $f(2)$

b) $f\left(-\frac{1}{2}\right)$

Solution. a) Substitute 2 for x.

$$\begin{aligned} f(x) &= 3x + \frac{1}{x} \\ f(2) &= 3(2) + \frac{1}{2} \\ &= 6.5 \end{aligned}$$

b) Substitute $-\frac{1}{2}$ for x.

$$\begin{aligned} f(x) &= 3x + \frac{1}{x} \\ f\left(-\frac{1}{2}\right) &= 3\left(-\frac{1}{2}\right) + \frac{1}{-\frac{1}{2}} \\ &= -1.5 - 2 \\ &= -3.5 \end{aligned}$$

Algebraic expressions may be substituted for variables in the equation of a function.

Example 2. If $g(x) = \frac{x - 3}{x}$, $x \neq 0$, find:

a) $g(1 - 2x)$

b) $g\left(\frac{5}{y}\right)$

Solution. a) $g(x) = \frac{x - 3}{x}$

Substitute $1 - 2x$ for x.

$$\begin{aligned} g(1 - 2x) &= \frac{(1 - 2x) - 3}{1 - 2x} \\ &= \frac{-2 - 2x}{1 - 2x} \\ &= \frac{2x + 2}{2x - 1}, x \neq \frac{1}{2} \end{aligned}$$

b) $g(x) = \frac{x - 3}{x}$

Substitute $\frac{5}{y}$ for x.

$$\begin{aligned} g\left(\frac{5}{y}\right) &= \frac{\frac{5}{y} - 3}{\frac{5}{y}} \times \frac{y}{y} \\ &= \frac{5 - 3y}{5}, y \neq 0 \end{aligned}$$

Function notation can be used even when an equation relating the variables is not given.

Example 3. From the graph of $y = f(x)$, find:
a) $f(1)$ b) $f(-2)$ c) $f(5)$ d) $f(0)$.

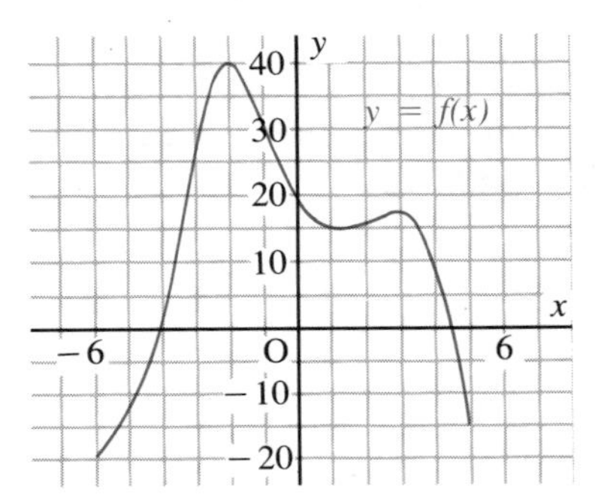

Solution. a) $f(1)$ is the value of y when $x = 1$. To find this value, draw a vertical line, $x = 1$, to intersect the graph. Then, draw a horizontal line to intersect the y-axis.
$f(1)$ appears to be 15.
b) $f(-2)$ appears to be 40.
c) $f(5)$ appears to be -15.
d) $f(0)$ appears to be 20.

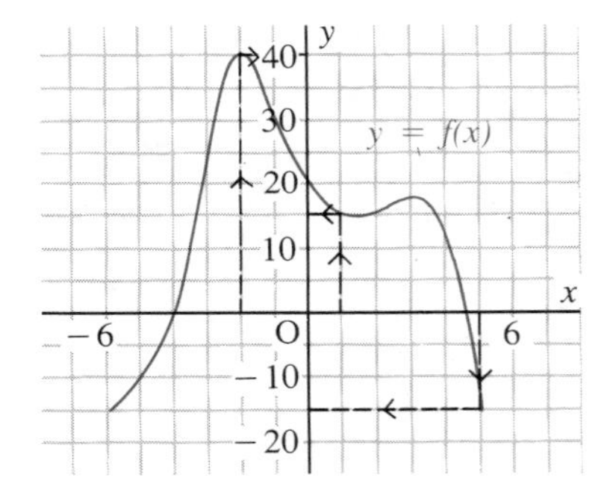

Example 4. Let n be a natural number, and let $f(n)$ represent the number of factors of n.
a) Find $f(5)$, $f(6)$, and $f(9)$.
b) Draw the graph of $y = f(n)$ for values of n from 1 to 12.

Solution. a) The factors of 5 are 1 and 5.
Since there are two factors, $f(5) = 2$.
The factors of 6 are 1, 2, 3, and 6.
Since there are four factors, $f(6) = 4$.
The factors of 9 are 1, 3, and 9.
Since there are three factors, $f(9) = 3$.
b) Make a table of values and draw the graph.

n	1	2	3	4	5	6	7	8	9	10	11	12
$f(n)$	1	2	2	3	2	4	2	4	3	4	2	6

Factors of natural numbers

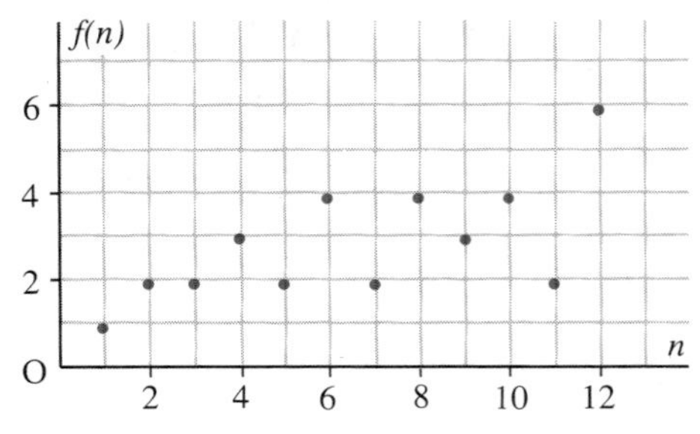

EXERCISES 1-2

Ⓐ

1. If $f(x) = x^2 + 3$, find:
   a) $f(1)$ b) $f(2)$ c) $f(0)$ d) $f(-1)$ e) $f(-2)$ f) $f(-3)$.

2. If $g(x) = 1 - 2x$, find:
   a) $g(1)$ b) $g(-2)$ c) $g(-5)$ d) $g(0)$ e) $g(6)$ f) $g\left(-\frac{1}{2}\right)$.

3. Find $f(-3)$, $f(4)$, and $f(-0.5)$ for each function.
   a) $f(x) = 5x - 2$ b) $f(x) = x^2 - 5$ c) $f(x) = x^2 + x$

4. For each graph of $y = f(x)$, find $f(-4)$, $f(0)$, and $f(6)$.
   a)

b)

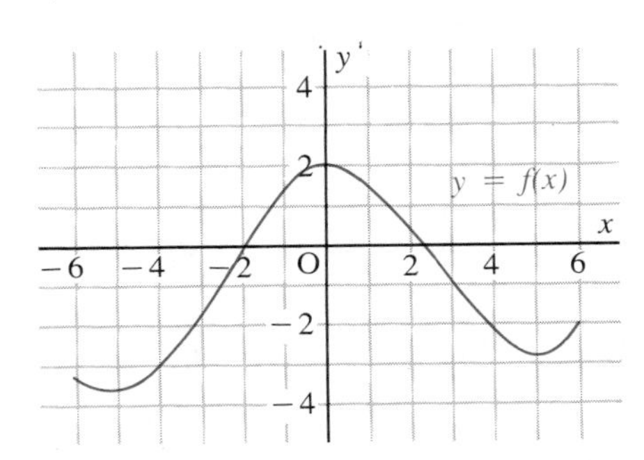

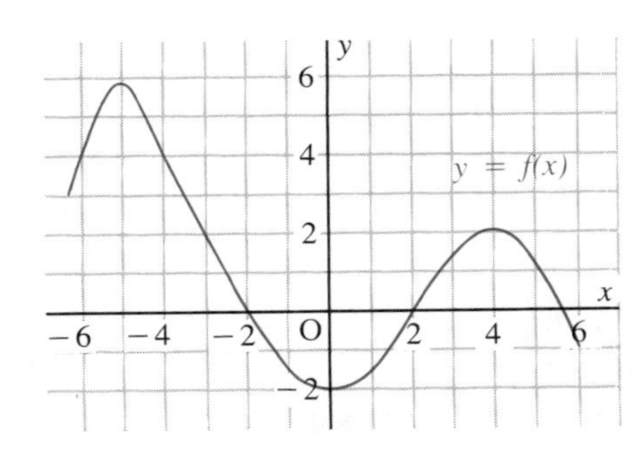

5. If $f(x) = 3x^2 - 5x + 2$, find:
   a) $f(4)$ b) $f(-2)$ c) $f(1)$ d) $f(-1)$ e) $f(0)$ f) $f(1.5)$.

6. If $g(x) = -2x^2 + 3x - 6$, find:
   a) $g(1)$ b) $g(2)$ c) $g(-2)$ d) $g(0)$ e) $g(-4)$ f) $g(-0.5)$.

Ⓑ

7. Let n be a positive integer, and let $d(n)$ represent the number of digits of n. For example, $d(15) = 2$, since 15 has 2 digits.
   a) Find. i) $d(6)$ ii) $d(47)$ iii) $d(803)$
   b) How many positive integers n are there such that:
      i) $d(n) = 1$ ii) $d(n) = 2$ iii) $d(n) = 3$?

8. If $f(x) = 2x + 1$, and $g(x) = 3 - x$, find:
   a) $f(a)$ b) $f(3a)$ c) $f(1 + y)$ d) $f(x + 1)$
   e) $g(y)$ f) $g(2 - y)$ g) $g(z - 1)$ h) $g(2x - 3)$
   i) $2f(x)$ j) $5g(n)$ k) $-3f(x)$ l) $-2g(a)$.

9. Graph each function and state its domain and range.
   a) $f(x) = 2x + 1$ b) $f(x) = x^2$ c) $f(x) = \sqrt{x}$

10. If $f(x) = 2 - 5x$, and $g(x) = x^2 - x - 1$, evaluate each expression.
    a) $f(1) + g(1)$ b) $f(2) + g(2)$ c) $f(-1) + g(-1)$
    d) $f(-1) - g(-1)$ e) $f(-3) - g(-3)$ f) $f(0) - g(0)$

11. If $g(x) = \frac{x+1}{x-1}$, $x \neq 1$, find:

a) $g(2x)$ b) $g(-x)$ c) $-g(x)$ d) $g\left(\frac{1}{x}\right)$

e) $g(x+1)$ f) $-g(x-1)$ g) $g(2x+1)$ h) $g(1-2x)$.

12. If $f(x) = 2x - 3$, and $g(x) = 1 - 4x$, find a value of x that satisfies each equation.
a) $f(x) = g(x)$ b) $f(x) = g(-x)$ c) $f(-x) = g(x)$
d) $f(x+1) = g(x-1)$ e) $f(2x-1) = g(x+1)$

13. If $f(x) = 3x - 5$, solve each equation.
a) $f(x) = 0$ b) $f(x) = 1$ c) $f(x) = -4$
d) $f(x) = f(-x)$ e) $f(x+1) = f(x-1)$

14. Let n be a positive integer, and let $s(n)$ represent the sum of the digits of n.
a) Find. i) $s(15)$ ii) $s(68)$ iii) $s(509)$
b) Give examples of positive integers n such that: i) $s(n) = 1$ ii) $s(n) = 2$.
c) How many solutions do these equations have?
i) $s(n) = 1$ ii) $s(n) = 2$

Ⓒ

15. If $f(x) = 1 + \frac{1}{x}$, prove that $f(x) + f\left(\frac{1}{x}\right) = f(x)f\left(\frac{1}{x}\right)$.

16. Let n be a positive integer, and let $f(n)$ represent the number of different prime factors of n.
a) Find. i) $f(1)$ ii) $f(6)$ iii) $f(9)$ iv) $f(20)$
b) What is the least number n such that: i) $f(n) = 3$ ii) $f(n) = 4$?

17. Let n be a natural number, and let $g(n)$ be the largest factor of n, other than n.
a) Explain why $g(n) \leqslant \frac{1}{2}n$ for all values of n.
b) Give an example of a natural number n such that:
i) $g(n) = \frac{1}{2}n$ ii) $g(n) < \frac{1}{2}n$.

18. $f(x)$ is a function with the following properties.
- The domain of $f(x)$ is the set of real numbers.
- $f(0) = 0$
- $f(x+1) = f(x) + 2x + 1$ for all real values of x

a) Find. i) $f(1), f(2), f(3), f(4)$
ii) $f(-1), f(-2), f(-3), f(-4)$
b) Describe the function $f(x)$.

19. Given $f(x) = 2^x$, show that:
a) $f(x)f(y) = f(x+y)$ b) $f(nx) = [f(x)]^n$, where $n \in \mathrm{N}$.

20. In *Exercise 19*, find another example of a function $f(x)$ such that $f(x)f(y) = f(x+y)$ and $f(nx) = [f(x)]^n$, $n \in \mathrm{N}$.

1-3 FUNCTIONS AS MAPPINGS

In the first section of this chapter we showed how the counter number on a videocassette recorder is a function of the playing time. The graph is reproduced here with arrows showing how it is read. The arrows suggest other ways to represent the relation between the variables.

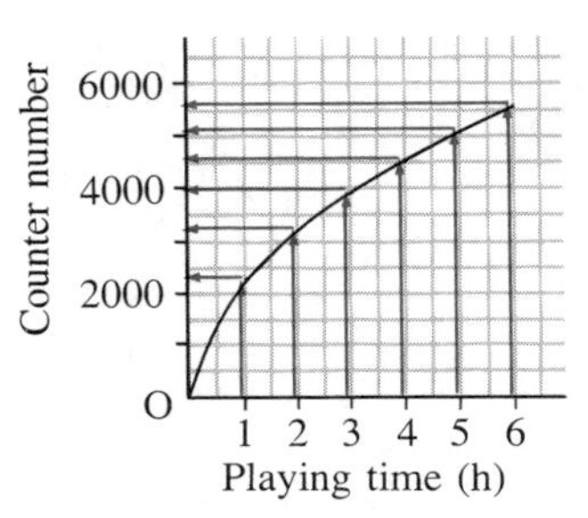

Counter number against playing time

Plotted points omitted

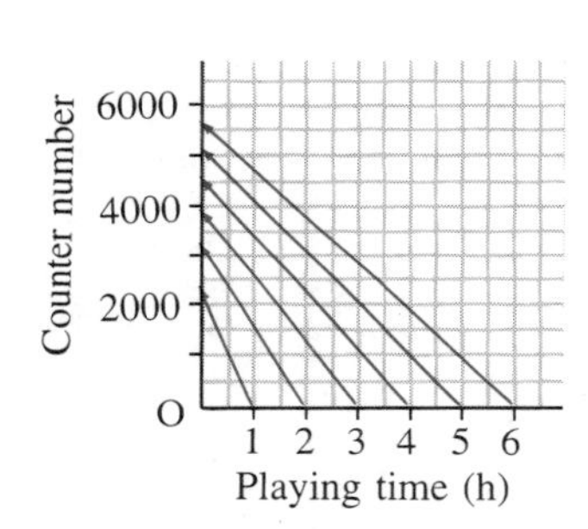

Points matched on parallel lines

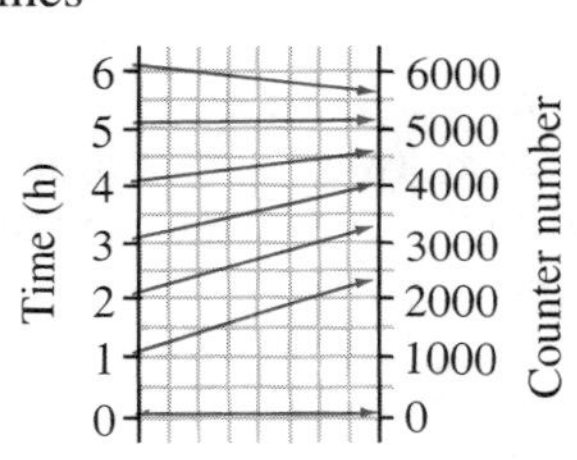

Points matched in sets

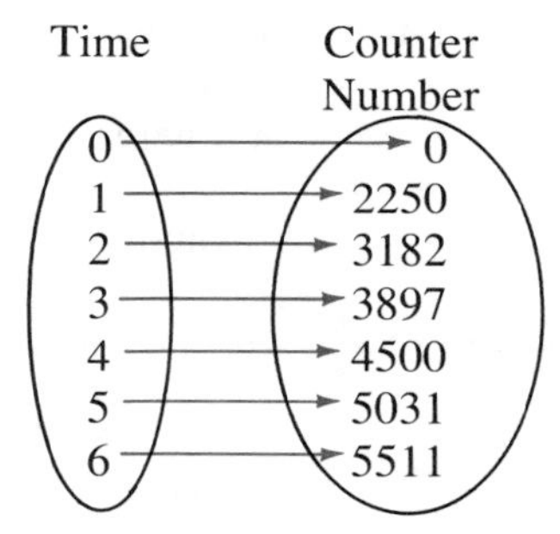

A graph that relates numbers in one set to numbers in another set by means of arrows is called a *mapping diagram*. The relation is referred to as a *mapping*.

Example 1. Graph each function on a mapping diagram.
a) $f(x) = 3x - 1$ b) $g(x) = x^2$

Solution. Substitute values of x, such as integers between -3 and 3 inclusive, and find the corresponding values of each function.

a)

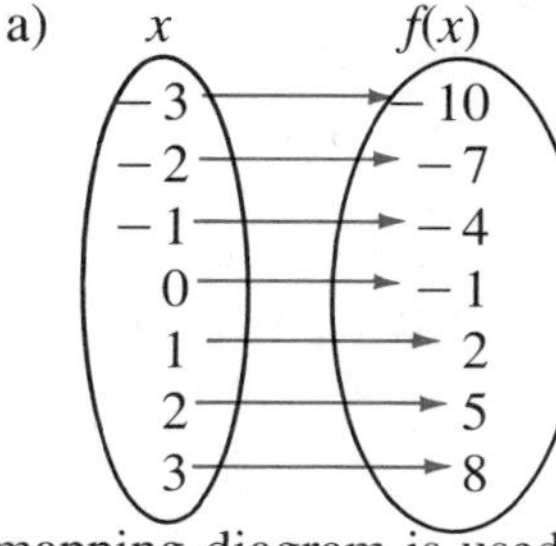

b)

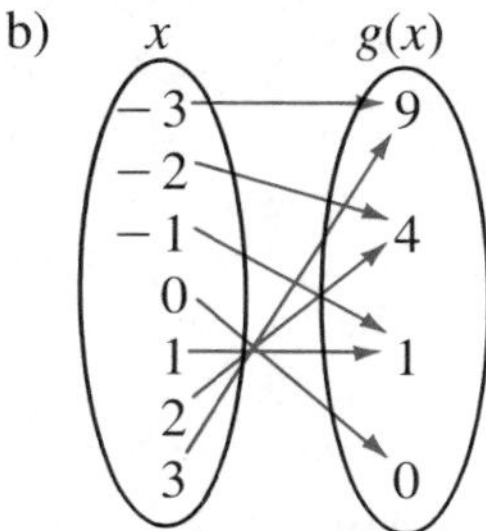

When a mapping diagram is used to represent a function, the first set of numbers is the domain, and the second set is the range. Since some numbers in the domain may map onto the same number in the range, it is possible to have more than one arrow pointing to the same number in the range. This is illustrated in *Example 1b*.

But if a mapping diagram represents a function, it is not possible to have two or more arrows starting at the same number in the domain. The reason for this is the requirement in the definition of a function that no two ordered pairs have the same first coordinate.

Example 2. Which mapping diagram represents a function?

a) x y

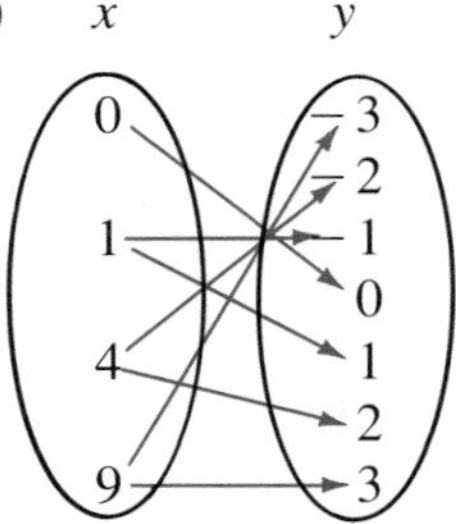

b) x y

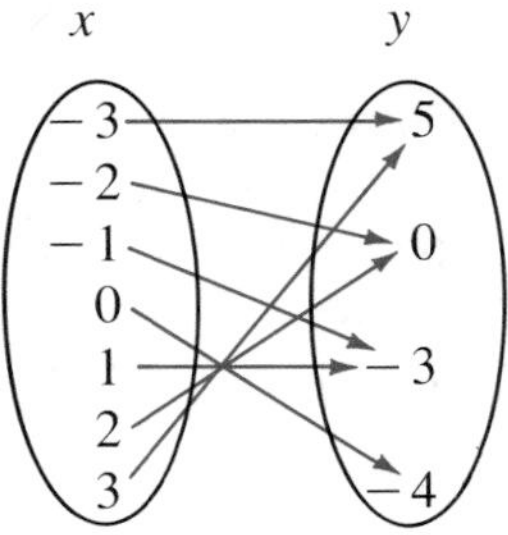

Solution. a) This mapping diagram does not represent a function, since there are 3 cases where two arrows start at the same number in the domain.

b) This mapping diagram represents a function, since each number in the domain corresponds to only one arrow.

Example 3. a) Write the function represented by the mapping diagram as a set of ordered pairs.

b) State the domain and the range of the function.

x $f(x)$

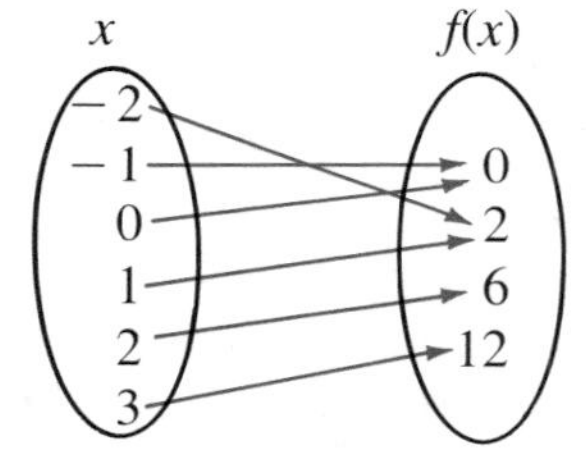

Solution. a) The tails of the arrows indicate the first coordinates of the ordered pairs, and the heads indicate the second coordinates. Therefore, the set of ordered pairs representing the function is:
$\{(-2,2), (-1,0), (0,0), (1,2), (2,6), (3,12)\}$.

b) The domain is the first set of numbers in the mapping diagram, $\{-2,-1,0,1,2,3\}$. The range is the second set, $\{0,2,6,12\}$.

It is impractical to draw mapping diagrams for functions containing many ordered pairs, because there would be too many arrows. However, when a function is represented by an equation it can also be described as a mapping. For example, the function $f(x) = x^2$ is sometimes written as $f: x \rightarrow x^2$. We say, "f is a function that maps x onto x^2". This way of writing a function is called *mapping notation*.

Example 4. Write each function using mapping notation.

a) $f(x) = x^2 + 2x - 3$

b) $\{(x,y) \mid y = 3(x - 1)^2 + 1\}$

c) $y = \frac{1}{x + 2}, x \neq -2$

Solution. a) $f: x \rightarrow x^2 + 2x - 3$

b) Let the name of the function be g. Then, in mapping notation, the function is expressed as $g: x \rightarrow 3(x - 1)^2 + 1$.

c) Let the name of the function be h. $h: x \rightarrow \frac{1}{x + 2}, x \neq -2$

EXERCISES 1-3

Ⓐ

1. Write the function represented by each mapping diagram as a set of ordered pairs.

a) x y

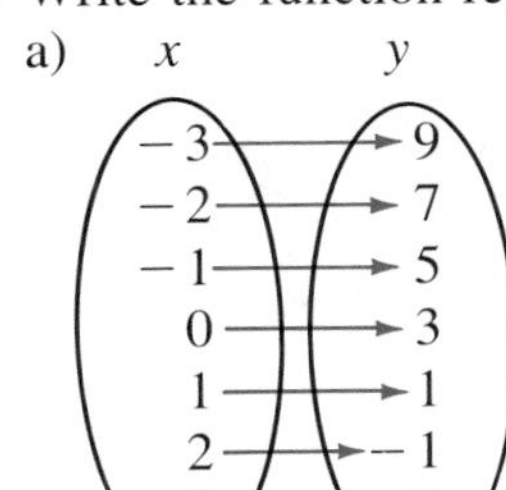

b) x y

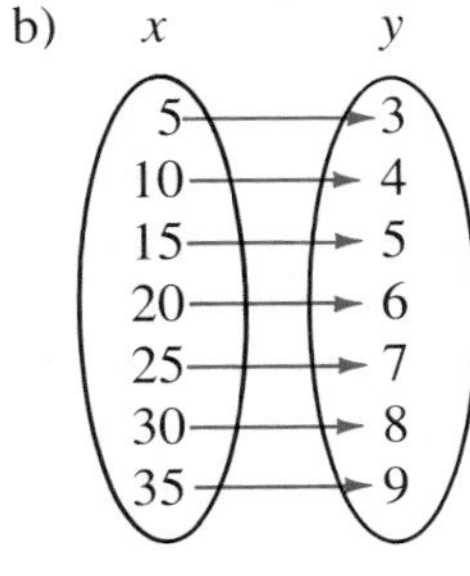

c) x y

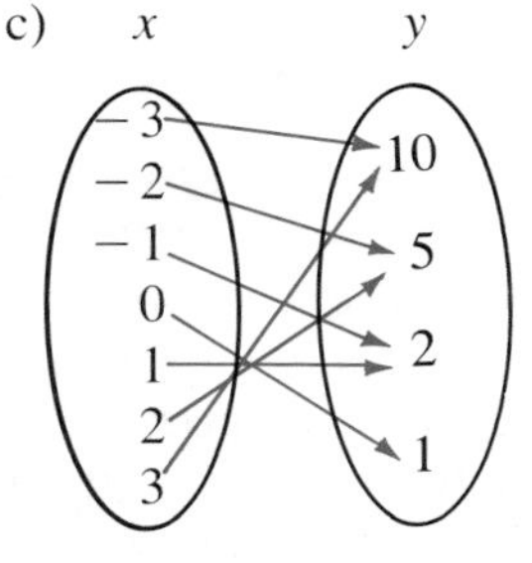

2. Draw a mapping diagram to represent each function.
   a) $\{(1,3), (2,5), (3,7), (4,9), (5,11)\}$
   b) $\{(-2,10), (-1,5), (0,2), (1,1), (2,2), (3,5)\}$
   c) $\{(2,1), (3,8), (4,4), (5,1), (6,-2), (7,5)\}$

3. Draw a mapping diagram for each function, using integral values of x between -3 and 3 inclusive.
   a) $\{(x,y) \mid y = 5x\}$
   b) $\{(x,y) \mid y = 2x^2 - 1\}$
   c) $f(x) = 10 - x^2$
   d) $g(x) = x^2 + x$

4. Write the functions in *Exercise 3* using mapping notation.

5. Draw a mapping diagram to represent each function. Use integral values between -3 and 3 inclusive.
   a) $f\colon x \rightarrow 3x - 2$
   b) $g\colon x \rightarrow x^2 - 4x$
   c) $h\colon z \rightarrow 2z^2 - 7$
   d) $f\colon u \rightarrow \dfrac{u}{u^2 + u}, u \neq -1, 0$

Ⓑ

6. Which mapping diagrams represent functions?

a) x y

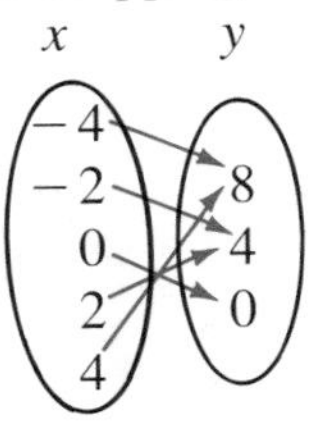

b) x y

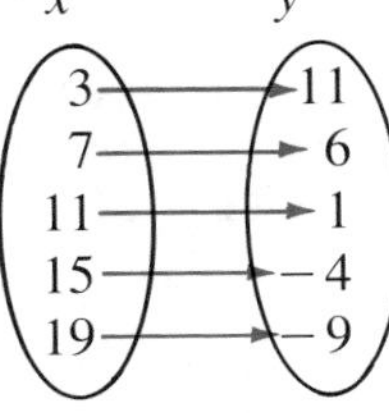

c) x y

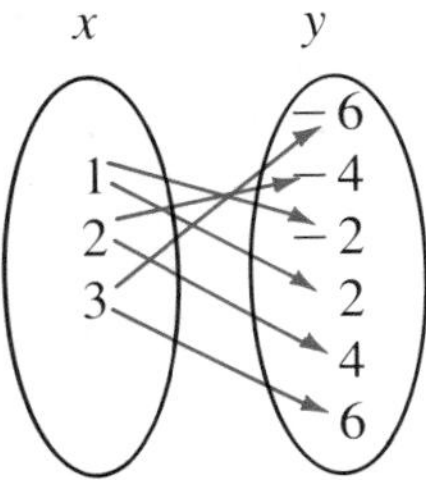

7. Given a mapping diagram, explain how you can tell if it represents a function.

8. Write each function using mapping notation, and draw a mapping diagram.
   a) $\{(x,y) \mid y = \frac{2}{3}x - 6\}$
   b) $\{(x,y) \mid y = 2^x - 1\}$
   c) $f(x) = \dfrac{x^2}{x - 1}, x \neq 1$
   d) $g(x) = \dfrac{\sqrt{2x - 3}}{x}, x \neq 0$

COMPUTER POWER

Graphing Functions

A computer is ideally suited for graphing functions, since it can rapidly calculate the values of a function for many values of x. The graph can be displayed on the computer screen or printed on paper. The most primitive programs plot symbols on the screen, which normally consists of about 20 rows of 40 characters each. The program below is of this type, and can be used on almost any computer. For more accurate graphs, other programs must be used, but the commands are specific to particular computers.

This program can be used to obtain an approximation to the graph of any function that can be defined by an equation. When the program is run, the computer asks for the first and last values of x to be used in the table of values. To reduce the length of the program, it is necessary that the first value be negative, and the second value positive. Also, the least and greatest y-values desired must be entered. Once again, the first must be negative, and the second positive.

When the program is run, the graph of $y = x^3 - 12x + 8$ results. The sample output shows this function graphed for values of x between -5 and 5, with values of y between -50 and 50.

```
100 REM *** FUNCTION GRAPHS ***
110 DIM P$(40,22):I=0
120 INPUT "FIRST AND LAST X-VALUES? ";X1,X2
130 INPUT "LEAST AND GREATEST Y-VALUES? ";Y1,Y2
140 INPUT "WHAT PLOTTING SYMBOL DO YOU WANT? ";S$
150 XAXIS=22-INT(-Y1*22/(Y2-Y1)):YAXIS=INT(-X1*40/(X2-X1))
160 FOR Y=1 TO 22:FOR X=1 TO 40
170 P$(X,Y)=" ":NEXT X:NEXT Y
180 FOR X=1 TO 40:P$(X,XAXIS)=".":NEXT X
190 FOR Y=1 TO 22:P$(YAXIS,Y)=".":NEXT Y
200 FOR X= X1 TO X2 STEP (X2-X1)/39
210     I=I+1
220     Y=X^3-12*X+8
230     IF Y<Y1 OR Y>Y2 THEN GOTO 250
240     P$(I,22-INT((Y-Y1)*22/(Y2-Y1)))=S$
250 NEXT X
260 FOR Y=1 TO 22:FOR X=1 TO 40
270 PRINT P$(X,Y);:NEXT X:NEXT Y
280 END
```

```
FIRST AND LAST X-VALUES? -5,5
LEAST AND GREATEST Y-VALUES? -50,50
WHAT PLOTTING SYMBOL DO YOU WANT? *
```

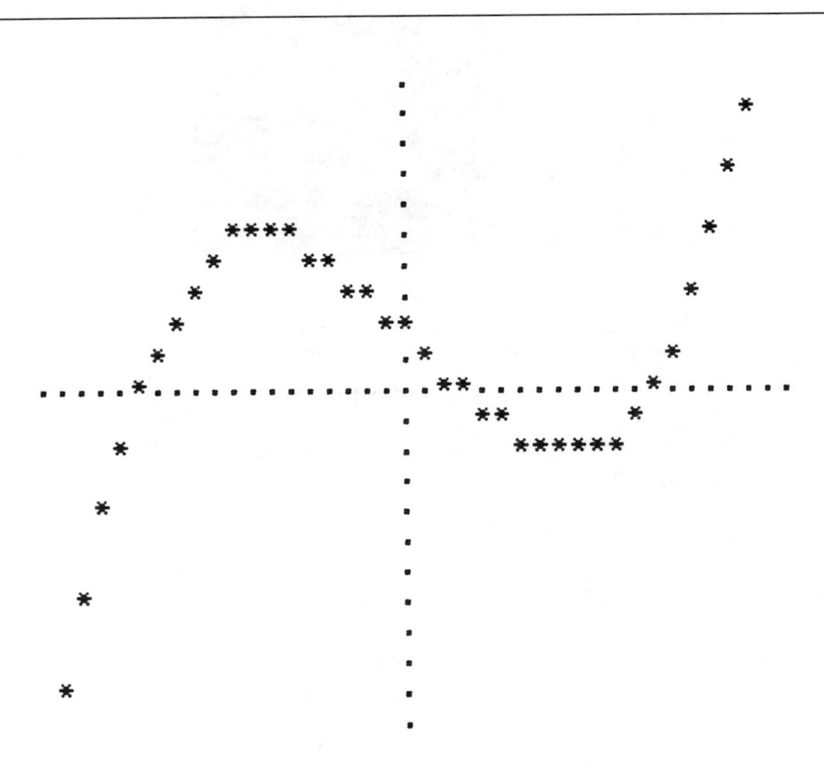

To graph a different function, type LIST, and then enter a new line 220. Some examples of functions that can be entered are given below.

Function	*Enter this line*
$y = x^2 - 4x$	`220 Y = X*X - 4*X`
$y = 2^x$	`220 Y = 2^X`
$y = \|2x + 1\|$	`220 Y = ABS(2*X+1)`
$y = \sqrt{x + 3}$	`220 Y = SQR(X+3)`

Error messages will result if values of x for which the function is not defined are used. For example, with reciprocal functions, a denominator of 0 must be avoided. For a reciprocal function such as $y = \frac{1}{x - 2}$, this can be achieved by entering this line.

```
215 IF X-2=0 THEN GOTO 250
```

Similarly, with square root functions, square roots of negative numbers must be avoided. For a function such as $y = \sqrt{x + 3}$, this can be achieved by entering this line.

```
215 IF X+3<0 THEN GOTO 250
```

Similar lines must be entered for other reciprocal or square root functions.

1-4 COMPOSITION OF FUNCTIONS

Consider the problem of expressing the cost of fuel, when taking a trip by car, as a function of the distance driven.

The cost of fuel, C cents, is a function of the amount of fuel consumed. If fuel costs 50 ¢/L, the cost for x litres of fuel is given by this equation.

$$C = 50x \ldots ①$$

The amount of fuel consumed is a function of the distance driven. If the car consumes fuel at the rate of 8.0 L/100 km, then in travelling d kilometres the amount of fuel consumed is given by this equation.

$$x = 0.080d \ldots ②$$

We can express the cost of fuel as a function of the distance driven by substituting $0.080d$ for x in ①.

$$\begin{aligned} C &= 50x \\ &= 50(0.080d) \\ C &= 4.0d \ldots ③ \end{aligned}$$

The cost of fuel to drive a distance of d kilometres is $C = 4.0d$, or 4 cents per kilometre.

When two functions are applied in succession, the resulting function is called the *composite* of the two given functions. The function described by equation ③ is the composite of the functions described by equations ① and ②.

Function composition can be illustrated with mapping diagrams.

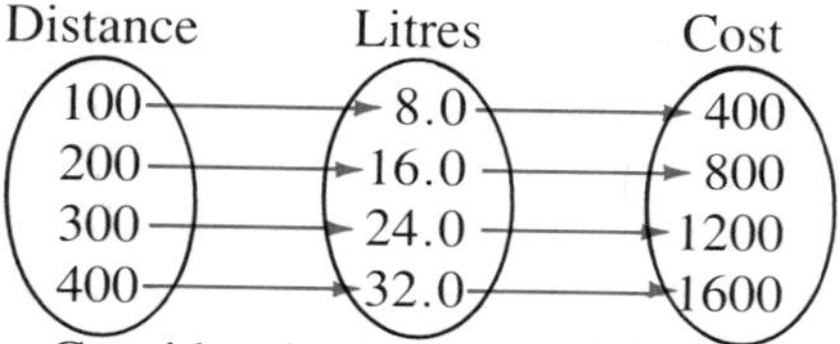

Consider the functions $f(x) = 2x + 3$ and $g(x) = x^2 - 1$. There are two different ways to form the composite of these functions.

Apply f first and g second

Double and add 3, then . . . square and subtract 1.

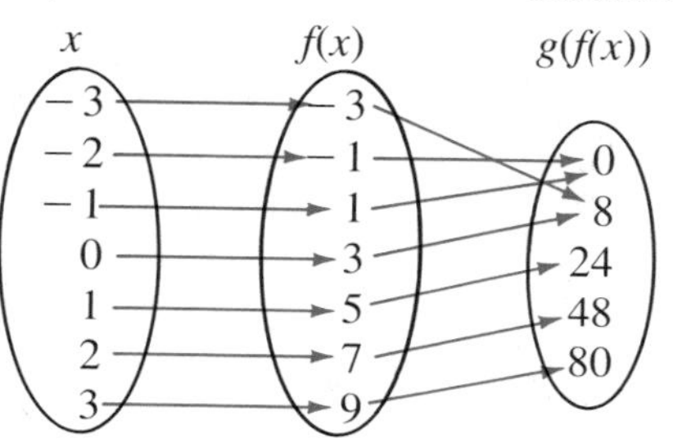

Apply g first and f second

Square and subtract 1, then . . . double and add 3.

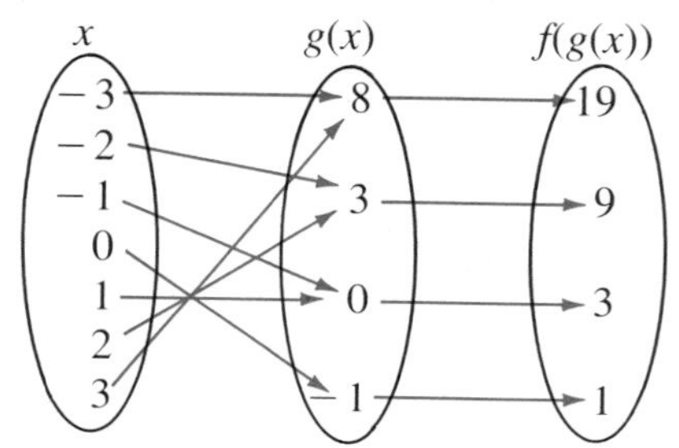

The composite function relates the numbers in the first set to those in the third, and is written as $g(f(x))$, or $g\circ f(x)$. We say, "g of f of x".

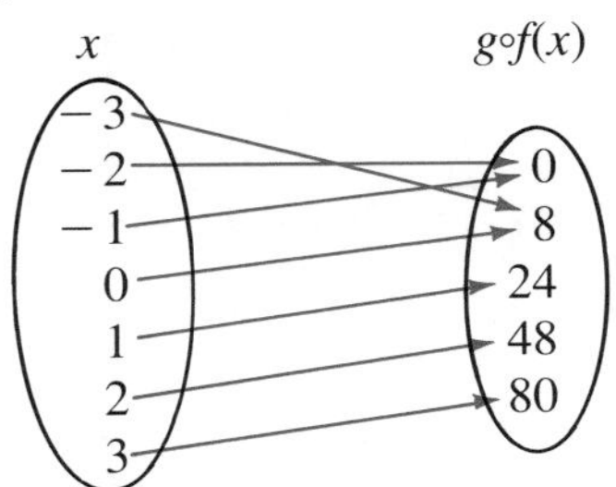

To express $g\circ f(x)$ as a function of x, substitute $f(x)$ for x in $g(x)$.

$$g(x) = x^2 - 1$$

$$\begin{aligned} g(f(x)) &= (f(x))^2 - 1 \\ &= (2x + 3)^2 - 1 \\ &= 4x^2 + 12x + 9 - 1 \\ &= 4x^2 + 12x + 8 \end{aligned}$$

In this case, the composite function is written as $f(g(x))$, or $f\circ g(x)$.

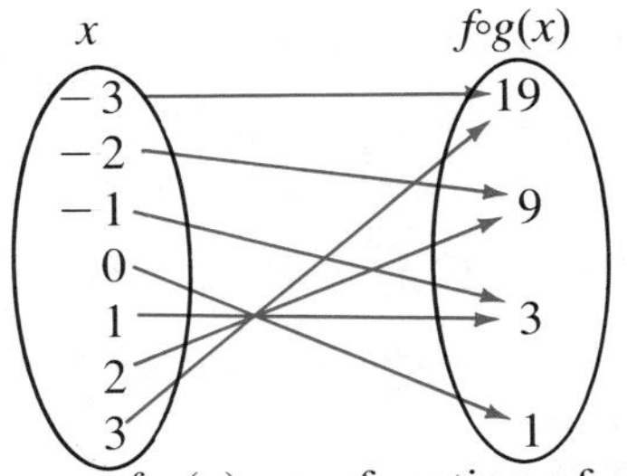

To express $f\circ g(x)$ as a function of x, substitute $g(x)$ for x in $f(x)$.

$$f(x) = 2x + 3$$

$$\begin{aligned} f(g(x)) &= 2g(x) + 3 \\ &= 2(x^2 - 1) + 3 \\ &= 2x^2 - 2 + 3 \\ &= 2x^2 + 1 \end{aligned}$$

Example 1. Given $f(x) = 3x - 5$ and $g(x) = x^2 - x$

a) Find $f\circ g(3)$ and $g\circ f(3)$.

b) Express $f\circ g(x)$ and $g\circ f(x)$ as functions of x.

Solution. a)

$$\begin{aligned} g(x) &= x^2 - x \\ g(3) &= 3^2 - 3 \\ &= 6 \\ f\circ g(3) &= f(g(3)) \\ &= f(6) \\ &= 3(6) - 5 \\ &= 18 - 5 \\ &= 13 \end{aligned}$$

$$\begin{aligned} f(x) &= 3x - 5 \\ f(3) &= 3(3) - 5 \\ &= 4 \\ g\circ f(3) &= g(f(3)) \\ &= g(4) \\ &= 4^2 - 4 \\ &= 16 - 4 \\ &= 12 \end{aligned}$$

b)

$$\begin{aligned} f\circ g(x) &= f(g(x)) \\ &= 3(g(x)) - 5 \\ &= 3(x^2 - x) - 5 \\ &= 3x^2 - 3x - 5 \end{aligned}$$

$$\begin{aligned} g\circ f(x) &= g(f(x)) \\ &= (f(x))^2 - f(x) \\ &= (3x - 5)^2 - (3x - 5) \\ &= 9x^2 - 30x + 25 - 3x + 5 \\ &= 9x^2 - 33x + 30 \end{aligned}$$

When finding the composite of two functions, it is not necessary for the functions to be different. In other words, we can find the composite of a function with itself.

Example 2. Given $f(x) = 3x - 1$, find $f\circ f(x)$.

Solution.

$$\begin{aligned} f\circ f(x) &= f(f(x)) \\ &= 3(f(x)) - 1 \\ &= 3(3x - 1) - 1 \\ &= 9x - 4 \end{aligned}$$

EXERCISES 1-4

(A)

1. Given $f(x) = 2x + 1$ and $g(x) = 3x + 1$, find:
   a) $f(3)$ b) $g(f(3))$ c) $g(3)$ d) $f(g(3))$.
2. For the functions in *Exercise 1*, find $g(f(x))$ and $f(g(x))$.
3. Given $f(x) = x^2 + 1$ and $g(x) = 2x$, find:
   a) $f(2)$ b) $g \circ f(2)$ c) $g(2)$ d) $f \circ g(2)$.
4. For the functions in *Exercise 3*, find $g \circ f(x)$ and $f \circ g(x)$.
5. Find $f(g(x))$ and $g(f(x))$ for each pair of functions.
   a) $f(x) = 3x + 4$; $g(x) = -2x + 5$
   b) $f(x) = x^2 + 5x$; $g(x) = 2x + 1$
   c) $f(x) = 2x^2 - 3x + 1$; $g(x) = 7 - 4x$
6. Given $f(x) = 3x^2 - 1$, find $f(g(x))$ and $g(f(x))$ for each function $g(x)$.
   a) $g(x) = x + 2$ b) $g(x) = 1 - 2x$ c) $g(x) = x^2$
   d) $g(x) = x^2 + x$ e) $g(x) = 2x^2 - 3x$ f) $g(x) = \frac{1}{x}$, $x \neq 0$
7. The area A of a circle is a function of its radius r, where $A = \pi r^2$. Express the area as a function of the diameter d.
8. The volume V of a sphere is a function of its radius r, where $V = \frac{4}{3}\pi r^3$. Express the volume as a function of the diameter d.

(B)

9. Given $f(x) = 2x - 1$ and $g(x) = 1 - 3x$, find:
   a) $f(g(2))$ b) $g(f(2))$ c) $f(f(2))$ d) $g(g(2))$.
10. For the functions in *Exercise 9*, find:
    a) $f(g(x))$ b) $g(f(x))$ c) $f(f(x))$ d) $g(g(x))$.
11. Given $f: x \to 4 - x$ and $g: x \to x^2 + x$, find:
    a) $f \circ g(-1)$ b) $g \circ f(-1)$ c) $f \circ f(-1)$ d) $g \circ g(-1)$.
12. For the functions in *Exercise 11*, find:
    a) $f \circ g(x)$ b) $g \circ f(x)$ c) $f \circ f(x)$ d) $g \circ g(x)$.
13. For each pair of functions, find $f \circ g(x)$, $g \circ f(x)$, $f \circ f(x)$, and $g \circ g(x)$.
    a) $f(x) = \sqrt{x}$; $g(x) = 4 - 2x$ b) $f(x) = \sqrt{2x}$; $g(x) = 1 + 3x$
    c) $f: x \to \frac{x}{x + 1}$; $g: x \to x^2 - 1$ d) $f: x \to 2^x$; $g: x \to 3x - 4$
14. The area A and perimeter P of a square are functions of its side length S. Express the area as a function of the perimeter.
15. Express the area of a square as a function of the length of its diagonal.
16. Given $f(x) = \frac{1}{x}$ and $g(x) = x^2$, show that $f(g(x)) = g(f(x))$.

17. Given $f(x) = 1 - x$ and $g(x) = \frac{x}{1 - x}$, $x \neq 1$

a) Show that $g(f(x)) = \frac{1}{g(x)}$. b) Does $f(g(x)) = \frac{1}{f(x)}$?

18. The temperature of the Earth's crust is a linear function of the depth below the surface. An equation expressing the relationship is $T = 0.01d + 20$. T is the temperature in degrees Celsius, and d is the depth in metres. If you go down the shaft in an elevator at the rate of 5 m/s, express the temperature as a function of the time of travel t seconds.

19. For each pair of functions, determine values of x such that $f(g(x)) = g(f(x))$.

a) $f(x) = 2x + 3$; $g(x) = x^2 - x + 3$ b) $f(x) = \frac{1}{x}$; $g(x) = 2x + 1$

20. From the functions listed in the box, find two whose composite function is $h(x)$.

a) $h(x) = (x + 1)^2$
b) $h(x) = \sqrt{x - 3}$
c) $h(x) = x^2 - 6x + 9$
d) $h(x) = x - 2$

$e(x) = x - 3$	$f(x) = x^2$
$g(x) = \sqrt{x}$	$k(x) = x + 1$

21. Find two functions whose composite function is $k(x)$.

a) $k(x) = x^6 + 2x^3 + 1$ b) $k(x) = (x - 4)^2 + 3(x - 4) + 4$
c) $k(x) = \sqrt{3x - 2}$ d) $k(x) = \frac{1}{x + 3}$

22. Given $f(x) = x - 3$ and $g(x) = \sqrt{x}$, find:

a) $f \circ g(x)$ b) the domain of $f \circ g(x)$ c) the range of $f \circ g(x)$
d) $g \circ f(x)$ e) the domain of $g \circ f(x)$ f) the range of $g \circ f(x)$.

23. Given $f\colon x \to x^2 + 1$ and $g\colon x \to \sqrt{x - 1}$, find:

a) $f \circ g(x)$ b) the domain of $f \circ g(x)$ c) the range of $f \circ g(x)$
d) $g \circ f(x)$ e) the domain of $g \circ f(x)$ f) the range of $g \circ f(x)$.

24. Find $f(f(x))$ for each function.

a) $f(x) = \frac{1}{1 - x}$, $x \neq 1$ b) $f(x) = \frac{x - 1}{x + 1}$, $x \neq -1$

Ⓒ

25. Given $f(x) = 2x + 1$

a) Find. i) $f \circ f(x)$ ii) $f \circ f \circ f(x)$ iii) $f \circ f \circ f \circ f(x)$
b) On the basis of the results in part a), predict what these functions would be.
i) $f \circ f \circ f \circ f \circ f(x)$ ii) $f \circ f \circ f \circ \ldots \circ f(x)$ (n functions)

26. Repeat *Exercise 25* using $f(x) = \frac{x}{x + 1}$, $x \neq -1$.

27. Given $f(x) = ax + b$, $g(x) = cx + d$, and $f(g(x)) = g(f(x))$, how are a, b, c, and d related?

MATHEMATICS AROUND US

The Waggle Dance of Honeybees

In 1973, Karl von Frisch received a Nobel Prize for his research in animal behaviour. One of his discoveries concerns a method used by honeybees to communicate the location of a food source to other bees inside a hive. Von Frisch observed bees returning to the hive when they had discovered a food source. Shortly after a bee returned, hundreds of bees left the hive, and went directly to the food source, although the bee which had found the food remained inside the hive. Somehow, the bee had informed the others where the food was located.

By marking the bees with paint, and using glass-walled hives, von Frisch learned how they do this. The bee which found the food performs a dance on the honeycomb inside the hive. It follows a figure-8 pattern and wags its body in the central part. Von Frisch observed that:

- the orientation of the central portion indicates the direction of the food source,
- the speed of the dance indicates the distance to the food.

Von Frisch made thousands of observations, comparing the speeds of the bees' dances with the distances to the food, and summarized his results on a graph like the one shown.

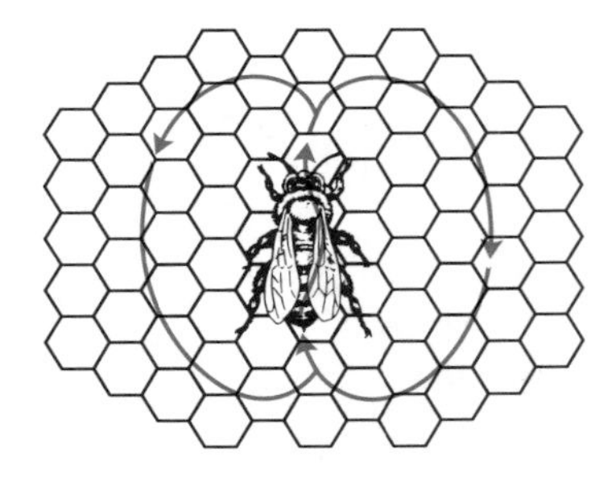

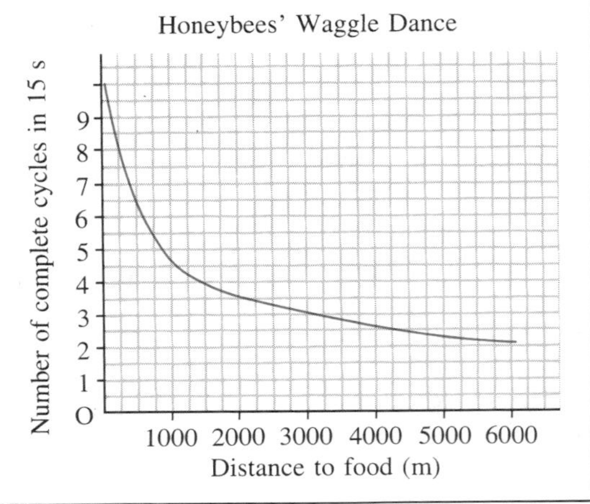

QUESTIONS

1. If the food is 1 km away, how many complete cycles does the bee make in 15 s? in 1 min?
2. If the bee makes 10 complete cycles in one minute, how far away is the food?
3. How would the graph differ if it were drawn to show the number of complete cycles in one minute instead of 15 s?

1-5 THE INVERSE OF A FUNCTION

Consider the functions $y = f(x)$ and $y = g(x)$ represented by the following mapping diagrams.

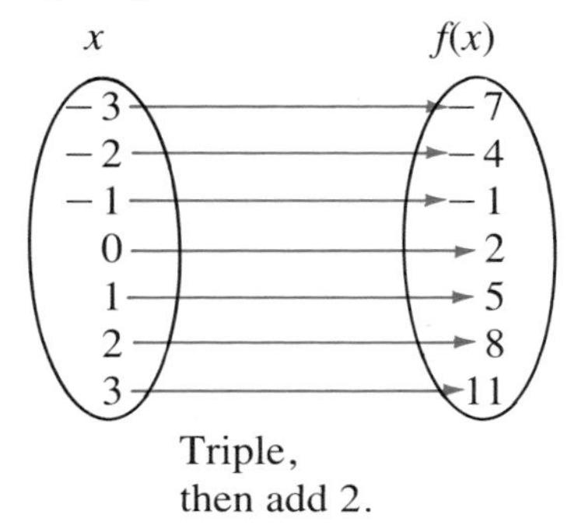

Triple, then add 2.

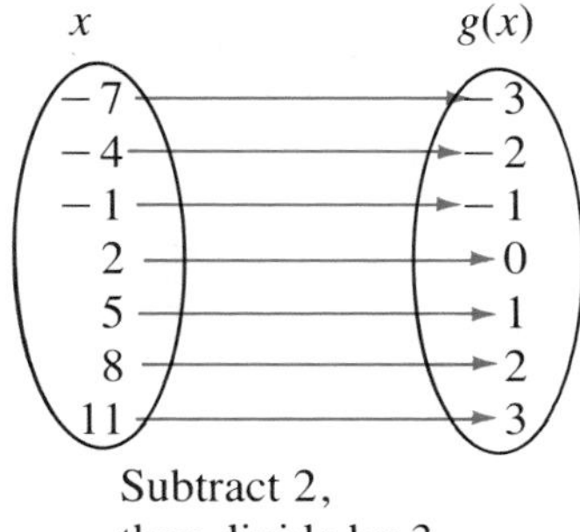

Subtract 2, then divide by 3.

The diagram on the right reverses the mapping of the diagram on the left, and vice versa. The ordered pairs of the function $y = g(x)$ are obtained by interchanging the members of the ordered pairs of $y = f(x)$. We say that the functions $y = f(x)$ and $y = g(x)$ are inverses of each other.

> The *inverse* of a function is the set of ordered pairs obtained by interchanging the members of each ordered pair of the function.

We can compare the graphs of the functions $y = f(x)$ and $y = g(x)$ by drawing them on the same grid.

The graphs appear to be reflections of each other in the line $y = x$. This is what we should expect since the members of the ordered pairs of one function are interchanged to obtain the ordered pairs of the other function.

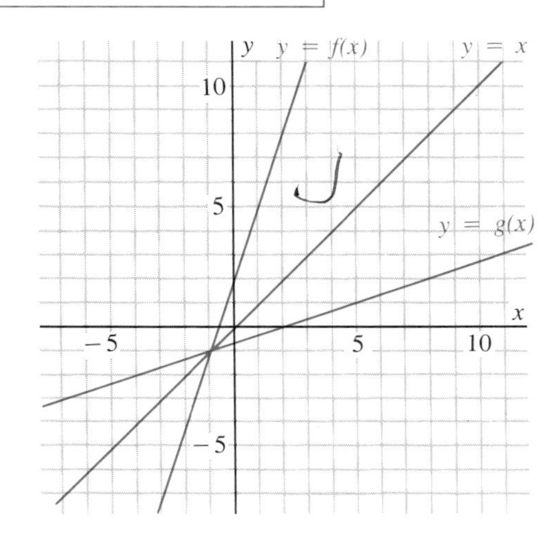

> **Reflection Property**
> When the members of each ordered pair of a function are interchanged, the graph of the function is reflected in the line $y = x$.

We can prove this reflection property as follows.

Given:
The graphs of $y = f(x)$ and its inverse $y = g(x)$

Required to Prove:
$y = g(x)$ is the reflection of $y = f(x)$ in the line $y = x$.

Analysis:
If we can prove that the line $y = x$ is the perpendicular bisector of the line segment joining two corresponding points on the graphs of $y = f(x)$ and $y = g(x)$, then $y = x$ must be the line of reflection for those graphs.

Proof:
Let $P(a,b)$ be a point on the graph of $y = f(x)$.
Since $y = g(x)$ is the inverse of $y = f(x)$, $Q(b,a)$ is the corresponding point on the graph of $y = g(x)$.
Since each coordinate of the midpoint of a line segment is the mean of the corresponding coordinates of the endpoints,

$M\left(\frac{a+b}{2}, \frac{b+a}{2}\right)$ is the midpoint of PQ.

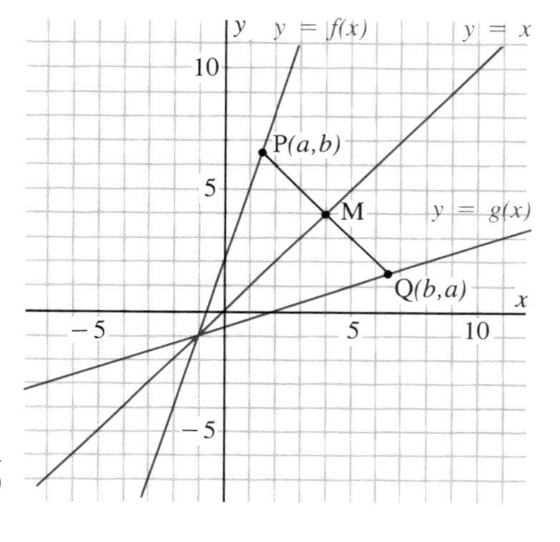

Since the coordinates of M are equal, M lies on the line $y = x$.
Hence, $y = x$ bisects PQ.

Assuming $a \neq b$, the slope of PQ is $\frac{a-b}{b-a} = \frac{a-b}{-(a-b)}$
$= -1$

The slope of the line $y = x$ is 1.

Since their slopes are negative reciprocals, PQ is perpendicular to the line $y = x$.
We have proved that the line $y = x$ bisects PQ, and is perpendicular to PQ.
Therefore, the line $y = x$ is the perpendicular bisector of PQ.

This proves that $y = g(x)$ is the reflection of $y = f(x)$ in the line $y = x$.

When a function is defined by an equation, we can obtain its inverse by interchanging x and y in the equation rather than in the ordered pairs. In the above example, the equation of the function $y = f(x)$ is $y = 3x + 2$. We can find the equation of the inverse by interchanging x and y.

$x = 3y + 2$

It is customary to solve this equation for y.

$3y = x - 2$

$y = \frac{x-2}{3}$

Therefore, the equation of the inverse function is $y = \frac{x-2}{3}$.

The inverse function of a given function $y = f(x)$ is written with a special notation, $y = f^{-1}(x)$. We say, "y equals the inverse function of x." For the function $f(x) = 3x + 2$, we write $f^{-1}(x) = \dfrac{x - 2}{3}$.

Example 1. a) Find the inverse of the function $f(x) = \dfrac{1}{x + 2}$.

b) Show that the inverse is a function and write it using function notation.

c) Determine the domain and the range of the inverse.

Solution. a) Write the equation of the function.

$$y = \frac{1}{x + 2}$$

Interchange x and y.

$$x = \frac{1}{y + 2}$$

Solve for y.

$$xy + 2x = 1$$
$$xy = 1 - 2x$$
$$y = \frac{1 - 2x}{x}$$

b) For each value of x, only one value of y can be calculated. Therefore, the inverse is a function.

In function notation, the inverse function is $f^{-1}(x) = \dfrac{1 - 2x}{x}$.

c) The inverse function is defined for all values of x except $x = 0$. Therefore, the domain of the inverse function is $\{x \mid x \neq 0, x \in R\}$. The domain of the given function is all values of x except $x = -2$. Since the ordered pairs are interchanged when finding the inverse, this corresponds to the range of the inverse. Therefore, the range of the inverse function is $\{y \mid y \neq -2, y \in R\}$.

Example 2. a) Find the inverse of the function $f(x) = (x - 3)^2$.

b) Graph the function $y = f(x)$ and its inverse on the same grid.

c) Is the inverse a function?

Solution. a) Write the equation of the function.

$$y = (x - 3)^2$$

Interchange x and y, and then solve for y.

$$x = (y - 3)^2$$

Take the square root of both sides, assuming $x \geqslant 0$.

$$\pm\sqrt{x} = y - 3$$
$$y = \pm\sqrt{x} + 3$$

b) We graph $f(x) = (x - 3)^2$ by making a table of values. Then we can graph the inverse by reflecting the graph of $y = f(x)$ in the line $y = x$.

$f(x) = (x - 3)^2$

x	y
0	9
1	4
2	1
3	0
4	1
5	4
6	9

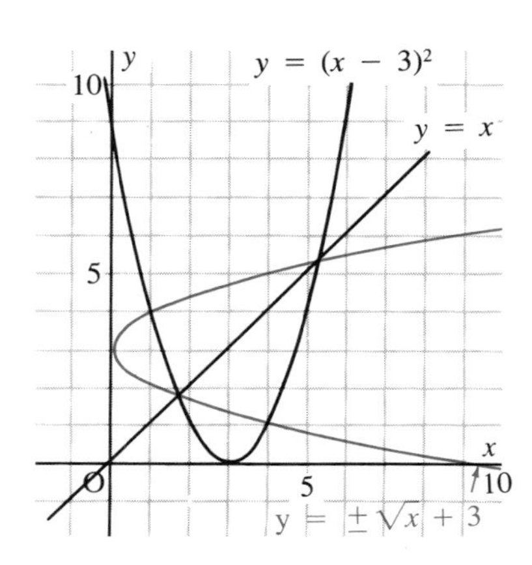

c) The inverse is not a function, since there are two values of y corresponding to a value of x. This is indicated by the term $\pm\sqrt{x}$ in the equation, and by the fact that the graph of the inverse does not pass the vertical-line test.

When the inverse of a function is not a function, we can usually restrict the domain of the given function so that its inverse is a function. Two ways of doing this for the function in *Example 2* are shown below. In principle, there are infinitely many ways of doing this.

Restrict the domain of $y = (x - 3)^2$ to values of $x \geqslant 3$.
Then, the inverse is $y = \sqrt{x} + 3$.

or

Restrict the domain of $y = (x - 3)^2$ to values of $x \leqslant 3$.
Then, the inverse is $y = -\sqrt{x} + 3$.

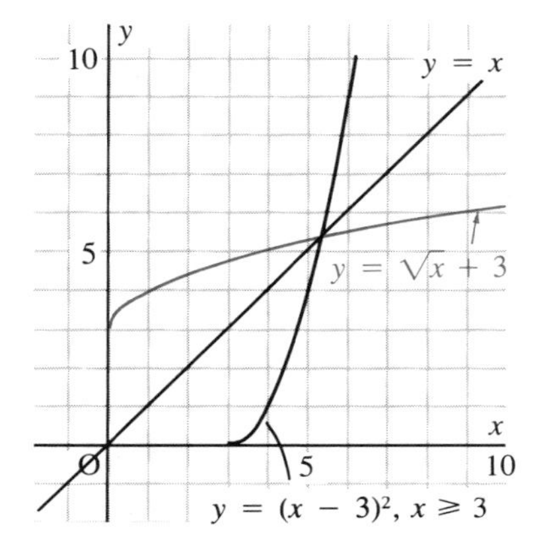

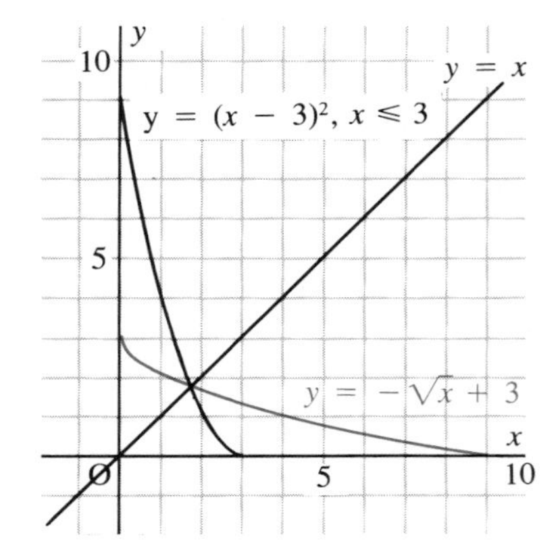

In both cases, the inverse is a function because its graph passes the vertical-line test.

Properties of the Inverse of a Function

- The inverse of a function is obtained by:
  - — reversing the mapping diagram
  - — interchanging the ordered pairs of the function
  - — interchanging x and y in the equation, and solving for y
  - — reflecting the graph of the function in the line $y = x$.
- The domain of the inverse is the range of the original function.
- The range of the inverse is the domain of the original function.
- The inverse of a function is not necessarily a function.

EXERCISES 1-5

Ⓐ

1. On each grid, is $y = g(x)$ the inverse of $y = f(x)$?

a)

$y = g(x)$

$y = f(x)$

b)

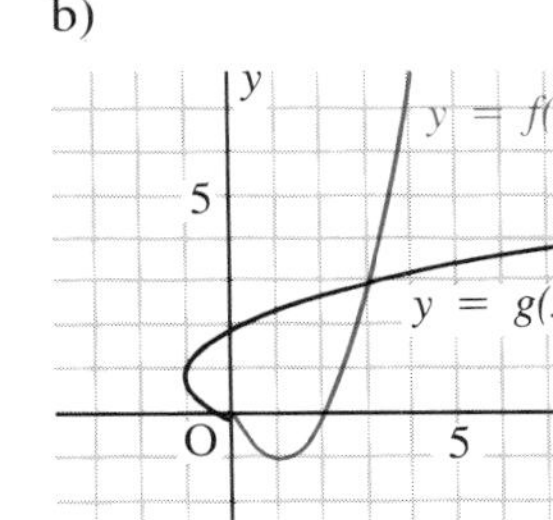

c)

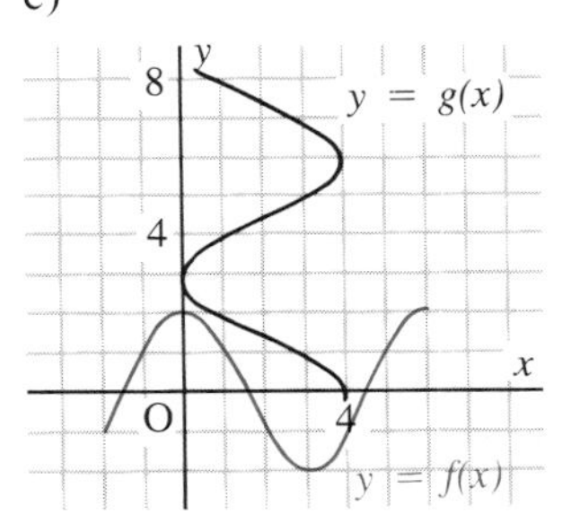

2. Find the equation for the inverse of each function. Is the inverse a function?

a) $y = 2x + 5$ b) $3x^2 - y = 4$ c) $5x + 2y = 10$

d) $f(x) = 4x^2 - 1$ e) $f(x) = \dfrac{x - 3}{x}$ f) $f(x) = \dfrac{2x + 3}{4}$

Ⓑ

3. Graph each function, its inverse, and the line $y = x$ on the same grid.

a) $f(x) = 5 - 2x$ b) $f(x) = \dfrac{1}{2}x^2 - 2, x \geqslant 0$

c) $f(x) = \dfrac{2x - 1}{x}, x > 0$ d) $f(x) = (x - 1)^2 + 2, x \geqslant 1$

4. Find the inverse of each function, and state whether the inverse is also a function. If the inverse is a function, state its domain and range.

a) $f(x) = 2x + 3$ b) $g(x) = 2x^2 - 3$ c) $h(x) = \dfrac{1}{x + 1}$

d) $f: x \to (x + 1)^2$ e) $g: x \to \dfrac{x + 1}{x}$ f) $\{(x,y) \mid y = \sqrt{x - 2}\}$

5. Restrict the domain of each function so that its inverse is a function. Illustrate the function and its inverse on a grid.
   a) $y = x^2 - 2$ b) $y = 2(x + 1)^2 - 3$ c) $y + x^2 = 5$
   d) $f(x) = 4 - x^2$ e) $f(x) = (x - 1)^2 - 1$ f) $f(x) = 4 - (x - 3)^2$

6. Find the inverse of each function.
   a) $f(x) = \frac{1}{1 - x}, x \neq 1$ b) $f(x) = \frac{x - 2}{x + 2}, x \neq -2$
   c) $f(x) = \frac{2x^2}{x^2 - 4}, x \neq 2, -2$ d) $f(x) = \frac{1}{3x^2 + 4}$

7. Two functions are described in words. Is each function the inverse of the other?
   a) i) The value of x is increased by 3.
      ii) The value of x is decreased by 3.
   b) i) Twice the value of x is decreased by 1.
      ii) Half the value of x is increased by 1.
   c) i) Twice the value of x is subtracted from 5.
      ii) The value of x is subtracted from 5, then divided by 2.
   d) i) x is reduced by 1, then squared and increased by 3.
      ii) x is reduced by 3, then the square root is found, which is then increased by 1.

8. Given $f(x) = 2x + 5$, find an expression for each function.
   a) $f^{-1}(x)$ b) $f \circ f^{-1}(x)$ c) $f^{-1} \circ f(x)$

9. Given $f(x) = \frac{x - 1}{x + 1}$, find an expression for each function.
   a) $f^{-1}(x)$ b) $f \circ f^{-1}(x)$ c) $f^{-1} \circ f(x)$

10. If $f(x)$ is any function which has an inverse, what do $f \circ f^{-1}(x)$ and $f^{-1} \circ f(x)$ represent?

Ⓒ

11. Show that $f(f^{-1}(x)) = x$ and $f^{-1}(f(x)) = x$, where $f^{-1}(x)$ is the inverse of $f(x)$.

12. Is the inverse of every linear function also a function? If you think it is, explain why. If you think it is not, give a counterexample.

13. Find the inverse of the inverse of each function. Is the inverse of the inverse of a given function always a function?
   a) $f(x) = \frac{3x - 5}{2}$ b) $g(x) = 2(x - 1)^2 + 3$ c) $h(x) = \frac{2x - 3}{x}$

14. Find two ways to restrict the domain of each function so that its inverse is a function.
   a) $g(x) = 2(x + 1)^2 - 5$ b) $y = \frac{4 - x^2}{3}$ c) $f: x \rightarrow |2x + 3| - 5$

INVESTIGATE

Find examples of functions that are equal to their own inverse functions. What property do these functions have in common?

1-6 GRAPHICAL ADDITION AND SUBTRACTION OF FUNCTIONS

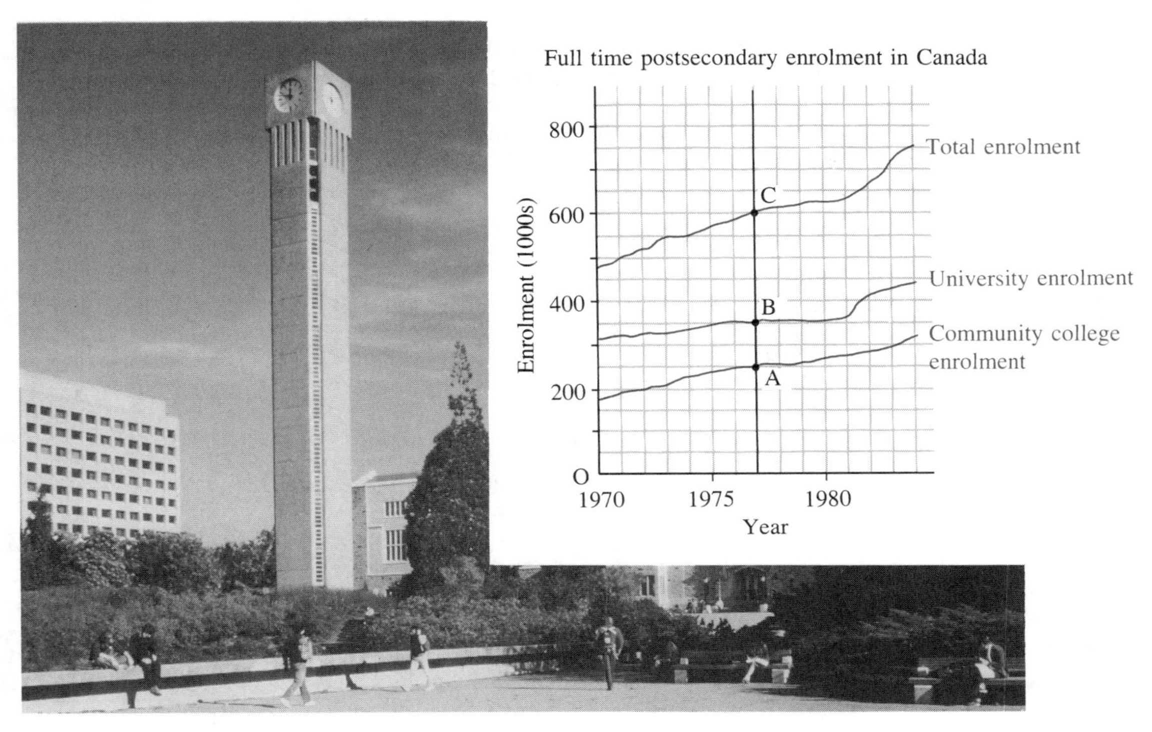

We often see graphs showing two or more functions on the same grid. In the example above, one function is the community college enrolment, the other is the university enrolment. The third function is the total postsecondary enrolment. The points on the graph of this function are obtained by adding the y-coordinates of the corresponding points on the graphs of the other two functions.

For example, in 1977 the community college enrolment is given by point A, and the university enrolment by point B. Since the total enrolment is given by point C, the y-coordinate of C is the sum of the y-coordinates of A and B.

Since the second coordinate of an ordered pair is sometimes called an ordinate, this method of graphing the sum of two functions is called the method of *adding ordinates*. The method can be used to graph the sum of two given functions.

For example, if $f(x) = x$ and $g(x) = \frac{1}{x}$, $x \neq 0$, then the sum of $y = f(x)$ and $y = g(x)$ is the function defined by

$$\begin{aligned} y &= f(x) + g(x) \\ &= x + \frac{1}{x}, \quad x \neq 0 \end{aligned}$$

Example 1. a) Graph the functions $f(x) = x$ and $g(x) = \frac{1}{x}$, $x \neq 0$.

b) Write $y = f(x) + g(x)$ as a function of x.

c) Use the result of part a) to graph the function $y = x + \frac{1}{x}$, $x \neq 0$.

Solution. a) Make a table of values for each function.

$f(x) = x$

x	-4	0	4
$f(x)$	-4	0	4

$g(x) = \frac{1}{x}$

x	-4	-2	-1	$-\frac{1}{2}$	$\frac{1}{2}$	1	2	4
$g(x)$	$-\frac{1}{4}$	$-\frac{1}{2}$	-1	-2	2	1	$\frac{1}{2}$	$\frac{1}{4}$

Graph $y = x$ and $y = \frac{1}{x}$ on the same grid.

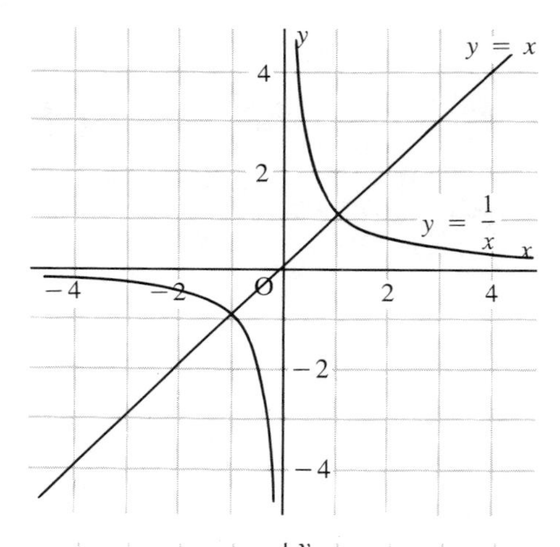

b) Since $f(x) = x$ and $g(x) = \frac{1}{x}$,

$$y = f(x) + g(x)$$
$$= x + \frac{1}{x}$$

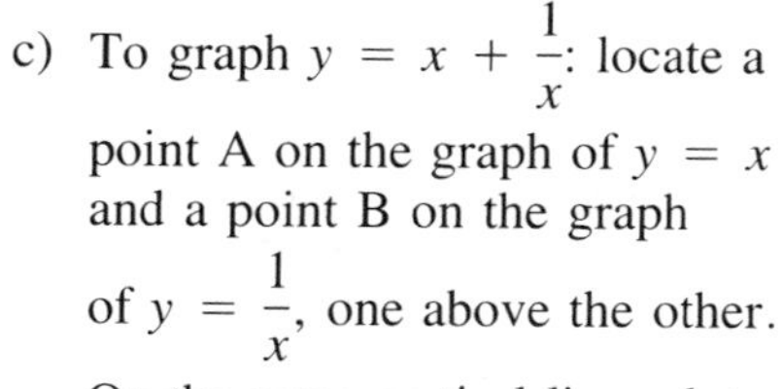

c) To graph $y = x + \frac{1}{x}$: locate a point A on the graph of $y = x$ and a point B on the graph of $y = \frac{1}{x}$, one above the other.

On the same vertical line, plot a point C whose ordinate is the ordinate of A plus the ordinate of B.

Repeat the process of adding ordinates for other pairs of points that are above each other.

Draw a smooth curve through the plotted points. This curve represents the function $y = x + \frac{1}{x}$.

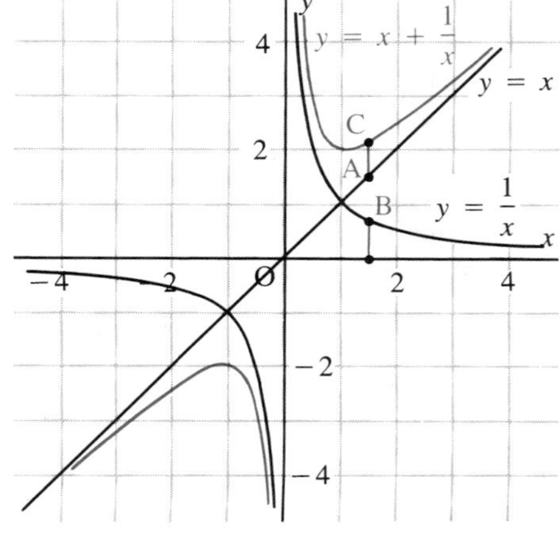

In *Example 1*, the domain of $f(x) = x$ is the set of all real numbers, but the domain of $g(x) = \frac{1}{x}$ is $\{x \mid x \neq 0, x \in R\}$. Since the function $y = f(x) + g(x)$ can only be defined for values of x for which both $f(x)$ and $g(x)$ are defined, the domain of $y = x + \frac{1}{x}$ is $\{x \mid x \neq 0, x \in R\}$.

> **Addition of Functions**
> The *sum* of any two functions $y = f(x)$ and $y = g(x)$ is the function defined by $y = f(x) + g(x)$. The domain of $y = f(x) + g(x)$ consists of all values of x which belong to the domain of $f(x)$ *and* to the domain of $g(x)$.

Frequently, when a graph shows the sum of two functions, only one of these functions is plotted. The graph of the other function can be drawn by *subtracting ordinates*.

Example 2. This graph was obtained from an experiment to determine the stopping distance for cars at different speeds. The total stopping distance is the sum of the reaction-time distance and the braking distance. Draw a graph on the same grid, showing the braking distance as a function of speed.

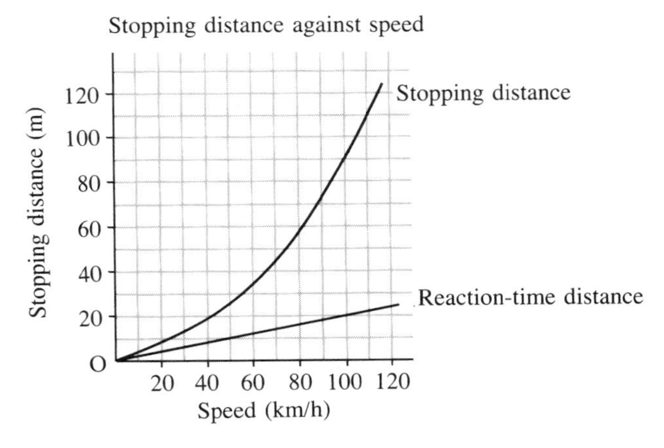

Solution. The braking distance is the difference between the stopping distance and the reaction-time distance. To plot this graph, locate a point on each of the given graphs such that one point is vertically above the other. Subtract the ordinates of these points, and plot the corresponding point with the same horizontal coordinate. Repeat, using other pairs of points which are vertically above each other. Draw a smooth curve through the plotted points.

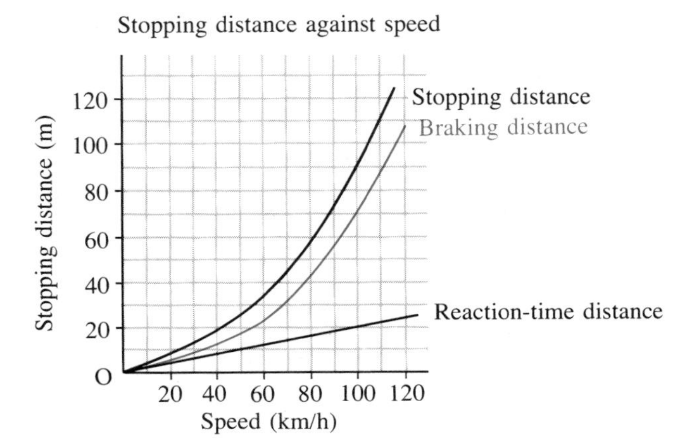

Subtraction of Functions
If $y = f(x)$ and $y = g(x)$ are any two functions, the function defined by $y = f(x) - g(x)$ represents their difference. The domain of $y = f(x) - g(x)$ consists of all values of x which belong to the domain of $f(x)$ *and* to the domain of $g(x)$.

Example 3. a) Graph the functions $f(x) = x + 2$ and $g(x) = x^2$.
b) Write $y = f(x) - g(x)$ as a function of x.
c) Use the result of part a) to graph the function $y = x + 2 - x^2$.
d) What is the domain of $y = x + 2 - x^2$?

Solution. a) Make a table of values for each function.

$f(x) = x + 2$

x	-3	0	3
$f(x)$	-1	2	5

$g(x) = x^2$

x	-3	-2	-1	0	1	2	3
$g(x)$	9	4	1	0	1	4	9

Graph $y = x + 2$ and $y = x^2$ on the same grid.

b) Since $f(x) = x + 2$ and $g(x) = x^2$,
$y = f(x) - g(x)$
$= x + 2 - x^2$

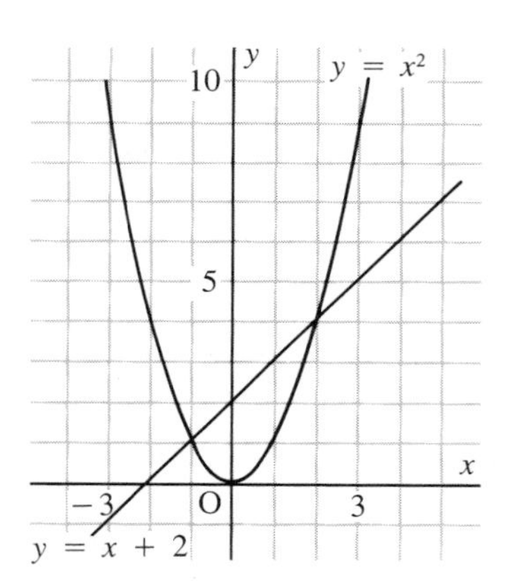

c) To graph $y = x + 2 - x^2$, locate a point A on the graph of $y = x + 2$ and a point B on the graph of $y = x^2$, one above the other. On the same vertical line, plot a point C whose ordinate is the ordinate of A minus the ordinate of B.

Repeat the process of subtracting ordinates for other pairs of points that are above each other.

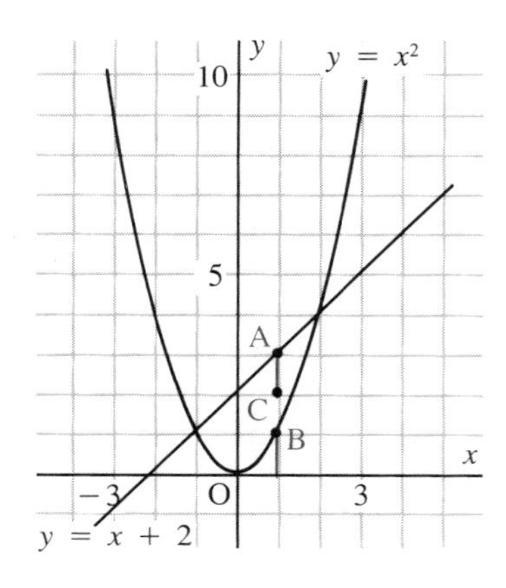

Draw a smooth curve through the plotted points. This curve represents the function $y = x + 2 - x^2$.

d) Since the functions $f(x) = x + 2$ and $g(x) = x^2$ are defined for all real values of x, the domain of $y = x + 2 - x^2$ is the set of all real numbers.

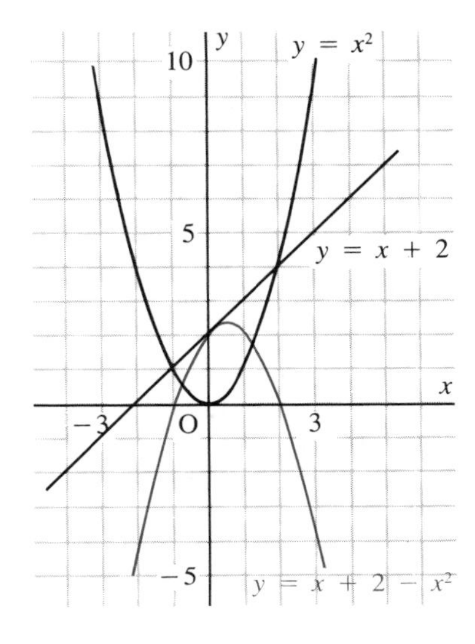

EXERCISES 1-6

Ⓐ

1. Given $f(x)$ and $g(x)$, write the function $y = f(x) + g(x)$ as a function of x.
   a) $f(x) = 2x + 3$; $g(x) = x - 5$
   b) $f(x) = x^2 - 4$; $g(x) = 2x + 3$
   c) $f(x) = x^2 + x - 1$; $g(x) = x^2 - 4x + 3$
   d) $f(x) = (x - 2)^2$; $g(x) = (2x - 1)^2$

2. Given $f(x)$ and $g(x)$, write the function $y = f(x) - g(x)$ as a function of x.
   a) $f(x) = x + 3$; $g(x) = 2 - 3x$
   b) $f(x) = x^2 + 5x$; $g(x) = x^2 - x - 2$
   c) $f(x) = (x + 1)^2$; $g(x) = (x - 1)^2$
   d) $f(x) = (2x - 3)^2$; $g(x) = (3x + 2)^2$

3. Copy each graph, and use the method of adding ordinates to draw the graph of $y = f(x) + g(x)$.

a)

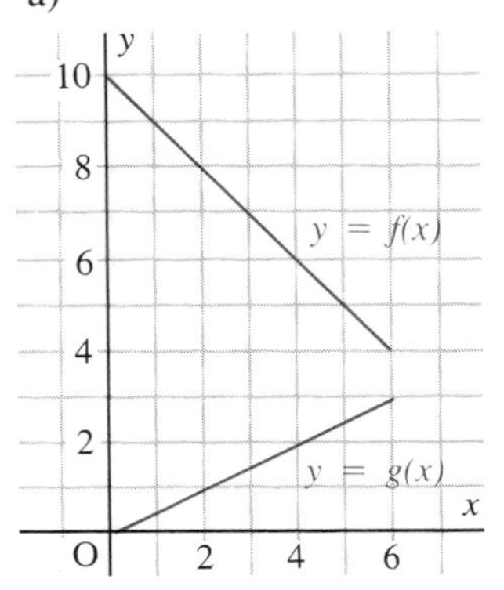

b)

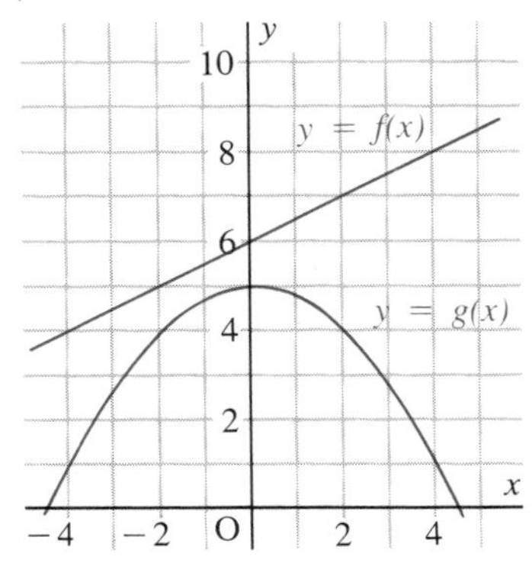

c)

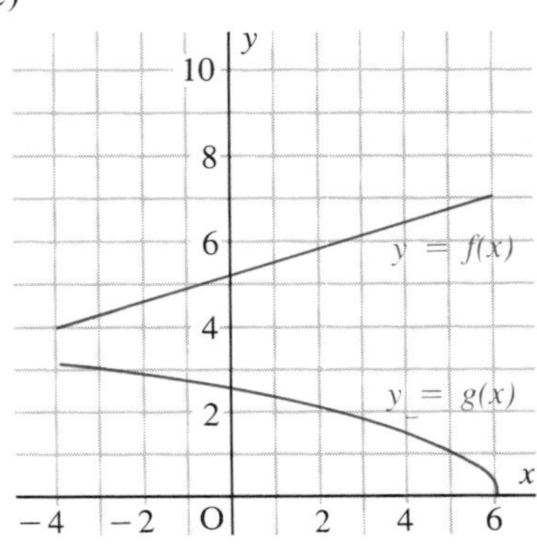

4. For each graph of *Exercise 3*, use the method of subtracting ordinates to draw the graph of $y = f(x) - g(x)$.

Ⓑ

5. Given $f(x) = x$ and $g(x) = x + 1$
   a) Write the function $y = f(x) + g(x)$ as a function of x.
   b) Graph $y = f(x)$ and $y = g(x)$ on the same grid.
   c) Use the graphs in part b) to draw the graph of $y = f(x) + g(x)$.
   d) What is the domain of $y = f(x) + g(x)$?

6. Given $f(x) = 2x + 4$ and $g(x) = x + 1$
   a) Write the function $y = f(x) - g(x)$ as a function of x.
   b) Graph $y = f(x)$ and $y = g(x)$ on the same grid.
   c) Use the graphs in part b) to draw the graph of $y = f(x) - g(x)$.
   d) What is the domain of $y = f(x) - g(x)$?

7. Each graph involves the addition of two functions. Describe the functions which are added, and identify the function which is their sum.

a)

Optimization of costs

Cost per unit ($)

4
3
2
1
O
4 8 12 16 20
Number of units (1000s)
Total cost
Storage cost
Manufacturing cost

b)

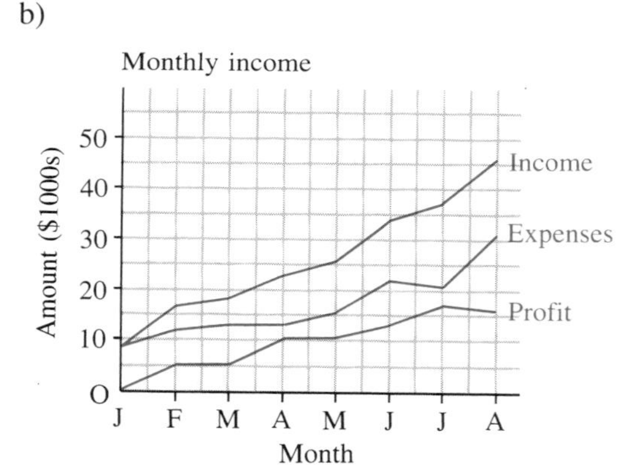

8. Copy each pair of graphs, and draw the graph of $y = f(x) + g(x)$.

a)

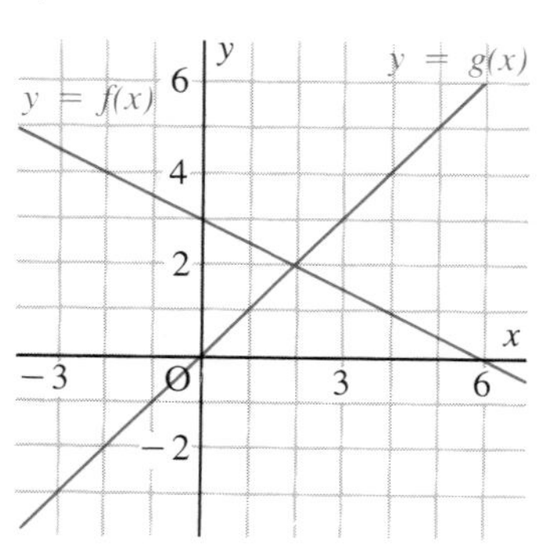

b)

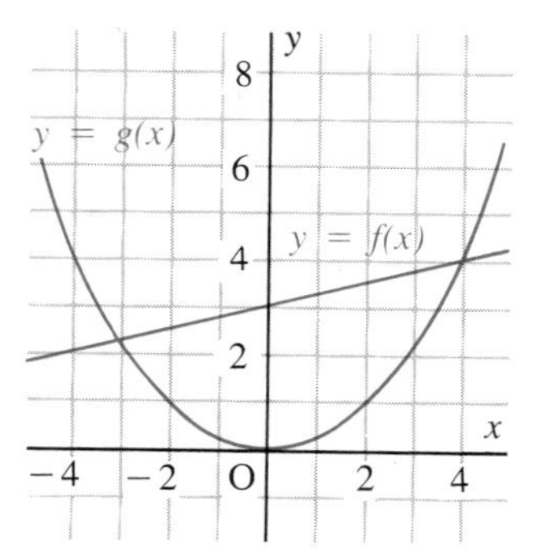

c)

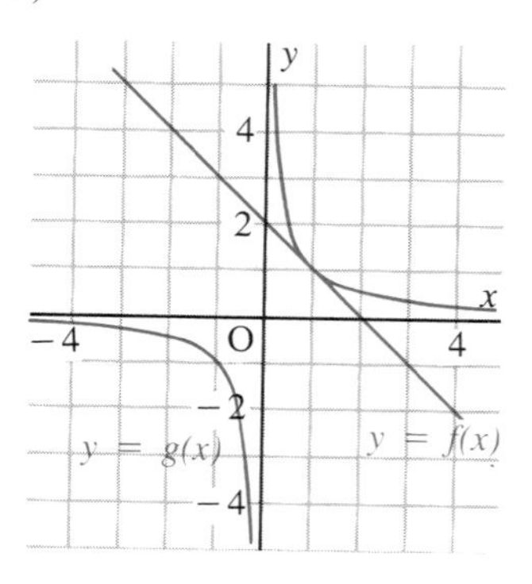

9. For each pair of graphs in *Exercise 8*, draw the graph of $y = f(x) - g(x)$.

10. Given $f(x) = x^2 - 4$ and $g(x) = 2x$, draw the graph of each function.
    a) $y = f(x)$ b) $y = g(x)$
    c) $y = f(x) + g(x)$ d) $y = f(x) - g(x)$

11. Given $f(x) = \sqrt{x}$ and $g(x) = x$, draw the graph of each function.
    a) $y = f(x)$ b) $y = g(x)$
    c) $y = f(x) + g(x)$ d) $y = f(x) - g(x)$

12. Draw the graph of $y = \dfrac{2x}{x^2 + 1}$. Use this graph to draw the graph of each function.
    a) $y = x + 3 + \dfrac{2x}{x^2 + 1}$ b) $y = \dfrac{2x}{x^2 + 1} - x$

13. Each graph involves the subtraction of two functions. Describe the functions which are subtracted, and identify the function which is their difference.
    a)

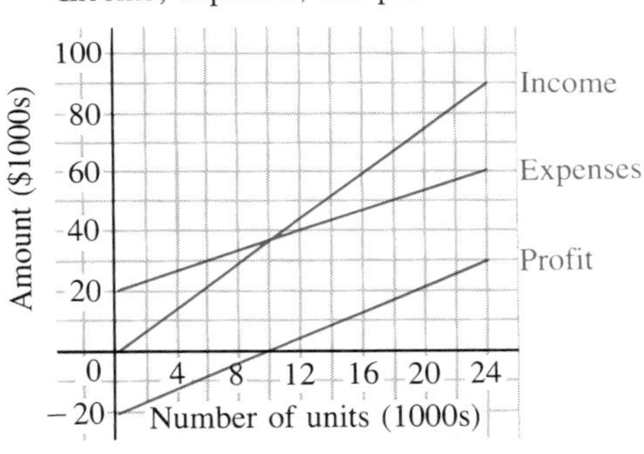

b)

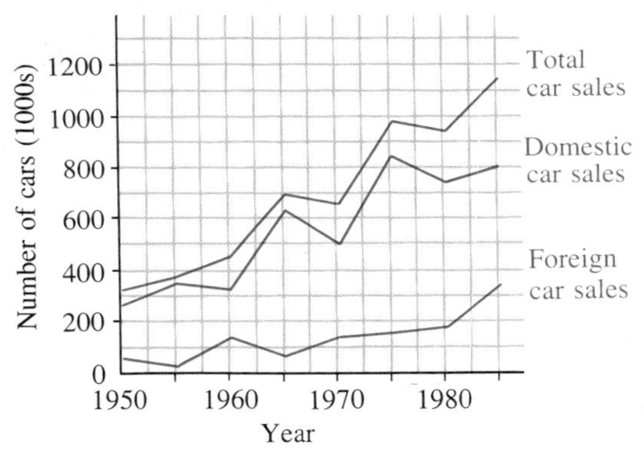

Ⓒ

14. The graph of a function is given. Copy the graph, and draw examples of functions $f(x)$ and $g(x)$ such that the given function represents
    a) $f(x) + g(x)$
    b) $f(x) - g(x)$
    c) $g(x) - f(x)$

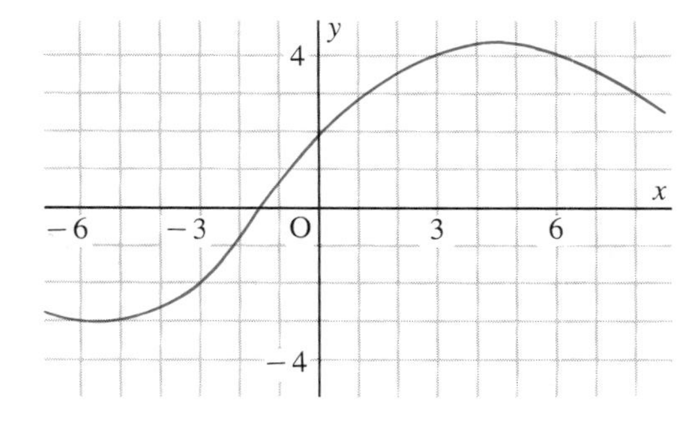

15. a) Draw the graph of each function for reasonable values of x, assuming that $x > 0$.
    i) $f(x) = 2^x - x^2$ ii) $f(x) = 1.5^x - x^2$ iii) $f(x) = 1.1^x - x^2$
    b) Use the graphs drawn in part a) to determine the values of x for which:
    i) $2^x - x^2 > 0$ ii) $1.5^x - x^2 > 0$ iii) $1.1^x - x^2 > 0$.

THE MATHEMATICAL MIND

The Origin of the Function Concept

The concept of a function originated in the seventeenth century, when scientists and mathematicians became interested in the study of motion.

- Galileo showed that the path of a projectile fired into the air is a parabola.

- The moon's motion was studied because knowledge of its position was used to determine longitude at sea.

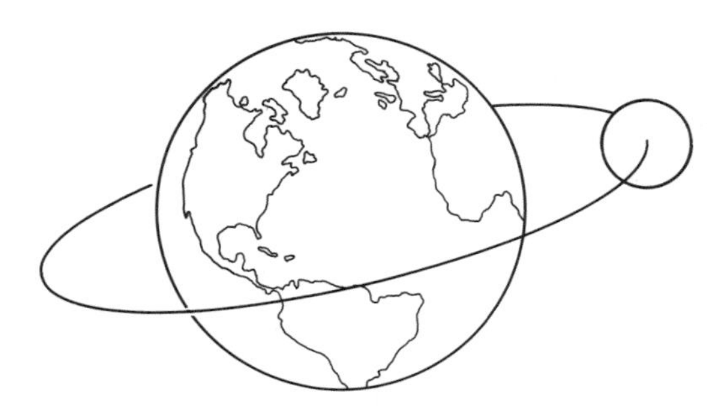

Since moving objects follow a single line or a curve, mathematicians thought that a function was defined by a single equation. For example, this definition was given by James Gregory in 1667.

> A function is a quantity obtained from other quantities by a succession of algebraic operations, or any other operation imaginable.

Leonhard Euler 1707–1783

As late as 1734, Leonhard Euler defined a function as any expression formed in any manner from a variable quantity and constants. He also introduced the $f(x)$ notation.

By 1750, scientists studying vibrating strings had encountered an example of a function that could not be defined by a single equation. This caused a controversy over the question of what a function was. Euler extended the definition to include cases where there were different expressions in different intervals of the domain. For example, Euler would have considered the following expression to be a single function.

$$f(x) = \begin{cases} x + 6, & \text{if } x \leqslant -2 \\ x^2, & \text{if } -2 \leqslant x \leqslant 2 \\ x + 2, & \text{if } x \geqslant 2 \end{cases}$$

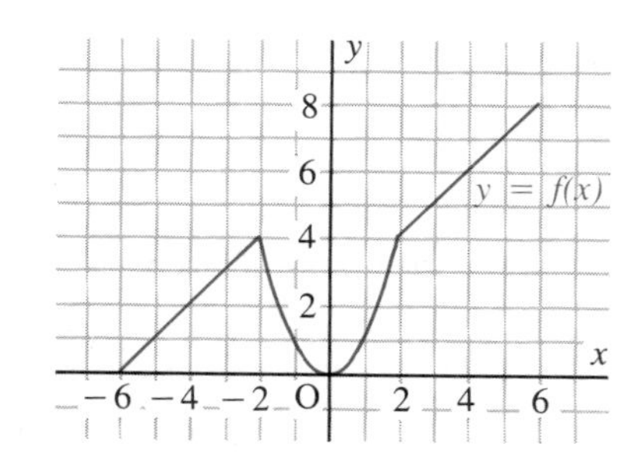

Most mathematicians found this new idea difficult to accept, and the concept of a function given by a single equation dominated mathematics until about 1800.

Joseph Fourier
1768-1830

But the definition of a function was soon to be extended even further. In 1807, Joseph Fourier published a paper about the flow of heat. He used functions whose component parts were not connected. Here is an example of such a function.

$$f(x) = \begin{cases} x + 4, & \text{if } x < -2 \\ x, & \text{if } -2 \leqslant x < 2 \\ x - 4, & \text{if } x \geqslant 2 \end{cases}$$

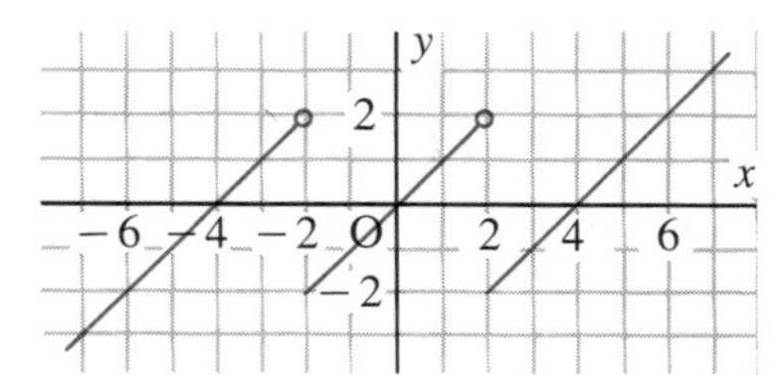

Moreover, Fourier's work implied that a function did not even have to be defined by equations. This led Lejeune Dirichlet to give a new definition of a function in 1837.

> *y* is a function of *x* when to each value of *x* in a given interval there corresponds a unique value of *y*.

Dirichlet's definition is equivalent to the one given on page 3 of this book. It is a very broad definition because it does not matter whether y depends on x according to one law or more, or whether the dependence can be expressed by equations.

QUESTIONS

1. Graph each function.

 a) $$f(x) = \begin{cases} 2 - x, & x \leqslant -2 \\ x^2, & -2 \leqslant x \leqslant 2 \\ 6 - x, & x \geqslant 2 \end{cases}$$

 b) $$f(x) = \begin{cases} x + 2, & x < -2 \\ -x, & -2 \leqslant x \leqslant 2 \\ x - 2, & x > 2 \end{cases}$$

 c) $$f(x) = \begin{cases} (x + 4)^2, & x \leqslant -2 \\ x^2, & -2 \leqslant x \leqslant 2 \\ (x - 4)^2, & x \geqslant 2 \end{cases}$$

2. Write the equations which define this function.

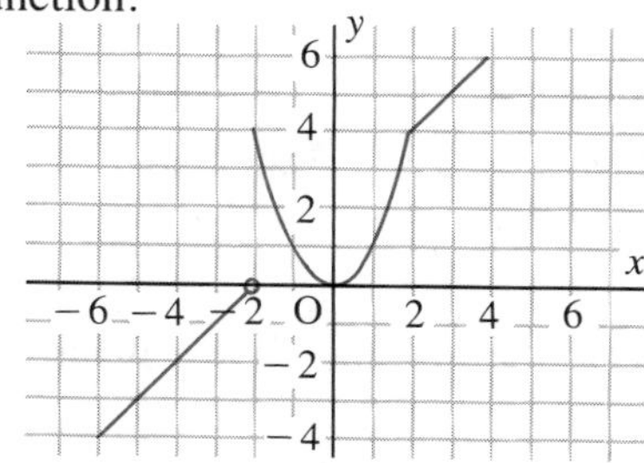

3. Refer to the functions in the examples and exercises of this chapter. Find an example of a function which does not satisfy any of the definitions given above, except the one given by Dirichlet.

4. In 1829 Dirichlet gave an example of a function of x that has one value for all rational values of x and a different value for all irrational values of x. Give an example of such a function.

Review Exercises

1. Graph each function. State the domain and the range.
   a) $y = \dfrac{2x + 1}{3}$ b) $y = (x - 2)^2 - 3$ c) $y = \dfrac{x + 3}{x}$

2. Write the inverse of each function in *Exercise 1*. State the domain and the range of the inverse.

3. If $f(x) = 5x - 2$, find:
   a) $f(-3)$ b) $f(2a)$ c) $f(x + 1)$ d) $f(3n - 2)$.

4. If $f(x) = 4 - 3x$ and $g(x) = x^2 + 2x - 5$, find:
   a) $f(2)$ b) $g(-3)$ c) $f(2x^2 + 1)$ d) $g(x - 1)$
   e) $f(g(x))$ f) $g(f(x))$ g) $2f(x) + g(x)$ h) $g(x) - f(x)$.

5. If $f(x) = 2x^2 - 5x + 1$, solve each equation.
   a) $f(x) = -1$ b) $f(x) = 13$ c) $f(2a) = 13$

6. If $g(x) = \dfrac{x + 1}{x - 1}$, $x \neq 1$, find:
   a) $g(3)$ b) $g\left(\frac{1}{2}a\right)$ c) $g\left(\dfrac{2x - 1}{x}\right)$ d) $g^{-1}(x)$.

7. a) Draw a mapping diagram to represent each function.
   i) $\{(1,-5), (2,3), (3,-2), (5,0), (-2,3)\}$
   ii) $\{(x,y) \mid 3x + y = 5, x, y \in I, -2 \leqslant x \leqslant 4\}$
   iii) $f{:}x \rightarrow 2(x - 1)^2 - 3, -3 \leqslant x \leqslant 2$
   b) Draw a mapping diagram that does *not* represent a function.

8. Given $f(x) = 3x + 2$ and $g(x) = 2x - 1$, find:
   a) $f(g(2))$ b) $g(f(-2))$ c) $f(f(3))$ d) $g(g(-1))$
   e) $f \circ g(x)$ f) $f^{-1} \circ g(x)$ g) $g \circ f^{-1}(x)$ h) $g^{-1}(f(x))$.

9. If $f(x) = 2x + 5$ and $g(x) = x^2 - 3x + 2$, find:
   a) $f \circ g(x)$ b) $g \circ f(x)$ c) $f \circ f(x)$ d) $g \circ g(x)$
   e) $f^{-1} \circ g(x)$ f) $g \circ f^{-1}(x)$ g) $f^{-1} \circ f(x)$ h) $f^{-1} \circ f^{-1}(x)$.

10. Find the inverse of each function. Is the inverse a function?
    a) $y = \dfrac{7 - x}{3}$ b) $y = \dfrac{2x^2 - 1}{5}$ c) $y = \dfrac{3x + 1}{x - 2}$

11. Graph each function and its inverse on the same axes. State the domain and the range of the inverse. Is the inverse a function?
    a) $f(x) = 4 - 2x$ b) $y = (x - 2)^2 + 3$ c) $y = 2\sqrt{x + 1} - 2$

12. Draw the graph of each function, given that:
    a) $f(x) = 3x + 2$ and $g(x) = 4 - 2x$
    b) $f(x) = 2x + 1$ and $g(x) = (x - 1)^2 - 2$.
    i) $y = f(x)$ ii) $y = g(x)$
    iii) $y = f(x) + g(x)$ iv) $y = f(x) - g(x)$

2 Algebraic Operations

A manufacturer produces cartons measuring 30 cm by 40 cm by 40 cm. If each dimension is increased by the same amount, how does the volume change? (See Section 2-1 *Example 5*.)

2-1 OPERATIONS WITH POLYNOMIALS

In your earlier work in mathematics, you studied polynomials. Polynomials are expressions that result from adding or subtracting terms such as $3x$, $2x^2y$, and $-7m$.

Example 1. Simplify.

a) $3(3x^2 - 6x + 2) + 2(4x^2 + 3x - 5)$
b) $4(5x - 3y + 2) - 3(2x + 4y - 1)$
c) $6x - [2y - (3x - y)]$

Solution.

a)
$$\begin{aligned} &3(3x^2 - 6x + 2) + 2(4x^2 + 3x - 5) \\ &= 9x^2 - 18x + 6 + 8x^2 + 6x - 10 \\ &= 17x^2 - 12x - 4 \end{aligned}$$

b)
$$\begin{aligned} &4(5x - 3y + 2) - 3(2x + 4y - 1) \\ &= 20x - 12y + 8 - 6x - 12y + 3 \\ &= 14x - 24y + 11 \end{aligned}$$

c)
$$\begin{aligned} 6x - [2y - (3x - y)] &= 6x - [2y - 3x + y] \\ &= 6x - [3y - 3x] \\ &= 6x - 3y + 3x \\ &= 9x - 3y \end{aligned}$$

Products of binomials are obtained by multiplying each term of one binomial by each term of the other binomial.

Example 2. Simplify.

a) $(x + 3)(2x - 4)$ b) $(3x + 4) - 2(5x - 1)(x + 3)$

Solution.

a)
$$\begin{aligned} (x + 3)(2x - 4) &= 2x^2 - 4x + 6x - 12 \\ &= 2x^2 + 2x - 12 \end{aligned}$$

b)
$$\begin{aligned} (3x + 4) - 2(5x - 1)(x + 3) &= 3x + 4 - 2(5x^2 + 14x - 3) \\ &= 3x + 4 - 10x^2 - 28x + 6 \\ &= -10x^2 - 25x + 10 \end{aligned}$$

The product of two binomials can be illustrated with a multiplication table. For $(x + 3)(2x - 4)$ in *Example 2a* each term in the table is a term in the product of the binomials.

	x	$+3$
$2x$	$2x^2$	$+6x$
-4	$-4x$	-12

There are two special cases of the product of two binomials.

Square of a Binomial

$$(x + y)^2 = x^2 + 2xy + y^2$$

Product of a Sum and a Difference

$$(x + y)(x - y) = x^2 - y^2$$

Example 3. Simplify.

a) $4a(3a - 2b)^2$ b) $xy(2x - 3y)(2x + 3y) - 4x^3y$

Solution. a) $4a(3a - 2b)^2 = 4a(9a^2 - 12ab + 4b^2)$

$= 36a^3 - 48a^2b + 16ab^2$

b) $xy(2x - 3y)(2x + 3y) - 4x^3y = xy(4x^2 - 9y^2) - 4x^3y$

$= 4x^3y - 9xy^3 - 4x^3y$

$= -9xy^3$

To find products involving polynomials other than binomials, multiply each term of one polynomial by each term of the other polynomial.

Example 4. Simplify.

a) $(2x - 3)(x^2 + 4x - 5)$

b) $(x^2 - 3x + 1)(2x^2 + x - 3)$

Solution. a) $(2x - 3)(x^2 + 4x - 5) = 2x^3 + 8x^2 - 10x - 3x^2 - 12x + 15$

$= 2x^3 + 5x^2 - 22x + 15$

b) $(x^2 - 3x + 1)(2x^2 + x - 3)$

$= 2x^4 + x^3 - 3x^2 - 6x^3 - 3x^2 + 9x + 2x^2 + x - 3$

$= 2x^4 - 5x^3 - 4x^2 + 10x - 3$

Example 5. The dimensions of a carton are 30 cm by 40 cm by 40 cm. If each dimension is increased by x centimetres, find a polynomial to represent the increase in volume.

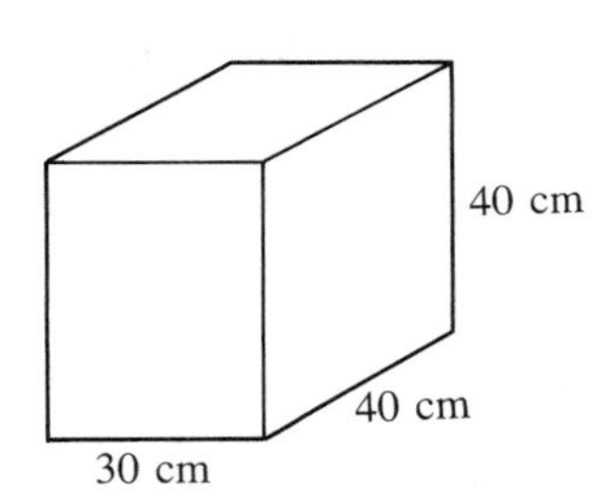

Solution. The volume of the carton, in cubic centimetres, is $30 \times 40 \times 40$, or 48 000.

When each dimension is increased by x centimetres, the dimensions of the larger carton are $(x + 30)$ cm by $(x + 40)$ cm by $(x + 40)$ cm.

(x + 40) cm
(x + 40) cm
(x + 30) cm

The volume of the larger carton is

$V = (x + 30)(x + 40)(x + 40)$

$= (x + 30)(x^2 + 80x + 1600)$

$= x^3 + 80x^2 + 1600x + 30x^2 + 2400x + 48\,000$

$= x^3 + 110x^2 + 4000x + 48\,000$

Subtract the original volume to obtain the increase in volume. The increase in volume is therefore represented by the polynomial $x^3 + 110x^2 + 4000x$.

EXERCISES 2-1

(A)

1. Simplify.
   a) $2(3x + 1) - 5(x - 3)$
   b) $6(a - 2) - 3(2a + 1)$
   c) $2(x + 3y) + 3(4x - y)$
   d) $4(3p - 6q) - 2(p + 5q)$
   e) $3x(x - 2y) - y(2x - 7y)$
   f) $2x(x^2 + 3) - x(5 - 3x)$

2. Simplify.
   a) $3(4x^2 - 13x + 5) - 2(4x^2 - 7)$
   b) $(4 - 11x + 5x^2) - 2(3x^2 - 2x)$
   c) $-5(2a - b + 3c) + 7(3a - 2b + c)$
   d) $n(3n^2 - 9n + 8) - 5n^2(2n - 1)$

3. Simplify.
   a) $(x - 4)(x + 3)$
   b) $(n + 7)(n - 9)$
   c) $(x - 8)^2$
   d) $(3x + 5)(2x - 3)$
   e) $(4a - 3b)(2a + b)$
   f) $(2x + 5y)(x - 3y)$
   g) $2(x - 4)(3x - 7)$
   h) $3(x - 2y)(x + 3y)$
   i) $x(3x - 2y)^2$

(B)

4. Simplify.
   a) $(x - 7)^2 - 3x$
   b) $6 - (x - 4)^2$
   c) $(2a - 5b)^2 - (a + 3b)^2$
   d) $(2x - 3y)(2x + 3y) - (2x + 5y)^2$

5. Simplify.
   a) $(a - 2)(a + 7) - 2(a + 4)(a - 1)$
   b) $3(2x - y)^2 - 2(x - 3y)^2$
   c) $(2x + 5y)(x - 3y) + (3x - 8y)(4x + y)$
   d) $(3x - y)(2x - 9y) - 3(x + 4y)(4x - 3y)$

6. Simplify.
   a) $(3x^2 - 2)^2 + (2x^2 - 3)^2$
   b) $(5y^2 + 2)^2 - (2y^2 + 5)^2$
   c) $x^2(x^2 - 1) - x^2(x + 1)(x + 2)$
   d) $(2x^2 - y^2)(2x^2 + y^2) - 2(3x^2 + 2y^2)^2$

7. Simplify.
   a) $(x - 3)(x + 2y - 5)$
   b) $(n + 2)(3n^2 - n + 3)$
   c) $(x + 2y + 3z)(3x + 2y + z)$
   d) $(x - 1)(x + 3)(x - 2)$
   e) $2(x - 3)^2(x - 1)$
   f) $(x + y)^3$

8. A square has sides of length 5 cm. If each side is increased by x centimetres, find the increase in:
   a) the perimeter
   b) the area.

9. A circle has radius 10 cm. If the radius is increased by x centimetres, find the increase in:
   a) the circumference
   b) the area.

10. The dimensions of a carton are 40 cm by 40 cm by 50 cm. If each dimension is increased by x centimetres, find a polynomial to represent the increase in:
    a) the volume
    b) the surface area.

11. The surface area A and volume V of a sphere of radius r are given by these formulas.

$A = 4\pi r^2 \qquad V = \frac{4}{3}\pi r^3$

A sphere has radius 6 cm. If the radius is increased by x centimetres, find the increase in:

a) the surface area b) the volume.

12. The surface area A and volume V of a cylinder of base radius r and height h are given by these formulas.

$A = 2\pi r(r + h) \qquad V = \pi r^2 h$

A cylinder has a base radius 4 cm and height 5 cm. If the radius is increased by x centimetres and the height by y centimetres, find the increase in:

a) the surface area b) the volume.

Ⓒ

13. The diagram at the right contains three squares. A, B, and C are the centres of the squares, and the side length of the smaller squares is a. Find an expression in terms of a for the area of:

a) $\triangle$ABC b) $\triangle$ADE.

14. Using the diagram of *Exercise 13*, find the fraction of:

a) the entire diagram that is shaded
b) the large square that is shaded
c) the small square that is shaded.

15. a) Simplify.

i) $(x + a)(x + b)$ ii) $(x + a)(x + b)(x + c)$

b) Examine the patterns in the results of part a). Use the patterns to simplify this product. $(x + a)(x + b)(x + c)(x + d)$

16. Use the patterns in *Exercise 15* to simplify these products.

a) $(x + 1)(x + 2)(x + 3)$ b) $(x - 2)(x + 3)(x + 5)$
c) $(x + 1)(x + 2)(x + 3)(x + 4)$ d) $(x - 4)(x - 1)(x + 3)(x + 5)$

INVESTIGATE

1. Use a multiplication table to find the product $(x + y + z)^2$.

2. Describe a rule that could be used to find the square of a trinomial, without having to multiply out all the terms.

3. Use the rule to find each product.

a) $(x + y + 5)^2$ b) $(a - b + 3)^2$ c) $(p - q - 4)^2$
d) $(2x - y + 3)^2$ e) $(3m - 2n - 5)^2$ f) $(4a + 5b - 3c)^2$

2-2 FACTORING: COMMON FACTORS AND TRINOMIALS

Factoring is the operation of changing a sum or a difference into a product. The following examples review some methods of factoring.

Common Factor

Example 1. Factor fully.

a) $12ax + 3ay - 15az$ b) $16x^3y - 24x^2y^2$

Solution. a) $12ax + 3ay - 15az = 3a(4x + y - 5z)$

b) $16x^3y - 24x^2y^2 = 8x^2y(2x - 3y)$

When using other methods of factoring, always check for a common factor first.

There are two methods of factoring trinomials, called decomposition and inspection. Both methods are outlined below.

Factoring Trinomials by Decomposition

This method of factoring a trinomial is suggested by the way the product of two binomials is obtained.

$$\begin{aligned}(2x + 3)(x - 7) &= 2x(x - 7) + 3(x - 7)\\ &= 2x^2 - 14x + 3x - 21\\ &= 2x^2 - 11x - 21\end{aligned}$$

The integers -14 and $+3$ have a sum of -11 and a product of -42. This is the same as the product of 2 and -21.

This implies that a trinomial of the form $ax^2 + bx + c$ can be factored if two integers can be found with a sum of b and a product of ac.

Example 2. Factor using decomposition. $2x^2 + 7x - 15$

Solution. $2x^2 + 7x - 15$

What two integers have a sum of $+7$ and a product of $(2)(-15)$, or -30? The integers are $+10$ and -3.

Therefore, we decompose the middle term, and then use common factors.

$$\begin{aligned}2x^2 + 7x - 15 &= 2x^2 + 10x - 3x - 15\\ &= 2x(x + 5) - 3(x + 5)\\ &= (x + 5)(2x - 3)\end{aligned}$$

If the decomposition of the middle term is written in the reverse order, we get the same result.

$$\begin{aligned}2x^2 + 7x - 15 &= 2x^2 - 3x + 10x - 15\\ &= x(2x - 3) + 5(2x - 3)\\ &= (2x - 3)(x + 5)\end{aligned}$$

Factoring Trinomials by Inspection

Trinomials can often be factored by inspection. For example, consider the possible factors of $3x^2 - 14x - 5$. There are only four possibilities.

All four of these products produce a first term of $3x^2$ and a last term of -5, but they produce different middle terms.

$(3x - 5)(x + 1)$	This produces a middle term of $+3x - 5x$, or $-2x$.
$(3x + 5)(x - 1)$	This produces a middle term of $-3x + 5x$, or $+2x$.
$(3x - 1)(x + 5)$	This produces a middle term of $+15x - x$, or $+14x$.
$(3x + 1)(x - 5)$	This produces a middle term of $-15x + x$, or $-14x$, which is the one we want.

Therefore, $3x^2 - 14x - 5 = (3x + 1)(x - 5)$

With practice, you should be able to use this method without writing down all the possible factors.

Example 3. Factor by inspection. $5a^2 - 12a + 4$

Solution. $5a^2 - 12a + 4$

Since the middle term is negative and the last term is positive, the signs in both brackets are negative. Since the first term is $5a^2$ and the last term is $+4$, the only possibilities are these.

$-5a$		$-20a$		$-10a$
$(5a - 4)(a - 1)$	or	$(5a - 1)(a - 4)$	or	$(5a - 2)(a - 2)$
$-4a$		$-a$		$-2a$

The third possibility is the one that produces a middle term of $-12a$.
Therefore, $5a^2 - 12a + 4 = (5a - 2)(a - 2)$

Example 4. Factor fully. a) $30x^3 + 35x^2y - 15xy^2$
b) $16a - 12a^2b - 18a^3b^2$

Solution. a) First remove the common factor.

$$30x^3 + 35x^2y - 15xy^2 = 5x(6x^2 + 7xy - 3y^2)$$
$$= 5x(2x + 3y)(3x - y)$$

b)
$$16a - 12a^2b - 18a^3b^2 = 2a(8 - 6ab - 9a^2b^2)$$
$$= 2a(4 + 3ab)(2 - 3ab)$$

EXERCISES 2-2

Ⓐ

1. Factor.
   a) $x^2 + 3x + 2$ b) $x^2 - 5x + 6$ c) $3x^2 + 7x + 2$
   d) $2x^2 + 3x + 1$ e) $2x^2 - 7x + 6$ f) $6x^2 - 19x + 10$

2. Factor.
   a) $x^2 + x - 6$ b) $3x^2 - 7x + 4$ c) $2x^2 + 9x + 10$
   d) $2x^2 - x - 15$ e) $4x^2 - 8x - 21$ f) $4x^2 - 17x + 15$

Ⓑ

3. Factor.
   a) $5x^2 + 11x + 2$ b) $7y^2 - 22y + 3$ c) $3x^2 + 20x + 25$
   d) $6 + 19a + 10a^2$ e) $6u^2 - 11u - 10$ f) $6x^2 - 13x + 6$

4. Factor.
   a) $6x^2 + 3x - 3$ b) $6m^2 - 17m - 14$ c) $4 + 12a - 40a^2$
   d) $-60 + 30x^2 - 5x$ e) $40 - 38x + 6x^2$ f) $23y + 10y^2 + 12$

5. Factor fully.
   a) $x^2 + 6xy + 8y^2$ b) $6x^2 - 27xy - 15y^2$ c) $11mn + 3m^2n^2 + 6$
   d) $16h^2 - 9hk - 25k^2$ e) $4st + 14t^2 - 10s^2$ f) $6x^2y^2 - 22xy + 20$

6. Factor fully.
   a) $3p^2 - 19pq - 14q^2$ b) $2a^2 + 15ab - 8b^2$ c) $21a^2 - 25ab - 4b^2$
   d) $20x^2 - 42xy + 18y^2$ e) $-12p^2 - 8pq + 15q^2$ f) $10x^2 + 19xy + 6y^2$

7. Factor fully.
   a) $9x^4 + 12x^2 + 4$ b) $6x^4 - x^2 - 12$ c) $6m^4 + 4m^2n^2 - 2n^4$
   d) $10x^4y^4 - 21x^2y^2 - 10$ e) $6a^4 + 3a^2b^2 - 18b^4$ f) $10x^4 + 25x^2 - 60$

8. Factor fully.
   a) $-12p^4 + 14p^2q^2 + 40q^4$ b) $-15x^4 - 2x^2y^2 + 24y^4$
   c) $-3a^4 - 7a^2b^2 - 4b^4$ d) $25a^4 - 25a^2b^2 + 6b^4$
   e) $-21x^4 - 51x^2y^2 - 18y^4$ f) $16x^2y^2 - 4y^4 - 7x^4$

Ⓒ

9. Factor.
   a) $8x^2(x + 1) + 2x(x + 1) - 3(x + 1)$
   b) $(a^2 - ab)^2 - 8b^2(a^2 - ab) + 12b^4$
   c) $3x^2(2x + 1) - 8xy(2x + 1) + 4y^2(2x + 1)$

10. Factor.
    a) $abx^2 + (an - bm)x - mn$ b) $3ax^2 + (ab + 6)xy + 2by^2$
    c) $mn^2x^4 - (3mn + n)ax^2 + 3a^2$ d) $12abx^2 + (8a^2 - 6b^2)xy - 4aby^2$

11. Factor.
    a) $x^4 + 2x^3y^2 - 3x^2y^4$ b) $4m^6 + 2m^4n^2 - 12m^2n^4$
    c) $a^2bx^4 - (a^2 - b^2)ax^2y^2 - a^2by^4$ d) $3m^2n^2x^2 - 2n^3x + 12m^3x - 8mn$

2-3 FACTORING: SPECIAL TRINOMIALS AND GROUPING

Some other methods of factoring are reviewed in this section.

Difference of Squares

Here is the general pattern for factoring a difference of squares.

$$a^2x^2 - b^2y^2 = (ax + by)(ax - by)$$

Example 1. Factor fully.

a) $49x^2 - 4y^2$ b) $18a^3 - 50ab^2$ c) $4(x + 1)^2 - 25a^2$

Solution. a) $49x^2 - 4y^2 = (7x + 2y)(7x - 2y)$

b) $18a^3 - 50ab^2 = 2a(9a^2 - 25b^2)$
$= 2a(3a + 5b)(3a - 5b)$

c) $4(x + 1)^2 - 25a^2 = [2(x + 1) + 5a][2(x + 1) - 5a]$
$= (2x + 2 + 5a)(2x + 2 - 5a)$

Trinomial Square

The patterns for factoring a trinomial square can be seen from an example of the square of a binomial.

$(3x - 5y)^2 = (3x - 5y)(3x - 5y)$
$= 9x^2 - 15xy - 15xy + 25y^2$
$= 9x^2 - 30xy + 25y^2$

Using a multiplication table

	$3x$	$-5y$
$3x$	$9x^2$	$-15y$
$-5y$	$-15y$	$25y^2$

$(3x - 5y)^2 = 9x^2 - 30xy + 25y^2$

These are the squares of the terms of the binomial.

This is twice the product of the terms of the binomial.

Reversing this pattern provides a strategy for recognizing a trinomial that is a perfect square. For example,

$16a^2 + 24ab + 9b^2$

The first and last terms are perfect squares.
$16a^2 = (4a)^2$ and $9b^2 = (3b)^2$

The middle term is twice the product of the square roots of the first and last terms.
$24ab = 2(4a)(3b)$

Here is the general pattern for factoring a trinomial square.

$$a^2x^2 + 2abxy + b^2y^2 = (ax + by)^2$$

Example 2. Factor fully.

a) $9x^2 + 24xy + 16y^2$ b) $50a^2 - 120ab + 72b^2$

Solution. a) $9x^2 + 24xy + 16y^2 = (3x + 4y)^2$

b) $50a^2 - 120ab + 72b^2 = 2(25a^2 - 60ab + 36b^2)$
$= 2(5a - 6b)^2$

Grouping

Occasionally, the terms of an expression may be grouped to obtain either a common factor or a difference of squares.

Example 3. Factor fully.

a) $ax - cx - ay + cy$ b) $a^2 - p^2 + 2a + 1$

Solution. a) $ax - cx - ay + cy = (ax - cx) - (ay - cy)$
$= x(a - c) - y(a - c)$
$= (a - c)(x - y)$

b) $a^2 - p^2 + 2a + 1 = (a^2 + 2a + 1) - p^2$
$= (a + 1)^2 - p^2$
$= [(a + 1) + p][(a + 1) - p]$
$= (a + 1 + p)(a + 1 - p)$

Strategies for Factoring

Always factor the expressions completely.

Common Factor: Look for the same variable occurring in each term.
Look for numerical coefficients with common factors.

When using the strategies below, always remove common factors first.

Trinomials: Look for a polynomial with three terms. The exponents of the variables form an increasing or decreasing pattern.

Trinomial Squares: Look for a trinomial whose first and last terms are perfect squares.

Difference of Squares: Look for two perfect squares with opposite signs.

Grouping: Look for parts of the expression that can be factored using the above methods. It may be necessary to rearrange the terms.

EXERCISES 2-3

Ⓐ

1. Factor.
   a) $b^2 - a^2$ b) $1 - 9b^2$ c) $81x^2 - 25$
   d) $49x^2 - y^2$ e) $4m^2 - 9$ f) $16p^2 - 49$

2. Factor.
   a) $x^2 + 2xy + y^2$ b) $9e^2 + 6e + 1$ c) $4x^2 - 20x + 25$
   d) $4m^2 + 12m + 9$ e) $9x^2 - 24x + 16$ f) $25x^2 - 20x + 4$

3. Factor.
   a) $ax - ay + bx - by$ b) $ax + by - bx - ay$
   c) $cx - dy + dx - cy$ d) $x^3 + x^2 + x + 1$
   e) $2xy + 4x + 3y + 6$ f) $6ab + 3a - 10b - 5$

Ⓑ

4. Factor.

a) $m^2p^2 - 100a^2$ b) $3 - 48x^2$ c) $a^2x^2 - b^2y^2$
d) $(x + y)^2 - w^2$ e) $y^4 - 81$ f) $16x^4 - 625y^4$
g) $49p^2 - 42pc + 9c^2$ h) $1 - 20y^2z^2 + 100y^4z^4$ i) $d^3a^2 + 2d^3a + d^3$
j) $12m^2 - 36m + 27$ k) $18a^3 + 12a^2 + 2a$ l) $25x^4 - 20x^3y^2 + 4x^2y^4$

5. Factor.

a) $(2x - 1)^2 - y^2$ b) $9m^2 - (5n - 1)^2$
c) $4a^2 - 9 - 2ab + 3b$ d) $x^2 - 9y^2 + x - 3y$
e) $x - a + (x - a)^2$ f) $4x^2 + 4xy + y^2 - 1$
g) $a^2 - b^2 + c^2 - 2ac$ h) $(5x + 2)^2 - 5xy - 2y$

6. Factor.

a) $ax - a + bx - b + cx - c$ b) $(x - b)^2 - c^2$
c) $x^3 + x^2 - 3x - 3$ d) $2y^3 + 5y - 4y^2 - 10$
e) $m^2 - 9 + 6n - n^2$ f) $6xy + 30x - 10y - 9x^2 - 25$
g) $25(x - 3y)^2 - 16(3x - y)^2$ h) $d(1 - r) - dr + dr^2$

Ⓒ

7. Two perfect squares with a difference of 48 are 64 and 16. How many other pairs of perfect squares are there with a difference of 48? Can you prove that you have found them all?

8. a) Show that $x^4 + x^2 + 1 = (x^2 + 1)^2 - x^2$.
b) Use the result of part a) to factor $x^4 + x^2 + 1$.

9. Use the method suggested by *Exercise 8* to factor each expression.

a) $x^4 + x^2 + 25$ b) $x^4 - 3x^2 + 1$
c) $x^4 + 4$ d) $x^4 + x^2y^2 + y^4$

INVESTIGATE

Here are some examples of polynomials having coefficients which are either +1 or −1.

Coefficients of +1	**Alternating coefficients**
$x^2 + x + 1$	$x^2 - x + 1$
$x^3 + x^2 + x + 1$	$x^3 - x^2 + x - 1$
$x^4 + x^3 + x^2 + x + 1$	$x^4 - x^3 + x^2 - x + 1$
$x^5 + x^4 + x^3 + x^2 + x + 1$	$x^5 - x^4 + x^3 - x^2 + x - 1$

1. a) Investigate which of the above polynomials can be factored by grouping.
b) Can any of these polynomials be factored in more than one way?
c) Given a polynomial with coefficients of +1, or with alternating coefficients of +1 and −1, explain how you could tell whether or not it can be factored by grouping.

2. Investigate other polynomials with coefficients of +1 or −1 which can be factored by grouping.

Using Factoring to Evaluate Polynomials

When we make a table of values for a given polynomial, we need to evaluate the polynomial for several values of the variable. We can often simplify the calculation by factoring the polynomial before substituting. For example, suppose we evaluate $x^2 + 12x + 27$ for $x = 8$. The calculation could proceed in either of two ways.

Without factoring

$$\begin{aligned} x^2 + 12x + 27 &= 8^2 + 12(8) + 27 \\ &= 64 + 96 + 27 \\ &= 187 \end{aligned}$$

This solution requires two multiplications and two additions.

With factoring

$$\begin{aligned} x^2 + 12x + 27 &= (x + 9)(x + 3) \\ &= (8 + 9)(8 + 3) \\ &= (17)(11) \\ &= 187 \end{aligned}$$

This solution requires two additions and only one multiplication.

Since the solution using the factored form involves one less multiplication, it is the more efficient procedure. If a polynomial is to be evaluated for many values of x, it is worth factoring the polynomial before substituting.

Not all polynomials can be factored. However, any polynomial in one variable can be expressed in a *nested form* by successive grouping and factoring. For example, the polynomial $3x^4 - 5x^3 + 7x^2 - 4x + 2$ can be expressed as follows.

$$\begin{aligned} 3x^4 - 5x^3 + 7x^2 - 4x + 2 &= (3x^3 - 5x^2 + 7x - 4)x + 2 \\ &= ((3x^2 - 5x + 7)x - 4)x + 2 \\ &= (((3x - 5)x + 7)x - 4)x + 2 \end{aligned}$$

When $x = 3$, the value of the polynomial can be found as follows.

Using the original form

$$\begin{aligned} & 3x^4 - 5x^3 + 7x^2 - 4x + 2 \\ &= 3(81) - 5(27) + 7(9) - 4(3) + 2 \\ &= 243 - 135 + 63 - 12 + 2 \\ &= 161 \end{aligned}$$

This solution requires calculating the powers, four multiplications, and four additions.

Using the nested form

$$\begin{aligned} & (((3x - 5)x + 7)x - 4)x + 2 \\ &= (((9 - 5)3 + 7)3 - 4)3 + 2 \\ &= ((19)3 - 4)3 + 2 \\ &= (53)3 + 2 \\ &= 161 \end{aligned}$$

This solution requires four multiplications and four additions.

It is easier to evaluate the polynomial using the nested form than it is using the original form.

1. Write each polynomial in nested form, and then evaluate it for $x = 1, 2, 3,$ 4, and 5.
   a) $5x^3 + 2x^2 - 7x + 8$
   b) $2x^3 - 5x^2 + 3x - 9$
   c) $6x^3 + x^2 - 4x + 12$
   d) $2x^4 + 3x^3 - 5x^2 + 6x - 11$

2. a) Evaluate $f(x) = x^2 + 12x + 11$ for $x = 1, 2, 3, \ldots, 10$
   b) For what value(s) of x is $f(x)$ a perfect square?
   c) For what value(s) of x is each polynomial a perfect square?
      i) $x^2 + 7x + 6$
      ii) $x^2 + 8x - 9$
      iii) $x^2 - 11x + 24$

3. The program below can be used to compare the time a computer takes to evaluate a polynomial, for a large number of values of x, when it is written in its usual form, with the time it takes to evaluate the polynomial, for the same values of x, when it is written in nested form. For convenience, it is assumed that the coefficient of every term is 3, and that the values of x start at 0 and increase by 0.01. The program can be used for polynomials up to the tenth degree.
   a) Run the program, and use a stopwatch to time how long the computer takes to evaluate a cubic polynomial 250 times using both methods.
   b) Copy and complete the table.

Degree of polynomial	1	2	3	...	10
Time to evaluate 250 terms in original form					
Time to evaluate 250 terms in nested form					

   c) Draw a graph of the results in part b).
   d) The time required to evaluate the polynomial 250 times is a function of its degree. What kind of function does it appear to be?

```
100 REM *** CALCULATING TEST ***
110 INPUT "WHAT IS THE DEGREE? ";N
120 INPUT "HOW MANY VALUES ARE DESIRED? ";H
130 INPUT "PRESS 1 - POLYNOMIAL, 2 - NESTED ";C
140 IF C=2 THEN GOTO 200
150 PRINT:PRINT "CALCULATING USING POLYNOMIAL FORM:":X=0
160 FOR K=1 TO H:Y=3:XP=X
170 FOR I=1 TO N:Y=Y+3*XP:XP=XP*X:NEXT I
180 X=X+.01:NEXT K
190 IF C=1 THEN GOTO 240
200 PRINT:PRINT "CALCULATING USING NESTED FORM:":X=0
210 FOR K=1 TO H:Y=3
220 FOR I=1 TO N:Y=Y*X+3:NEXT I
230 X=X+.01:NEXT K
240 PRINT:INPUT "PRESS S TO STOP, RETURN TO REPEAT ";Y$
250 PRINT:IF Y$<>"S" THEN 110:END
```

2-4 DIVIDING A POLYNOMIAL BY A POLYNOMIAL

Dividing a polynomial by a polynomial is similar to long division in arithmetic. Compare the steps in these two examples.

$$\begin{array}{r} 32 \\ 21\overline{)679} \\ \underline{63} \\ 49 \\ \underline{42} \\ 7 \end{array} \qquad \begin{array}{rl} 3x + 2 & \text{— Quotient} \\ 2x + 1\overline{)6x^2 + 7x + 9} & \text{— Dividend } (2x + 1 \text{ — Divisor}) \\ \underline{6x^2 + 3x} & \\ 4x + 9 & \\ \underline{4x + 2} & \\ 7 & \text{— Remainder} \end{array}$$

Divisor
Quotient
Dividend
Remainder

To check, multiply the divisor by the quotient and add the remainder. The result should be the dividend.

$21 \times 32 + 7 = 679 \qquad (2x + 1)(3x + 2) + 7 = 6x^2 + 7x + 9$

Example 1. Divide $2x^2 + 5x - 2$ by $x + 3$ and check. Assume that $x \neq -3$.

Solution.

$$\begin{array}{r} 2x \phantom{{}-2} \\ x + 3\overline{)2x^2 + 5x - 2} \end{array}$$

Divide $2x^2$ by x to get $2x$.

$$\begin{array}{r} 2x \phantom{{}-2} \\ x + 3\overline{)2x^2 + 5x - 2} \\ \underline{2x^2 + 6x} \phantom{{}-2} \\ -x \phantom{{}-2} \end{array}$$

Multiply $2x$ by $x + 3$ to get $2x^2 + 6x$.
Subtract $2x^2 + 6x$ from $2x^2 + 5x$ to get $-x$.

$$\begin{array}{r} 2x - 1 \\ x + 3\overline{)2x^2 + 5x - 2} \\ \underline{2x^2 + 6x} \downarrow \\ -x - 2 \end{array}$$

Bring down the -2.
Divide $-x$ by x to get -1.

$$\begin{array}{r} 2x - 1 \\ x + 3\overline{)2x^2 + 5x - 2} \\ \underline{2x^2 + 6x} \phantom{{}-2} \\ -x - 2 \\ \underline{-x - 3} \\ 1 \end{array}$$

Multiply -1 by $x + 3$ to get $-x - 3$.
Subtract $-x - 3$ from $-x - 2$ to get 1.

Since the remainder has a lower degree than the divisor, the division is now complete.

Check.

$$\begin{aligned} (x + 3)(2x - 1) + 1 &= 2x^2 + 5x - 3 + 1 \\ &= 2x^2 + 5x - 2 \end{aligned}$$

Example 2. Divide $-4x^3 + 6x^2 + 4x - 7$ by $2x - 3$.

Solution.

$$\begin{array}{r} -2x^2 \phantom{{}+4x} + 2 \\ 2x - 3\overline{)-4x^3 + 6x^2 + 4x - 7} \\ \underline{-4x^3 + 6x^2} \phantom{{}+4x-7} \\ 0 + 4x - 7 \\ \underline{+4x - 6} \\ -1 \end{array}$$

Since the remainder is zero, bring down the next *two* terms.

The quotient is $-2x^2 + 2$ with a remainder of -1.

If a power is missing in the dividend, it must be included using zero as the coefficient.

Example 3. Divide $t^4 - 25t^2 + 62t - 36$ by $t^2 + 3t - 18$.

Solution.

$$
\begin{array}{r}
t^2 - 3t + 2 \\
t^2 + 3t - 18 \overline{) t^4 + 0t^3 - 25t^2 + 62t - 36} \\
\underline{t^4 + 3t^3 - 18t^2} \qquad\qquad \\
-3t^3 - 7t^2 + 62t \qquad \\
\underline{-3t^3 - 9t^2 + 54t} \qquad \\
2t^2 + 8t - 36 \\
\underline{2t^2 + 6t - 36} \\
2t
\end{array}
$$

The quotient is $t^2 - 3t + 2$, with a remainder of $2t$.

When dividing polynomials, we must write both expressions in descending (or ascending) powers of the variable.

Example 4. Divide $-7x - 6 + x^3$ by $x + 1$ and check.

Solution. Write $-7x - 6 + x^3$ as $x^3 + 0x^2 - 7x - 6$.

$$
\begin{array}{r}
x^2 - x - 6 \\
x + 1 \overline{) x^3 + 0x^2 - 7x - 6} \\
\underline{x^3 + x^2} \qquad\qquad \\
-x^2 - 7x \qquad \\
\underline{-x^2 - x} \qquad \\
-6x - 6 \\
\underline{-6x - 6} \\
0
\end{array}
$$

Check. $(x^2 - x - 6)(x + 1) = x^3 - 7x - 6$

In *Example 4*, the quotient can be factored.

We can write $x^3 - 7x - 6 = (x^2 - x - 6)(x + 1)$

$$= (x - 3)(x + 2)(x + 1)$$

This example illustrates that if one factor of a polynomial is known, other factors can be found by dividing, and then factoring the quotient.

Example 5. Show that $x - 5$ is a factor of $x^3 - 2x^2 - 33x + 90$ and use the result to factor the polynomial.

Solution.

$$
\begin{array}{r}
x^2 + 3x - 18 \\
x - 5 \overline{) x^3 - 2x^2 - 33x + 90} \\
\underline{x^3 - 5x^2} \qquad\qquad \\
3x^2 - 33x \qquad \\
\underline{3x^2 - 15x} \qquad \\
-18x + 90 \\
\underline{-18x + 90} \\
0
\end{array}
$$

Since the remainder is 0, $x - 5$ is a factor of the given polynomial. Since the quotient can be factored, we can factor the polynomial.

$$x^3 - 2x^2 - 33x + 90 = (x - 5)(x^2 + 3x - 18)$$

$$= (x - 5)(x + 6)(x - 3)$$

EXERCISES 2-4

Ⓐ

1. Find each quotient and remainder. Assume that the divisor is not equal to zero.
   a) $(x^2 + 7x + 14) \div (x + 3)$
   b) $(x^2 - 3x + 5) \div (x - 2)$
   c) $(c^2 + c - 2) \div (c + 3)$
   d) $(n^2 - 11n + 6) \div (n + 5)$

2. Divide.
   a) $x^3 - 5x^2 + 10x - 15$ by $x - 3$
   b) $m^3 - 5m^2 - m - 10$ by $m - 2$
   c) $3s^3 + 11s^2 - 6s - 10$ by $s + 4$
   d) $2x^3 + x^2 - 27x - 36$ by $x + 3$

3. When a certain polynomial is divided by $x + 2$, the quotient is $x^2 - 4x + 1$ and the remainder is 8. What is the polynomial?

4. When a certain polynomial is divided by $x - 3$, the quotient is $x^2 + 2x - 5$ and the remainder is -3. What is the polynomial?

Ⓑ

5. Divide.
   a) $2x^2 - 1 + 5x$ by $x + 1$
   b) $3x^2 - 5 + 2x$ by $x - 2$
   c) $25u^2 + 1$ by $5u + 3$
   d) $6x^2 - 3$ by $2x + 4$
   e) $8x^2 + 11 - 6x$ by $2x - 3$
   f) $9m^2 - 5$ by $3m + 2$

6. Divide.
   a) $c^3 + 13c^2 + 39c + 20$ by $c + 9$
   b) $x^3 + x - 8x^2 + 37$ by $x - 2$
   c) $6 + 7n - 11n^2 - 2n^3$ by $6 + n$
   d) $x^3 - 12x - 20$ by $2 + x$
   e) $5a^3 - 5a + 3a^2 + 3$ by $a - 1$
   f) $m^3 - 19m - 24$ by $m - 3$

7. Divide.
   a) $x^3 - 10x - 15 + 7x^2$ by $x + 8$
   b) $-2a^2 + 29a - a^3 - 40$ by $-3 + a$
   c) $-6m^3 + 7m + 29m^2 - 13$ by $2m - 1$
   d) $4s^3 - 13s - 6$ by $2s + 1$

8. Divide each polynomial by $x - 2$ and factor the quotient.
   a) $x^3 - 9x^2 + 26x - 24$
   b) $3x^3 - 8x^2 + 3x + 2$
   c) $-x^3 + 3x + 2$
   d) $5x^3 - 56x + 13x^2 + 20$
   e) $16x^3 - 2x^2 - 51x - 18$
   f) $-10x^3 + x - 6 + 21x^2$

9. Divide.
   a) $x^3 + 5x^2 - 2x - 24$ by $x^2 + 7x + 12$
   b) $y^3 - y^2 + 4y + 15$ by $y^2 + 2y - 3$
   c) $10a^4 - a^3 + 11a^2 + 7a + 5$ by $5a^2 + 2a - 1$
   d) $6t^4 + 4t^3 - 13t^2 - 10t - 5$ by $2t^2 - 5$

10. Find each quotient.
    a) $\dfrac{x^3 + 3x^2 - 4x - 12}{x - 2}$
    b) $\dfrac{2m^3 - 3m^2 - 8m - 3}{2m + 1}$
    c) $\dfrac{3x^3 + 2x^2 - 11x - 12}{x + 1}$
    d) $\dfrac{a^3 - 28a - 41}{a + 4}$

11. Find each quotient then factor it.
    a) $(x^3 + x^2y - 9xy^2 - 9y^3) \div (x + y)$
    b) $(-x^3 - 5x^2y - 2xy^2 + 8y^3) \div (x - y)$
    c) $(-8a^3 + 37a^2b - 33ab^2 - 18b^3) \div (a - 2b)$
    d) $(-15m^3 + 47mn^2 + 28m^2n + 12n^3) \div (5m + 4n)$

12. Find the quotient.
    a) $(x^3 + 4x^2 - 3x - 12) \div (x + 4)$
    b) $(6a^3 + 4a^2 + 9a + 6) \div (3a + 2)$
    c) $(9m^3 + 6m - 15m^2 - 10) \div (3m - 5)$
    d) $(4x^3 - 10x^2 + 6x - 15) \div (2x - 5)$

13. One factor of $4x^3 + 15x^2 - 31x - 30$ is $x - 2$. Find the other factors.

14. Two factors of $12a^4 - 39a^2 + 8a - 8a^3 + 12$ are $a - 2$ and $2a + 1$. Find the other factors.

15. Find the quotient.
    a) $(x^4 + x^3 + 7x^2 - 6x + 8) \div (x^2 + 2x + 8)$
    b) $(-2a^3 - 10 + 16a + 39a^2 - 15a^4) \div (2 - 4a - 5a^2)$
    c) $(s^5 - 4s^3 + 19s^2 - 2s^4 + 15 - 31s) \div (s^3 - 7s + 5)$

Ⓒ

16. Find the quotient.
    a) $(x^3 + 1) \div (x + 1)$
    b) $(a^5 - 1) \div (a - 1)$
    c) $(s^4 + s^2t^2 + t^4) \div (s^2 + st + t^2)$
    d) $(m^4 + 4n^4) \div (m^2 + 2mn + 2n^2)$

17. When $10x^3 + mx^2 - x + 10$ is divided by $5x - 3$, the quotient is $2x^2 + nx - 2$ and the remainder is 4. Find the values of m and n.

18. Find the value of k such that when $2x^3 + 9x^2 + kx - 15$ is divided by $x + 5$, the remainder is 0.

19. Divide $x^3 + (a + b)x^2 + (ab + c)x + ac$ by $x + a$.

20. a) Divide $x^3 + (a + b + c)x^2 + (ab + bc + ac)x + abc$ by $x + a$.
    b) Using the result of part a), predict the quotient when $x^3 + (a + b + c)x^2 + (ab + bc + ac)x + abc$ is divided by:
       i) $x + b$ ii) $x + c$.

INVESTIGATE

1. Let $f(x) = x^3 - 2x^2 + 7x - 4$.
   a) Divide $f(x)$ by $x - 1$, and note the remainder.
   b) Evaluate $f(1)$ and compare with the result of part a).
   c) Find the remainders when $f(x)$ is divided by $x - 2$ and by $x + 3$, and compare the results with $f(2)$ and $f(-3)$.
   d) Based on your results in parts b) and c), state a probable conclusion.
2. Investigate whether similar relations hold for other polynomials.

2-5 THE REMAINDER THEOREM

In some problems involving division, only the remainder is needed. For example, to find the day of the week 60 days from now, it is necessary to divide 60 by 7.

$$\begin{array}{lrl} & 8 & \text{——— Quotient} \\ \text{Divisor} & 7\overline{)60} & \text{——— Dividend} \\ & \underline{56} & \\ & 4 & \text{——— Remainder} \end{array}$$

Since the remainder is 4, in 60 days the day of the week will be four days after today.

In algebra, we can find remainders without actually dividing. To understand the method, it is necessary to recognize the relations among the dividend, divisor, quotient, and remainder in a division problem. For the division illustrated above, we can write:

$$60 = (7)(8) + 4$$

dividend = (divisor) (quotient) + remainder

> **Division Statement**
> In any division problem,
> dividend = (divisor)(quotient) + remainder

Example 1. Given $f(x) = x^3 + 4x^2 + x - 2$, find the remainder when $f(x)$ is divided by $x - 1$. Write the corresponding division statement.

Solution.

$$\begin{array}{r} x^2 + 5x + 6 \\ x - 1\overline{)x^3 + 4x^2 + x - 2} \\ \underline{x^3 - x^2} \qquad\quad \\ 5x^2 + x \qquad \\ \underline{5x^2 - 5x} \qquad \\ 6x - 2 \\ \underline{6x - 6} \\ 4 \end{array}$$

The corresponding division statement is

$$x^3 + 4x^2 + x - 2 = (x - 1)(x^2 + 5x + 6) + 4$$

In *Example 1*, notice that the remainder is a constant, otherwise we could have continued the division. Notice also what happens if we substitute 1 for x in both sides of the division statement.

In the left side, the result is

$$1^3 + 4(1)^2 + 1 - 2 = 4$$

In the right side, the result is

$$(1 - 1)(1^2 + 5(1) + 6) + 4 = 0(12) + 4 = 4$$

Hence, $f(1) = 4$

Therefore, $f(1)$ is equal to the remainder. In other words, when the polynomial $x^3 + 4x^2 + x - 2$ is divided by $x - 1$, the remainder is $f(1)$.

This is an example of a general result which is true for any polynomial, and is called the remainder theorem.

> **Remainder Theorem**
> When a polynomial $f(x)$ is divided by $x - a$, the remainder is $f(a)$.

This theorem is proved below.

Given:
A polynomial $f(x)$ is divided by $x - a$.

Required to Prove:
The remainder is $f(a)$.

Analysis:
If we can write the division statement, then we can use the same reasoning that we used above. We should substitute a for x in the division statement.

Proof:
When $f(x)$ is divided by $x - a$, the division can be continued until the remainder is a constant, r.
If $q(x)$ represents the quotient, then the division statement is
$f(x) = (x - a)q(x) + r$.
Substitute a for x in both sides of the division statement.
In the left side, the result is $f(a)$.
In the right side, the result is $(a - a)q(a) + r$, or r.
Since these two results must be equal, $f(a) = r$
Therefore, the remainder is $f(a)$.

We can use the remainder theorem to find the remainder without actually dividing.

Example 2. Find the remainder when $x^3 - 4x^2 + 5x - 1$ is divided by:
a) $x - 2$ b) $x + 1$.

Solution. a) Let $f(x) = x^3 - 4x^2 + 5x - 1$.
The remainder when $f(x)$ is divided by $x - 2$ is $f(2)$.

$$\begin{aligned} f(2) &= 2^3 - 4(2)^2 + 5(2) - 1 \\ &= 8 - 16 + 10 - 1 \\ &= 1 \end{aligned}$$

The remainder is 1.

b) Since $x + 1 = x - (-1)$, the remainder when $f(x)$ is divided by $x + 1$ is $f(-1)$.

$$\begin{aligned} f(-1) &= (-1)^3 - 4(-1)^2 + 5(-1) - 1 \\ &= -1 - 4 - 5 - 1 \\ &= -11 \end{aligned}$$

The remainder is -11.

Example 3. When $x^3 + 3x^2 - kx + 10$ is divided by $x - 5$, the remainder is 15. Find the value of k.

Solution. Let $f(x) = x^3 + 3x^2 - kx + 10$.
The remainder when $f(x)$ is divided by $x - 5$ is $f(5)$.

$$\begin{aligned} f(5) &= 5^3 + 3(5)^2 - 5k + 10 \\ &= 125 + 75 - 5k + 10 \\ &= 210 - 5k \end{aligned}$$

Since the remainder is 15,

$$\begin{aligned} 210 - 5k &= 15 \\ -5k &= -195 \\ k &= 39 \end{aligned}$$

EXERCISES 2-5

(A)

1. Divide, and write the corresponding division statement.
   a) $a^2 - 2a - 13$ by $a + 3$
   b) $x^3 + x^2 + x + 11$ by $x + 2$
   c) $2p^3 + 5p^2 - 2p - 3$ by $p + 1$
   d) $2s^3 - 7s^2 + 16s - 22$ by $2s - 3$

2. Find the remainder when $x^3 + 3x^2 - 5x + 4$ is divided by each binomial.
   a) $x - 1$
   b) $x - 2$
   c) $x - 3$
   d) $x + 1$
   e) $x + 2$
   f) $x + 3$

3. Find the remainder when each polynomial is divided by $x - 2$.
   a) $x^2 - 5x + 2$
   b) $x^3 + x^2 - 2x + 3$
   c) $-x^3 - x^2 + 10x - 8$
   d) $3x^3 - 5x^2 + 2x + 8$
   e) $2x^3 + x^2 + 4x - 7$
   f) $-x^4 - 3x^3 + 2x^2 - 5x - 1$

4. Without using long division, find each remainder.
   a) $(2a^2 + 6a + 8) \div (a + 1)$
   b) $(n^2 + 4n + 12) \div (n - 4)$
   c) $(y^3 + 6y^2 - 4y + 3) \div (y + 2)$
   d) $(-p^3 + 2p^2 + 5p + 9) \div (p + 1)$
   e) $(3m^3 + 7m^2 - 2m - 11) \div (m - 2)$
   f) $(-c^4 + 3c^2 - c + 1) \div (c + 2)$

5. What is the remainder when each polynomial is divided by x?
   a) $x^2 + 3x$
   b) $x^3 - 2x + 8$
   c) $-x^3 - 7x^2 + 4x - 6$
   d) $-x^4 + 2x^2 + 1$
   e) $x^3 - x^2 + 5x$
   f) $-x^4 - 3x^3 + 2$

(B)

6. Find each remainder.
   a) $(2m^2 + m - 6) \div (m + 3)$
   b) $(-a^3 + 2a^2 - 5a + 1) \div (a - 2)$
   c) $(2x^3 + 7x^2 - 3x + 10) \div (1 + x)$
   d) $(n^3 - n^2 + 7n + 4) \div (n - 3)$
   e) $(-3y^3 - 9y^2 + 12) \div (2 + y)$
   f) $(-2x^4 + 3x^2 - 5x + 14) \div (-2 + x)$

7. Find k.
   a) When $x^3 + kx^2 + 2x - 3$ is divided by $x + 2$, the remainder is 1.
   b) When $x^4 - kx^3 - 2x^2 + x + 4$ is divided by $x - 3$, the remainder is 16.
   c) When $2x^3 - 3x^2 + kx - 1$ is divided by $x - 1$, the remainder is 1.

8. When $kx^3 + px^2 - x + 3$ is divided by $x - 1$, the remainder is 4. When this polynomial is divided by $x - 2$, the remainder is 21. Find the values of k and p.

9. When $x^3 + kx^2 + 2x + 9$ is divided by $x - 1$, the remainder is 7. What is the remainder when $x^3 + kx^2 + 2x + 9$ is divided by $x + 1$?

Ⓒ

10. $f(x)$ is a polynomial which leaves a remainder of 3 when it is divided by $x + 2$. Find the remainder when each polynomial is divided by $x + 2$.
    a) $f(x) + 1$ b) $f(x) + x + 2$ c) $2f(x)$

11. When the polynomial $f(x)$ is divided by $x - a$, the quotient is $q(x)$ and the remainder is r. Show that the remainder is equal to each of these expressions.
    a) $f(0) + aq(0)$ b) $f(a + 1) - q(a + 1)$ c) $f(a - 1) + q(a - 1)$
    Illustrate your answers with an example in which $f(x)$ is a cubic polynomial and $q(x)$ is a quadratic polynomial.

12. Without using long division, find the remainder.
    a) $(6x^2 - 10x + 7) \div (3x + 1)$ b) $(-8a^2 - 2a - 3) \div (4a - 1)$
    c) $(-4x^3 - 9x + 10) \div (1 - 2x)$ d) $(6m^3 - 15m^2 + 3) \div (2m + 1)$

13. a) If a fourth-degree polynomial is divided by a quadratic polynomial, would it be possible for the remainder to be: i) a cubic polynomial
       ii) a quadratic polynomial iii) a linear polynomial?
    b) Use the result of part a) to find the remainder when $x^4 + 2x^3 - 5x^2 + x + 3$ is divided by $x^2 + x - 2$.

14. Without using long division, find the remainder.
    a) $(x^3 + 3x^2 - x - 2) \div (x + 3)(x + 1)$
    b) $(2x^3 + x^2 - 4x + 12) \div (x^2 + x - 2)$
    c) $(x^4 - 4x^2 + 2) \div (x - 1)(x + 1)(x - 2)$

15. Find the remainder if the polynomial $f(x)$ is divided by each expression.
    a) $ax + b$ b) $(x - a)(x - b)$

16. If $f(x) = (x - a)q(x) + r$, where r is a constant, what multiples of $x - a$ are closest to $f(x)$? Illustrate your answer with an example in which $f(x)$ is a cubic polynomial and $q(x)$ is a quadratic polynomial.

The remainder theorem was proved by substituting a for x in the division statement $f(x) = (x - a)q(x) + r$. Investigate what happens if values of x other than a are substituted in this statement. Illustrate your results with specific examples.

2-6 THE FACTOR THEOREM

According to the remainder theorem, if a number a is substituted for x in a polynomial, the value obtained is the remainder when the polynomial is divided by $x - a$. If this remainder is 0, then $x - a$ is a factor of the polynomial. This special case of the remainder theorem is called the factor theorem.

> **Factor Theorem**
> If $x = a$ is substituted into a polynomial in x, and the resulting value is 0, then $x - a$ is a factor of the polynomial.

Example 1. a) Find the remainder when $x^3 - 4x^2 + x + 6$ is divided by $x - 3$.
b) State a factor of $x^3 - 4x^2 + x + 6$.

Solution. a) Let $f(x) = x^3 - 4x^2 + x + 6$.
The remainder when $f(x)$ is divided by $x - 3$ is $f(3)$.

$$\begin{aligned} f(3) &= 3^3 - 4(3)^2 + 3 + 6 \\ &= 27 - 36 + 3 + 6 \\ &= 0 \end{aligned}$$

b) By the factor theorem, $x - 3$ is a factor of $x^3 - 4x^2 + x + 6$.

The factor theorem provides a simple method for determining whether a binomial of the form $x - a$ is a factor of a given polynomial.

Example 2. Determine which binomials are factors of $x^3 - 6x^2 + 3x + 10$.
a) $x - 2$ b) $x - 3$ c) $x + 1$ d) $x - 5$

Solution. Let $f(x) = x^3 - 6x^2 + 3x + 10$.

a) $$\begin{aligned} f(2) &= 2^3 - 6(2)^2 + 3(2) + 10 \\ &= 8 - 24 + 6 + 10 \\ &= 0 \end{aligned}$$

Since $f(2) = 0$, $x - 2$ is a factor of $x^3 - 6x^2 + 3x + 10$.

b) $$\begin{aligned} f(3) &= 3^3 - 6(3)^2 + 3(3) + 10 \\ &= 27 - 54 + 9 + 10 \\ &= -8 \end{aligned}$$

Since $f(3) \neq 0$, $x - 3$ is not a factor of $x^3 - 6x^2 + 3x + 10$.

c) $$\begin{aligned} f(-1) &= (-1)^3 - 6(-1)^2 + 3(-1) + 10 \\ &= -1 - 6 - 3 + 10 \\ &= 0 \end{aligned}$$

Since $f(-1) = 0$, $x + 1$ is a factor of $x^3 - 6x^2 + 3x + 10$.

d) $$\begin{aligned} f(5) &= 5^3 - 6(5)^2 + 3(5) + 10 \\ &= 125 - 150 + 15 + 10 \\ &= 0 \end{aligned}$$

Since $f(5) = 0$, $x - 5$ is a factor of $x^3 - 6x^2 + 3x + 10$.

In *Example 2*, we found three factors of $x^3 - 6x^2 + 3x + 10$. The product of these three factors must be $x^3 - 6x^2 + 3x + 10$. This can be checked by multiplication.

$$(x - 5)(x + 1)(x - 2) = x^3 - 6x^2 + 3x + 10$$

Notice that the product of the constant terms in the factors is $(-5)(+1)(-2)$, or 10. This is also the constant term in the polynomial. This suggests the following property of the factors of a polynomial.

> **Factor Property**
> If a polynomial has any factor of the form $x - a$, then the number a is a factor of the constant term of the polynomial.

The factor property indicates which factors to test when attempting to factor a polynomial.

Example 3. Find one factor of the polynomial $x^3 + 2x^2 - 5x - 6$.

Solution. Let $f(x) = x^3 + 2x^2 - 5x - 6$.
We must find a value of x such that $f(x)$ has a value of 0.
According to the factor property, the numbers to test are the factors of -6: that is, 1, 2, 3, 6, -1, -2, -3, and -6.

Try $x = 1$.
$$\begin{aligned} f(1) &= 1^3 + 2(1)^2 - 5(1) - 6 \\ &= 1 + 2 - 5 - 6 \\ &\neq 0 \end{aligned}$$

$x - 1$ is not a factor of $x^3 + 2x^2 - 5x - 6$.

Try $x = -1$.
$$\begin{aligned} f(-1) &= (-1)^3 + 2(-1)^2 - 5(-1) - 6 \\ &= -1 + 2 + 5 - 6 \\ &= 0 \end{aligned}$$

$x + 1$ is a factor of $x^3 + 2x^2 - 5x - 6$.
Therefore, one factor of $x^3 + 2x^2 - 5x - 6$ is $x + 1$.

From *Example 3*, we know that $x + 1$ is one factor of $x^3 + 2x^2 - 5x - 6$. The other factors can be found using either of the following strategies.

Using long division

$$\begin{array}{r} x^2 + x - 6 \\ x + 1 \overline{) x^3 + 2x^2 - 5x - 6} \\ \underline{x^3 + x^2} \\ x^2 - 5x \\ \underline{x^2 + x} \\ -6x - 6 \\ \underline{-6x - 6} \\ 0 \end{array}$$

The other factor is $x^2 + x - 6$. Therefore,
$$\begin{aligned} x^3 + 2x^2 - 5x - 6 &= (x + 1)(x^2 + x - 6) \\ &= (x + 1)(x + 3)(x - 2) \end{aligned}$$

By equating coefficients

One factor of $x^3 + 2x^2 - 5x - 6$ is $x + 1$. Let the other factor be $x^2 + bx + c$. Then,

$(x + 1)(x^2 + bx + c) = x^3 + 2x^2 - 5x - 6$

When the product on the left side is expanded, the constant term must equal the constant term on the right side. Also, the term containing x must equal the term containing x on the right side. These terms are found as follows.

The constant term: $(x + 1)(x^2 + bx + c) = x^3 + 2x^2 - 5x - 6$

$$+1c$$

$$c = -6$$

The x term: $(x + 1)(x^2 + bx + c) = x^3 + 2x^2 - 5x - 6$

$$cx \qquad +1bx$$

$$cx + bx = -5x$$
$$(c + b)x = -5x$$

Since this equation is true for all values of x, the coefficients are equal.

$$c + b = -5$$
$$-6 + b = -5$$
$$b = 1$$

The other factor of $x^3 + 2x^2 - 5x - 6$ is $x^2 + x - 6$. Therefore,

$$\begin{aligned} x^3 + 2x^2 - 5x - 6 &= (x + 1)(x^2 + x - 6) \\ &= (x + 1)(x + 3)(x - 2) \end{aligned}$$

Example 4. Factor fully. $x^3 - 6x^2 - x + 30$

Solution. Let $f(x) = x^3 - 6x^2 - x + 30$.

Since the constant term 30 is much larger than the coefficients of the other terms, we can see that substituting $x = 1$ or $x = -1$ would not give zero.

Try $x = 2$. $$\begin{aligned} f(2) &= 2^3 - 6(2)^2 - 2 + 30 \\ &= 8 - 24 - 2 + 30 \\ &\neq 0 \end{aligned}$$

Try $x = -2$. $$\begin{aligned} f(-2) &= (-2)^3 - 6(-2)^2 - (-2) + 30 \\ &= -8 - 24 + 2 + 30 \\ &= 0 \end{aligned}$$

Therefore, $x + 2$ is one factor of $x^3 - 6x^2 - x + 30$.

The other factor can be found using long division or by equating coefficients. We use the method of equating coefficients.

Let the other factor be $x^2 + bx + c$. Then,

$(x + 2)(x^2 + bx + c) = x^3 - 6x^2 - x + 30$

Equate coefficients.

Since the constant term is 30, $$\begin{aligned} 2c &= 30 \\ c &= 15 \end{aligned}$$

Since the term containing x is $-x$, $$\begin{aligned} 2b + c &= -1 \\ 2b + 15 &= -1 \\ b &= -8 \end{aligned}$$

Therefore, the other factor of $x^3 - 6x^2 - x + 30$ is $x^2 - 8x + 15$.

$$\begin{aligned} x^3 - 6x^2 - x + 30 &= (x + 2)(x^2 - 8x + 15) \\ &= (x + 2)(x - 3)(x - 5) \end{aligned}$$

Example 5. Factor fully. $2x^3 + 7x^2 + 2x - 3$

Solution. Let $f(x) = 2x^3 + 7x^2 + 2x - 3$.

Try $x = -1$.

$$\begin{aligned} f(-1) &= 2(-1)^3 + 7(-1)^2 + 2(-1) - 3 \\ &= -2 + 7 - 2 - 3 \\ &= 0 \end{aligned}$$

Therefore, $x + 1$ is one factor of $2x^3 + 7x^2 + 2x - 3$.

We use the method of equating coefficients to find the other factor.

Let the other factor be $ax^2 + bx + c$. Then,

$(x + 1)(ax^2 + bx + c) = 2x^3 + 7x^2 + 2x - 3$

Equate coefficients.

Since the term containing x^3 is 2, $a = 2$

Since the term containing x^2 is 7, $a + b = 7$

$2 + b = 7$

$b = 5$

Since the constant term is -3, $c = -3$

Therefore, the other factor of $2x^3 + 7x^2 + 2x - 3$ is $2x^2 + 5x - 3$.

$$\begin{aligned} 2x^3 + 7x^2 + 2x - 3 &= (x + 1)(2x^2 + 5x - 3) \\ &= (x + 1)(2x - 1)(x + 3) \end{aligned}$$

In *Example 5*, since $2x - 1$ is a factor of $2x^3 + 7x^2 + 2x - 3$, substituting $x = \frac{1}{2}$ into the polynomial should give a value of zero.

That is, $f(x) = 2x^3 + 7x^2 + 2x - 3$

$$\begin{aligned} f\left(\frac{1}{2}\right) &= 2\left(\frac{1}{2}\right)^3 + 7\left(\frac{1}{2}\right)^2 + 2\left(\frac{1}{2}\right) - 3 \\ &= \frac{1}{4} + \frac{7}{4} + 1 - 3 \\ &= 0 \end{aligned}$$

EXERCISES 2-6

(A)

1. Given $f(x) = x^3 + x^2 - 9x - 9$
   a) Show that $f(3) = 0$.
   b) Use long division to show that $x - 3$ is a factor of $f(x)$.

2. Given $g(x) = x^3 + 4x^2 + 5x + 2$
   a) Show that $g(-2) = 0$.
   b) Use long division to show that $x + 2$ is a factor of $g(x)$.

3. Given $p(x) = 2x^3 + x^2 - 27x - 36$
   a) Show that $p(-3) = 0$.
   b) Use long division to show that $p(x)$ is divisible by $x + 3$.

4. If $x + 7$ is a factor of $f(x)$, then what is the value of $f(-7)$?

5. If $f(5) = 0$, then what must be a factor of $f(x)$?

6. Which polynomials have $x - 2$ as a factor?
   a) $x^3 - 3x^2 - 4x + 12$
   b) $x^3 + x^2 - 16x + 20$
   c) $-x^3 + 3x - 2$
   d) $x^4 - 8x^3 + 24x^2 - 32x + 16$

7. Which polynomials have $x + 3$ as a factor?
   a) $x^3 + 2x^2 - 9x - 18$
   b) $-x^3 - 2x^2 + 21x - 18$
   c) $x^3 + 6x^2 + 9x$
   d) $-x^4 - 8x^3 - 14x^2 + 8x + 15$

8. Which of the following polynomials has $x - 2$ as a factor?
   a) $x^3 - 5x^2 - 17x + 21$
   b) $-x^3 - 5x^2 + 2x + 24$
   c) $x^3 - x^2 - 17x - 15$
   d) $x^3 + 7x^2 + 7x - 15$

9. a) Which polynomial in *Exercise 8* has $x + 5$ as a factor?
   b) Which polynomial in *Exercise 8* has $x - 7$ as a factor?

10. If $y^3 + 2y^2 - 5y - 6$ has a value of 0 when -1, 2, and -3 are substituted for y, then what are the factors of $y^3 + 2y^2 - 5y - 6$?

11. Determine which binomials are factors of $x^3 - 4x^2 + x + 6$ without dividing.
    a) $x - 2$
    b) $x + 2$
    c) $x - 3$

12. Given $f(x) = x^3 - 3x^2 - 6x + 8$, determine which binomials are factors of $f(x)$.
    a) $x + 1$
    b) $x - 2$
    c) $x - 4$
    d) $x - 1$

13. Given $p(x) = 2x^3 + 11x^2 - 7x - 6$, determine if $p(x)$ is divisible by each binomial.
    a) $x - 1$
    b) $x + 6$
    c) $x + 2$

(B)

14. Show that the first two binomials are factors of the cubic polynomial, and use the results to factor the polynomial.
    a) $a - 2$, $a - 1$; $a^3 - 6a^2 + 11a - 6$
    b) $a + 2$, $a - 2$; $a^3 + 3a^2 - 4a - 12$
    c) $x + 3$, $x + 2$; $x^3 + 4x^2 + x - 6$

15. Determine whether each binomial is a factor of the higher-degree polynomial, without dividing.
    a) $x - 1$; $x^2 - 7x + 6$
    b) $x + 2$; $x^2 + 8x + 6$
    c) $x - 2$; $x^3 - 3x^2 - 4x + 12$
    d) $x - 3$; $x^3 + 6x^2 - 2x + 3$
    e) $x + 1$; $x^7 - 5x^4 - 4x + 2$
    f) $2x - 1$; $4x^3 - 6x^2 + 8x - 3$

16. Find a linear factor of each polynomial.
    a) $x^3 - 4x + 3$
    b) $x^3 + x^2 + x + 1$
    c) $-y^3 - 19y^2 - 19y - 1$
    d) $x^3 - 27$
    e) $-y^3 + y^2 + y + 2$
    f) $x^3 + 2x^2 + 5x + 4$

17. a) Show that both $x - 1$ and $x + 2$ are factors of $x^3 - 3x^2 - 6x + 8$.
    b) Find another factor of $x^3 - 3x^2 - 6x + 8$.

18. a) Show that both $x - 2$ and $x - 3$ are factors of $2x^3 - 11x^2 + 17x - 6$.
    b) Find another factor of $2x^3 - 11x^2 + 17x - 6$.

19. Three students were discussing their methods of factoring cubic polynomials.
Scott, "After finding one factor by the factor theorem, I always use long division to get another factor."
Megan, "I don't like using long division, so I always use the method of equating coefficients."
Ivan, "I have found a faster method. I try to use the factor theorem three times. If I can get three values of x which make the expression equal 0, then I know what the three factors are."
Megan, "But that method won't work for all cubic polynomials."
a) Factor $x^3 - 8x^2 + 19x - 12$ using Ivan's method.
b) Give two examples which show that Megan is correct.

20. Factor completely.
a) $x^3 + 5x^2 + 2x - 8$
b) $x^3 + 9x^2 + 23x + 15$
c) $x^3 + 2x^2 - 19x - 20$
d) $x^3 - 7x - 6$
e) $5x^3 - 7x^2 - x + 3$
f) $x^3 - 9x^2 + 17x - 6$
g) $x^3 + 8x^2 + 17x + 10$
h) $2x^3 - x^2 - 13x - 6$

21. Factor completely.
a) $x^3 - 8x^2 + 17x - 6$
b) $x^3 - 3x^2 - 24x - 28$
c) $x^3 + 6x^2 - 31x - 36$
d) $x^3 - 28x - 48$
e) $3x^3 + 2x^2 - 11x - 10$
f) $10x^3 - 21x^2 - x + 6$
g) $x^3 - 39x - 70$
h) $3x^3 + 4x^2 - 35x - 12$

22. Find k.
a) $x - 2$ is a factor of $x^3 - 6x^2 + kx - 6$.
b) $x + 4$ is a factor of $3x^3 + 11x^2 - 6x + k$.
c) $x - 3$ is a factor of $x^3 + kx^2 + kx + 21$.

Ⓒ

23. Is $2x + 1$ a factor of $2x^3 - x^2 - 13x - 6$?

24. Is $x^2 - 1$ a factor of $2x^4 - 3x^3 + 3x^2 + 3x - 5$?

25. Is $x^3 - 6x^2 + 3x + 10$ divisible by $x^2 - x - 2$?

26. Solve by factoring.
a) $x^3 - 2x^2 - 19x + 20 = 0$
b) $x^3 - 8x^2 + x + 42 = 0$
c) $6x^3 + 13x^2 - 16x - 3 = 0$
d) $5x^3 - 13x^2 - 56x - 20 = 0$

27. Prove that $x - y$ is a factor of $x^n - y^n$ for all values of $n \in N$.

28. Prove that $x + a$ is a factor of $(x + a)^5 + (x + c)^5 + (a - c)^5$.

29. Show that for any polynomial $f(x)$ there exists a polynomial $g(x)$ such that $f(x) = xg(x) + c$, where c is a constant.

Investigate whether or not $x + y$ is a factor of $x^n + y^n$ for all values of $n \in N$. If it is not, then for what values of n is $x + y$ a factor of $x^n + y^n$?

COMPUTER POWER

Factors of Cubic Polynomials

The program below finds the linear factors of cubic polynomials of the form $x^3 + bx^2 + cx + d$, in which the coefficient of x^3 is 1. It does this by evaluating the polynomial for integral values of x between -50 and $+50$. When a value of 0 is encountered, the computer prints the corresponding factor. To use the program, we must enter the coefficients in order of descending powers of x.

```
100 REM *** CUBIC FACTORS ***
110 PRINT "ENTER THE COEFFICIENTS (PRESS RETURN"
120 PRINT "AFTER ENTERING EACH COEFFICIENT):"
130 FOR I=0 TO 3
140     INPUT A(I)
150 NEXT I
160 FOR X=-50 TO 50
170     Y=A(0)
180     FOR I=1 TO 3
190         Y=Y*X+A(I)
200     NEXT I
210     IF Y=0 AND X<0 THEN PRINT "(X + ";-X;") IS A FACTOR"
220     IF Y=0 AND X=0 THEN PRINT "X IS A COMMON FACTOR"
230     IF Y=0 AND X>0 THEN PRINT "(X - ";X;") IS A FACTOR"
240 NEXT X
250 END
```

When the program was used to factor the cubic polynomial $x^3 - 4x^2 - 44x + 96$, the following results were obtained.

```
ENTER THE COEFFICIENTS
?1
?-4
?-44
?96
(X + 6) IS A FACTOR
(X - 2) IS A FACTOR
(X - 8) IS A FACTOR
```

This shows that $x^3 - 4x^2 - 44x + 96 = (x + 6)(x - 2)(x - 8)$.

The program only finds linear factors, and does not show if a factor is repeated. However, once one or more linear factors are known, the other factors can be found by equating coefficients.

1. Use the program to factor these polynomials.
   a) $x^3 + 7x^2 - 14x - 120$
   b) $x^3 + 11x^2 - 310x + 1000$
   c) $2x^3 - x^2 - 87x + 126$
   d) $x^3 - 2x^2 - 64x - 160$
   e) $x^3 - 4x^2 - 35x + 150$
   f) $x^3 + 17x^2 - 55x + 100$

2-7 FACTORING THE SUM AND THE DIFFERENCE OF CUBES

Both the sum and the difference of cubes can be factored using the factor theorem.

To factor a difference of cubes such as $x^3 - 8$, write

$$f(x) = x^3 - 8$$

Observe that $f(2) = 2^3 - 8$
$= 0$

Therefore, $x - 2$ is a factor of $x^3 - 8$. By division or equating coefficients, the other factor is found to be $x^2 + 2x + 4$.

$x^3 - 8 = (x - 2)(x^2 + 2x + 4)$

To factor a sum of cubes such as $x^3 + 125$, write

$$f(x) = x^3 + 125$$

Observe that $f(-5) = (-5)^3 + 125$
$= 0$

Therefore, $x + 5$ is a factor of $x^3 + 125$. By division or equating coefficients, the other factor is found to be $x^2 - 5x + 25$.

$x^3 + 125 = (x + 5)(x^2 - 5x + 25)$

These results suggest general patterns for factoring the sum and the difference of cubes. They can be checked by multiplying.

$$x^3 - y^3 = (x - y)(x^2 + xy + y^2)$$
$$x^3 + y^3 = (x + y)(x^2 - xy + y^2)$$

Example. Factor. $27y^3 - 1000$

Solution. $27y^3 - 1000 = (3y)^3 - (10)^3$
$= (3y - 10)[(3y)^2 + (3y)10 + (10)^2]$
$= (3y - 10)(9y^2 + 30y + 100)$

EXERCISES 2-7

1. Factor.

a) $x^3 + 8$ b) $x^3 + 27$ c) $x^3 - 125$ d) $p^3 - d^3$ e) $x^3 + \frac{1}{8}$

(B)

2. Factor.

a) $64x^3 + 125$ b) $125x^3 - 216y^3$ c) $27 - a^3b^3$
d) $(x + 3)^3 - 8$ e) $(y + 1)^3 - 1000$ f) $(x + 2)^3 - (x - 2)^3$
g) $5x^3 - 40$ h) $2x^3 + 16y^3$ i) $mc^3 + 1000m$
j) $x^4 + x$ k) $3y - 24y^4$ l) $16(x + 1)^3 + 2$

3. Factor.

a) $x^9 - y^9$ b) $\frac{1}{x^3} + \frac{64}{y^3}$ c) $(x + 1)^3 - (y - 2)^3$

4. Show that $x^3 + y^3 = (x + y)(x^2 - xy + y^2)$ by:
a) using the factor theorem
b) replacing y with $-y$ in $x^3 - y^3 = (x - y)(x^2 + xy + y^2)$.

(C)

5. Factor $x^6 - y^6$ by considering it as:
a) a difference of cubes b) a difference of squares.

2-8 RADICALS

The ancient Greeks encountered radicals when they considered the lengths of the sides of squares and the edges of cubes.

The Greeks asked, "If the area of this square is 2, then what is the length of the side AB?"
The answer, of course, is the square root of 2.

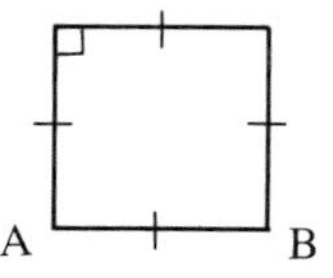

They also asked, "If the volume of this cube is 2, then what is the length of the edge CD?"
The answer, they concluded, is the cube root of 2.

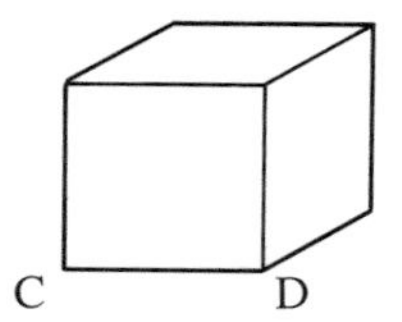

In this way, the idea of a radical was introduced to mathematics, but it was many centuries before symbols such as $\sqrt{2}$ and $\sqrt[3]{2}$ appeared.

Square Roots

The square roots of 25 are 5 and -5 because $5^2 = 25$ and $(-5)^2 = 25$. The square root of any positive number a is a number x such that $x^2 = a$.

A positive number has two square roots, one positive and the other negative. The radical sign $\sqrt{}$ always denotes the positive square root.

Example 1. Simplify.

a) $\sqrt{\frac{4}{49}}$ b) $4\sqrt{25 + 144}$ c) $-\sqrt{1.21}$ d) $(\sqrt{6})^2$

Solution. a) $\sqrt{\frac{4}{49}} = \frac{2}{7}$

b) $4\sqrt{25 + 144} = 4\sqrt{169}$
$= 4(13)$
$= 52$

c) $-\sqrt{1.21} = -1.1$

d) By definition, $(\sqrt{6})^2 = 6$

Cube Roots

The cube root of 125 is 5 because $5^3 = 125$. We write $\sqrt[3]{125} = 5$.

The cube root of $-\frac{1}{8}$ is $-\frac{1}{2}$ because $\left(-\frac{1}{2}\right)^3 = -\frac{1}{8}$. We write $\sqrt[3]{-\frac{1}{8}} = -\frac{1}{2}$.

The cube root of any number a is a number x such that $x^3 = a$.

Example 2. Simplify.

a) $\sqrt[3]{8} + 5\sqrt[3]{-27}$ b) $10\sqrt[3]{\frac{-1}{125}}$ c) $\sqrt[3]{0.001}$ d) $(\sqrt[3]{6})^3$

Solution. a) $\sqrt[3]{8} + 5\sqrt[3]{-27} = 2 + 5(-3)$
$= -13$

b) $10\sqrt[3]{\frac{-1}{125}} = 10\left(\frac{-1}{5}\right)$
$= -2$

c) $\sqrt[3]{0.001} = 0.1$

d) By definition, $(\sqrt[3]{6})^3 = 6$

Roots of Higher Order

Other roots are defined in a manner similar to square roots and cube roots. The fourth roots of 81 are 3 and -3 because $3^4 = 81$ and $(-3)^4 = 81$.
Thus, $\sqrt[4]{81} = 3$
Similarly, the fifth root of -32 is -2 because $(-2)^5 = -32$.
Thus, $\sqrt[5]{-32} = -2$

In general, if n is a positive integer, the symbol $\sqrt[n]{x}$ denotes the nth root of x. The previous examples illustrate the following properties of $\sqrt[n]{x}$.

- $(\sqrt[n]{x})^n = x$
- When n is even, x must be greater than or equal to 0, and $\sqrt[n]{x}$ denotes the positive nth root of x.
- When n is odd, there is no restriction on x. $\sqrt[n]{x}$ is positive if $x > 0$ and negative if $x < 0$.

Example 3. Simplify.

a) $\sqrt[4]{\frac{16}{81}}$ b) $\sqrt[5]{243}$ c) $\sqrt[9]{-1}$

Solution. a) $\sqrt[4]{\frac{16}{81}} = \frac{2}{3}$ b) $\sqrt[5]{243} = 3$ c) $\sqrt[9]{-1} = -1$

Example 4. Which is greater, $4\sqrt{3}$ or $5\sqrt{2}$?

Solution. The expressions can be evaluated using a calculator, but a simpler method is to square each expression.

$$(4\sqrt{3})^2 = 4^2(\sqrt{3})^2 = 16(3) = 48 \qquad (5\sqrt{2})^2 = 5^2(\sqrt{2})^2 = 25(2) = 50$$

Therefore, $5\sqrt{2} > 4\sqrt{3}$

Care must be taken with radicals involving variables to ensure that the roots of even order are positive. This is done by using the absolute-value sign.

Example 5. Simplify.

a) $\sqrt{x^2}$ b) $\sqrt{x^4}$ c) $\sqrt[4]{16a^4b^8}$ d) $\sqrt[3]{-y^6}$

Solution. a) $\sqrt{x^2} = |x|$ b) $\sqrt{x^4} = x^2$

c) $\sqrt[4]{16a^4b^8} = |2ab^2| = 2|a|b^2$ d) $\sqrt[3]{-y^6} = -y^2$

In *Example 5a*, the absolute-value signs are needed because $\sqrt{x^2} = x$ would be incorrect for negative values of x.
In *Example 5b*, absolute-value signs are not needed since $x^2 \geqslant 0$ for all real values of x.

EXERCISES 2-8

(A)

1. Simplify.
   a) $\sqrt{81}$ b) $3\sqrt{25}$ c) $-2\sqrt{49}$ d) $\sqrt{400}$
   e) $-5\sqrt{900}$ f) $-2\sqrt{10\,000}$ g) $\sqrt{0.16}$ h) $\sqrt{0.04}$

2. Simplify.
   a) $\sqrt[3]{-8}$ b) $-11\sqrt[3]{8}$ c) $\sqrt[4]{16}$ d) $\sqrt[5]{-32}$
   e) $\sqrt[6]{1}$ f) $-2\sqrt[3]{-27}$ g) $-5\sqrt[3]{-64}$ h) $\sqrt[3]{0.008}$

3. Simplify.
   a) $\sqrt{4} + \sqrt[3]{8} + \sqrt[4]{16}$ b) $-\sqrt{64} - \sqrt[3]{64}$ c) $\sqrt[3]{27 + 64 + 125}$
   d) $-\sqrt{\frac{4}{9}} + \sqrt[3]{\frac{1}{27}}$ e) $\sqrt[3]{\frac{8}{125}} + \sqrt[3]{\frac{27}{125}}$ f) $\sqrt[4]{\frac{1}{16}} - \sqrt[3]{\frac{27}{8}}$

4. Simplify.
   a) $(\sqrt{37})^2$ b) $-(\sqrt[3]{-125})^3$ c) $(\sqrt[5]{121})^5$ d) $3(\sqrt[4]{12})^4$
   e) $8(\sqrt[3]{17})^3$ f) $(5\sqrt{3})^2$ g) $-7(\sqrt{11})^4$ h) $-4(\sqrt[3]{-6})^6$

5. Simplify.
   a) $\sqrt{36x^2}$ b) $\sqrt[3]{125m^3}$ c) $-\sqrt[4]{81a^4}$ d) $\sqrt[3]{8x^3y^6}$
   e) $\sqrt[5]{-32x^5y^{10}}$ f) $-\sqrt[4]{16a^8b^{12}}$ g) $-\sqrt[3]{-27x^6y^3}$ h) $\sqrt[6]{64m^6n^{12}}$

6. Simplify.
   a) $\sqrt{121x^2y^4}$ b) $-\sqrt[3]{27m^6n^9}$ c) $\sqrt[5]{-243a^{10}b^5}$ d) $\sqrt[4]{256x^8y^{12}}$
   e) $\sqrt[5]{32p^5q^{10}r^5}$ f) $\sqrt[3]{-8m^9n^{15}}$ g) $-\sqrt[6]{729x^{12}y^{18}}$ h) $\sqrt[3]{-125a^6b^{12}c^9}$

7. A square has an area of x square centimetres. Write an expression for its perimeter.

(B)

8. Simplify.
   a) $\sqrt{25x^8y^6}$ b) $\sqrt[4]{16m^4n^{12}}$ c) $-\sqrt[3]{-27a^{12}b^6c^{18}}$
   d) $-\sqrt[6]{64x^{12}y^6}$ e) $\sqrt[5]{-32m^{10}n^{15}}$ f) $\sqrt{225x^6y^{10}z^{16}}$
   g) $-\sqrt[4]{81m^4n^{12}p^8}$ h) $\sqrt[3]{1000a^6b^{15}c^{21}}$ i) $\sqrt[5]{243x^{10}y^5z^5}$

9. Which is the greater number of each pair?
   a) $2\sqrt{5}, 3\sqrt{2}$ b) $3\sqrt{5}, 2\sqrt{11}$ c) $5\sqrt{3}, 4\sqrt{5}$
   d) $2\sqrt{15}, 3\sqrt{7}$ e) $3\sqrt{6}, 2\sqrt{14}$ f) $6\sqrt{3}, 4\sqrt{6}$

10. a) Enter the number 81 in your calculator and press the [$\sqrt{\ }$] key twice. Express the answer as a root of 81.
    b) Suppose you enter a positive number in your calculator and then press the [$\sqrt{\ }$] key repeatedly. Which roots of the original number appear in the display?
    c) Some calculators have a [$\sqrt[3]{\ }$] key. Which roots can be calculated by entering a number and pressing the [$\sqrt[3]{\ }$] key repeatedly?

11. A cube has a volume of x cubic centimetres. Write an expression for its total surface area.

12. Which of these radicals are equal?
$4\sqrt{3}$, $3\sqrt{8}$, $3\sqrt{6}$, $2\sqrt{12}$, $6\sqrt{2}$, $2\sqrt{15}$

13. Arrange in order from least to greatest.
a) $\sqrt{30}$, $3\sqrt{3}$, $4\sqrt{2}$
b) $5\sqrt{3}$, $6\sqrt{2}$, $4\sqrt{5}$
c) $7\sqrt{2}$, $4\sqrt{6}$, $6\sqrt{3}$, $4\sqrt{7}$
d) $3\sqrt[3]{5}$, $2\sqrt[3]{12}$, $3\sqrt[3]{4}$, $4\sqrt[3]{2}$

14. The area A of a triangle can be found using *Heron's formula*.
$A = \sqrt{s(s - a)(s - b)(s - c)}$
a, b, and c are the lengths of the sides of the triangle and s is half the perimeter. Find the area of a triangle with sides 34 cm, 16 cm, and 30 cm.

15. This diagram contains three squares. A, B, and C are the centres of the squares, and the side length of the smaller squares is a. Find an expression in terms of a for the perimeter of $\triangle$ABC.

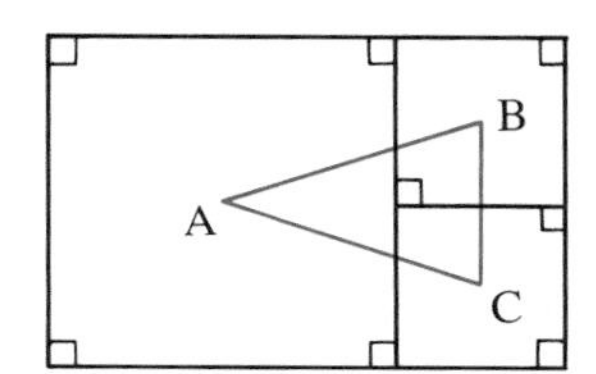

Ⓒ

16. The length, width, and height of a rectangular prism are in the ratio 3 : 2 : 1. Find the ratio of the body diagonal to:
a) the length
b) the width
c) the height.

17. Repeat *Exercise 16* for a prism with its length, width, and height in the ratio $l : w : h$.

18. Without evaluating each radical, determine which is the greater number of each pair.
a) $\sqrt{15}$, $\sqrt[3]{65}$
b) $\sqrt{10}$, $\sqrt[3]{30}$
c) $\sqrt{5}$, $\sqrt[3]{15}$

19. Given two radicals of the form $a\sqrt{b}$ and $c\sqrt{d}$, state the conditions that a, b, c, and d must satisfy for each statement to be true.
a) $a\sqrt{b} = c\sqrt{d}$
b) $a\sqrt{b} < c\sqrt{d}$
c) $a\sqrt{b} > c\sqrt{d}$

INVESTIGATE

1. Notice that $\sqrt{16} < 16$, since $\sqrt{16} = 4$.
Is it always true that the square root of a number is less than the number? If not, then explain how you can tell, for any given number, whether or not the square root of the number is less than the number.

2. Notice that $\sqrt{64} > \sqrt[3]{64}$, since $\sqrt{64} = 8$ and $\sqrt[3]{64} = 4$.
Is it always true that the square root of a number is greater than the cube root of the same number? If not, then explain how you can tell, for any given number, whether or not its square root is greater than its cube root.

Review Exercises

1. Simplify.
   a) $4x(2x + 5y) - 2x(5x - 8y)$
   b) $6a(3a - b + 4c) - 2a(a + 4b - 3c)$
   c) $3x(x + 7y - 2) + x(5 - 2x + y)$
   d) $4m(3m - 9) + 3m(m + 4) - m(5m - 2)$

2. Simplify.
   a) $(2x + 7)(x + 3y - 5)$
   b) $(m + 2)(4m^2 - 5n - 3)$
   c) $(x + 2y - 3z)(3x - 5y + z)$
   d) $(2x + 3)^2 - (3x + 1)^2$
   e) $(x + 2)(2x - 1)(3x - 2)$
   f) $4(3x - 2)(2x + 3)^2$

3. Factor.
   a) $x^2 - 11x + 24$
   b) $2m^2 + m - 15$
   c) $3x^2 - 2xy - 8y^2$
   d) $9x^2 - 30xy + 25y^2$
   e) $10a^2 + 21ab + 9b^2$
   f) $6x^2 - xy - 15y^2$

4. Factor.
   a) $64x^2 - 49y^2$
   b) $80x^4 - 45x^2y^2$
   c) $30a^2 - 57a + 18$
   d) $8x^3 + 10x^2y - 12xy^2$
   e) $2x^2(2x + 1) - x(2x + 1) + 3(2x + 1)$
   f) $4x^2 + 12xy + 9y^2 - 25$

5. Divide, then factor the quotient if possible.
   a) $2a^3 - 5a^2 - 9a + 18$ by $a + 2$
   b) $2x^3 - 13x + 5x^2 - 30$ by $x + 3$
   c) $6x^3 + 17x^2y - 26xy^2 + 8y^3$ by $x + 4y$
   d) $32x^3 - 18x - 16x^2 + 9$ by $2x + 1$

6. Find the remainder when $x^3 + 2x^2 - x + 3$ is divided by each binomial.
   a) $x - 1$
   b) $x + 3$
   c) $x + 2$

7. When $x^4 - 3x^3 - kx^2 + 5x - 2$ is divided by $x - 3$, the remainder is -5. Find the value of k.

8. Which polynomials have $x - 3$ as a factor?
   a) $x^3 - 29x + 2x^2 + 40$
   b) $x^3 - 9x^2 + 26x - 24$
   c) $5x^3 - 18x^2 - 5x + 42$
   d) $8x^3 + 33x - 37x^2 + 18$

9. Factor completely.
   a) $x^3 + 3x^2 - 4x - 12$
   b) $x^3 - 3x - 2$
   c) $x^3 + 5x^2 + 2x - 8$
   d) $x^3 + x^2 - 9x - 9$

10. Find k if $x + 2$ is a factor of $x^3 - 5x^2 + kx - 4$.

11. Factor.
    a) $8x^3 - 27$
    b) $64m^3 + 125n^3$
    c) $54x^6 + 16y^3$
    d) $5y - 40y^4$
    e) $343a^3 - (2a - 1)^3$
    f) $81p^3 - 3000q^3$

12. Simplify.
    a) $5\sqrt[3]{27}$
    b) $-3\sqrt{17^2}$
    c) $6\sqrt[4]{16m^4}$
    d) $\sqrt[3]{64x^6y^9}$

13. Arrange in order from least to greatest.
    a) $3\sqrt{5}, 5\sqrt{2}, 4\sqrt{3}, 2\sqrt{10}$
    b) $3\sqrt[3]{6}, 5\sqrt[3]{2}, 2\sqrt[3]{21}, 4\sqrt[3]{3}$

3 Equations and Inequalities

Modern communications systems depend on geosynchronous satellites which are placed in orbit above the equator. Such a satellite is synchronized with the Earth's rotation, and appears to be stationary. Its height and speed are adjusted so that it travels once around the Earth in exactly 24 h. How high should a communications satellite be placed? (See Section 3-8 *Example 3*.)

3-1 SOLVING LINEAR EQUATIONS

A company makes microwave ovens. Suppose that it costs \$100 000 to set up the factory to produce a certain type of microwave oven and \$200 to make each one. If the ovens are sold at \$450 each, how many ovens must be sold to break even? This problem can be answered using an equation.

Let n represent the number of ovens sold. To break even, the cost of producing the ovens must equal the income from selling them.

Cost of producing n ovens: $100\ 000 + 200n$
Income from selling n ovens: $450n$

At the break-even point:

$$\begin{aligned} 450n &= 100\ 000 + 200n \\ 250n &= 100\ 000 \\ n &= \frac{100\ 000}{250} \\ &= 400 \end{aligned}$$

To break even, the company must sell 400 ovens. If more than this number are sold, the company will make a profit.

If the company priced the ovens at \$500, how many would have to be sold to break even?

The above example is typical of many applied problems in business, industry and science which are solved using equations. The values of the variable which satisfy an equation are called the *roots* of the equation.

Example 1. Solve. $4(x + 3) - 2(3x - 9) = 5(2 - x)$

Solution.

$$\begin{aligned} 4(x + 3) - 2(3x - 9) &= 5(2 - x) \\ 4x + 12 - 6x + 18 &= 10 - 5x \\ -2x + 30 &= 10 - 5x \\ 3x &= -20 \\ x &= -\frac{20}{3} \end{aligned}$$

Notice in *Example 1* that the terms containing the variable are all of the first degree. Such equations are called *linear equations*, and they are solved by reducing them to the form $ax = b$.

To solve an equation containing fractions, multiply both sides by a common denominator to obtain an equivalent equation without fractions.

Example 2. Solve and check. $\frac{x}{3} + \frac{2x - 5}{4} = 7$

Solution.

$$\frac{x}{3} + \frac{2x - 5}{4} = 7$$

Multiply both sides by 12.

$$\begin{aligned} 12\left(\frac{x}{3} + \frac{2x - 5}{4}\right) &= 12(7) \\ 4x + 3(2x - 5) &= 84 \\ 10x - 15 &= 84 \\ 10x &= 99 \\ x &= \frac{99}{10} \\ &= 9.9 \end{aligned}$$

Check.

$$\begin{aligned} \text{Left side} &= \frac{x}{3} + \frac{2x - 5}{4} \\ &= \frac{9.9}{3} + \frac{2(9.9) - 5}{4} \\ &= 3.3 + 3.7 \\ &= 7 \end{aligned}$$

Right side $= 7$

Hence, 9.9 is the root.

Equations with literal coefficients are solved in the same way.

Example 3. Solve for x. $\frac{ax + b}{c} + \frac{bx + c}{d} = 1$, where $c \neq 0$ and $d \neq 0$

Solution.

$$\frac{ax + b}{c} + \frac{bx + c}{d} = 1$$

Multiply both sides by cd.

$$\begin{aligned} cd\left(\frac{ax + b}{c} + \frac{bx + c}{d}\right) &= cd(1) \\ d(ax + b) + c(bx + c) &= cd \\ adx + bd + bcx + c^2 &= cd \\ (ad + bc)x &= cd - bd - c^2 \end{aligned}$$

Assume that $ad + bc \neq 0$, and divide both sides by $ad + bc$.

$$x = \frac{cd - bd - c^2}{ad + bc}$$

Some equations are not linear equations, but can still be reduced to linear equations of the form $ax = b$.

Example 4. Solve. $\frac{2}{3} + \frac{1}{2x} = \frac{2 - x}{x}$

Solution.

$$\frac{2}{3} + \frac{1}{2x} = \frac{2 - x}{x}$$

The equation is not defined when $x = 0$.
Assume that $x \neq 0$, and multiply both sides by $6x$.

$$\begin{aligned} 6x\left(\frac{2}{3} + \frac{1}{2x}\right) &= 6x\left(\frac{2 - x}{x}\right) \\ 4x + 3 &= 6(2 - x) \\ 4x + 3 &= 12 - 6x \\ 10x &= 9 \\ x &= \frac{9}{10} \end{aligned}$$

Example 5. Solve. $\frac{x + 1}{x - 3} = \frac{2x}{2x - 6}$

Solution.

$$\frac{x + 1}{x - 3} = \frac{2x}{2x - 6}$$

The equation is not defined when

$x - 3 = 0$ or $2x - 6 = 0$

$x = 3$ $\quad x = 3$

Assume that $x \neq 3$, and cross-multiply.

$$\begin{aligned} 2x(x - 3) &= (x + 1)(2x - 6) \\ 2x^2 - 6x &= 2x^2 - 4x - 6 \\ -2x &= -6 \\ x &= 3 \end{aligned}$$

But this is the value of x for which the equation is not defined.
Therefore, the equation has no root.

or

$$\frac{x + 1}{x - 3} = \frac{2x}{2x - 6}$$

$$\frac{x + 1}{x - 3} = \frac{2x}{2(x - 3)}$$

$$\frac{x + 1}{x - 3} = \frac{x}{x - 3}$$

Assuming that $x \neq 3$, the numerators must be equal.

$x + 1 = x$

$1 = 0$ This is not possible.

As *Example 5* indicates, when we follow the steps of solving an equation, we may obtain a value of the variable for which the equation is not defined. Such a value cannot be a root of the equation.

EXERCISES 3-1

1. Solve.
   a) $2(3x - 4) = 5(x - 3)$
   b) $7(x - 3) - 2(x + 5) = 39$
   c) $3(x + 2) + 2(2x - 1) = 5(x - 4)$
   d) $5(3x + 14) - 2(x - 15) = 9(2x + 5)$

2. Solve and check.

a) $\frac{x}{5} + \frac{1}{2} = \frac{3}{10}$

b) $\frac{4x}{3} + \frac{5}{6} = \frac{x}{2} - \frac{1}{4}$

c) $\frac{2(x + 7)}{5} = \frac{3x}{4}$

d) $\frac{2x + 1}{5} - \frac{x}{3} = \frac{x - 3}{3}$

e) $\frac{2(x - 3)}{9} - \frac{x - 5}{6} = \frac{x - 1}{6}$

f) $\frac{3(x - 1)}{2} - \frac{2x}{3} = \frac{2x - 1}{2}$

3. Solve for x.

a) $ax + b = c$

b) $\frac{x}{a} + b = c$

c) $\frac{ax}{b} + c = d$

d) $\frac{ax + b}{c} = d$

e) $\frac{ax}{b} + \frac{c}{d} = e$

f) $ax + \frac{b}{c} = d$

4. The average cost A dollars of producing n microwave ovens is given by this formula.

$$A = \frac{100\ 000 + 200n}{n}$$

a) Solve this formula for n.

b) How many microwave ovens would have to be produced for the average cost to be:

i) \$400 ii) \$300 iii) \$250 iv) \$225?

5. The formulas for the volume V and the surface area A of a cylinder are $V = \pi R^2 h$ and $A = 2\pi R(R + h)$. Solve these formulas for h.

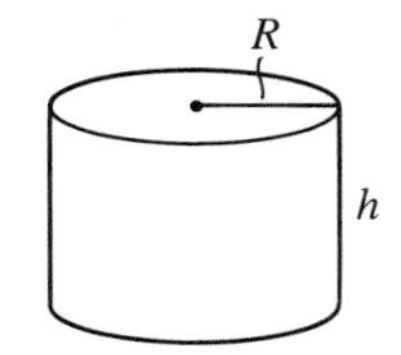

6. The formula for the area A of a trapezoid is $A = \frac{1}{2}h(a + b)$, where a and b are the lengths of the parallel sides, and h is the perpendicular distance between them. Solve this formula for:

a) a b) b c) h.

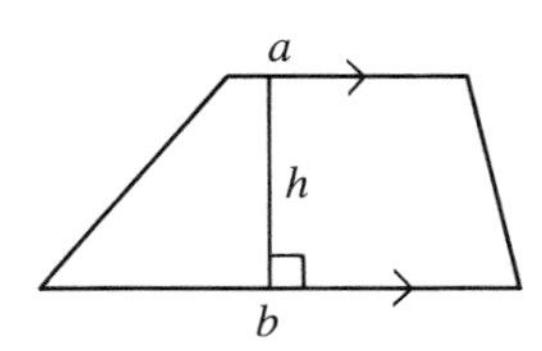

B

7. Find the root of each equation.

a) $4(3x - 1) - 9(x - 3) = 2(x + 1)$

b) $2(3x - 2) = 4(2x - 5) - 5(x - 8)$

c) $3(4 - x) - 4(2 + x) = 2(1 - 3x)$

d) $14(x - 3) + 12(2x + 7) = 8(x + 6)$

e) $3x(x - 5) - 3x(x - 7) = 2$

f) $3(2x - 5) + 7(2 - 3x) = 12 - 5(3x + 4)$

g) $5x(3x - 2) - 3x(2x - 9) = 3x(3x + 7) - 8$

h) $2(5x - 1) - (x - 7) - 6 = 2(x - 7) - 15$

8. Solve for x and check.
   a) $4(3x + 2) - 6(x - 3) = 4(2x + 5) + 34$
   b) $2x(3x + 4) - 5(2x + 1) = 3x(2x - 1) - (x + 7)$
   c) $\frac{5(x - 3)}{4} = \frac{6(x - 2)}{5} + \frac{x}{2}$
   d) $\frac{2x}{3} - \frac{3x}{4} = \frac{5x}{6} - \frac{1}{2}$
   e) $\frac{ax - b}{c} + d = e$
   f) $\frac{ax}{b} - c = \frac{d}{e}$

9. Solve.
   a) $\frac{2}{3} + \frac{1}{3x} = \frac{5 + x}{x}$
   b) $\frac{1}{3x} + \frac{3}{4} = \frac{2 - x}{x}$
   c) $\frac{2x}{6x + 5} = \frac{x + 3}{3x - 1}$
   d) $\frac{2x^2 - 2x + 8}{x + 1} = 2x - 1$
   e) $\frac{2x + 3}{2x} - \frac{1}{3} = \frac{x - 4}{2x} + \frac{1}{3}$
   f) $\frac{3x + 4}{2x} - \frac{7 + x}{4x} = \frac{5x + 4}{3x} + \frac{2}{3}$

10. A regular polygon has equal sides and equal angles. If there are n sides, the measure x degrees of each angle is given by this formula.
    $x = \left(\frac{n - 2}{n}\right)180$

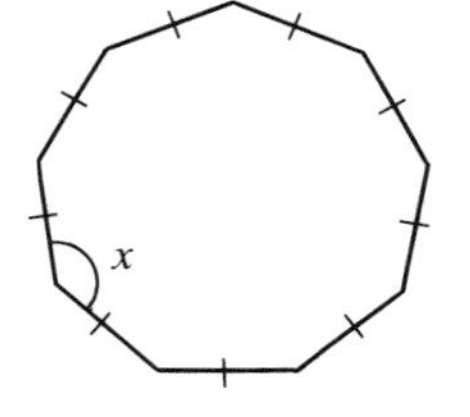

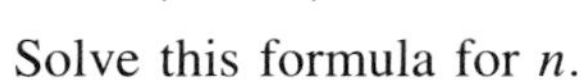

Solve this formula for n.

11. Solve for the variable indicated.
    a) $F = G\frac{m_1m_2}{d^2}$, m_1
    b) $\frac{1}{f} = \frac{1}{p} + \frac{1}{q}$, p
    c) $a = \frac{v - u}{t}$, v
    d) $C = \frac{nE}{nr + R}$, R
    e) $u = \frac{2s - gt^2}{2t}$, s
    f) $A = \pi r(r + 2h)$, h

12. One tank holds 50 L of water and a second tank holds 40 L of antifreeze. Equal samples were taken from each tank and mixed. Each tank was filled with the mixture and the contents of each tank stirred. This was done a second time, after which the contents of the first tank were 17.75% antifreeze. What size sample was taken each time?

INVESTIGATE

Is it possible for a linear equation to have more than one root? If it is, give an example. If it is not, explain why not. Discuss the answer!

3-2 SOLVING QUADRATIC EQUATIONS BY FACTORING

Have you ever wondered how high you would have to go to be able to see from one coast of Canada to the other? If you were in Vancouver, the answer to this question, h kilometres, is the positive root of the equation $h^2 + 12\,740h - 20\,000\,000 = 0$. If you were in Winnipeg, the equation to solve is $h^2 + 12\,740h - 6\,000\,000 = 0$. These are examples of *quadratic equations*.

Quadratic equations without a first-degree term can always be reduced to the form $x^2 = c$. The solution is completed by taking the square root of both sides.

Example 1. Solve the equation $3.5x^2 = 9.1$. Express the roots to three decimal places.

Solution. $3.5x^2 = 9.1$

Divide both sides by 3.5.

$$x^2 = 2.6$$
$$x = \pm\sqrt{2.6}$$
$$\doteq \pm 1.612$$

Quadratic equations usually have first-degree terms, and many of these equations can be solved by factoring.

Example 2. Solve.

a) $x^2 - x - 12 = 0$ b) $4t^2 - 20t + 25 = 0$

Solution. a) $x^2 - x - 12 = 0$

$(x - 4)(x + 3) = 0$

Either $x - 4 = 0$ or $x + 3 = 0$

$x = 4$ $x = -3$

b) $4t^2 - 20t + 25 = 0$

$(2t - 5)(2t - 5) = 0$

$2t - 5 = 0$

$t = 2.5$

In *Example 1* and *Example 2a*, the quadratic equations have two different roots. In *Example 2b*, we say that the quadratic equation has two equal roots.

Some equations are not quadratic equations, but quadratic equations may occur in the solutions.

Example 3. Solve. $\dfrac{3}{x + 1} = \dfrac{3}{4} - \dfrac{x - 1}{3x + 1}$

Solution. The equation is not defined when $x + 1 = 0$ or when $3x + 1 = 0$

$x = -1$ $\qquad$ $x = -\frac{1}{3}$

Assume that $x \neq -1$ and $x \neq -\frac{1}{3}$.

Multiply both sides of the equation by $4(x + 1)(3x + 1)$.

$$
\begin{aligned}
4(x + 1)(3x + 1)\left(\frac{3}{x + 1}\right) &= 4(x + 1)(3x + 1)\left(\frac{3}{4} - \frac{x - 1}{3x + 1}\right) \\
12(3x + 1) &= 3(x + 1)(3x + 1) - 4(x + 1)(x - 1) \\
36x + 12 &= 3(3x^2 + 4x + 1) - 4(x^2 - 1) \\
36x + 12 &= 9x^2 + 12x + 3 - 4x^2 + 4 \\
36x + 12 &= 5x^2 + 12x + 7 \\
0 &= 5x^2 - 24x - 5 \\
0 &= (5x + 1)(x - 5)
\end{aligned}
$$

Either $5x + 1 = 0$ or $x - 5 = 0$

$x = -\frac{1}{5}$ $\qquad$ $x = 5$

EXERCISES 3-2

(A)

1. Solve, expressing the roots to two decimal places.
   a) $6x^2 = 45$ b) $19m^2 = 608$ c) $5.8c^2 - 29 = 0$
   d) $37a^2 = 1776$ e) $2.7t^2 - 13.77 = 0$ f) $0.38x^2 - 5.85 = 0$

2. Solve and check.
   a) $x^2 - 9x + 14 = 0$ b) $m^2 - 2m - 15 = 0$
   c) $x^2 - 14x + 33 = 0$ d) $t^2 + 12t + 32 = 0$
   e) $y^2 + 7y - 18 = 0$ f) $x^2 + 15x + 54 = 0$

(B)

3. Find the roots of each equation.
   a) $2x^2 + 11x + 15 = 0$ b) $12n^2 - 17n - 7 = 0$
   c) $6x^2 - 13x + 6 = 0$ d) $2c^2 + 11c + 12 = 0$
   e) $5t^2 - 11t - 12 = 0$ f) $12a^2 - 25a - 7 = 0$

4. Solve.
   a) $5x(x - 2) = x^2 - 3(2x - 1)$
   b) $3y(y + 4) = y(y + 5) - 3$
   c) $3n(n - 3) - 23 = (n - 4)(n + 2)$
   d) $(6x - 4)(4x + 2) = 4x(x - 1) - x + 4$
   e) $(3a - 7)(2a + 7) = (2a + 1)(a + 3) + 48$
   f) $(2x + 1)(2x - 3) + 5 = (x + 8)(x - 5) + 48$

5. Write a quadratic equation with the given roots.

a) $3, 7$ b) $-4, 9$ c) $\frac{2}{3}, -5$

d) $-\frac{1}{2}, -\frac{3}{4}$ e) $-8, \frac{3}{2}$ f) $\frac{3}{5}, -\frac{4}{3}$

6. Solve for the variable indicated. Assume that all the variables are positive.

a) $E = mc^2$, c b) $E = \frac{1}{2}mv^2$, v

c) $v^2 = u^2 + 2as$, u d) $s^2 = h^2 + (R - r)^2$, R

e) $F = G\frac{m_1m_2}{d^2}$, d f) $V = \pi r^2h$, r

7. Solve.

a) $\frac{5}{x + 1} + \frac{4}{3} = \frac{x + 1}{x - 1}$ b) $\frac{2m + 3}{m + 3} + \frac{1}{2} = \frac{m + 1}{m - 1}$

c) $\frac{a}{a + 1} = \frac{1}{3} + \frac{a - 1}{a + 3}$ d) $\frac{3x + 2}{2x + 1} = \frac{3x + 1}{x - 1} - \frac{1}{3}$

e) $\frac{2x - 1}{2x + 1} + \frac{x + 1}{x + 3} = \frac{3x - 1}{2x + 1} + \frac{1}{6}$ f) $\frac{2x - 3}{x - 1} - \frac{x - 1}{x + 2} = \frac{2x - 5}{x + 2} + \frac{x - 2}{x - 1}$

8. In the open sea, the distance between the waves, the wavelength L metres, is approximated by the formula $L = 0.64v^2$, where v is the velocity in metres per second of the waves.
   a) What is the wavelength when the velocity is: i) 2 m/s ii) 3 m/s?
   b) Solve the formula for v.
   c) What is the velocity to 1 decimal place when the wavelength is: i) 10 m ii) 15 m?
   d) What happens to the wavelength if the velocity is: i) doubled ii) tripled?

9. Solve for x.

a) $x^2 - 2xy + y^2 = 0$ b) $x^2 + 3xy - 10y^2 = 0$

c) $x^2 + 20xy + 51y^2 = 0$ d) $2x^2 + 11xy + 12y^2 = 0$

e) $3x^2 - 11xy + 10y^2 = 0$ f) $6x^2 - xy - 12y^2 = 0$

10. The speed with which water flows out of a hole at the bottom of a reservoir is related to the depth of the water. According to Torricelli's theorem, $d \doteq 0.05s^2$, where d is the depth of the water in metres and s is the speed in metres per second.
    a) Solve the formula for s.
    b) What is the speed to 1 decimal place of the water if the depth is: i) 1 m ii) 2 m iii) 5 m?
    c) What happens to the speed if the depth is: i) doubled ii) tripled?

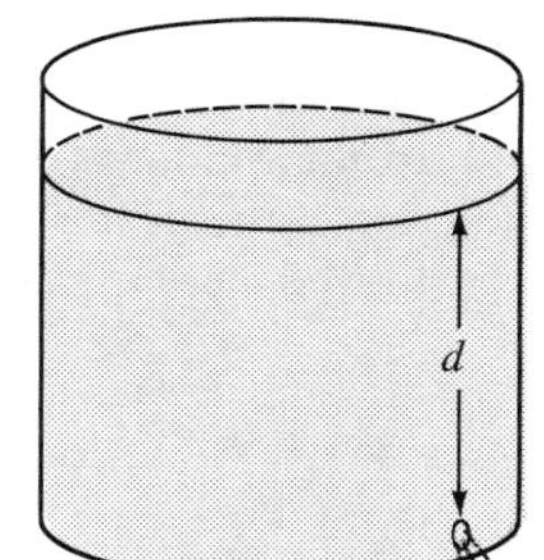

11. The volume of a cone is given by the formula $V = \frac{1}{3}\pi r^2 h$, where r is the radius of the base and h is the height.
    a) Find the volume of a cone with radius 15 m and height 12 m.
    b) Solve the formula for r.
    c) What is the radius of a conical pile of sand with volume 425 000 m^3 and height:
    i) 45 m ii) 60 m?

12. In △PQR, QR $= 10\sqrt{2}$, ∠P $= 90°$, and D is a point on QR such that PD is perpendicular to QR. If QD $= 4\sqrt{2}$, find the length of PD.

13. In △ABC, ∠C $= 60°$; the lengths of the three sides in such a triangle are related by the formula
$c^2 = a^2 + b^2 - ab$.
If AC $=$ 8 cm and AB $=$ 7 cm, find the length of BC. Explain why there are two answers.

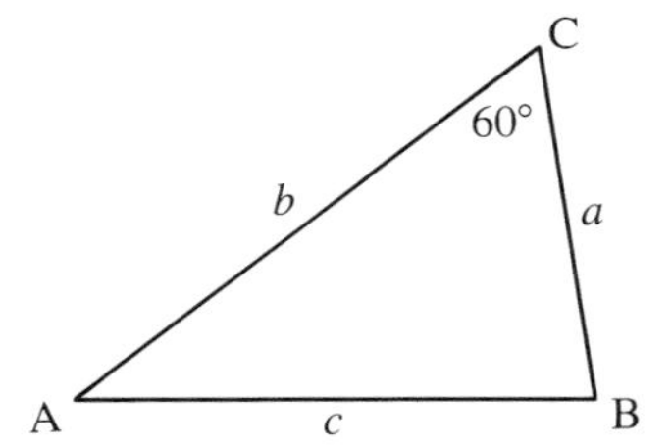

14. In *Exercise 13*, if ∠C $= 60°$ and AC $=$ 8 cm, how long would side AB have to be such that there is only one value for the length of BC?

15. A tin can has a base radius of 4.2 cm and a height of 4.0 cm. The manufacturer decides to increase its volume by 50% by increasing the radius but not changing the height. What increase in radius is needed?

16. A tin can has a base radius of r centimetres. The manufacturer decides to increase its volume by x% by increasing its radius by y centimetres. Express y as a function of r and x.

17. The weight w newtons of an object on the Earth's surface is given by this formula.
$$w = \frac{4 \times 10^{14} m}{d^2}$$
m kilograms is its mass and d metres is its distance from the centre of the Earth. The Earth's radius is 6370 km.
    a) Find the weight to the nearest newton of a 100 kg person at:
       i) sea level
       ii) the summit of Mount Everest, 8850 m
       iii) the bottom of the Marianas Trench, −11 000 m.
    b) Determine how far to the nearest kilometre above the Earth's surface the person would have to go to experience a reduction in weight of: i) 10% ii) 50%.

MATHEMATICS AROUND US

The Rising Fast Ball

Some baseball fans believe that pitchers can throw a baseball that rises as it approaches the batter. This appears to contradict common experience that the ball falls because of gravity. However, it has been observed that a ball delivered with backspin experiences an upward lift that acts against gravity. In one study, a computer was programmed to calculate the amount of lift that could be expected when a baseball is pitched with backspin. It was found that, in the absence of gravity, the lifting force due to backspin caused the ball to rise about 15 cm. Thus, the question of whether the ball actually rises depends on how much the ball falls due to gravity on its way to the batter.

The study showed that the rising fast ball is just an illusion. A ball thrown with backspin may appear to rise simply because it does not fall as much as the batter expects it to. You can confirm this by completing the questions below.

QUESTIONS

1. It is about 18.4 m from the pitcher's mound to the batter. A reasonably fast pitch travels at about 150 km/h. Calculate how long it takes the ball to reach the batter at this speed, to the nearest hundredth of a second.
2. Once the ball leaves the pitcher's hand, it begins to fall. The distance s metres that it falls is given by the formula $s = 4.9t^2$, where t is the elapsed time in seconds. Using your answer to *Question 1*, find how far the ball has fallen by the time it reaches the batter. Give your answer to the nearest centimetre.
3. If the ball is thrown with backspin, how far should it fall by the time it reaches the batter?
4. How fast would a pitcher have to throw the ball before it would actually rise on its way to the batter?

3-3 SOLVING QUADRATIC EQUATIONS USING A FORMULA

Many quadratic equations cannot be solved by factoring. But all quadratic equations can be solved using the method of *completing the square*.

Example 1. Solve. $x^2 + 8x + 2 = 0$

Solution. $x^2 + 8x + 2 = 0$

Isolate the constant term.

$$x^2 + 8x = -2$$

Add the square of one-half the coefficient of x to both sides.

$$x^2 + 8x + 16 = -2 + 16$$

$$(x + 4)^2 = 14$$

Take the square root of both sides.

$$x + 4 = \pm\sqrt{14}$$

$$x = -4 \pm \sqrt{14}$$

The method of completing the square can be used to prove the formula for solving any quadratic equation.

Given:

The general quadratic equation $ax^2 + bx + c = 0$, where $a \neq 0$

Required to Prove:

$$x = \frac{-b \pm \sqrt{b^2 - 4ac}}{2a}$$

Proof:

Statement	Reason
$ax^2 + bx + c = 0$	
$x^2 + \frac{b}{a}x + \frac{c}{a} = 0$	Dividing both sides by a
$x^2 + \frac{b}{a}x = -\frac{c}{a}$	Isolating the constant term
$x^2 + \frac{bx}{a} + \frac{b^2}{4a^2} = \frac{b^2}{4a^2} - \frac{c}{a}$	Completing the square on the left side, and adding the same term to the right side
$\left(x + \frac{b}{2a}\right)^2 = \frac{b^2 - 4ac}{4a^2}$	Writing the left side as a complete square
$x + \frac{b}{2a} = \pm\frac{\sqrt{b^2 - 4ac}}{2a}$	Taking the square root of both sides
$x = \frac{-b}{2a} \pm \frac{\sqrt{b^2 - 4ac}}{2a}$	
$x = \frac{-b \pm \sqrt{b^2 - 4ac}}{2a}$	

This result is called the quadratic formula.

Quadratic Formula

The roots of the equation $ax^2 + bx + c = 0$ are $x = \dfrac{-b \pm \sqrt{b^2 - 4ac}}{2a}$.

Example 2. Find the roots of each equation.

a) $9x^2 - 12x + 2 = 0$
b) $9x^2 - 12x + 3 = 0$
c) $9x^2 - 12x + 4 = 0$
d) $9x^2 - 12x + 5 = 0$

Solution. Compare each equation with the general equation $ax^2 + bx + c = 0$.

a) $9x^2 - 12x + 2 = 0 \qquad a = 9, b = -12, c = 2$

$$\begin{aligned} x &= \frac{-b \pm \sqrt{b^2 - 4ac}}{2a} \\ &= \frac{-(-12) \pm \sqrt{(-12)^2 - 4(9)(2)}}{2(9)} \\ &= \frac{12 \pm \sqrt{72}}{18} \\ &= \frac{12 \pm 6\sqrt{2}}{18} \\ &= \frac{2 \pm \sqrt{2}}{3} \end{aligned}$$

The roots of the equation are $\dfrac{2 + \sqrt{2}}{3}$ and $\dfrac{2 - \sqrt{2}}{3}$.

b) $9x^2 - 12x + 3 = 0 \qquad a = 9, b = -12, c = 3$

$$\begin{aligned} x &= \frac{-(-12) \pm \sqrt{(-12)^2 - 4(9)(3)}}{2(9)} \\ &= \frac{12 \pm \sqrt{36}}{18} \\ &= \frac{12 \pm 6}{18} \\ &= 1 \text{ or } \frac{1}{3} \end{aligned}$$

The roots are 1 and $\frac{1}{3}$.

c) $9x^2 - 12x + 4 = 0 \qquad a = 9, b = -12, c = 4$

$$\begin{aligned} x &= \frac{-(-12) \pm \sqrt{(-12)^2 - 4(9)(4)}}{2(9)} \\ &= \frac{12 \pm 0}{18} \\ &= \frac{2}{3} \end{aligned}$$

The equation has two equal roots, $\frac{2}{3}$.

d) $9x^2 - 12x + 5 = 0$

$a = 9,\ b = -12,\ c = 5$

$$x = \frac{-(-12) \pm \sqrt{(-12)^2 - 4(9)(5)}}{2(9)}$$

$$= \frac{12 \pm \sqrt{-36}}{18}$$

Since the square root of a negative number is not defined as a real number, the equation has no real roots.

In *Example 2d*, the number under the radical sign is negative. We can extend the number system to include square roots of negative numbers by defining the number i with the property that $i^2 = -1$, or $i = \sqrt{-1}$. Then we can define $\sqrt{-36}$.

$$\sqrt{-36} = \sqrt{36} \times \sqrt{-1}$$
$$= 6i$$

With this definition, the solution of *Example 2d* can be completed.

$$x = \frac{12 \pm \sqrt{-36}}{18}$$

$$x = \frac{12 \pm 6i}{18}$$

$$= \frac{2}{3} + \frac{1}{3}i \text{ or } \frac{2}{3} - \frac{1}{3}i, \text{ where } i = \sqrt{-1}$$

These roots are examples of complex numbers. We can check that they satisfy the equation by using the fact that $i^2 = -1$.

Check the root $x = \frac{2}{3} + \frac{1}{3}i$.

Left side $= 9x^2 - 12x + 5$ Right side $= 0$

$$= 9\left(\frac{2}{3} + \frac{1}{3}i\right)^2 - 12\left(\frac{2}{3} + \frac{1}{3}i\right) + 5$$

$$= 9\left(\frac{4}{9} + \frac{4}{9}i + \frac{1}{9}i^2\right) - 8 - 4i + 5$$

$$= 4 + 4i - 1 - 8 - 4i + 5$$

$$= 0$$

Hence, $\frac{2}{3} + \frac{1}{3}i$ is a root of the equation. We can also check the root $\frac{2}{3} - \frac{1}{3}i$. These two roots are called conjugates, since they differ only in the sign of the term containing i.

- An expression of the form $a + bi$, where a and b are real numbers, and $i^2 = -1$, is called a *complex number*.
- The complex numbers $a + bi$ and $a - bi$ are called *conjugates*.
- The set of complex numbers includes real numbers, since any real number x can be written in the form $x + 0i$.

As *Example 2* suggests, the number under the radical sign indicates the types of roots the equation has. This number is called the *discriminant* of the equation.

Properties of Quadratic Equations

- Every quadratic equation has two complex roots. The roots of the equation $ax^2 + bx + c = 0$, $a \neq 0$, are:
$\dfrac{-b + \sqrt{b^2 - 4ac}}{2a}$ and $\dfrac{-b - \sqrt{b^2 - 4ac}}{2a}$.
- The nature of the roots is indicated by the discriminant.
If $b^2 - 4ac > 0$, there are two different real roots.
If $b^2 - 4ac = 0$, there are two equal real roots.
If $b^2 - 4ac < 0$, there are two conjugate complex roots.

Example 3. One root of a quadratic equation is $3 - 2i$.
a) What is the other root of the equation?
b) Write a quadratic equation with these roots.

Solution. a) Since $3 - 2i$ is a complex root, and complex roots occur in conjugate pairs, the other root is $3 + 2i$.
b) A quadratic equation with these roots is

$$\begin{aligned} [x - (3 - 2i)][x - (3 + 2i)] &= 0 \\ x^2 - (3 - 2i + 3 + 2i)x + (3 - 2i)(3 + 2i) &= 0 \\ x^2 - 6x + 9 - 4i^2 &= 0 \\ x^2 - 6x + 9 - 4(-1) &= 0 \\ x^2 - 6x + 13 &= 0 \end{aligned}$$

EXERCISES 3-3

1. Solve.
a) $3x^2 - 5x + 2 = 0$ b) $5x^2 + 6x + 1 = 0$ c) $2x^2 - 6x - 1 = 0$
d) $4x^2 - 24x + 36 = 0$ e) $2x^2 - 13x + 10 = 0$ f) $4x^2 - 4x - 3 = 0$

2. Solve and check.
a) $12x^2 - x - 6 = 0$ b) $15x^2 - 7x - 1 = 0$ c) $4x^2 - 17x + 3 = 0$
d) $6x^2 - x - 2 = 0$ e) $9x^2 + 24x + 15 = 0$ f) $2x^2 - 7x - 15 = 0$

3. Solve.
a) $x^2 + 7x - 12 = 0$ b) $x^2 - 8x + 14 = 0$ c) $3x^2 + 5x + 1 = 0$
d) $4x^2 - 9x + 5 = 0$ e) $2x^2 + 5x + 6 = 0$ f) $5x^2 + 4x + 2 = 0$

4. Solve.
a) $4x^2 + 20x + 15 = 0$ b) $4x^2 + 20x + 21 = 0$ c) $4x^2 + 20x + 10 = 0$
d) $4x^2 + 20x + 25 = 0$ e) $4x^2 + 20x + 30 = 0$ f) $4x^2 + 20x + 35 = 0$

5. Write the conjugate of each complex number.
a) $1 + 2i$ b) $5 - 3i$ c) $4i + 1$ d) $i - 2$ e) i

Ⓑ

6. Find the discriminant of each equation.
   a) $3x^2 + 7x + 4 = 0$ b) $2x^2 + 3x - 8 = 0$ c) $5x^2 - x + 2 = 0$
   d) $4x^2 + 12x + 9 = 0$ e) $2x^2 - 9x - 5 = 0$ f) $3x^2 + 4x + 7 = 0$

7. Which equations in *Exercise 6* have:
   a) 2 different real roots b) 2 equal real roots c) 2 complex roots?

8. Determine the nature of the roots of each equation.
   a) $4x^2 + 7x - 2 = 0$ b) $2x^2 - 7x - 15 = 0$ c) $3x^2 - 8x + 7 = 0$
   d) $7x^2 + 10x - 3 = 0$ e) $16x^2 + 8x + 1 = 0$ f) $12x^2 - 9x + 5 = 0$

9. Solve.
   a) $5x^2 + 4x - 1 = 0$ b) $2x^2 - 8x + 5 = 0$ c) $3x^2 + 5x + 1 = 0$
   d) $4x^2 + 7x + 5 = 0$ e) $3x^2 - 8x + 4 = 0$ f) $2x^2 - 4x + 5 = 0$

10. A complex root of a quadratic equation is given below. Write the other root, and then write a quadratic equation with these roots.
    a) $3 + 4i$ b) $1 - 2i$ c) $2 + 7i$ d) $3i + 2$ e) $i - 1$

11. Solve.
    a) $5x(x + 3) = (3x + 2)(x - 1)$
    b) $(2x + 5)(x - 3) = (4x + 7)(3x - 1)$
    c) $(3x + 1)(2x + 5) = (2x - 3)(x - 2)$
    d) $(x + 2)(x - 5) = (2x + 1)(x - 4)$
    e) $(x + 2)(5x + 1) = 5x - (2x + 1)(2x + 2)$
    f) $(2x + 7)(x + 4) = (3x + 5)(x - 2)$

12. Solve.
    a) $\frac{x^2 + 5}{3} - \frac{7}{2} = \frac{x + 8}{2}$ b) $\frac{1}{x} + \frac{x}{2} = \frac{2}{3}$
    c) $\frac{8}{x} + \frac{5}{x + 2} = 1$ d) $\frac{3}{2x + 1} - \frac{x + 2}{3x - 1} = \frac{x - 3}{2x + 1}$
    e) $\frac{4}{x + 1} - \frac{1}{x + 3} = \frac{2}{3}$ f) $\frac{2x + 1}{x} + \frac{x - 3}{x + 2} = \frac{x - 1}{x} + \frac{5}{x + 2}$

13. Write a quadratic equation with these roots.
    a) $7, -2$ b) $-\frac{3}{5}, -\frac{2}{3}$ c) $2 - \sqrt{5}, 2 + \sqrt{5}$
    d) $3 + i, 3 - i$ e) $\frac{3 + 2\sqrt{6}}{2}, \frac{3 - 2\sqrt{6}}{2}$ f) $\frac{2 + 3i}{4}, \frac{2 - 3i}{4}$

14. For what value(s) of k does each equation have two equal real roots?
    a) $3x^2 - kx + 8 = 0$ b) $5x^2 + 8x - 2k = 0$
    c) $kx^2 + 9 = 18x$ d) $(3k + 1)x^2 + kx + 1 = 0$

15. For what values of m does each equation have two real roots?
    a) $2x^2 + mx + 9 = 0$ b) $5mx^2 + 6x + 2 = 0$
    c) $3(x^2 - 2m) = 9x$ d) $4x^2 - 2mx + 3 = 0$

16. A sum of money earns interest at a rate i, compounded semi-annually. A slightly higher rate r, compounded annually, yields the same interest in a year. These rates are related by this formula.
$r = (1 + 0.5i)^2 - 1$, where r and i are percents expressed as decimals
a) If $i = 10\%$, find r. b) If $r = 18\%$, find i.

17. Some soup is sold in 284 mL cans with a height of 9.4 cm and a base radius of 3.2 cm. The manufacturer plans to introduce a new kind of soup in cans containing twice as much soup. If the height of the new cans is the same as the old ones, determine the radius of the new cans.

18. In a certain programming language, the instruction CALL –856 executes a delay loop of length t microseconds, where $t = 2.5x^2 + 13.5x + 13$, and x is a number stored in memory. What number x should be stored to have a delay loop of length:
a) 1 s b) 30 s?

19. A square with sides of length 6 cm is divided into 3 right triangles and a larger isosceles triangle. The three right triangles have equal areas.
a) Find the value of x.
b) Find the area of the larger isosceles triangle.

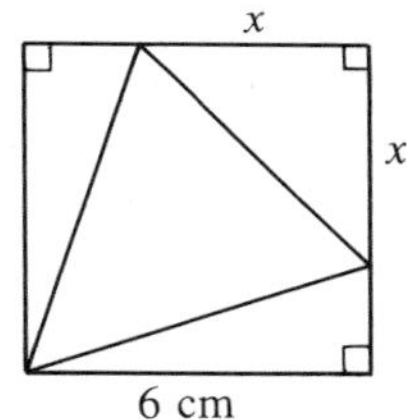

20. Solve the equations given on page 79 to determine how high you would have to go until you could see from one coast of Canada to the other coast:
a) from above Vancouver b) from above Winnipeg.

21. Find values of k such that each quadratic equation can be solved by factoring.
a) $x^2 + kx + 12 = 0$ b) $x^2 + kx = 8$ c) $x^2 - 3x = k$

Ⓒ

22. Find the condition that must be satisfied by a, b, and c if the roots of the equation $ax^2 + bx + c = 0$ are in each ratio.
a) 1 : 1 b) 2 : 1 c) 1 : 2 d) $m : n$

23. a) Explain why the equation $(x - 1)^2 + (x + 1)^2 = 0$ has no real roots.
b) Find the complex roots of the equation $(x - 1)^2 + (x + 1)^2 = 0$.

24. Determine whether or not there are any real numbers x and y with the property that the reciprocal of their sum is equal to the sum of their reciprocals.

25. a) Show that the product of two consecutive natural numbers can never be a perfect square.
b) If n is a natural number, determine the least value of x such that $n + x$ is a rational number and $n(n + x)$ is a perfect square.

26. In the proof of the quadratic formula on page 84, the first step was to make the first term a perfect square by dividing both sides by a. But the first term can be made a perfect square by multiplying both sides by $4a$. Use this approach to develop the formula for solving a quadratic equation.

3-4 SOLVING POLYNOMIAL EQUATIONS BY GRAPHING

When we drop a stone into a well, a certain amount of time passes before we hear it hit the water. The time interval t seconds for a well 100 m deep can be calculated from this equation.

$0.015t^3 - 4.9t^2 + 100 = 0$

This is an example of a cubic equation. Quadratic and cubic equations are special cases of a more general type of equation called a *polynomial equation*. Here are some other examples of polynomial equations.

Quartic equation (fourth degree): $x^4 + 2x^3 - 6x^2 + 3x + 1 = 0$

Quintic equation (fifth degree): $3x^5 + 2x^4 - 5x^2 - 3 = 0$

Polynomial equations with a cubic term, such as $x^3 - 12x + 8 = 0$, first appeared in Babylonian tablets dated about 2000 B.C. Although the Babylonians lacked a general technique for solving such equations, they developed numerical methods for solving certain types of cubic equations. During the last four thousand years, a number of different methods have been developed to solve such equations. The most useful method is one that has been employed only recently — in most practical applications, computers are now used to solve polynomial equations.

One method of solving a polynomial equation is to use a grid. When the graph of the polynomial expression is plotted, the expression equals zero where the graph intersects the x-axis.

Example 1. Solve by graphing. $x^3 - 12x + 8 = 0$

Solution. Let $y = x^3 - 12x + 8$. Make a table of values for various values of x, plot the ordered pairs (x,y) on a grid, and draw a smooth curve through them.

x	y
−5	−57
−4	−8
−3	17
−2	24
−1	19
0	8
1	−3
2	−8
3	−1
4	24
5	73

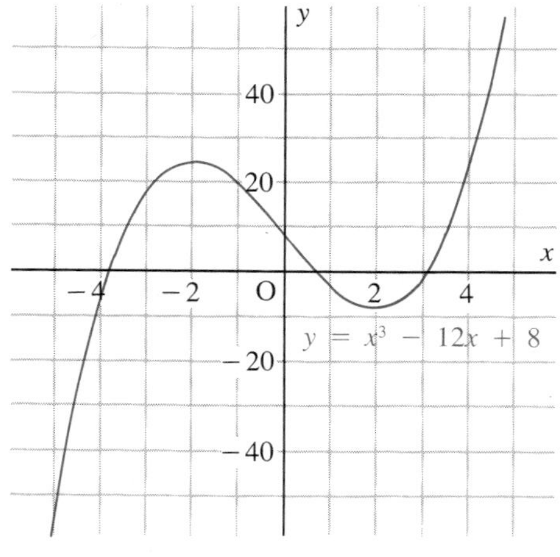

The expression is equal to 0 where the graph intersects the x-axis. The roots of the equation $x^3 - 12x + 8 = 0$ are approximately −3.8, 0.7, and 3.1.

Example 2. Solve graphically. a) $x^3 - 12x - 16 = 0$ b) $x^3 - 12x + 32 = 0$

Solution. Compare the given equation with the equation in *Example 1*.

a) Since the constant term in $y = x^3 - 12x - 16$ is 24 less than the constant term in $y = x^3 - 12x + 8$, the table of values can be written directly. Each y-value for $y = x^3 - 12x - 16$ is 24 less than the corresponding y-value for $y = x^3 - 12x + 8$.

b) Similarly, each y-value for $y = x^3 - 12x + 32$ is 24 greater than the corresponding y-value for $y = x^3 - 12x + 8$.

Plot the ordered pairs and draw the graphs.

	a)	b)
x	y	y
−5	−81	−33
−4	−32	16
−3	−7	41
−2	0	48
−1	−5	43
0	−16	32
1	−27	21
2	−32	16
3	−25	23
4	0	48
5	49	97

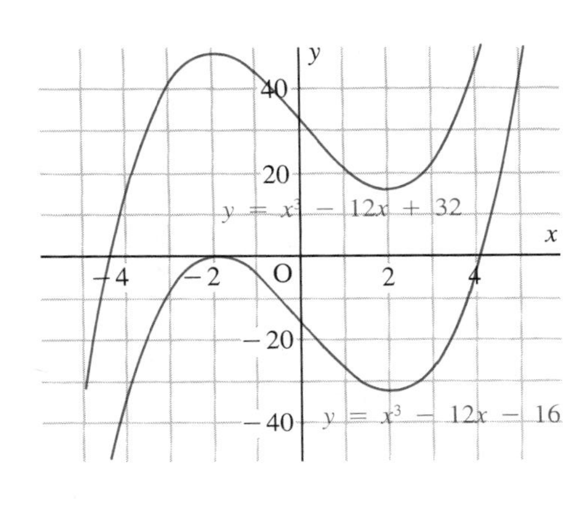

a) The graph of $y = x^3 - 12x - 16$ appears to cross the x-axis at one point and touch it at another. The equation $x^3 - 12x - 16 = 0$ has three real roots, two of which are equal: -2, -2, and 4.

b) The graph of $y = x^3 - 12x + 32$ intersects the x-axis at only one point. The equation $x^3 - 12x + 32 = 0$ has one real root, which is approximately -4.4.

Example 3. Solve graphically. $x^4 - 20x^2 + 10x + 30 = 0$

Solution. Make a table of values for the equation $y = x^4 - 20x^2 + 10x + 30$ and graph the ordered pairs.

x	y
−5	105
−4	−74
−3	−99
−2	−54
−1	1
0	30
1	21
2	−14
3	−39
4	6

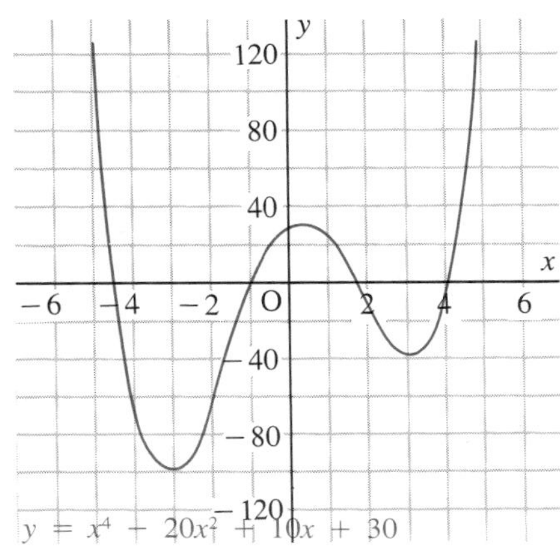

The roots of the equation $x^4 - 20x^2 + 10x + 30 = 0$ are approximately -4.6, -1.0, 1.6, and 3.9. There are four real roots.

EXERCISES 3-4

Ⓐ

1. Use the graph to estimate the root(s) of the equation.

a) $x^3 + 2x^2 - 10 = 0$

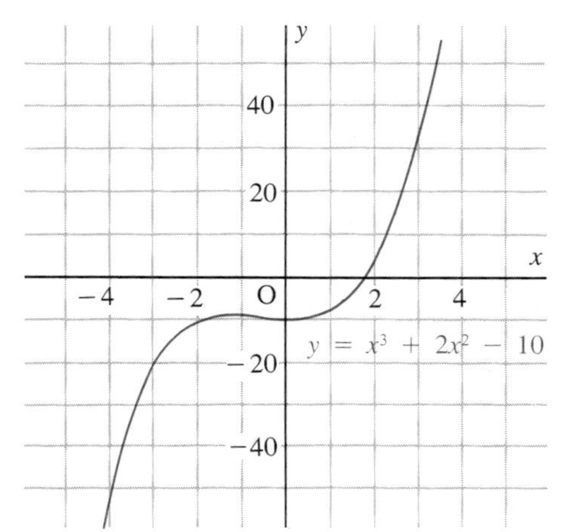

b) $-x^3 - 3x^2 + 5x + 16 = 0$

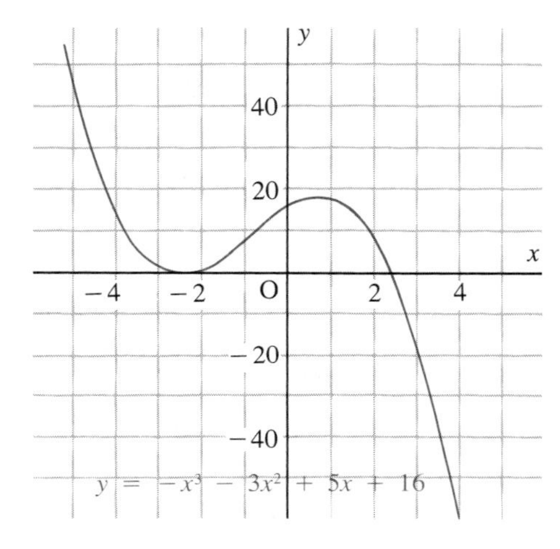

c) $x^4 - 10x^2 - 5x + 5 = 0$

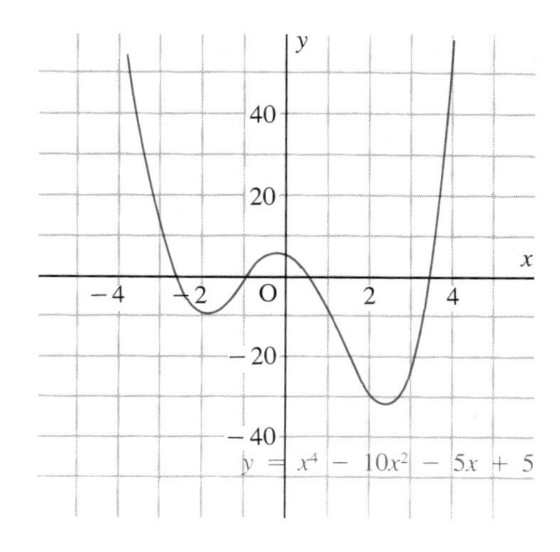

d) $x^5 - 10x^3 + 15x = 0$

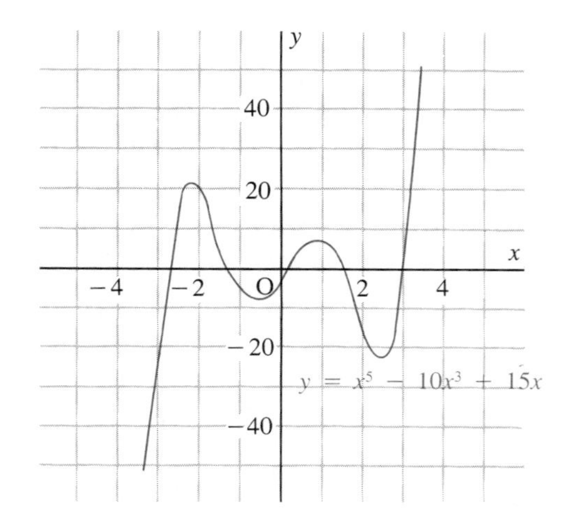

Ⓑ

2. Solve graphically.

a) $x^3 - 10x = 0$

b) $x^3 - 10x + 12 = 0$

c) $x^3 - 10x - 12 = 0$

d) $x^3 - 10x - 24 = 0$

3. Solve graphically.
   a) $x^3 - 15x - 10 = 0$
   b) $x^3 + x - 15 = 0$
   c) $x^4 - 15x^2 + 20 = 0$
   d) $x^4 - 5x^2 - 10x - 25 = 0$

4. Use a graph to find the x-intercepts of the graph of each function.
   a) $f(x) = x^3 + 10x - 20$
   b) $f(x) = x^3 - 3x^2 + x - 10$
   c) $f(x) = x^4 - 10x^2 + 5x + 7$
   d) $f(x) = x^4 - 4x^3 + 16x - 25$

5. In *Exercise 1 b)*, is it possible to tell for certain if there are two equal negative roots? If there are not two equal negative roots, then what other possibilities are there for this equation?

6. Explain why every cubic equation has at least one real root.

7. Sketch an example of a cubic function which has:
   a) three equal roots
   b) two equal roots and a third root which is less than they are
   c) two equal roots and a third root which is greater than they are
   d) one real root and two complex roots.

8. Sketch an example of a quartic function which has:
   a) four equal roots
   b) two pairs of two equal roots
   c) one pair of equal roots and two other real roots
   d) one pair of equal roots and two complex roots.

9. Solve the equation given on page 90 to determine how long it is between dropping a stone into a well 100 m deep and hearing the stone hit the water.

10. It is given that the equations $x^3 - 12x + 16 = 0$ and $x^3 - 12x - 16 = 0$ both have two different real roots.
    a) Which of the equations below have:
       i) three different real roots ii) only one real root?
       $x^3 - 12x + 20 = 0$ $x^3 - 12x + 10 = 0$ $x^3 - 12x - 20 = 0$
    b) For what values of k does the equation $x^3 - 12x + k = 0$ have:
       i) 3 different real roots ii) 2 different real roots iii) only 1 real root?

Ⓒ

11. A Babylonian tablet gives the values of $n^3 + n^2$ for integral values of n from 1 to 30.
    a) Make a table of values for $n = 1$ to 10.
    b) Use your table to find a root of the equation $x^3 + 2x^2 = 441$.
    c) Determine whether or not the equation $x^3 + 2x^2 = 441$ has any other real roots.

12. Individual packets of juice measure 6.4 cm by 3.8 cm by 10.3 cm. The packets contain 250 mL of juice. The manufacturer plans to introduce a new line of juice in packets containing twice as much juice. If each dimension of the original packets is increased by the same amount, find the dimensions of the new packets.

10.3 cm
6.4 cm
3.8 cm

3-5 SOLVING POLYNOMIAL EQUATIONS BY FACTORING

Although there are formulas for solving cubic and quartic equations, they involve cube and fourth roots, and are too complicated to be of practical significance. There are no formulas for solving polynomial equations of degree higher than the fourth. (See *THE MATHEMATICAL MIND*, page 100.)

Some polynomial equations can be solved by factoring.

Example 1. Solve for x. $x^3 - x = 0$

Solution. The left side of the equation has a common factor.

$$x^3 - x = 0$$
$$x(x^2 - 1) = 0$$
$$x(x - 1)(x + 1) = 0$$

Either $x = 0$ or $x - 1 = 0$ or $x + 1 = 0$

$x = 1$ $\quad$ $x = -1$

Example 2. Solve for x. $x^3 - 3x^2 - 4x + 12 = 0$

Solution. We recognize that the left side can be factored by grouping because a factor of $x - 3$ remains when common factors are removed from the first two terms and from the last two terms.

$$x^3 - 3x^2 - 4x + 12 = 0$$
$$x^2(x - 3) - 4(x - 3) = 0$$
$$(x - 3)(x^2 - 4) = 0$$
$$(x - 3)(x + 2)(x - 2) = 0$$

Either $x - 3 = 0$ or $x + 2 = 0$ or $x - 2 = 0$

$x = 3$ $\quad$ $x = -2$ $\quad$ $x = 2$

Example 3. Solve for x. $x^3 + 9x^2 + 13x + 5 = 0$

Solution. Since grouping does not produce a common factor, we try the factor theorem.

Let $f(x) = x^3 + 9x^2 + 13x + 5$.

The factors of 5 are ± 1 and ± 5.

By inspection, we see that $f(1) \neq 0$. All the terms are positive and hence cannot have a sum of zero.

$$\begin{aligned} f(-1) &= (-1)^3 + 9(-1)^2 + 13(-1) + 5 \\ &= -1 + 9 - 13 + 5 \\ &= 0 \end{aligned}$$

Since $f(-1) = 0$, $x + 1$ is a factor of the left side of the given equation. Also, 5 is the last term in the quadratic factor. The quadratic factor can be found by long division, or by equating coefficients.

Let $(x + 1)(x^2 + bx + 5) = x^3 + 9x^2 + 13x + 5$.

(Diagram brackets: $5x$ from $x \cdot 5$; bx from $1 \cdot bx$.)

The term containing x is $5x + bx$ on the left side, and $13x$ on the right side. Since the coefficients are equal,

$$5 + b = 13$$
$$b = 8$$

Therefore, the given equation can be written in the form

$$(x + 1)(x^2 + 8x + 5) = 0$$

Either $x + 1 = 0$ or $x^2 + 8x + 5 = 0$

$x = -1$

$$x = \frac{-8 \pm \sqrt{8^2 - 4(1)(5)}}{2} = \frac{-8 \pm \sqrt{64 - 20}}{2} = \frac{-8 \pm \sqrt{44}}{2} = -4 \pm \sqrt{11}$$

Example 4. Solve for x. $x^3 + 1 = 0$

Solution. The left side of the equation is a sum of cubes.

$$x^3 + 1 = 0$$
$$(x + 1)(x^2 - x + 1) = 0$$

Either $x + 1 = 0$ or $x^2 - x + 1 = 0$

$x = -1$

$$x = \frac{1 \pm \sqrt{(-1)^2 - 4(1)(1)}}{2} = \frac{1 \pm \sqrt{-3}}{2}$$

There is only one root, $x = -1$, in the set of real numbers. In the set of complex numbers, there are two additional roots, $\frac{1 \pm \sqrt{3}i}{2}$.

Example 5. A rectangular piece of cardboard measuring 10 cm by 8 cm is made into an open box by cutting squares from the corners and turning up the sides. If the box is to hold a volume of 48 cm^3, what size of square must be removed?

Solution. Draw a diagram.

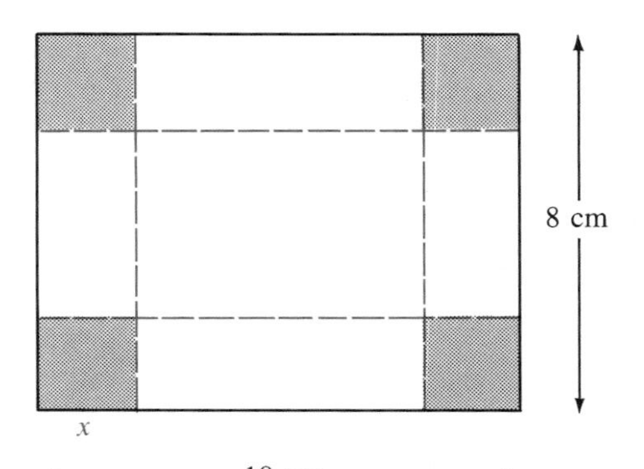

Let the side of the square to be removed be represented by x centimetres. Then the volume of the box is given by this expression.

$$V = x(10 - 2x)(8 - 2x)$$

Since the volume is 48 cm^3,

$$x(10 - 2x)(8 - 2x) = 48$$
$$4x(5 - x)(4 - x) = 48$$
$$x(20 - 9x + x^2) = 12$$
$$x^3 - 9x^2 + 20x = 12$$
$$x^3 - 9x^2 + 20x - 12 = 0 \quad \ldots ①$$

Solve using the factor theorem.
Let $f(x) = x^3 - 9x^2 + 20x - 12$.

$$\begin{aligned} f(1) &= 1^3 - 9(1)^2 + 20(1) - 12 \\ &= 1 - 9 + 20 - 12 \\ &= 0 \end{aligned}$$

Since $f(1) = 0$, $x - 1$ is a factor of the left side of equation ①. The other factors can be found by division, by inspection, or by using the factor theorem again.

$$\begin{aligned} f(2) &= 2^3 - 9(2)^2 + 20(2) - 12 \\ &= 8 - 36 + 40 - 12 \\ &= 0 \end{aligned}$$

Since $f(2) = 0$, $x - 2$ is a factor of the left side of equation ①.
Since $x - 1$ and $x - 2$ are factors, using the factor property the third factor has the form $x - a$, where

$$\begin{aligned} (-1)(-2)(-a) &= -12 \\ a &= 6 \end{aligned}$$

Therefore, the third factor is $x - 6$.
That is, the equation may be written $(x - 1)(x - 2)(x - 6) = 0$.
Either $x = 1$, $x = 2$, or $x = 6$

When $x = 1$, the dimensions of the box are 8 cm by 6 cm by 1 cm, and it has a volume of 48 cm^3.
When $x = 2$, the dimensions are 6 cm by 4 cm by 2 cm, and the volume is also 48 cm^3.
It is impossible for x to be 6 since four squares with sides of this length cannot be cut from the cardboard.

Therefore, four squares with 1 cm sides, or four squares with 2 cm sides can be removed to form a box with a volume of 48 cm^3.

As the above examples suggest, only certain polynomial equations can be solved by factoring. More general methods are needed to solve other polynomial equations.

EXERCISES 3-5

1. Solve for x.
   a) $x(x - 2)(x + 5) = 0$
   b) $x(2x + 3)(x - 4) = 0$
   c) $x(x^2 + 10x + 21) = 0$
   d) $x(6x^2 + 5x - 21) = 0$
   e) $x^3 - 4x = 0$
   f) $2x^3 + 10x^2 + 12x = 0$

2. a) One root of each equation below is the same for every equation. What is this root?
   i) $10x^3 - 25x^2 - 15x = 0$
   ii) $12x^3 = 27x$
   iii) $6x^3 + 45x = 33x^2$
   iv) $3x^4 + 14x^3 + 8x^2 = 0$
   v) $18x^4 - 50x^2 = 0$
   vi) $35x^2 - 5x^3 = 60x$

   b) Find the other roots of each equation in part a).

(B)

3. Solve.
   a) $x^3 - 2x^2 + 3x - 6 = 0$
   b) $x^3 + 5x^2 - 9x - 45 = 0$
   c) $2x^3 - 3x^2 - 11x + 6 = 0$
   d) $3x^3 - 2x^2 - 12x + 8 = 0$

4. Solve.
   a) $x^3 + 3x^2 - 10x - 24 = 0$
   b) $x^3 - x^2 + 9x - 9 = 0$
   c) $2x^3 - 3x^2 - 5x + 6 = 0$
   d) $8x^3 + 4x^2 - 18x - 9 = 0$

5. Solve.
   a) $x^3 + x - 10 = 0$
   b) $2x^3 - 4x^2 - 18x + 36 = 0$
   c) $2x^3 + 10x^2 + 13x + 5 = 0$
   d) $3x^3 - 2x^2 + 75x - 50 = 0$

6. Find three consecutive integers with a product of: a) -24 b) -120.

7. What number and its cube differ by: a) 24 b) -120?

8. A rectangular piece of cardboard measuring 12 cm by 8 cm is made into an open box by cutting squares from the corners and turning up the sides. If the volume of the box is 60 cm^3, what are its dimensions?

(C)

9. The product of the squares of two consecutive integers is 256 036. Find the integers.

10. Write a polynomial equation with these roots.
    a) 2, 5, 1
    b) $-1, 2 + \sqrt{3}, 2 - \sqrt{3}$
    c) $-\frac{1}{2}, 3, -3, 1$
    d) $-1, \frac{3 + 2\sqrt{5}}{2}, \frac{3 - 2\sqrt{5}}{2}$
    e) $3, 2 + i, 2 - i$
    f) $1, \frac{-1 + \sqrt{3}i}{2}, \frac{-1 - \sqrt{3}i}{2}, -2$

11. If one root is 2, find each value of k, and the other roots.
    a) $2x^3 - 13x^2 + kx + 10 = 0$
    b) $25x^4 + kx^2 + 16 = 0$
    c) $3x^3 - 15x^2 + kx - 4 = 0$
    d) $3x^4 - kx^3 + 49x^2 - 23x - 14 = 0$

12. Solve.
    a) $3x^4 - 15x^2 + 12 = 0$
    b) $\frac{3}{x^2} + \frac{2x}{x + 2} = \frac{3x}{x + 2} + \frac{1}{x^2}$

13. The diagrams show the first four pyramidal numbers. The number of balls in each layer of the pyramids is a perfect square. An expression for the nth pyramidal number is $\frac{n(n + 1)(2n + 1)}{6}$.

    a) Verify that the expression is correct by using it to find the number of balls in the pyramids shown in the diagrams.
    b) The only pyramidal number (other than 1) which is a perfect square is 4900. How many layers are in the pyramid for this number?

COMPUTER POWER

Solving Polynomial Equations

The computer is an ideal tool for solving polynomial equations such as $x^3 - 12x + 8 = 0$ (see *Example 1* in Section 3-4). The program below can be used to find decimal approximations to the roots of polynomial equations up to the tenth degree.

```
100 REM *** POLYNOMIAL EQUATIONS ***
110 INPUT "WHAT IS THE DEGREE? ";N
120 PRINT "ENTER ";N+1;" COEFFICIENTS"
130 FOR I=0 TO N:INPUT A(I):NEXT I
140 INPUT "WHAT IS THE FIRST VALUE OF X? ";X:T=0
150 INPUT "WHAT IS THE INCREMENT? ";D:Y1=0:Y2=0
160 FOR K=1 TO 11:Y=A(0)
170     FOR I=1 TO N:Y=Y*X+A(I):NEXT I
180     Y2=Y1:Y1=Y:PRINT X,Y
190     IF Y=0 THEN PRINT:PRINT X;" IS A ROOT":PRINT
200     IF Y1*Y2>=0 THEN GOTO 320
210     PRINT:PRINT "THERE IS A ROOT BETWEEN ";X-D;" AND ";X
220     PRINT:PRINT "PRESS:"
230     PRINT "1 - FOR A MORE ACCURATE APPROXIMATION"
240     PRINT "2 - TO CONTINUE"
250     PRINT "3 - TO REPEAT"
260     PRINT "4 - TO STOP":PRINT:INPUT Q
270     IF T=0 THEN XT=X:DT=D
280     IF Q=1 THEN T=T+1:Y1=0:Y2=0:X=X-D:D=D/10:GOTO 160
290     IF Q=2 THEN T=0:X=XT:D=DT:GOTO 160
300     IF Q=3 THEN GOTO 140
310     IF Q=4 THEN GOTO 340
320     X=X+D
330 NEXT K
340 END
```

When the program is run, the computer first asks for the degree of the polynomial, and then for the coefficients. These must be entered in descending order, including zero coefficients for missing terms. For example, to solve the equation $x^3 - 12x + 8 = 0$, the degree is 3 and the coefficients are 1, 0, -12, and 8.

The program instructs the computer to evaluate the polynomial for eleven successive values of x. You must enter the first value of x desired, and the increment. For example, if you enter -5 for the first value of x, and 1 for the increment, the computer will evaluate the polynomial for these values of x: $-5, -4, -3, \ldots, 5$. For the polynomial $x^3 - 12x + 8 = 0$, the computer is calculating the table of values shown on page 90. In this table, notice that some of the y-values are negative, while others are positive.

Also, a root of the equation occurs between the values of x for which the corresponding values of y change sign. The program uses this fact to calculate the root of the equation.

When the computer encounters two consecutive values of y with opposite signs, it indicates that a root exists between the two corresponding values of x. At this point, four options are given. Simply follow the instructions on the screen. For example, if you indicate that a more accurate approximation is desired, the computer will calculate values of x between those found, using a smaller increment. If this option is chosen several times in succession, the root can be found very accurately.

The following result was obtained for the root of the equation $x^3 - 12x + 8 = 0$ which lies between -4 and -3.

```
THERE IS A ROOT BETWEEN -3.7587705 AND -3.7587704
```

This shows that one root of the equation is $-3.758\ 770$, to six decimal places.

Use the program to answer these questions.

1. Find the other roots of the equation $x^3 - 12x + 8 = 0$, to six decimal places.
2. Each equation has a root between -3 and $+3$. Find this root to four decimal places.
   a) $x^3 + 6x^2 + 5x - 15 = 0$
   b) $x^5 + 5x^4 + 5x^3 - 5x^2 - 6x - 40 = 0$
   c) $x^3 - 3x - 5 = 0$
3. Find all the real roots of each equation, to four decimal places.
   a) $x^3 + 2x^2 - 11x - 5 = 0$
   b) $x^4 - 4x^3 - 4x^2 + 16x - 1 = 0$
   c) $x^5 - 2x^3 + x^2 - 10x + 25 = 0$
4. The volume V of a spherical segment with base radius a and height h is given by this formula.

   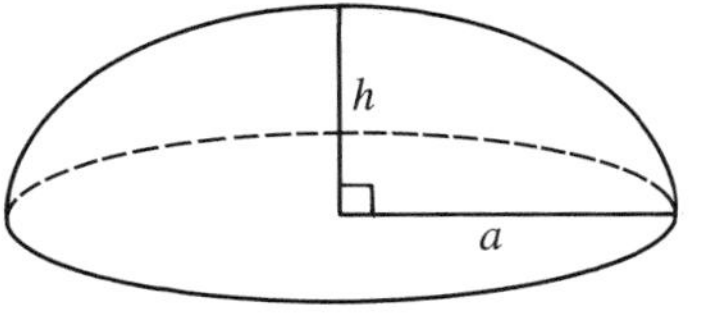

   $$V = \frac{1}{6}\pi h(3a^2 + h^2)$$

   A domed stadium is designed to be in the shape of a spherical segment with a base radius of 150 m. If the dome is to contain a volume of 3 500 000 m^3, find the height of the dome at its centre, to the nearest tenth of a metre.
5. Give an example of a polynomial equation which has a real root that would not likely be found by the program. Use the program to illustrate that it cannot be found this way.

THE MATHEMATICAL MIND

The Cubic Equation Controversy

One of the most important mathematical achievements of the sixteenth century was the discovery by Italian mathematicians of formulas for the solution of cubic and quartic equations. This accomplishment occurred at a time when discoveries were often kept secret, and rivals were challenged to solve the same problem.

About 1510, a professor at the University of Bologna revealed to a student a method he had found of solving cubic equations without a quadratic term, such as $x^3 + 5x = 8$.

Nicolo Tartaglia
1499-1557

In 1535, when Nicolo Tartaglia claimed to have found a method of solving cubic equations without a linear term, such as $x^3 + 2x^2 = 6$, the former student challenged him to a public equation-solving contest. But before the contest, Tartaglia learned how to solve an equation of the first type as well, and he won the contest triumphantly.

Tartaglia knew that, by substituting $y - \frac{b}{3a}$ for x, any cubic equation $ax^3 + bx^2 + cx + d = 0$ could be reduced to the form $y^3 + my = n$.
He proved that a root of this equation is

$$y = \sqrt[3]{\sqrt{\left(\frac{m}{3}\right)^3 + \left(\frac{n}{2}\right)^2} + \frac{n}{2}} - \sqrt[3]{\sqrt{\left(\frac{m}{3}\right)^3 + \left(\frac{n}{2}\right)^2} - \frac{n}{2}}.$$

Girolamo Cardano
1501-1576

Later, Girolamo Cardano urged Tartaglia to show him his method. When Cardano promised to keep it secret, Tartaglia gave it to him. But in 1545 Cardano published his *Ars Magna*, a Latin text on algebra, and included Tartaglia's solution of cubic equations. When Tartaglia protested the breach of his promise, Cardano claimed to have received his information from another party, and accused Tartaglia of plagiarism from the same source. There followed a bitter dispute between the two men over the question of who was the first to discover the formula for solving cubic equations.

Tartaglia's solution gave only one root, and later mathematicians found improved solutions. They also discovered formulas for quartic equations. Much work was done attempting to find a formula for quintic equations, but without success. This was proved to be impossible in 1824 by the Norwegian mathematician, Niels Henrik Abel.

QUESTIONS

1. Use a calculator and the formula given above to solve these cubic equations. Verify each solution.
   a) $y^3 + 6y = 2$
   b) $y^3 + 4y + 3 = 0$
   c) $x^3 - 3x^2 + 5x + 4 = 0$

3-6 SOLVING EQUATIONS INVOLVING ABSOLUTE VALUE

On the number line, the numbers -4 and 4 are each located 4 units from 0. Each number is said to have an absolute value of 4.
We write $|-4| = 4$ and $|4| = 4$.

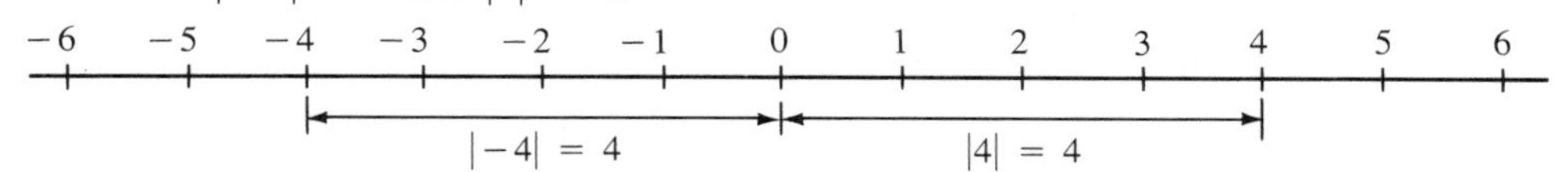

Example 1. Simplify.
a) $|12|$
b) $|-7|$

Solution.
a) The absolute value of a positive number is the number itself.
$|12| = 12$

b) The absolute value of a negative number is the opposite number.
$|-7| = 7$

As *Example 1* indicates, the definition of the absolute value of a number depends on whether the number is positive or negative.

> **Definition of Absolute Value**
> If a number is positive or zero, its *absolute value* is the number itself.
> If $x \geqslant 0$, then $|x| = x$
>
> If a number is negative, its *absolute value* is the opposite number.
> If $x < 0$, then $|x| = -x$

When this definition is used, both cases must be considered separately.

Example 2. Solve for x. $|x - 2| = 3$

Solution. *Case 1.* Let $x - 2 \geqslant 0$
$x \geqslant 2$

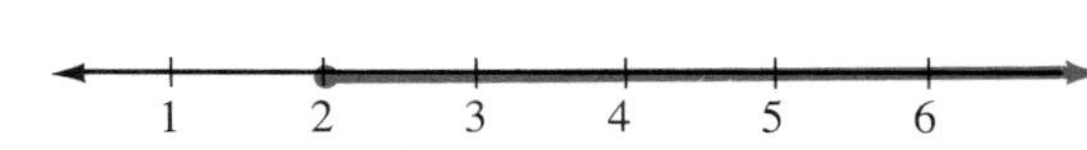

The solution below is valid only if $x \geqslant 2$.
For these values of x, $|x - 2| = x - 2$
The given equation becomes: $x - 2 = 3$
$x = 5$

Case 2. Let $x - 2 < 0$
$x < 2$

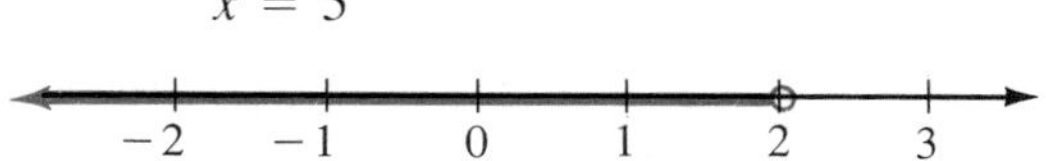

The solution below is valid only if $x < 2$.
For these values of x, $|x - 2| = -(x - 2)$
$= -x + 2$
The given equation becomes: $-x + 2 = 3$
$x = -1$

Therefore, the given equation has two roots, $x = 5$ and $x = -1$.

In some equations, one or both of the roots obtained are not possible values of the variable, and must be rejected.

Example 3. Solve and check. $|x - 3| = 2x$

Solution. *Case 1.* Let $x - 3 \geqslant 0$
$$x \geqslant 3$$

The solution below is valid only if $x \geqslant 3$.
For these values of x, $|x - 3| = x - 3$
The given equation becomes: $x - 3 = 2x$
$$-3 = x$$
$$x = -3$$
This solution is rejected because it is not among the possible values of x.

Case 2. Let $x - 3 < 0$
$$x < 3$$

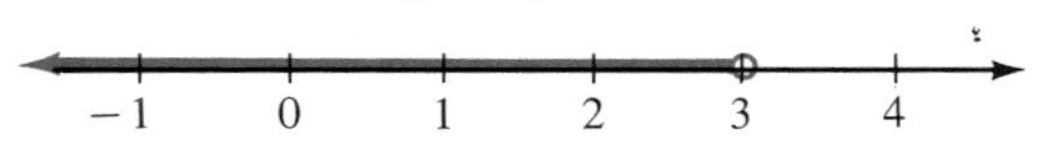

The solution below is valid only if $x < 3$.
For these values of x, $|x - 3| = -(x - 3)$
$$= -x + 3$$
The given equation becomes: $-x + 3 = 2x$
$$3 = 3x$$
$$x = 1$$
Therefore, the given equation has only one root, $x = 1$.

Check. When $x = 1$, L.S. $= |x - 3|$ $\qquad$ R.S. $= 2x$
$= |1 - 3|$ $\qquad$ $= 2(1)$
$= |-2|$ $\qquad$ $= 2$
$= 2$

Therefore, $x = 1$ is correct.

In *Example 3*, you can check that the possible root $x = -3$, which was obtained in the first case, does not satisfy the equation $|x - 3| = 2x$.

Occasionally, an equation is encountered that has no roots. This can sometimes be determined by inspection.

Example 4. Solve for x.

a) $|2x + 3| = -5$ $\qquad$ b) $|x - 2| + |2x + 6| = 0$

Solution. a) $|2x + 3| = -5$
The expression on the left side is greater than or equal to 0.
Therefore, it is impossible for it to be equal to the right side, -5.
This equation has no roots.

b) $|x - 2| + |2x + 6| = 0$
Each expression on the left side is greater than or equal to 0.
The only way their sum can be zero is for each term to be equal to 0.
But this is impossible, since $|x - 2|$ equals 0 when $x = 2$, and $|2x + 6|$ equals 0 when $x = -3$.
Since there is no value of x which makes both expressions equal 0, the equation has no roots.

EXERCISES 3-6

(A)

1. Solve for x.
   a) $|x| = 5$ b) $|x| = 2$ c) $|x| = 0$ d) $|x| = -4$

(B)

2. Solve for x.
   a) $|x - 2| = 7$ b) $|x + 4| = 3$ c) $|x + 1| = 5$
   d) $0 = |x - 7|$ e) $|3x - 2| = 4$ f) $|x - 4| = -2$
   g) $|1 - x| = 8$ h) $6 = |x - 5|$ i) $|2 - 3x| = 7$

3. Solve for x.
   a) $|x + 1| = 2x$ b) $|x + 4| = x - 1$
   c) $|3 - x| = 4$ d) $3x = |x - 2|$
   e) $x = |2x + 1|$ f) $|4x - 1| = x$

4. Solve for x.
   a) $|x + 3| = 4x$ b) $3x = |2 - x|$ c) $|4 + 3x| = 7x$
   d) $|4x - 1| = 8x$ e) $|10x + 3| = x - 1$ f) $|2 - 5x| = 2 - 3x$

5. Solve for x.
   a) $2|x + 1| = 8$ b) $9 = 3|2 + x|$ c) $2|x - 1| = 5$
   d) $4|4x - 3| = 7x$ e) $\frac{1}{2}|6x + 4| = 2x$ f) $\frac{1}{4}|3 - 2x| = \frac{3}{2}$

6. Solve for x.
   a) $|3x - 4| + |7 - 2x| = 0$ b) $|2x - 8| + |12 - 3x| = 0$
   c) $|2x - 6| = -|x + 4|$ d) $|x - 3| + |3 - x| = 0$

(C)

7. Solve for x.
   a) $|x| = 5|x| - 8$ b) $7|x + 2| = 2|x + 2| + 15$
   c) $|x + 1| + 2 = 3|x + 1|$ d) $|2x - 1| = |2x - 1| + 1$
   e) $|2x + 3| = |2x + 3|$ f) $|5x - 1| = |1 - 5x|$

8. Solve for x.
   a) $|x - 3| + |x - 8| = 17$ b) $|1 - 5x| = |x|$
   c) $|x - 1| + |x - 3| = 6$ d) $|x - 1| + |x - 3| = 2$

9. Solve for x.
   a) $|x + 2| + |2 - x| = 8$ b) $|2x - 1| + |1 - 2x| = 0$
   c) $|2x - 1| - |1 - 2x| = 4$ d) $|2x - 1| - |1 - 2x| = 0$

10. Draw a graph of the function $f(x) = |x - 1| + |x - 4|$ and use it to solve each equation.
    a) $|x - 1| + |x - 4| = 5$
    b) $|x - 1| + |x - 4| = 3$
    c) $|x - 1| + |x - 4| = 1$

3-7 SOLVING INEQUALITIES INVOLVING ABSOLUTE VALUE

To solve inequalities involving absolute value, use the definition of absolute value. The cases where the expression inside the absolute value signs is positive and negative must be considered separately.

Example 1. Solve for x. $|3x - 1| < 5$

Solution. *Case 1*. Let $3x - 1 \geqslant 0$

$$x \geqslant \frac{1}{3}$$

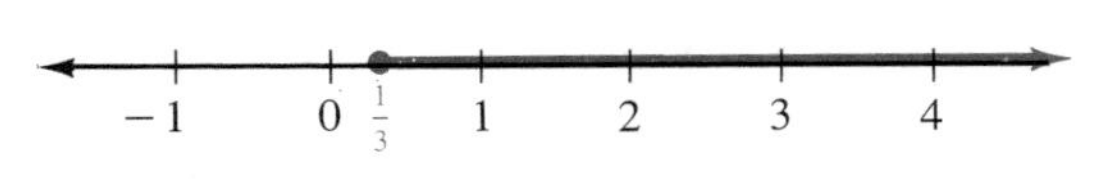

The solution below is valid only if $x \geqslant \frac{1}{3}$.

For these values of x, $|3x - 1| = 3x - 1$

The given inequality becomes: $3x - 1 < 5$

$$3x < 6$$

$$x < 2$$

Since the only possible values of x are those shown on the number line above, the values of x which satisfy the inequality lie between $\frac{1}{3}$ (including $\frac{1}{3}$) and 2.

$$\frac{1}{3} \leqslant x < 2$$

Case 2. Let $3x - 1 < 0$

$$x < \frac{1}{3}$$

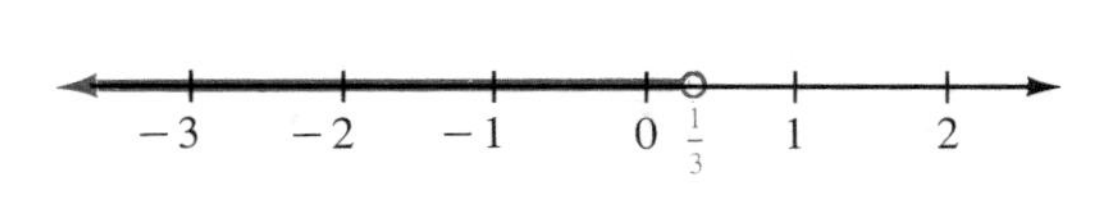

The solution below is valid only if $x < \frac{1}{3}$.

For these values of x, $|3x - 1| = -(3x - 1)$

$$= -3x + 1$$

The given inequality becomes: $-3x + 1 < 5$

$$-3x < 4$$

$$x > -\frac{4}{3}$$

Since the only possible values of x are those shown on the number line above, the values of x which satisfy the inequality lie between $-\frac{4}{3}$ and $\frac{1}{3}$.

$$-\frac{4}{3} < x < \frac{1}{3}$$

Combining the results of Cases 1 and 2, we see that the solution set of the given inequality consists of all real numbers between $-\frac{4}{3}$ and 2.

$$\left\{x \mid -\frac{4}{3} < x < 2\right\}$$

−4 −3 −2 $-\frac{4}{3}$ −1 0 1 2 3 4

Any inequality involving absolute value expressions can be solved in the same way. In some cases, the solutions obtained are not possible values of x and must be rejected.

Example 2. Solve for x. $|x - 2| > 2x$

Solution. *Case 1.* Let $x - 2 \geqslant 0$

$x \geqslant 2$

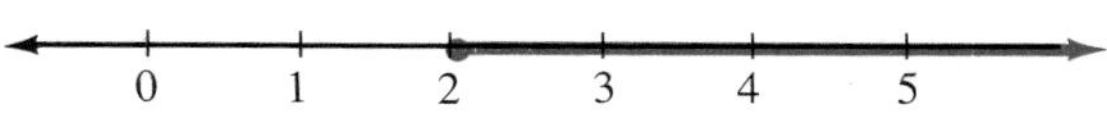

The solution below is valid only if $x \geqslant 2$.
For these values of x, $|x - 2| = x - 2$

The given inequality becomes: $x - 2 > 2x$

$$x - 2x > 2$$
$$-x > 2$$
$$x < -2$$

This result contradicts the initial statement that $x \geqslant 2$. Hence, there is no solution for this case.

Case 2. Let $x - 2 < 0$

$x < 2$

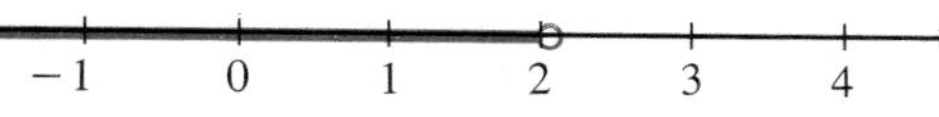

The solution below is valid only if $x < 2$.
For these values of x, $|x - 2| = -(x - 2)$
$= -x + 2$

The given inequality becomes: $-x + 2 > 2x$

$$-3x > -2$$
$$x < \frac{2}{3}$$

Since the only possible values of x are those shown on the number line above, the values of x which satisfy the inequality are less than $\frac{2}{3}$.

Hence, the solution set of the given inequality consists of all real numbers less than $\frac{2}{3}$.

$\left\{x \mid x < \frac{2}{3}\right\}$

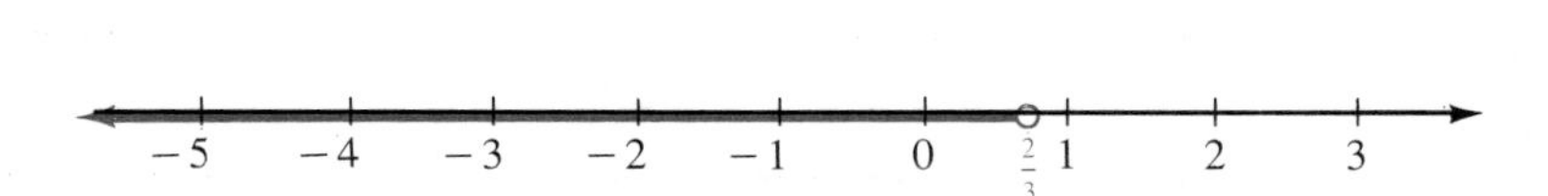

EXERCISES 3-7

Ⓐ

1. Solve.

a) $|x| < 3$ b) $|x| > 4$ c) $|2x| \leqslant 12$
d) $|x - 2| < 5$ e) $|5x| \geqslant 8$ f) $|x + 1| \leqslant 9$

2. Solve.

a) $|x - 1| \leqslant 4$ b) $|x + 1| > 7$ c) $|2x + 1| < 9$
d) $|3x - 1| < 5$ e) $|x + 3| \geqslant 10$ f) $|4x - 1| \geqslant 11$

Ⓑ

3. Solve.
   a) $|x| > x - 2$
   b) $|2x - 5| \leqslant 7$
   c) $|5x + 2| > 3$
   d) $|3x - 2| < x + 1$
   e) $|7x + 12| \leqslant -5$
   f) $|x + 1| > 3x$

4. Solve.
   a) $|2x + 1| < 9$
   b) $|\frac{1}{2}x + 1| \leqslant 2$
   c) $|4x - 9| > 15$
   d) $|3 - x| < 2x$
   e) $|2 - 3x| < 3x - 4$
   f) $|3x + 2| < 5x + 1$

5. Solve.
   a) $|7x - 3| \geqslant 11$
   b) $\left|\frac{x - 2}{3}\right| < 1$
   c) $|x + 1| > x - 1$
   d) $|2x + 1| < 3x$
   e) $|6 - 3x| \leqslant x - 2$
   f) $|5x + 2| < 3x + 1$

Ⓒ

6. Solve.
   a) $|x| + |x - 1| < 5$
   b) $|3x - 1| \leqslant |2x + 18|$
   c) $|x + 2| - |x| > 4$
   d) $|12x + 5| \leqslant |5x + 12|$

7. Solve.
   a) $|x + |x|| < 10$
   b) $||x| - 2| > 6$
   c) $\left|\frac{x - 3}{x + 5}\right| < 2$
   d) $\left|\frac{3x - 6}{4x - 8}\right| \geqslant 1$

8. a) If the area of a rectangle, in square centimetres, is represented by $7x - x^2 - 9$, and its width in centimetres is represented by $x - 2$, find an expression for its length.
   b) Assuming that the length is greater than or equal to the width, for what values of x does the expression found in part a) represent the length of the rectangle?

9. Write an absolute value inequality whose solution set is each given graph.
   a)
   2
   b)
   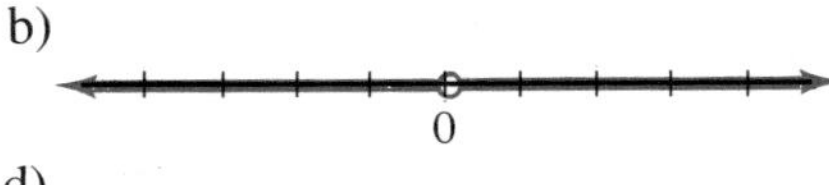

   c)
   −1
   3
   d)
   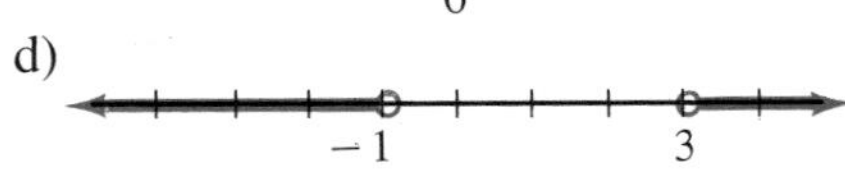

10. Write an absolute value inequality for each solution set.
   a) $\{x| \ x \geqslant 3\}$
   b) $\{x| \ 0 \leqslant x \leqslant 4\}$
   c) $\{x| \ x < 0 \text{ or } x > 4\}$
   d) $\{x| \ x \neq 2\}$

11. Write an absolute value inequality which has:
   a) no solution
   b) every real number as a solution
   c) only one solution.

3-8 SOLVING RADICAL EQUATIONS

The design of a domed stadium calls for a roof which is part of a sphere. If the diameter of the base of the stadium is 200 m, and the roof is 75 m above the centre of the playing field, what is the radius of the sphere?

This problem can be answered by solving the following equation for r, where h is the height of the roof, and c is the diameter of the base.

$$\sqrt{4h(2r - h)} = c$$

Substitute 200 for c and 75 for h.

$$\sqrt{300(2r - 75)} = 200$$

In this equation, the variable occurs under a radical sign. For this reason the equation is called a *radical equation*. The equation can be solved by squaring both sides.

$$\begin{aligned}(\sqrt{300(2r - 75)})^2 &= 200^2\\ 300(2r - 75) &= 40\,000\\ 6r - 225 &= 400\\ 6r &= 625\\ r &\doteq 104.2\end{aligned}$$

The radius of the sphere is approximately 104 m.

The steps used in solving the above equation are used to solve other radical equations.

Example 1. Solve.

a) $\sqrt{x - 3} - 3 = 0$

b) $\sqrt{x - 3} + 3 = 0$

Solution.

a) $\sqrt{x - 3} - 3 = 0$

Isolate the radical.

$$\sqrt{x - 3} = 3$$

Square both sides.

$$\begin{aligned}(\sqrt{x - 3})^2 &= 3^2\\ x - 3 &= 9\\ x &= 12\end{aligned}$$

Check.

When $x = 12$,

$$\begin{aligned}\text{L.S.} &= \sqrt{x - 3} - 3\\ &= \sqrt{9} - 3\\ &= 0\end{aligned}$$

R.S. $= 0$

The solution is correct.

That is, 12 is the only root of the equation $\sqrt{x - 3} - 3 = 0$.

b) $\sqrt{x - 3} + 3 = 0$

Isolate the radical.

$$\sqrt{x - 3} = -3$$

Square both sides.

$$\begin{aligned}(\sqrt{x - 3})^2 &= (-3)^2\\ x - 3 &= 9\\ x &= 12\end{aligned}$$

When $x = 12$,

$$\begin{aligned}\text{L.S.} &= \sqrt{x - 3} + 3\\ &= \sqrt{9} + 3\\ &= 6\end{aligned}$$

R.S. $= 0$

The solution is not correct.

That is, 12 is not a root of the equation $\sqrt{x - 3} + 3 = 0$. This equation has no real roots.

In *Example 1b* we could have predicted that the equation has no real roots. Since the radical sign always denotes the positive square root, it is impossible for the left side of the equation, $\sqrt{x-3}+3$, to be equal to 0. This example shows that the operation of squaring both sides of an equation may lead to numbers that do not satisfy the original equation. These are called *extraneous roots*. They are roots of the equation that was obtained after squaring, but they are not roots of the original equation.

Extraneous roots are often introduced when you square both sides of an equation. For this reason, you must identify extraneous roots.

> To solve a radical equation, follow these steps.
> *Step 1*. Isolate the radical on one side of the equation.
> *Step 2*. Square both sides of the equation.
> *Step 3*. Identify extraneous roots and reject them.

Example 2. Solve.

a) $4+\sqrt{2+x}=x$ b) $4-\sqrt{2+x}=x$

Solution. a) $4+\sqrt{2+x}=x$

Isolate the radical.

$$\sqrt{2+x}=x-4$$

Square both sides.

$$(\sqrt{2+x})^2=(x-4)^2$$
$$2+x=x^2-8x+16$$
$$x^2-9x+14=0$$
$$(x-7)(x-2)=0$$

Either $x-7=0$ or $x-2=0$

$x=7$ $x=2$

Check.

When $x=7$,
L.S. $=4+\sqrt{2+7}$
$=4+3$
$=7$
R.S. $=7$
7 is a root.

When $x=2$,
L.S. $=4+\sqrt{2+2}$
$=4+2$
$=6$
R.S. $=2$
2 is an extraneous root.

The equation has only one root, $x=7$.

b) $4-\sqrt{2+x}=x$

Isolate the radical.

$$-\sqrt{2+x}=x-4$$

Square both sides.

$$(-\sqrt{2+x})^2=(x-4)^2$$
$$2+x=x^2-8x+16$$

The same equation was obtained in part a), and the solution from here on is the same. The possible roots are 7 and 2.

Check.

When $x = 7$,	When $x = 2$,
$\text{L.S.} = 4 - \sqrt{2 + 7}$	$\text{L.S.} = 4 - \sqrt{2 + 2}$
$= 4 - 3$	$= 4 - 2$
$= 1$	$= 2$
$\text{R.S.} = 7$	$\text{R.S.} = 2$
7 is an extraneous root.	2 is a root.

The equation has only one root, $x = 2$.

In *Example 2*, the extraneous roots were identified by checking the possible roots obtained. Another method is to identify the possible values of x after the radical has been isolated. For example, this equation was obtained in *Example 2a*, $\sqrt{2 + x} = x - 4$.
Since the left side of the equation cannot be negative, the right side cannot be negative either. This introduces a restriction on x, namely, $x - 4 \geqslant 0$, or $x \geqslant 4$. From this point on, the solution is valid only if $x \geqslant 4$. Since 2 was one of the possible roots, it can then be rejected. If this method is used, it is not necessary to check the roots.

Example 3. When a satellite is h kilometres above the Earth the period, or time for one complete orbit, T minutes is given by this formula.
$T = 1.66 \times 10^{-4}\sqrt{(6370 + h)^3}$.
How high should a satellite be placed above the equator so that it always appears to be above the same point on the ground? Give your answer to the nearest hundred kilometres.

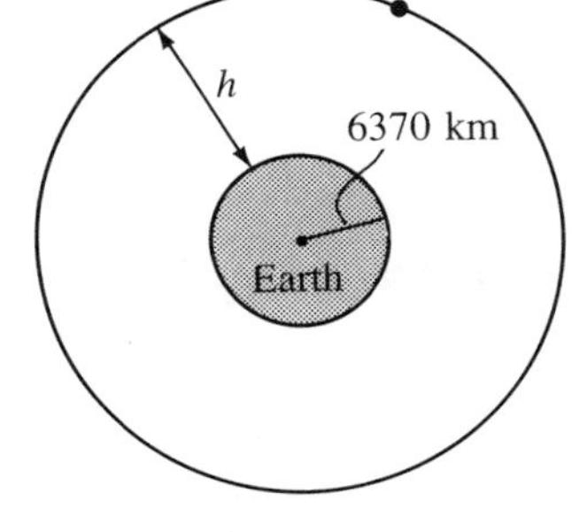

Solution. The period of the satellite has to equal the period of the Earth's rotation, which is 24 h, or 1440 min.
Substitute 1440 for T in the formula.

$$1440 = 1.66 \times 10^{-4}\sqrt{(6370 + h)^3}$$

Isolate the radical.

$$\frac{1440}{1.66 \times 10^{-4}} = \sqrt{(6370 + h)^3}$$

Since the left side is positive, there are no restrictions on h.
Therefore, there are no extraneous roots.
Square both sides.
$7.525\,039\,9 \times 10^{13} = (6370 + h)^3$
Solve by taking the cube root of both sides.

$$42\,219 = 6370 + h$$
$$35\,849 = h$$

To the nearest hundred kilometres, the satellite should be placed 35 800 km above the ground.

EXERCISES 3-8

(A)

1. Solve.
   a) $\sqrt{3x + 1} = 7$
   b) $\sqrt{2x + 7} = 5$
   c) $2\sqrt{x} = 8$
   d) $12\sqrt{x} = 30$
   e) $\sqrt{x} + 3 = 4$
   f) $\sqrt{x} - 6 = -3$

2. Solve.
   a) $\sqrt{x + 2} - 5 = 0$
   b) $\sqrt{x - 4} - 7 = 0$
   c) $\sqrt{2x + 7} - 9 = 0$
   d) $\sqrt{2x + 1} + 5 = 8$
   e) $\sqrt{7x - 3} - 2 = 3$
   f) $\sqrt{3x - 1} + 7 = 10$

3. Solve.
   a) $2 = 3\sqrt{2x - 5}$
   b) $\sqrt{5x + 2} - 3 = 1$
   c) $-2\sqrt{6x + 1} = 14$
   d) $5 + \sqrt{4x - 3} = 9$
   e) $-7 + 5\sqrt{2x + 3} = 8$
   f) $-3\sqrt{2x + 1} + 5 = -4$

4. Determine, by inspection, which of the following equations have extraneous roots.
   a) $\sqrt{x + 3} + 5 = 0$
   b) $\sqrt{3x - 2} - 2 = 3$
   c) $4 + \sqrt{2x - 7} = 0$
   d) $-4 + \sqrt{3x + 1} = 0$
   e) $7 + 5\sqrt{2x + 3} = 4$
   f) $3\sqrt{x + 1} + 2 = 8$

(B)

5. The formula for the length d of the diagonal of a rectangle with sides of length a and b is $d = \sqrt{a^2 + b^2}$. Solve the formula for a.

6. Solve.
   a) $4\sqrt{2x + 7} - 5 = 7$
   b) $4 + 2\sqrt{5x - 3} = 12$
   c) $3 + 4\sqrt{8x - 3} = 15$
   d) $-5\sqrt{8x - 4} + 3 = 18$
   e) $7\sqrt{9x + 12} - 5 = 16$
   f) $-20 + 6\sqrt{2x + 17} = -2$

7. Solve.
   a) $x + \sqrt{x - 5} = 7$
   b) $x - \sqrt{x - 5} = 7$
   c) $\sqrt{x + 7} + 5 = x$
   d) $\sqrt{x^2 + 3} = x + 1$
   e) $6 - \sqrt{x + 6} = x$
   f) $\sqrt{x - 2} - x = -8$

8. Solve.
   a) $x + \sqrt{3 + x} = 3$
   b) $x - \sqrt{2x - 5} = 4$
   c) $1 + \sqrt{6 - 2x} = x + 2$
   d) $5 + \sqrt{x + 1} = 2x + 1$
   e) $\sqrt{3x + 4} + 9 = 2x$
   f) $x + \sqrt{3x + 1} = 9$

9. Solve.
   a) $x - 3 = \sqrt{3x - 11}$
   b) $2\sqrt{5 - 4x} + x = 3$
   c) $3\sqrt{2x + 9} - x = 7$
   d) $\sqrt{2x + 7} + x - 4 = 10$
   e) $2x - \sqrt{4x + 1} = 7$
   f) $\sqrt{3x + 4} + x = 12$

10. At the scene of an accident, police can estimate the speed a car had been travelling by the length of the skid marks. One formula used for this purpose is $v = -7 + 8.2\sqrt{d}$, where v is the speed in kilometres per hour and d is the length of the skid marks in metres.
    a) Solve the formula for d.
    b) How long would be the skid marks of a car braking from:
       i) 60 km/h ii) 90 km/h iii) 120 km/h?
    c) What was the speed of the car if the length of its skid marks were:
       i) 50 m ii) 100 m iii) 150 m?

11. Solve for the variable indicated.
    a) $T = 2\pi\sqrt{\frac{l}{g}}$, l
    b) $u = \sqrt{v^2 - 2as}$, a
    c) $V = \sqrt{\frac{2gE}{W}}$, W
    d) $m = \dfrac{M}{\sqrt{1 - \frac{v^2}{c^2}}}$, c
    e) $v = \sqrt{\frac{F}{mk} - u^2}$, k
    f) $e = \sqrt{\dfrac{h^2 - 2ma^2E}{2ma}}$, E

12. The total surface area A of a cone with base radius r and height h is given by the formula $A = \pi r(r + \sqrt{r^2 + h^2})$. Solve this formula for h.

13. In $\triangle ABC$, $\angle B = 90°$, and AB is 1 cm longer than BC. If the perimeter of the triangle is 70 cm, find the lengths of the three sides.

Ⓒ

14. Solve the equation $x - 7\sqrt{x} + 12 = 0$ in two different ways.
    a) As a radical equation
    b) As a quadratic equation in $\sqrt{x}$

15. The diagram shows a sector of a circle with radius r. If h is as defined on the diagram, then the chord length c is given by this formula.
    $c = \sqrt{4h(2r - h)}$
    Solve the formula for h.

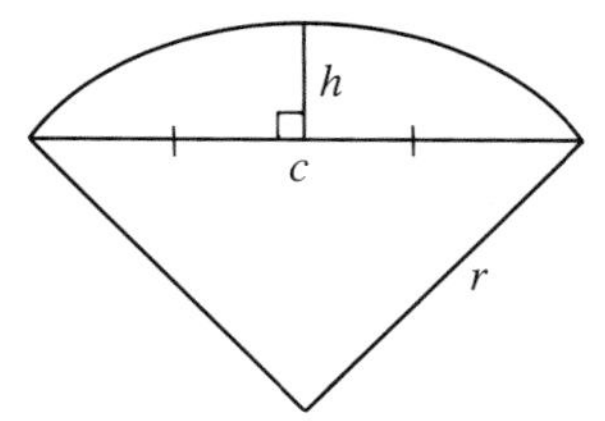

16. Check the results of *Exercise 15* as follows.
    a) Substitute the value of c which would result if the sector were a semicircle.
    b) Determine a condition that must be satisfied by r and c.

17. Without solving, find three equations which have no real roots.
    a) $\sqrt{x - 5} = 8 - x$
    b) $\sqrt{2x + 10} = -2 - x$
    c) $2x - 12 = \sqrt{17 - 3x}$
    d) $\sqrt{-7 - 3x} = 5x + 4$
    e) $4 + \sqrt{6 - 20x} = 10x$
    f) $-100x = \sqrt{15x - 1.5} - 11$

18. Explain the difference between an equation having extraneous roots and one having no real roots. Illustrate your answer with specific examples.

Review Exercises

1. Solve for x.
   a) $5(2x + 3) - 2(3x + 4) = 12$
   b) $3(x + 4) - 4(2x + 7) = 2(5x + 7)$
   c) $\frac{3(2x + 1)}{4} = \frac{2(x + 1)}{3} - \frac{x}{2}$
   d) $\frac{x - 2}{3x} + \frac{1}{2} = \frac{2x - 1}{2x} - \frac{1}{5}$

2. Solve and check.
   a) $3x^2 - 15.87 = 0$
   b) $2x^2 - 7x - 15 = 0$
   c) $6x^2 + 19x + 10 = 0$
   d) $3x(x - 5) = x(x + 2) + 9$

3. Solve.
   a) $x^2 + 2x - 4 = 0$
   b) $3x^2 - 5x + 1 = 0$
   c) $2x^2 - 5x - 4 = 0$
   d) $x^2 - 2x + 3 = 0$
   e) $4x^2 + 6x + 5 = 0$
   f) $5x^2 + 3x + 2 = 0$

4. Write a quadratic equation with roots of:
   a) $4, -\frac{5}{3}$
   b) $-\frac{2}{3}, -\frac{3}{2}$
   c) $0, -\frac{1}{3}$

5. Solve for the variable indicated.
   a) $V = \frac{1}{3}\pi r^2 h$, r
   b) $d = 4.9t^2 - 20$, t
   c) $t = 3s\sqrt{2v - 1}$, v

6. For what value of m will $3x(x + 2) = mx - 8$ have equal roots?

7. Determine the nature of the roots of these equations.
   a) $3x^2 - 8x + 4 = 0$
   b) $3x^2 - 8x + 6 = 0$
   c) $4x^2 - 12x + 9 = 0$

8. Write a quadratic equation, given one root.
   a) $3 - 2i$
   b) $5 + 3i$
   c) $3i - 4$

9. Solve.
   a) $\frac{x + 1}{x} + \frac{x + 2}{x - 2} = \frac{x - 1}{x - 2} + \frac{3}{x}$
   b) $(x^2 + 4x)^2 - 9(x^2 + 4x) - 36 = 0$

10. For what values of p does each equation have complex roots?
    a) $2x^2 + px + 7 = 0$
    b) $5px^2 + 3x = 2$
    c) $4x(x - 2) = 2p$

11. Solve graphically.
    a) $x^3 - 5x + 9 = 0$
    b) $\frac{x^3}{3} - 3x = 0$

12. Solve.
    a) $x^3 - x^2 - 4x + 4 = 0$
    b) $x^3 - 4x^2 + x + 6 = 0$
    c) $x^3 - x^2 - 3x + 6 = 0$
    d) $x^4 - 3x^3 - 2x^2 + 12x - 8 = 0$

13. Solve.
    a) $|3x| = 12$
    b) $|x - 3| = 5$
    c) $2|x + 2| - 8 = 0$

14. Solve.
    a) $|2x - 1| \leq 7$
    b) $|x + 1| > 4x$
    c) $|5x - 2| < 3x + 1$

15. Solve.
    a) $\sqrt{3x - 2} = 4$
    b) $4\sqrt{2x - 1} - 3 = 9$
    c) $2\sqrt{5x + 7} + 3 = 0$

1. For each function, find:
   i) $f(-2)$, $f(3)$, $f(1.2)$ ii) the domain and the range iii) the inverse
   a) $f(x) = 3x - 2$ b) $f(x) = 2x^2 - 3x + 1$ c) $f(x) = \dfrac{2 - x}{x}$

2. If $f(x) = x^2 - 3x + 1$, find:
   a) $f(2k)$ b) $f(-2k)$ c) $-f(z)$
   d) $f(x + 2)$ e) $f(2x - 1)$ f) $f\left(\dfrac{1}{x}\right)$.

3. If $f(x) = 2x^2 - 5$, show that $f(x + 3) \neq f(x) + f(3)$.

4. If $f(x) = 2x^2 - 5x + 1$, solve each equation.
   a) $f(x) = -1$ b) $f(x) = 13$ c) $f(2a) = 13$

5. Draw a mapping diagram to represent each set of ordered pairs. Which sets represent functions?
   a) $\{(1,9), (2,7), (3,5), (4,3), (5,1)\}$
   b) $\{(-3,2), (-1,4), (1,2), (-3,7), (5,-1), (6,5)\}$
   c) $\{(-4,13), (-3,7), (-2,3), (-1,1), (0,3), (1,7)\}$

6. If $f(x) = 2x + 5$ and $g(x) = x^2 - 3x + 2$, find:
   a) $g(f(x))$ b) $f(f(x))$ c) $f^{-1}(f^{-1}(x))$ d) $f(g(x))$.

7. Given $f(x) = 3x - 1$ and $g(x) = 2\sqrt{x + 1}$
   a) Find.
      i) $f\left(\dfrac{2x - 1}{2}\right)$ ii) $g\left(\dfrac{5}{x - 2}\right)$ iii) $f(g(x))$ iv) $g(f(x))$
   b) State the domain and the range of each function.
      i) $f(x)$ ii) $g(x)$ iii) $f(g(x))$ iv) $g(f(x))$

8. If $f(x) = 2x - 5$ and $g(x) = (x + 2)^2 - 3$, sketch these graphs.
   a) $f(x)$ and $g(x)$ on the same axes. b) $f(x) + g(x)$ c) $f(x) - g(x)$

9. The perimeter of a rectangle is 10 m. Express the length of its diagonal as a function of its width.

10. Simplify.
    a) $2(3x + 2y) - 5(x - 4y)$
    b) $3m(5m - 7n) - 2m(12m + 5n)$
    c) $x(4x - 3y + 7) - 3x(2x + 5y - 8)$
    d) $(5a - 3b)(2a + 7b)$
    e) $(3x + 2)^2 - 2(4x - 1)(x + 3)$
    f) $3(2m - 1)(-4m + 7n - 1) - (2m + n - 3)^2$

11. Factor.
    a) $15x^2 - 6xy + 21x$ b) $x^2 - 17x + 42$
    c) $10x^2 + 7xy - 12y^2$ d) $m^2(3m - 2) - 5m(3m - 2) + 9m - 6$
    e) $15x^3 + 21x^2y - 18xy^2$ f) $100p^2 - 36q^2$

12. Factor.
    a) $x^2 + 8xy + 16y^2 - 9$
    b) $16x^2 - 4y^2 + 12y - 9$
    c) $4(x + 2y + z)^2 - 9(x - 2y + z)^2$
    d) $a^2 - 2a + 1 - x^2 - 2xy - y^2$
    e) $2x^2(3x - 1) - 5x(3x - 1) + 6x - 2$
    f) $(3x + 2)^2 + 6xy + 4y + y^2$

13. One factor of $6m^3 - 6 - 29m - 31m^2$ is $1 + 3m$. Find the other factors.

14. Divide $x^4 - 4x^3 - 6x^5 + x + 5x^2 + 15$ by $2x^2 - x + 3$.

15. If $p(x) = 2x^2 + 5x - 4$, evaluate:
    a) $p(-2)$
    b) $p(3a)$
    c) $p(8x - 5)$

16. Factor completely.
    a) $x^3 + 4x^2 + 5x + 2$
    b) $x^3 + 2x^2 - 3$
    c) $27x^3 + 125y^3$
    d) $4x^3 - x + 8x^2 - 2$

17. Solve and check.
    a) $6(x + 1) - 12x = 3 - 4(2x - 1)$
    b) $\dfrac{2x - 4}{5} - \dfrac{x - 3}{4} = \dfrac{5 - 3x}{8}$
    c) $3x^2 - x - 14 = 0$
    d) $2x^2 + 4x - 7 = 0$
    e) $5x^2 + 8x + 3 = 0$
    f) $\dfrac{4}{x - 1} - \dfrac{5}{x + 2} = \dfrac{3}{x}$

18. Solve.
    a) $2x^2 - 5x + 4 = 0$
    b) $4x^3 - 3x^2 + 2x = 0$
    c) $x^3 - 7x - 6 = 0$
    d) $2x^3 - 3x^2 - 8x + 12 = 0$
    e) $(x^2 - 4x + 5)(x^2 - 4x + 2) = -2$
    f) $\dfrac{4}{x + 1} - \dfrac{12}{x + 3} = \dfrac{-5}{x + 2}$

19. Solve for the variable indicated.
    a) $s = 3u + \frac{1}{2}at^2$, t
    b) $m = 2\sqrt{3n + 5} - 1$, n

20. Determine the nature of the roots of each equation.
    a) $4x^2 + 20x + 25 = 0$
    b) $2x^2 - 5x + 2 = 0$
    c) $3x^2 - 4x + 8 = 0$

21. Write a quadratic equation given:
    a) the roots $\frac{3}{4}$ and -2
    b) the root $-2 + 3i$.

22. For what values of k does:
    a) $3x^2 - kx + 2 = 0$ have equal roots
    b) $2x^2 - 5x - k = 0$ have complex roots?

23. Solve.
    a) $|2x - 1| = 7$
    b) $|x + 5| - x + 2 = 3$
    c) $x + 2|x + 1| = 8$
    d) $|3x + 2| = 2x - 4$

24. Solve.
    a) $\sqrt{5x + 4} = 7$
    b) $\sqrt{2x - 3} + 3 = x$
    c) $\sqrt{x + 5} + x = 7$
    d) $2x + 2\sqrt{x} = 5$

4 Geometry

Why is the triangle the fundamental shape used in the construction of most structures? (See *Section 4-4*.)

4-1 THE LANGUAGE OF DEDUCTIVE GEOMETRY

Deductive geometry may be the oldest branch of formal mathematics. Over 2300 years ago, the ancient Greek mathematician Euclid assembled in his 13 books titled *Elements*, the essentials of a logically deductive system of theorems. His idea of postulating self-evident facts called "axioms" and deducing from them less obvious facts called "theorems" remains with us to this day as the standard format for all branches of mathematics. The branch of mathematics which deals with geometry in the plane is often called *Euclidean geometry* in his honour.

The construction of a rigorous deductive system requires a starting point; a set of undefined concepts which we can describe in non-mathematical language and which are sufficiently fundamental as to be intuitively and perhaps universally understood.

To begin our study of geometry we choose to introduce the concepts of a point, a line, and a plane as the *primitives*, that is, the basic undefined terms. We will use informal language to describe them.

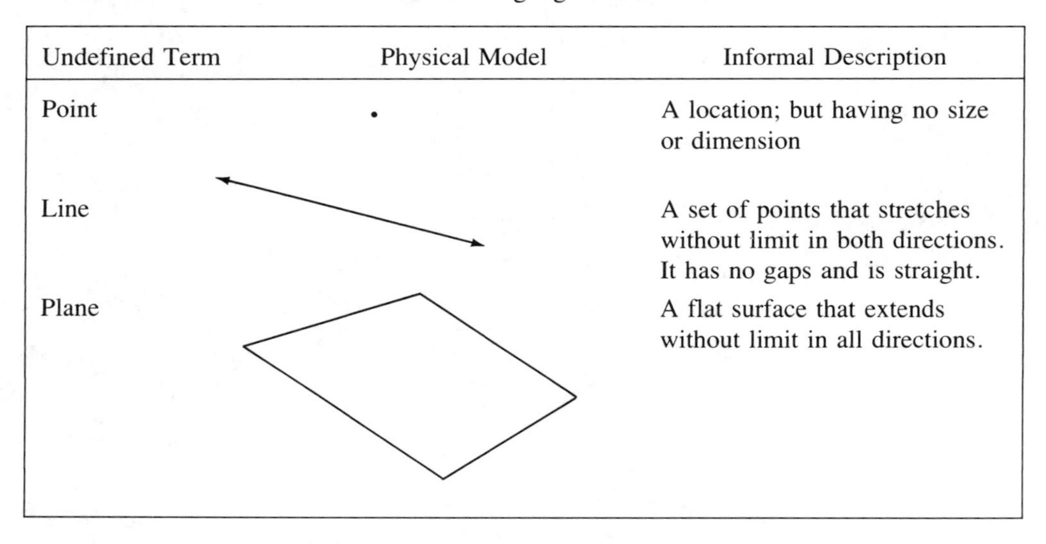

Undefined Term	Physical Model	Informal Description
Point	•	A location; but having no size or dimension
Line		A set of points that stretches without limit in both directions. It has no gaps and is straight.
Plane		A flat surface that extends without limit in all directions.

Using the concepts of a point and a line, we could write formal definitions of a line segment, a ray, and an angle. However, for our purposes it is more appropriate to describe these concepts informally.

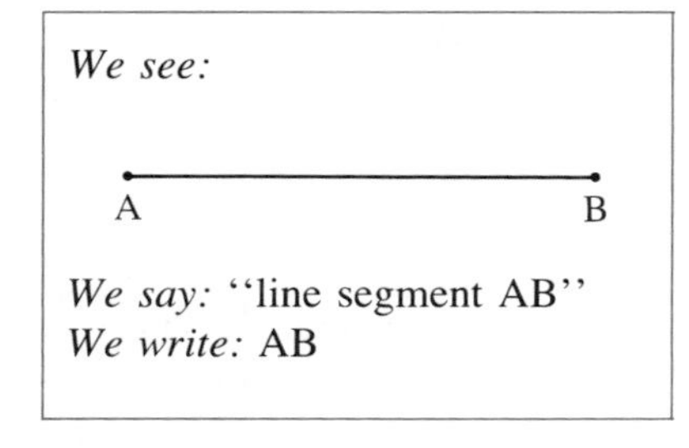

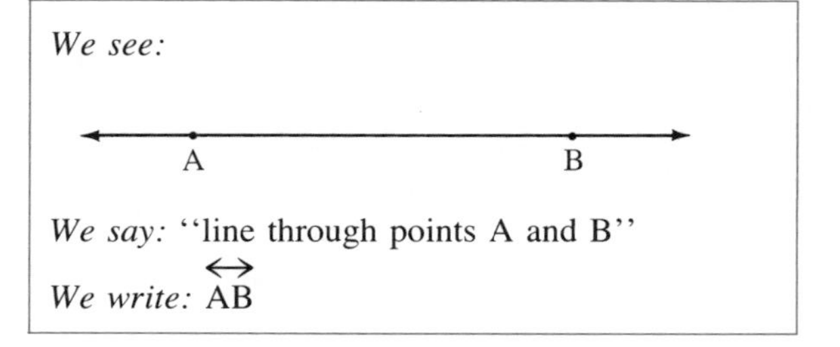

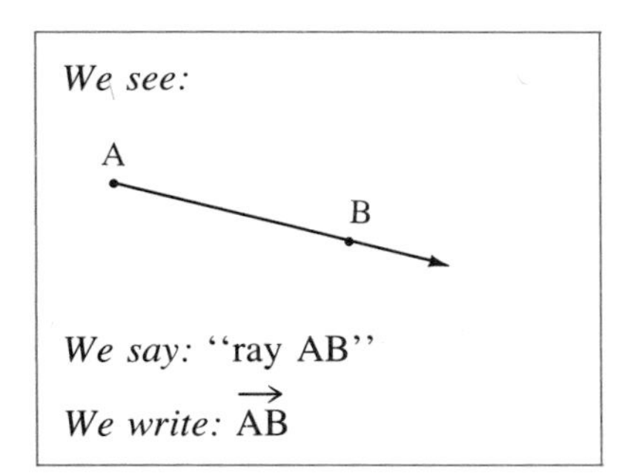

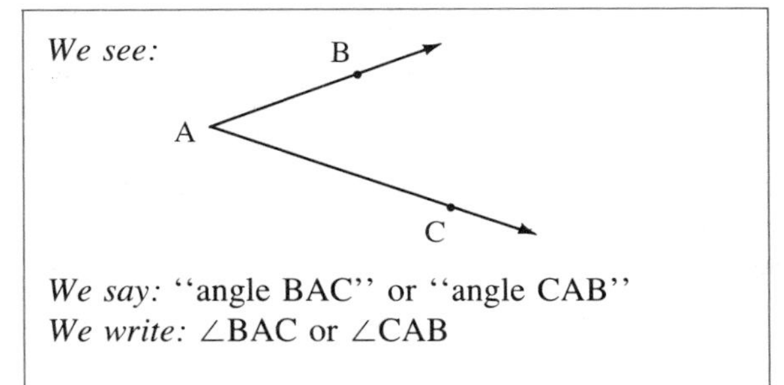

We say that $\triangle ABC$ is *congruent* to any triangle $\triangle A'B'C'$ if $\triangle ABC$ can be made to coincide with $\triangle A'B'C'$ through a physical motion; that is, through a series of slides, flips, and turns.

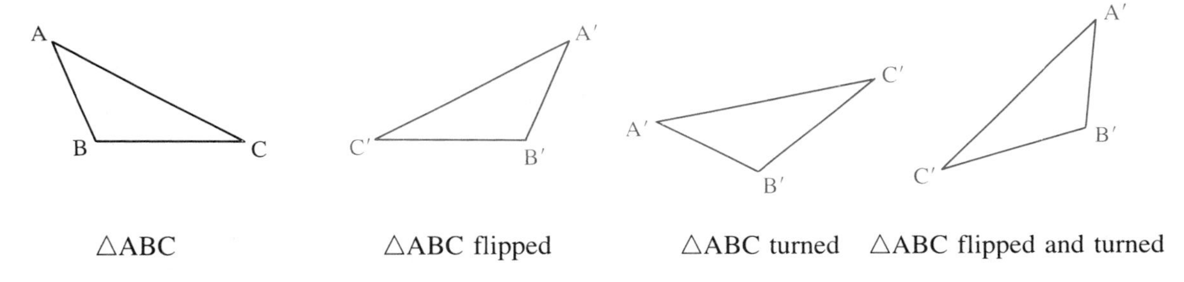

This idea of congruent figures as figures which can be made to coincide is applied to line segments and angles as well as triangles.

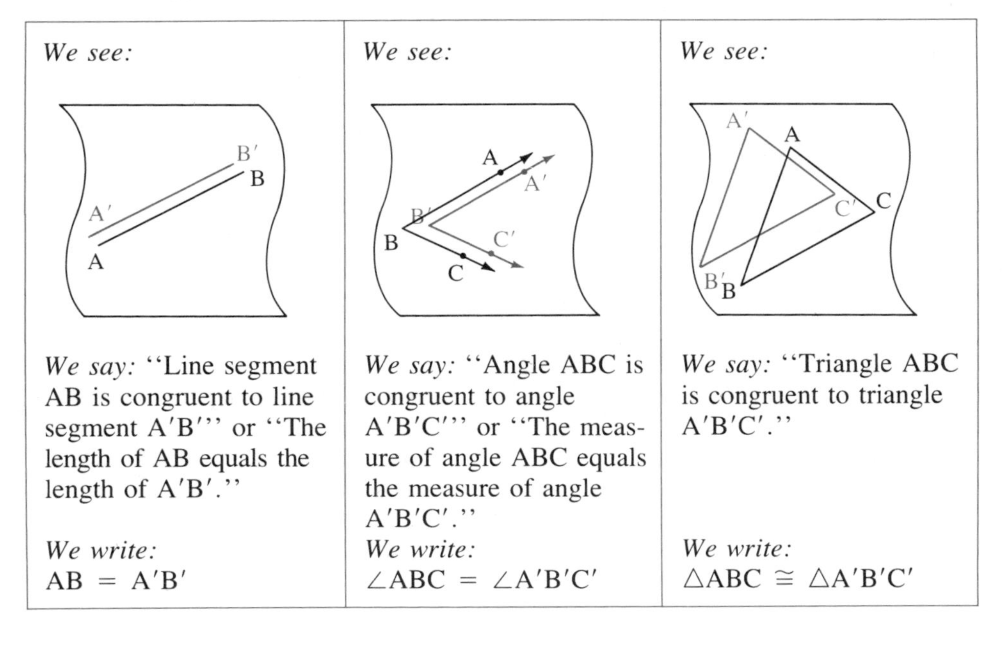

The statement that two line segments are congruent is equivalent to the statement that their lengths are equal. Also, the statement that two angles are congruent is equivalent to the statement that their measures are equal. Therefore, we can write = instead of ≅ when comparing congruent line segments and congruent angles. However, when we compare congruent triangles, we use the symbol ≅ to remind us that the statement $\triangle ABC \cong \triangle A'B'C'$ represents six equations. That is,

$$\triangle ABC \cong \triangle A'B'C' \text{ means } \begin{array}{ll} \angle A = \angle A' & \text{and } AB = A'B' \\ \angle B = \angle B' & AC = A'C' \\ \angle C = \angle C' & BC = B'C' \end{array}$$

To demonstrate that a pair of line segments, angles or triangles are congruent, we must show that they can be made to coincide by a suitable series of slides, flips, and turns. To show a change of position of a point, a line segment or a geometric figure we use the mapping notation illustrated below.

To show that point P moves to point P′

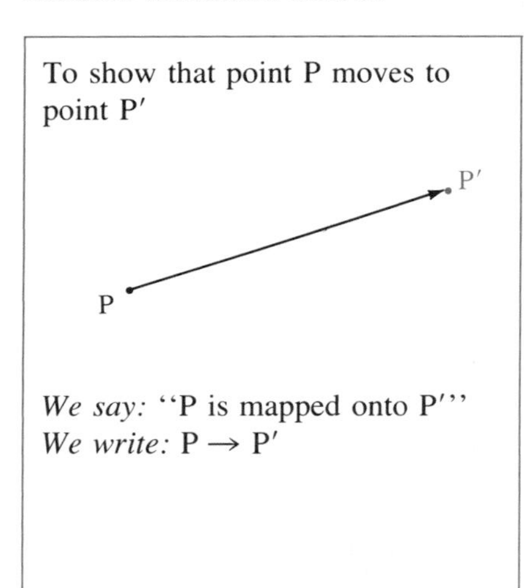

We say: "P is mapped onto P′"
We write: $P \rightarrow P'$

To show that $\triangle ABC$ moves to the position of $\triangle A'B'C'$

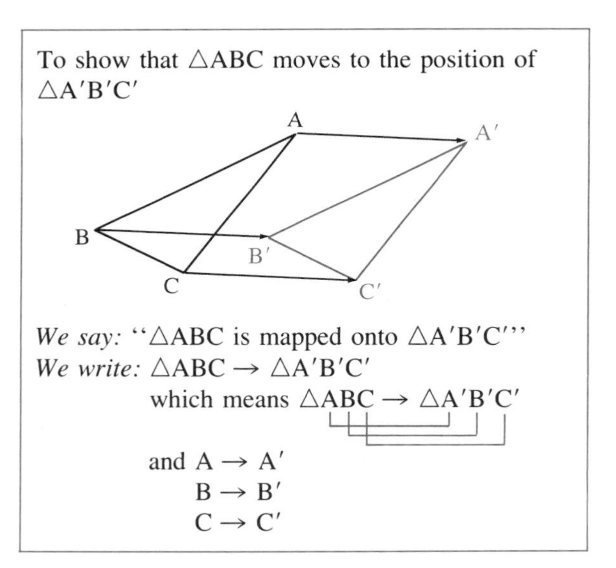

We say: "$\triangle ABC$ is mapped onto $\triangle A'B'C'$"
We write: $\triangle ABC \rightarrow \triangle A'B'C'$
which means $\triangle ABC \rightarrow \triangle A'B'C'$

and $A \rightarrow A'$
$B \rightarrow B'$
$C \rightarrow C'$

In these diagrams point P′ is the *image* of P and $\triangle A'B'C'$ is the *image* of $\triangle ABC$.

A mapping which associates each point P with an image P′ is called a *transformation*. Here are 3 examples of transformations that you may have studied. Adjacent to each transformation is the physical motion associated with it.

Transformation	Motion
translation	slide
rotation	turn
reflection	flip

These transformations correspond to rigid motions in the plane and therefore they preserve length. For this reason, they are called isometries.

The word *isometry* derives from the Greek "isos" meaning equal and "metron" meaning measure. Under an isometry the lengths of all line segments are unchanged. Furthermore, it can be shown that the measures of angles and areas are also unchanged under isometries.

Not all transformations are isometries. A dilatation is an example of a transformation which is not an isometry, since it does not preserve length.

EXERCISES 4-1

(A)

1. What point is the vertex of $\angle ABC$?
2. How many different ways can we name: a) $\triangle ABC$ b) parallelogram PQRS?
3. Write 6 equations which correspond to the statement $\triangle ABC \cong \triangle DEF$.
4. In how many points can two lines intersect?
5. Does the term "line" mean the same as the expression "straight line"?
6. How many lines pass through: a) a given point b) 2 given points?
7. Write the letter of the phrase which completes a true statement.

i) collinear points	a) are images of one another under isometries
ii) an isometry	b) is an isometry which reverses orientation
iii) a translation	c) has a measure of 180°
iv) a rotation	d) is any mapping which preserves lengths and angles
v) a reflection	e) is an isometry which leaves no points invariant
vi) congruent figures	f) lie on the same line
vii) a straight angle	g) is an isometry which leaves only one point invariant

8. Explain the difference between a trapezoid and a parallelogram.
9. Explain the classification of triangles into the categories: scalene, isosceles, equilateral.

(B)

10. a) Explain the term "perpendicular bisector".
    b) How many perpendicular bisectors has a given line segment? Support your answer with a reason.
11. Explain how you would determine whether two figures were identical.
12. Explain the difference between a transformation and a motion in the plane. Compare:
    a) a slide and a translation b) a flip and a reflection c) a turn and a rotation.
13. An isometry maps $\angle ABC$ onto $\angle A'B'C'$. Explain your answers to these questions.
    a) Is $\angle ABC = \angle A'B'C'$? b) Is B′ the image of B?
    c) Is $\overrightarrow{B'A'}$ the image of $\overrightarrow{BA}$? d) Is B′A′ the image of BA?

4-2 AXIOMS AND THEOREMS

In their quest for knowledge and ultimate truth, the ancient Greeks cultivated and developed the art of careful logical argument and step-by-step deductive thinking. Their mathematical investigations required detailed, carefully expressed ideas supported by basic assumptions called *axioms*.

One of the most famous axioms stated by Euclid is the ''Parallel Postulate'' or ''Parallel Axiom''.

> **Euclid's Parallel Axiom**
> There is exactly one line which is parallel to a given line and passes through a given point.

That is, there is no line other than l_1, which is parallel to l and passes through a given point P.

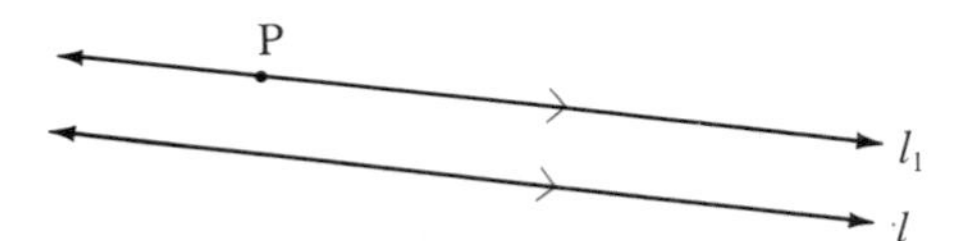

Here are four more of Euclid's axioms.

- Things which coincide with one another are equal to one another.
- It is possible to draw a straight line from one point to any other point.
- It is possible to describe a circle with a given centre and radius.
- All right angles are equal to one another.

Though Euclid's original set of axioms was a remarkable achievement for its time, it was incomplete. A modern approach to Euclidean geometry would identify as axioms some of the assumptions which Euclid overlooked. We shall highlight in this section some of these axioms which underpin Euclidean geometry. These axioms are, in fact, properties of the isometries studied in previous grades.

To build the language of geometry, we began with a set of basic terms, or primitives which we left undefined. New terms were then defined or expressed using these primitives.

In a similar way, we build the *theorems* of geometry by starting with a set of basic *axioms*. A theorem may be regarded as a logical consequence of a set of axioms. The sequence of logical steps which displays the theorem is called a *proof*.

To *prove* a theorem is to display the theorem as a logical consequence of some basic facts and axioms. In such a proof, we start with the facts which we know and then deduce the statement of the theorem using reasoning.

To construct a proof

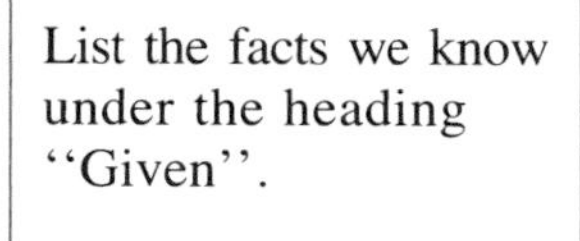

⇨ State what we need to prove, under the heading "Required to Prove".

⇨ Apply the given facts, the axioms or other theorems to deduce the required fact under the heading "Proof".

The proofs of some theorems are more easily understood with the use of an *Analysis*. This serves a dual purpose: it explains the thoughts that are necessary before the proof can proceed; and it lists any constructions that are not part of the *Given* statement.

In the following development, we introduce some basic definitions which are used to state fundamental theorems about angles. Each theorem is then proved, using the format of the flow chart above.

When proving theorems, we shall occasionally refer to the axioms. A more rigorous use of axioms is presented in *THE MATHEMATICAL MIND* on page 140.

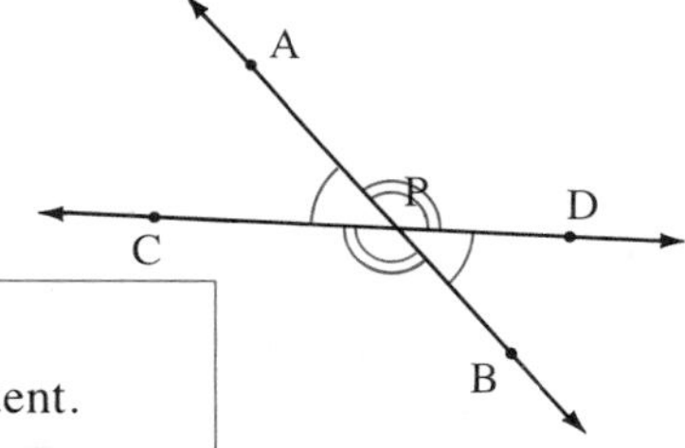

Definition: If $\overleftrightarrow{AB}$ and $\overleftrightarrow{CD}$ intersect at point P, then two pairs of *opposite angles* are formed: $\angle$DPB and $\angle$APC; $\angle$APD and $\angle$CPB.

> **Opposite Angles Theorem**
> If two lines intersect, then the opposite angles are congruent.

Given: $\overleftrightarrow{AB}$ and $\overleftrightarrow{CD}$ intersect at point P.

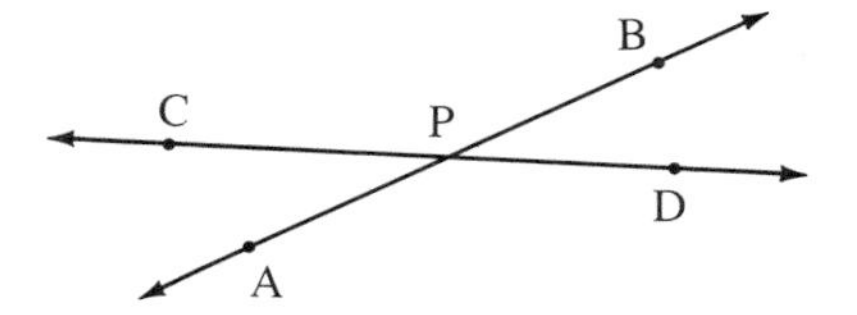

Required to Prove: $\angle$DPB = $\angle$APC
Proof:

Statement	Reason
$\angle DPB + \angle APD = 180°$	Supplementary angles
$\angle APC + \angle APD = 180°$	Supplementary angles
$\angle DPB - \angle APC = 0°$	Subtracting the equations
$\angle DPB = \angle APC$	

This proof applies to all opposite angles.
Hence, it is also true that $\angle$APD = $\angle$CPB.

This proof covers the main logical steps in arriving at the conclusion. However, if we were striving for more rigour we would have to include in our reasons an arithmetic axiom which states that if equals are subtracted from equals, the results are equal. In our treatment of geometry we will assume the arithmetic axioms without quoting them explicitly.

Definition: Any line which intersects two or more other lines is called a *transversal*.

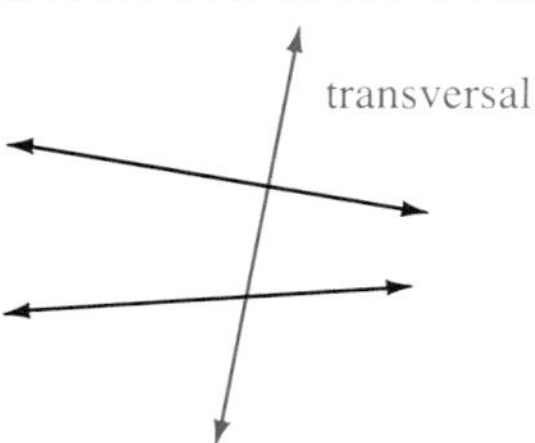

When a transversal intersects two other lines, eight angles are formed. The angles may be grouped in pairs.

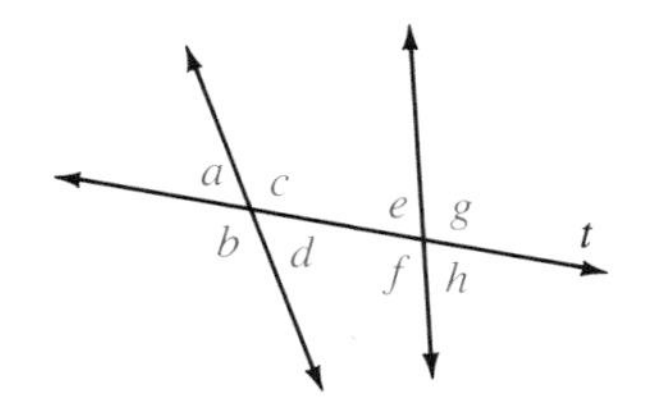

Corresponding Angles	Alternate Angles	Interior Angles
$\angle a$ and $\angle e$ $\angle b$ and $\angle f$ $\angle c$ and $\angle g$ $\angle d$ and $\angle h$	$\angle c$ and $\angle f$ $\angle d$ and $\angle e$	$\angle c$ and $\angle e$ $\angle d$ and $\angle f$

The following theorem shows the special relationships among the eight angles formed when a transversal intersects two *parallel* lines.

Parallel Lines Theorem
If a transversal intersects two parallel lines, then the corresponding angles are congruent.

Given: t is a transversal which intersects parallel lines l_1 and l_2 at points P_1 and P_2 respectively.

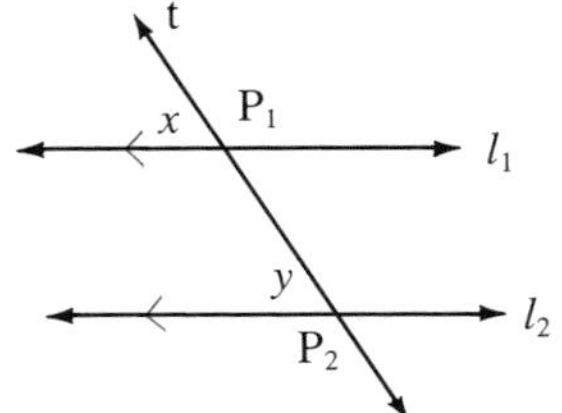

Required to Prove: $\angle x = \angle y$

Proof:

Statement	Reason
We can "slide" the line l_1 in the direction of line segment P_1P_2 until P_1 coincides with P_2 and l_1 coincides with l_2.	l_1 and l_2 are given parallel.
$\angle x$ is mapped onto $\angle y$.	$l_1 \rightarrow l_2$; $P_1 \rightarrow P_2$; $t \rightarrow t$
$\angle x = \angle y$	Definition of congruent angles

How can we be sure that there is a translation that maps any given line onto any line parallel to it?

How do we know that $\angle x$ does not change during a slide?

This proof, though correct, would not be regarded as rigorous. The first statement is an intuitive assertion, which is not based on a definition, a stated axiom, or a proven theorem.

The questions asked above will be addressed in *THE MATHEMATICAL MIND*, page 140.

A theorem that is closely related to another theorem and which is a self-evident consequence of that theorem is called a *corollary* of that theorem. The following corollaries of the Parallel Lines Theorem are easily deduced using this theorem and the Opposite Angles Theorem.

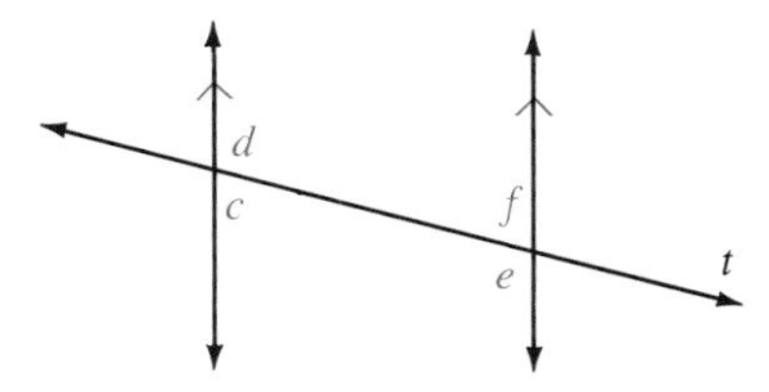

Corollary 1 of Parallel Lines Theorem
If a transversal intersects two parallel lines, then the alternate angles are congruent.

For example, $\angle c = \angle f$ and $\angle e = \angle d$

Corollary 2 of Parallel Lines Theorem
If a transversal intersects two parallel lines, then the interior angles on the same side of the transversal are supplementary.

For example,
$\angle c$ and $\angle e$ are supplementary; $\angle d$ and $\angle f$ are supplementary.

We can use the Parallel Lines Theorem to deduce an interesting and useful theorem about angles in a triangle.

Sum of the Angles Theorem
The sum of the measures of the angles in a triangle is 180°.

Given: $\triangle ABC$ with angle measures x, y, and z.
Required to Prove: $x + y + z = 180°$
Analysis: Draw l, a line through A parallel to $\overleftrightarrow{BC}$. z' and x' are the measures of the angles formed.

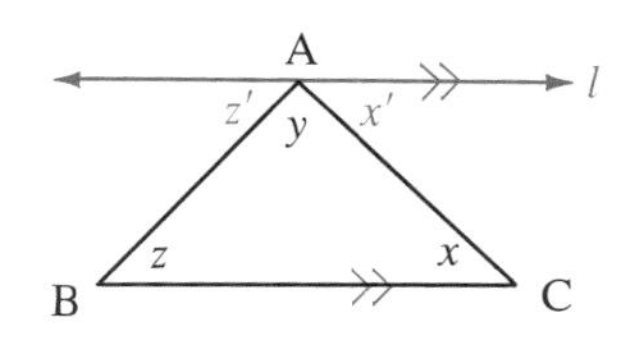

Proof:

Statement	Reason
$x = x'$	Parallel Lines Theorem — alternate angles
$z = z'$	Parallel Lines Theorem — alternate angles
$x' + y + z' = 180°$	Definition of a straight angle
Therefore, $x + y + z = 180°$	Substituting x for x' and z for z'

The Sum of the Angles Theorem asserts that the sum of the measures of the interior angles of any triangle is 180° no matter what the shape or size of the triangle. The fact that this result applies to any triangle, even those which have not been drawn and measured, demonstrates the power of deductive proof.

> **Corollary of the Sum of the Angles Theorem**
> If two angles of one triangle are congruent to two angles of another triangle, then the third angles are congruent.

The line and letters in color on the diagram above are drawn as a result of the *Analysis*. In many of the theorems that follow, you will see that constructions are necessary. These constructions are always drawn in color on the original diagram that is given.

The listing of a proof is sometimes made easier if the statements are numbered. This is illustrated in *Exercises 12* and *13*, page 126.

EXERCISES 4-2

Ⓐ

1. What is an axiom?
2. Why did Euclid attempt to base the study of geometry on axioms?
3. If axioms are self evident, why must they be stated?
4. Is the axiomatic method still used in mathematics?
5. Why do we not prove axioms?
6. Find the values of x and y.

a)

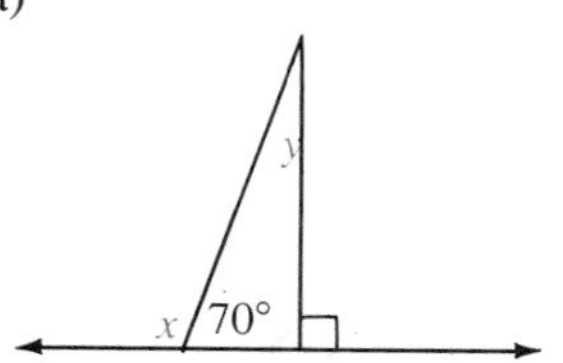

b)

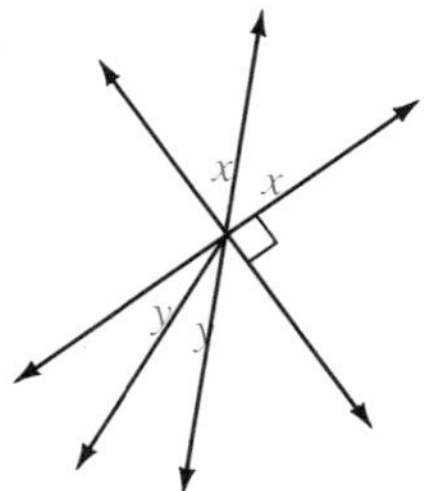

c)

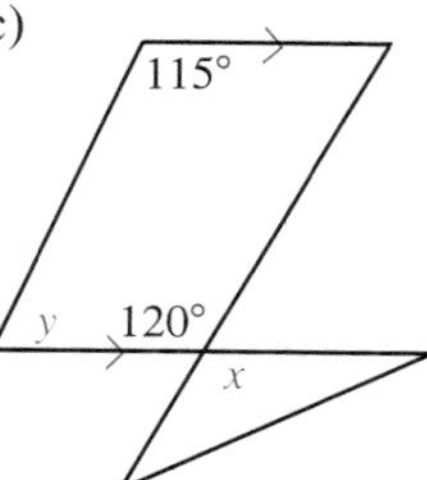

7. a) If you knew each value of x, how could you find the corresponding value of y?
   b) Write an equation relating x and y.

i)

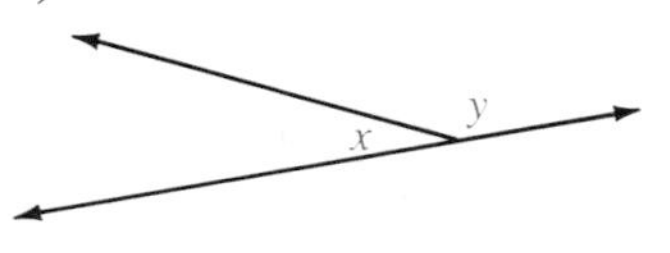

ii)

iii)

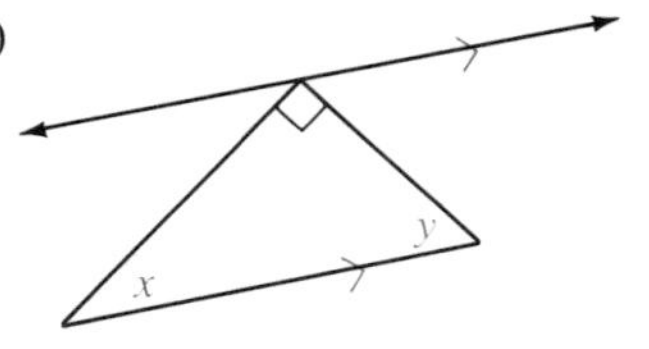

8. Write an equation relating x, y, and z in each diagram.

a)

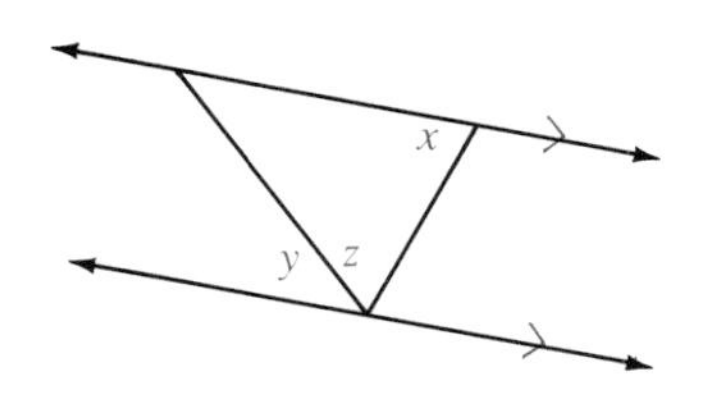

b)

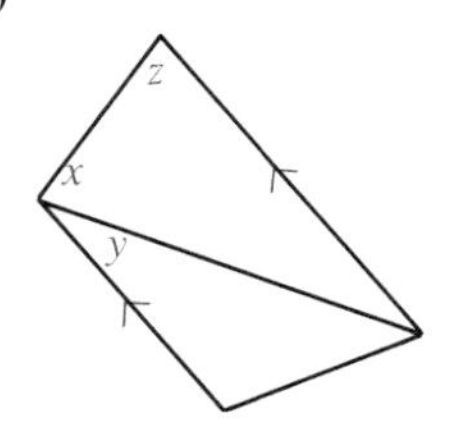

c)

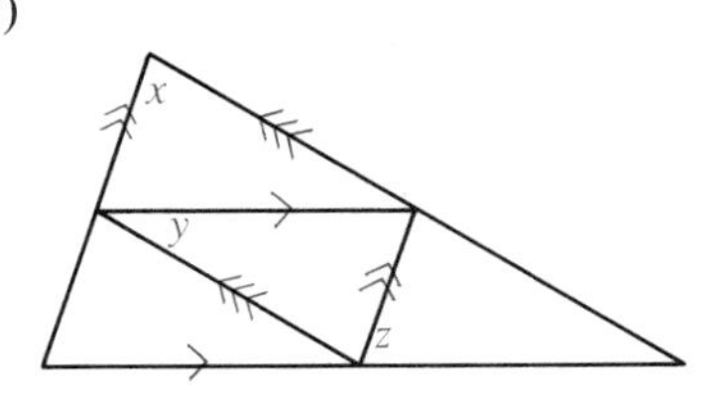

9. Explain why each statement is true.
   a) If 2 angles of one triangle are respectively congruent to 2 angles of another triangle, then the third angles are congruent.
   b) Each angle of a triangle with all angles congruent has a measure of 60°.
   c) If one angle of a triangle is congruent to the sum of the other two, then that angle is a right angle.

Ⓑ

10. For each theorem, draw and label a diagram marking all the given information. Then state the information which is given and that which it is required to prove.
    a) Theorem: In an isosceles triangle, the angles opposite the congruent sides are congruent.
    b) Theorem: Any point on the perpendicular bisector of a line segment is equidistant from the ends of the line segment.
    c) Theorem: A point is on the perpendicular bisector of a line segment if it is equidistant from the ends of the line segment.

11. For each theorem, draw and label a diagram marking all the given information. Then state the information which is given and that which it is required to prove.
    a) Theorem: If two sides of a triangle are congruent, then the median drawn to the third side is perpendicuar to it.
    b) Theorem: Chords which are equidistant from the centre of a circle are equal in length.
    c) Theorem: A line segment joining the midpoints of 2 sides of a triangle is parallel to the third side and equal to one-half of its length.
    d) Theorem: The diagonals of a rhombus bisect each other at right angles.

12. Copy all the statements in this proof and write the reasons.
    Given: ABCD is a parallelogram with AB ∥ DC and AD ∥ BC.

    Required to Prove: $\angle A = \angle C$ and $\angle B = \angle D$

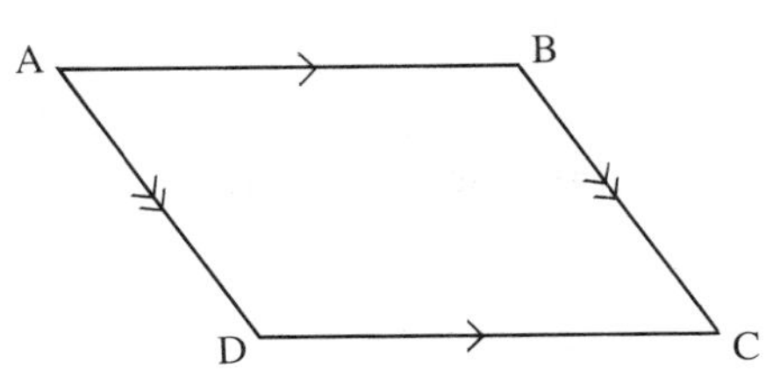

Proof:

Statement	Reason
1. AB ∥ DC	Given
2. $\angle A + \angle D = 180°$	______
3. AD ∥ BC	______
4. $\angle C + \angle D = 180°$	______
5. $\angle A = \angle C$	Statements __ and __
6. $\angle C + \angle B = 180°$	______
7. $\angle B = \angle D$	Statements __ and __

13. Copy all the statements in this proof and write the reasons.
Given: Quadrilateral WXYZ
Required to Prove:
$\angle W + \angle X + \angle Y + \angle Z = 360°$
Analysis: Draw diagonal WY and mark the angles a, b, c, and d as shown.

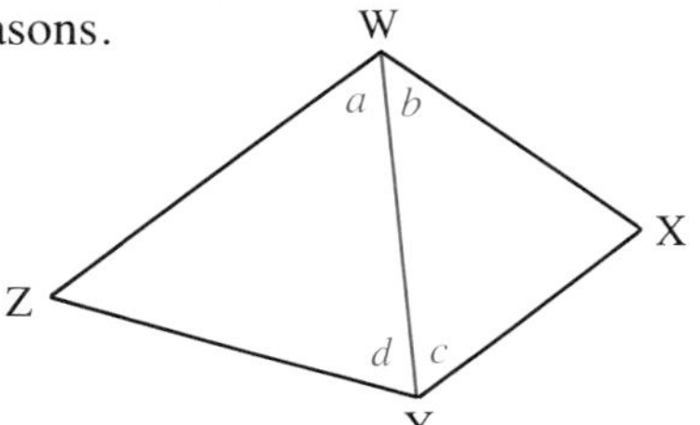

Proof:

Statement	Reason
1. $\angle X + b + c = 180°$	______
2. $a + d + \angle Z = 180°$	______
3. $\angle X + b + c + a + d + \angle Z = 360°$	Statements __ and __
4. $\angle X + (a + b) + (c + d) + \angle Z = 360°$	Statement __
5. $\angle X + \angle W + \angle Y + \angle Z = 360°$	Statement __

14. Prove corollary 1 of the Parallel Lines Theorem.

15. Prove corollary 2 of the Parallel Lines Theorem.

16. Prove that the sum of the measures of the angles of a pentagon is 540°.

17. Write an algebraic expression for the sum of the measures of the angles in a polygon of n sides.

18. Prove that if STUV is a parallelogram with $\angle T = 90°$, then STUV is a rectangle.

Ⓒ

19. Triangle ABC is a triangle with $\angle ABC = \angle ACB$. BD is the perpendicular from B to AC. Prove that $\angle DBC$ has a a measure of one-half the measure of $\angle A$.

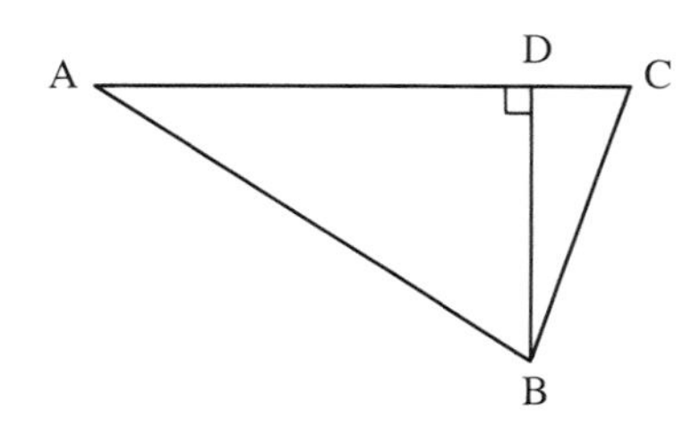

4-3 CONGRUENT TRIANGLE THEOREMS: PART ONE

The concept of congruence is an important aspect of many real-life situations. In forensic sciences, the proof that a fingerprint on an object matches that of a particular suspect is achieved by superimposing the two fingerprints and verifying that they are congruent.

In the manufacture of replacement parts for intricate machines, it is critical that each part and its replacement be identical in all respects. If the part and its replacement deviate from congruence by more than a prescribed tolerance, the machine will not function properly.

Even the spare key for your house or car must not deviate significantly from the original if it is to serve its purpose.

Though photocopy machines, printing presses, and computer disks produce copies which appear to be identical to the original, true congruence is a purely mathematical concept.

Definition: $\triangle ABC$ and $\triangle A'B'C'$ are *congruent* if there is an isometry which maps
$A \to A'$
$B \to B'$
$C \to C'$
We write $\triangle ABC \cong \triangle A'B'C'$.

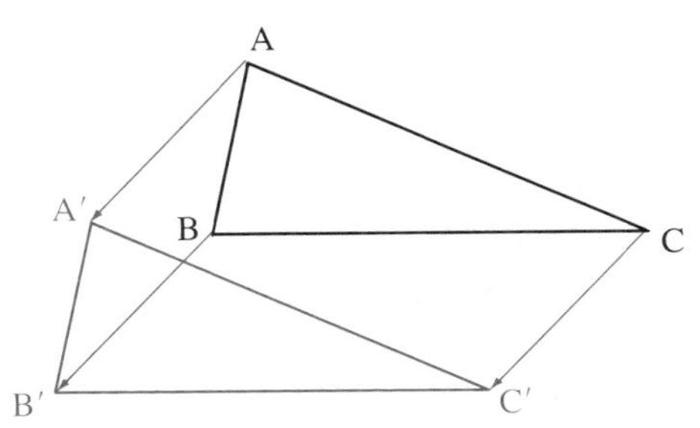

Congruent triangles are identical in all respects. That is, if $\triangle ABC \cong \triangle A'B'C'$, then corresponding sides and corresponding angles are equal. For this reason, knowing that two triangles are congruent helps us to prove theorems relating corresponding angles or corresponding sides. Hence, it is important to know what conditions are sufficient to prove that two triangles are congruent.

Some texts develop Euclidean geometry using the congruence theorems as axioms. We shall prove the congruence theorems before using them to prove a variety of other theorems.

To prove two triangles are congruent, we need only show that there is an isometry which maps each vertex of one triangle onto a corresponding vertex on the other.

The following theorem provides a simple set of conditions, which are sufficient to prove two triangles congruent.

> **Side-Angle-Side Theorem (SAS)**
> If two sides and the contained angle of one triangle are congruent to two sides and the contained angle of another triangle, then the triangles are congruent.

Given: $\triangle ABC$ and $\triangle A'B'C'$ such that $BA = B'A'$, $BC = B'C'$, and $\angle B = \angle B'$

Required to Prove: $\triangle ABC \cong \triangle A'B'C'$

Analysis: There is an isometry which maps $\triangle ABC \rightarrow \triangle A'B'C'$ so that $A \rightarrow A'$, $B \rightarrow B'$, and $C \rightarrow C'$.

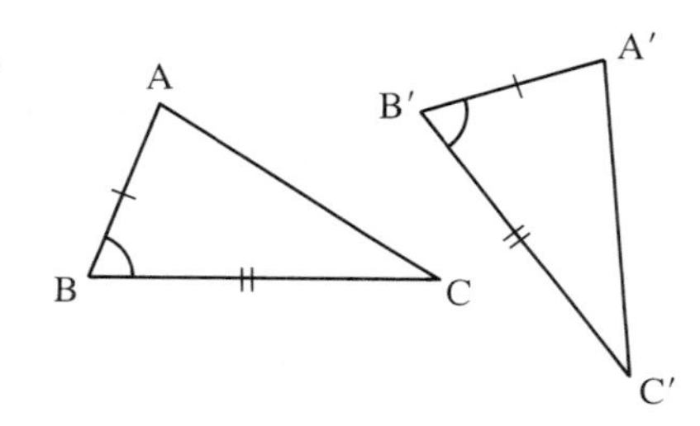

Proof:

Statement	Reason
1. $\angle B = \angle B'$	Given
2. We can move $\triangle ABC$ onto $\triangle A'B'C'$ so that $B \rightarrow B'$, BC falls along B′C′, and BA falls along B′A′.	Statement 1
3. $BC = B'C'$	Given
4. $BA = B'A'$	Given
5. $C \rightarrow C'$ and $A \rightarrow A'$	Statements 3 and 4
6. The motion described in statement 2 maps $\triangle ABC$ onto $\triangle A'B'C'$ so that $A \rightarrow A'$, $B \rightarrow B'$, and $C \rightarrow C'$.	Statements 2 and 5
7. $\triangle ABC \cong \triangle A'B'C'$	Statement 6

How do we know that there is a physical motion that maps $\angle B$ onto $\angle B'$?

The question will be addressed in THE MATHEMATICAL MIND on page 140.

The following theorems indicate that two triangles are congruent if two angles and one side of one triangle are congruent to the corresponding angles and side of the other triangle.

> **Angle-Side-Angle Theorem (ASA)**
> If two angles and the contained side of one triangle are congruent to two angles and the contained side of another triangle, then the triangles are congruent.

Given: △ABC and △A′B′C′ such that ∠B = ∠B′, ∠C = ∠C′, and BC = B′C′

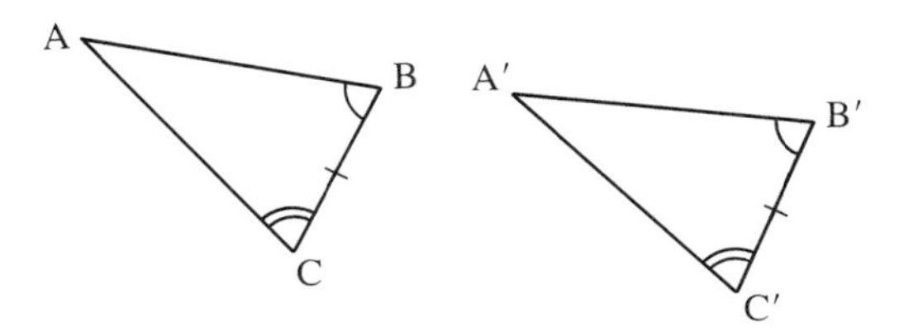

Required to Prove: △ABC ≅ △A′B′C′
Proof:

Statement	Reason
1. ∠B = ∠B′	Given
2. We can move △ABC onto △A′B′C′ so that B → B′, BC falls along B′C′, and BA falls along B′A′.	Statement 1
3. BC = B′C′	Given
4. C → C′	Statement 3
5. ∠C = ∠C′	Given
6. CA falls along C′A′	Statement 5
7. A lies on B′A′ and C′A′.	From Statement 2, BA falls along B′A′. From Statement 6, CA falls along C′A′.
8. A → A′	From Statement 7, A falls on the intersection of B′A′ and C′A′; that is, on A′.
9. The motion described in statement 2 maps △ABC onto △A′B′C′ so that A → A′, B → B′, and C → C′.	Statements 2, 4, and 8
10. △ABC ≅ △A′B′C′	Statement 9

We can combine the ASA theorem and the Sum of the Angles theorem to prove the following theorem.

> **Angle-Angle-Side Theorem (AAS)**
> If two angles and a side of one triangle are respectively congruent to two angles and a side of another triangle, then the two triangles are congruent.

Given: $\triangle ABC$ and $\triangle A'B'C'$ such that $\angle A = \angle A'$, $\angle B = \angle B'$, and $BC = B'C'$

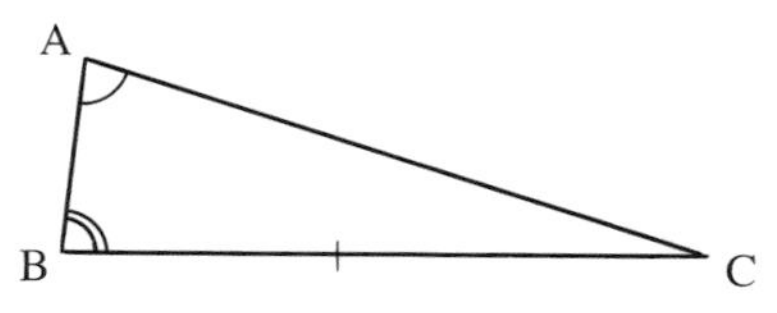

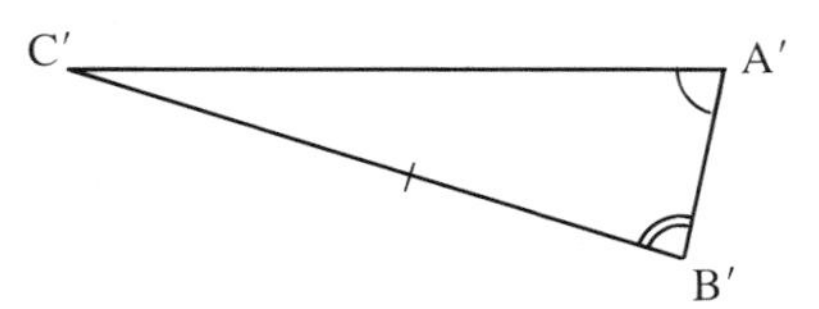

Required to Prove: $\triangle ABC \cong \triangle A'B'C'$

Proof:

Statement	Reason
$\angle A = \angle A'$	Given
$\angle B = \angle B'$	Given
$\angle C = \angle C'$	Sum of the Angles Theorem
In $\triangle ABC$ and $\triangle A'B'C'$	
$\angle B = \angle B'$	Given
$BC = B'C'$	Given
$\angle C = \angle C'$	Proved
Therefore, $\triangle ABC \cong \triangle A'B'C'$	ASA

The following Isosceles Triangle Theorem was also called ''Pons Asinorum'' (Bridge of Fools) by ancient mathematicians who believed that only those who were not fools could successfully cross this bridge into deductive thinking.

> **Isosceles Triangle Theorem**
> If two sides of a triangle are congruent, then the angles opposite the congruent sides are congruent.

Given: Isosceles $\triangle ABC$ with $AB = AC$
Required to Prove: $\angle B = \angle C$
Analysis: Draw AD, the bisector of $\angle BAC$.
Attempt to prove that $\triangle BAD$ is congruent to $\triangle CAD$.

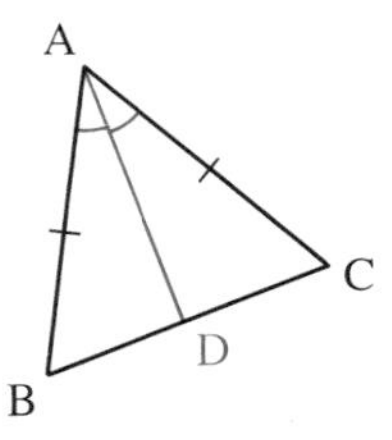

Proof:

Statement	Reason
In $\triangle BAD$ and $\triangle CAD$	
$AB = AC$	Given
$\angle BAD = \angle CAD$	AD bisects $\angle BAC$.
AD is common	
Therefore, $\triangle BAD \cong \triangle CAD$	SAS
$\angle B = \angle C$	Congruent triangles

EXERCISES 4-3

1. For each pair of triangles, name two pairs of sides which if equal would be sufficient to prove that the triangles are congruent.

a)
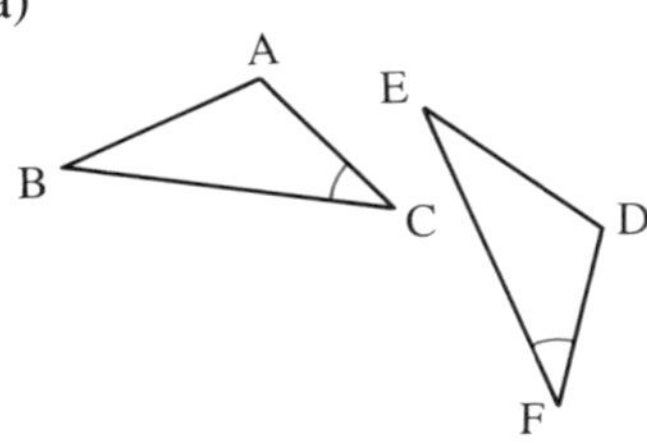

b)
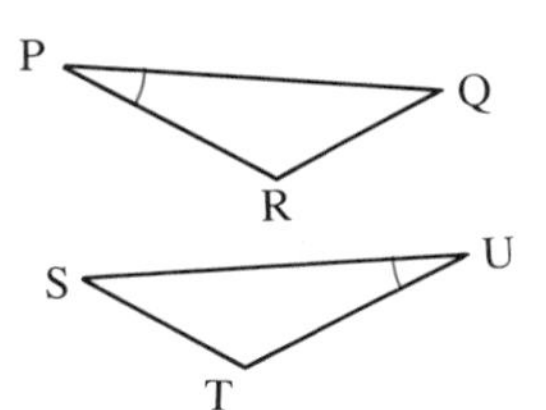

c)
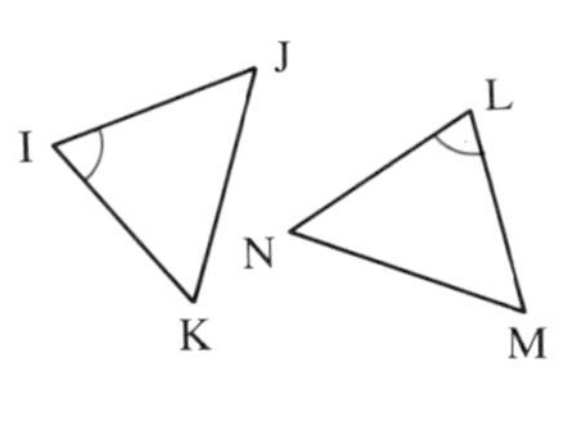

2. For each pair of triangles, name a pair of angles which if equal would be sufficient to prove the triangles congruent.

a)
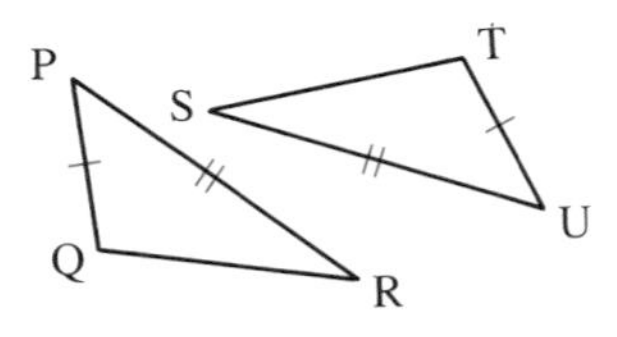

b)
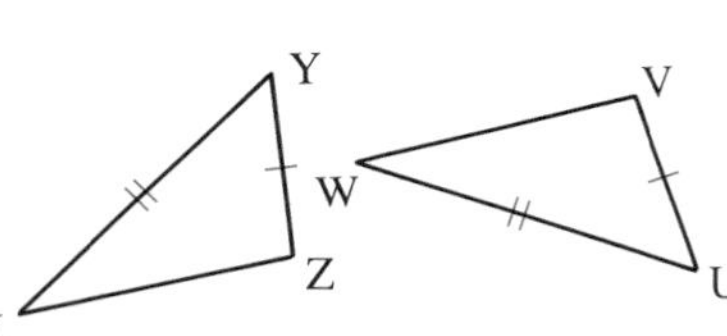

c)
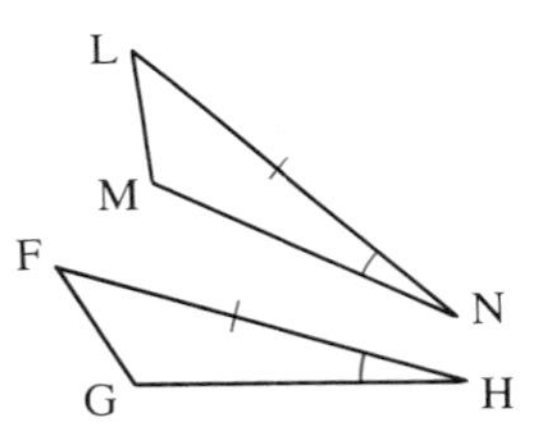

3. In each diagram, name a pair of congruent triangles. State the theorem that guarantees each congruence.

a)
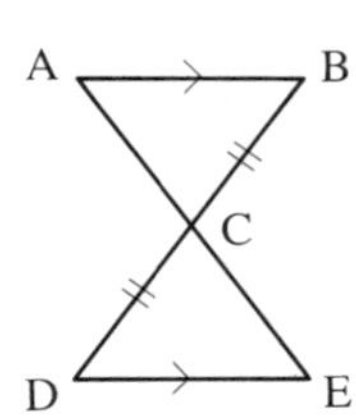

b)
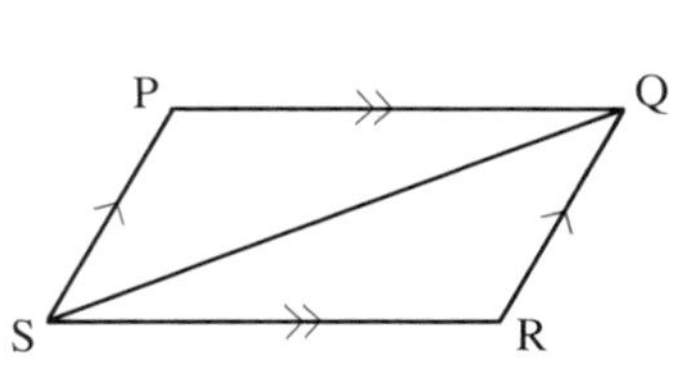

c)
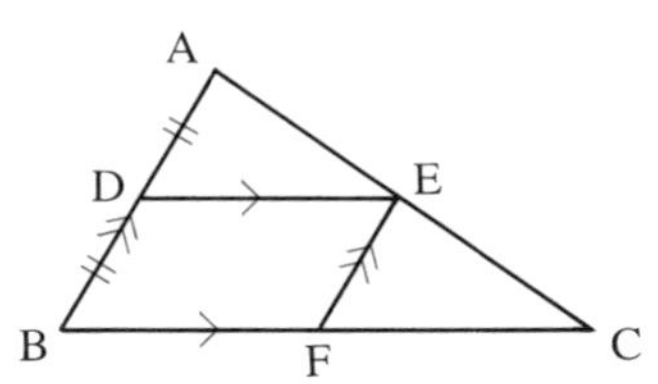

4. Calculate the measures of the angles marked x, y, and z.

a)
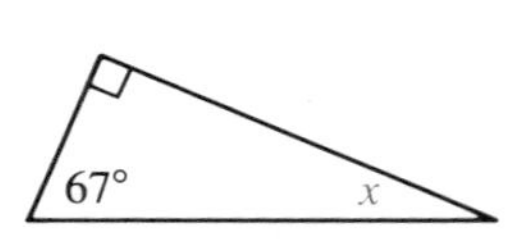

b)
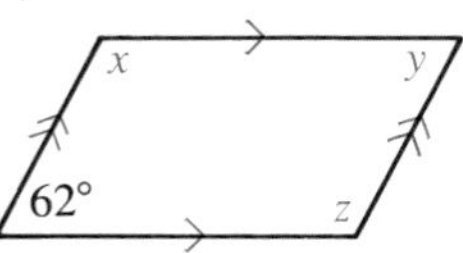

c)
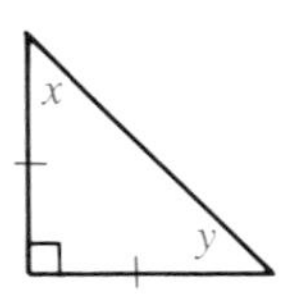

d)
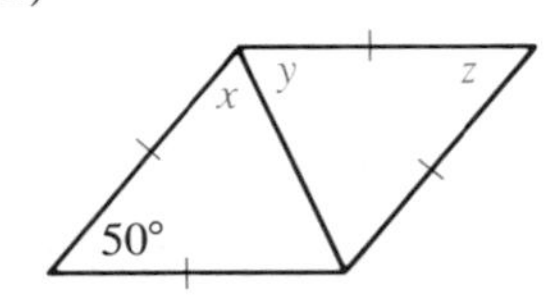

e)
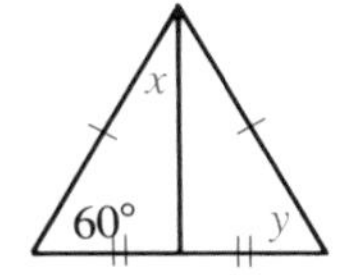

f)
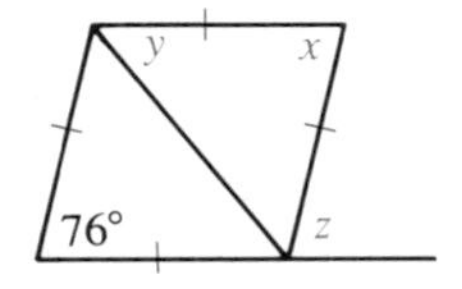

Ⓑ

5. Calculate the measures of the angles marked x, y, and z.

a)

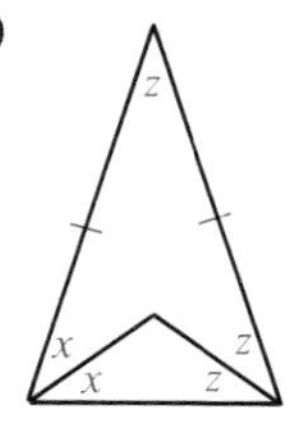

b)

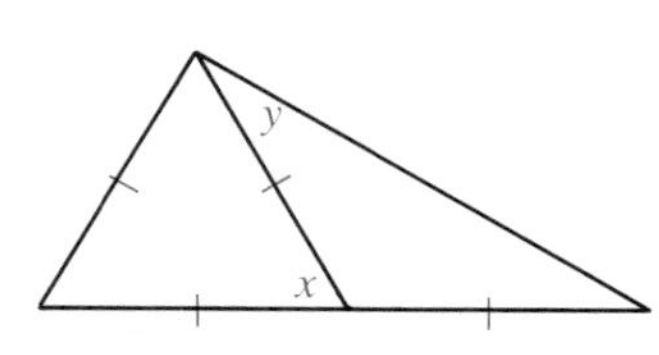

c)

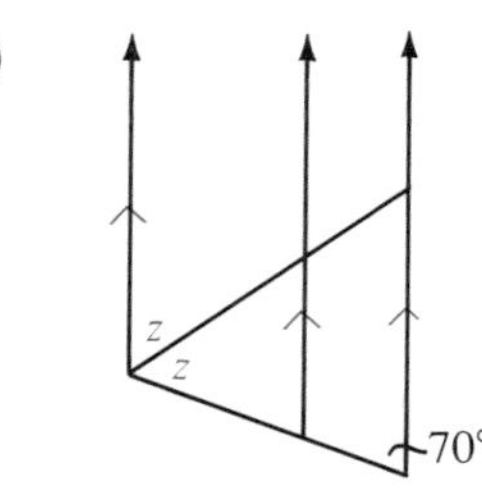

6. Copy the statements in this proof and write the reasons.
Given: MN is a diameter of a circle with centre O, and ML ∥ OK
Required to Prove: ∠LOK = ∠NOK

Proof:

Statement	Reason
1. OM = OL	______
2. ∠OML = ∠OLM	______
3. ML ∥ OK	______
4. ∠OML = ∠NOK	______
5. ∠OLM = ∠LOK	______
6. ∠OLM = ∠NOK	Statements __ and __
7. ∠LOK = ∠NOK	Statements __ and __

7. Copy the statements in this proof and write the reasons.
Given: △ABC is isosceles with AB = AC. BE and CD are medians drawn to AC and AB respectively.
Required to Prove: BE = CD

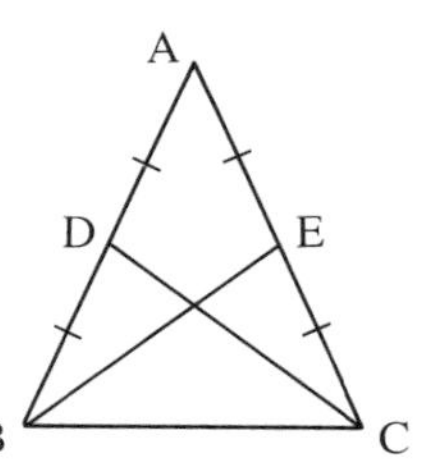

Proof:

Statement	Reason
AB = AC	Given
In △BDC and △CEB	
BD = CE	______
∠ABC = ∠ACB	______
BC is common	
Therefore, △BDC ≅ △CEB	______
CD = BE	______

8. Triangle XYZ (below left) is equilateral and XU = YW = ZV. Prove that △UVW is equilateral.

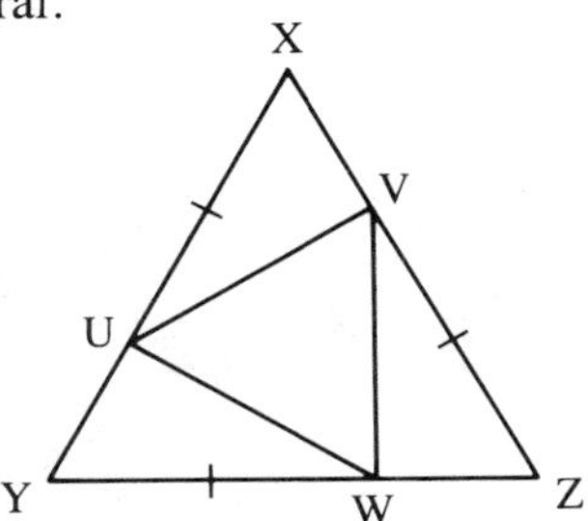

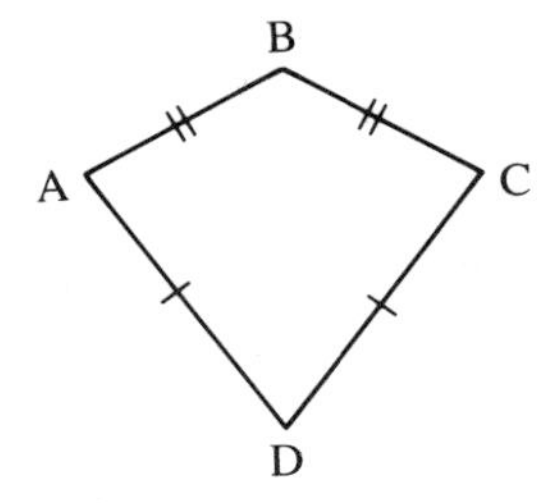

9. In quadrilateral ABCD (above right), AB = BC and AD = DC; prove that ∠A = ∠C.

10. Given parallelogram PQRS (below left) with diagonal PR and points M and N on PQ and RS respectively such that MN bisects PR at point T; prove that MT = TN.

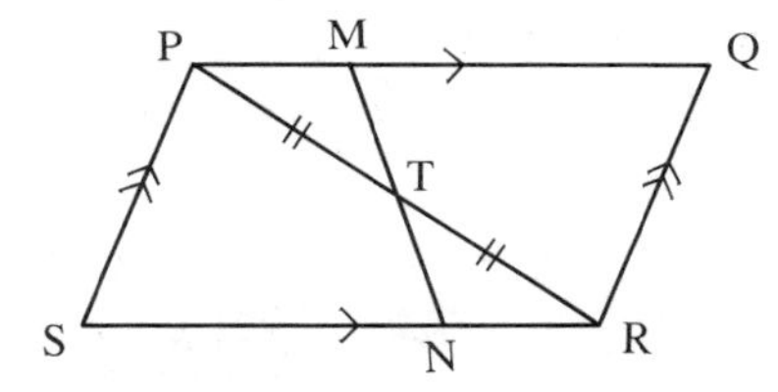

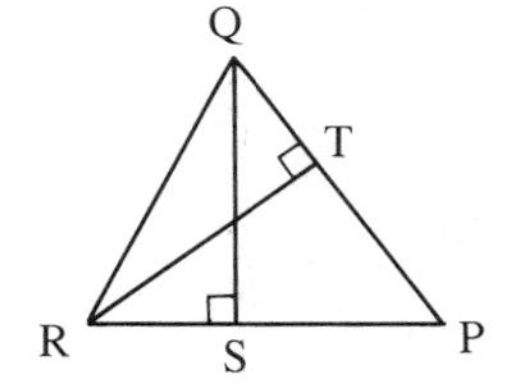

11. Triangle PQR (above right) is isosceles with PQ = PR. Prove that the altitudes QS and RT are equal.

12. To find the distance AB across a river, a surveyor placed stakes at points D and E so that DE ⊥ AB and BD = BE. A stake was then placed at point C so that ∠BDC = ∠BEA. The surveyor measured the distance from B to C to determine the distance from A to B. Is AB = BC? Explain your answer.

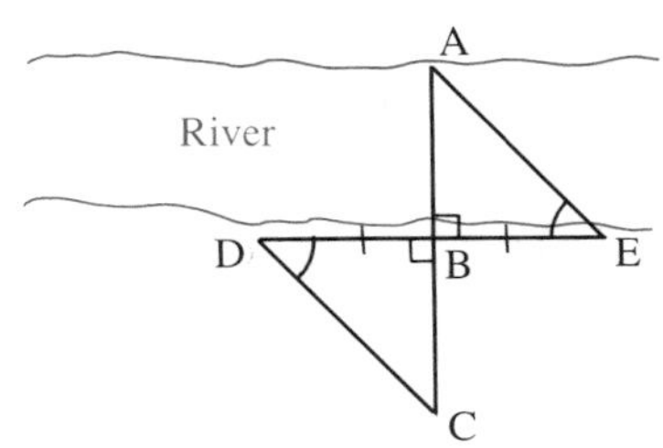

13. Prove that any point on the bisector of an angle is equidistant from the arms of the angle.

Ⓒ

14. Prove that two triangles are congruent if the three sides of one triangle are respectively congruent to the three sides of the other triangle.

15. Construct △ABC so that ∠BAC = 20°, AB = 6 cm, and BC = 2 cm. Construct another △ABC which satisfies these requirements but is not congruent to △ABC.

16. △ABC is a right triangle with ∠A = 90°. Median AD is drawn to the midpoint D of BC. Prove that BC is twice the length of AD.

4-4 CONGRUENT TRIANGLE THEOREMS: PART TWO

Why is the triangle the fundamental shape used in the construction of most structures?

If we construct a parallelogram from four metal strips and rivet the strips at the vertices, we can change the shape of the parallelogram.

We may start with a rectangle . . . and press into another shape . . . or yet another

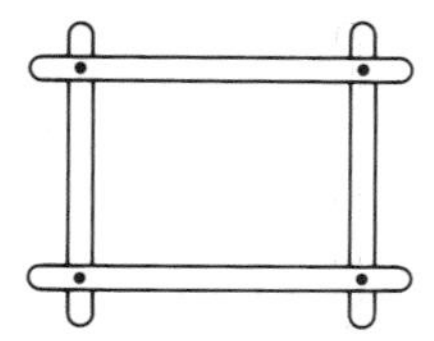

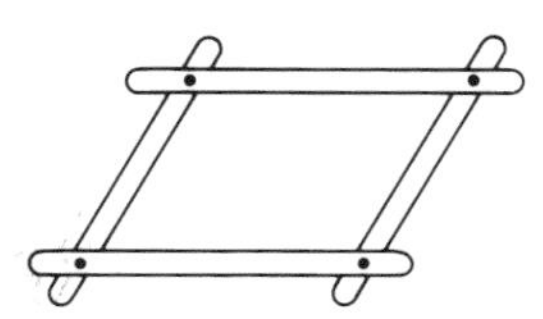

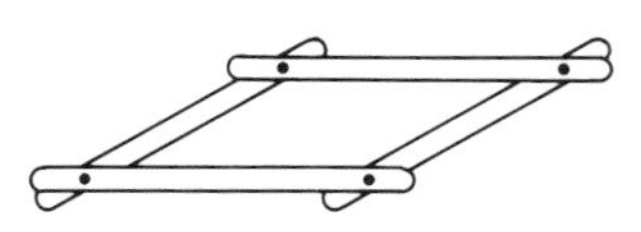

. . . without removing the rivets! That is, we can change the shape of a quadrilateral without changing the lengths of its sides. Engineers say that the quadrilateral is *unstable*.

The triangle, on the other hand, is *stable*. Three metal strips which are riveted to form a triangle can form only one triangle and there is no way to change the shape of such a triangle without bending one of its sides. That is, given three metal strips, we can make at most one triangle. Any two triangles with sides the same length must be congruent. The following theorem proves this fact.

> **Side-Side-Side Theorem (SSS)**
> If the sides of one triangle are congruent to the corresponding sides of another triangle, then the triangles are congruent.

Given: △ABC and △A′B′C′ such that AB = A′B′, AC = A′C′, BC = B′C′

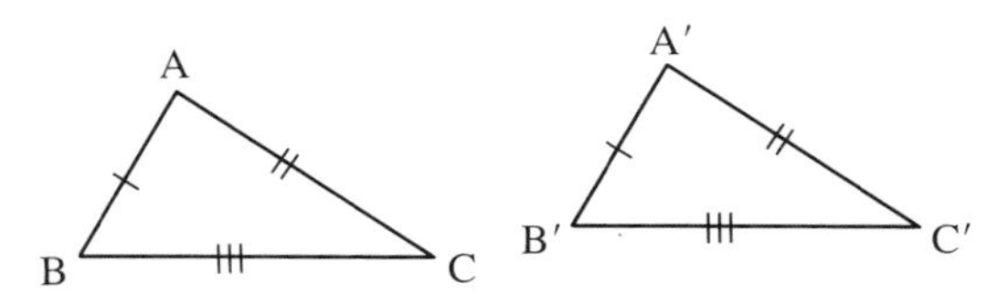

Required to Prove: △ABC ≅ △A′B′C′

Analysis: Move △ABC to △A′B′C′ so that BC falls along B′C′ and A falls on the side of BC remote from A′. It is sufficient to prove that △AB′C′ is congruent to △A′B′C′. Join AA′.

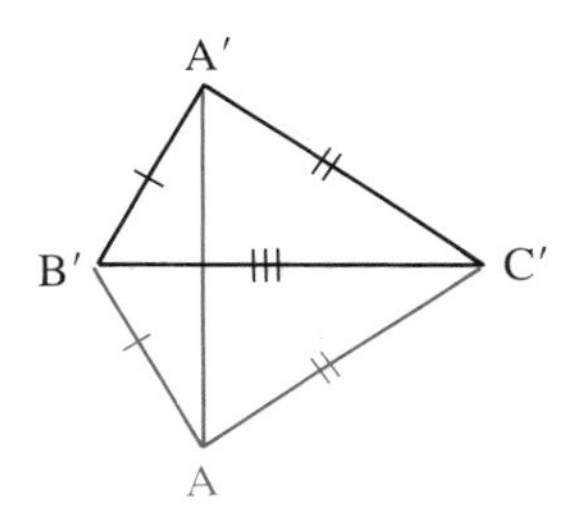

How do we know that such a physical motion exists?

Proof:

Statement	Reason
1. Since A′B′ = AB′, then ∠B′A′A = ∠B′AA′	Isosceles Triangle Theorem
2. Since A′C′ = AC′, then ∠AA′C′ = ∠A′AC′	Isosceles Triangle Theorem
3. ∠B′A′C′ = ∠B′AC′	Statements 1 and 2
4. In △A′B′C′ and △AB′C′	
B′A′ = B′A	Given
∠B′A′C′ = ∠B′AC′	Statement 3
A′C′ = AC′	Given
5. Therefore, △A′B′C′ ≅ △AB′C′	SAS
6. Since △AB′C′ ≅ △ABC, then △ABC ≅ △A′B′C′	

The question asked above will be addressed in *THE MATHEMATICAL MIND* on page 140.

The following congruent triangle theorem provides another example of a proof which is facilitated by mapping one side of one triangle onto the corresponding side of another triangle. This theorem is used frequently to prove right triangles congruent.

Hypotenuse-Side Theorem (HS)
If the hypotenuse and one side of a right triangle are congruent to the hypotenuse and one side of another right triangle, then the triangles are congruent.

Given: △ABC and △DEF such that AB = DE, AC = DF, and ∠B = ∠E = 90°

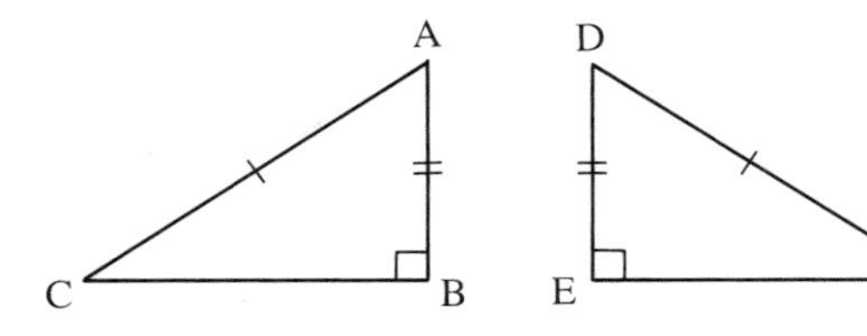

Required to Prove: △ABC ≅ △DEF
Analysis: Move △DEF onto △ABC so that DE falls along AB, and F falls on the side of AB remote from C. It is sufficient to prove that △ABC ≅ △ABF.

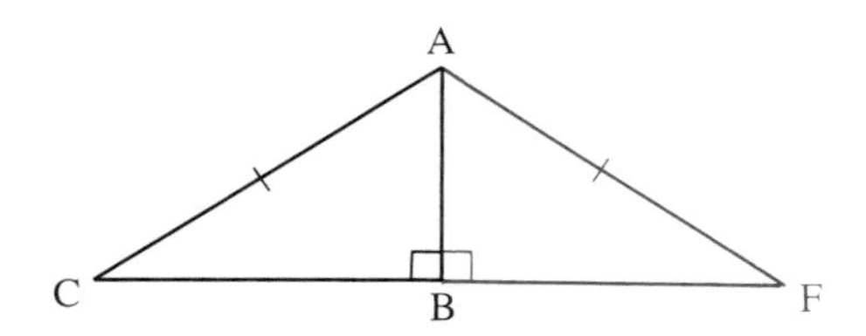

Proof:

Statement	Reason
AC = AF	Given
∠C = ∠F	Isosceles Triangle Theorem
In △ABC and △ABF	
∠C = ∠F	
∠ABC = ∠ABF	Given
AC = AF	Given
Therefore, △ABC ≅ △ABF	AAS

Since △ABF ≅ △DEF, then △ABC ≅ △DEF

The congruence theorems can be used to prove a variety of other theorems. The Side-Angle-Side Theorem can be used to prove the famous Pythagorean Theorem.

Pythagorean Theorem
The square of the hypotenuse of a right triangle is equal to the sum of the squares of the other two sides.

Given: $\triangle ABC$ is a right triangle with $\angle C = 90°$.
a, b, and c are the lengths of the sides opposite vertices A, B, and C respectively.

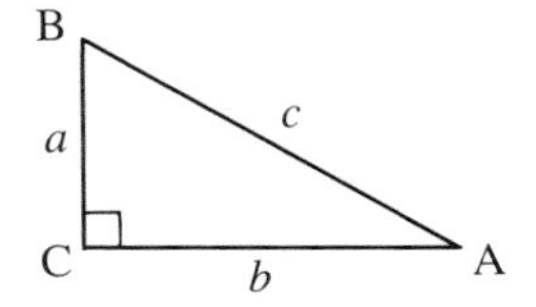

Required to Prove: $c^2 = a^2 + b^2$

Analysis: Consider a square PQRS with sides of length $a + b$. Let WXYZ be the quadrilateral formed by joining the points which divide each side of the square internally in the ratio $a : b$.

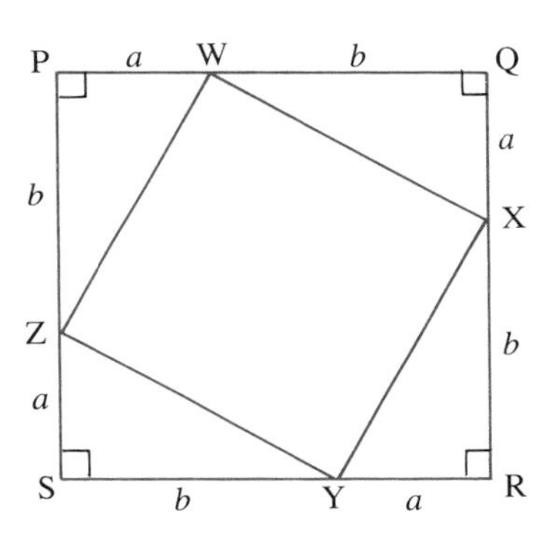

Proof:

Statement	Reason
1. Each colored triangle is a right triangle with shorter sides of length a and b.	From the diagram
2. Each colored triangle is congruent to $\triangle ABC$.	SAS
3. $\angle PWZ + \angle ZWX + \angle QWX = 180°$	Straight angle
4. $\angle PWZ + \angle QWX = 90°$	Statements 2 and 3, and the Sum of the Angles Theorem
5. $\angle ZWX = 90°$	Statements 3 and 4
6. All the angles in quadrilateral WXYZ are right angles.	Repeating the argument in statements 1 to 5 for the angles at X, Y, and Z
7. WXYZ is a square.	Statements 2 and 6
8. Area of PQRS is $(a + b)^2$.	Each side is $a + b$.
9. Area of PQRS is $c^2 + 4\left(\frac{1}{2}ab\right)$	Area of WXYZ plus area of the four shaded triangles
10. $c^2 + 2ab = (a + b)^2$	Statements 8 and 9
11. $c^2 = a^2 + b^2$	Statement 10

EXERCISES 4-4

1. Explain how you would prove that BD bisects ∠B and ∠D in the quadrilateral ABCD (below left).

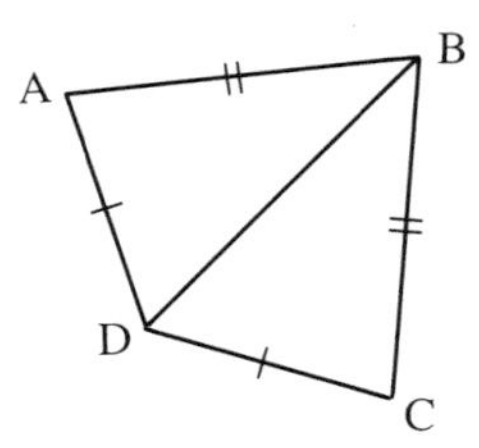

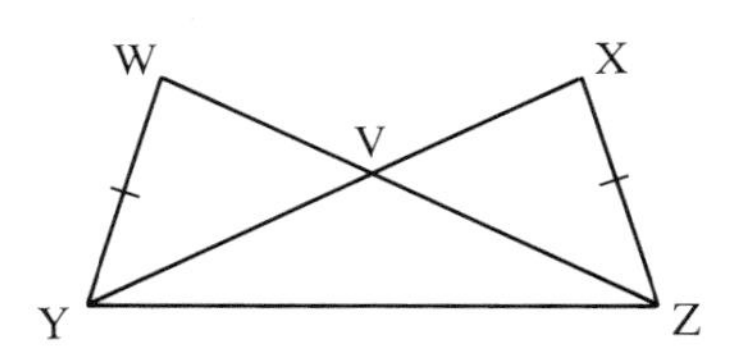

2. In the diagram (above right) WZ = XY and WY = XZ; explain why △VZY is isosceles.
3. Right △ABC has sides of length 3 cm, 4 cm, and 5 cm. Explain why any triangle with sides of length 3 cm, 4 cm, and 5 cm must be a right triangle.
4. Name two pairs of equal angles in each diagram. Name the theorems which support your answers.

a)

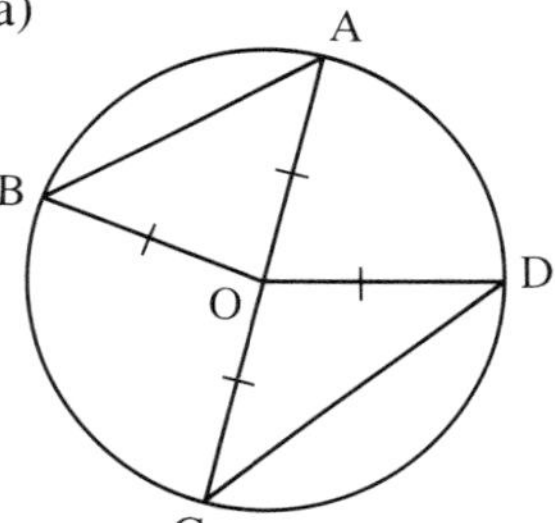

b)

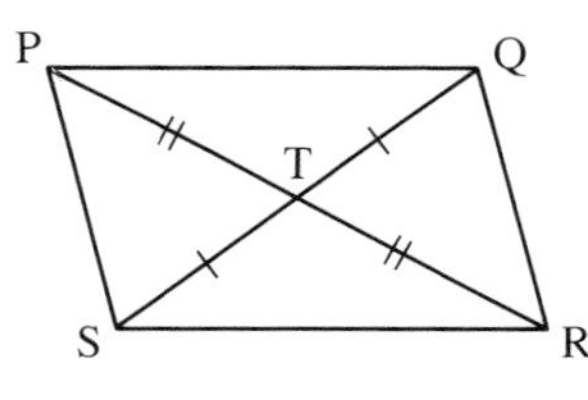

c)

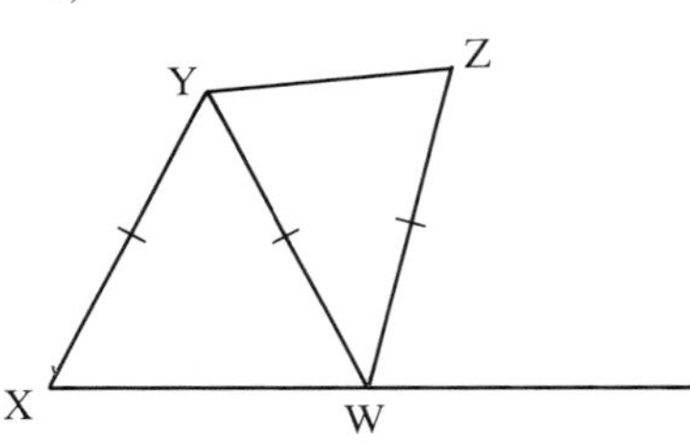

5. Triangle PQR (below left) represents an A-frame chalet with base QR 18 m, slant heights PQ = PR = 15 m, and height PS.
   a) Does PS bisect QR? Explain your answer.
   b) How long is SR?
   c) What is the height of the chalet?

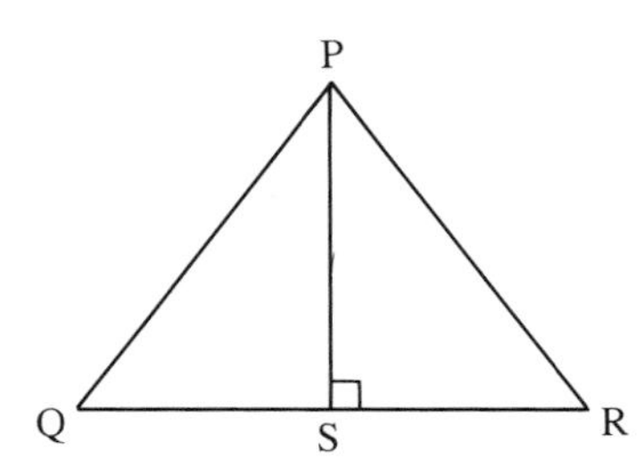

6. A chord AB of length 24 cm is constructed in a circle of diameter 26 cm (above right). How far is the chord from the centre of the circle?

Ⓑ

7. Copy the statements in this proof and write the reasons.

   Given: Quadrilateral ABCD with diagonals AC and BD intersecting at G; AD = DC and AB = BC

   Required to Prove: AG = CG and ∠CGD = 90°

   Proof:

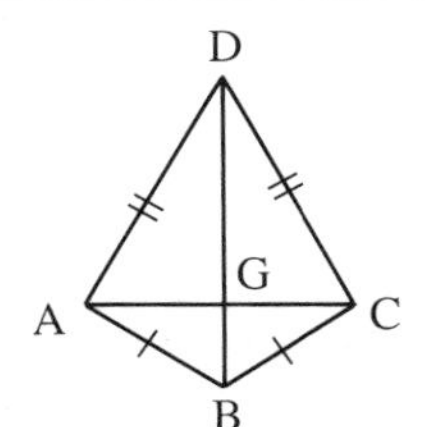

Statement	Reason
1. In △ABD and △CBD	
AB = CB	________
AD = CD	________
BD is common	
2. Therefore, △ABD ≅ △CBD	____
3. In △ADG and △CDG	
AD = CD	________
∠ADG = ∠CDG	Statement __
DG is common	
4. Therefore, △ADG ≅ △CDG	____
5. AG = CG	________
6. ∠AGD = ∠CGD	________
7. ∠CGD = 90°	Straight angle and Statement __

8. Isosceles △DEF has DE = DF. Prove that the median from D to EF is also an altitude of △DEF.

9. Prove that two chords of a circle that are equal in length must be equidistant from the centre of the circle.

10. The bisectors of ∠Q and ∠R of △PQR meet at point S. Prove that S is equidistant from all three sides of △PQR.

11. Prove that in any parallelogram the opposite angles are congruent and the opposite sides are congruent.

12. Prove that any point that is equidistant from the arms of an angle lies on the bisector of that angle.

13. Prove that if all the medians of a triangle are altitudes, then the triangle is equilateral.

Ⓒ

14. In parallelogram PQRS, T and U are the midpoints of PS and QR respectively. TR and PU intersect SQ at V and W respectively. Prove that SW = QV.

15. The Pythagorean Theorem states that if c is the length of the hypotenuse of a right triangle, and a and b are the lengths of the remaining sides, then $c^2 = a^2 + b^2$. Prove the converse of the Pythagorean Theorem; that is, if a triangle has sides of length a, b, and c such that $c^2 = a^2 + b^2$, then the triangle is a right triangle with hypotenuse of length c.

THE MATHEMATICAL MIND

The Axiomatic Approach

The ancient Greeks attempted to build a foundation for mathematical proof. With this effort was born the so-called ''axiomatic'' method whereby all theorems were to be deduced from universally accepted ''self-evident'' truths.

In the ninetenth century, the requirement that axioms be self-evident was abandoned. Mathematics became a purely abstract science which no longer asserted that ''such and such is true''; but rather ''If the following axioms are assumed, then the following theorems are logical consequences''. This apparently inconsequential change in focus enabled mathematicians to shift their study of geometry from an investigation of *the* geometry to an investigation of various geometries. Each geometry was defined by a different set of axioms. Euclid's parallel postulate was an axiom in Euclidean geometry but was not included in the sets of axioms for non-Euclidean geometries.

Many textbooks begin with the congruence theorems as axioms and proceed from there. This approach obviates the need to prove the congruence theorems. However, Euclid in his *Elements* chose a more ''self-evident'' system of axioms and deduced the congruence theorems from them. Euclid's proofs of the congruence theorems, while a remarkable achievement for their time, would not withstand the scrutiny of modern day rigour. In *Sections 4-3* and *4-4* we have reproduced the essence of Euclid's proofs, offering on occasion some rhetorical questions where a proof may be suspect. In this feature, we present as axioms some of the properties of isometries which might be used to bridge some of the gaps in Euclid's proofs. We do concede, however, that even this ''more rigorous'' treatment of Euclidean geometry is not the ultimate, for there is no ultimate certainty!

In the proofs of the congruent triangle theorems, one triangle was moved to the location of another triangle and superimposed upon it. Plausible argument was used to establish that the sides and the vertices of the two triangles coincided and so it was concluded that the two triangles were congruent. This physical movement of two triangles into coincidence carries at least two implicit assumptions.

- The lengths of the sides and the measures of the angles of a triangle are not changed during a physical motion.
- Any two triangles having corresponding angles and corresponding sides congruent can be placed into coincidence by a physical motion.

While these assumptions may appear innocuous, they are not trivial. Before we can accept the first assumption we must establish that all physical motions can be expressed as a series of slides, flips, and turns and that under the corresponding isometries, the lengths of all line segments and the measures of all angles are preserved. To emphasize the significance of the second assumption we observe, for example, that the two triangles, positioned as shown below, though congruent cannot be made to coincide using only slides and turns — a flip is required to give them the same orientation.

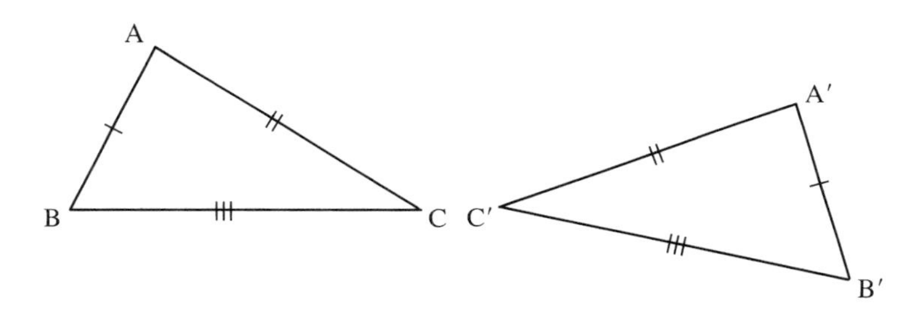

The Euclidean proofs of the congruence theorems can be made more rigorous by identifying the assumptions described above and stating them explicitly as a set of axioms.

Invariant Length Axiom
Any line segment AB and its image A′B′ under an isometry are congruent. Conversely, if AB and A′B′ are congruent line segments, then there is an isometry which maps AB onto A′B′.

Invariant Angle Axiom
Any ∠ABC and its image ∠A′B′C′ under an isometry are congruent. Conversely, if ∠ABC = ∠A′B′C′, then there is an isometry which maps ∠ABC onto ∠A′B′C′ such that $\overrightarrow{BA} \rightarrow \overrightarrow{B'A'}$ and $\overrightarrow{BC} \rightarrow \overrightarrow{B'C'}$.

The axioms above are self-evident and seem to follow directly from the definition and properties of isometries. Now we use these axioms to prove the congruence theorems.

> **Side-Angle-Side Theorem**
> If two sides and the contained angle of one triangle are congruent to two sides and the contained angle of another triangle, then the triangles are congruent.

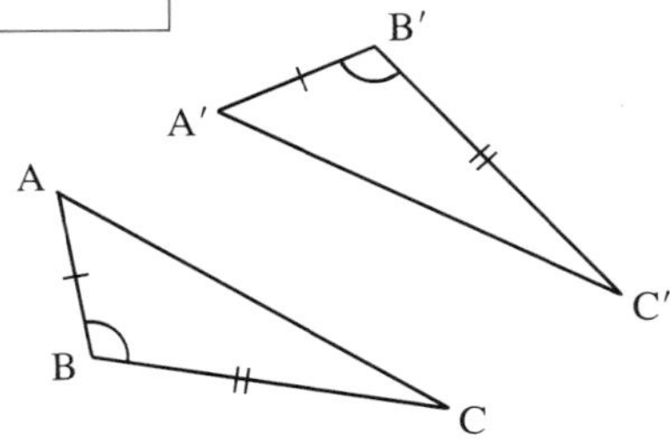

Given: Triangles ABC and A′B′C′ such that
BA = B′A′
BC = B′C′
∠B = ∠B′

Required to Prove: There is an isometry which maps △ABC → △A′B′C′ so that A → A′, B → B′, C → C′.

Proof:

Statement	Reason
1. Since ∠B = ∠B′, there is an isometry which maps B → B′ so that $\overrightarrow{BC} \to \overrightarrow{B'C'}$, and $\overrightarrow{BA} \to \overrightarrow{B'A'}$. 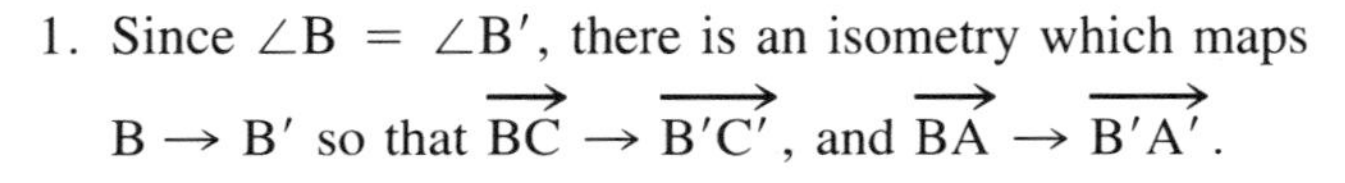	Invariant Angle Axiom
2. Since BC = B′C′ and BA = B′A′, the isometry maps C → C′ and A → A′.	Statement 1 and Invariant Length Axiom
3. There is an isometry which maps △ABC → △A′B′C′ so that A → A′ B → B′ C → C′	Statements 1 and 2

> **Angle-Side-Angle Theorem**
> If two angles and the contained side of one triangle are congruent to two angles and the contained side of another triangle, then the triangles are congruent.

Given: △ABC and △A′B′C′ such that
∠B = ∠B′
∠C = ∠C′
BC = B′C′

Required to Prove: △ABC ≅ △A′B′C′

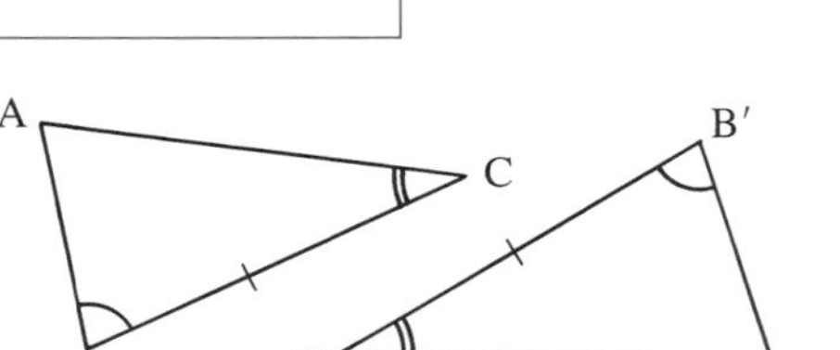

Proof:

Statement	Reason
1. Since $\angle B = \angle B'$, there is an isometry which maps $B \to B'$ so that $\overrightarrow{BC} \to \overrightarrow{B'C'}$, and $\overrightarrow{BA} \to \overrightarrow{B'A'}$.	Invariant Angle Axiom
2. Since $BC = B'C'$, the isometry maps $C \to C'$.	Invariant Length Axiom
3. The isometry maps $B \to B'$ $C \to C'$ A into $\overrightarrow{B'A'}$	Statements 1 and 2
4. The isometry maps A into $\overrightarrow{C'A'}$	Given $\angle C = \angle C'$
5. The isometry maps A into $\overrightarrow{C'A'}$ and $\overrightarrow{B'A'}$	Statements 3 and 4
6. The isometry maps $A \to A'$	Statement 5
7. The isometry maps $A \to A'$ $B \to B'$ $C \to C'$	Statement 3 and 6
8. $\triangle ABC \cong \triangle A'B'C'$	Statement 7

Side-Side-Side Theorem
If the sides of one triangle are congruent to the corresponding sides of another triangle, then the triangles are congruent.

Given: $\triangle ABC$ and $\triangle A'B'C'$ such that
$AB = A'B'$
$AC = A'C'$
$BC = B'C'$

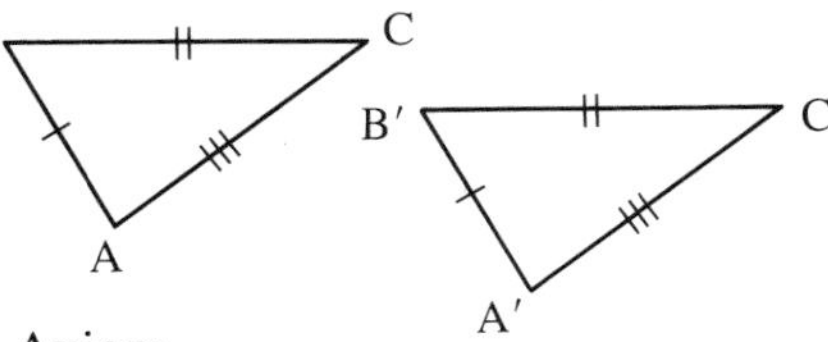

Required to Prove: $\triangle ABC \cong \triangle A'B'C'$

Analysis: It follows from the Invariant Length Axiom that there is some isometry which maps $\triangle ABC$ onto $\triangle AB'C'$ so that $B \to B'$ and $C \to C'$. Since this mapping is an isometry, $\triangle ABC \cong \triangle AB'C'$. It is therefore sufficient to prove that $\triangle A'B'C' \cong \triangle AB'C'$.
Join AA'.

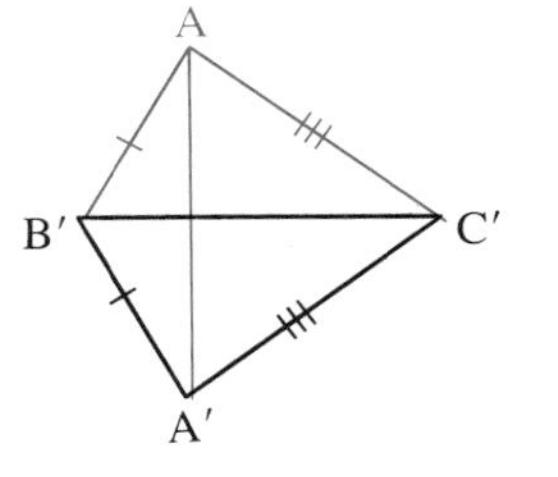

Proof:

Statement	Reason
1. $BC = B'C'$	Given
2. There is an isometry which maps $B \rightarrow B'$ and $C \rightarrow C'$.	Statement 1 and Invariant Length Axiom
3. We may assume without loss of generality that A is mapped onto a point which lies on the opposite side of $\overleftrightarrow{B'C'}$ from A. (If not, the isometry is followed by a reflection in $B'C'$.)	
4. $B'A' = B'A$	Invariant Length Axiom
5. $\angle B'A'A = \angle B'AA'$	Isosceles Triangle Theorem
6. $C'A' = C'A$	Invariant Length Axiom
7. $\angle C'A'A = \angle C'AA'$	Isosceles Triangle Theorem
8. $\angle B'A'C' = \angle B'AC'$	Statements 5 and 7
9. In $\triangle B'A'C'$ and $\triangle B'AC'$	
$B'A' = B'A$	Proved
$\angle B'A'C' = \angle B'AC'$	Proved
$A'C' = AC'$	Proved
10. Therefore, $\triangle B'A'C' \cong \triangle B'AC'$	SAS

QUESTIONS

1. Let A be any point on the perpendicular bisector of line segment BC and let D be the midpoint of BC.
   a) Name the isometry which maps $BD \rightarrow CD$ so that $B \rightarrow C$, $A \rightarrow A$, and $D \rightarrow D$.
   b) How do we know that under this isometry $AB \rightarrow AC$?
   c) How do we know that $AB = AC$ and that A is equidistant from points B and C?
   d) How do we know that any point on the perpendicular bisector of a line segment is equidistant from the ends of the line segment?

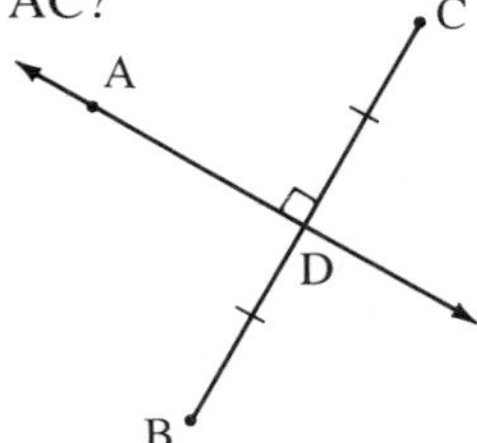

2. Triangle ABC is isosceles with $AB = AC$. $\overleftrightarrow{AD}$ bisects $\angle BAC$ so that $\angle BAD = \angle CAD$.
   a) How do we know there is an isometry which maps $\angle BAD$ onto $\angle CAD$ so that $A \rightarrow A$, $\overrightarrow{AB} \rightarrow \overrightarrow{AC}$ and $\overrightarrow{AD} \rightarrow \overrightarrow{AD}$?

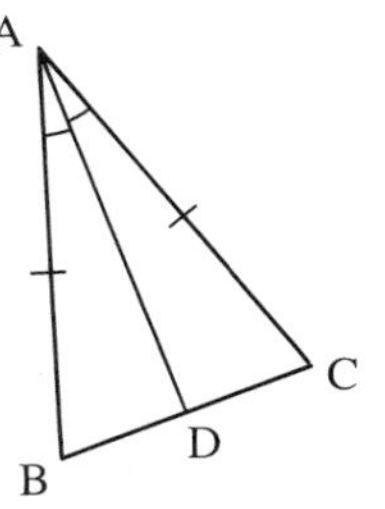

b) Explain how we can deduce from part a) that under that isometry A → A, B → C, and D → D.
c) Why can we deduce from part b) that $\triangle BAD \cong \triangle CAD$?
d) Why can we conclude from part c) that $\angle B = \angle C$ and $\angle BDA = \angle CDA = 90°$?
e) Why can we deduce from part c) that BD = CD?

3. Copy and complete this proof.
Prove that any point equidistant from the ends of a line segment lies on the perpendicular bisector of that line segment.
Given: Point A equidistant from points B and C; that is, AB = AC
Required to Prove: A lies on the perpendicular bisector of BC.
Analysis: Draw AD, the bisector of $\angle BAC$; then $\angle BAD = \angle CAD$

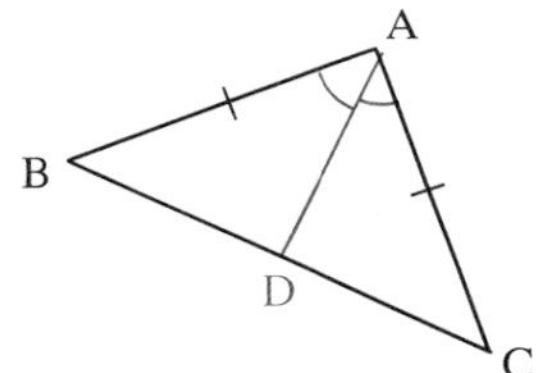

Proof:

Statement	Reason
1. AB = AC	______
2. $\angle BAD = \angle CAD$	______
3. There is an isometry which maps $\angle BAD$ onto $\angle CAD$.	Statement __ and ______ Axiom
4. $\overrightarrow{AB} \to \overrightarrow{AC}$ and $\overrightarrow{AD} \to \overrightarrow{AD}$	______ Axiom
5. Under the isometry A → A, B → C, D → D	Statements __ and __
6. BD = CD	Statement __
7. $\angle ADB = \angle ADC = 90°$	Statement __
8. AD is the perpendicular bisector of BC.	Statements __ and __

4. Use the axioms below and Euclid's Parallel Axiom to deduce that a line segment has exactly one perpendicular bisector.
Axiom A: A line segment has exactly one midpoint.
Axiom B: If two lines are perpendicular to the same line, then they are parallel to each other.

4-5 INDIRECT PROOF IN GEOMETRY

About 300 B.C. Euclid used the method of indirect proof to prove that the set of prime numbers is infinite. The logical basis for the indirect method remained unchallenged until the early 20th century when mathematicians began to develop the theory of sets and discovered some fundamental paradoxes. Fortunately these paradoxes do not apply to indirect proof as we shall use it in our study of geometry. You may therefore use indirect proof as an alternative to direct proof and regard both approaches as equally valid.

An indirect proof has four steps.

- We begin the proof with the statement that we are required to prove, and the opposite statement.
- We assume that the statement that we are required to prove is false, and the opposite statement is true.
- We show that this assumption leads to a contradiction.
- Since there is a contradiction, we conclude that the initial statement that we were required to prove is true.

These steps are illustrated in the following proof.

Prove that the diagonals of a rhombus are perpendicular.

Given: ABCD is a rhombus. E is the point of intersection of diagonals AC and BD.

Required to Prove: BD is perpendicular to AC; that is, $\angle AED = \angle AEB = 90°$

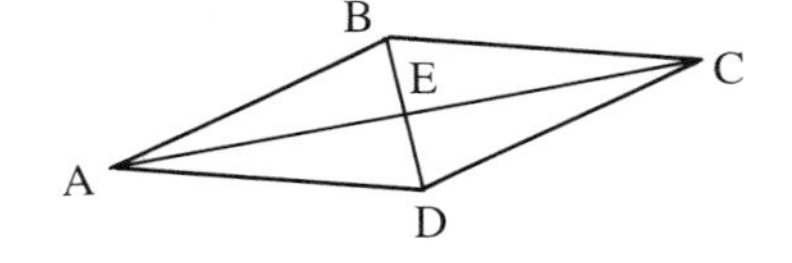

Proof: Either the diagonals AC and BD are perpendicular, or they are not.
Suppose the diagonals are not perpendicular; that is, BD is not perpendicular to AC.

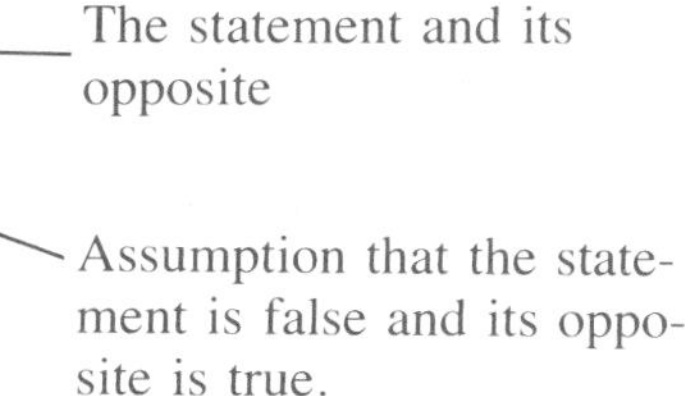

Statement	Reason
1. $\angle AED + \angle AEB = 180°$	Straight angle
2. $\angle AED \neq \angle AEB$	Assumption that BD is not perpendicular to AC
3. In $\triangle ABC$ and $\triangle ADC$	
AB = AD	Given a rhombus
BC = DC	Given a rhombus
AC is common	
4. Therefore, $\triangle ABC \cong \triangle ADC$	SSS
5. $\angle DAE = \angle BAE$	Congruent triangles

6. In $\triangle AED$ and $\triangle AEB$	
AE is common	
$\angle DAE = \angle BAE$	Statement 5
$AD = AB$	Given a rhombus
7. Therefore, $\triangle AED \cong \triangle AEB$	SAS
8. $\angle AED = \angle AEB = 90°$	Congruent triangles and Statement 1

Statement 8 contradicts statement 2. Hence, the initial statement is true. Therefore, $\angle AED = \angle AEB = 90°$ — The assumption leads to a contradiction.

The Parallel Lines Theorem can be proved using the method of indirect proof. But first we shall introduce the concept of an exterior angle of a triangle and prove the Exterior Angle Theorem using the direct method of proof.

Definition: When one side of a triangle is extended, the new angle formed is called an *exterior* angle.

Definition: The exterior angle together with the adjacent interior angle of a triangle form a straight angle. The other two interior angles of the triangle are called the *remote interior* angles.

In both diagrams below, side BC is extended to form exterior angle $\angle ACD$. In both cases, $\angle BAC$ and $\angle ABC$ are remote interior angles.

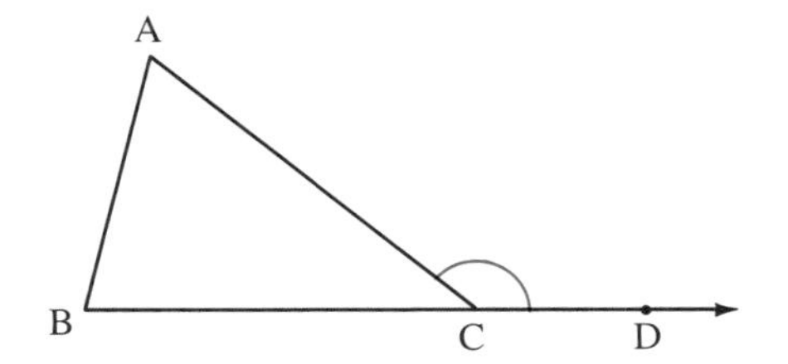

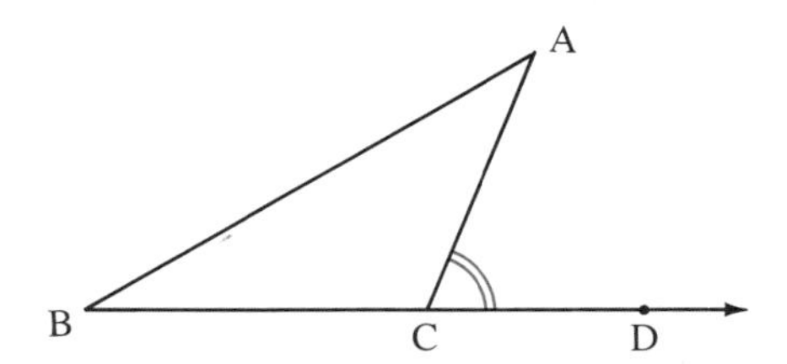

Similarly, each of the other two sides could be extended to form an exterior angle, with two corresponding remote interior angles.

Exterior Angle Theorem
The measure of an exterior angle of a triangle is equal to the sum of the measures of its remote interior angles.

Given: $\triangle ABC$ with exterior angle $\angle ACD$
Required to Prove: $\angle ACD = \angle CAB + \angle ABC$

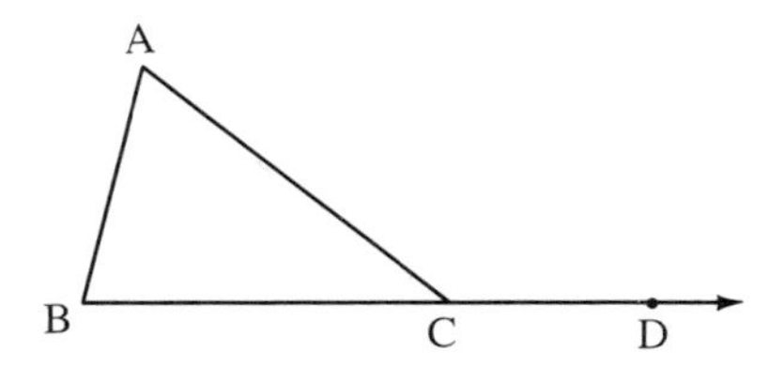

Proof:

Statement	Reason
$\angle BCA + \angle ACD = 180°$	Straight angle
$\angle BCA + \angle CAB + \angle ABC = 180°$	Sum of the Angles Theorem
Therefore, $\angle ACD = \angle CAB + \angle ABC$	

We now use the Exterior Angle Theorem to prove the Parallel Lines Theorem, using the method of indirect proof.

> **Parallel Lines Theorem**
> If a transversal intersects two parallel lines, then the corresponding angles are congruent.

Given: Transversal t intersects parallel lines l_1 and l_2 at points P_1 and P_2 respectively.

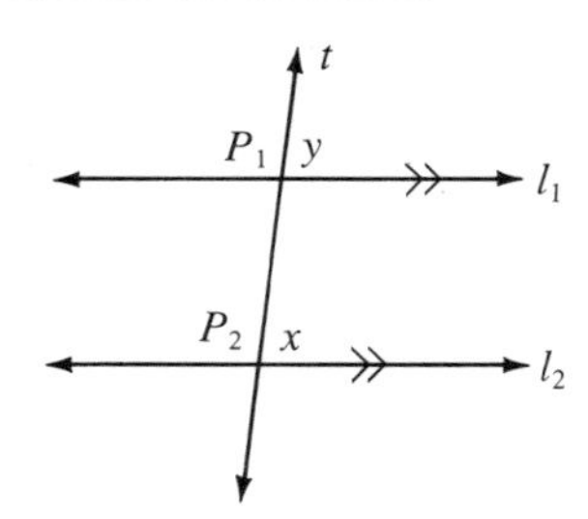

Required to Prove: $\angle x = \angle y$

Proof: Either $\angle x = \angle y$ or $\angle x \neq \angle y$ — The statement and its opposite

Suppose that $\angle x \neq \angle y$ — Assumption that the statement is false and its opposite is true

Let m be a line through P_1 which intersects t such that $\angle z = \angle x$.
By Euclid's Parallel Axiom, there cannot be two distinct lines through P_1 which are parallel to l_2. Since we are given l_1 parallel to l_2, m cannot be parallel to l_2, and hence m must intersect l_2 at some point Q.

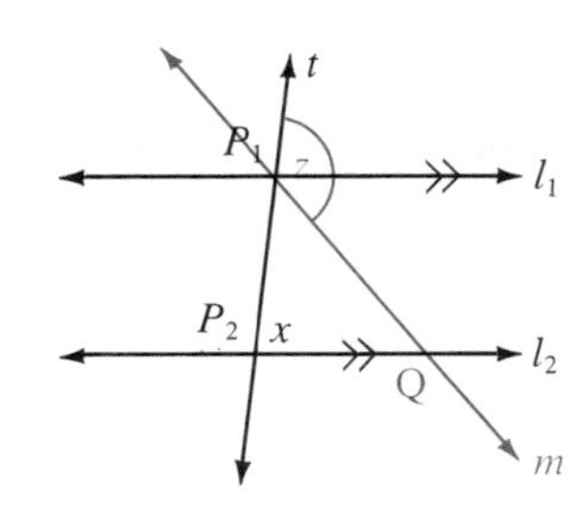

Statement	Reason
1. $\angle x \neq \angle y$	Assumption
2. $\angle x = \angle z$	Definition of line m
3. For $\triangle P_1P_2Q$, $\angle x + \angle Q = \angle z$	Exterior Angle Theorem
4. $\angle x < \angle z$	Statement 3 and $\angle Q > 0$

Statement 4 contradicts statement 2.
Hence, the initial statement is true.
Therefore, $\angle x = \angle y$

EXERCISES 4-5

Ⓐ

1. Find each value of x.
   a) b) c) d)

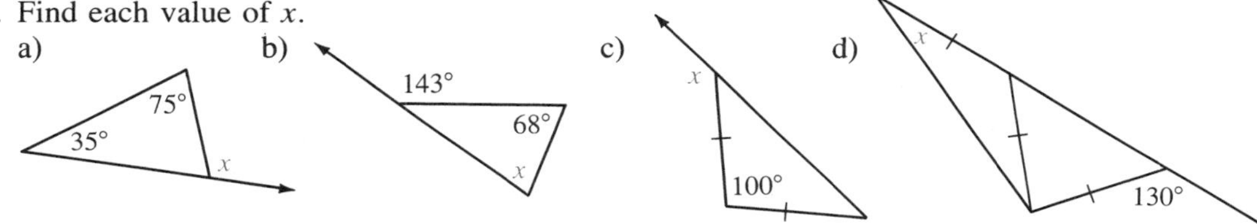

2. Find the sum of the colored angles in each figure.
   a) b) c)

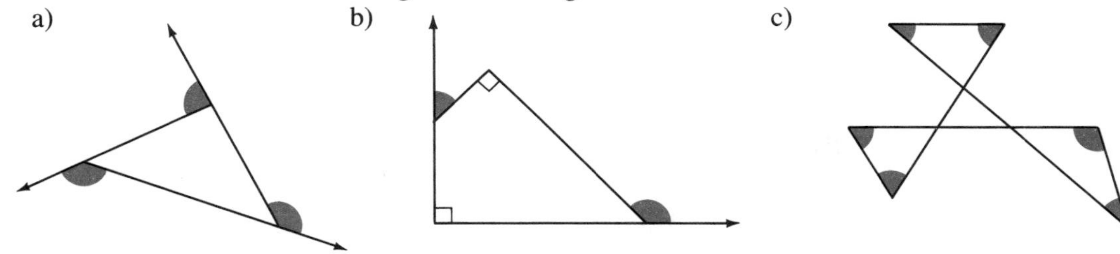

3. State which of the following statements are true.
   a) $\angle AEF = \angle GAE + \angle BGC$
   b) $\angle GCD > \angle BAG$
   c) $\angle CGE = \angle ABG + \angle BAE$
   d) $\angle GCD = \angle GBC + \angle GAE + \angle AEG$
   e) $\angle AEF < \angle BAE + \angle ABG$
   f) $\angle GBC + \angle GCB \leqslant \angle GAE + \angle GEA$

4. For each theorem, write the first two steps of an indirect proof.
   a) Theorem: If two lines intersect, then they do so in one point.
      Given: Lines l_1 and l_2 intersect at P.
      Required to Prove: P is the only point of intersection.
   b) Theorem: In an isosceles triangle, the angles opposite the congruent sides are congruent.
      Given: $\triangle ABC$ with $AB = AC$
      Required to Prove: $\angle ABC = \angle ACB$

c) Theorem: If two lines intersect, then the opposite angles are congruent.
Given: AB and CD intersect at E.
Required to Prove: ∠AEC = ∠BED

Ⓑ

5. Copy the statements in this proof and write the reasons.
Prove that if two lines are perpendicular to the same line, then the two lines are parallel.
Given: l_1 and l_2 are perpendicular to m.
Required to Prove: l_1 is parallel to l_2.

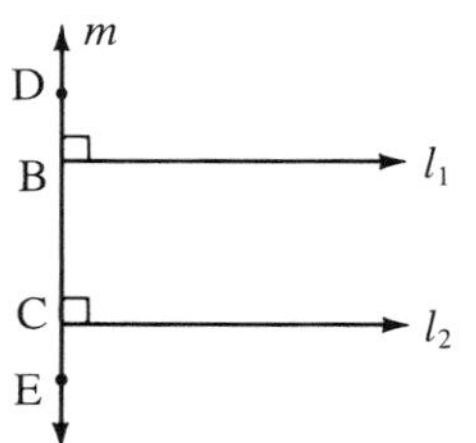

Proof: Either l_1 is parallel to l_2 or l_1 is not parallel to l_2.
Suppose that l_1 is not parallel to l_2.
Since l_1 is not parallel to l_2, they intersect at some point A. Let B and C be the points of intersection of l_1 and l_2 respectively, with m.

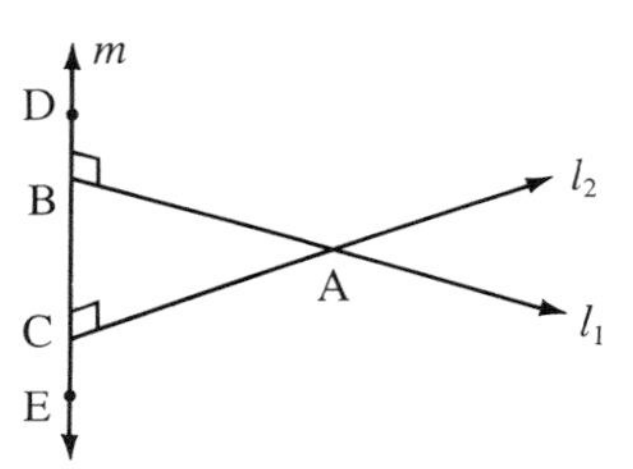

Statement	Reason
1. ∠ABD = 90°	______
2. ∠ACB = 90°	______
3. ∠ABD = ∠ACB + ∠BAC	______
4. ∠ABD > 90°	Statements __ and __

Statement 4 contradicts statement 1.
Hence, the initial statement is true.
Therefore, l_1 is parallel to l_2.

6. Given the diagram (below left), use the method of indirect proof to prove that ∠SQR > ∠TRV.

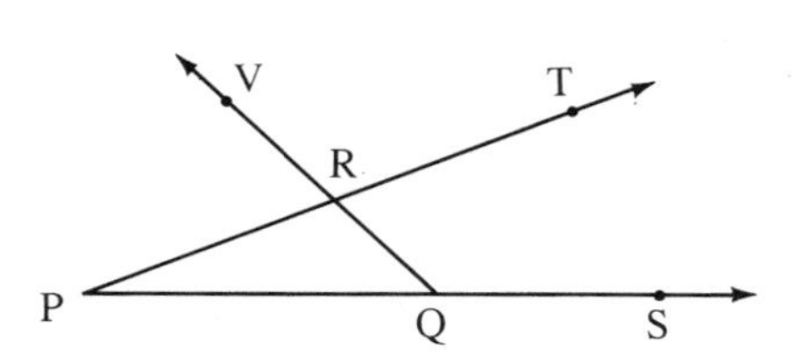

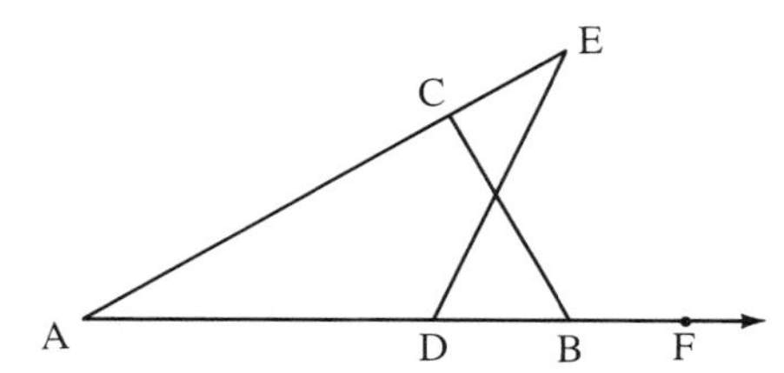

7. Given the diagram (above right), use the method of indirect proof to prove that ∠FBC > ∠AED.

8. Triangle ABC (below left) is scalene. Use the method of indirect proof to prove that $\angle A \neq \angle B$.

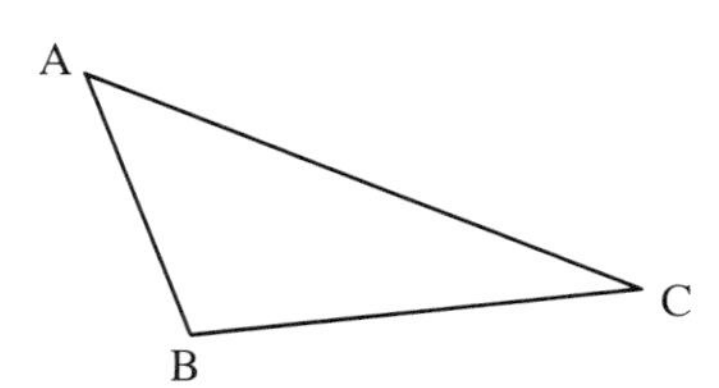

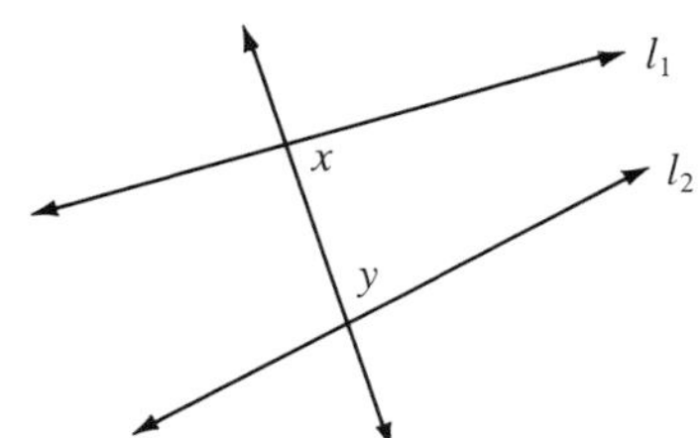

9. Given the diagram (above right) in which $x + y < 180°$, use the method of indirect proof to prove that l_1 is not parallel to l_2.

10. Use the method of indirect proof to prove that a triangle cannot contain two right angles.

11. Copy and complete this proof.
Given: Scalene $\triangle ABC$ where AD bisects $\angle A$ and meets BC in D
Required to Prove: AD is not perpendicular to BC.

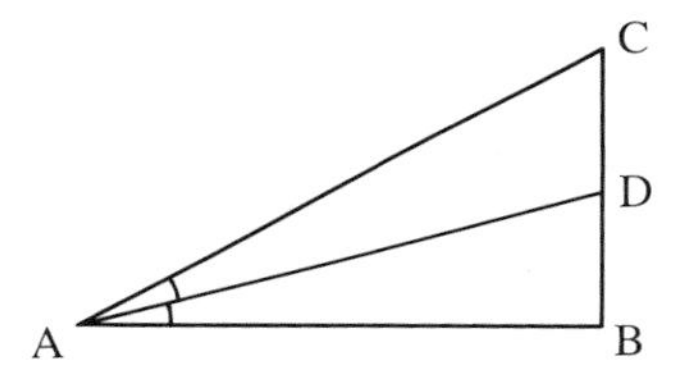

Proof: Either ________
or ________ .
Assume ________ .

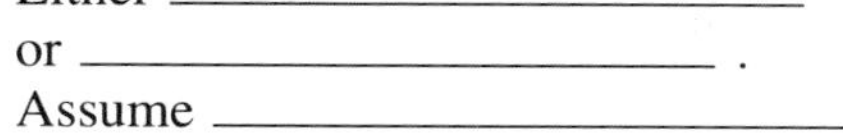

Statement	Reason
1. In $\triangle ABD$ and $\triangle ACD$	
________	________
________	________
________	
2. Therefore, $\triangle$______ $\cong$ $\triangle$______	ASA
3. ________	________

Statement 3 contradicts the given information that $\triangle ABC$ is scalene.
Hence, ________ .
Therefore, ________ .

Use the method of indirect proof in the following exercises.

12. Prove that the angles opposite the congruent sides of an isosceles triangle are congruent.

13. Prove that the medians of a triangle cannot bisect each other.

14. Prove that if a transversal intersects two lines so that the interior angles on the same side of the transversal are supplementary, then the lines cannot intersect.

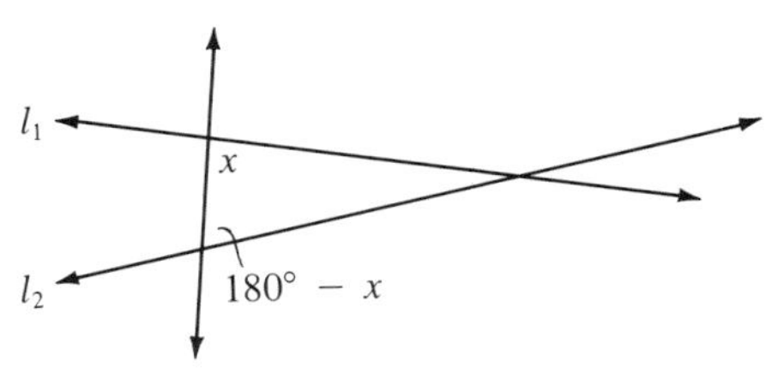

4-6 THE TRIANGLE INEQUALITIES

Now that we have learned the method of indirect proof, we can use it to prove a stronger version of the Isosceles Triangle Theorem.

First we consider the following corollaries, which are direct consequences of the Exterior Angle Theorem. The proof of each corollary is left for the exercises.

> **Corollary 1 of the Exterior Angle Theorem**
> If the length of one side of a triangle is greater than the length of another side, then the measure of the angle opposite the longer side is greater than the measure of the angle opposite the shorter side.

> **Corollary 2 of the Exterior Angle Theorem**
> If the measure of one angle of a triangle is greater than the measure of another angle, then the length of the side opposite the greater angle is greater than the length of the side opposite the lesser angle.

> **Corollary 3 of the Exterior Angle Theorem**
> The sum of the lengths of any two sides of a triangle is greater than the length of the third side.

The following example shows that Corollary 2 can be used to derive the Isosceles Triangle Theorem.

Example. Prove the Isosceles Triangle Theorem using the method of indirect proof.

Solution. The Isosceles Triangle Theorem asserts that the angles opposite the congruent sides of an isosceles triangle are congruent.

Given:
$\triangle ABC$ is isosceles with $AB = AC$
Required to Prove:
$\angle ABC = \angle ACB$

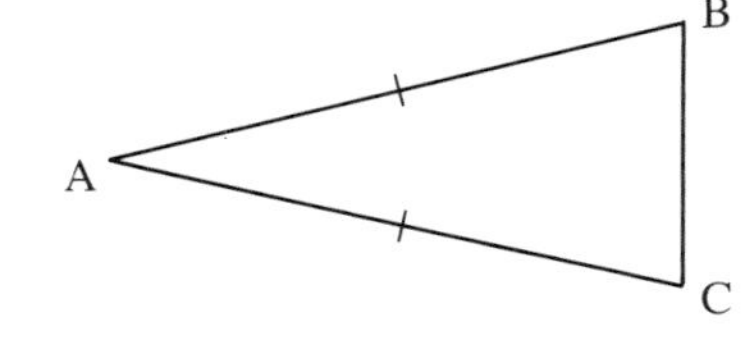

Proof:
Use indirect proof.
Either the angles opposite the congruent sides are congruent or they are not.
Assume that the angles are not congruent; that is, assume $\angle ABC \neq \angle ACB$.
Suppose A, B, and C are chosen so that $\angle ABC > \angle ACB$.

Statement	Reason
1. ∠ABC > ∠ACB	Assumption
2. AC > AB	Corollary 1, Exterior Angle Theorem
3. AC = AB	Given

Statement 3 contradicts statement 2.
Hence, the assumption that ∠ABC ≠ ∠ACB is false.
Therefore, ∠ABC = ∠ACB
If we had assumed that ∠ACB > ∠ABC, we could have used a similar argument to prove that ∠ABC ≠ ∠ACB.

EXERCISES 4-6

Ⓐ

1. Name the smallest angle in each triangle.

a)

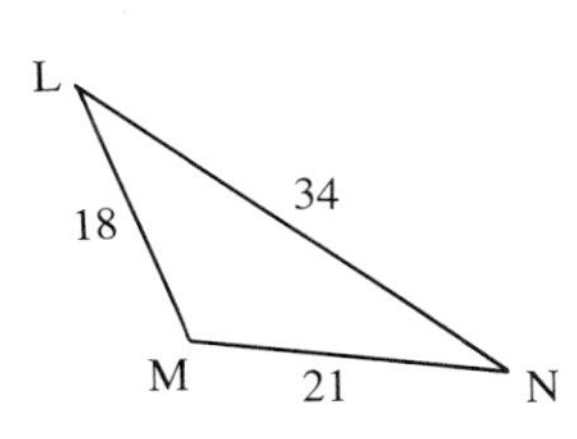

b)

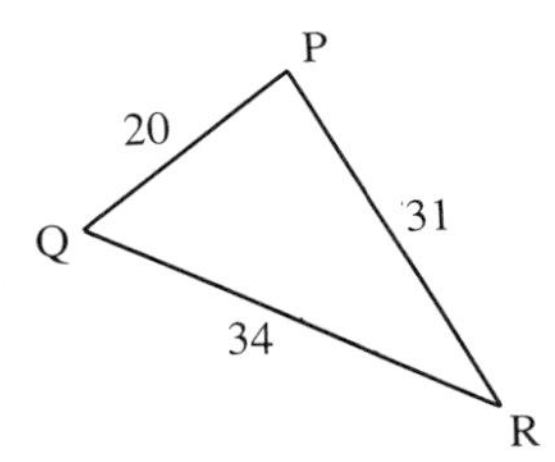

c)

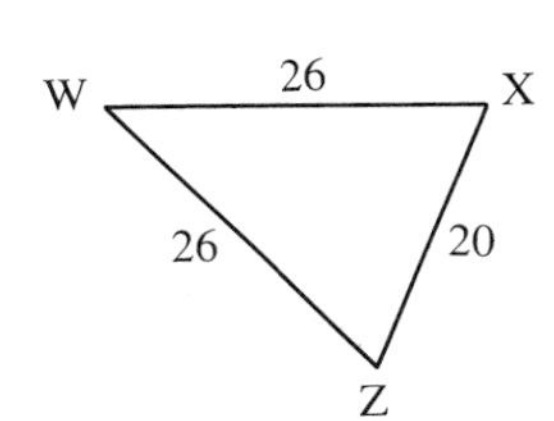

2. Name the shortest line segment in each diagram.

a)

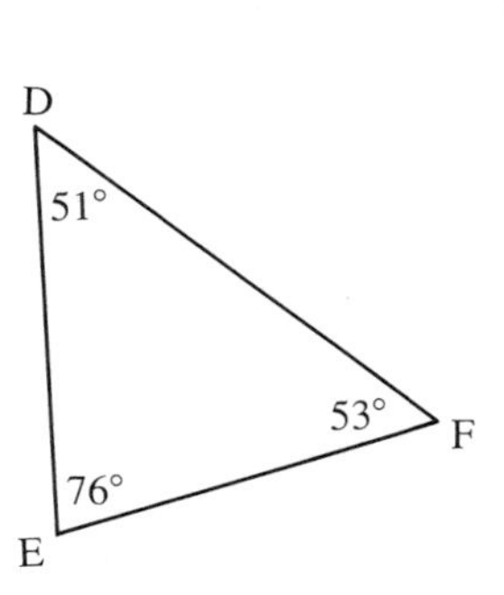

b)

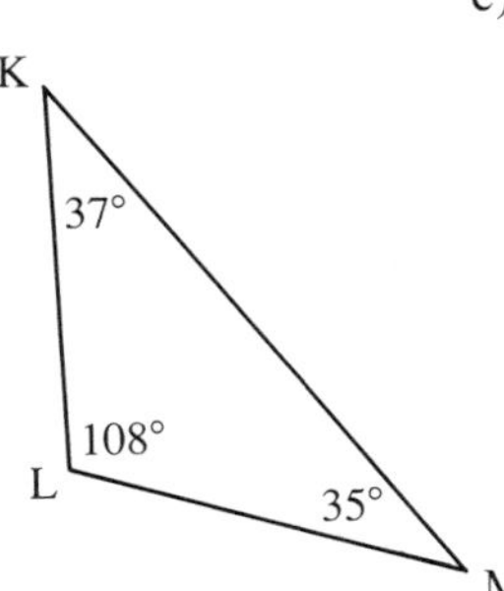

c)

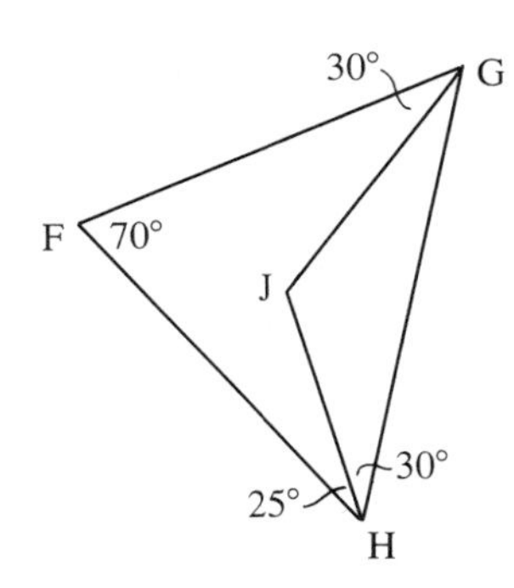

Ⓑ

3. Explain how the Exterior Angle Theorem (Corollary 2) can be used to prove that the longest side of a right triangle must be the side opposite the right angle.

4. If an equilateral triangle is defined as a triangle with the lengths of all sides equal, which corollary of the Exterior Angle Theorem guarantees that the measures of all the angles of an equilateral triangle are equal? Explain your answer.

5. Use the given information to state a numerical inequality for x in each diagram.

a)

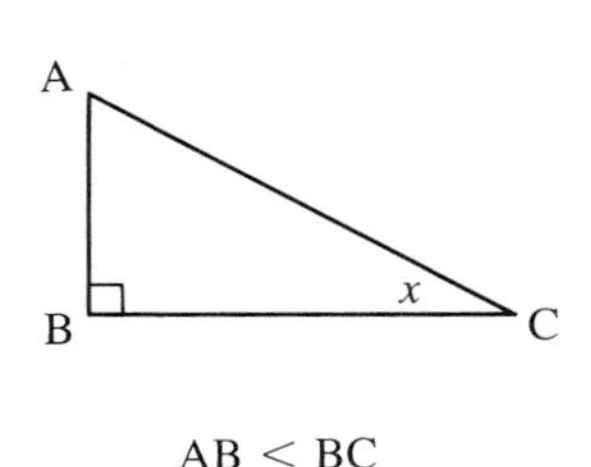

AB < BC

b)

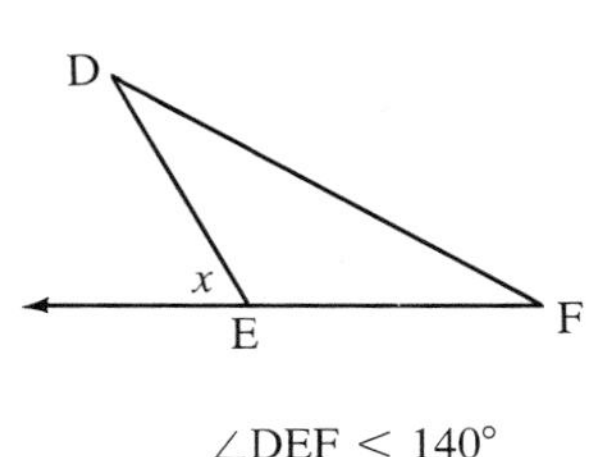

∠DEF < 140°

c)

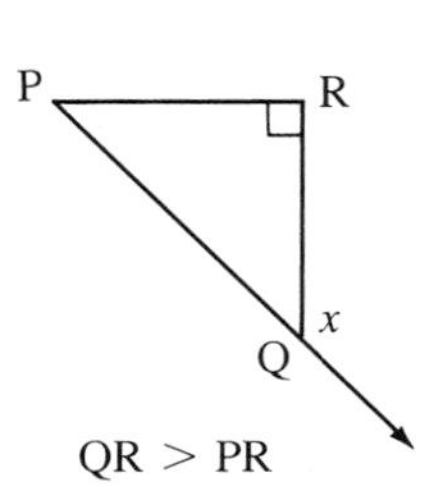

QR > PR

6. In this exercise we will prove corollary 1 of the Exterior Angle Theorem. Copy the statements in the proof and write the reasons.
Given: △ABC with AC > AB
Required to Prove: ∠ABC > ∠ACB
Analysis: Let D be a point on AC such that AB = AD.

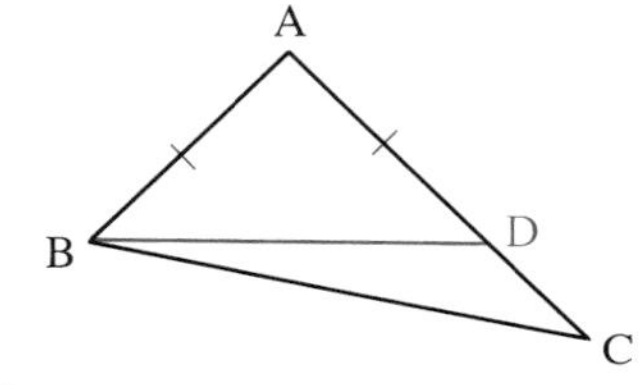

Proof:

Statement	Reason
1. ∠ABD = ∠ADB	____________
2. ∠ADB > ∠ACB	____________
3. ∠ABD > ∠ACB	Statements __ and __
4. ∠ABC > ∠ABD	____________
5. ∠ABC > ∠ACB	Statements __ and __

7. In this exercise we will use the method of indirect proof to prove corollary 2 of the Exterior Angle Theorem. Copy the statements in the proof and write the reasons.
Given: △ABC with ∠B > ∠C
Required to Prove: AC > AB

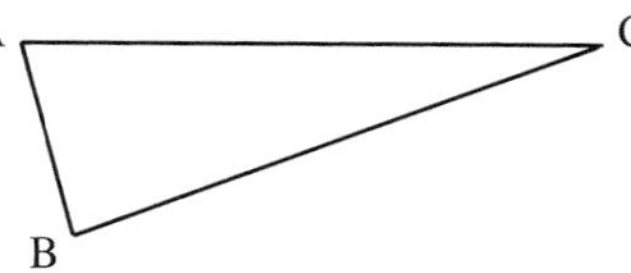

Proof: There are 3 possible cases: AC = AB, AC < AB, and AC > AB. Consider each case in turn.

Statement	Reason
Case 1: Suppose AC = AB.	
∠B = ∠C	____________
This contradicts the given fact that ∠B > ∠C. Hence, AC ≠ AB	
Case 2: Suppose AC < AB.	
∠B < ∠C	____________
This contradicts the given fact that ∠B > ∠C. Hence, AC < AB is false.	

Since AC is not less than or equal to AB, then AC > AB.

8. The inequality in corollary 3 of the External Angle Theorem is called the *triangle inequality*. The triangle inequality asserts that the sum of the lengths of any two sides of a triangle is greater than the length of the third side.

   Copy and complete this proof of corollary 3.

   Given: △ABC

   Required to Prove: AB + BC > AC

   Analysis: Extend AB to a point D such that BD = BC.

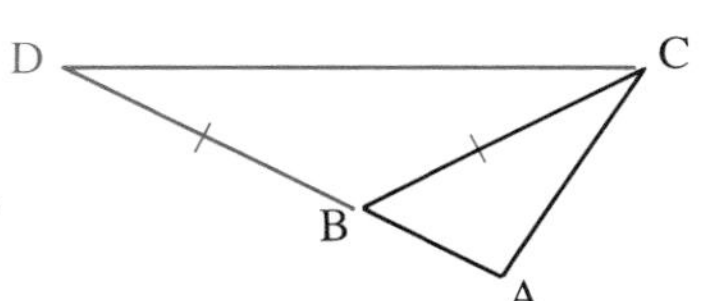

   Proof:

Statement	Reason
1. AB + BC = AB + BD	________
2. ∠BCD = ∠BDC	________
3. ∠ACD > ∠BDC	________
4. AD > AC	________
5. AB + BD > AC	________
6. AB + BC > AC	________

9. The diagonals of quadrilateral ABCD intersect at E. Prove that:
   a) AE + EB > AB
   b) DE + EC > DC
   c) AC + DB > AB + DC

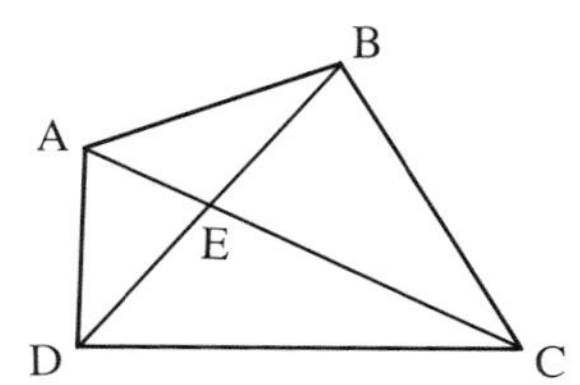

10. Use *Exercise 9* to prove that the sum of the lengths of the diagonals of any quadrilateral is greater than the total length of any pair of opposite sides.

Ⓒ

11. a) Prove that the sum of the lengths of any three sides of a quadrilateral is greater than the length of the fourth side.
    b) Prove that the sum of the lengths of $n - 1$ sides of a polygon of n sides is greater than the length of the remaining side.
    c) Use the result in part b) to prove that the shortest path (composed of line segments) between any two points A and B in the plane is the line segment AB.

12. The light from an object placed at position O is reflected off a mirror m at R and into the eye of a viewer at V. The reflected image of O appears at position O′. S is a point on the perpendicular to the mirror at R. Prove that:
    a) ∠ORS = ∠VRS
    b) If R′ is any point on m, then the distance VR′ + R′O is a minimum when R = R′.

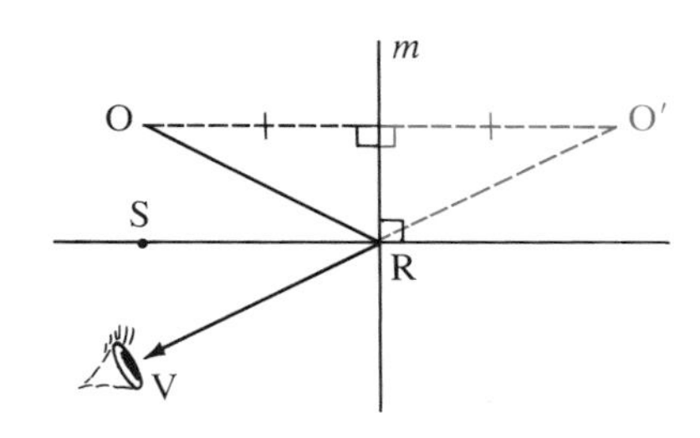

MATHEMATICS PROJECT

Functions in Geometry

Two angles on a diagram are often related. For example, in this diagram y can be expressed as a function of x as follows.

Since $\triangle ABC$ is isosceles,
$\angle ABC = \angle ACB = 180° - x$. Then, since the sum of the angles in $\triangle ABC$ is 180°,

$$y + 2(180° - x) = 180°$$
$$y = 180° - 2(180° - x)$$
$$y = 2x - 180°$$

This is a linear function whose graph is a straight line with slope 2 and y-intercept -180. Since x is defined on the diagram as an exterior angle of $\triangle ABC$, x is limited to values of x between 90° and 180°, and the domain of the function is $\{x \mid 90° < x < 180°\}$. Therefore, the graph of the function is the line segment between P(90,0) and Q(180,180), not including the end points. This is indicated by open circles at P and Q.

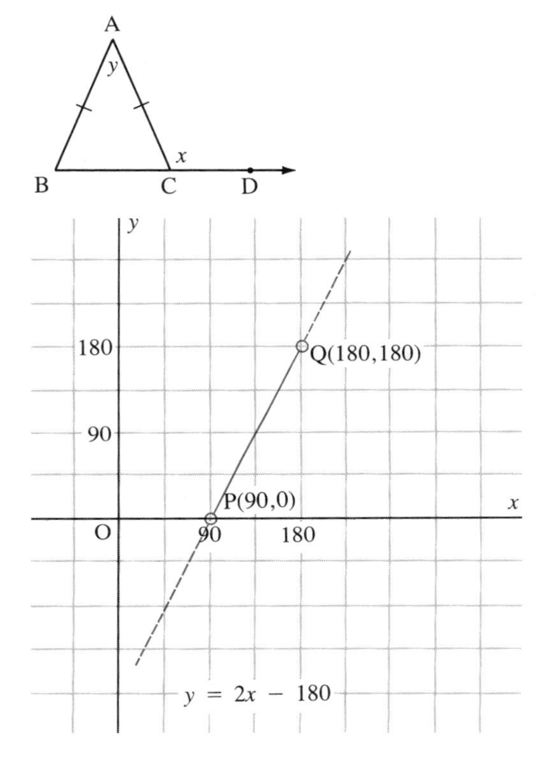

1. For each diagram, express y as a function of x and draw its graph. What is the domain of the function?

a)

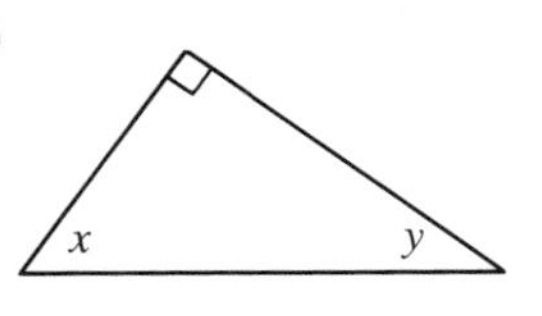

b)

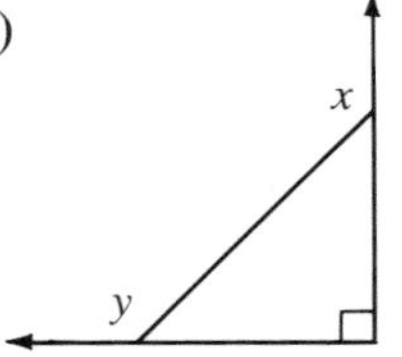

c)

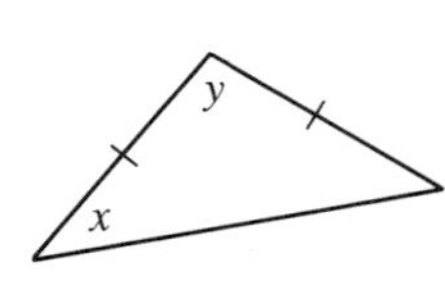

d)

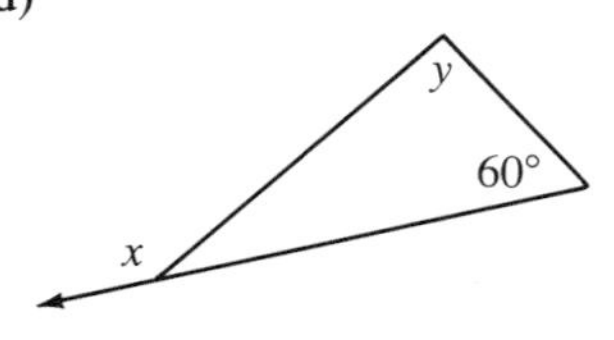

e)

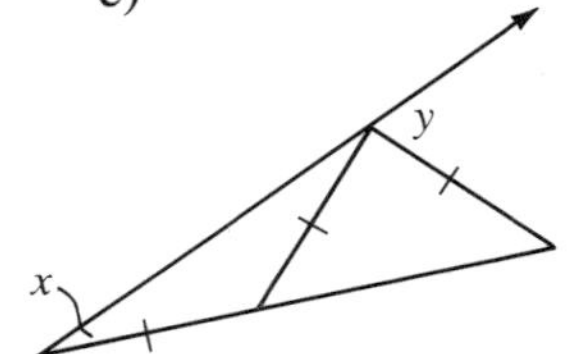

f)

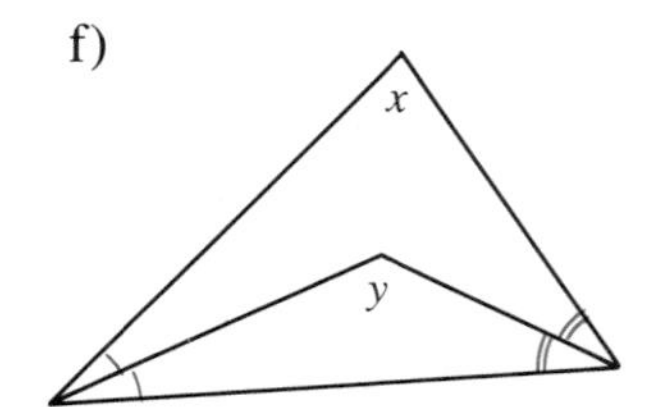

For the isosceles △ABC (left), the domain of the function can be extended to include all real values of x. This is done by redefining x as follows.

Imagine that AB and AC represent rods hinged at A and C, with end B free to move along line ED. Then x can be defined to be the angle, in degrees, which rod CA makes with CD, measured in a counterclockwise direction.

The sequence of diagrams shows the positions of the rods for values of x from 90° to 270°. By continuing the movement of B along CD, we can draw similar diagrams for values of x greater than 270°, or less than 90°. Notice how y is defined on the diagrams; it is the angle through which rod AC has turned relative to rod AB.

2. a) Determine the value of y for each diagram.
   b) Draw similar sequences of diagrams for values of x:
      i) increasing from 270° to 360°
      ii) decreasing from 90° to 0°
      iii) decreasing from 0° to −180°.
   Indicate how y should be defined on each diagram.

3. For each diagram of *Question 1*, investigate how x and y can be redefined in a similar manner such that the domain of the function can be extended to include all real numbers.

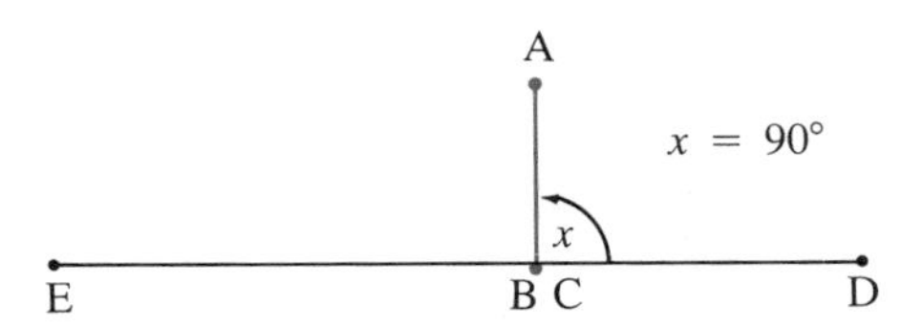

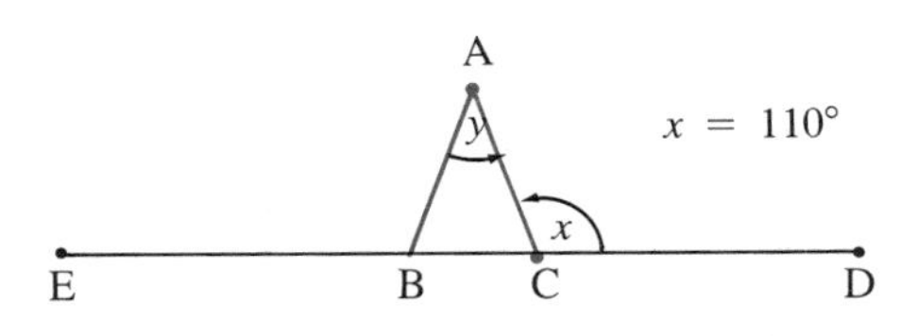

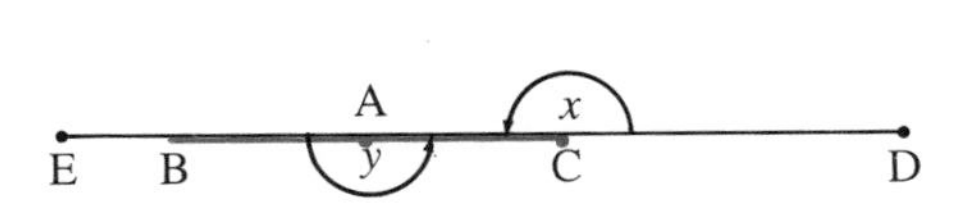

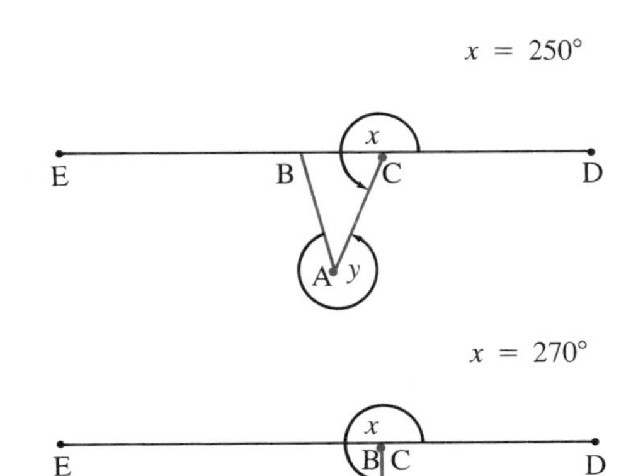

4-7 CONDITIONAL STATEMENTS

The statement in the cartoon has an "if" clause and a "then" clause. A statement of this form is called a conditional statement.

If a person is a father	then he is a male.
"if" clause	"then" clause

The "if" clause is called the *hypothesis* and the "then" clause is called the *conclusion*.

Definition: A statement which begins with an "if" clause (or some equivalent) and ends with a "then" clause (or some equivalent) is called a *conditional statement*.

Definition: The *converse* is the statement obtained by interchanging the hypothesis and the conclusion. For example,

If a person is a male	then	he is a father	is the converse of
If a person is a father	then	he is a male	

Clearly, the converse of a true statement is not necessarily true. Apparently the gentleman in the cartoon above does not understand this.

Sometimes "if . . . then" statements are disguised in other forms. The table shows a variety of conditional statements which are equivalent to the "if . . . then" format. The table also shows the converse of each statement.

Statement	Converse
If a computer is too expensive, then few people will buy it.	If few people buy a computer, then it is too expensive.
All Canadians are people.	All people are Canadians.
Every rhombus is a parallelogram.	Every parallelogram is a rhombus.
A triangle is equilateral if it has exactly 3 lines of symmetry.	A triangle is equilateral only if it has exactly 3 lines of symmetry.

We observe in the table above that the converses of the first three statements are false while the fourth statement and its converse are true. When a statement and its converse are both true, we can combine them into a single *biconditional statement* using the "if and only if" construction.

A triangle is equilateral if and only if it has exactly 3 lines of symmetry.

The "if and only if" construction is used so often that mathematicians have created the symbol "iff" to read "if and only if". Therefore this statement and its converse can be written as follows.

A triangle is equilateral iff it has exactly 3 lines of symmetry.

Example. Write each statement and its converse. If both statements are true, write them as a biconditional statement using "iff".

a) If a chord passes through the centre of a circle, then the chord is a diameter.

b) If a point P is mapped onto P′ under a reflection in l, then P and P′ are equidistant from l.

Solution. This table shows each statement and its converse.

	Statement	Converse
a)	If a chord passes through the centre of a circle, then the chord is a diameter.	If a chord is a diameter of a circle, then it passes through the centre.
b)	If a point P is mapped onto P′ under a reflection in l, then P and P′ are equidistant from l.	If points P and P′ are equidistant from l, then P is mapped onto P′ under a reflection in l.

The converse of the statement in part a) is true. To express both statements as a single biconditional statement, we write "A chord of a circle is a diameter iff it passes through the centre."

The converse of the statement in part b) is false since P and P′ could be on the same side of l and equidistant from l, but P′ would not necessarily be the reflection image of P in l.

EXERCISES 4-7

Ⓐ

1. Write each statement in the "if . . . then" form. State the hypothesis and the conclusion of each statement.
   a) If a man is afraid of sharks he may choose to swim in the pool.
   b) A professional golfer will hit a longer drive if she uses a high compression ball.
   c) When the battery is dead, the flashlight does not work.
   d) All mathematicians like music.
   e) Every king is a male.
   f) If one geometric figure is the image of another under an isometry the figures are congruent.
   g) A triangle is equilateral if it is mapped onto itself under a rotation of 60° about its centre.
   h) Triangles are polygons.

2. Write the converse of each statement in *Exercise 1*. Rewrite each statement which has a true converse as a biconditional statement.

Ⓑ

3. Write an example of each phrase.
   a) a true statement which has a false converse
   b) a true statement which has a true converse
   c) a false statement which has a true converse
   d) a false statement which has a false converse

4. To prove that a statement is not true in general, we need only provide a single example which violates the statement. Such an example is called a *counter-example*. Give one counterexample to disprove each statement.
   a) All prime numbers are odd.
   b) A quadrilateral with a pair of parallel sides is a parallelogram.
   c) The diagonals of a trapezoid bisect each other.
   d) If all the angles of one triangle are respectively congruent to the angles of another triangle, then the two triangles are congruent.
   e) For any two congruent figures, there is a translation that will map one figure onto the other.
   f) Every isometry is a translation or a rotation or a reflection.

5. Test the statements to find out which are true. Give a counterexample for any statement that is not true.
   a) Any point on the perpendicular bisector of a line segment is equidistant from the ends of that line segment.
   b) The angles opposite the congruent sides of an isosceles triangle are congruent.
   c) The angle opposite the longest side of a triangle is the greatest angle inside the triangle.
   d) If two triangles are congruent, then they have equal areas.
   e) If a quadrilateral is mapped onto itself under a rotation, then it is a parallelogram.
   f) If the four vertices of a quadrilateral lie on the same circle, then the quadrilateral is a parallelogram.

4-8 THEOREMS AND THEIR CONVERSES

In this section we shall prove some theorems and their converses. Each pair of theorems will then be combined into a single biconditional theorem using the iff notation.

> **Theorem**
> If a point is on the perpendicular bisector of a line segment, then it is equidistant from the ends of the line segment.

Given: P is any point on the perpendicular bisector of AB. O is the point of intersection of the perpendicular with AB.
Required to Prove: PA = PB

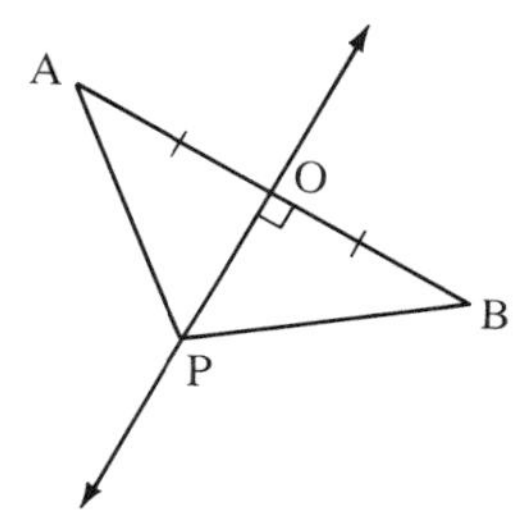

Proof:

Statement	Reason
In △POA and △POB	
OA = OB	$\overleftrightarrow{PO}$ is the perpendicular bisector.
∠POA = ∠POB	$\overleftrightarrow{PO}$ is the perpendicular bisector.
PO is common	
Therefore, △POA ≅ △POB	SAS
PA = PB	Congruent triangles

Now we prove the converse of the theorem above.

> **Theorem**
> If a point is equidistant from two given points, then it is on the perpendicular bisector of the line segment joining those points.

Given: AB is any line segment.
P is any point such that PA = PB.
Required to Prove: P is on the perpendicular bisector of AB.
Analysis: Try using congruent triangles.
To obtain two triangles, let the bisector of ∠APB meet AB at O.

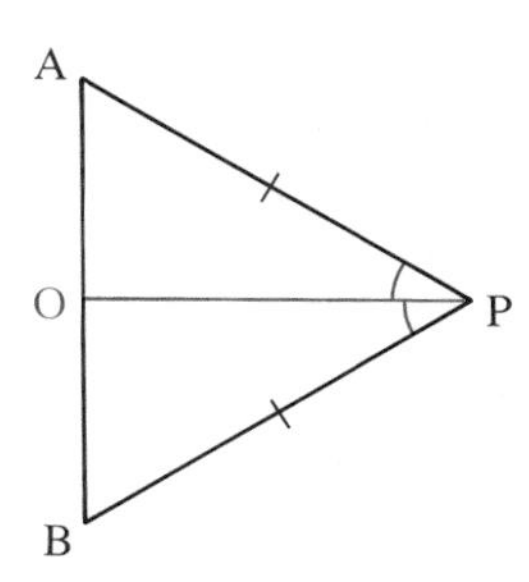

Proof:

Statement	Reason
In $\triangle POA$ and $\triangle POB$	
$PA = PB$	Given
$\angle APO = \angle BPO$	Since PO bisects $\angle APB$
PO is common	
Therefore, $\triangle POA \cong \triangle POB$	SAS
$OA = OB$	Congruent triangles
$\angle AOP = \angle BOP = 90°$	Congruent triangles
$OP \perp AB$	Property of a straight angle
Therefore, P is on the perpendicular bisector of AB.	$OA = OB$ and $OP \perp AB$

The two theorems proved above can be combined into a single biconditional statement called the Perpendicular Bisector Theorem.

> **Perpendicular Bisector Theorem**
> A point is on the perpendicular bisector of a line segment iff it is equidistant from the ends of the line segment.

The next pair of theorems describe an important property of points on the bisector of an angle.

> **Theorem**
> If a point is on the bisector of an angle, then it is equidistant from the arms of the angle.

Given: P is a point on the bisector of $\angle BAC$.

Required to Prove: P is equidistant from $\overrightarrow{AB}$ and $\overrightarrow{AC}$.

Analysis: Drop the perpendiculars from P onto AB and $\overrightarrow{AC}$ at D and E respectively. We are required to prove that $DP = PE$.

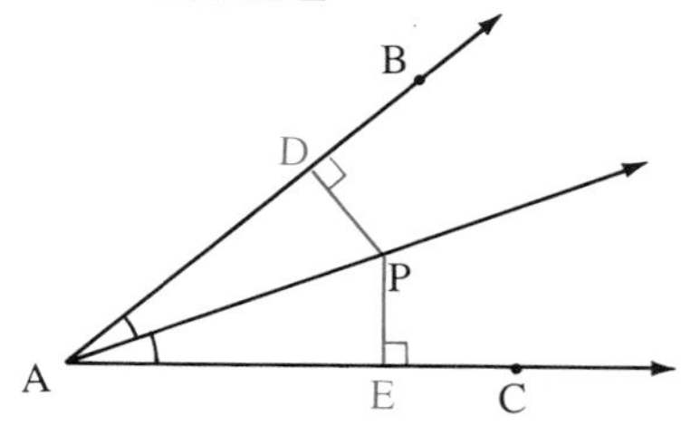

Proof:

Statement	Reason
In $\triangle DAP$ and $\triangle EAP$	
$\angle DAP = \angle EAP$	Given
$\angle PDA = \angle PEA$	$PD \perp AB$; $PE \perp AC$
AP is common	
Therefore, $\triangle DAP \cong \triangle EAP$	AAS
$PD = PE$	Congruent triangles

Here is the converse theorem.

> **Theorem**
> If a point is equidistant from the arms of an angle, then it is on the bisector of the angle.

Given: PD and PE are the perpendiculars from a point P to the arms $\overrightarrow{AB}$ and $\overrightarrow{AC}$ respectively of $\angle BAC$ such that PD = PE.
Required to Prove: $\angle PAD = \angle PAE$

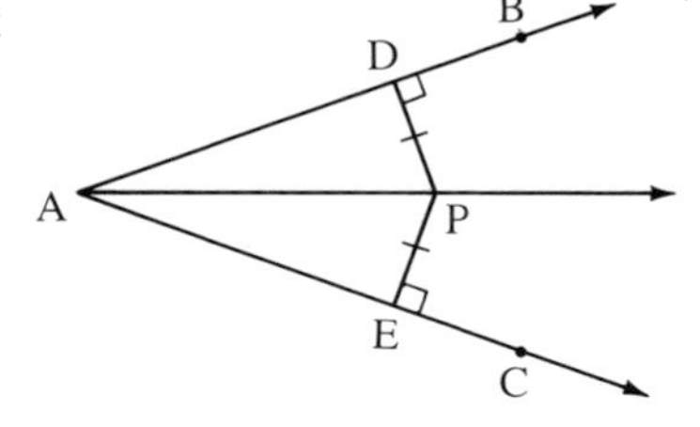

Proof:

Statement	Reason
In $\triangle DAP$ and $\triangle EAP$	
$\angle ADP = \angle AEP$	Given
$PD = PE$	Given
AP is common	
Therefore, $\triangle DAP \cong \triangle EAP$	HS
$\angle PAD = \angle PAE$	Congruent triangles

This theorem and its converse can be combined into the biconditional statement called the Angle Bisector Theorem.

> **Angle Bisector Theorem**
> A point is on the bisector of an angle iff it is equidistant from the arms of the angle.

In *Section 4-3* we proved the Isosceles Triangle Theorem. The following theorem is the converse of it.

> **Theorem**
> If two angles of a triangle are congruent, then the sides opposite the congruent angles are congruent.

Given: $\triangle ABC$ with $\angle B = \angle C$
Required to Prove: AB = AC
Analysis: Let AD be the bisector of $\angle BAC$; that is, $\angle BAD = \angle CAD$.

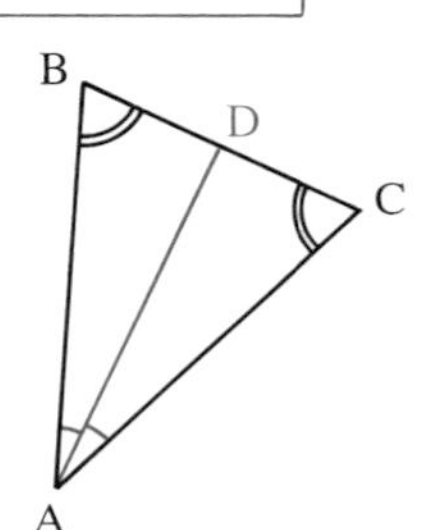

Proof:

Statement	Reason
In △ABD and △ACD	
∠ABD = ∠ACD	Given
∠BAD = ∠CAD	AD bisects ∠BAC
AD is common	
Therefore, △ABD ≅ △ACD	AAS
AB = AC	Congruent triangles

We can now write the Isosceles Triangle Theorem as a biconditional statement.

> **Isosceles Triangle Theorem**
> Two angles of a triangle are congruent iff the sides opposite those angles are congruent.

In *Section 4-2* and *Section 4-5* we proved the Parallel Lines Theorem; that is, if a transversal intersects two parallel lines, then corresponding angles are congruent. We now prove the converse of that theorem using the method of indirect proof.

> **Theorem**
> If a transversal intersects two lines so that corresponding angles are congruent, then the lines are parallel.

Given: $\overleftrightarrow{AB}$ is a transversal which intersects lines l_1 and l_2 in points E and F respectively so that ∠BFD = ∠BEC.

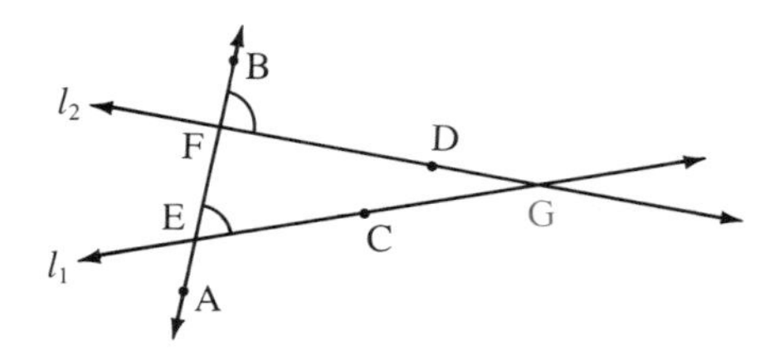

Required to Prove: l_1 is parallel to l_2.

Proof: Either l_1 and l_2 are parallel, or they are not. Assume that l_1 is not parallel to l_2; that is, l_1 and l_2 intersect at some point G.

Statement	Reason
∠BFD > ∠BEC	Exterior Angle Theorem
∠BFD = ∠BEC	Given

These two statements are contradictory.
Hence, the assumption that l_1 is not parallel to l_2 is false.
Therefore, l_1 is parallel to l_2.

We can now write the Parallel Lines Theorem as a biconditional statement.

Parallel Lines Theorem
The corresponding angles formed by a transversal, which intersects two lines, are congruent iff the lines are parallel.

We can also write the corollaries of the Parallel Lines Theorem as biconditional statements.

Corollary 1 of Parallel Lines Theorem
The alternate angles formed by a transversal, which intersects two lines, are congruent iff the lines are parallel.

Corollary 2 of Parallel Lines Theorem
The interior angles on the same side of a transversal, which intersects two lines, are supplementary iff the lines are parallel.

EXERCISES 4-8

Ⓐ

1. Identify pairs of parallel line segments. Name the theorems which support your answers.

a)

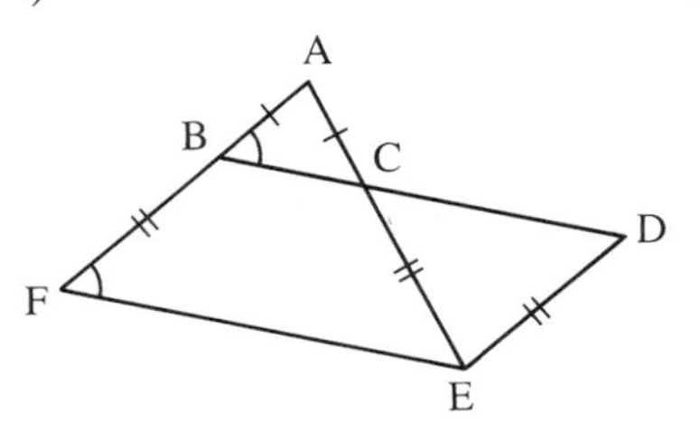

b)

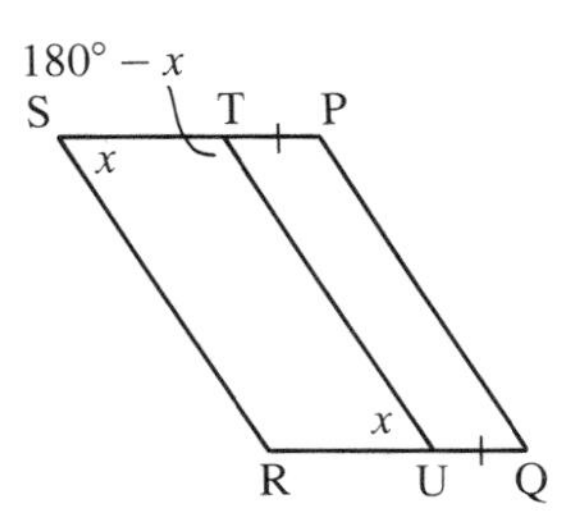

c)

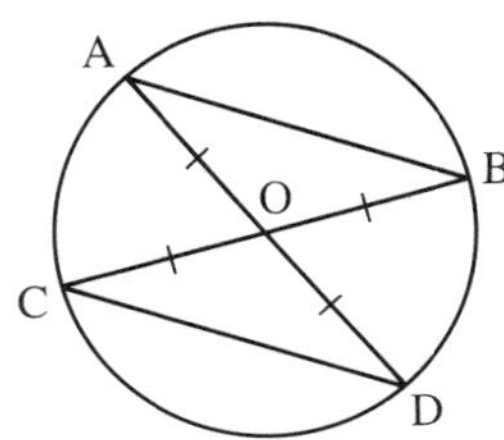

2. Explain why a circle with centre O can be drawn to pass through the points X, Y, and Z.

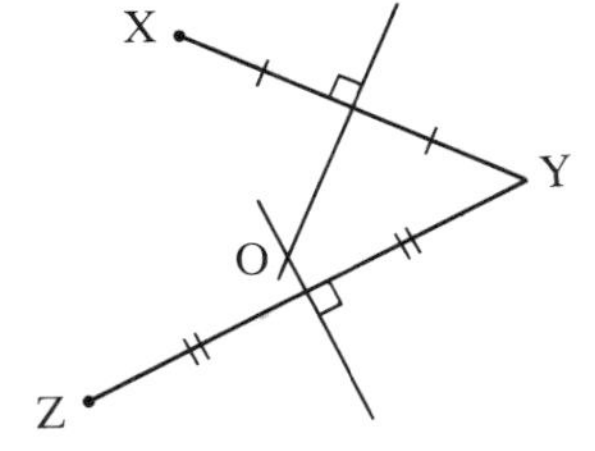

3. How many circles can be drawn which pass through:
   a) 2 given points
   b) 3 given points?

4. Explain why the centre of a circle which passes through points P and Q lies on the perpendicular bisector of line segment PQ.

5. When light passes from air into water, parallel rays are refracted (bent) through the same angle. Parallel rays $\overrightarrow{AB}$ and $\overrightarrow{DE}$ are bent into rays $\overrightarrow{BC}$ and $\overrightarrow{EF}$ respectively. Are BC and EF parallel? Explain your answer.

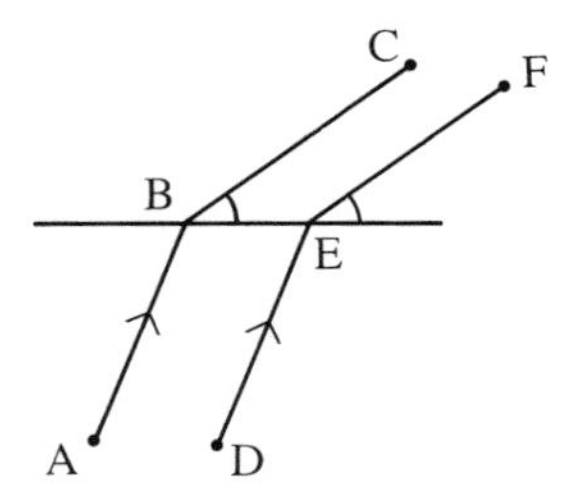

6. a) Explain how Corollary 1 follows directly from the Parallel Lines Theorem.
   b) Explain how Corollary 2 can be deduced from the Parallel Lines Theorem.

(B)

7. Two line segments AC and BD bisect each other. Prove that ABCD is a parallelogram.

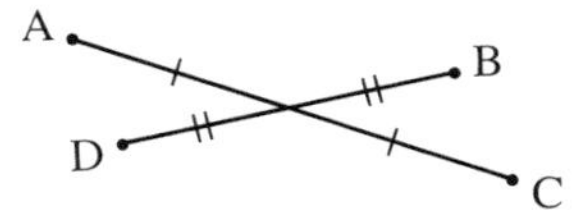

8. A quadrilateral with all sides of equal length is called a rhombus. Prove that a rhombus is a parallelogram; that is, the opposite sides are parallel.

9. Quadrilateral PQRS has $\angle P = \angle R$, $\angle Q = \angle S$, and PQ parallel to SR. Prove that PQRS is a parallelogram.

10. Quadrilateral EFGH has EF = HG and EF parallel to HG. Prove that EFGH is a parallelogram.

11. Prove that if two opposite angles of a quadrilateral are right angles, then the bisectors of the other two angles are parallel.

12. Two distinct lines l_1 and l_2 are both parallel to line l_3. Prove that l_1 is parallel to l_2.

13. In quadrilateral ABCD, $\angle A = \angle D$ and $\angle B = \angle C$. Prove that AD is parallel to BC.

14. Prove that any radius of a circle which bisects a chord is perpendicular to the chord.

15. A billiard ball reflects off two adjacent banks of a billiard table. Prove that the lines of approach and reflection are parallel; that is, prove AB is parallel to DC.

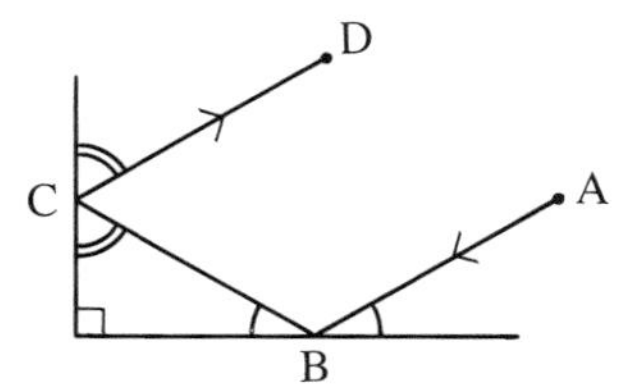

16. Prove that two lines drawn from different vertices of a triangle and terminating in the opposite sides cannot bisect each other.

(C)

17. a) Prove that the line drawn parallel to one side of a triangle and passing through the midpoint of another side, bisects the third side.
    b) Use part a) to show that the line segment joining the midpoints of two sides of a triangle is parallel to the third side and equal to one-half its length.

4-9 PROOFS USING TRANSFORMATIONS

In the previous sections we proved most theorems by identifying congruent triangles and deducing that corresponding sides or angles were congruent. This technique was the cornerstone of the traditional Euclidean proofs in deductive geometry. However, if we use the following properties of isometries as our basic set of axioms, then theorems can be proved using transformations.

Recall that the first two axioms shown below were introduced in *THE MATHEMATICAL MIND*, page 140.

Invariant Length Axiom
Two line segments AB and A′B′ are congruent iff there is an isometry which maps AB onto A′B′ so that $A \to A'$ and $B \to B'$.

Invariant Angle Axiom
Two angles $\angle ABC$ and $\angle A'B'C'$ are congruent iff there is an isometry which maps $\angle ABC$ onto $\angle A'B'C'$ so that $\overrightarrow{BA} \to \overrightarrow{B'A'}$ and $\overrightarrow{BC} \to \overrightarrow{B'C'}$.

Angle Bisector Axiom
A line is a bisector of an angle iff a reflection in the line maps each arm of the angle into the other arm.

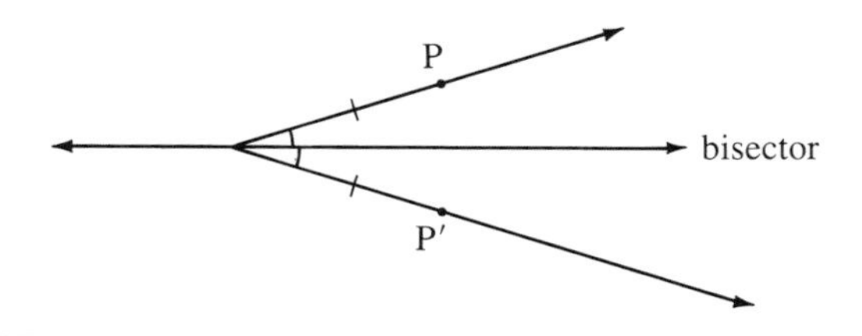

Reflection Line Axiom
Under a reflection in a line l

- Every point on l is mapped onto itself.
- Any point P not on l is mapped onto a point P′ on the other side of l such that l is the perpendicular bisector of PP′.

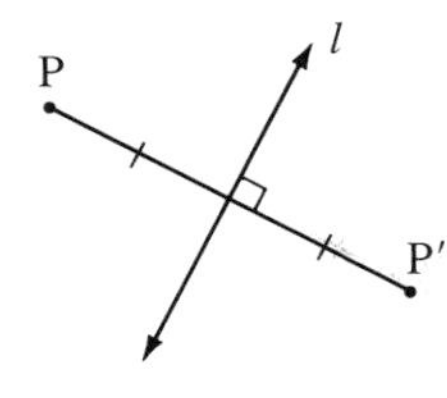

> **Half-Turn Invariance Axiom**
> Under a 180° turn about the midpoint of a line segment AB
> - AB is mapped onto itself such that A → B and B → A.
> - Any line segment CD is mapped onto a parallel line segment C′D′ where C → C′ and D → D′.

Certain theorems can be proved using transformational geometry rather than Euclidean geometry. The power in transformational proofs derives from the fact that certain attributes such as length, angle measure, parallelism, and perpendicularity are invariant under an isometry. The following examples show how these invariants can be used in transformational proofs.

Example 1. Triangle ABC is isosceles with AB = AC. CD and BE intersect at F and AF bisects ∠A. Prove that CD = BE.

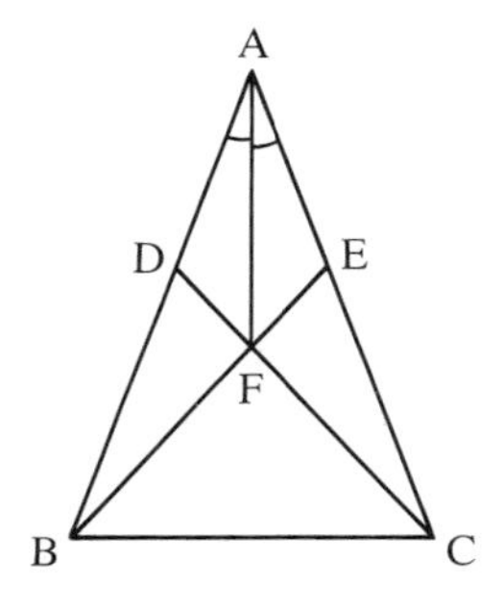

Solution.

Statement	Reason
1. AB = AC	Given
Under a reflection in $\overleftrightarrow{AF}$,	
2. B → C and C → B	Statement 1 and Angle Bisector Axiom
3. A → A and F → F	Reflection Line Axiom
4. AB → AC and AC → AB BF → CF and CF → BF	Statements 2 and 3
5. $\overrightarrow{BF} \rightarrow \overrightarrow{CF}$ and $\overrightarrow{CF} \rightarrow \overrightarrow{BF}$	Statement 4
6. Since D is the intersection of $\overrightarrow{CF}$ and AB, then the image of D is the intersection of $\overrightarrow{BF}$ and AC; that is, E is the image of D.	Statements 4 and 5
7. CD → BE	Statements 2 and 6
8. CD = BE	Statement 7 and Invariant Length Axiom

Example 2. Prove that the midpoints of a pair of opposite sides of a parallelogram together with a pair of opposite vertices of that parallelogram are themselves the vertices of a parallelogram.

Solution. *Given:*
DEFG is a parallelogram and H and J are respectively the midpoints of DE and FG.
Required to Prove:
DHFJ is a parallelogram;
that is, DH || JF and HF || DJ.
Proof:

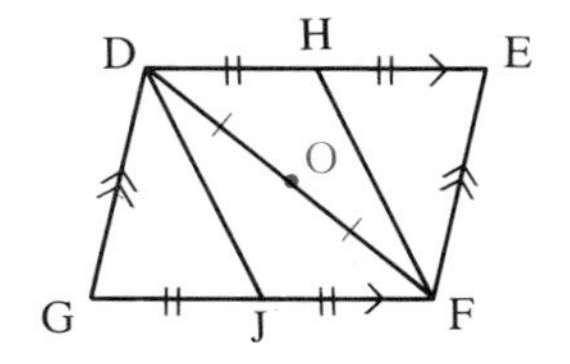

Statement	Reason
Let O be the midpoint of diagonal DF. Under a 180° rotation about O,	
1. D → F and F → D	Half-Turn Invariance Axiom
2. The image of DE is parallel to DE and has end point F.	Statement 1 and Half-Turn Invariance Axiom
3. DE → FG and FG → DE	Statement 2 and Euclid's Parallel Axiom
4. Since H and J are the midpoints of DE and FG respectively, H → J and J → H	Statement 3
5. HF → JD and JD → HF	Statements 1 and 4
6. HF || DJ	Statement 5 and Half-Turn Invariance Axiom
7. DH || JF	Given

For many problems in deductive geometry, Euclidean proofs are more readily apparent because pairs of congruent triangles are easily identified and the proofs often follow routinely from a listing of congruent sides and angles. However, for certain types of problems, transformation techniques are more effective.

EXERCISES 4-9

1. Under a reflection R, describe:
   a) what points are invariant
   b) what line segments are invariant
   c) what lines are invariant
   d) what polygons are invariant.

2. For a rotation of 90°, describe:
   a) what points are invariant
   b) what line segments are invariant
   c) what lines are invariant
   d) what geometric figures are invariant.

3. Repeat *Exercise 2* for a rotation of 180°.

4. a) In the isosceles $\triangle ABC$, $AB = AC$. The line segment AD bisects $\angle BAC$. Under a reflection in AD what is the image of:
   i) point B ii) point C
   iii) segment BD iv) segment CD?
   b) What property of reflections implies that $BD = CD$?
   c) What property of reflections implies that $\angle ABD = \angle ACD$?
   d) How can we conclude from part a) iv) that $\angle ADB = \angle ADC = 90°$?

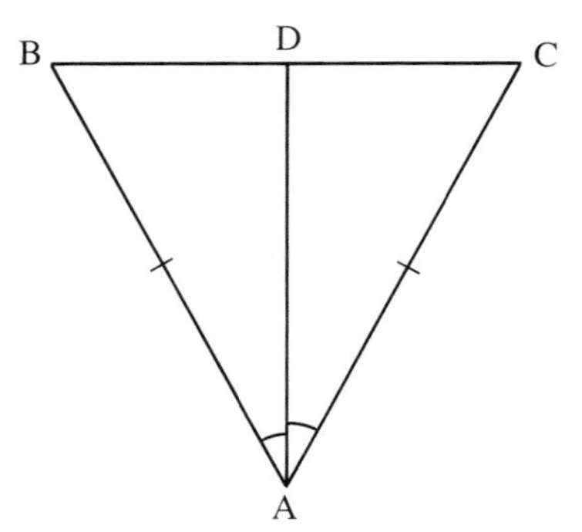

5. a) P is any point on l, the perpendicular bisector of line segment AB. D is the point of intersection of l and AB. Under a reflection in l what is the image of:
   i) point A ii) point B
   iii) point P iv) AP?
   b) What property of reflections implies that $AP = BP$?

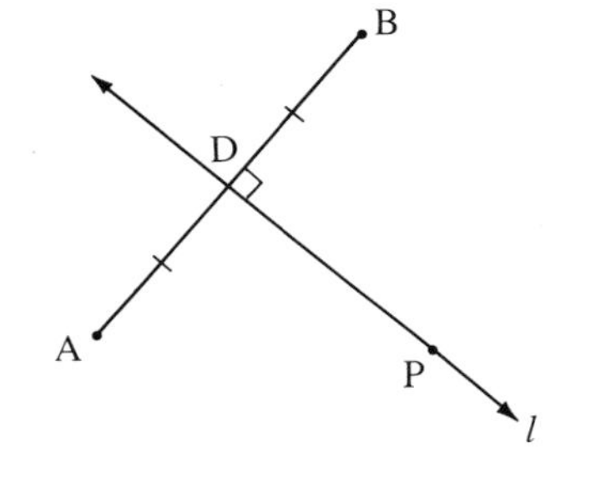

6. Line segment XY is perpendicular to lines l and m. If Z is the midpoint of XY, prove that l maps onto m under a rotation of 180° about Z.

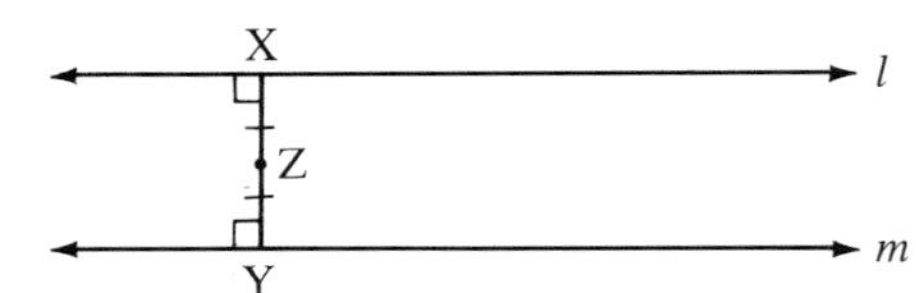

(B)

7. Copy and complete this proof.
   Prove that in an isosceles triangle the angles opposite the equal sides are equal.
   Given: $\triangle ABC$ is isosceles with $AB = AC$.
   Required to Prove: $\angle ABC = \angle ACB$
   Analysis: Let AD be the bisector of $\angle BAC$.

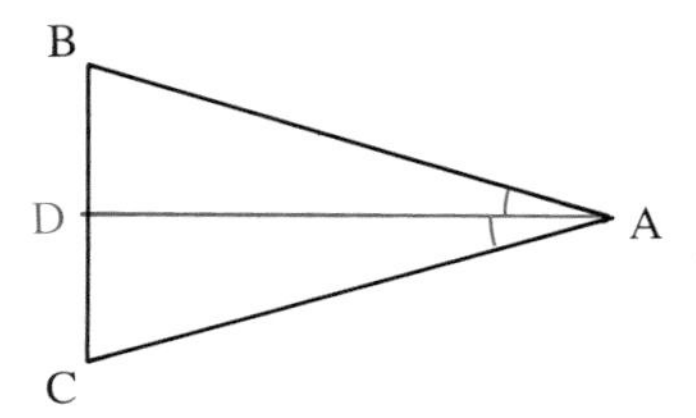

Proof:

Statement	Reason
1. A reflection in $\overleftrightarrow{AD}$ maps $A \to A$, $B \to C$, and $C \to B$.	________ Axiom
2. $\angle ABC$ is mapped onto $\angle ACB$.	Statement __
3. $\angle ABC = \angle ACB$	________ Axiom

8. Use the properties of rotations to deduce that if a quadrilateral maps onto itself under a rotation of 180°, then it is a parallelogram.

9. Parallelogram PQRS has A, B, C, and D as the midpoints of PQ, QR, RS, and SP respectively. Use the properties of rotations to deduce that ABCD is a parallelogram.

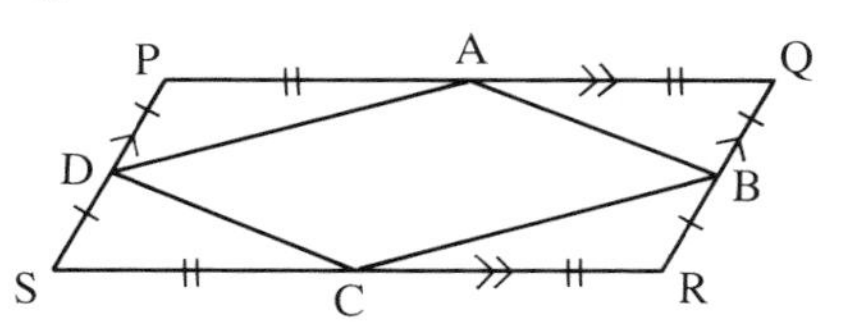

10. Prove that the diagonals of a rhombus bisect each other at right angles.

11. a) In isosceles $\triangle STU$, ST = SU and SW is the bisector of $\angle S$. Also, TV and UX are the altitudes from T and U respectively. Under a reflection in SW, what is the image of:
    i) T ii) U iii) ST iv) SU?
    b) What is the measure of the angle between the image of TV and the image of SU under a reflection in SW?
    c) Use your answer to part b) to show that UX is the image of TV under a reflection in SW.
    d) Explain why part c) implies that UX = TV.

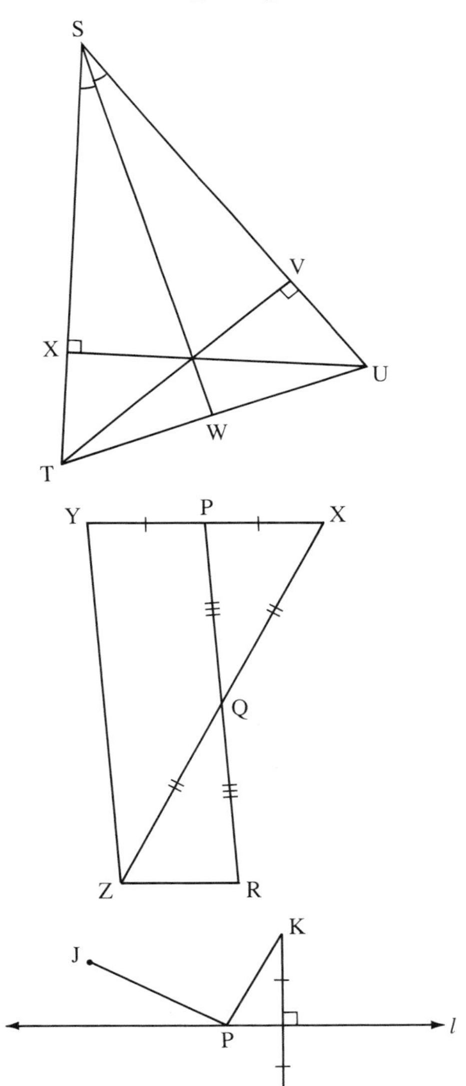

12. a) In the diagram, P and Q are the respective midpoints of sides XY and XZ of $\triangle XYZ$. PQ is extended to R so that PQ = QR. Use the properties of rotations to prove that:
    i) $PQ \parallel YZ$ ii) $PQ = \frac{1}{2}YZ$.
    b) Use part a) to deduce the following property of triangles.
    The line segment joining the midpoints of two sides of a triangle is parallel to the third side and half its length.

13. Prove that if P is any point on the line l, and K and K′ are images of one another under a reflection in l, then the total length JP + PK is a minimum when P lies on line segment JK′.

Review Exercises

1. Write a sentence to define each word or phrase.

a) parallel	b) perpendicular	c) equidistant
d) parallelogram	e) quadrilateral	f) polygon
g) rhombus	h) diagonal	i) midpoint
j) perpendicular bisector	k) angle bisector	l) supplementary angles

2. Find the values of x and y.

a)

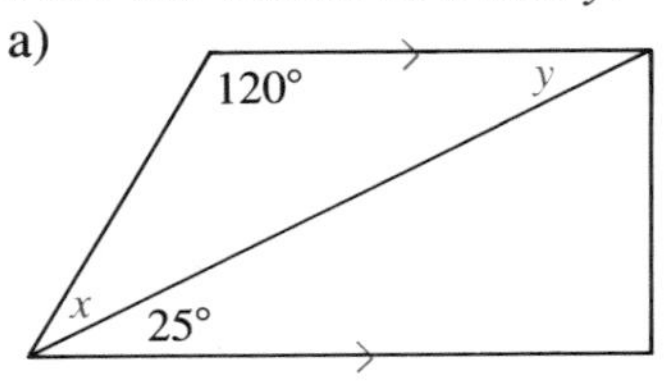

b)

c)

3. Diagonal PR of quadrilateral PQRS (below left) bisects $\angle$P and $\angle$R. Prove that PR is perpendicular to diagonal QS.

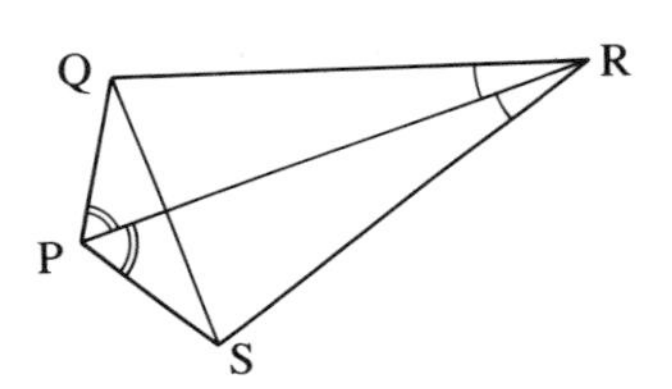

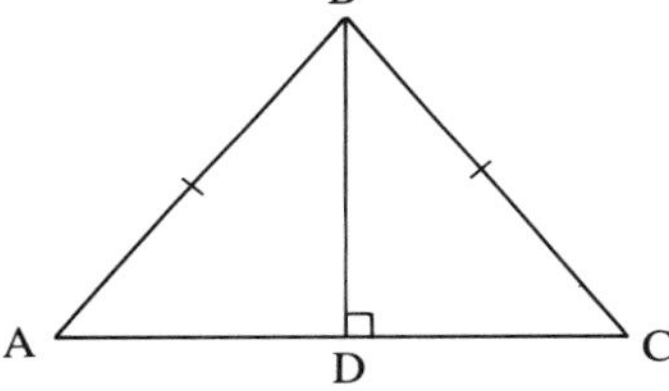

4. Triangle ABC (above right) is isosceles with AB = BC.
   a) Prove that the perpendicular BD divides $\triangle$ABC into two congruent triangles, $\triangle$ABD and $\triangle$CBD.
   b) Use the result in part a) to prove that if the hypotenuse and one side of a right triangle are respectively congruent to the hypotenuse and one side of another right triangle, then the triangles are congruent.

5. In the diagram (below left), AM and BN are parallel radii. C and D are the points where $\overleftrightarrow{MN}$ intersects the circles. Prove that AC is parallel to BD.

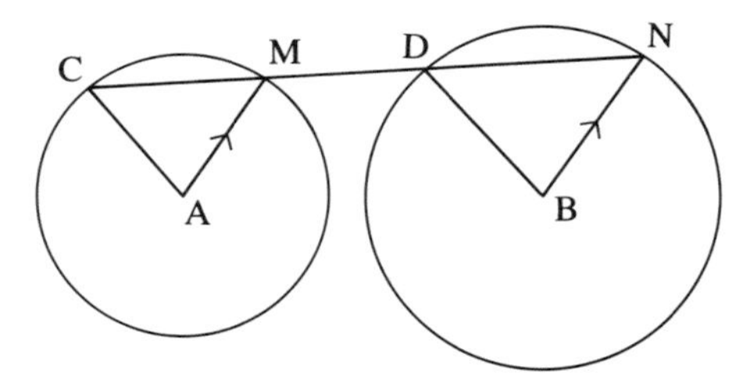

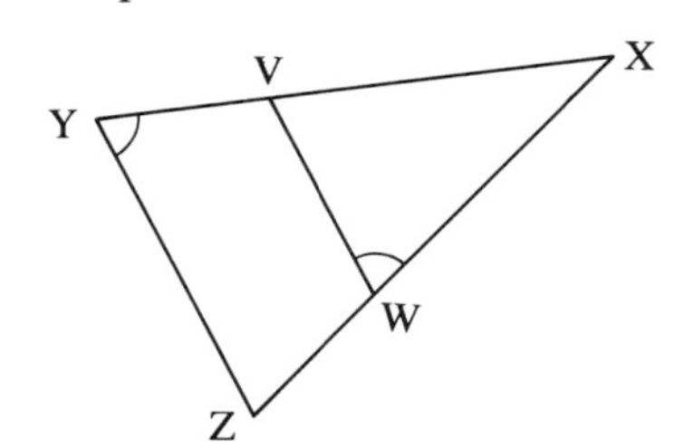

6. In the diagram (above right), XY = XZ and $\angle$XWV = $\angle$XYZ. Prove that VW is parallel to YZ.

7. In $\triangle$PQR, PQ > PR. S is a point on PQ such that PS = PR. Prove that $\angle$SRQ = $\angle$PRS − $\angle$Q.

5 Similarity

To estimate the height of a tree, a forester held a metre stick perpendicular to the ground and observed the length of its shadow was 72 cm. Then she measured the length of the tree's shadow as 18.5 m. What was the approximate height of the tree? (See Section 5-5 *Example 1*.)

5-1 SIMILAR FIGURES

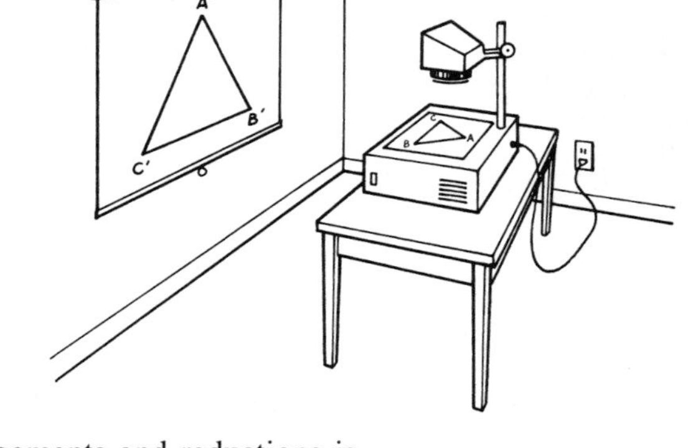

This overhead projector projects △ABC onto △A′B′C′. △A′B′C′ is the same shape as △ABC but it is larger. We say that △ABC has been *enlarged*.

If △A′B′C′ were smaller than △ABC, we would say that △ABC had been *reduced*.

Two figures such as △ABC and △A′B′C′ which have the same shape but not necessarily the same size are said to be *similar*.
We say: △ABC is similar to △A′B′C′.
We write: △ABC ~ △A′B′C′.

The transformation associated with enlargements and reductions is called a *dilatation*. The factor by which a dilatation increases (or decreases) lengths is called the *scale factor* of the dilatation.

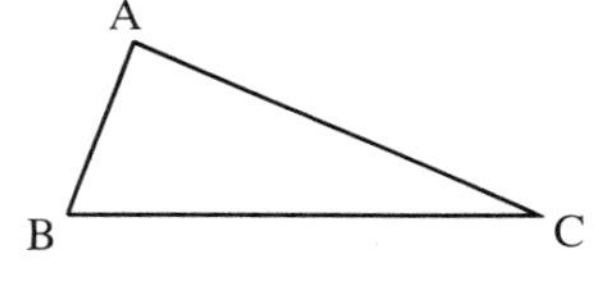

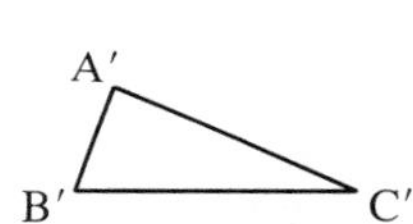

If a dilatation exists which maps A → A′
B → B′
C → C′
then △ABC and △A′B′C′ are similar.

Conversely, if △ABC ~ △A′B′C′, then each triangle is congruent to a dilatation image of the other triangle.

We shall use the following properties of dilatations as axioms for the study of similar figures.

> **Scale Factor Axiom for Line Segments**
> Under a dilatation with scale factor k, the image of every line segment is a line segment k times as long, where k is a positive constant. When $k > 1$ the dilatation corresponds to an enlargement and when $k < 1$ the dilatation corresponds to a reduction.

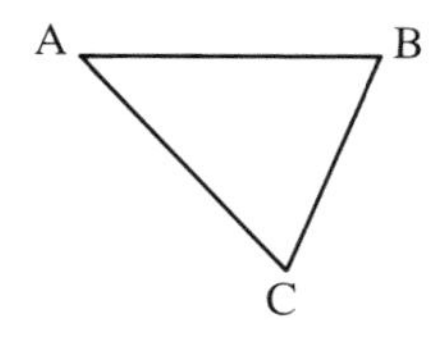

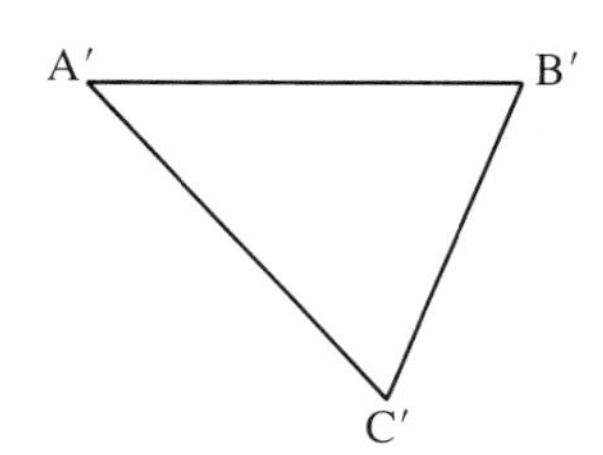

If △ABC is mapped onto △A′B′C′ by a dilatation with scale factor k, then △ABC ~ △A′B′C′.

And $\frac{A'B'}{AB} = k$, $\frac{B'C'}{BC} = k$, $\frac{A'C'}{AC} = k$

We can combine these three equations into a continued proportion.

$$\frac{A'B'}{AB} = \frac{B'C'}{BC} = \frac{A'C'}{AC} = k$$

The concept of similarity can be applied to any geometric figures. The knowledge that two figures are similar can be used to find the lengths of the sides of those figures, given the lengths of some of the sides.

Example 1. Find the values of x and y for each pair of similar figures.

a) $\triangle ABC \sim \triangle DEF$

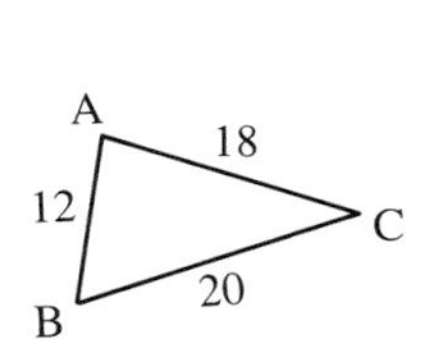

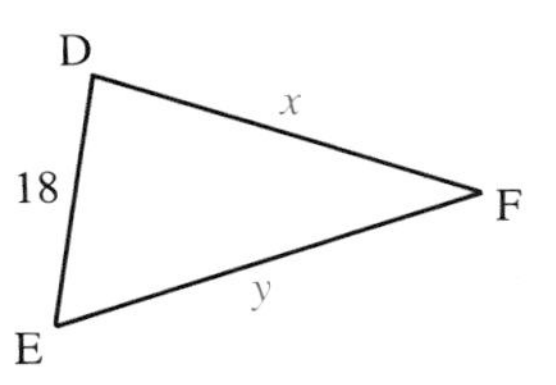

b) Figure KLMN $\sim$ figure K′L′M′N′

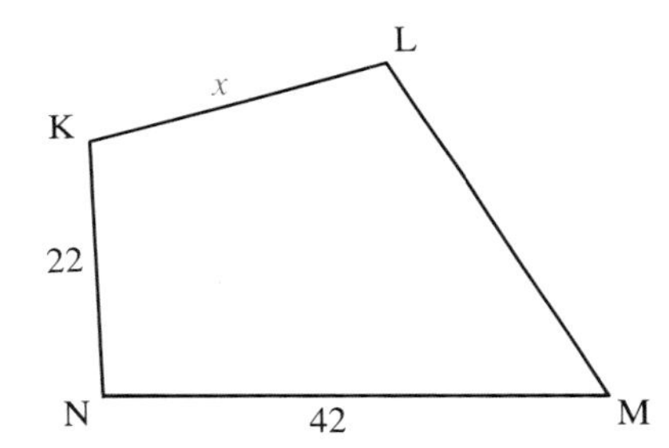

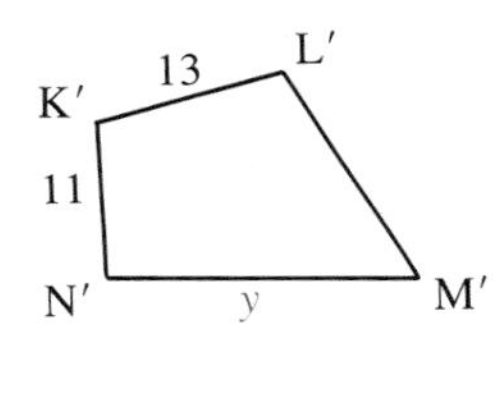

Solution. a) Since $\triangle ABC \sim \triangle DEF$

$$\frac{DF}{AC} = \frac{DE}{AB}$$
$$\frac{x}{18} = \frac{18}{12}$$
$$x = 18\left(\frac{18}{12}\right)$$
$$= 27$$
$$\frac{EF}{BC} = \frac{DE}{AB}$$
$$\frac{y}{20} = \frac{18}{12}$$
$$y = 20\left(\frac{18}{12}\right)$$
$$= 30$$

b) Since figure KLMN $\sim$ figure K′L′M′N′

$$\frac{KL}{K'L'} = \frac{KN}{K'N'}$$
$$\frac{x}{13} = \frac{22}{11}$$
$$x = 13\left(\frac{22}{11}\right)$$
$$= 26$$
$$\frac{M'N'}{MN} = \frac{K'N'}{KN}$$
$$\frac{y}{42} = \frac{11}{22}$$
$$y = 42\left(\frac{11}{22}\right)$$
$$= 21$$

Example 1 could have been completed by observing that since DE is 1.5 times as long as the corresponding side AB, all the sides of $\triangle DEF$ are 1.5 times as long as the corresponding sides of $\triangle ABC$. Similarly, the sides of figure K′L′M′N′ are one-half as long as their corresponding sides in figure KLMN.

Under a dilatation with scale factor k, a rectangle with sides 2 units and 3 units is mapped onto a rectangle with sides $2k$ units and $3k$ units.

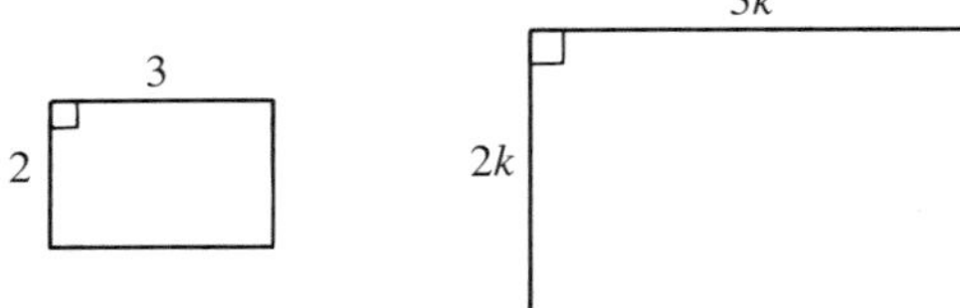

The original rectangle has an area of 6 square units. The image rectangle has an area of $6k^2$ square units. This result suggests the following axiom.

> **Scale Factor Axiom for Areas**
> Under a dilatation with scale factor k, a geometric figure of area A has an image figure of area k^2A.

Example 2. Two circles on a target are such that the circumference of the larger circle is 2.5 times the circumference of the smaller circle.

Find the ratio of the areas of the two circles.

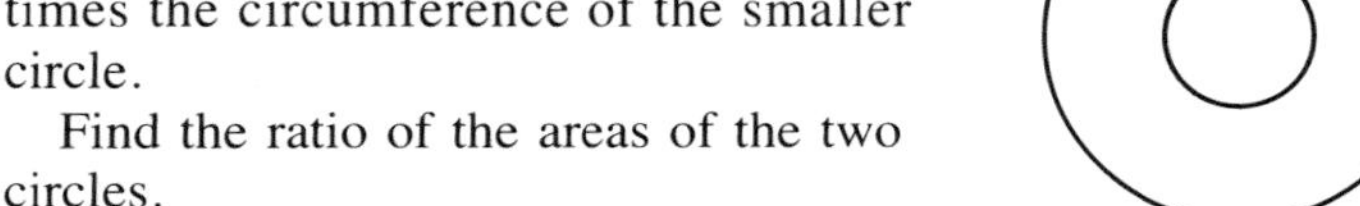

Solution. A dilatation with scale factor 2.5 will map the smaller circle onto the larger circle.

It follows from the Scale Factor Axiom for Areas that the larger circle has an area which is $(2.5)^2$, or 6.25 times the area of the smaller circle.

From the definition of similarity, rectangle PQRS is similar to rectangle P′Q′R′S′ if and only if the rectangles have the same shape; that is, they have the same length to width ratio.

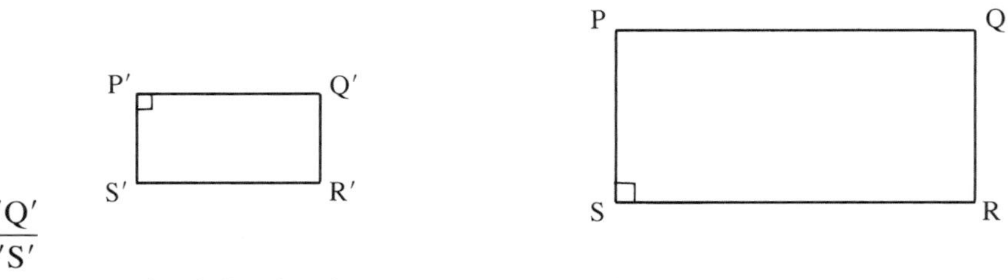

$$\frac{PQ}{PS} = \frac{P'Q'}{P'S'}$$

This demonstrates the following important property of dilatations.

> **Ratio Invariance Axiom**
> The ratio of the lengths of any two sides of a polygon is preserved under a dilatation.

The following axiom enables us to determine the unknown angles of a polygon given some of the angles of a similar polygon.

> **Angle Invariance Axiom**
> The measure of an angle is preserved under a dilatation.

Example 3. Find the values of x and y, if $\triangle ABC \sim \triangle DEF$.

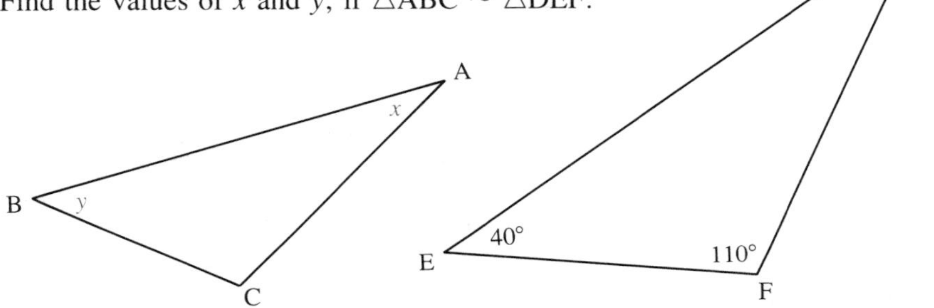

Solution. From the Angle Invariance Axiom, corresponding angles of similar figures are congruent.
Therefore, $\angle A = \angle D$ and $\angle B = \angle E$
From the Sum of the Angles Theorem
$\angle D = 30°$
Therefore, $\angle A = 30°$
that is, $x = 30°$
Also, $\angle B = \angle E = 40°$
so $y = 40°$

EXERCISES 5-1

1. For each pair of similar figures
   a) Name the congruent angles.
   b) Write the ratio of the corresponding sides as a continued proportion.
      i) $\triangle ABC \sim \triangle DEF$ ii) Figure PQRS ~ figure TWVU iii) $\triangle KLM \sim \triangle GHJ$

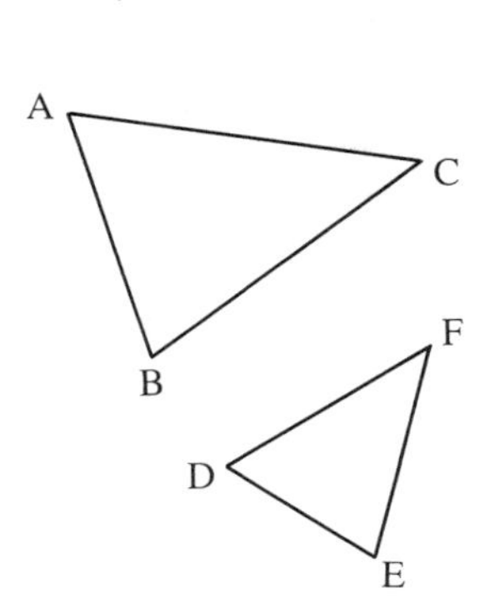

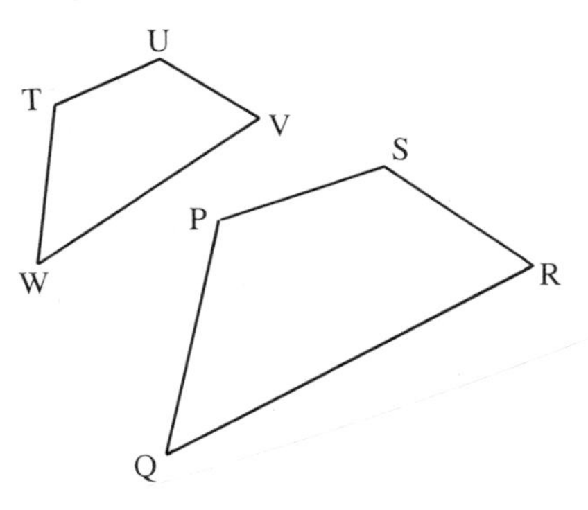

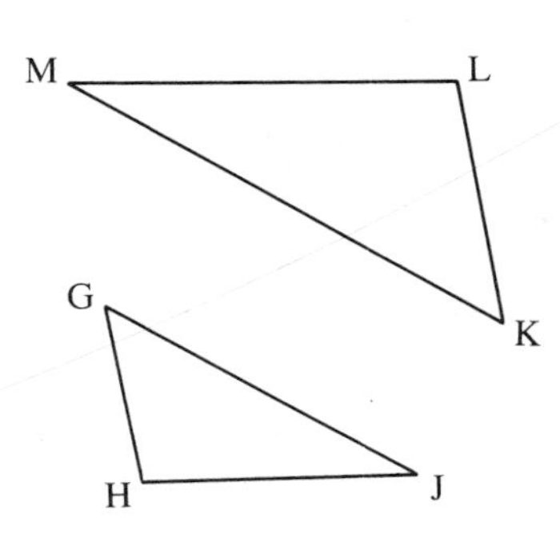

2. State why the pairs of figures are not similar.

a)

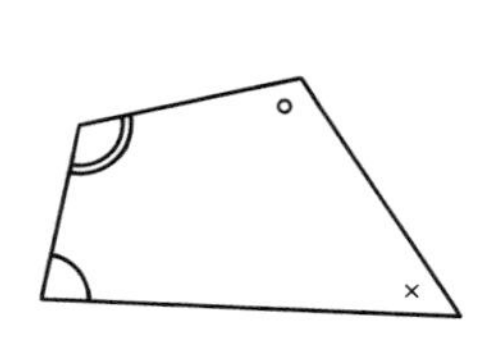

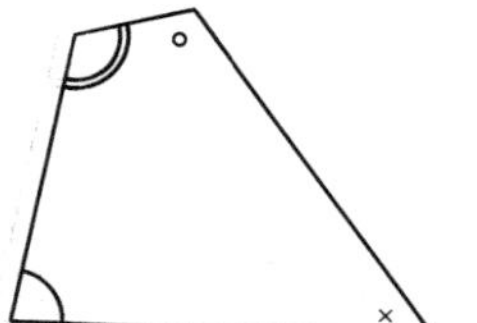

b)

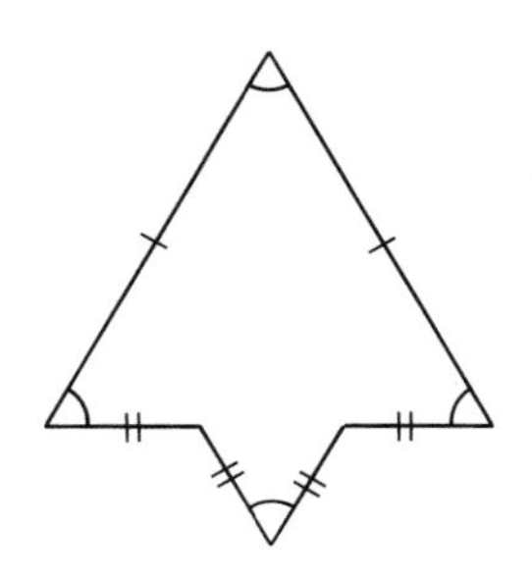

3. a) Given $\triangle ABC \cong \triangle DEF$, is $\triangle ABC \sim \triangle DEF$? Explain your answer.
b) Given $\triangle PQR \sim \triangle STU$, is $\triangle PQR \cong \triangle STU$? Explain your answer.

4. Find the ratio of the areas of two circles if the smaller one has a diameter with length equal to 0.75 of the length of the diameter of the larger circle.

5. Find the values of x, y, and z for each pair of similar figures.

a)

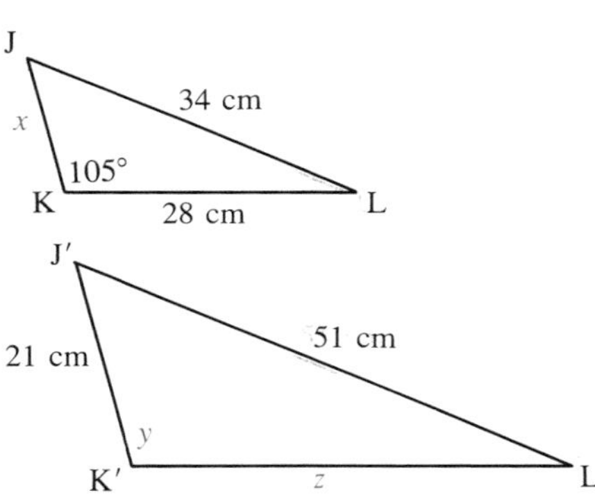

b)

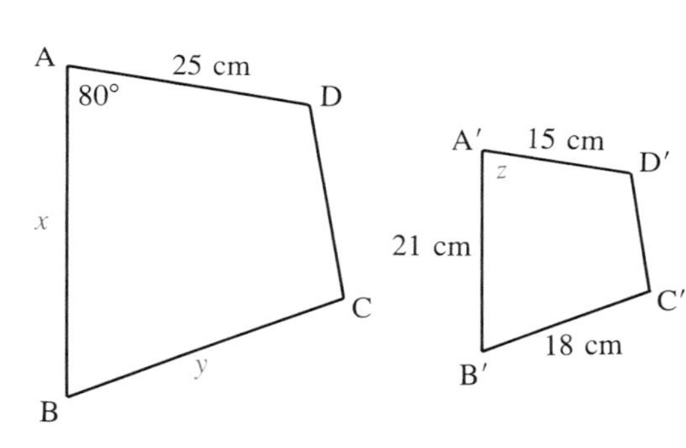

6. Find the scale factor of the dilatation for each pair of similar figures in *Exercise 5*.

7. For the similar figures in *Exercise 5*, find the area of the image figure, given the area of the original figure.
a) $\triangle JKL$ has area of 189 cm^2.
b) Figure ABCD has area of 741 cm^2.

(B)

8. A triangle has sides of length 3.2 cm, 4.5 cm, and 2.8 cm. Find the dimensions of a similar triangle for a dilatation with each scale factor.
a) 3
b) 0.8
c) 1.4

9. A rectangle has dimensions 2.5 m by 1.8 m. Find the dimensions and the area of a similar rectangle for a dilatation with each scale factor.
a) 1.5
b) 0.6

10. The area of a triangle is 248 cm^2. Find the scale factor of the dilatation if a similar triangle is constructed with each area.
a) 992 cm^2
b) 635 cm^2
c) 27.5 cm^2

11. Figure ABCD has an area of 5.4 m^2. Find the area of a similar figure A′B′C′D′ if $\frac{AB}{A'B'} = 2.1$.

12. Draw two triangles that are similar, but one is not a dilatation image of the other.

13. The ratio of the areas of two similar triangles is 49 : 121.
    a) Find the ratio of a pair of corresponding sides.
    b) Find the length of one side if the corresponding side of:
       i) the larger triangle   ii) the smaller triangle   is 5.5 cm.

14. The three figures are similar. Find the value of each variable to 1 decimal place.

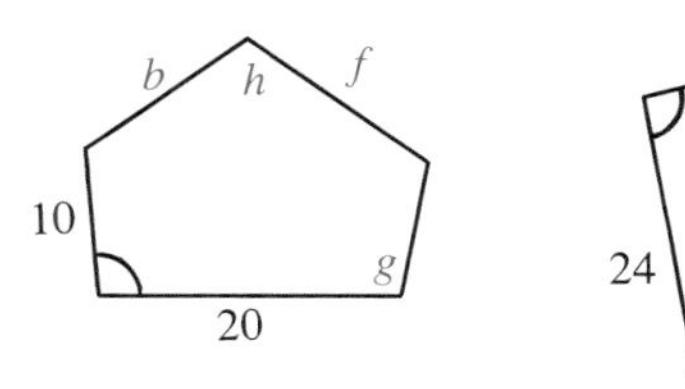

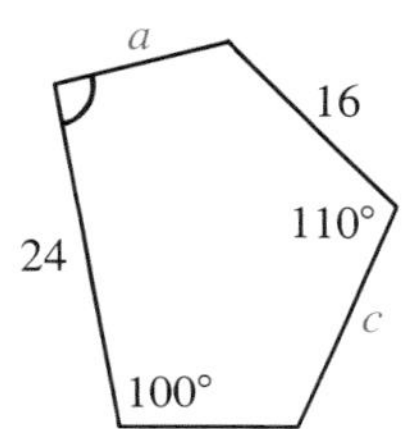

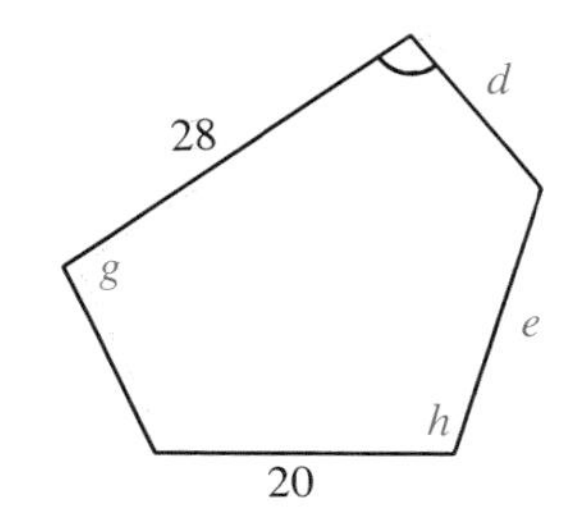

INVESTIGATE

The Pythagorean Theorem states that the squares constructed on the sides of a right triangle are related by this equation.
$a^2 + b^2 = c^2$

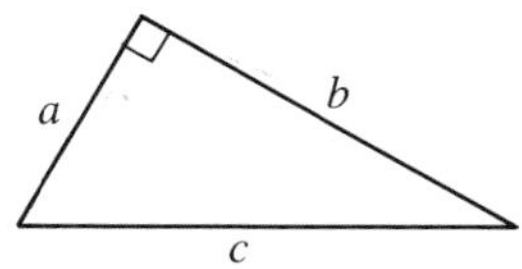

If other figures are constructed on the sides of a right triangle, does the relation still hold?

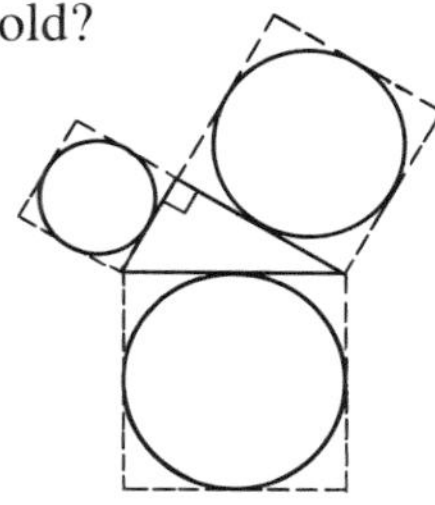

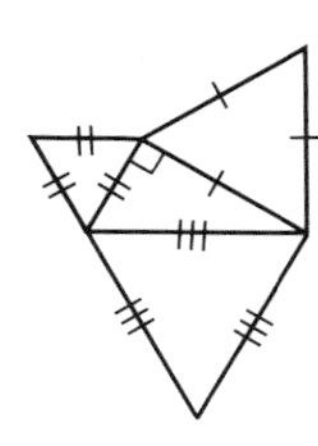

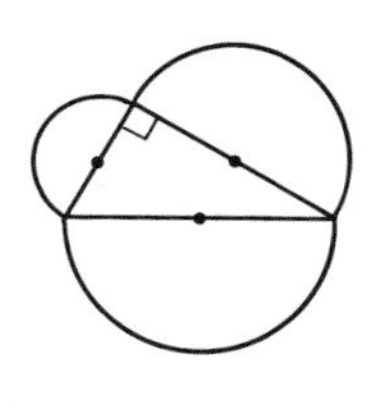

a) i) Draw a circle inside each square on the side of a right triangle.
   ii) Draw an equilateral triangle on each side of a right triangle.
   iii) Draw a semicircle on each side of a right triangle such that the side is a diameter.
   iv) Draw a triangle on the hypotenuse, and a similar triangle on each of the other two sides.

b) For each situation above, how are the areas of the figures you drew related?

c) Does the Pythagorean Theorem as stated for the squares drawn on the sides of a right triangle apply to other figures drawn on the sides?

5-2 SUFFICIENCY CONDITIONS FOR SIMILAR TRIANGLES

The floorplan of a house is similar to the actual configuration of the house. Consequently the ratios of all the distances in the floorplan are equal to the ratios of the actual distances in the house. Furthermore, the angles in the house are equal in measure to those in the floorplan. This fact enables the builder to locate positions of walls, doors, etc., by measuring angles in the floorplan.

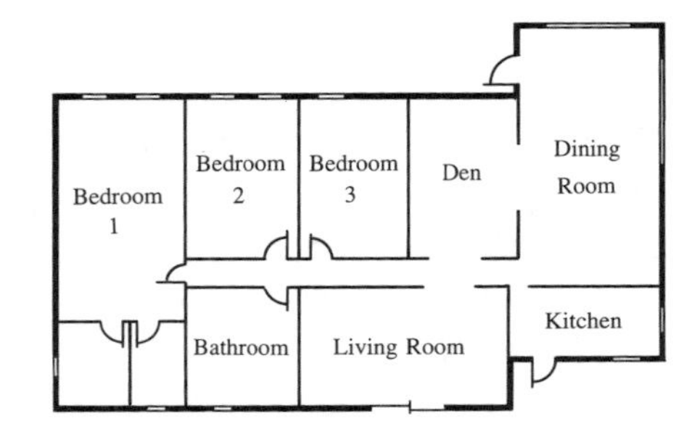

In the previous section we observed the following properties for two triangles that are similar.

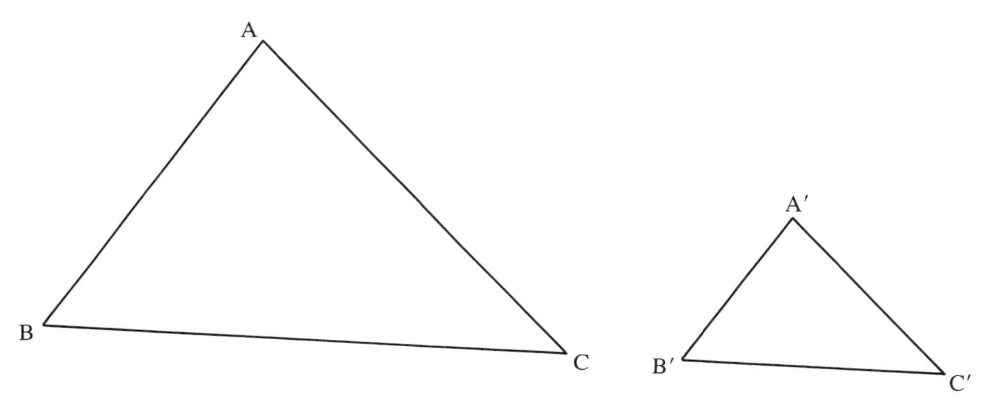

$\triangle ABC \sim \triangle A'B'C'$

- The measures of corresponding angles are equal.
  $\angle A = \angle A' \qquad \angle B = \angle B' \qquad \angle C = \angle C'$
- The lengths of corresponding sides are in the same ratio.
  $\frac{A'B'}{AB} = \frac{A'C'}{AC} = \frac{B'C'}{BC}$
- The ratio of the lengths of any two sides of one triangle equals the ratio of the lengths of the corresponding sides of the other triangle.
  $\frac{AB}{BC} = \frac{A'B'}{B'C'} \qquad \frac{AB}{AC} = \frac{A'B'}{A'C'} \qquad \frac{AC}{BC} = \frac{A'C'}{B'C'}$

Now we will prove the converses of the statements listed above.

The converse of the first statement is the Angle-Angle-Angle Similarity Theorem. The second and third statements combine into one converse statement, which is the Side-Side-Side Similarity Theorem.

In addition, we prove a third theorem, the Side-Angle-Side Similarity Theorem. This theorem also provides sufficient conditions to prove that two triangles are similar.

> **Angle-Angle-Angle Similarity Theorem (AAA~)**
> If the corresponding angles of two triangles are congruent, then the triangles are similar.

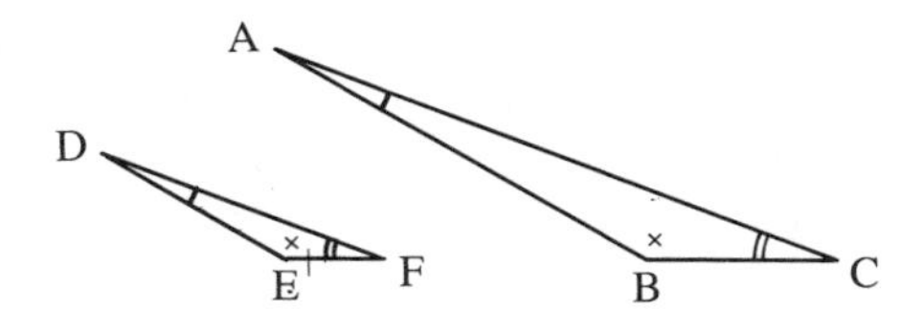

Given: △ABC and △DEF with ∠A = ∠D, ∠B = ∠E, and ∠C = ∠F
Required to Prove: △ABC ~ △DEF
Analysis: Let Q be a point on BC such that BQ = EF.
Let P be a point on AB such that ∠BQP = ∠EFD.
Show that △PBQ ≅ △DEF.
Map △PBQ onto △P′BC and show that △P′BC is coincident with △ABC. That is, P′ is coincident with A and so △ABC is the dilatation image of △PBQ and so △ABC ~ △PBQ.
Then conclude that △ABC ~ △DEF.

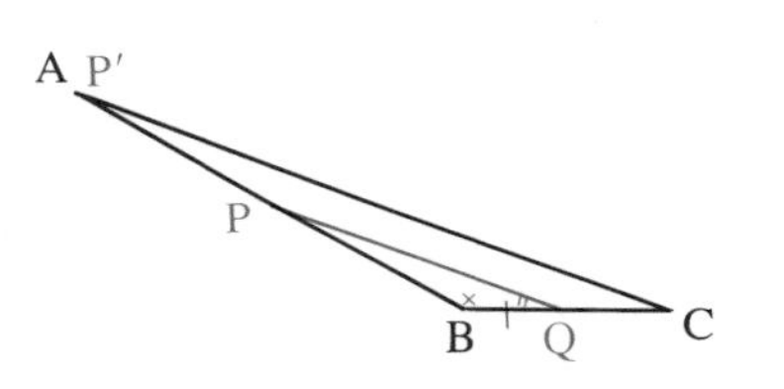

Proof:

Statement	Reason
1. In △PBQ and △DEF	
∠B = ∠E	Given
BQ = EF	Definition of Q
∠BQP = ∠EFD	Definition of P
2. Therefore, △PBQ ≅ △DEF	ASA
3. There is a dilatation that maps B → B, Q → C, and P → P′, where P′ is on AB.	Q is on BC.
4. Therefore, △BQP ~ △BCP′	
5. ∠P′CB = ∠PQB	Angle Invariance Axiom
6 ∠PQB = ∠DFE	Congruent triangles
7. ∠DFE = ∠ACB	Given
8. ∠P′CB = ∠ACB	Statements 5, 6, and 7
9. In △P′BC and △ABC	
∠P′BC = ∠ABC	Angle Invariance Axiom
BC is common	
∠P′CB = ∠ACB	Statement 8
10. Therefore, △P′BC ≅ △ABC	ASA
11. △ABC ~ △DEF	Statements 2, 4, and 10

The following corollary of this theorem indicates that we need know that only two angles of one triangle are respectively congruent to two angles of another triangle, to prove that the triangles are similar.

Angle-Angle Similarity Theorem (AA~) If two angles of one triangle are respectively congruent to two angles of another triangle, then the two triangles are similar.

The previous theorem asserted that if two triangles are mutually equiangular, then the triangles are similar. The following theorem asserts that if two triangles have sides which are in the same ratio, then the triangles are similar.

Side-Side-Side Similarity Theorem (SSS~) If three sides of one triangle are proportional to three sides of another triangle, the triangles are similar.

Given: $\triangle ABC$ and $\triangle DEF$ such that

$$\frac{DE}{AB} = \frac{EF}{BC} = \frac{DF}{AC} = k$$

Required to Prove: $\triangle ABC \sim \triangle DEF$

Analysis: Let $\triangle A'B'C'$ be the image of $\triangle ABC$ under a dilatation with scale factor k.
Prove that $\triangle A'B'C' \cong \triangle DEF$ and conclude that since $\triangle A'B'C' \sim \triangle ABC$, then $\triangle ABC \sim \triangle DEF$.

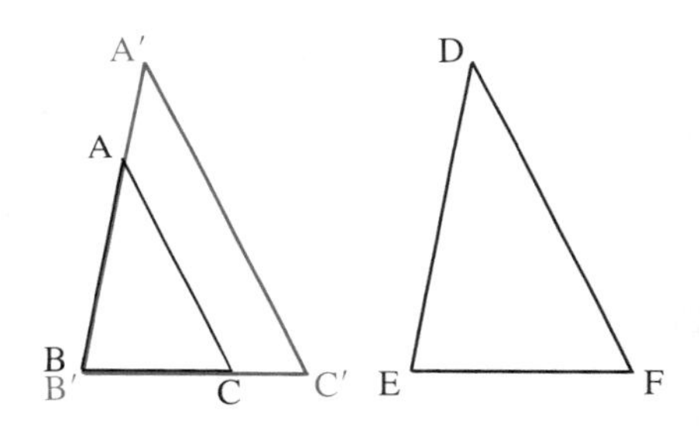

Proof:

Statement	Reason
1. $DE = kAB$, $EF = kBC$ and $DF = kAC$	Given
2. $\triangle A'B'C' \sim \triangle ABC$	Definition of $\triangle A'B'C'$
3. $A'B' = kAB$, $A'C' = kAC$ and $B'C' = kBC$	Scale Factor Axiom for Line Segments
4. In $\triangle A'B'C'$ and $\triangle DEF$	
$A'B' = DE$	Statements 1 and 3
$A'C' = DF$	Statements 1 and 3
$B'C' = EF$	Statements 1 and 3
5. Therefore, $\triangle A'B'C' \cong \triangle DEF$	SSS
6. $\triangle ABC \sim \triangle DEF$	Statements 2 and 5

The SSS congruence theorem asserts that two triangles are congruent if corresponding sides are equal, while the SSS similarity theorem asserts that two triangles are similar if corresponding sides are proportional.

The SAS congruence theorem asserts that if two sides of one triangle are congruent to two sides of another triangle and the contained angles are congruent, then the triangles are congruent. The following theorem asserts that if the condition that the sides are congruent is replaced by the condition that they are proportional, then the triangles are similar (and not necessarily congruent).

> **Side-Angle-Side Similarity Theorem (SAS~)**
> If two sides of one triangle are proportional to two sides of another triangle and the contained angles are congruent, then the two triangles are similar.

Given: $\triangle ABC$ and $\triangle DEF$ such that $\angle B = \angle E$ and $\frac{DE}{AB} = \frac{EF}{BC} = k$

Required to Prove: $\triangle ABC \sim \triangle DEF$
Analysis: Let $\triangle A'B'C'$ be the image of $\triangle ABC$ under a dilatation with scale factor k.

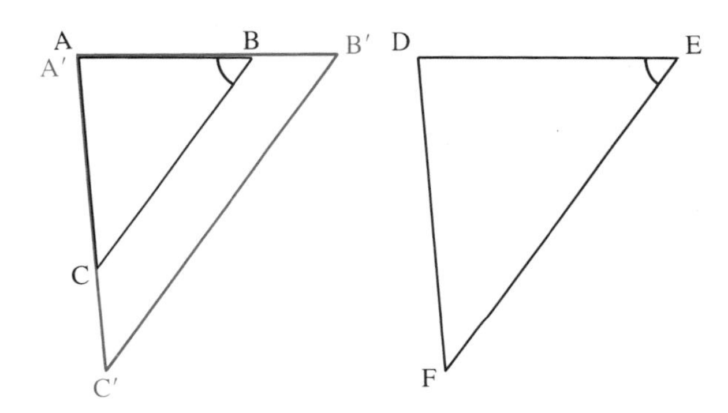

Proof:

Statement	Reason
1. $DE = kAB$ and $EF = kBC$	Given
2. $\angle E = \angle B$	Given
3. $\triangle A'B'C' \sim \triangle ABC$	Definition of $\triangle A'B'C'$
4. $A'B' = kAB$ and $B'C' = kBC$	Scale Factor Axiom for Line Segments
5. $\angle B = \angle B'$	Angle Invariance Axiom
6. In $\triangle A'B'C'$ and $\triangle DEF$	
$A'B' = DE$	Statements 1 and 4
$\angle A'B'C' = \angle DEF$	Statements 2 and 5
$B'C' = EF$	Statements 1 and 4
7. Therefore, $\triangle A'B'C' \cong \triangle DEF$	SAS
8. $\triangle ABC \sim \triangle DEF$	Statements 3 and 7

The three similarity theorems above are very useful for finding the lengths of unknown sides of a triangle or the measures of unknown angles. The following examples show how these theorems can be applied.

Example 1. To find the distance AB across a pond, a surveyor makes the measurements shown in the diagram. What is the distance from A to B?

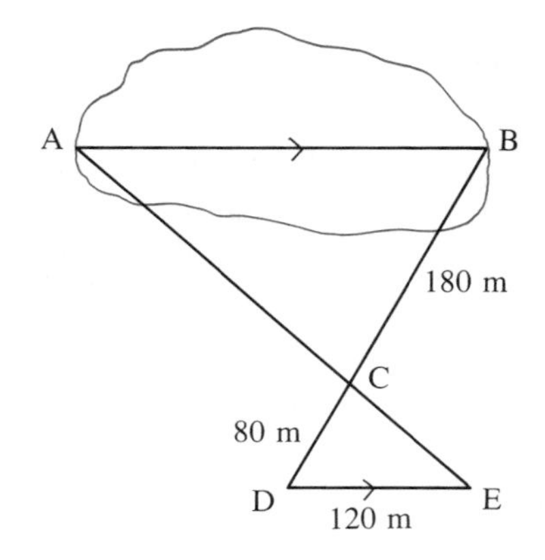

Solution. Since AB is parallel to DE, from the Parallel Lines Theorem

$\angle A = \angle E$ and $\angle B = \angle D$

From the Opposite Angles Theorem

$\angle ACB = \angle DCE$

Therefore, $\triangle ABC \sim \triangle EDC$ AAA ~

Then, $\dfrac{AB}{ED} = \dfrac{BC}{DC}$

Substitute the known values.

$$AB = 120\left(\frac{180}{80}\right)$$
$$= 270$$

The distance from A to B is 270 m.

Example 2. Two roads AB and AC intersect at 65°. Roads AB and BC intersect at 70°. AB and AC are respectively 375 m and 498 m. If D and E are locations on AB and AC respectively such that AD = 250 m and AE = 332 m, find the measure of $\angle AED$.

Solution. In $\triangle ADE$ and $\triangle ABC$

$$\frac{AD}{AB} = \frac{250}{375} = \frac{2}{3} \qquad \frac{AE}{AC} = \frac{332}{498} = \frac{2}{3}$$

So, $\dfrac{AD}{AB} = \dfrac{AE}{AC}$

The contained angle, $\angle A$, is common to $\triangle ADE$ and $\triangle ABC$.

Therefore, $\triangle ADE \sim \triangle ABC$ SAS ~

Then, $\angle AED = \angle ACB$

From the Sum of the Angles Theorem

$$\angle ACB = 180° - 65° - 70°$$
$$= 45°$$

$\angle AED = 45°$

EXERCISES 5-2

Ⓐ

1. Name the condition which guarantees similarity.
   a) $\triangle ABC \sim \triangle DEF$ b) $\triangle JKL \sim \triangle MNO$

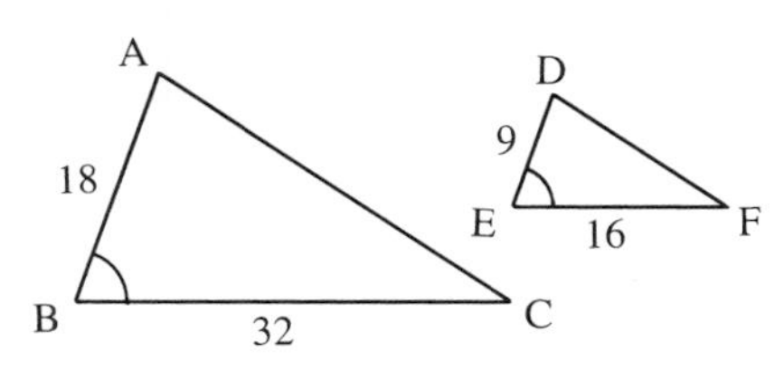

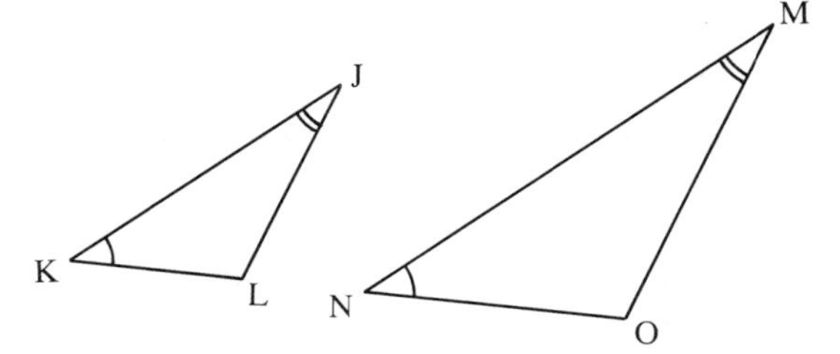

2. a) State the triangles that are similar and the condition for their similarity.
   b) State the proportions relating the sides of the triangles.
   i) ii)

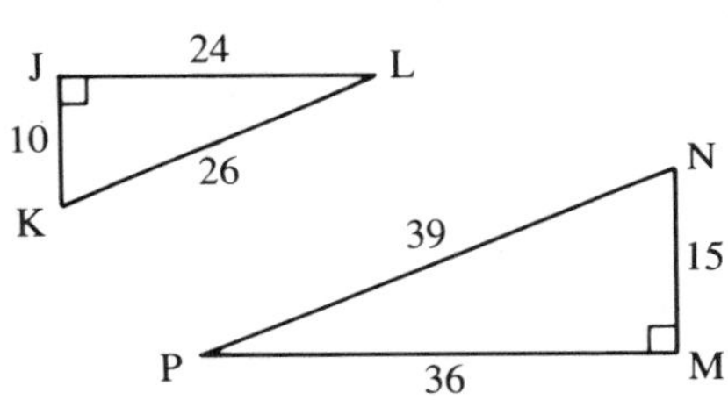

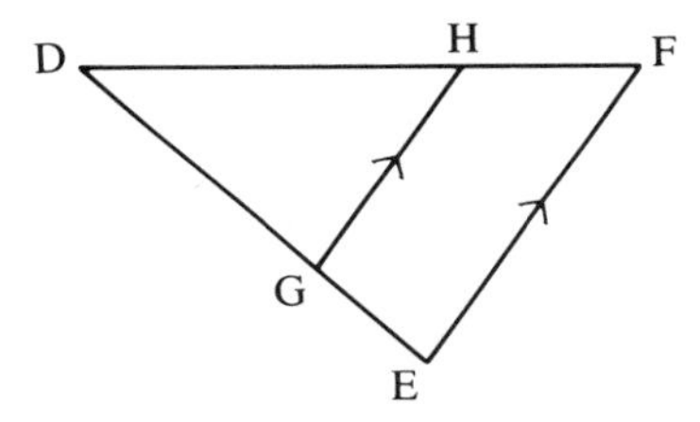

3. Find the values of x and y to 1 decimal place.
   a) $\triangle JKL \sim \triangle NML$ b) $\triangle PQR \sim \triangle PRS$

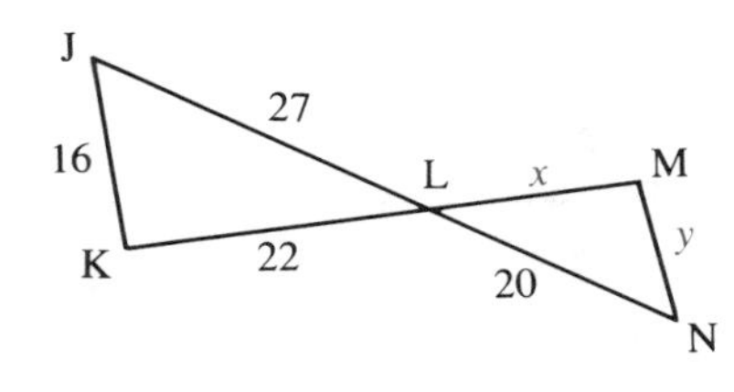

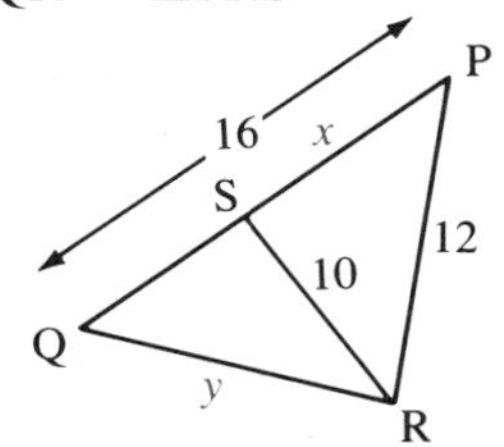

Ⓑ

4. In each diagram
   a) Identify two triangles that are similar and state the condition for their similarity.
   b) Find the values of x and y to 1 decimal place.
   i) ii) iii)

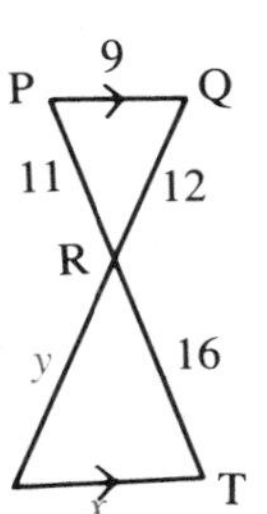

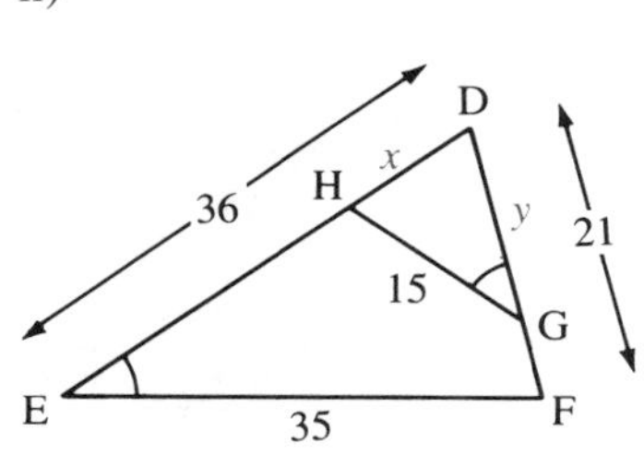

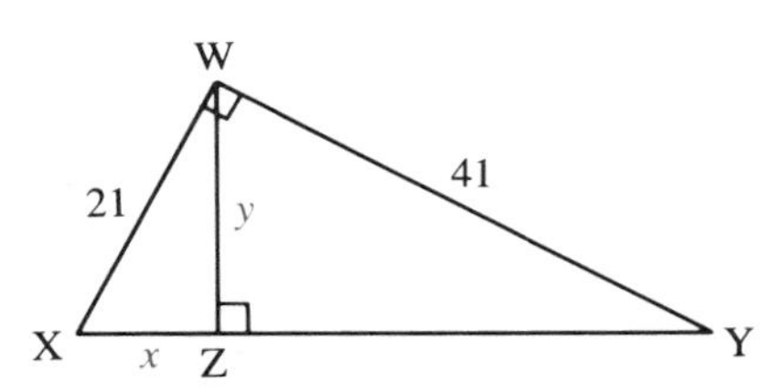

5. For the diagram (below left), list pairs of similar triangles and state why they are similar.

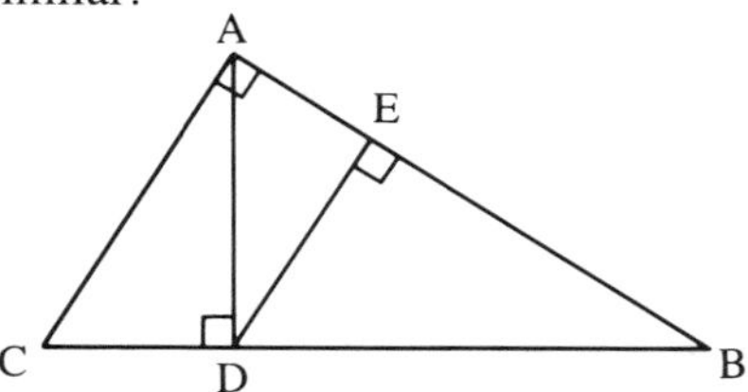

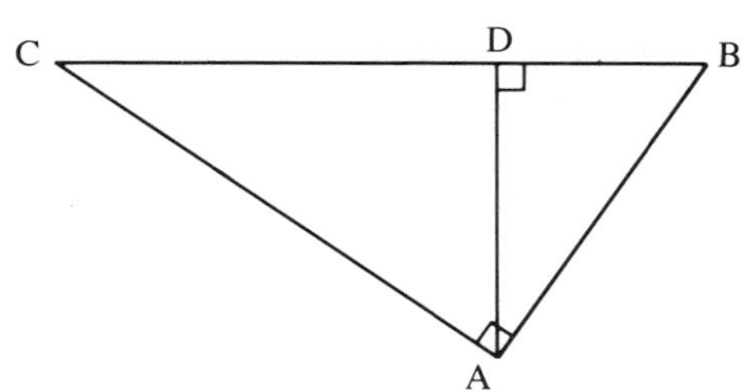

6. For the diagram (above right), prove that:
   a) $\triangle ABC \sim \triangle DBA$ b) $\triangle ABC \sim \triangle DAC$ c) $\triangle DBA \sim \triangle DAC$

7. Find the values of x and y to 1 decimal place.

a)

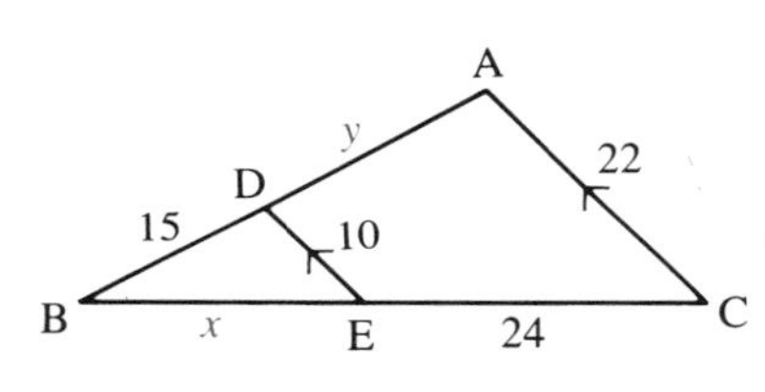

b)

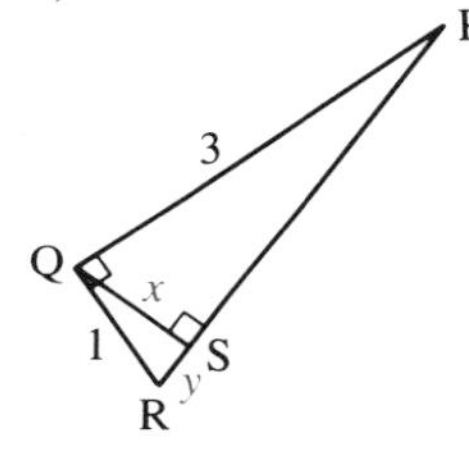

c)

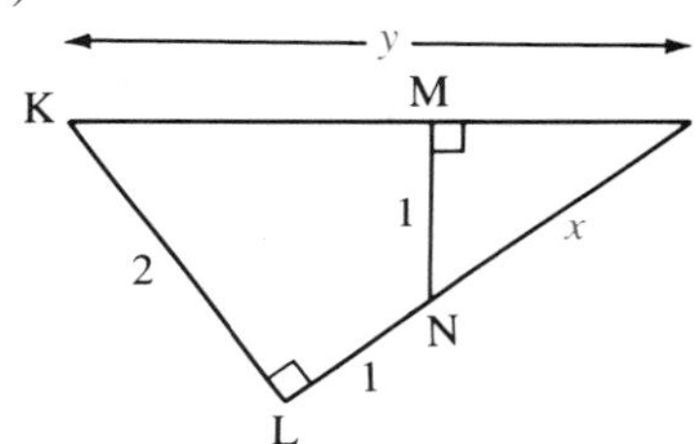

8. In rectangle ABCD, P is located on CD such that $\angle APB = 90°$ and $\dfrac{AP}{PB} = 2$.

   Find $\dfrac{AB}{AD}$.

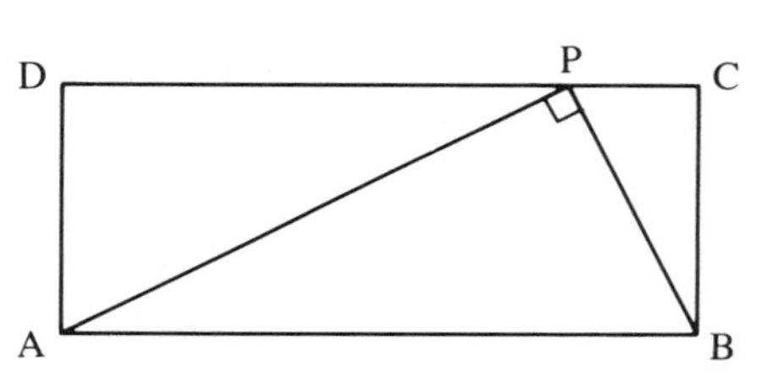

9. For each part
   a) Identify two similar triangles and prove that they are similar.
   b) Find the values of x and y to 1 decimal place.

i)

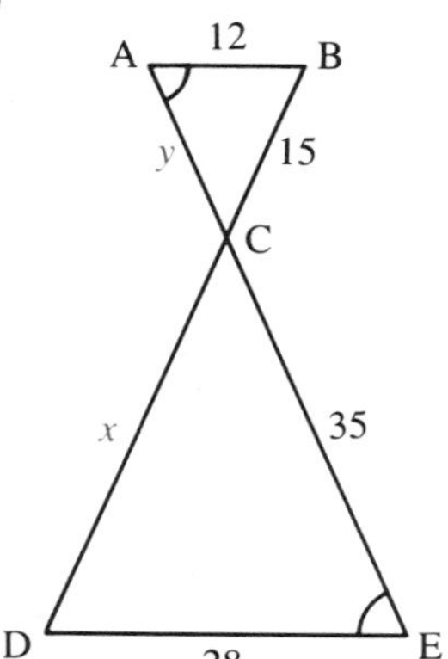

ii)

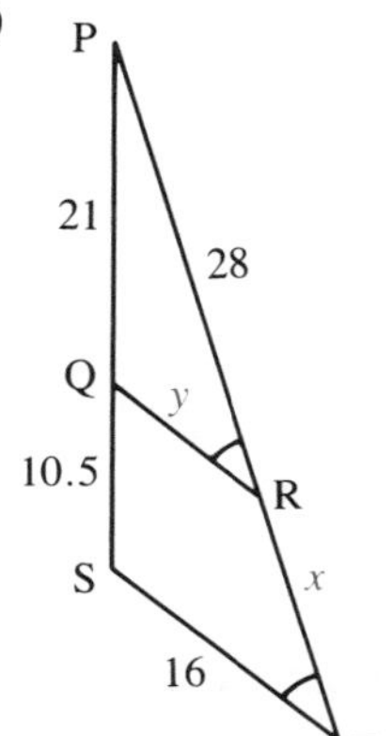

iii)

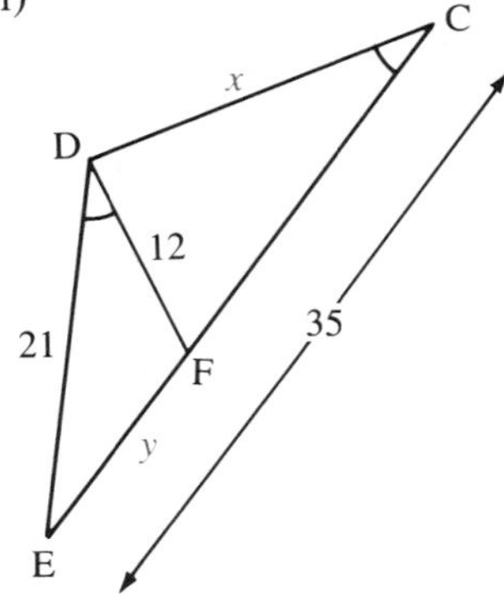

10. The diagram represents the blueprint for a cottage deck. The scale is 1:300.
    a) Find the dimensions of the deck.
    b) Find the area of the deck.

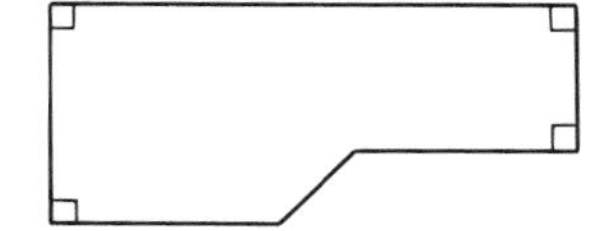

11. The base of a triangle has length b centimetres, and its altitude has length h centimetres. A rectangle of width x centimetres is inscribed in the triangle, with its length coinciding with the base of the triangle. Find the area of the rectangle in terms of b, h, and x.

12. A negative measuring 36 mm by 24 mm is enlarged to form a picture 16.2 cm by 10.8 cm. The image of a tower on the negative is 30.5 mm. How high is the tower in the picture?

13. On a blueprint, a triangular roof truss has dimensions 52 mm by 40 mm by 20 mm.
    a) If the actual length of the truss is 4.55 m, find the lengths of the two shorter sides.
    b) If the family room on the same blueprint measures 44 mm by 32 mm, what are its actual dimensions? (Assume that the scale is the same.)

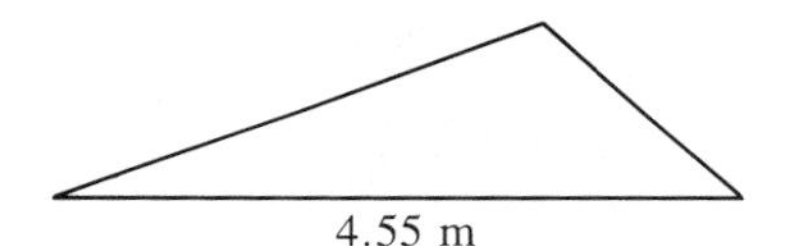

Ⓒ

14. From a window 2.5 m above the ground, Lisa notices that the top of a building B is in line with the top of a lamp post P. The lamp post is 5.5 m high, 6.9 m from Lisa, and 19.5 m from the building. How high is the building?

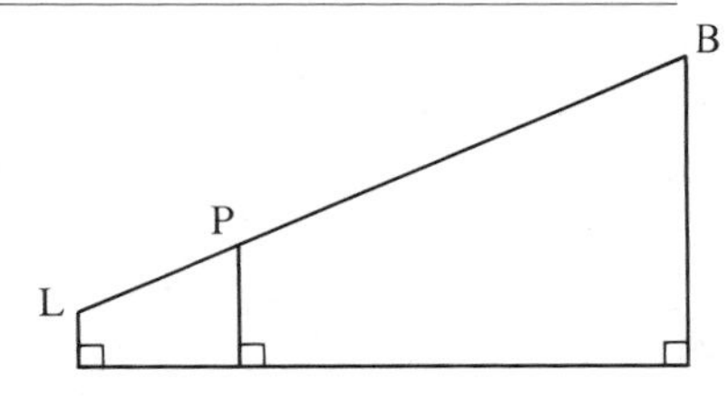

15. In $\triangle ABC$ (below left), EFG is parallel to BDC. Prove that $\frac{EF}{FG} = \frac{BD}{DC}$.

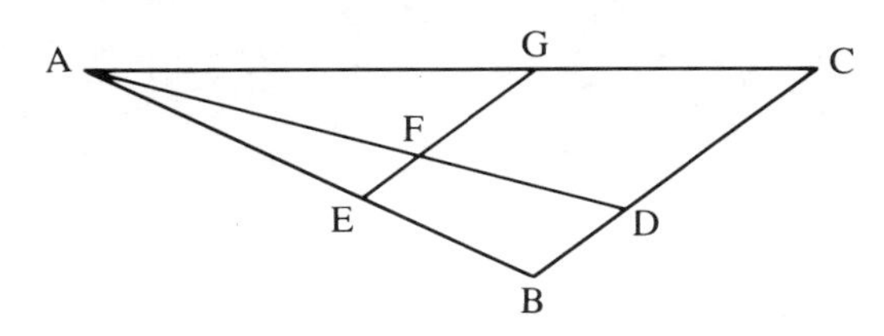

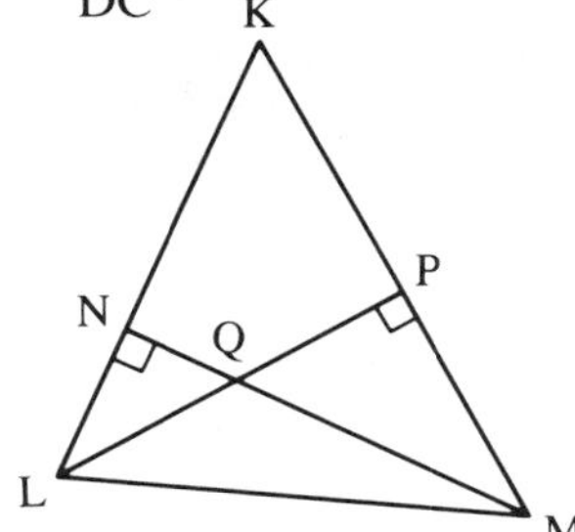

16. In $\triangle KLM$ (above right), prove that:
    a) $\frac{KL}{KM} = \frac{KP}{KN}$
    b) $\frac{NQ}{QP} = \frac{LQ}{QM}$.

17. E is the point of intersection of the diagonals of a trapezoid. Prove that E divides each diagonal into segments which are proportional to the segments of the other diagonal.

MATHEMATICS AROUND US

Aerial Photographs

Surveyors, town planners, engineers, rescue teams, and military personnel frequently use aerial photographs. The scale of a photograph, or *representative fraction* RF, must be known. It is related to the *photo distance* PD, and the *ground distance* GD by the formula $\text{RF} = \frac{\text{PD}}{\text{GD}}$.

To calculate the RF, the dimensions of a known object in the photograph, for example, a tennis court, can be compared with the actual dimensions of a tennis court.

If no ground distance can be determined, similar triangles can be used. The height h of the airplane, the focal length f of the camera lens, and the image size x on the negative are known.

When the photo is printed it is enlarged k times from the negative.

That is, $\text{PD} = kx$ or $\dfrac{x}{\text{PD}} = \dfrac{1}{k}$

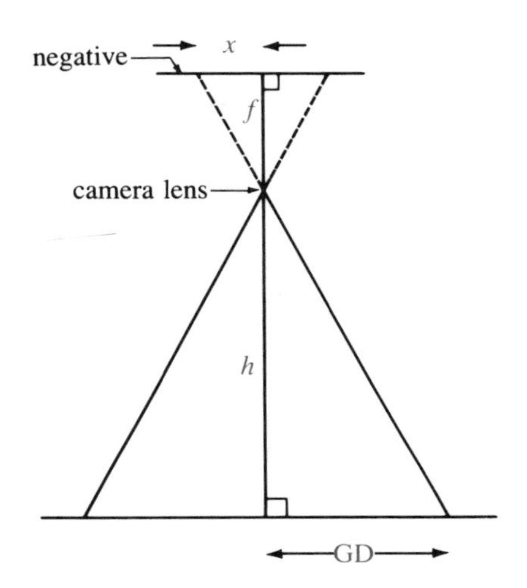

QUESTIONS

1. a) If a bridge, which is 450 m long, is 5 cm long on the photograph, what is the RF?
   b) On the same photograph, a river is 36.9 cm long. How long is the river?
   c) How large will a wheat field, measuring 800 m by 250 m, be on the photograph?
2. Use the diagram above to explain how would you find the GD, if you knew the values of h, f, and x.
3. How is the RF related to f and h?
4. a) A photograph taken at an altitude of 1000 m with a lens of focal length 150 mm is enlarged six times from the negative. What is the RF?
   b) On the photograph, a fence is 27.5 cm long. What is its actual length?
5. The terrain being photographed is hilly and the altitude varies from 950 m to 1050 m. How would this affect the RF?
6. The areas of regions on the ground, which have shapes that are regular geometric figures, can easily be calculated by measuring the photograph. What is the area of a hardwood bush measuring 5 cm by 10 cm on a 1 : 5000 photograph?
7. If the area is irregular in shape, a grid of uniformly spaced dots on a transparency can be laid over the photograph. If there are 25 dots/cm^2, the centres of the dots will be 0.2 cm apart. Each dot will represent 0.04 cm^2 of area.
   a) What area on the ground is represented by one dot on a grid in a 1 : 5000 photo?
   b) If 1435 dots are needed to cover a strip mine, how large is the mine?

5-3 THE SIDE-SPLITTING THEOREM

Though its name might suggest otherwise, there is nothing funny about the so-called "side-splitting" theorem. However, the application of this theorem to the mechanical device called the *pantograph* is somewhat amusing. By merely tracing the figure at F we obtain the enlargement at E.

The clue as to why the pantograph works is provided by the side-splitting theorem which we study in this section.

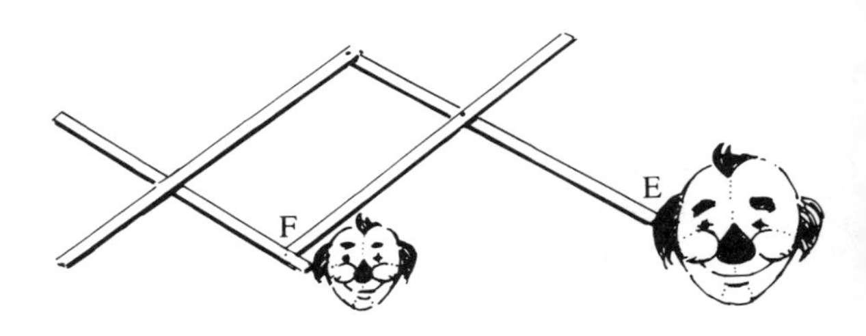

"Sport that wrinkled care derides
And laughter holding both his sides"
John Milton

> **Theorem**
> If a line is drawn parallel to one side of a triangle, through the midpoint of a second side, then it bisects the third side.

Given: $\triangle$ABC with line $\overleftrightarrow{DE}$ parallel to BC, and passing through the midpoint D of side AB
Required to Prove: AE = EC

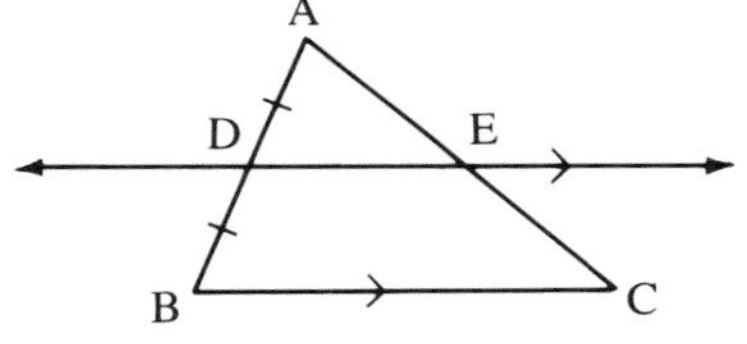

Proof:

Statement	Reason
DE is parallel to BC	Given
$\angle$ADE = $\angle$ABC	Parallel Lines Theorem
In $\triangle$ADE and $\triangle$ABC $\angle$A is common $\angle$ADE = $\angle$ABC	 Proved
Therefore, $\triangle$ADE ~ $\triangle$ABC	AA~
$\frac{AD}{AB} = \frac{AE}{AC}$	Similar triangles
$\frac{AD}{AB} = \frac{1}{2}$	D is the midpoint of AB
Therefore, $\frac{AE}{AC} = \frac{1}{2}$	
That is, $AE = \frac{1}{2}AC$	
Hence, AE = EC	

The theorem can help us understand how the pantograph works.
Suppose AC and CE are of equal length.
Suppose also that the pantograph is set so that B and D are the midpoints of AC and CE respectively and BF = FD = CD.
Then BCDF is a rhombus.
Therefore, BC is parallel to FD and CD is parallel to BF because opposite sides of a rhombus are parallel.
It follows from the theorem above that F is the midpoint of side AE of △CAE.

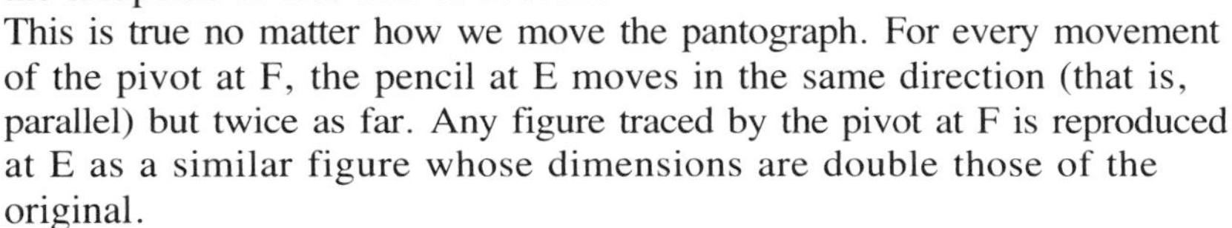

This is true no matter how we move the pantograph. For every movement of the pivot at F, the pencil at E moves in the same direction (that is, parallel) but twice as far. Any figure traced by the pivot at F is reproduced at E as a similar figure whose dimensions are double those of the original.

The theorem previously proved is a special case of the Proportionality Theorem. To state this theorem, we introduce the following definition.

Definition: The line DE divides AB and AC *proportionally* means that

$$\frac{AD}{DB} = \frac{AE}{EC} \quad \text{or} \quad \frac{AD}{AB} = \frac{AE}{AC}.$$

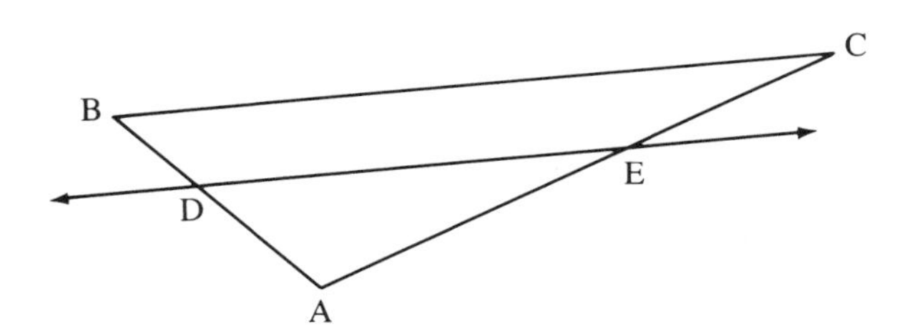

Proportionality Theorem
If a line is parallel to one side of a triangle and intersects the other two sides, then the line divides those two sides proportionally.

Given: △ABC with a line drawn parallel to BC, which intersects AB and AC respectively at points D and E.

Required to Prove: $\frac{AD}{DB} = \frac{AE}{EC}$

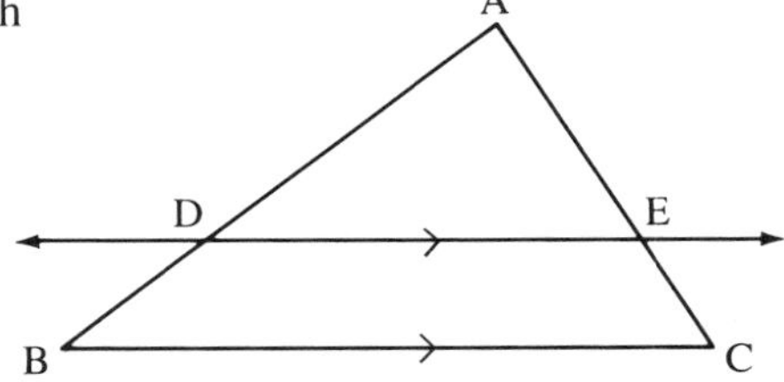

Proof:

Statement	Reason
DE is parallel to BC	Given
$\angle ADE = \angle ABC$	Parallel Lines Theorem
In $\triangle ABC$ and $\triangle ADE$	
$\angle A$ is common	
$\angle ABC = \angle ADE$	Proved
Therefore, $\triangle ABC \sim \triangle ADE$	AA~
$\frac{AB}{AD} = \frac{AC}{AE}$	Similar triangles
$\frac{AD + DB}{AD} = \frac{AE + EC}{AE}$	Expressing two sides as the sums of their parts
$1 + \frac{DB}{AD} = 1 + \frac{EC}{AE}$	Dividing
$\frac{DB}{AD} = \frac{EC}{AE}$	Subtracting 1 from both sides
$\frac{AD}{DB} = \frac{AE}{EC}$	Taking reciprocals

Example 1. Find the values of x and y.

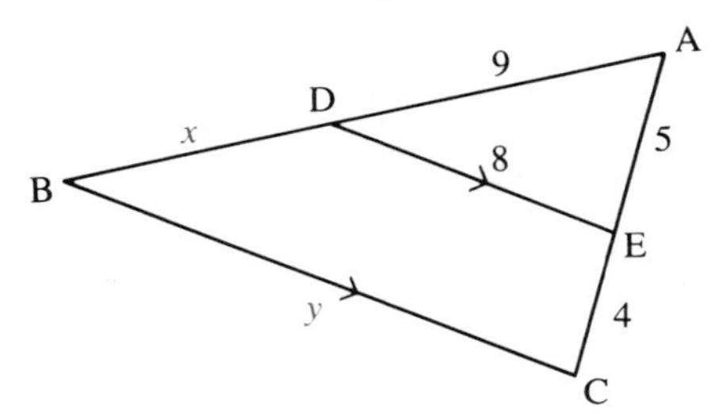

Solution. Since DE is parallel to BC, we can use the Proportionality Theorem.

$$\frac{AD}{DB} = \frac{AE}{EC}$$

$$\frac{9}{x} = \frac{5}{4}$$

$$x = 9\left(\frac{4}{5}\right)$$

$$= 7.2$$

In $\triangle ABC$ and $\triangle ADE$

$\angle A$ is common

Since DE is parallel to BC

$\angle ABC = \angle ADE$

Therefore, $\triangle ABC \sim \triangle ADE$ AA~

Hence, $\frac{BC}{AC} = \frac{DE}{AE}$

$$\frac{y}{9} = \frac{8}{5}$$

$$y = \frac{8}{5}(9)$$

$$= 14.4$$

In the solution of *Example 1*, the Proportionality Theorem could only be applied to the sides that were "split"; that is, to find x. For the third sides of the triangles, we had to use similar triangles to find y.

So far, the Parallel Lines Theorem is the only one we have for proving that lines are parallel. The converse of the Proportionality Theorem provides another way of proving lines or line segments parallel.

> **Converse of the Proportionality Theorem**
> If two sides of a triangle are divided proportionally, then the line segment joining the points of division is parallel to the third side.

Given: $\triangle$ABC with D and E on sides AB and AC respectively, such that

$$\frac{AB}{AD} = \frac{AC}{AE} = k$$

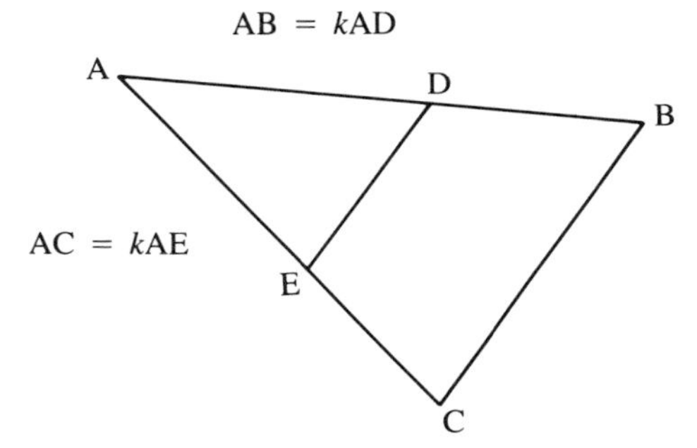

Required to Prove: DE is parallel to BC.
Proof:

Statement	Reason
In $\triangle$ADE and $\triangle$ABC	
$\frac{AB}{AD} = \frac{AC}{AE} = k$	Given
$\angle$A is common	
Therefore, $\triangle ADE \sim \triangle ABC$	SAS~
$\angle ADE = \angle ABC$	Similar triangles
DE is parallel to BC	Parallel Lines Theorem

We can combine the Proportionality Theorem and its converse into a single statement which we shall call the Side-Splitting Theorem.

> **Side-Splitting Theorem**
> Two sides of a triangle are divided proportionally iff the line segment joining the points of division is parallel to the third side.

Example 2. $\triangle ABC$ is a right triangle with sides AB = 10, AC = 24, and BC = 26. In which triangles is DE parallel to BC?

a)

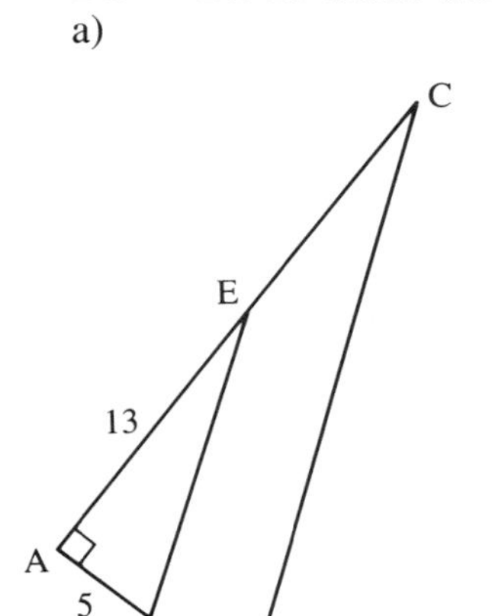

b)

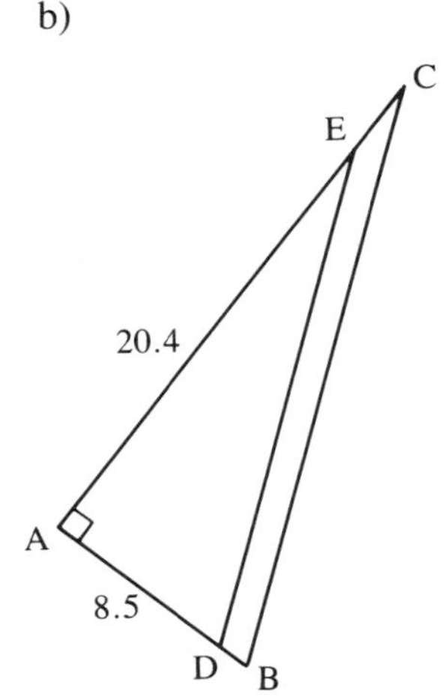

c)

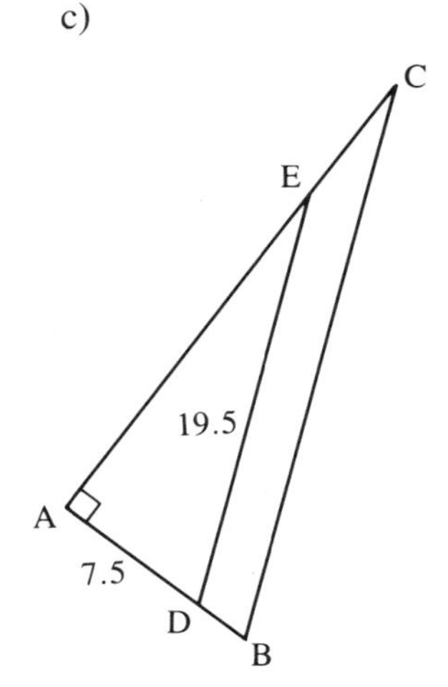

Solution. From the Side-Splitting Theorem, DE is parallel to BC if $\frac{AD}{AB} = \frac{AE}{AC}$.

That is;

a) Is $\frac{5}{10} = \frac{13}{24}$?

Comparing cross products

$(5)(24) \neq (13)(10)$

Hence, $\frac{5}{10} \neq \frac{13}{24}$, and DE is not parallel to BC.

b) Is $\frac{8.5}{10} = \frac{20.4}{24}$?

Comparing cross products

$(8.5)(24) = (20.4)(10)$

Hence, $\frac{8.5}{10} = \frac{20.4}{24}$, and DE is parallel to BC.

c) We cannot use the Side-Splitting Theorem because we do not know the length of AE.

However, DE is parallel to BC if $\triangle ADE \sim \triangle ABC$.

$\triangle ADE \sim \triangle ABC$ if $\frac{AD}{AB} = \frac{DE}{BC}$

That is, if $\frac{7.5}{10} = \frac{19.5}{26}$

Comparing cross products

$$(7.5)(26) = (19.5)(10)$$

Hence, $\frac{7.5}{10} = \frac{19.5}{26}$, and DE is parallel to BC.

EXERCISES 5-3

1. In $\triangle$ABC
   a) Are the sides AB and AC divided proportionally?
   b) Is DE parallel to BC?
   c) Do parts a) and b) illustrate a contradiction of the Side-Splitting Theorem? Explain your answer.

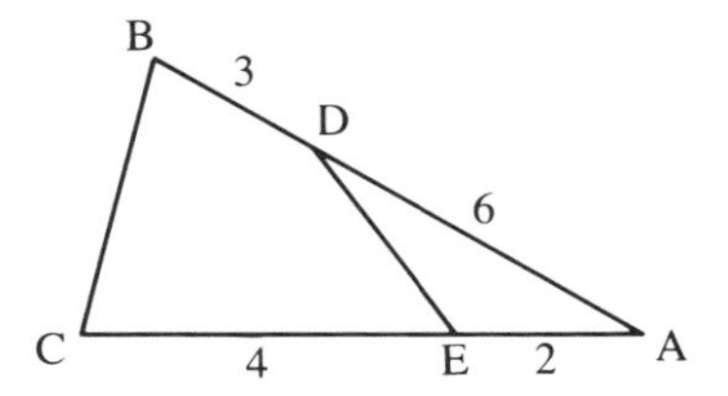

2. Find each value of x.

a)

7
10
7
x

b)

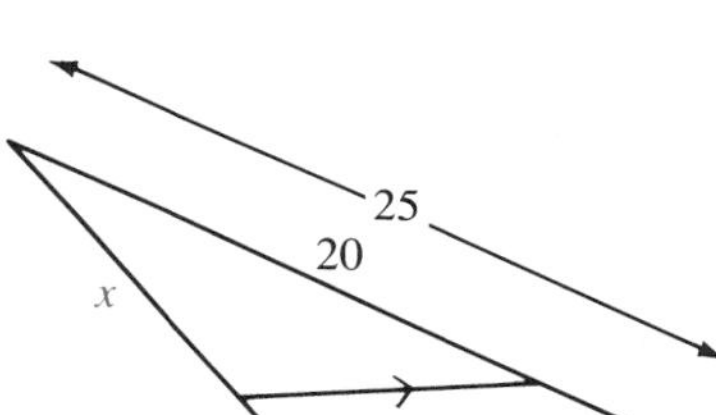

c)

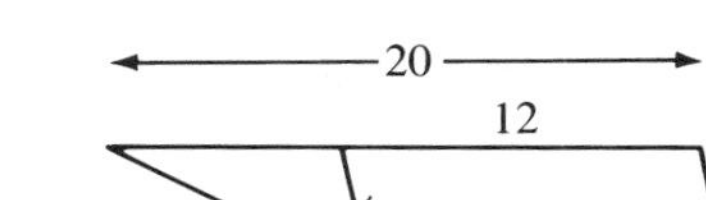

3. Is DE parallel to BC?

a)

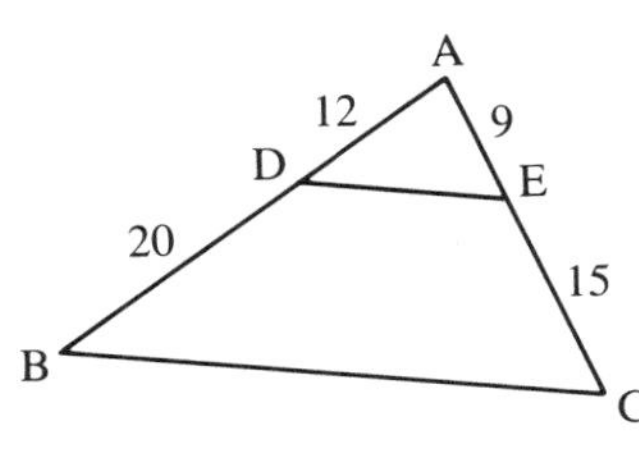

b)

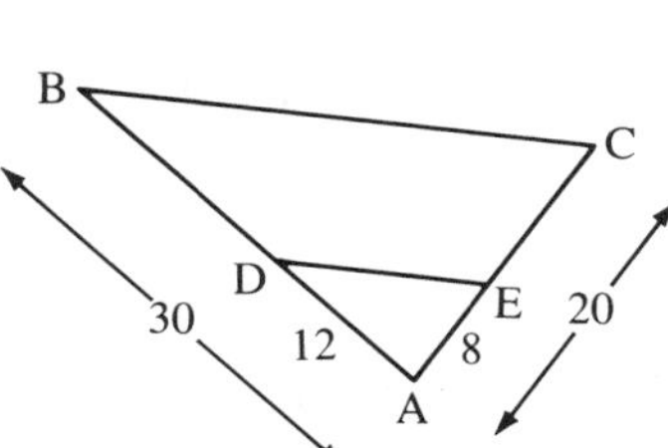

c)

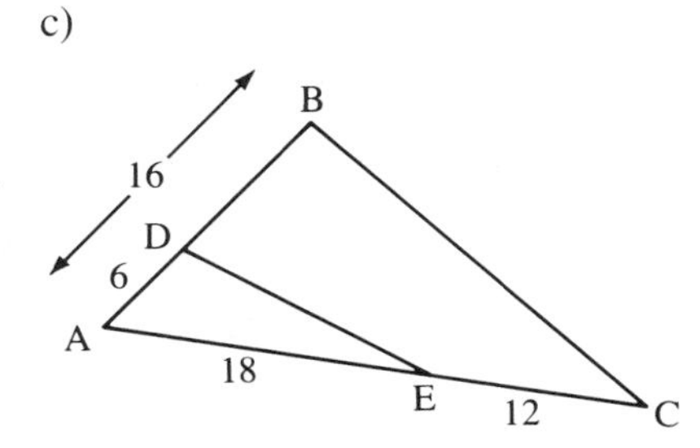

4. In $\triangle$ABC (below left), DE is parallel to BC.
   a) Find the value of x.
   b) If DE is 12 cm, how long is BC?

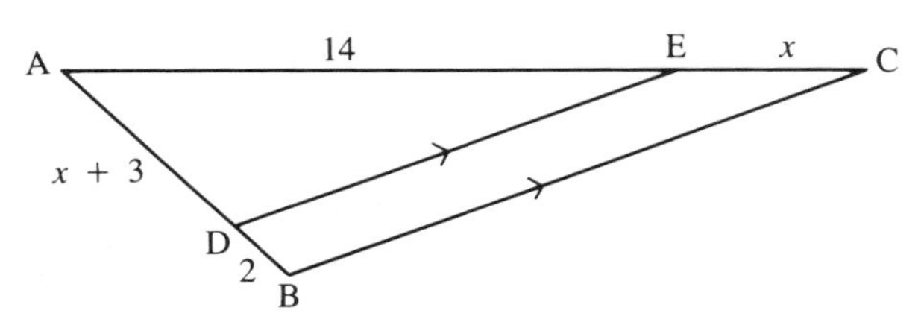

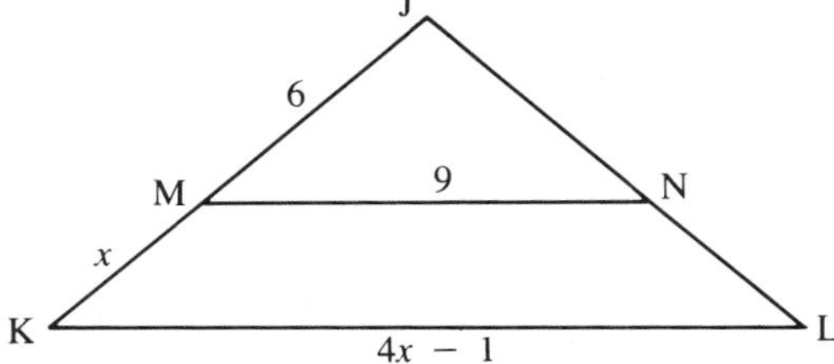

5. Triangle JKL is similar to $\triangle$JMN (above right).
   a) Find the value of x.
   b) If JL is 10 cm, how long is NL?

B

6. For each condition shown, state whether ST is parallel to QR.

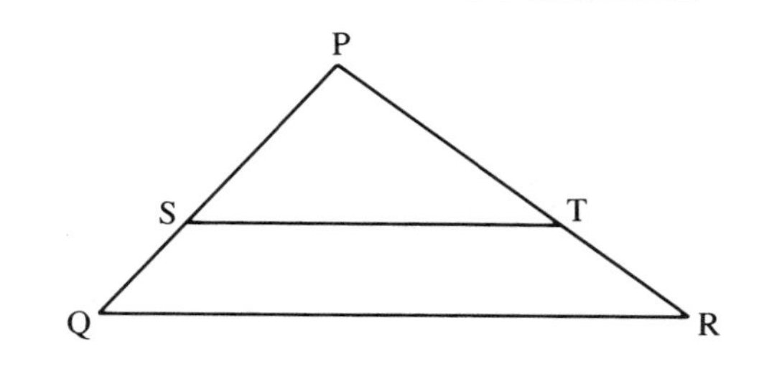

a) $\frac{PS}{PQ} = \frac{PT}{PR}$ b) $\frac{PS}{QS} = \frac{PR}{PT}$

c) $\frac{QS}{PQ} = \frac{RT}{PR}$ d) $\frac{PQ}{PS} = \frac{PR}{PT}$

e) $\frac{PS}{PT} = \frac{QS}{RT}$ f) $\frac{PS}{PR} = \frac{PT}{PQ}$

7. Triangle ABC (below left) has an area of 900 cm^2. Find the areas of $\triangle$ADE if AB = 50 cm and AD has these lengths.

a) 25 cm b) 30 cm c) 40 cm d) 20 cm

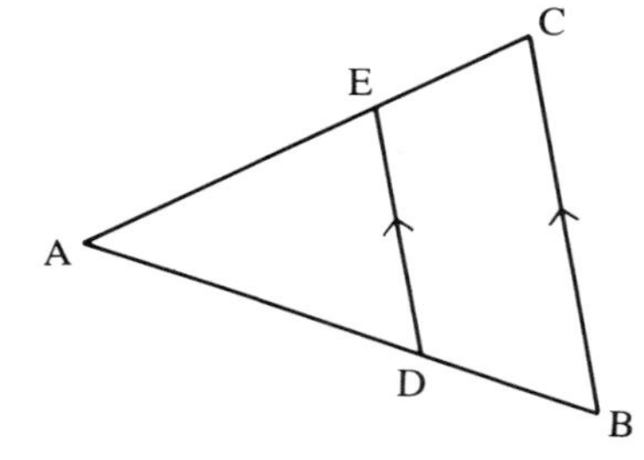

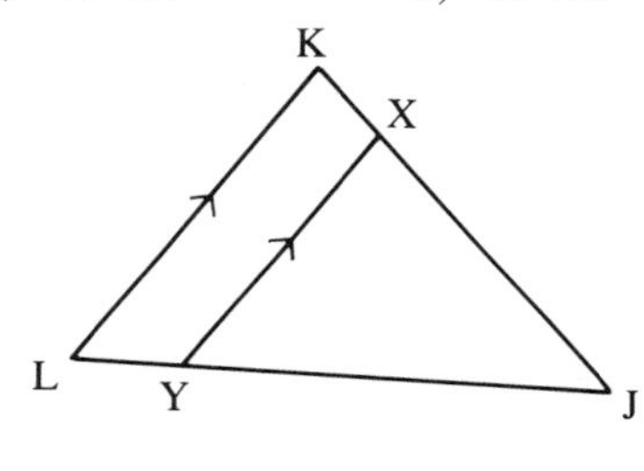

8. Triangle JKL (above right) has an area of 3600 mm^2. XY is parallel to KL. Find the values of $\frac{JX}{JK}$ if $\triangle$JXY has these areas.

a) 900 mm^2 b) 144 mm^2 c) 2025 mm^2 d) 2304 mm^2

9. P, Q, and R are the midpoints of the sides of $\triangle$XYZ. Find the areas of $\triangle$PQR if $\triangle$XYZ has these areas.

a) 72 cm^2 b) 200 cm^2 c) 122 cm^2 d) 525 cm^2

10. In trapezoid PQRS (below left), PS, XY, and QR are parallel; $\frac{QZ}{ZS} = \frac{3}{2}$, PQ = 20 cm, and RS = 28 cm. Find the lengths of PX and RY.

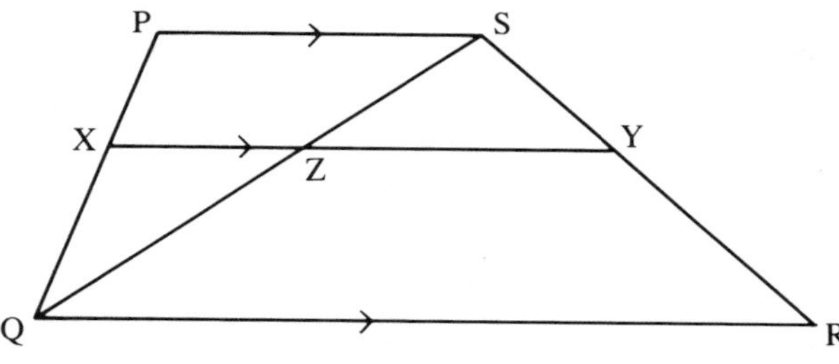

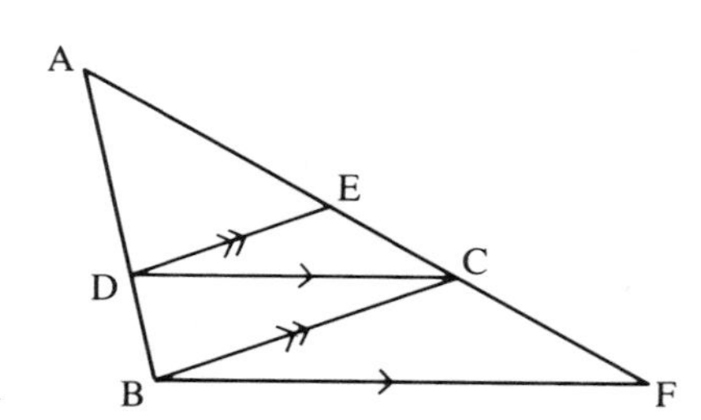

11. In the diagram (above right), prove that $\frac{AC}{EC} = \frac{AF}{CF}$.

12. In the pantograph, the point F moves:
    i) 5 cm ii) 12 cm. For each of these distances, how far does E move if:
    a) AB = BC
    b) AB = 6 cm, BC = 18 cm
    c) AB = 4 cm, AC = 12 cm
    d) AC = 15 cm, BC = 9 cm.

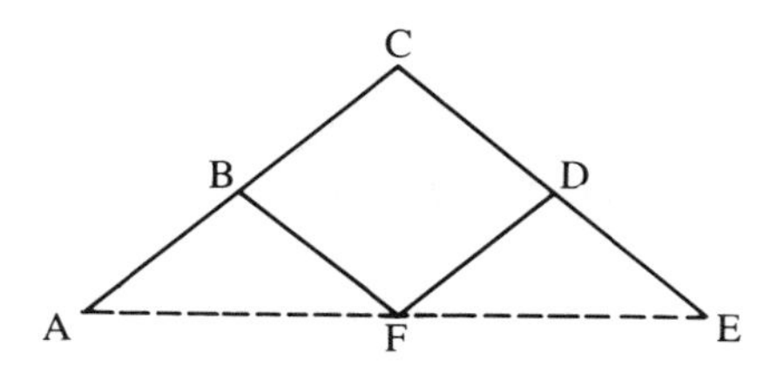

13. In the diagram (below left), ST is parallel to QR and ST bisects $\angle PSR$. Prove that $\frac{PS}{SR} = \frac{PT}{TR}$.

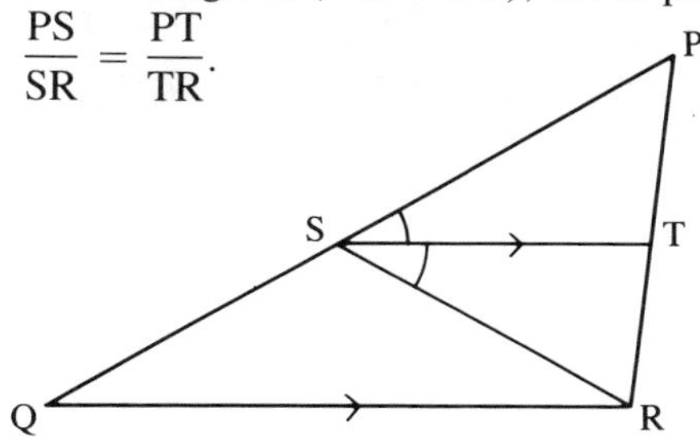

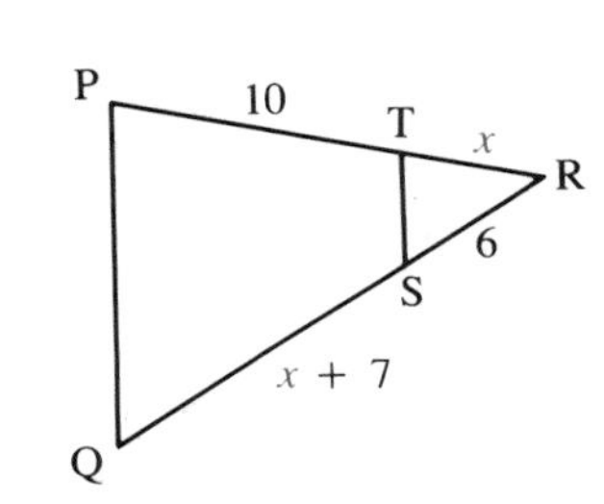

14. In the diagram (above right), $\triangle PQR$ is similar to $\triangle TSR$.
    a) Find the value of x.
    b) If PQ = 18 cm, find the length of ST.

15. a) Prove that $\triangle ABC \sim \triangle DEC$.
    b) If DE = 10 cm, find the length of AB to the nearest centimetre.
    c) If the area of $\triangle DEC$ is 440 cm^2, find the area of quadrilateral ABED to the nearest square centimetre.

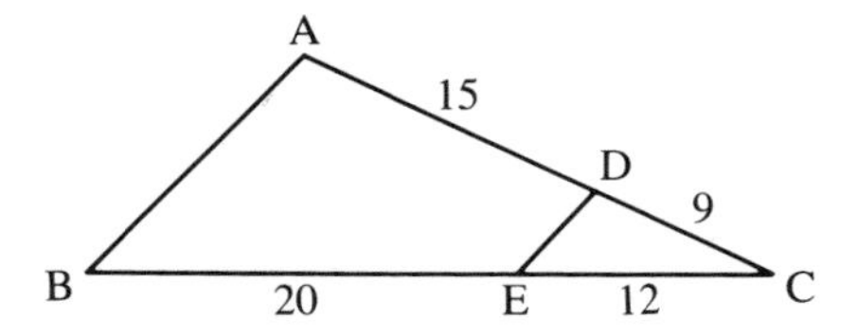

Ⓒ

16. In $\triangle ABC$ (below left), G and E trisect AC; D and F divide AB and CB respectively in the ratio 2 : 1. Find the ratio of the area of $\triangle GHE$ to the area of $\triangle ABC$.

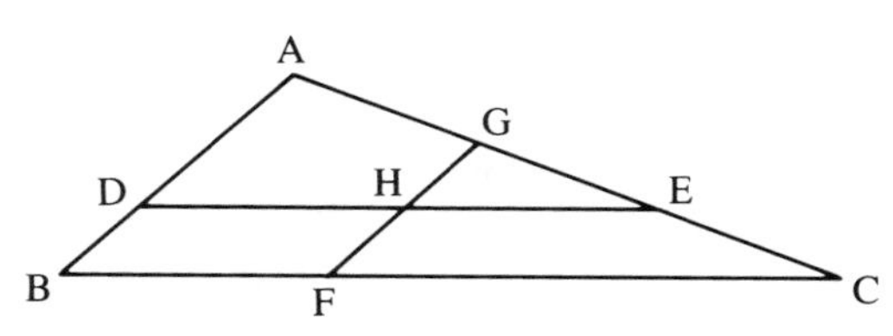

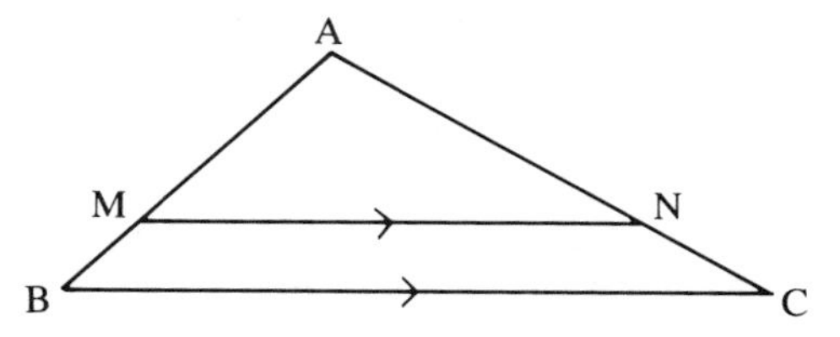

17. In $\triangle ABC$ (above right), MN is parallel to BC and divides $\triangle ABC$ into two regions with equal areas. Find these ratios. a) MN : BC b) AN : NC

18. In $\triangle XYZ$, MN is parallel to YZ and PQ is parallel to XY. Both MN and PQ divide $\triangle XYZ$ into regions with equal areas. If $\triangle XYZ$ has an area of k square centimetres, find an expression for the area of each of the four regions.

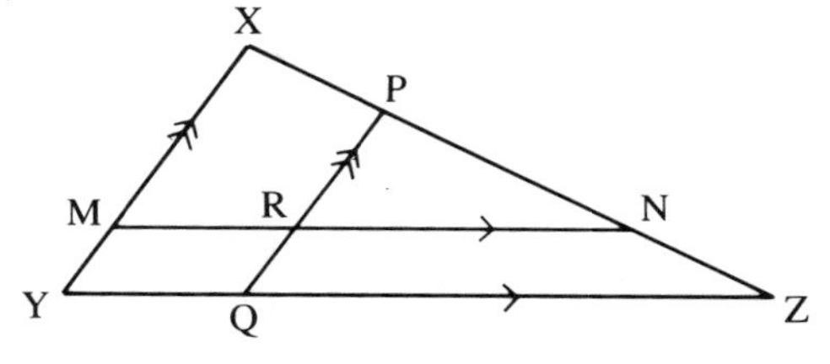

5-4 THE MEAN PROPORTIONAL THEOREM

How high is the moon above the Earth?

We can say that the surface of the moon is about 380 000 km above the Earth's surface, but this does not provide us with a visual sense of this height. Sometimes it is helpful to make comparisons such as this. "The height of the moon above the Earth is to the height of the CN tower as the height of the CN tower is to the height (thickness) of a dime."

That is, $\frac{\text{height of the moon}}{\text{height of the CN tower}} = \frac{\text{height of the CN tower}}{\text{height of a dime}}$

This equation is a proportion in which the denominator of one ratio is the same as the numerator of the other ratio. That is, it has the form

$$\frac{a}{b} = \frac{b}{c}.$$

The common element b is called the *mean proportional* between a and c. In the example above, we say that the height of the CN tower is the mean proportional between the thickness of a dime and the height of the moon.

In general, if b is the mean proportional between a and c, then

$$\frac{a}{b} = \frac{b}{c}$$

$$b^2 = ac$$

That is, $b = \pm\sqrt{ac} \quad ac \geqslant 0$

This shows that there are two mean proportionals between any two non-zero numbers with the same sign.

The mean proportional is sometimes called the *geometric mean*.

Mean Proportional Theorem

The perpendicular to the hypotenuse of a right triangle from the opposite vertex is the mean proportional between the segments into which it divides the hypotenuse.

Given: Right $\triangle$ABC, where AD is the perpendicular from A to the hypotenuse BC

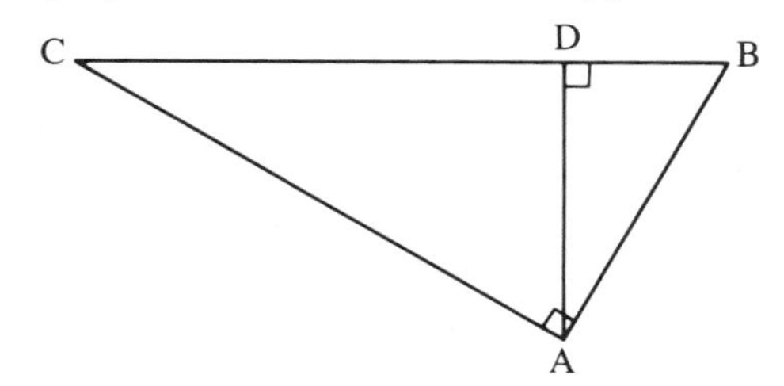

Required to Prove: $\frac{BD}{AD} = \frac{AD}{CD}$

Proof:

Statement	Reason
In $\triangle ABC$ and $\triangle DBA$	
$\angle A = \angle D$	Given right angles
$\angle B$ is common	
Therefore, $\triangle ABC \sim \triangle DBA$	AA~
Similarly, $\triangle ABC \sim \triangle DAC$	AA~
Therefore, $\triangle DBA \sim \triangle DAC$	
$\frac{BD}{AD} = \frac{AD}{CD}$	Similar triangles

> **Corollary of the Mean Proportional Theorem**
> Each of the shorter sides of a right triangle is the mean proportional between the adjacent segment of the hypotenuse and the hypotenuse.

In $\triangle ABC$

$$\frac{BD}{BA} = \frac{BA}{BC} \quad \text{and} \quad \frac{CD}{CA} = \frac{CA}{CB}$$

The proof of this corollary is left to the exercises.

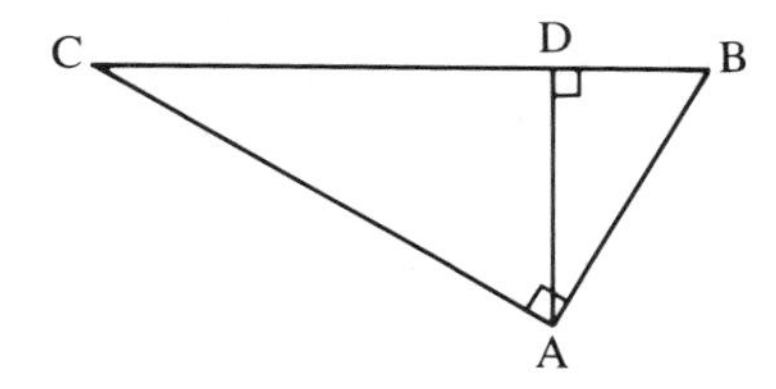

Example 1. Find each value of x.

a)

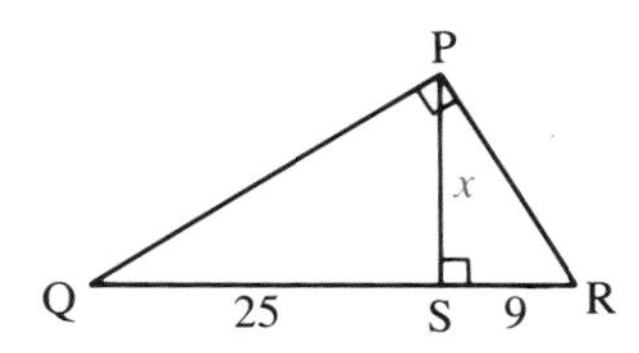

b)

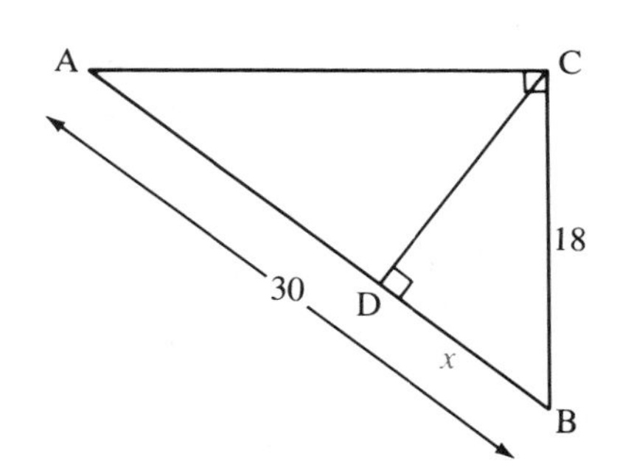

Solution.

a) From the Mean Proportional Theorem

$$\frac{QS}{PS} = \frac{PS}{RS}$$

$$\frac{25}{x} = \frac{x}{9}$$

$$x^2 = 225$$

$$x = 15$$

b) From the corollary of the Mean Proportional Theorem

$$\frac{BD}{BC} = \frac{BC}{BA}$$

$$\frac{x}{18} = \frac{18}{30}$$

$$x = 10.8$$

Example 2. Prove the Pythagorean Theorem using the Mean Proportional Theorem.

Solution. Draw right $\triangle ABC$ with $\angle A = 90°$.
Draw the altitude AD.
Label the lengths as indicated.
In $\triangle ABC$, the Pythagorean Theorem states that $a^2 = b^2 + c^2$.
To prove this, use the corollary of the Mean Proportional Theorem.

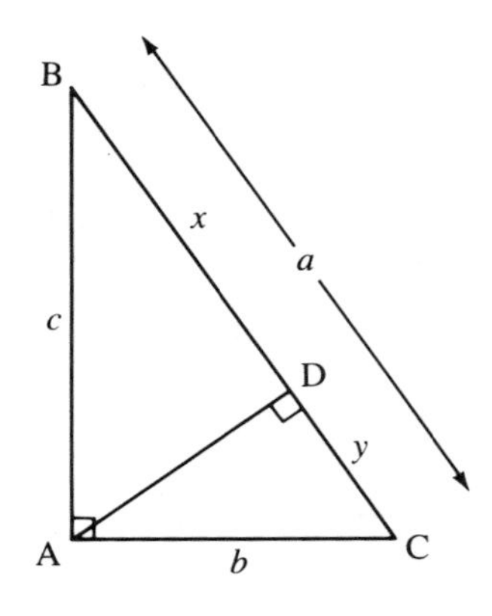

$\frac{y}{b} = \frac{b}{a}$ and $\frac{x}{c} = \frac{c}{a}$

$b^2 = ay$ . . . ① $c^2 = ax$ . . . ②

Add ① and ②.

$$\begin{aligned} b^2 + c^2 &= ax + ay \\ &= a(x + y) \\ &= a(a) \\ &= a^2 \end{aligned}$$

Hence, $a^2 = b^2 + c^2$

Example 3. In rectangle ABCD, AE and CF are perpendiculars from A and C to the diagonal BD. Find an expression for the length of EF.

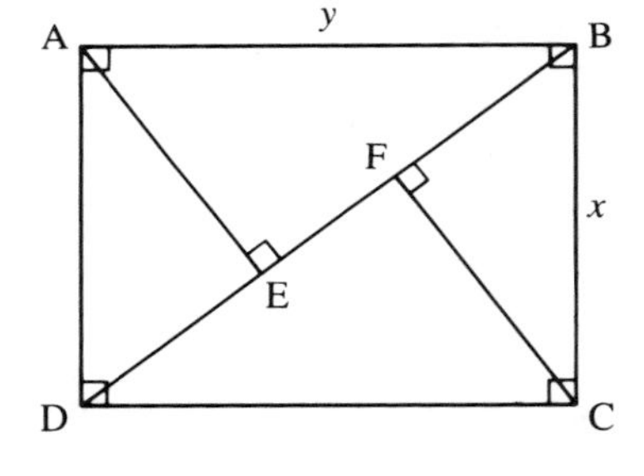

Solution. From the corollary of the Mean Proportional Theorem

In $\triangle ABD$

$$\frac{BE}{BA} = \frac{BA}{BD}$$

$$BE = \frac{BA^2}{BD} = \frac{y^2}{BD}$$

In $\triangle BCD$

$$\frac{BF}{BC} = \frac{BC}{BD}$$

$$BF = \frac{BC^2}{BD} = \frac{x^2}{BD}$$

$$EF = BE - BF = \frac{y^2}{BD} - \frac{x^2}{BD}$$

$$EF = \frac{y^2 - x^2}{BD} \quad . . . ①$$

From the Pythagorean Theorem in $\triangle BCD$

$BD = \sqrt{x^2 + y^2}$ . . . ②

Substitute from ② into ①.

$$EF = \frac{y^2 - x^2}{\sqrt{x^2 + y^2}}$$

EXERCISES 5-4

(A)

1. Find the mean proportionals between each pair of numbers.
   a) 2 and 8 b) 9 and 4 c) 4 and 16
   d) 3 and 27 e) 9 and 16 f) 8 and 50
2. Find the mean proportionals between each pair of terms.
   a) 6 and 10 b) -12 and -20 c) $4a$ and $18a$
   d) mn and $\frac{m}{n}$ e) $15xy$ and $75x$ f) $-\frac{18s^2}{t}$ and $-\frac{8t^2}{s}$
3. b is the mean proportional between a and c. If $b = 30$, find the value of c for each value of a.
   a) 25 b) -12 c) 50 d) 45 e) -150 f) -10

(B)

4. Find two numbers which have a mean proportional of 4 and a sum of 10.
5. Find two numbers which have a mean proportional of 12 and a difference of 45.
6. The length of a virus is to the length of a shoelace as the length of the shoelace is to the length of the St. Lawrence River. If the lengths of the shoelace and the St. Lawrence River are approximately 60 cm and 3000 km, about how long is the virus?
7. The mass of a 320 kg polar bear is to the mass of a 6300 kg elephant as the mass of the elephant is to the mass of a blue whale. What is the mass of the blue whale?
8. Find each value of x to 1 decimal place.
   a)

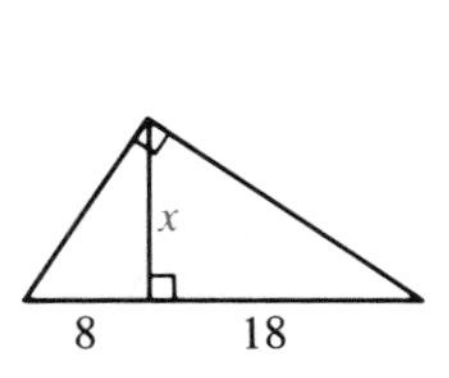

b)

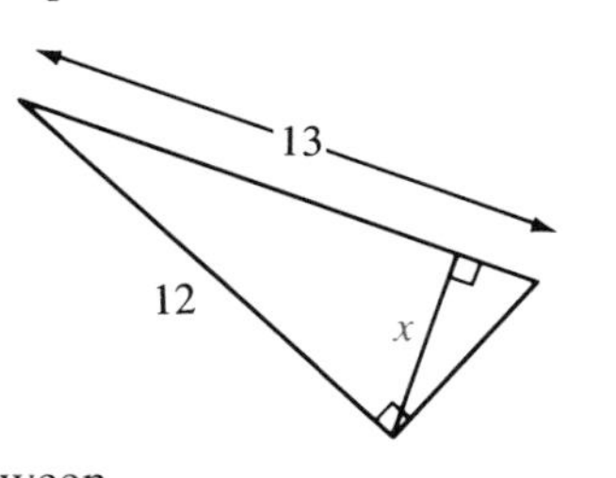

c)

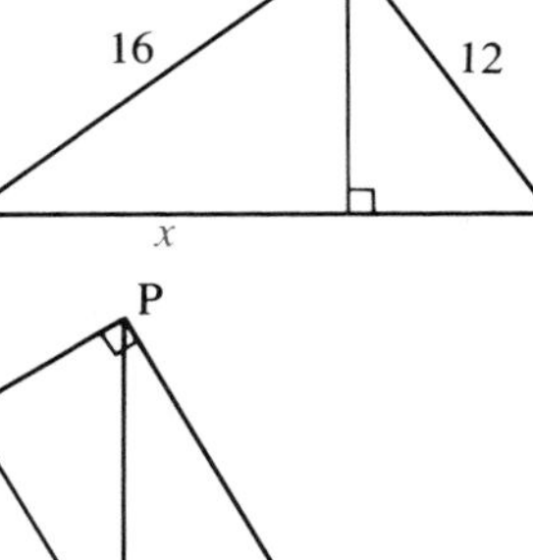

9. Name the mean proportional between each pairs of sides.
   a) QS and RS b) QS and QR
   c) PT and QT d) RS and RQ
   e) PT and PQ f) QT and PQ

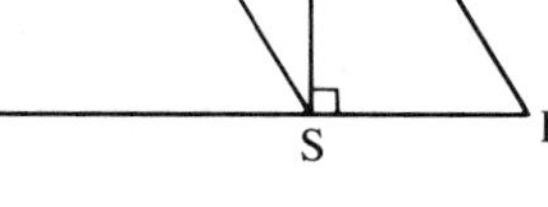

10. Find the values of x and y to 1 decimal place.
    a)

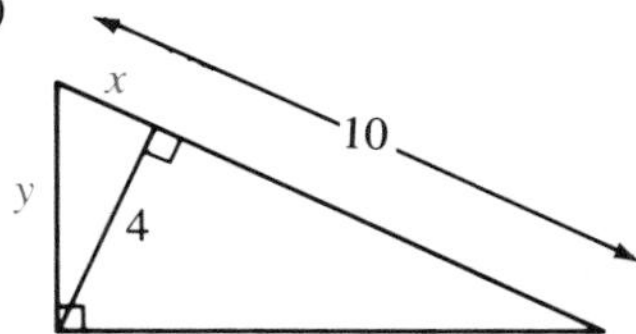

b)

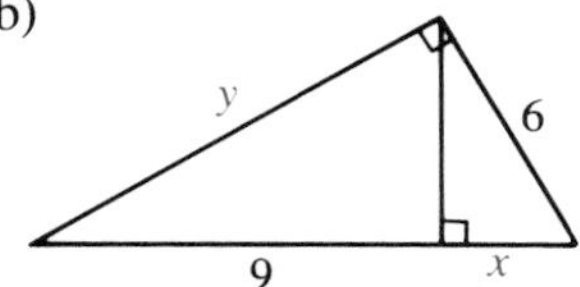

c)

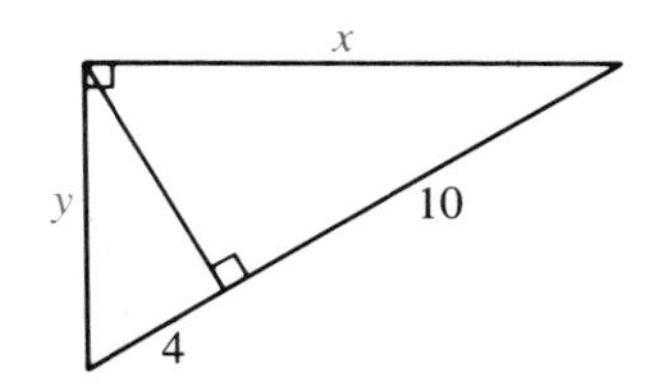

11. A 35 cm cord is divided into three pieces such that the ratio of the lengths of the shortest to the longest is 1 : 4. The length of the middle piece is the mean proportional between the other two pieces. Find the lengths of the pieces.

12. Brubacker, Martin, and Weber are partners in a business which makes a profit of \$61 420. The ratio of Brubacker's share to Weber's share is 9 : 16. Martin's share is the mean proportional of the other two shares. How much does each partner receive?

13. In $\triangle ABC$ (below left), $\angle C = 90°$, and CD is perpendicular to AB.
   a) If CD is 12 cm and AD : DB = 3 : 1, find the length of AD.
   b) If AD is 9 cm and DB is 7 cm, find the area of $\triangle ABC$.
   Give the answers to the nearest whole number.

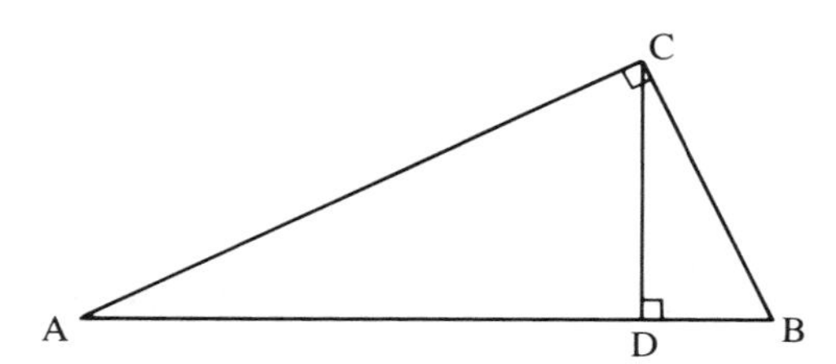

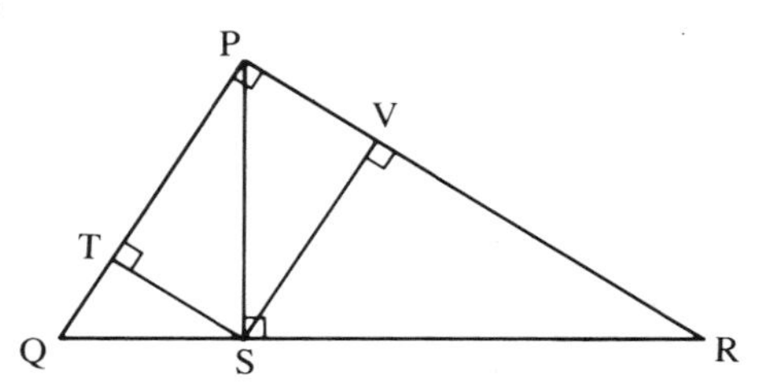

14. In $\triangle PQR$ (above right), $\angle P = 90°$, PS is perpendicular to QR, TS is perpendicular to PQ, and SV is perpendicular to PR.
   Show that the area of the rectangle PTSV $= \sqrt{QT \times TP \times PV \times VR}$.

15. Prove the corollary of the Mean Proportional Theorem.

Ⓒ

16. A chambered nautilus shell (below left), can be approximated by a sequence of perpendicular line segments. Prove that the length of each segment is the geometric mean between the lengths of the preceding and succeeding segments.

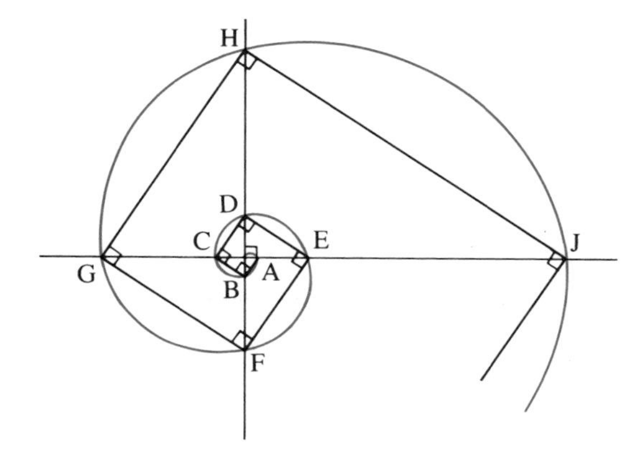

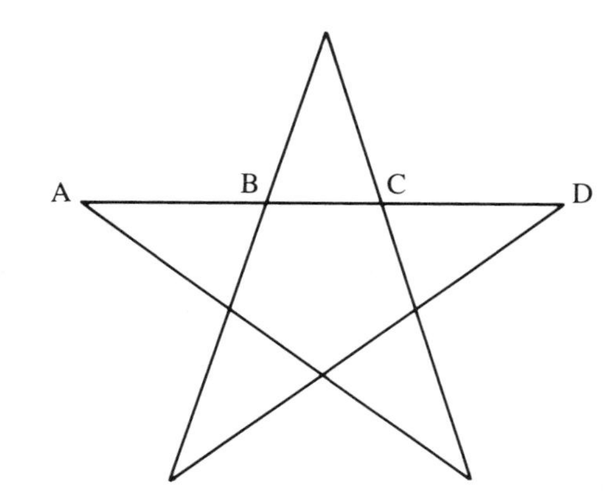

17. If the sides of a regular pentagon are extended (above right), a five-pointed star is formed. If AB is the mean proportional between BC and AC, show that AC is the mean proportional between AB and AD.

5-5 APPLICATIONS OF SIMILAR TRIANGLES

The properties of similar triangles are used in many applications, such as optics, electromagnetic theory, astronomy, and engineering.

The fact that the lengths of corresponding sides of similar figures are proportional is perhaps the most useful and powerful property of similarity. The following examples and exercises hint at the diversity of the applications.

Example 1. To estimate the height of a tree, a forester held a metre stick perpendicular to the ground and observed the length of its shadow was 72 cm. Then she measured the length of the tree's shadow as 18.5 m. What was the approximate height of the tree?

Solution. Since the heights of the metre stick and the tree were measured at the same time, the sun's rays striking the tree are parallel to the rays striking the metre stick.

In $\triangle TRE$ and $\triangle T'R'E'$

From the Parallel Lines Theorem

$\angle TRE = \angle T'R'E'$

Since TE and T′E′ are vertical

$\angle TER = \angle T'E'R' = 90°$

Therefore, $\triangle TRE \sim \triangle T'R'E'$ AA~

Hence, $\frac{TE}{T'E'} = \frac{RE}{R'E'}$

Substitute the known values.

$$\frac{TE}{1} = \frac{18.5}{0.72}$$

$$TE \doteq 25.69$$

The tree is about 25.7 m high.

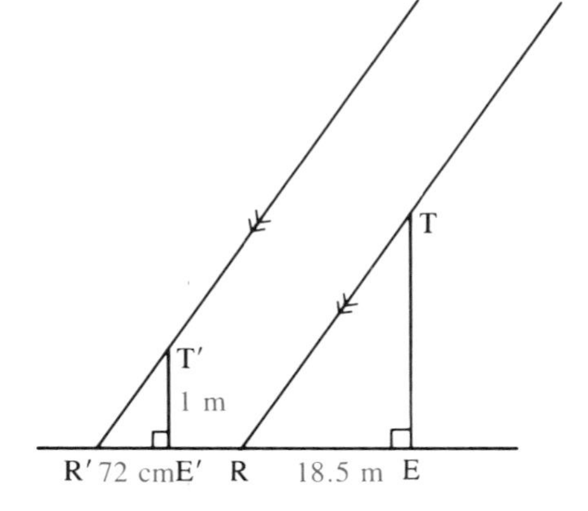

Example 2. The approximate radii of the sun, the Earth, and the moon are 695 000 km, 6380 km, and 1740 km respectively. The sun is about 149 000 000 km from the Earth, while the moon is about 380 000 km from the Earth.

Show that when the Earth lies on the line segment joining the sun and the moon, the moon is entirely contained in the Earth's umbra (shadow); that is, show that the eclipse of the moon is total.

Solution.

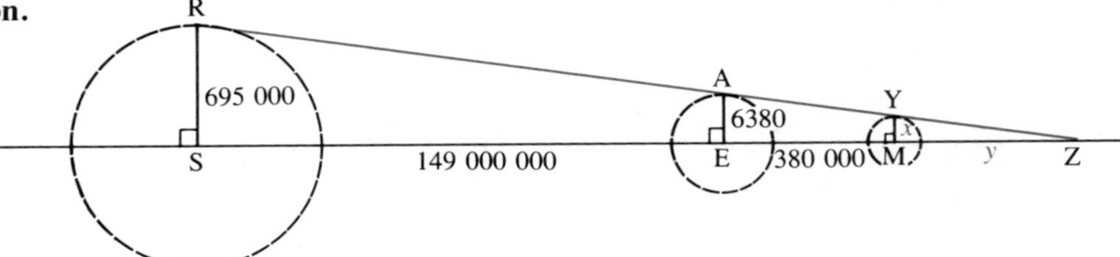

The diagram shows the parallel radii of the sun and the Earth, and their distances from the sun. A circle of radius x is drawn with its centre at the moon. The colored line represents a ray of light from the sun.

We shall use similar triangles to calculate x, and compare it with the radius of the moon.

Since RS, AE, and YM are parallel, from the Parallel Lines Theorem
$\angle SRA = \angle EAY = \angle MYZ$
Since RS, AE, and YM are perpendicular to SZ,
$\angle RSE = \angle AEM = \angle YMZ = 90°$
Therefore, $\triangle RSZ \sim \triangle AEZ \sim \triangle YMZ$ AA~

Hence, $\dfrac{RS}{SZ} = \dfrac{AE}{EZ} = \dfrac{YM}{MZ}$

Substitute the given information.

$$\frac{695\ 000}{149\ 380\ 000 + y} = \frac{6380}{380\ 000 + y} = \frac{x}{y}$$

Consider the first part of the proportion.

$$\frac{695\ 000}{149\ 380\ 000 + y} = \frac{6380}{380\ 000 + y}$$

Solve for y.

$$\begin{aligned} 695\ 000(380\ 000 + y) &= 6380(149\ 380\ 000 + y) \\ 2.641 \times 10^{11} + 695\ 000y &= 9.530\ 444 \times 10^{11} + 6380y \\ 688\ 620y &= 6.889\ 444 \times 10^{11} \\ y &\doteq 1\ 000\ 471 \end{aligned}$$

Substitute for y in the second part of the proportion.

$$\frac{6380}{380\ 000 + y} = \frac{x}{y}$$

$$\begin{aligned} x &= 1\ 000\ 471 \left(\frac{6380}{380\ 000 + 1\ 000\ 471} \right) \\ &\doteq 4624 \end{aligned}$$

The radius of the moon is only 1740 km.
Hence, the moon is contained entirely within the Earth's shadow.

In Chapter 7, another application of similar triangles will be illustrated when we study the trigonometry of triangles. This is based on the property that the ratio of the lengths of any two sides of a triangle is the same as the ratio for the corresponding sides of a similar triangle. That is, the ratios of lengths are preserved under dilatations.

EXERCISES 5-5

1. A tree casts a shadow 28 m long at a time when a person 178 cm tall casts a shadow 240 cm long. What is the height of the tree to the nearest metre?

2. Shannon is 136 cm tall and she is standing 3 m from the aperture of a pinhole camera. How tall will her photographic image be if the film is 8 cm behind the aperture?

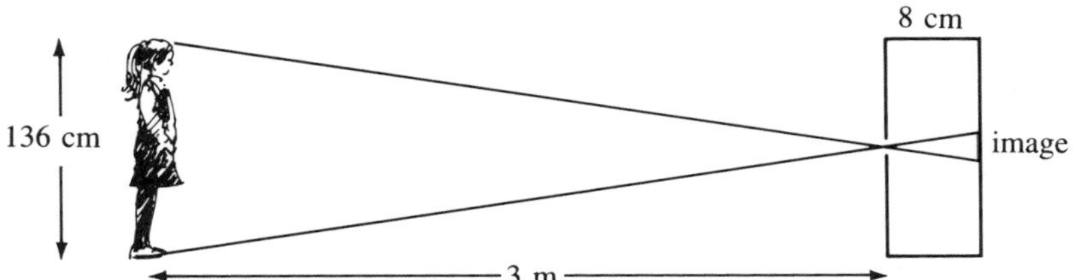

3. An A-frame ski chalet (below left) has a span of 20 m at its base. What is the height of the chalet if a beam parallel to the base and 6 m above it, has a length of 13 m?

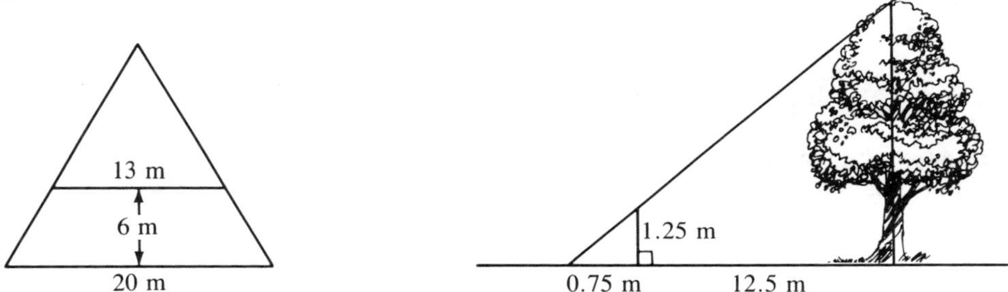

4. Jeremy notices that the end of the shadow of a tree coincides with the end of the shadow of a post (above right). If the post is 1.25 m high and 12.5 m from the tree, and the post's shadow is 0.75 m long, how high is the tree?

5. A person 195 cm tall sees the reflection of the top of a building in a puddle 7 m away (below left). How high is the building if it is located 40 m from the puddle?

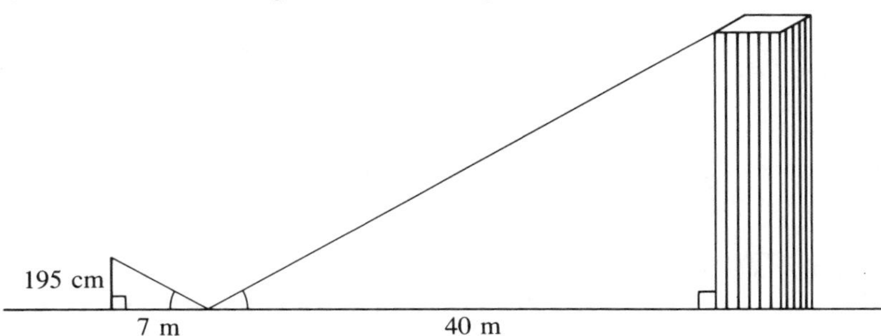

6. If metric sized paper is folded in half along its length, the resulting dimensions are proportional to the original dimensions. Find the width of a piece of metric paper if its length is 28.5 cm.

7. When playing tennis, Birgit hits the ball from a point 2.4 m high. She is 10.8 m from the net, which is 0.9 m high. If the ball just clears the net travelling perpendicular to it, where does it strike the other court?

8. The 210.3 m towers of the Verrazano-Narrows suspension bridge (below left) joining Brooklyn to Staten Island are 4.1 cm out of parallel due to the curvature of the Earth. If the distance between the towers at road level is 1298.4 m, estimate the radius of the Earth.

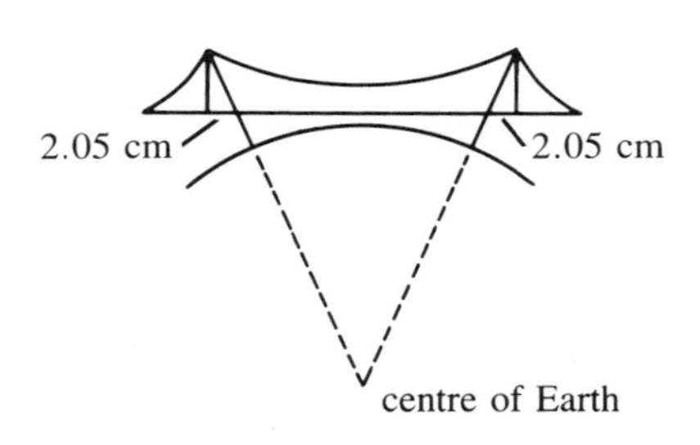

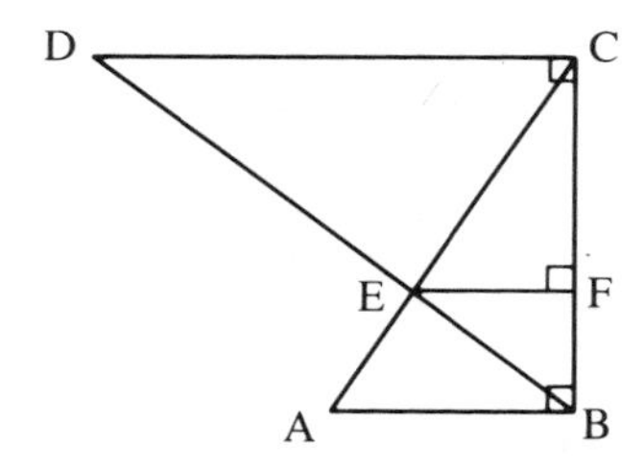

9. In the diagram (above right), AB is 2 cm, BC is 3 cm, and CD is 4 cm.
   a) Find the length of EF.
   b) If AB = x, BC = y, and CD = z, how long is EF?
   c) Is the length of EF dependent on BC?

10. The holding pens (below left) at a livestock auction have the dimensions shown.
    a) Find the lengths of AB, BC, and CD to 1 decimal place.
    b) How long are BG and CF?

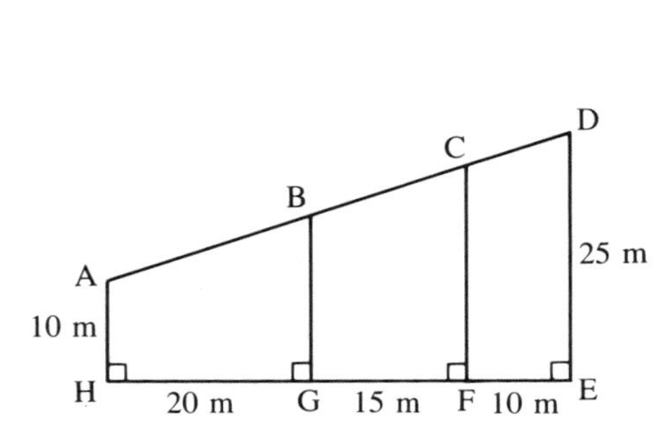

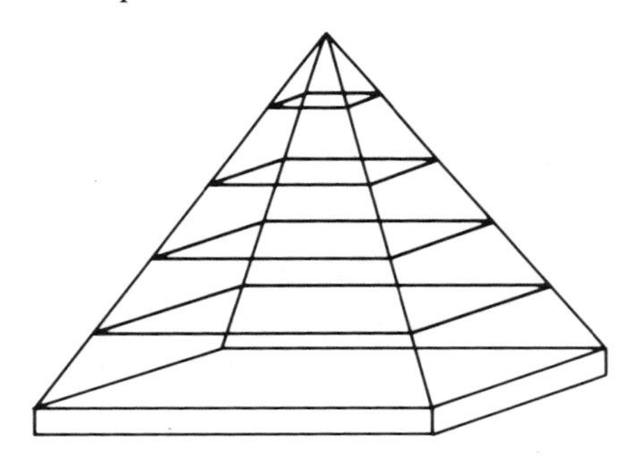

11. The manager of a china and gifts boutique constructed a display stand (above right). The base measures 1.5 m by 0.8 m and is 25 cm high. Find the dimensions of the four shelves if they are all equally spaced and the entire stand is 1.85 m tall.

12. A second display stand is constructed using the same base dimensions as in *Exercise 11*. The first shelf measures 1.20 m by 0.64 m and is 0.40 m above the base. The second shelf is 0.96 m by 0.51 m and is 0.32 m above the first shelf. The next two shelves are 0.26 m and 0.22 m above the previous lower shelves.
    a) Find the dimensions of the top two shelves.
    b) How tall is the display stand?

Ⓒ

13. When resistors R_1 and R_2 are connected in parallel, the total resistance R ohms is given by $\frac{1}{R} = \frac{1}{R_1} + \frac{1}{R_2}$. Explain how the side of the square contained in the triangle (below left) formed by joining values of R_1 and R_2 gives the value of R. Find the value of R if:
   a) $R_1 = 40\ \Omega$ and $R_2 = 120\ \Omega$
   b) $R_1 = 60\ \Omega$ and $R_2 = 30\ \Omega$
   c) $R_1 = 70\ \Omega$ and $R_2 = 110\ \Omega$.

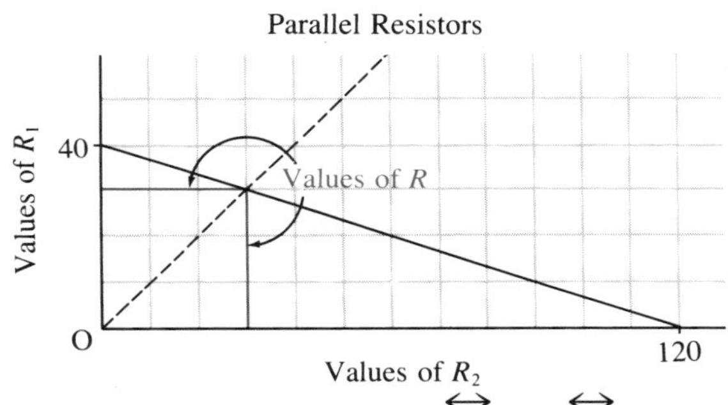

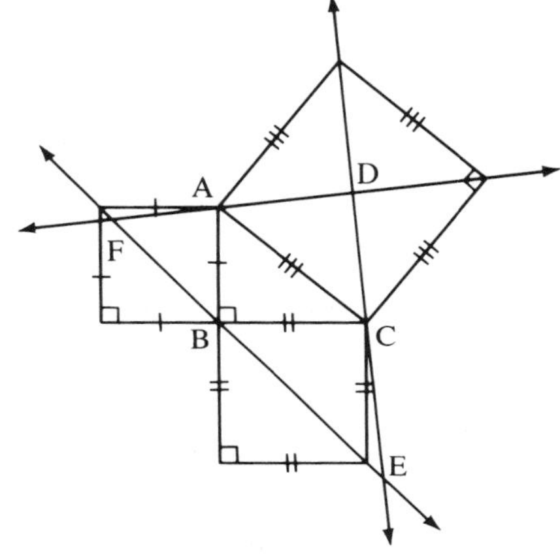

14. In the diagram (above right), $\overleftrightarrow{CD}$ and $\overleftrightarrow{BF}$ contain the diagonals of the squares. D is the centre of the square on the hypotenuse. Prove that $\triangle ABC \sim \triangle FDE$.

15. Under what conditions is it possible to divide a rectangle with dimensions l by w into two similar non-congruent rectangles?

16. a) The moon takes about 27.5 days to complete one orbit of the Earth. Calculate the speed of the moon in kilometres per hour.
    b) Calculate the time, in minutes, that a total eclipse of the moon should last.

17. A conical cup of depth h centimetres has a diameter of 2R centimetres at its widest part (below left). It is filled with water to a depth of x centimetres. Write an expression for the volume of water in the cup.

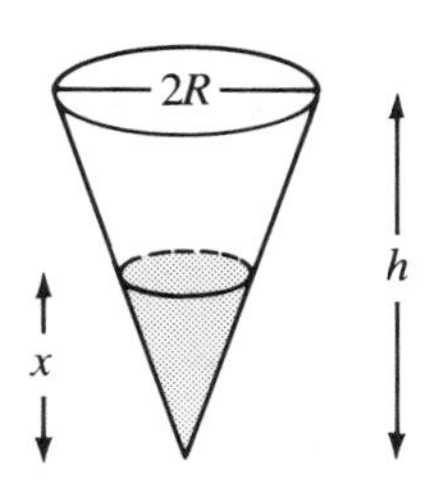

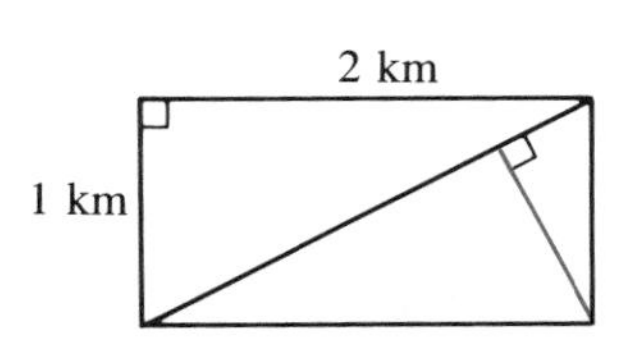

18. A rectangular tree farm is 2 km long and 1 km wide (above right). A road is cut along a diagonal of the rectangular farm. A second road is cut from an opposite corner to the first road and perpendicular to it. Calculate the length of the second road and verify that it is the mean proportional between the two segments into which it divides the first road.

Review Exercises

1. Find the values of x, y, and z for each pair of similar figures.

   a)

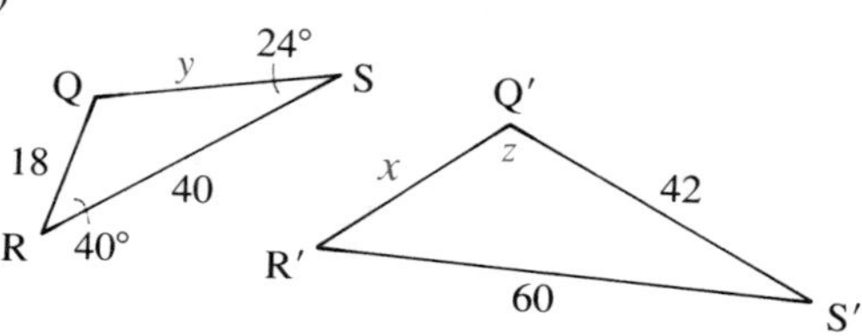

   b)

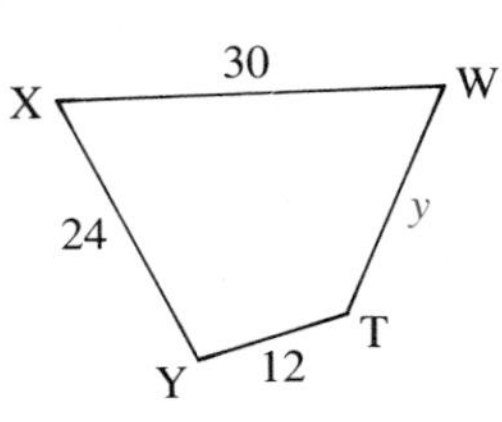

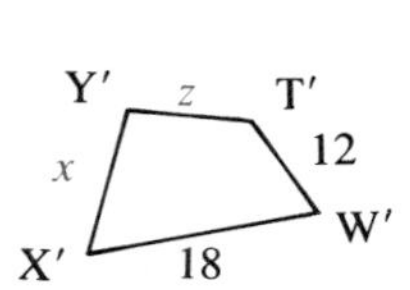

2. The area of the smaller of two similar triangles is $\frac{1}{16}$ of the area of the larger triangle.

   Find the length of the corresponding side of the other triangle if one side of:

   a) the smaller triangle b) the larger triangle is 3.6 cm.

3. Find a pair of similar triangles and prove that they are similar.

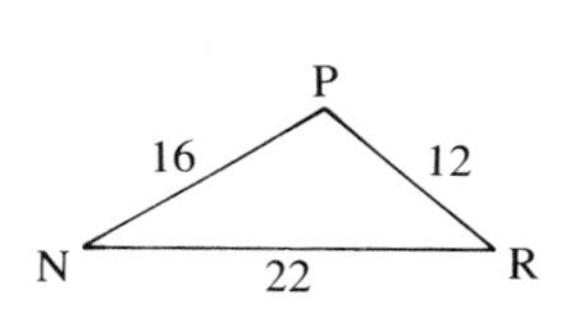

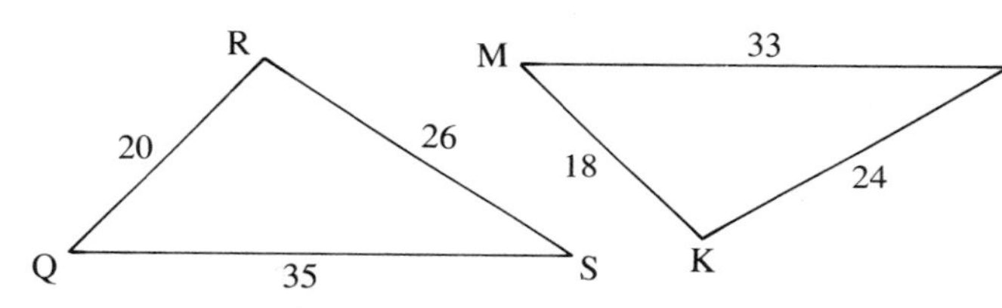

4. The tops of posts (1.0 m and 1.4 m high) line up with the top of a barn, as shown. The posts are 2 m apart and the centre of the barn is 42 m from the 1.0 m post. How high is the barn?

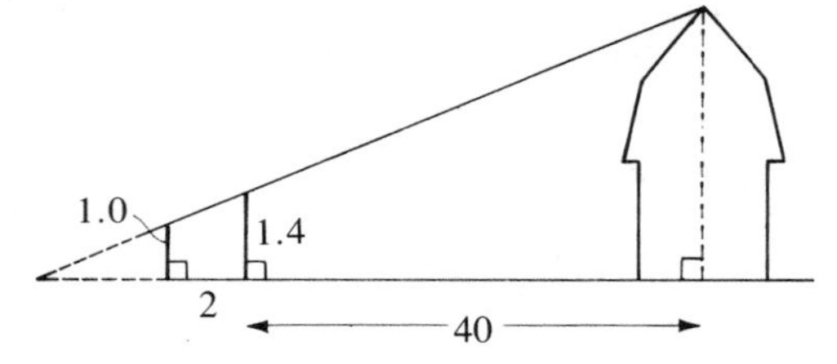

5. In $\triangle XYZ$ (below left), UV is parallel to XZ.

   a) Find the value of x. b) If XZ is 9 m, find UV.

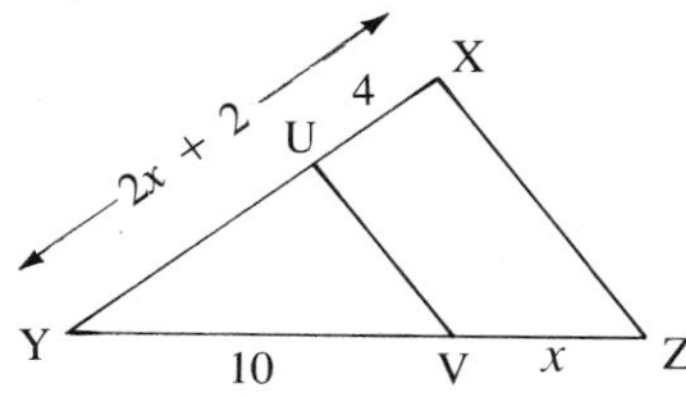

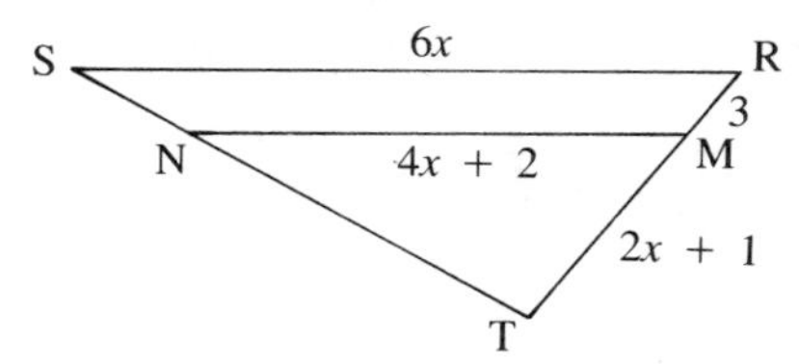

6. Triangle RST (above right) is similar to $\triangle MNT$.

   a) Find the value of x. b) Find ST if SN is 4 cm.

7. In $\triangle ABC$, $\angle B = 90°$, BD is perpendicular to AC, and E is the midpoint of AC. If BC = 10 cm and BD = 8 cm, find the length of DE to 1 decimal place.

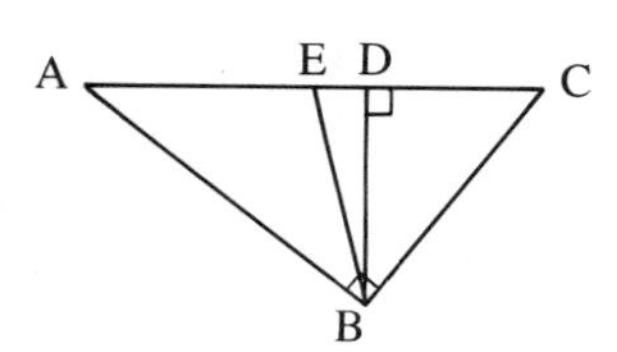

6 Circle Geometry

Andy and Brinkley are seated at opposite ends of a diameter of a Ferris wheel. What is Andy's angle of elevation as seen from the bottom of the Ferris wheel, in terms of his angle of elevation as seen by Brinkley? (See the *Example* in Section 6-7.)

6-1 DEFINITIONS AND CONCEPTS OF A CIRCLE

The concept of a circle has intrigued the human intellect since the beginnings of recorded time. The circle has been used by various religious groups as the symbol of eternity, perfection, and completeness. Circles are also employed in a variety of logos, such as the familiar Olympic symbol.

The association of the circle with qualities such as perfection, eternity, and completeness derives from the following geometric properties of circles.

- A circle is a closed curve.
- There is a unique point, the centre of the circle, which is equidistant from all points on the circle.
- Any line which passes through the centre of a circle is a line of symmetry of the circle.
- A circle has an infinite number of lines of symmetry.
- The intersection of a sphere with a plane is a circle.

The last of these properties explains why the sun and the moon (which are essentially spherical) appear to us as disks with a circular rim.

The ancient Ptolemaic theory of planetary motion asserted that each planet moved in a circle about the sun, which in turn moved in a circle about the Earth. This theory was predominant for about 1500 years, until the publication in 1543 of the Copernican theory which asserted that all planets, including the Earth, travel in circular orbits around the sun. We know today that the planets actually travel in elliptical orbits but their orbits are in most cases almost circular. The successive theories of planetary motion are suggestive of the all-pervasive role of the circle in scientific models. This fact alone makes the study of the circle and its geometric properties of critical importance.

Following the axiomatic approach, we begin our study of circles with some undefined terms (the point, the line, and the plane) together with terms which we defined previously.

Definition: A *circle* is the set of all points which lie a fixed distance, r (called the *radius*) from a fixed point C (called the *centre*).

Using this definition of a circle and its centre together with the terms, point, line, and line segment, we can write definitions of a chord, a diameter, a radius, and a sector of a circle (see *Exercises 3* and *4*, page 212).

The diagram on the next page illustrates examples of other familiar terms.

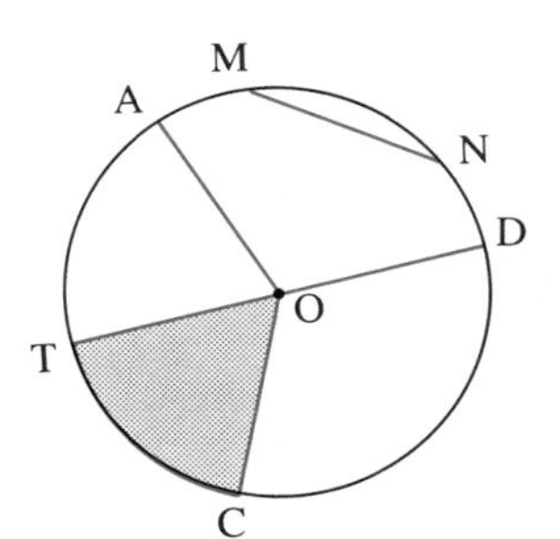

- Point O is the centre of the circle.
- Point A is any point on the circle.
- Line segment OA is a radius.
- Line segment DT (which contains O) is a diameter.
- Line segment MN is a chord.
- TC is an arc.
- The shaded region TOC is a sector, and $\angle TOC$ is the sector angle.

The diagrams below show the three possible cases for the intersection of a line with a circle.

There is no point of intersection. 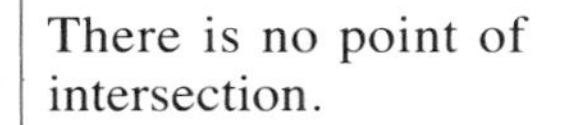 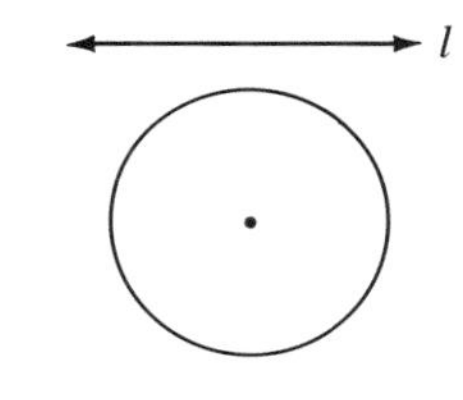	There is one point of intersection. 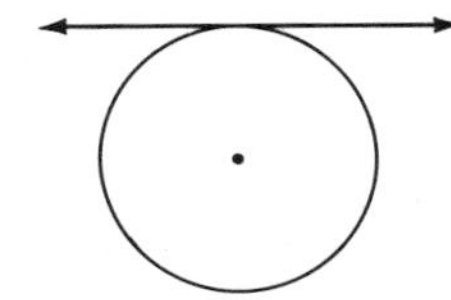 We say: l is a *tangent* to the circle.	There are 2 points of intersection. 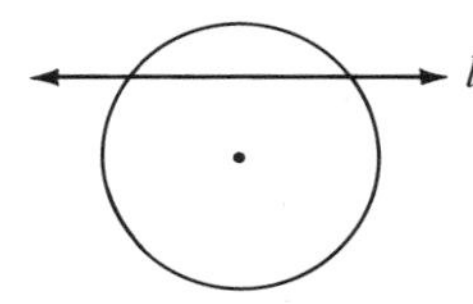 We say: l is a *secant* of the circle.

The diagrams illustrate the definitions of a tangent and a secant. In Sections 6-6 to 6-8 we will study interesting and important properties of tangents and secants of circles.

Example. Calculate the perimeter of a regular octagon inscribed in a circle of diameter 15 cm. Each side of the octagon is 6.9 cm from the centre of the circle.

Solution. Draw a diagram.

Figure ABCDEFGH is a regular octagon.
Join AO and OB, which are radii of the circle.
Then, AO = OB = 7.5 cm
Drop the perpendicular from O onto AB at R.
Then, OR = 6.9 cm
Use the Pythagorean Theorem in $\triangle BOR$.

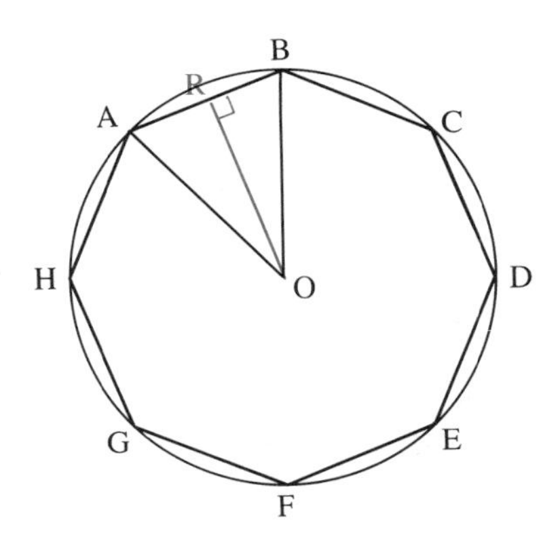

$$RB^2 = OB^2 - OR^2$$
$$= 7.5^2 - 6.9^2$$
$$RB = \sqrt{7.5^2 - 6.9^2}$$
$$\doteq 2.939$$
$$AB = 2RB$$
$$\doteq 5.878$$

The perimeter of the octagon is 8(5.878) cm, or about 47 cm.

EXERCISES 6-1

Ⓐ

1. What point is equidistant from all the points that lie on a circle?

2. What is the greatest possible distance between two points which lie on a circle with radius R?

3. Define each term as it pertains to a circle.
   a) centre b) radius c) diameter d) chord e) tangent

4. a) Define the term sector. b) Can a semicircle be a sector?

5. Explain the difference between a secant and a tangent to a circle.

6. How many secants pass through a particular point on a circle?

Ⓑ

7. a) What is the greatest number of points in which three circles can intersect?
   b) What is the least number of points in which three circles can intersect?
   c) Draw diagrams to illustrate three circles intersecting in all possible numbers of points from the least to the greatest.

8. Given a circle and a point outside the circle
   a) How many secants can be drawn from the point to the circle?
   b) How many tangents can be drawn from the point to the circle?

9. Two intersecting circles of equal radii are drawn. How many points on each circle are equidistant from both centres?

10. How far is a chord of length 8 cm from the centre of a circle with diameter 10 cm?

11. Calculate the perimeter of each inscribed regular polygon.

a)

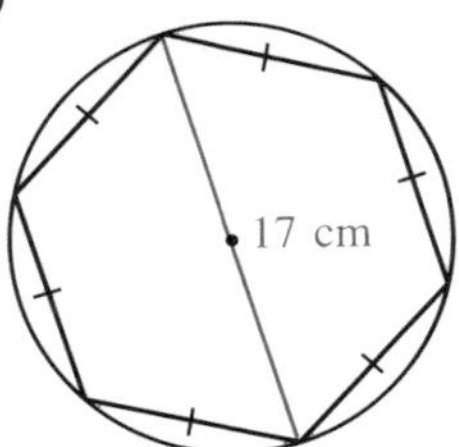

b)

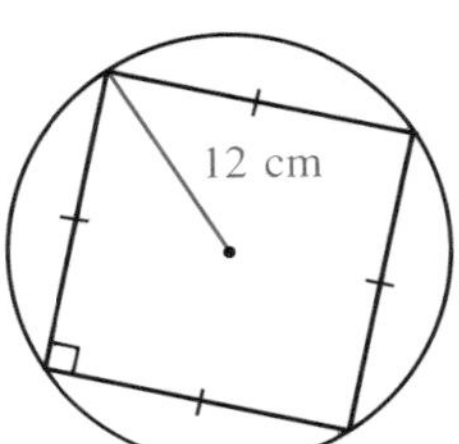

c)

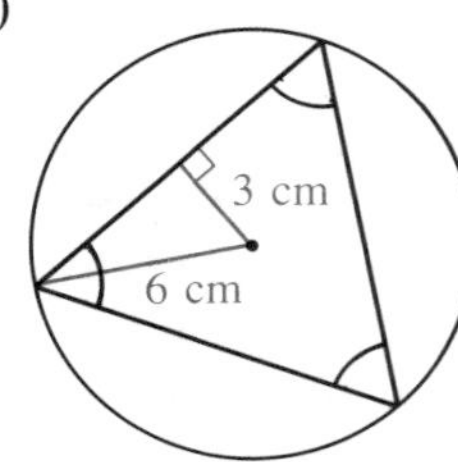

Ⓒ

12. a) Prove that any point on the perpendicular bisector of a chord of a circle is equidistant from the ends of the chord.
    b) Write the converse of the theorem in part a) and prove it.
    c) Use part b) to deduce that the centre of a circle lies on the perpendicular bisector of every chord of that circle.
    d) Use part c) to deduce that the point of intersection of the perpendicular bisectors of two (non-parallel) chords of a circle is the centre of that circle.

13. Using the information in *Exercise 12*, describe how to locate the centre of a circular disk using only a ruler (marked in millimetres) and a set square.

6-2 PROPERTIES OF CHORDS IN A CIRCLE

In the construction of a wheel for a train, a disk is cut from a steel cylinder. A hole is then drilled in the centre of the circular disk.

How can the centre of the disk be located?

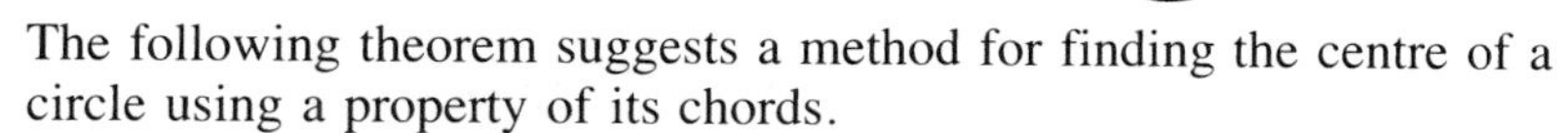

The following theorem suggests a method for finding the centre of a circle using a property of its chords.

> **Chord Perpendicular Bisector Theorem**
> The perpendicular bisector of a chord of a circle passes through the centre of the circle.

Given: A chord AB of a circle with centre O
Required to Prove: The perpendicular bisector of AB passes through O.
Analysis: Draw the radii OA and OB.

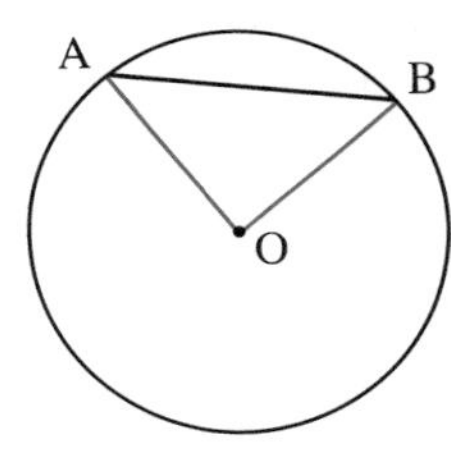

Proof:

Statement	Reason
OA = OB	Radii
O is on the perpendicular bisector of AB.	Perpendicular Bisector Theorem

Therefore, the perpendicular bisector of AB passes through O.

> **Corollary 1**
> If a radius bisects a chord, then the radius is perpendicular to that chord.

A radius that bisects a chord passes through the midpoint of the chord and the centre of the circle. The perpendicular bisector passes through the same two points. Therefore, the two lines are coincident.

> **Corollary 2**
> If a radius is perpendicular to a chord, then the radius bisects that chord.

A radius that is perpendicular to a chord must be parallel to the perpendicular bisector. Since the radius and the perpendicular bisector both pass through the centre of the circle, they must be coincident.

It follows from the Chord Perpendicular Bisector Theorem that the centre of a circle is the point of intersection of the perpendicular bisectors of any two (non-parallel) chords of the circle.

l is the perpendicular bisector of chord AB.
m is the perpendicular bisector of chord CD.
O is the centre of the circle.

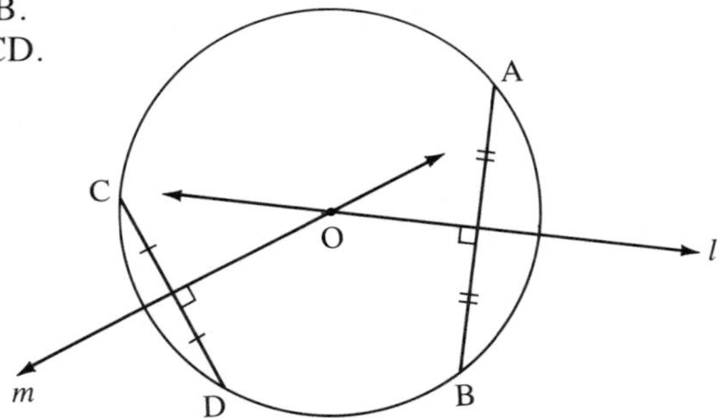

We can use the Hypotenuse-Side Theorem and the Chord Perpendicular Bisector Theorem to prove the following important property of chords in a circle.

> **Theorem**
> If two chords are equidistant from the centre of a circle, then the chords are congruent.

Given: Chords AB and DE which are equidistant from O. That is, OF = OG; OF ⊥ AB; OG ⊥ ED

Required to Prove: AB = DE

Analysis: Draw radii OA, OB, OE, and OD to produce △AOB and △ODE. Consider congruent triangles.

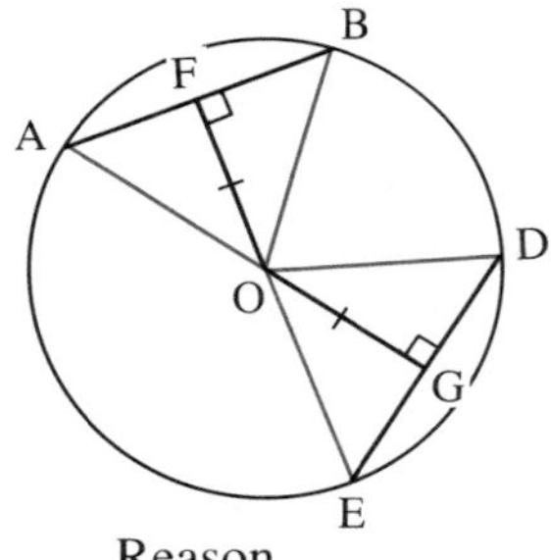

Proof:

Statement	Reason
In △OFB and △OGE	
OF = OG	Given
OB = OE	Radii
∠OFB = ∠OGE = 90°	Given
Therefore, △OFB ≅ △OGE	HS
FB = GE	Congruent triangles
FB = $\frac{1}{2}$AB and GE = $\frac{1}{2}$DE	Chord Perpendicular Bisector Theorem
Therefore, AB = DE	

The Hypotenuse-Side Theorem can also be used to prove the converse of the theorem above.

> **Theorem**
> If chords in a circle are equal, then the chords are equidistant from the centre of the circle.

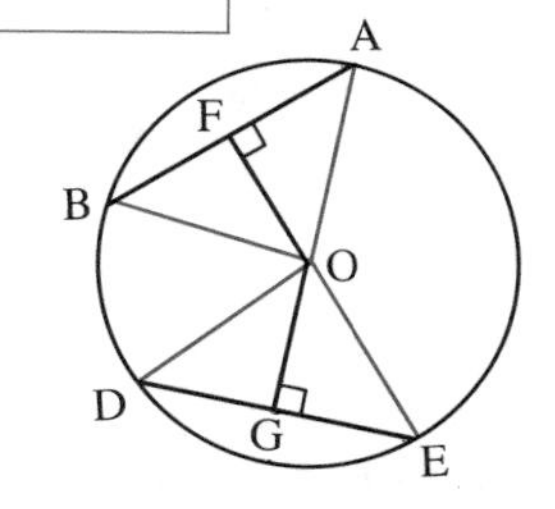

Given: Chords AB and DE such that AB = DE
OF and OG are perpendiculars from O to AB and DE respectively.

Required to Prove: OF = OG

Analysis: Draw radii OA, OB, OE, and OD to produce △OAB and △ODE.

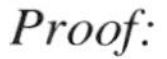
Proof:

Statement	Reason
AB = DE	Given
F and G are the midpoints of AB and DE respectively	Chord Perpendicular Bisector Theorem
Therefore, AF = FB = DG = GE	
In △OFB and △OGE	
OB = OE	Radii
BF = EG	Proved
∠OFB = ∠OGE = 90°	Given
Therefore, △OFB ≅ △OGE	HS
OF = OG	Congruent triangles

The two theorems above can be combined into a single statement using the "iff" notation. This biconditional statement is called the Equal Chords Theorem.

> **Equal Chords Theorem**
> Chords of a circle are equal iff they are equidistant from the centre.

EXERCISES 6-2

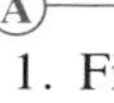

1. Find each value of x to 1 decimal place where necessary.

a)

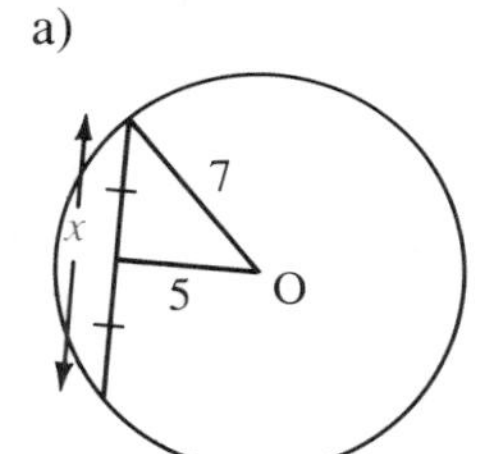

b)

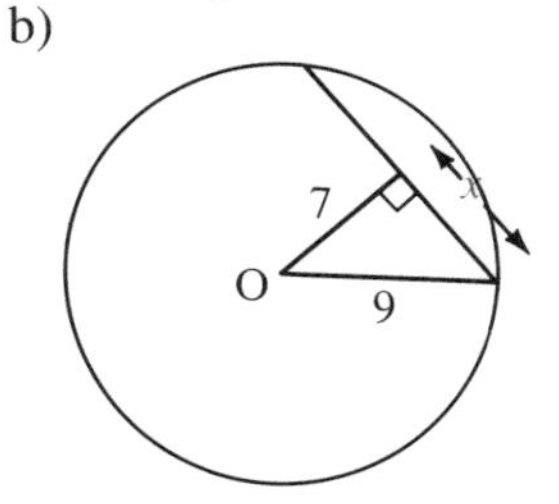

c)

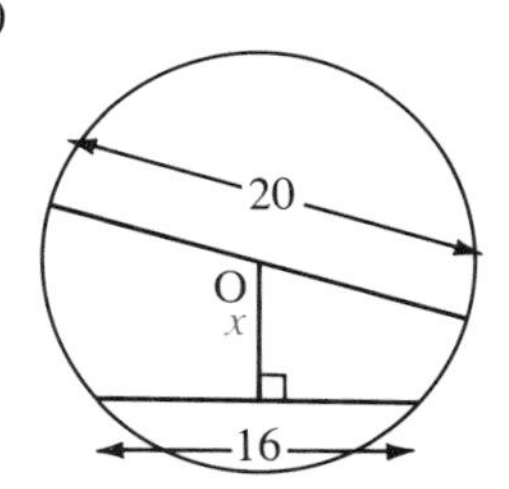

2. Find each value of x to 1 decimal place where necessary.

a)

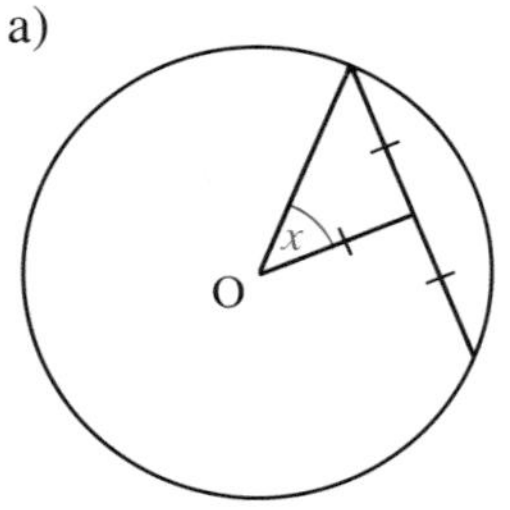

b)

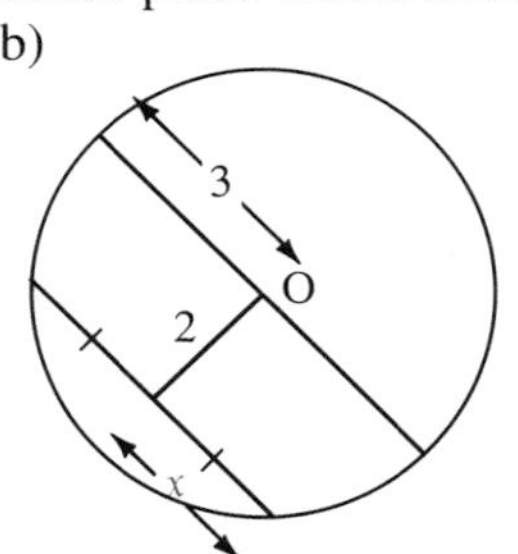

c)

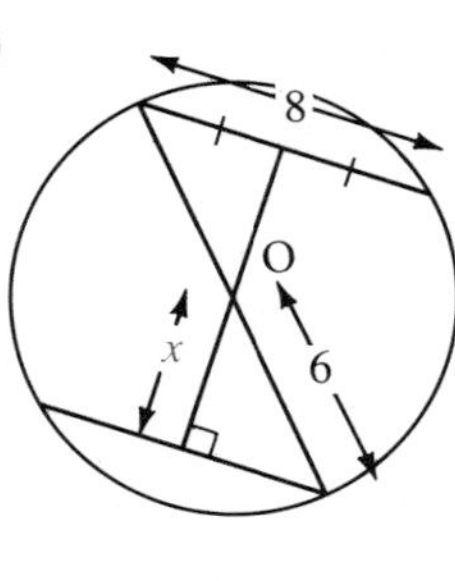

3. A circle has a diameter of 14 cm. How far from the centre of the circle is a chord of length 7 cm?

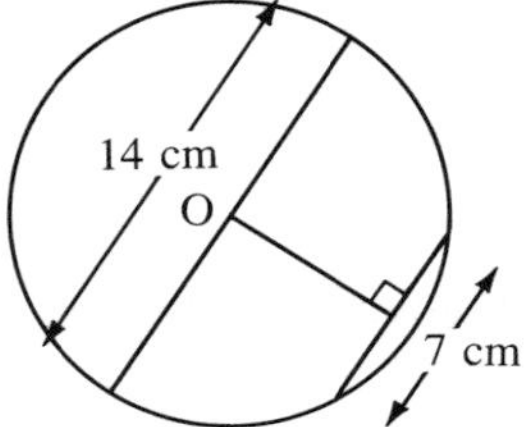

4. Find each value of z to 1 decimal place where necessary.

a)

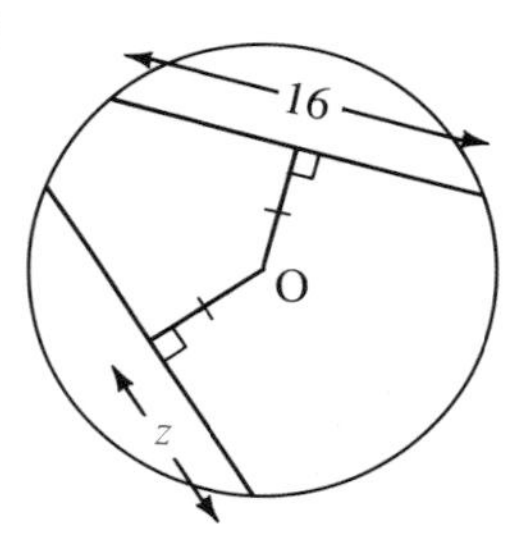

b)

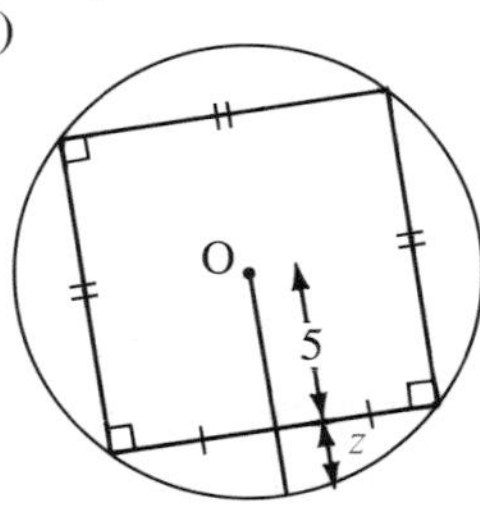

c)

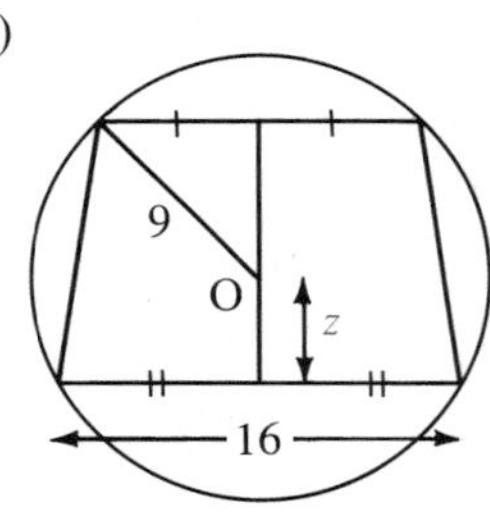

(B)

5. Describe how you would find the centre of a circle which passes through three non-collinear points.

6. Describe how you would find the centre and the radius of a circle which circumscribes (passes through the vertices of) a given triangle.

7. What is the diameter of a circle in which a chord 16 cm long is 15 cm from the centre?

8. The base of a large hemispherical dome is a circle of diameter 80 m. How far apart are two 20 m parallel support beams which form "chords" of the circular base?

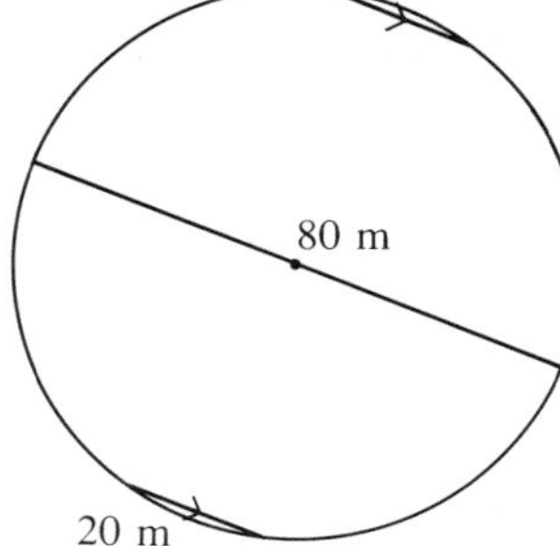

9. A square (below left) is inscribed in a circle of diameter 20 cm. What is the distance between the midpoints of adjacent sides of the square?

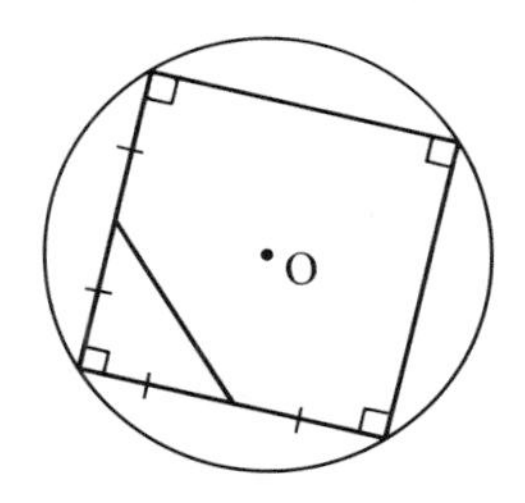

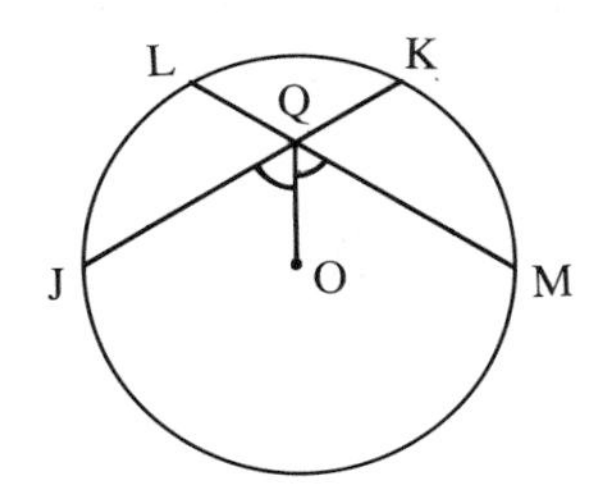

10. Two chords JK and LM of a circle with centre O intersect at point Q so that OQ bisects ∠JQM (above right). Prove that JK = LM.

11. Two equal chords JK and LM of a circle with centre O intersect at a point Q. Prove that OQ bisects one of the angles formed by the chords.

12. In the diagram, PQ and RS are equal chords of the circle with centre O. If T is the point of intersection of PQ and RS, prove that:

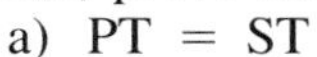
a) PT = ST

b) QT = RT

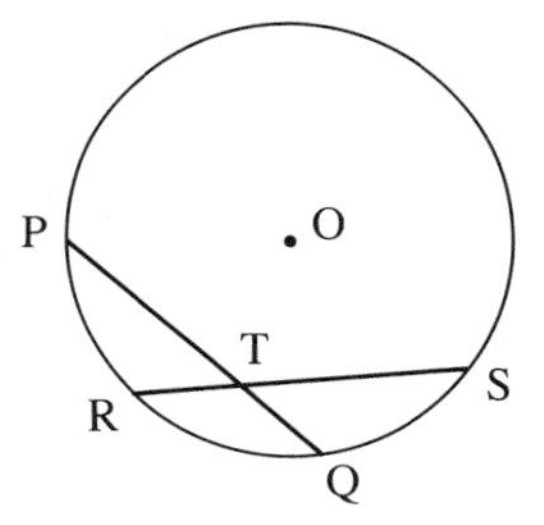

Ⓒ

13. Prove that there exists one and only one circle which passes through any 3 non-collinear points.

14. Prove that the perpendicular bisectors of the three sides of a triangle are concurrent.

15. Two circles of radii r and R intersect in two points A and B (below left). The distance between the centres of the circles is d units. Write an algebraic expression in terms of r, R, and d for the distance of chord AB from the centre of each circle.

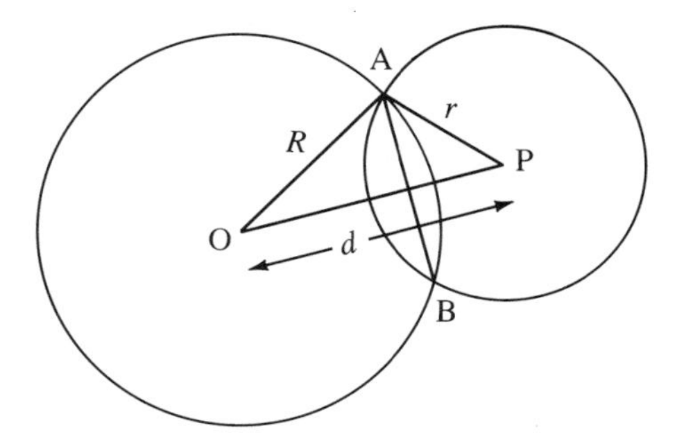

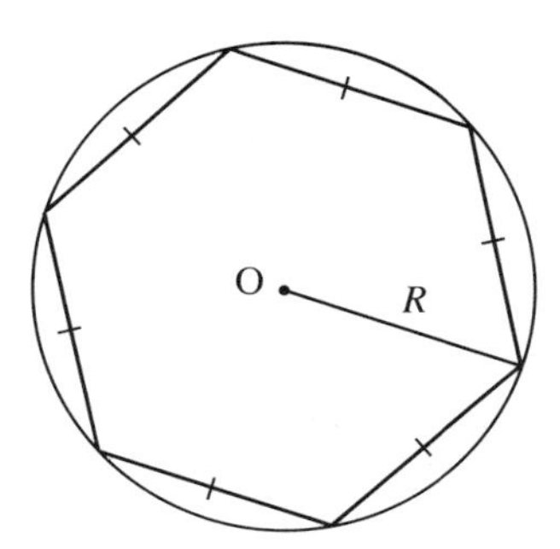

16. Write an algebraic expression for the area of a regular hexagon inscribed in a circle with radius R (above right).

6-3 PROPERTIES OF ANGLES IN A CIRCLE

When the balls on a billiard table are positioned as shown, the ⑦ ball is easier to sink than the ⑥ ball even though both balls are the same distance from the pocket.

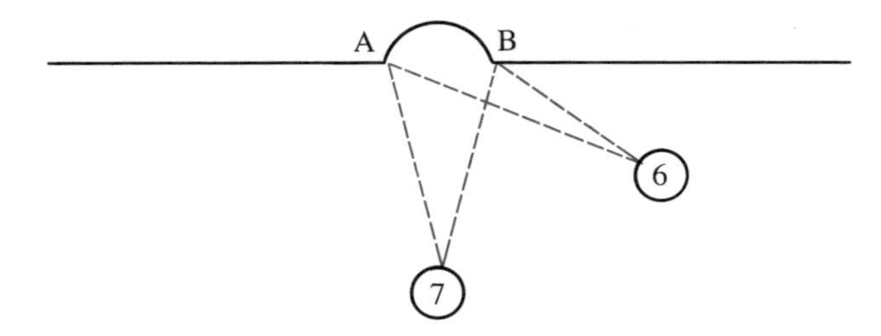

The diagram shows why. The dotted lines show the boundary of the paths for each ball. The permissible paths for the ⑥ ball lie within a small angle. The permissible paths for the ⑦ ball lie within a larger angle. We say that the angle subtended by line segment AB at the ⑦ ball is greater than the angle subtended by AB at the ⑥ ball.

Definition: If AB is a chord of a circle with centre O, then ∠AOB is called the angle *subtended at the centre of the circle* by the chord AB.

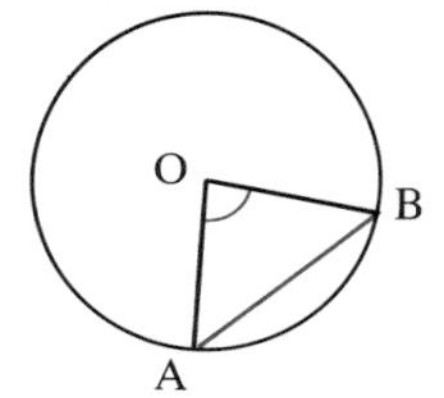

Definition: If C is a point on the circumference of a circle and AB is any chord, then ∠ACB is called an angle *subtended at the circumference of the circle* by chord AB.

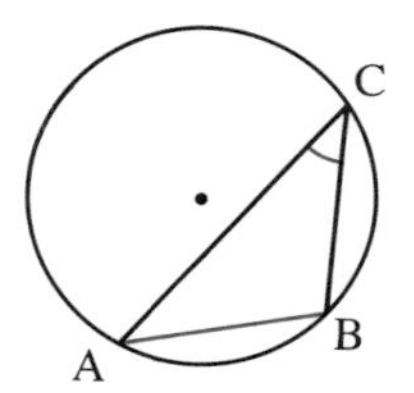

From investigations in previous grades, you may have discovered that the angle subtended at the centre of a circle by a chord is twice the measure of any angle subtended at the circumference of that circle by that same chord (provided both angles are located on the same side of the chord).

Angles in a Circle Theorem
If the angle at the centre of a circle and an angle at the circumference are subtended by the same chord and lie on the same side of that chord, then the angle at the centre is twice the measure of the angle at the circumference.

To prove this theorem we must consider the two possible cases shown below in which the centre lies inside (Case I) and outside (Case II) the angle at the circumference.

Case I

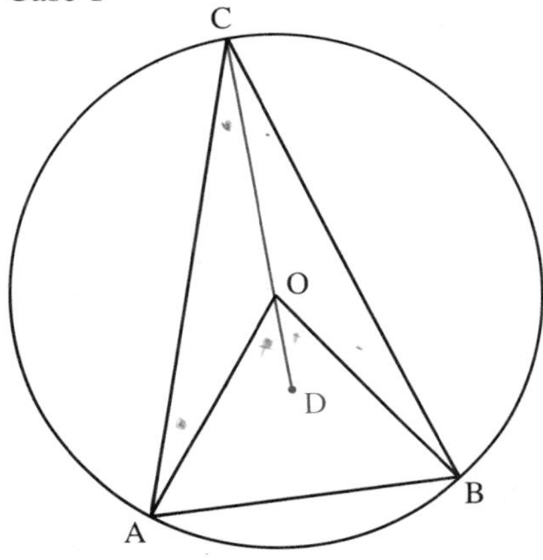

Case II

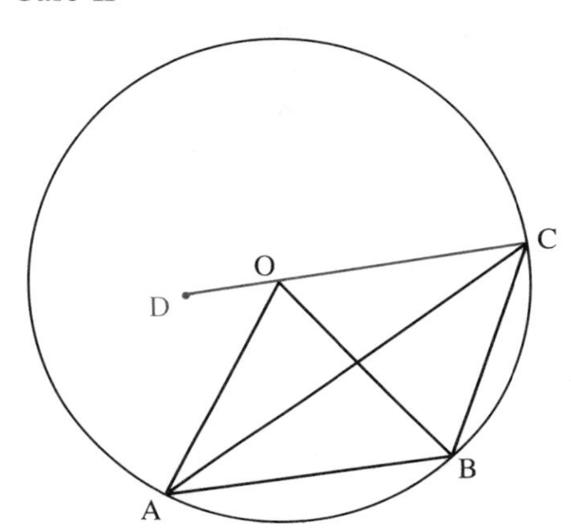

Given: AB is a chord of a circle with centre O, and C is a point on the circumference of the circle.

Required to Prove: ∠AOB = 2∠ACB

Analysis: Extend CO to a point D and consider the angles so formed.

Proof: The first 4 statements apply to Case I and Case II.

Statement	Reason
1. OC = OA	Radii
2. ∠ACO = ∠CAO	Isosceles Triangle Theorem
3. ∠DOA = 2∠ACO	Exterior Angle Theorem and Statement 2
4. ∠DOB = 2∠BCO	Reasoning as in Statements 1 to 3
5. Case I : ∠AOB = ∠DOB + ∠DOA	
= 2∠BCO + 2∠ACO	Statements 3 and 4
= 2(∠BCO + ∠ACO)	
= 2∠ACB	
Case II: ∠AOB = ∠DOB − ∠DOA	
= 2(∠BCO − ∠ACO)	Statements 3 and 4
= 2∠ACB	

Corollary 1
If two angles are subtended by the same chord on the circumference of a circle, and lie on the same side of the chord, then the angles are congruent.

This corollary can be extended to any number of angles subtended by the same arc. In the diagram

- $\angle C = \angle D = \angle E$ because all these angles are subtended by chord AB and are on the same side of AB.
- $\angle F$ is not equal to the other labelled angles because it is *not* on the same side of chord AB.

  However $\angle F$ is equal to other angles subtended by AB on the same side as $\angle F$.

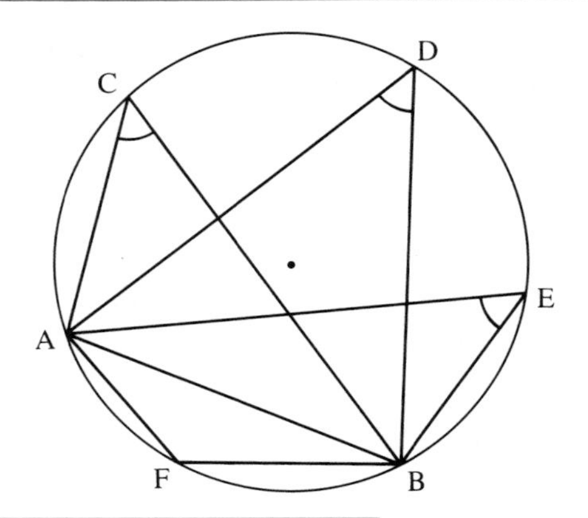

> **Corollary 2**
> If an angle on the circumference of a circle is subtended by a diameter of the circle, then that angle is a right angle.

In the diagram, AB is a diameter and $\angle AOB = 180°$.
AB subtends $\angle ADB$ and $\angle AEB$ at the circumference.

Therefore, $\angle ADB = \frac{1}{2}\angle AOB$

$= 90°$

Similarly, $\angle AEB = 90°$

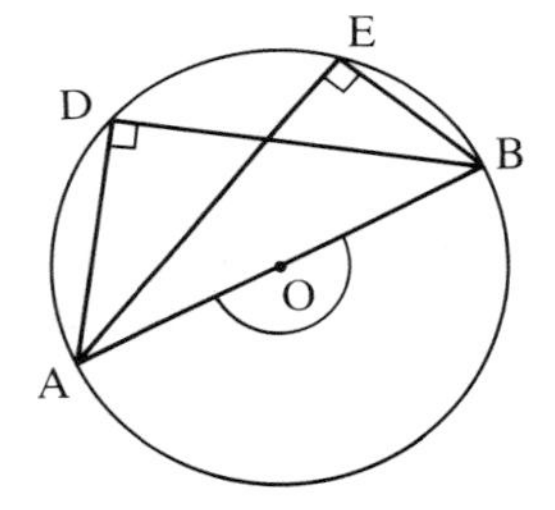

> **Corollary 3**
> If a chord subtends an angle of 90° at the circumference of a circle, then that chord is a diameter of the circle.

The next example shows how the Angles in a Circle Theorem and its corollaries can be used to determine the measures of angles in a circle.

Example. In the diagram, the chord AB has a length equal to the radius of the circle, centre O. Find the measure of $\angle APB$.

Solution. Join OA and OB.
Since AB is equal to the radius of the circle, $\triangle OAB$ is equilateral.
Hence, $\angle AOB = 60°$
Since AB subtends $\angle O$ at the centre and $\angle P$ at the circumference,

$\angle APB = \frac{1}{2}\angle AOB$

$= \frac{1}{2}(60°)$, or 30°

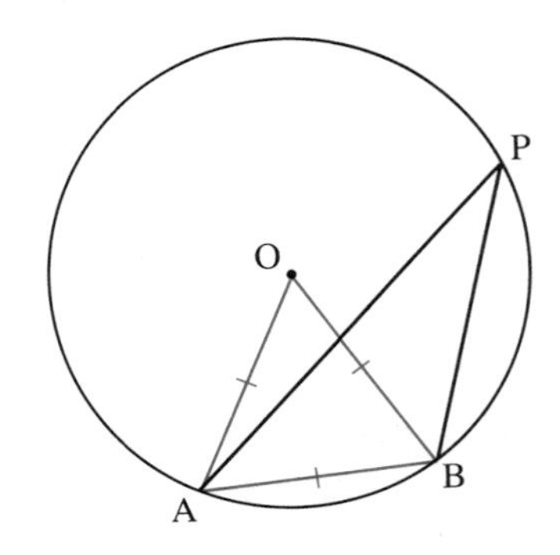

EXERCISES 6-3

Ⓐ

1. Use the diagram to name the angles in the circle, centre O.
   a) Five angles subtended by chord AB on the circumference of the circle
   b) Two angles subtended by chord AB on the circumference, and located on the same side of AB as ∠AEB
   c) Two angles subtended by chord AB on the circumference, and located on opposite sides of AB
   d) An angle subtended by chord AB on the circumference, and located on the same side as ∠AGB
   e) An angle subtended by chord AB at the centre of the circle.

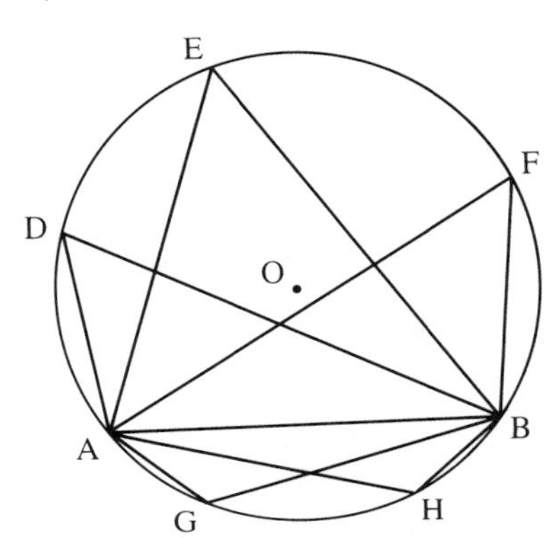

2. a) What is the measure of an angle at the circumference of a circle, subtended by a diameter?
   b) What is the measure of an angle at the centre of a circle, subtended by a diameter?

3. Find each value of x.

a)

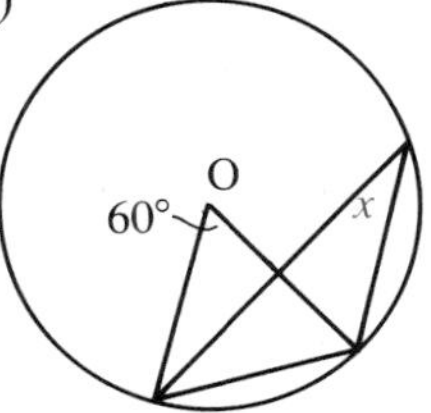

b)

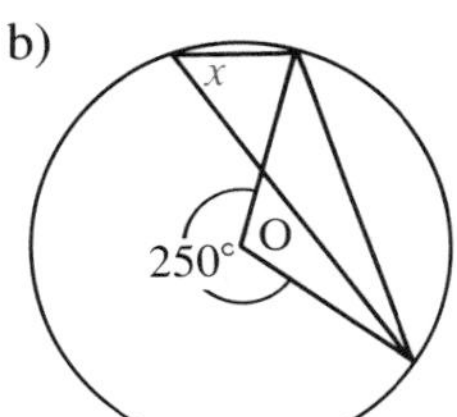

c)

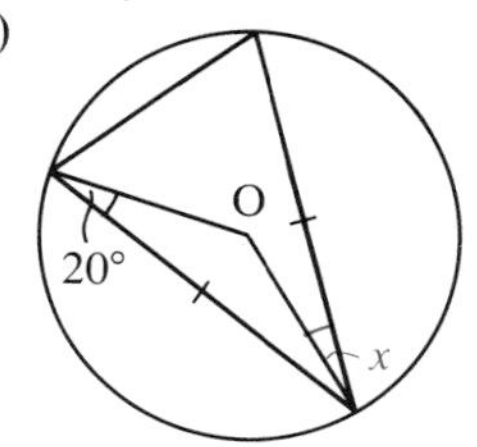

4. Find the values of x, y, and z.

a)

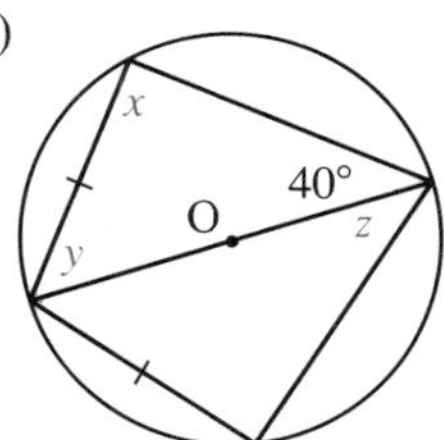

b)

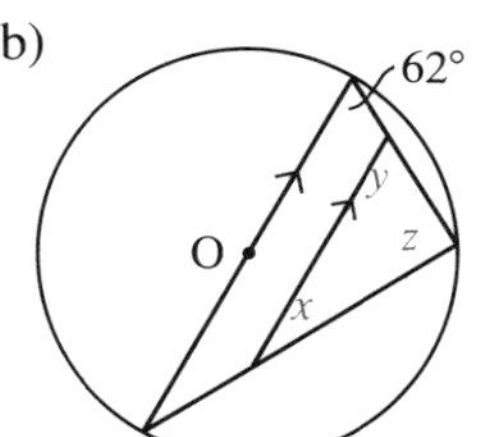

c)

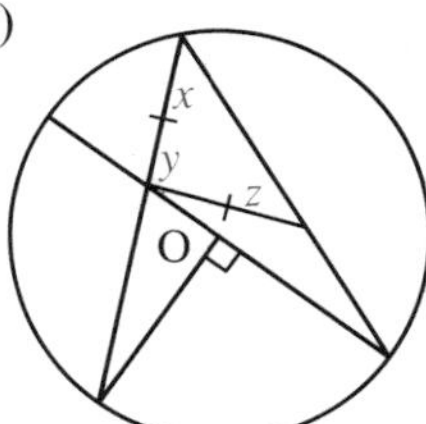

5. AB, BC, DE, and EF are equal chords of a circle with centre O, and ∠BAC = 30°. Find the measures of ∠DEF and ∠DFE.

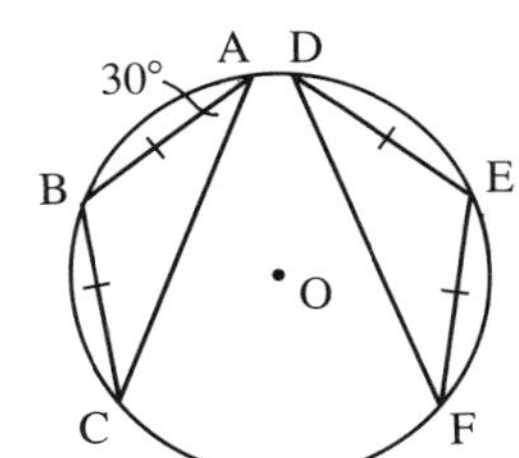

6. Trapezoid ABCD (below left) is inscribed in a circle and AD is parallel to BC. If $\angle ABD = 35°$ and $\angle DAC = 40°$, find the measures of $\angle DAB$ and $\angle ADC$.

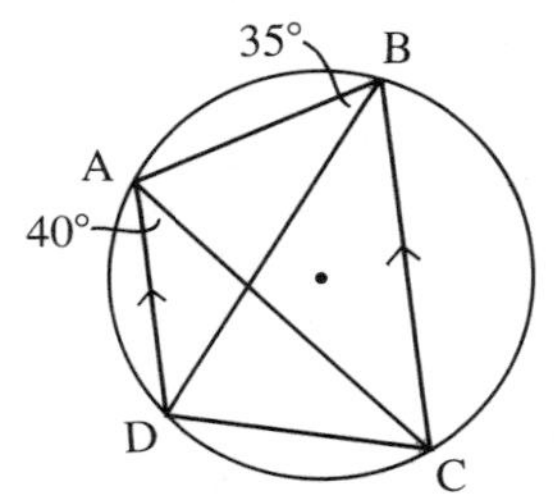

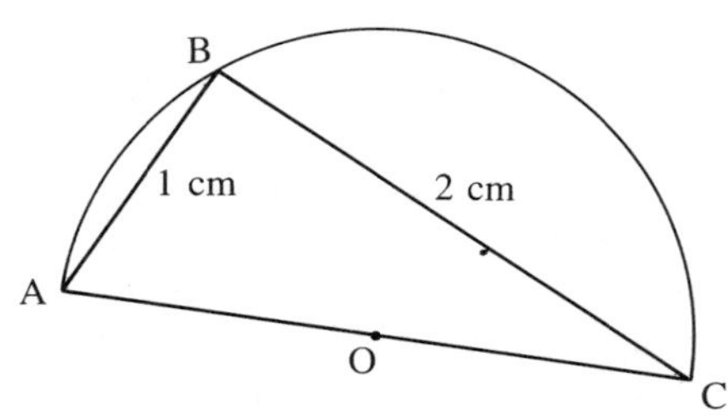

7. Calculate the radius of the semicircle (above right).

8. AB and AD are equal chords of a circle with centre O (below left). Prove that $\angle OAD = \angle OBA$.

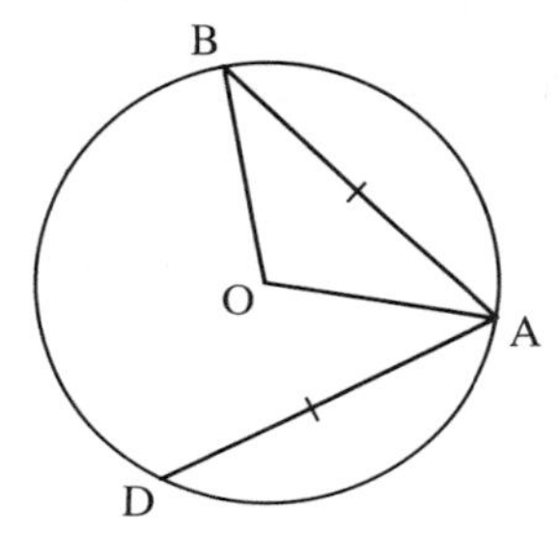

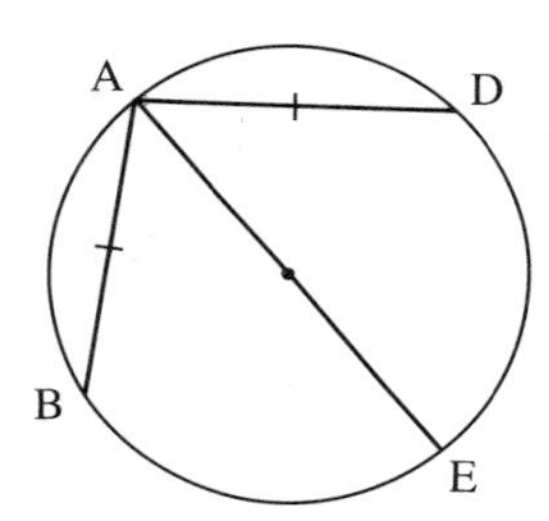

9. AB and AD are equal chords in a circle with diameter AE (above right). Prove that $\angle BAE = \angle DAE$.

10. OD and OE bisect respectively chords AB and AC of a circle with centre O and diameter BC (below left). Prove that OD is perpendicular to OE.

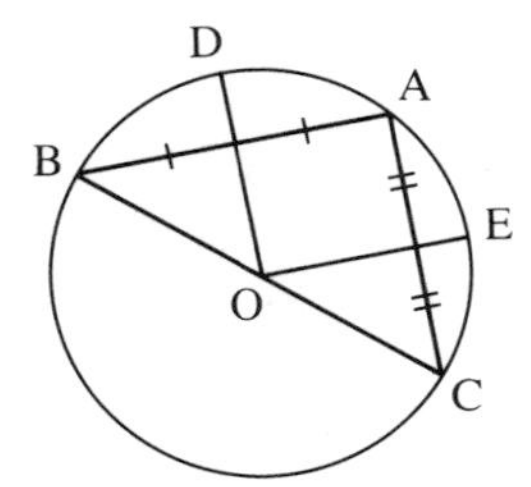

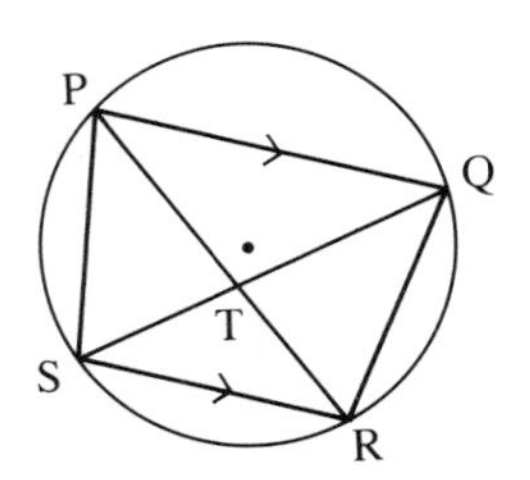

11. Trapezoid PQRS is inscribed in a circle, and PQ is parallel to SR (above right). If diagonals PR and SQ intersect at T, prove that TS = TR and TP = TQ.

12. Prove that any trapezoid inscribed in a circle is an isosceles trapezoid; that is, at least one pair of opposite sides are equal.

13. Prove that equal chords subtend equal angles at the centre of a circle.

14. WXYZ is a quadrilateral inscribed in a circle and WX = YZ. Prove that the diagonals of WXYZ are equal in length.

15. ABCD is a quadrilateral inscribed in a circle with centre O (below left). Prove that $\angle A + \angle C = 180°$ and $\angle B + \angle D = 180°$.

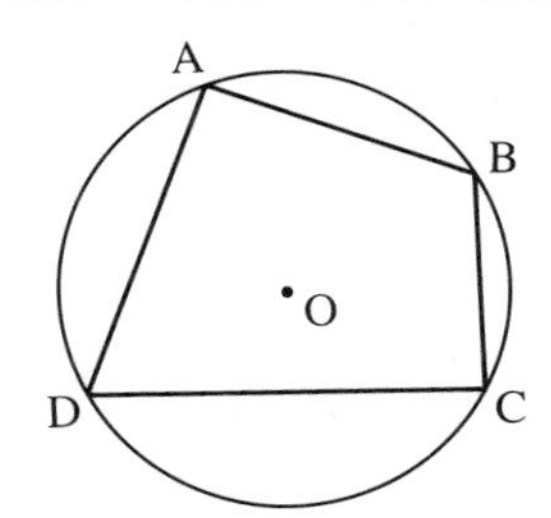

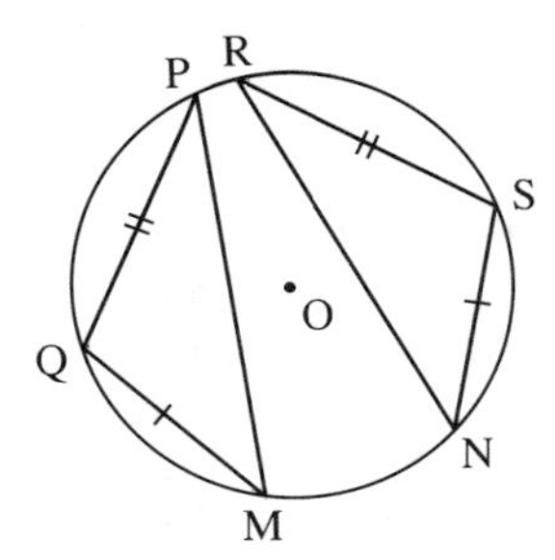

16. PQ and RS are equal chords of a circle with centre O (above right). If M and N are points on the circumference of the circle such that QM = SN, prove that $\angle QMP = \angle RNS$.

17. AB is a chord of a circle, centre O and radius 12 cm. C and D are points on the circle such that $\angle ACB$ and $\angle ADB$ are on opposite sides of chord AB. What is the length of chord AB if $\angle ACB = \angle ADB$?

Ⓒ

18. a) State and prove the converse of corollary 2 of the Angles in a Circle Theorem.
    b) Prove that if two equal angles are subtended by the same chord but on opposite sides of that chord, then the chord is a diameter.

19. Use *Exercise 18* to prove that if a parallelogram is inscribed in a circle, then that parallelogram is a rectangle.

20. In a semicircle, three connected chords have lengths 1, 2, and 3 respectively. Calculate the radius of the semicircle to 1 decimal place.

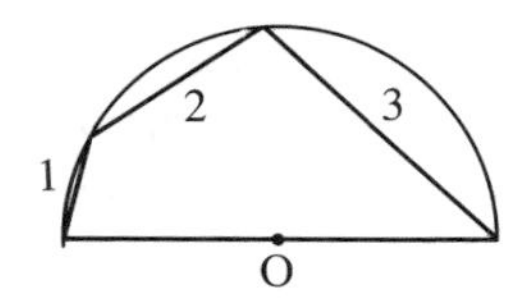

21. a) In $\triangle ABC$, the altitudes from B to AC and from C to AB intersect at O. Prove that AO is perpendicular to BC.
    b) State a theorem about the altitudes of a triangle that you have proved in part a).

In the diagram, major arc AOB subtends $\angle APB$ and $\angle AQB$ at the circumference of the circle.

Does the Angles in a Circle Theorem apply in this situation? If so, do its corollaries also apply?

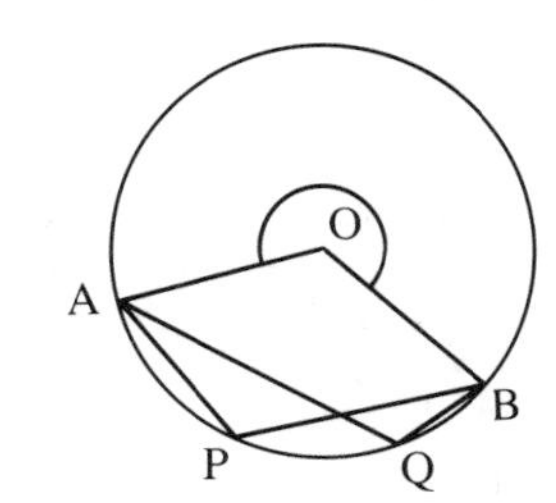

6-4 CONCYCLIC POINTS

Some of the most important theorems in mathematics have grown out of attempts to answer simple questions. Three such questions are posed below.

Question 1: Is there a circle which passes through any two given points?

The diagram suggests that infinitely many circles can be drawn through the two given points A and B.

We can deduce this by observing that any point on the perpendicular bisector of AB is equidistant from A and B (Perpendicular Bisector Theorem) and is therefore the centre of a circle through points A and B.

Since there are infinitely many points on the perpendicular bisector of AB, there are infinitely many circles through A and B.

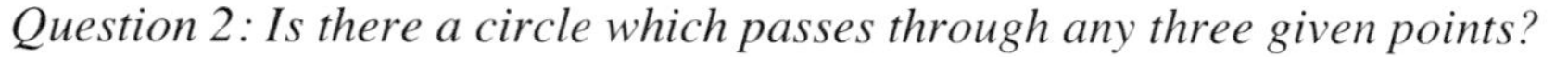

Question 2: Is there a circle which passes through any three given points?

If the three given points are collinear, then there is no circle which passes through them.

Since A, B, and C are non-collinear, the perpendicular bisectors of AB and BC intersect in a single point O. That is, there is only one point that is equidistant from A, B, and C and therefore only one circle which contains them all.

Since any three non-collinear points form the vertices of a triangle, we can say that for any given triangle there is a unique circle which passes through its vertices. This is called the *circumcircle* of the triangle.

Question 3: Is there a circle which passes through any four given points?

Given any four points (no three of which are collinear) we can find a unique circle which passes through any 3 of them. However, if the points are chosen arbitrarily, the fourth point will not necessarily lie on that circle. The following definition will be helpful in expressing conditions under which four points lie on a circle.

Definition: Any set of points which lie on a circle are said to be *concyclic*.

The search for conditions under which points lie on a circle may now be expressed as the search for conditions under which points are concyclic. The following theorem is the converse of corollary 1 of the Angles in a Circle Theorem, page 219.

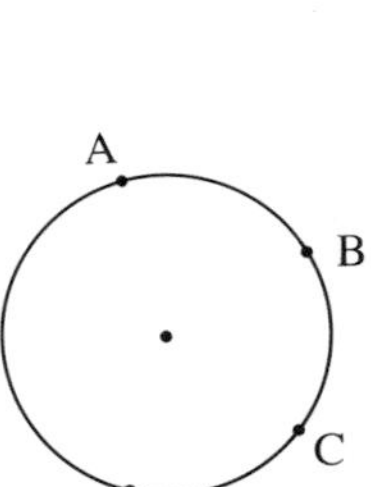

A, B, C, and D are concyclic

> **Theorem**
> If a line segment subtends equal angles at two points on the same side of the segment, then the two points and the ends of the line segment are concyclic.

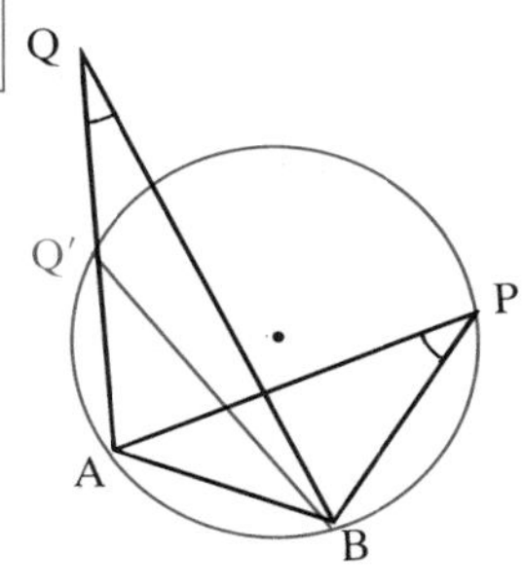

Given: Chord AB and points P and Q such that
$\angle AQB = \angle APB$

Required to Prove: A, B, P, and Q are concyclic.

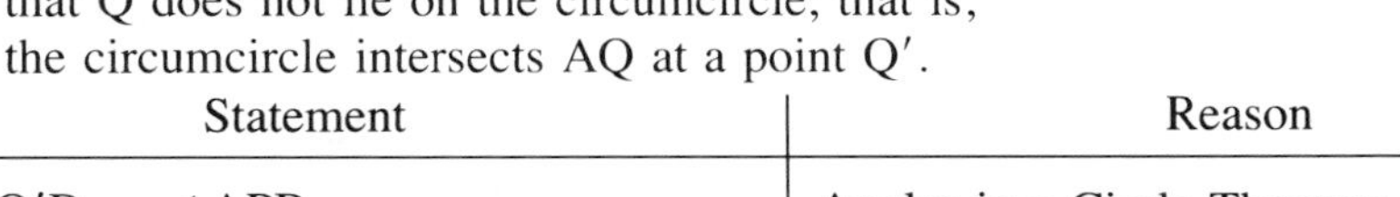

Proof: Consider the circumcircle of $\triangle APB$. Either Q lies on the circumcircle or it does not. Suppose that Q does not lie on the circumcircle; that is, the circumcircle intersects AQ at a point Q′.

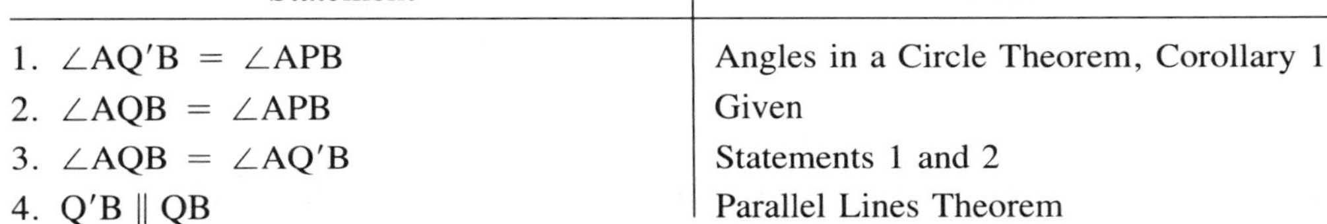

Statement	Reason
1. $\angle AQ'B = \angle APB$	Angles in a Circle Theorem, Corollary 1
2. $\angle AQB = \angle APB$	Given
3. $\angle AQB = \angle AQ'B$	Statements 1 and 2
4. $Q'B \parallel QB$	Parallel Lines Theorem

Statement 4 contradicts the fact that QB and Q′B intersect at B.
Similarly, we can prove that Q′ does not lie on AQ extended.
Therefore, Q lies on the circumcircle of $\triangle ABP$.
That is, A, B, P, and Q are concyclic.

Example. Prove that the midpoint of the hypotenuse of a right triangle is equidistant from the vertices of that triangle.

Solution. *Given:* $\triangle PQR$ is a right triangle with $\angle Q = 90°$.
O is the midpoint of hypotenuse PR.

Required to Prove: $OP = OQ = OR$

Analysis: Construct a circle centre O and diameter PR. Let S be any point on the circle on the same side of PR as point Q.

Proof:

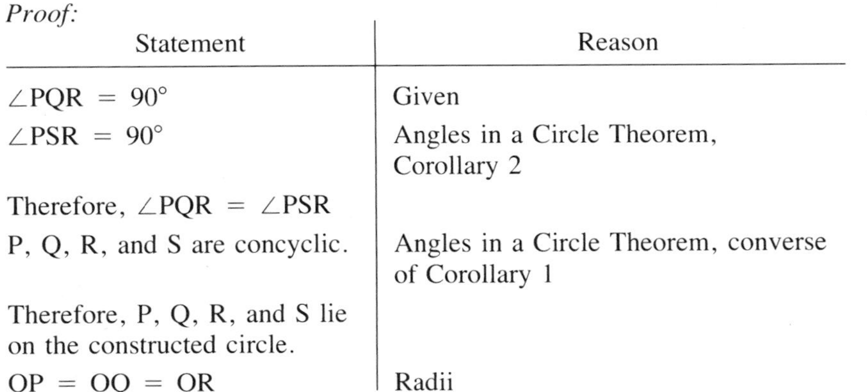

Statement	Reason
$\angle PQR = 90°$	Given
$\angle PSR = 90°$	Angles in a Circle Theorem, Corollary 2
Therefore, $\angle PQR = \angle PSR$	
P, Q, R, and S are concyclic.	Angles in a Circle Theorem, converse of Corollary 1
Therefore, P, Q, R, and S lie on the constructed circle.	
$OP = OQ = OR$	Radii

EXERCISES 6-4

1. What property is shared by points A, B, and C if there is no circle on which all three points lie?

2. In the diagram (below left), AD, BE, and CF are the altitudes of $\triangle ABC$ and they intersect at G.
   a) Explain how we know that points B, F, E, and C are concyclic.
   b) Use part a) to deduce that $\angle GCE = \angle FBG$.
   c) Name two other pairs of acute angles which are equal.

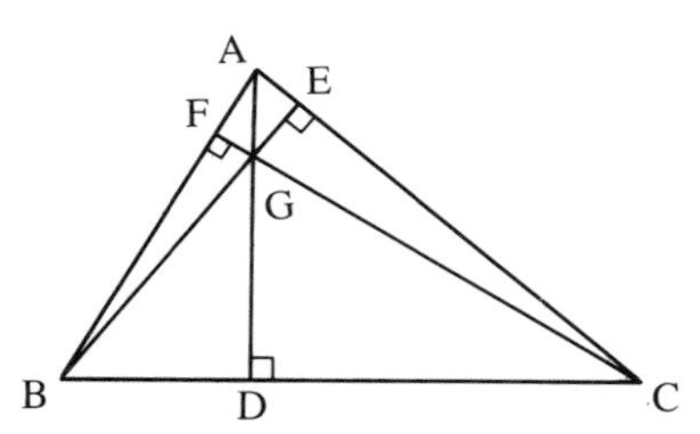

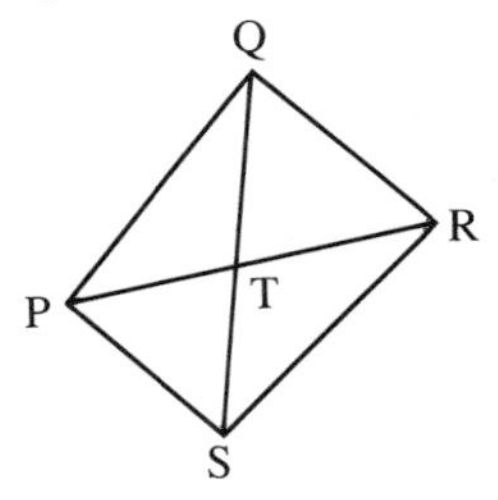

3. In the diagram (above right), PQRS is a quadrilateral with vertices which are concyclic. Diagonals PR and QS intersect at T. Name five pairs of equal angles.

4. A television camera moves in a horizontal plane so that a rectangular billboard subtends a fixed angle at the lens of the camera. What is the shape of the camera's path?

5. In the diagram (below left), PQRS is a quadrilateral with concyclic vertices.
   a) Prove that $\angle QRS = \angle PQS + \angle PSQ$.
   b) Use part a) to prove that $\angle SPQ + \angle QRS = 180°$.
   c) Prove that two angles subtended at the circumference by the same chord but on opposite sides of the chord are supplementary.

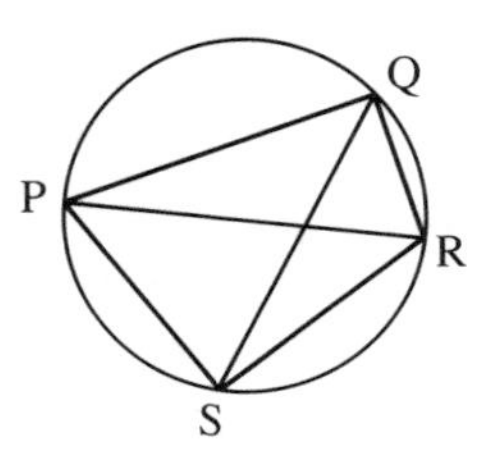

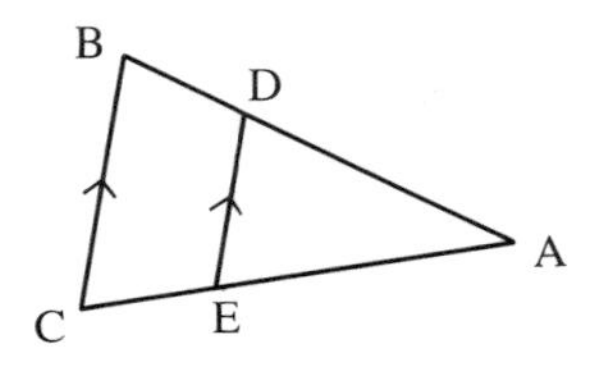

6. In the diagram (above right), isosceles $\triangle ABC$ has $AB = AC$. Points D and E are located on sides AB and AC respectively so that DE is parallel to BC. Prove that points D, E, C, and B are concyclic.

7. Prove that there is a circle which passes through two vertices of a triangle and also passes through the base of each altitude drawn from those vertices.

8. AB and AC are two equal chords of a circle, and D and E are the midpoints of AB and AC respectively. Prove that B, C, E, and D are concyclic points.

6-5 CYCLIC QUADRILATERALS

In the previous section we proved that any three non-collinear points are concyclic. We can express this alternatively as follows.

> The vertices of a triangle are concyclic.

We also observed in the previous section that four points chosen arbitrarily are not necessarily concyclic. We might express this as follows.

> The vertices of a quadrilateral are not necessarily concyclic.

To investigate the conditions under which four points are concyclic, it is convenient to introduce the concept of a cyclic quadrilateral.

Definition: A quadrilateral with concyclic vertices is said to be a *cyclic quadrilateral.*

The statement that A, B, C, and D are concyclic

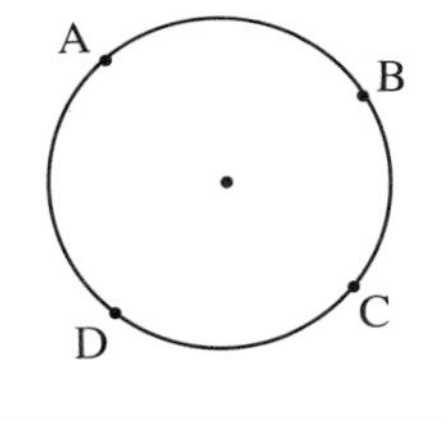

is equivalent to

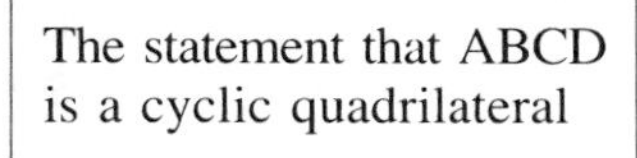
The statement that ABCD is a cyclic quadrilateral

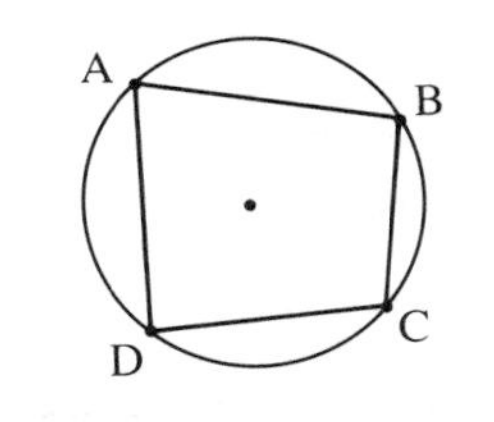

The converse of the Angles in a Circle Theorem (proved in the previous section) can be expressed in terms of a cyclic quadrilateral.

> **Theorem**
> If one side of a quadrilateral subtends equal angles at its other two vertices, then the quadrilateral is cyclic.

The following theorem provides another set of conditions which are sufficient to establish that a quadrilateral is cyclic.

> **Theorem**
> If a quadrilateral is cyclic, then its opposite angles are supplementary.

Given: Cyclic quadrilateral ABCD inscribed in a circle centre O

Required to Prove: $\angle A + \angle C = 180°$
$\angle B + \angle D = 180°$

Analysis: Join O to A, B, C, and D to form 4 isosceles triangles. Label the measures of the equal angles.

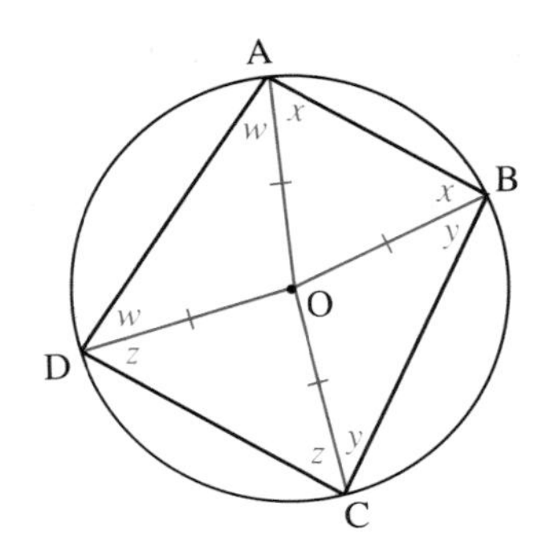

Proof:

Statement	Reason
$OA = OB = OC = OD$	Radii
$\angle OAB = \angle OBA = x$	Isosceles Triangle Theorem
$\angle OBC = \angle OCB = y$	Isosceles Triangle Theorem
$\angle OCD = \angle CDO = z$	Isosceles Triangle Theorem
$\angle ODA = \angle OAD = w$	Isosceles Triangle Theorem
$2(w + x + y + z) = 360°$	Sum of the angles in a quadrilateral is 360°
$(w + x) + (y + z) = 180°$	
$w + x = \angle A;\ y + z = \angle C$	Analysis
Therefore, $\angle A + \angle C = 180°$	
Similarly, $\angle B + \angle D = 180°$	

The theorem proved above enables us to relate angles subtended by the same chord but located on opposite sides of that chord. In the diagram, $\angle C$ and $\angle D$ are both on the circumference of the circle and subtended by the chord AB. Since they are opposite angles of a cyclic quadrilateral, they are supplementary.

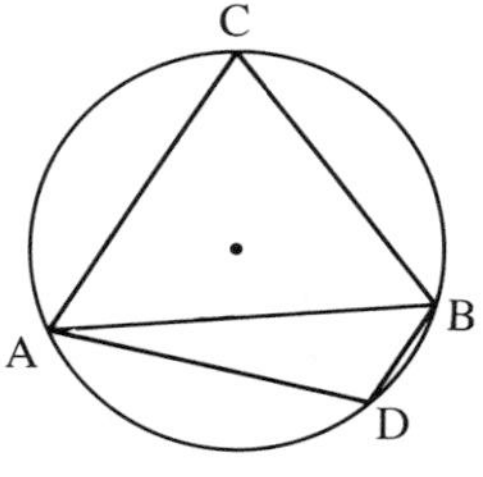

$\angle C + \angle D = 180°$

This theorem can be used to prove its converse, stated below.

> **Theorem**
> If the opposite angles of a quadrilateral are supplementary, then the quadrilateral is cyclic.

Given: Quadrilateral PQRS such that
$\angle S + \angle Q = 180°$ and $\angle P + \angle R = 180°$

Required to Prove: PQRS is a cyclic quadrilateral.

Analysis: Let T be any point on the circumcircle of $\triangle PQR$, on the same side of PR as S. Join TR and TP.

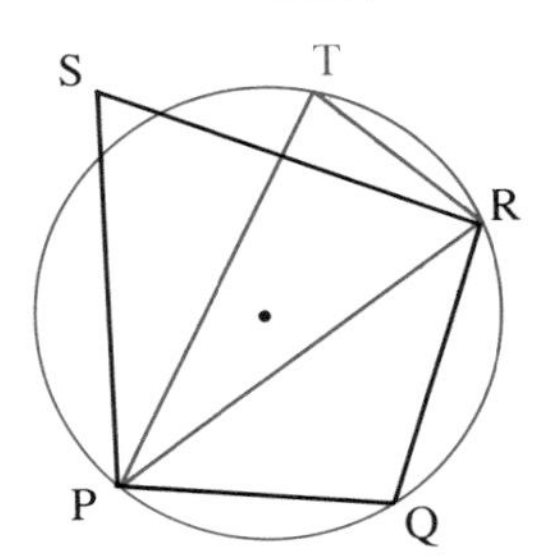

Proof:

Statement	Reason
$\angle S + \angle Q = 180°$	Given
$\angle T + \angle Q = 180°$	Analysis — P, Q, R, T are concyclic
Therefore, $\angle S = \angle T$	
P, R, T, and S are concyclic	Converse of Angles in a Circle Theorem
Therefore, S lies on the circle through P, R, and T	
But Q lies on the circle through P, R, and T	Analysis
Therefore, PQRS is a cyclic quadrilateral	

The foregoing theorem and its converse can be combined into a biconditional statement called the Cyclic Quadrilateral Theorem.

> **Cyclic Quadrilateral Theorem**
> A quadrilateral is cyclic iff its opposite angles are supplementary.

> **Corollary of the Cyclic Quadrilateral Theorem**
> A quadrilateral is cyclic iff any of its exterior angles is equal to the interior and opposite angle.

In the diagram, $\angle BCE$ is an exterior angle of cyclic quadrilateral ABCD.
Since ABCD is a cyclic quadrilateral
$\angle BAD + \angle BCD = 180°$
Since DCE is a straight line
$\angle BCE + \angle BCD = 180°$
Therefore, $\angle BAD = \angle BCE$

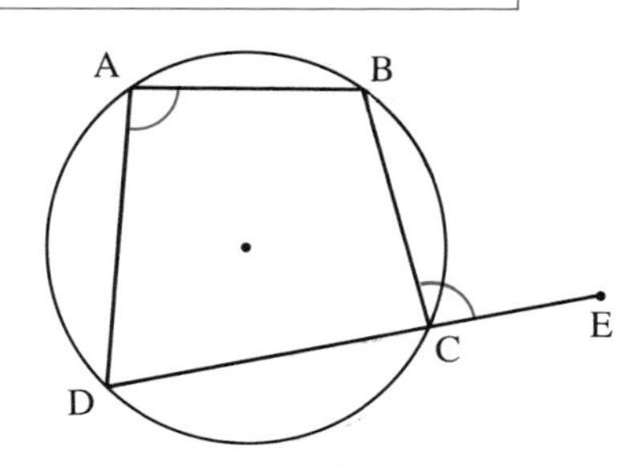

EXERCISES 6-5

Ⓐ

1. Find each value of x.

a)

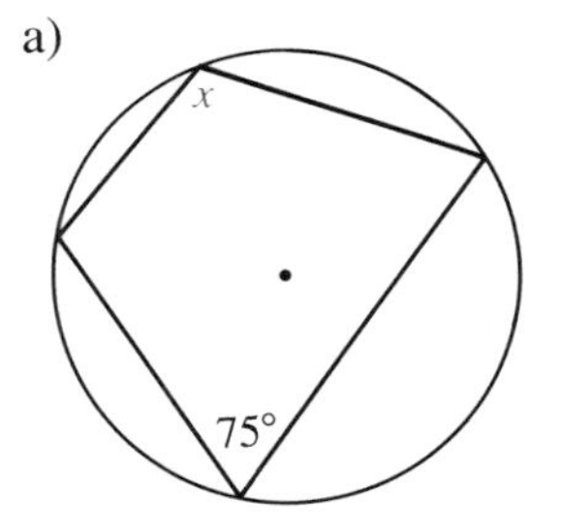

b)

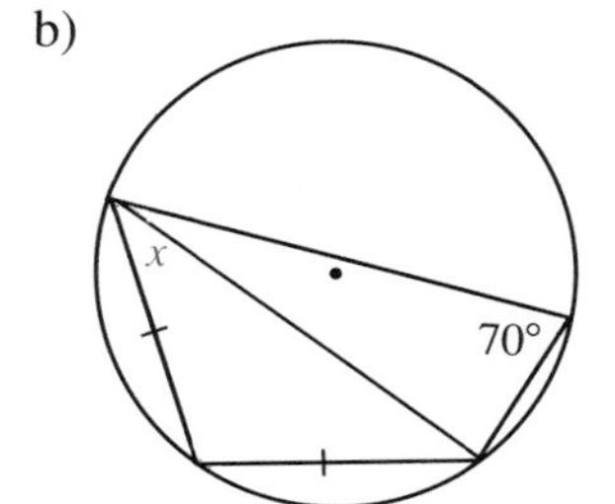

c)

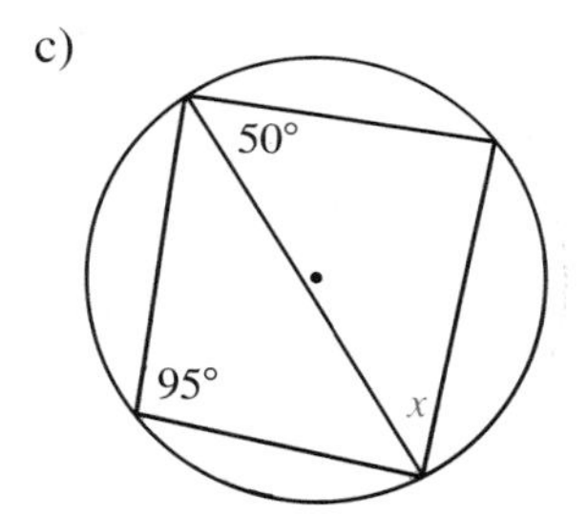

2. Find the values of x and y.

a)

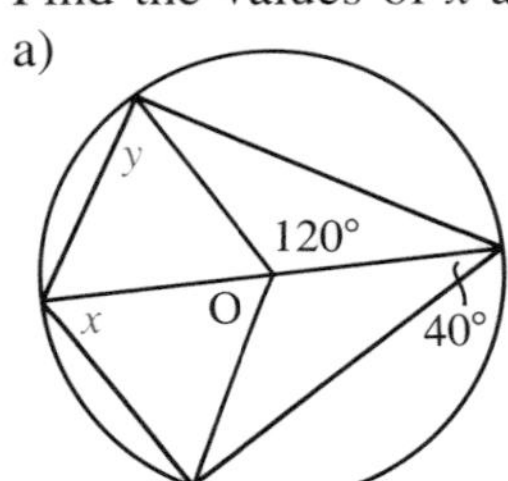

b)

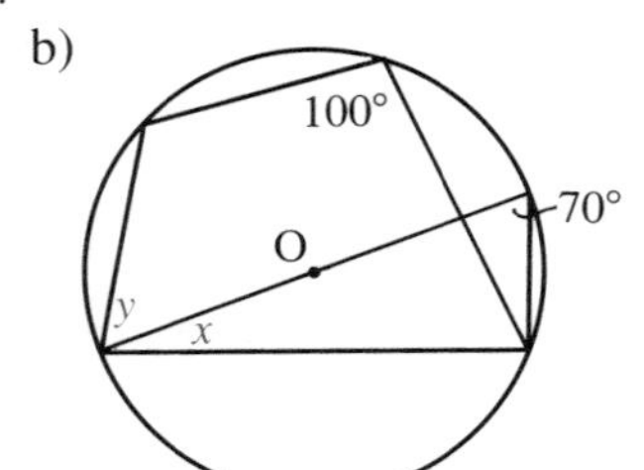

c)

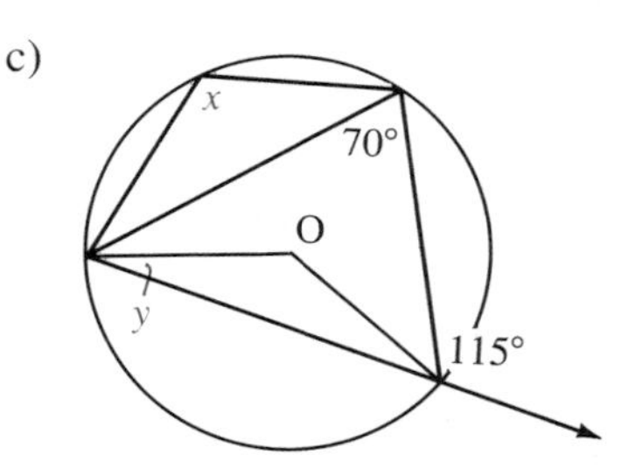

3. Name three different conditions, each of which is sufficient to prove that a quadrilateral is cyclic.

4. PQRS (below left) is a cyclic quadrilateral with PQ = PS and RQ = RS. Prove that △PQR and △PSR are right triangles.

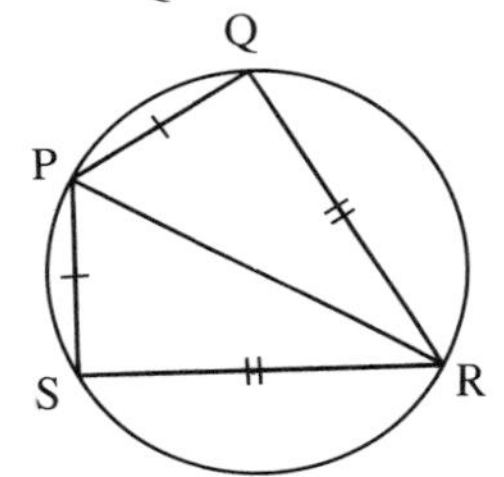

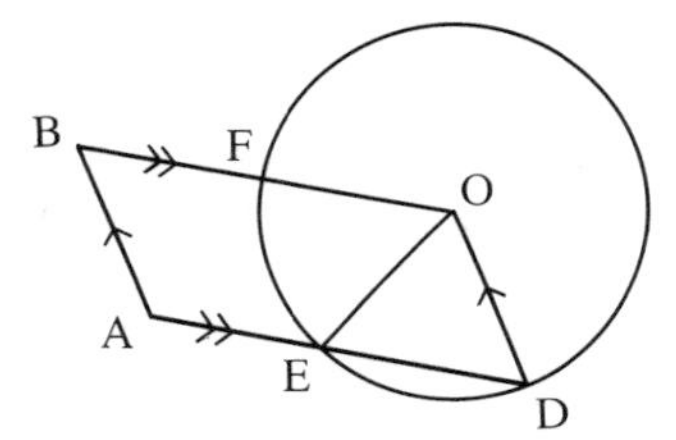

5. In the diagram (above right), a circle with centre O intersects parallelogram ABOD at points D, E, and F. Prove that BOEA is a cyclic quadrilateral.

6. PQRS is a trapezoid with PQ parallel to SR, and PS = QR. Prove that if PQRS is not a parallelogram, then it is a cyclic quadrilateral.

7. W, X, Y, and Z are points on a circle with centre O and diameter WZ (below left). V is a point outside the circle such that VW is perpendicular to VX. Prove that ∠VWX = ∠ZWY.

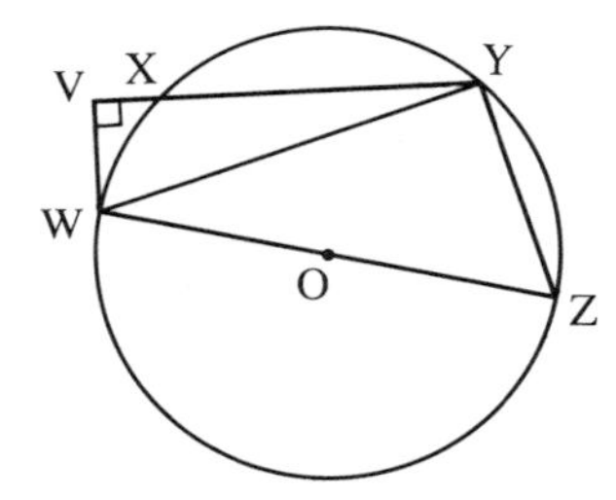

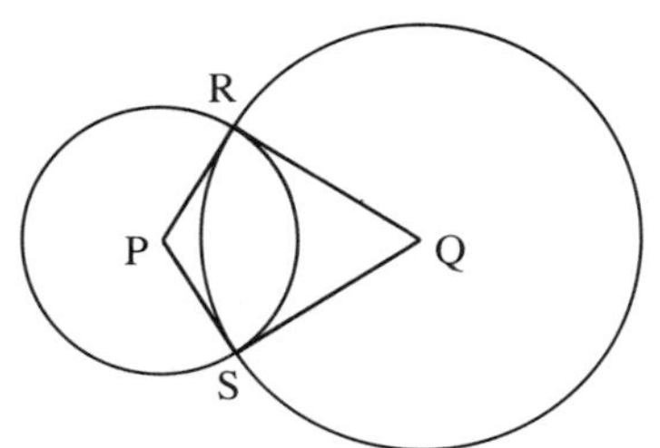

8. R and S are the points of intersection of circles with centres P and Q (above right). If RQSP is a cyclic quadrilateral, prove that ∠R = ∠S = 90°.

9. ABCD is a cyclic quadrilateral with AB = AD and CB = CD. Prove that the quadrilateral formed by joining the midpoints of adjacent sides is a rectangle.

10. Prove that the three altitudes of a triangle are concurrent.

6-6 PROPERTIES OF TANGENTS

Many geometric theorems are intuitively obvious to us in their everyday application. However, the creation of a rigorous deductive geometry requires that even the most "obvious" theorems be proved. The history of mathematics has shown that major errors, when they occurred, resulted from the unquestioned assumption of "truths" which appeared "self-evident".

Whenever we cross a street, we intuitively know that the shortest path to the other side is a line perpendicular to the curb. This can be expressed as a theorem, which will be important in the proofs of the other theorems in this section. This theorem, while apparently self-evident, must be proved in a rigorous treatment of geometry.

> **Distance Theorem**
> Given any line l and any point P not on l, there is exactly one point Q on l such that PQ is perpendicular to l. Furthermore, PQ is the shortest distance from P to l.

To prove this theorem we shall use the method of indirect proof.

Given: A line l, a point P not on l, and a point Q on l, such that PQ is perpendicular to l.

Required to Prove: a) There is no other point on l such that a line drawn to it from P is perpendicular to l.
b) PQ is the shortest distance from P to l.

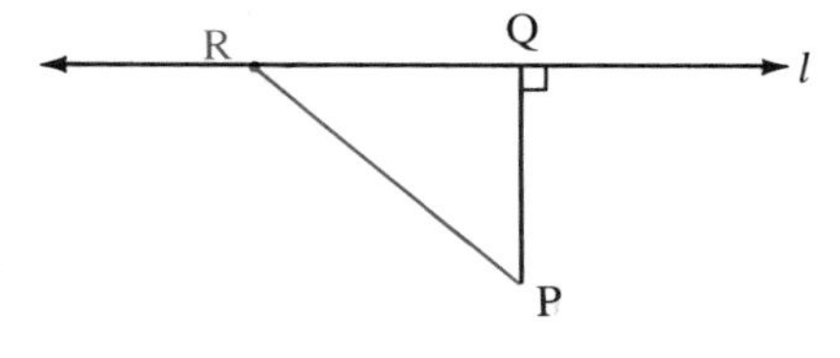

Proof: Let R be any point on l, distinct from Q.
Then, we are required to prove that PR is not perpendicular to l, and that $PQ < PR$.
Either $PQ < PR$, or it is not.
Assume that $PQ > PR$.

Statement	Reason
In $\triangle PQR$	
1. $\angle Q = 90°$	Given
2. $\angle R < 90°$	Sum of the Angles Theorem
3. $PQ < PR$	Corollary 2 of Exterior Angle Theorem

It follows from statement 2 that PR is not perpendicular to l.
Statement 3 contradicts the assumption that $PQ > PR$.
Hence, the assumption is false.
Therefore, $PQ < PR$.

You may recall in *Section 6-1* we defined a tangent to a circle as a line which intersects that circle in exactly one point. The word tangent is derived from the Latin verb "tangere," which means to touch.

> **Theorem**
> If a line is perpendicular to a radius of a circle at a point of intersection with the circle, then the line is a tangent to the circle at that point.

Given: A circle with centre O and a line l which intersects the circle at point Q such that OQ is perpendicular to l

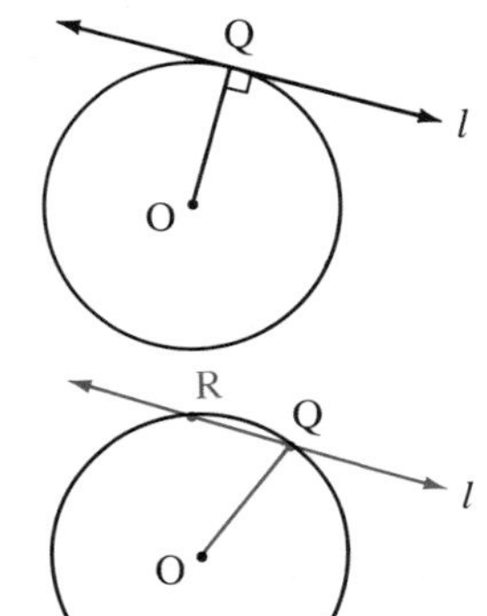

Required to Prove: l is tangent to the circle at Q.
Proof: We use indirect proof.
Either l is a tangent to the circle, or it is not.
Assume that l is not a tangent to the circle.
Then, l intersects the circle in another point R which is distinct from Q.

Statement	Reason
1. OQ is perpendicular to l.	Given
2. $OQ < OR$	Distance Theorem
3. $OQ = OR$	Radii

Statement 3 contradicts statement 2.
Hence, the assumption that l is not a tangent is false.
Therefore, l is a tangent to the circle at Q.

> **Theorem**
> A tangent to a circle is perpendicular to the radius of the circle at the point of tangency.

Given: A circle with centre O and radius r.
Line l is a tangent to the circle at Q.
Required to Prove: OQ is perpendicular to l.
Analysis: Let R be any point on l distinct from Q. Then, using the Distance Theorem, it is sufficient to prove that $OQ < OR$.

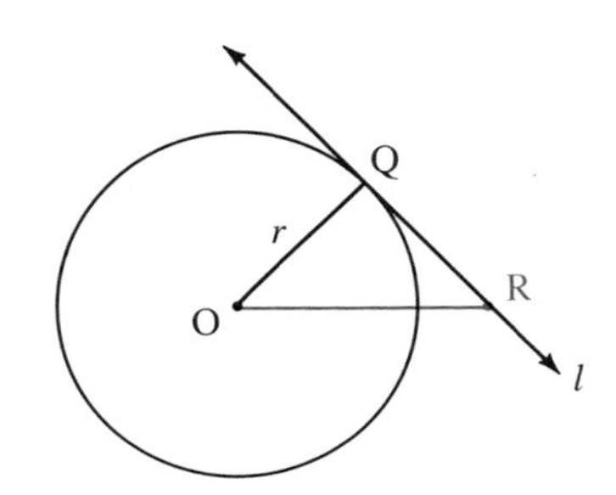

Proof:

Statement	Reason
R lies outside the circle.	l intersects the circle in exactly one point, Q.
Therefore, OR $>$ r	
OQ $=$ r	Radius
Therefore, OQ $<$ OR for all points R on l	
OQ is perpendicular to l.	Distance Theorem

> **Corollary**
> Any line perpendicular to a tangent to a circle at the point of tangency passes through the centre of the circle.

The two theorems above which illustrate the perpendicularity of a tangent to the radius at the point of tangency can be combined into a biconditional statement called the Tangent-Radius Theorem.

> **Tangent-Radius Theorem**
> A line is a tangent to a circle iff it is perpendicular to the radius of the circle at a point of intersection.

The Tangent-Radius Theorem shows that tangents drawn to a circle, centre O, from an external point P must be perpendicular to the radii drawn to their points of contact, Q and R.

Hence, two right triangles can be drawn with OP as their hypotenuse.

We discovered earlier in this chapter (page 220) that if a circle is drawn with diameter OP, then $\angle OQP = \angle ORP = 90°$ only if Q and R lie on the circumference of the circle.

This diagram illustrates that the only points of tangency from P to the circle, centre O, are the points of intersection of the two circles. Since these circles intersect in exactly two points, then exactly two points of tangency exist.

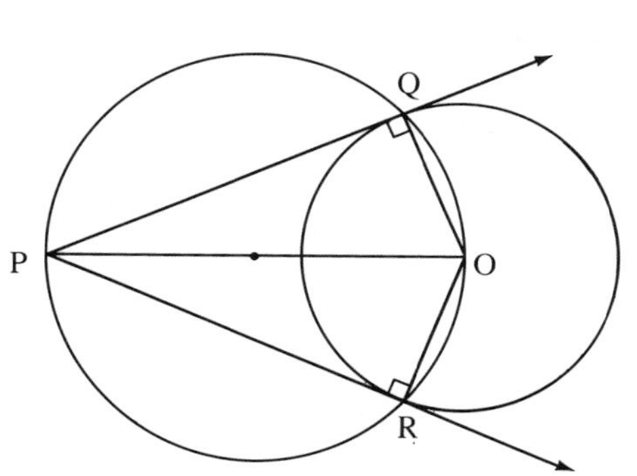

The foregoing discussion can be formalized and extended to establish the Equal Tangents Theorem.

> **Equal Tangents Theorem**
> From a point P outside a circle there are exactly two tangents which can be drawn. Furthermore, PQ = PR where Q and R are the points of tangency.

Given: Circle, centre O, and any point P outside the circle.

Required to Prove: There are exactly two tangents which can be drawn to the circle from P, and those tangents are equal in length.

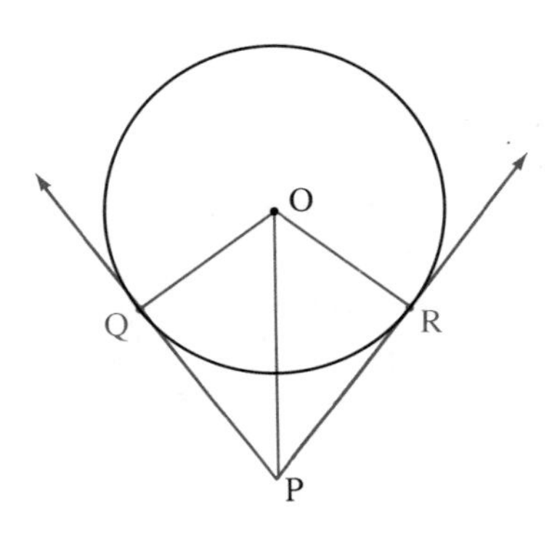

Analysis: Let Q and R be points on the circle to which tangents are drawn from P.
We showed previously that two circles can intersect, at most, in two points.
Hence, there are exactly two points Q and R such that $\overleftrightarrow{PQ}$ and $\overleftrightarrow{PR}$ are tangents to the circle.
It remains only to prove that PQ = PR.

Proof:

Statement	Reason
In △POQ and △POR	
∠OQP = ∠ORP = 90°	Tangent-Radius Theorem
OP is common	
OQ = OR	Radii
Therefore, △POQ ≅ △POR	HS
PQ = PR	Congruent triangles

EXERCISES 6-6

Ⓐ

1. Find each value of y.
   a) b) c)

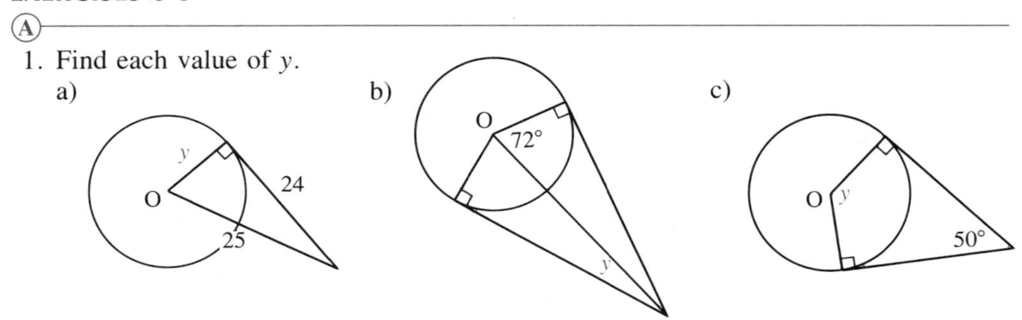

2. Find the values of x and y. O and M mark the centres of circles.

a)

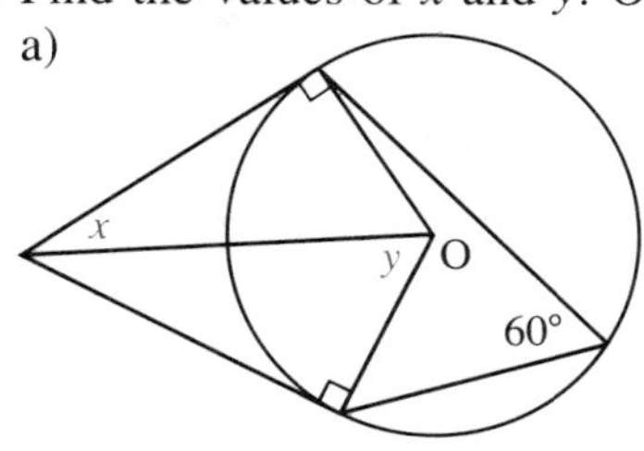

b)

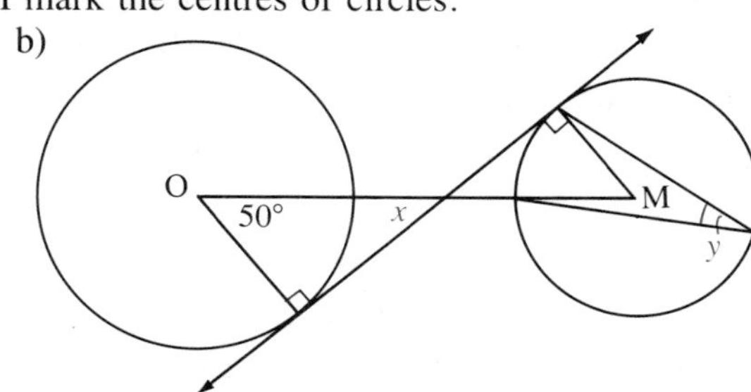

Ⓑ

3. In the diagram (below left), PQ is a tangent at point Q to the circle with centre O. If QO = QR, prove that OR = RP.

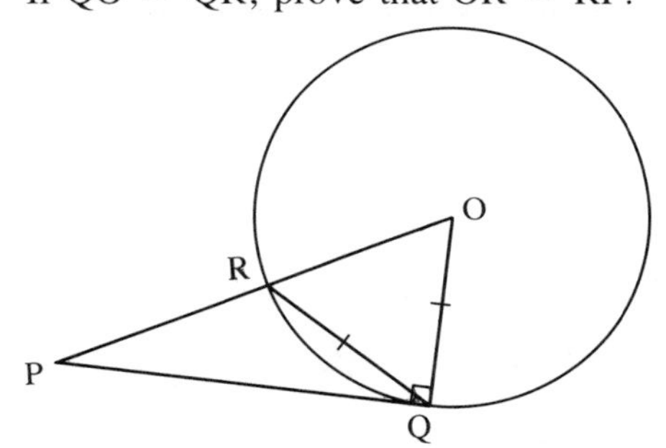

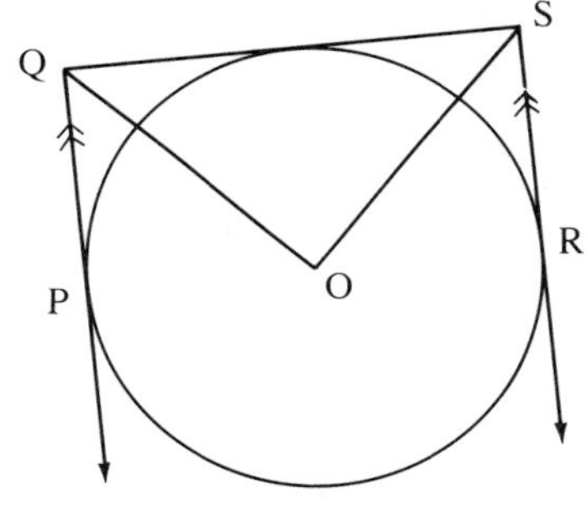

4. PQ and RS (above right) are tangents at points P and R to a circle with centre O. QS is also a tangent to the circle. If PQ is parallel to RS, prove that △QOS is a right triangle.

5. Two tangents are drawn from an external point P to points A and B on a circle with centre O. Prove that the points P, A, B, and O are concyclic.

6. PQ and RS (below left) are chords of a circle with centre O, and are tangents to a smaller concentric circle. Prove that PQ = RS.

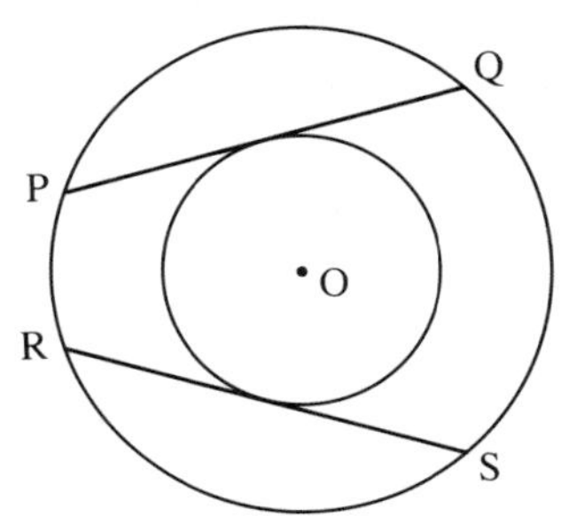

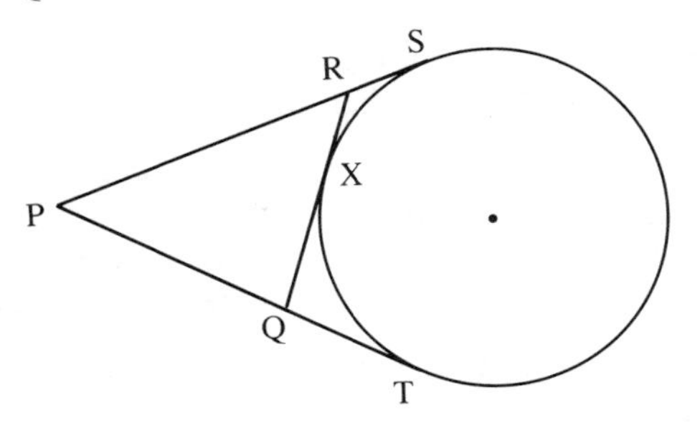

7. PS, PT, and QR (above right) are tangents to a circle at the points S, T, and X respectively. Prove that the perimeter of △PQR is equal to 2PS.

8. AB and CD are tangents to a circle at points B and D. If BD is a diameter of the circle, prove that AB is parallel to CD.

9. Prove that if two circles intersect in distinct points L and M, then the centres of the circles, and the midpoint of LM, are collinear.

10. P is a point external to a circle with centre O. From P, tangents PA and PB are drawn to the circle. Prove that PO bisects $\angle$BPA.

11. Two circles of radii 10 cm and 17 cm share a common chord of length 16 cm. What is the distance between their centres?

12. When the tangents at the point of intersection of two circles are perpendicular, we say the circles intersect at right angles.

    Two circles with centres O and C and radii r and R respectively, intersect at right angles at points A and B (below left).
    a) Prove that AB is perpendicular to OC.
    b) Prove that $\triangle$AOD $\sim$ $\triangle$CAD, where D is the intersection point of AB and OC.
    c) Find an expression in terms of r and R for the length of AB.

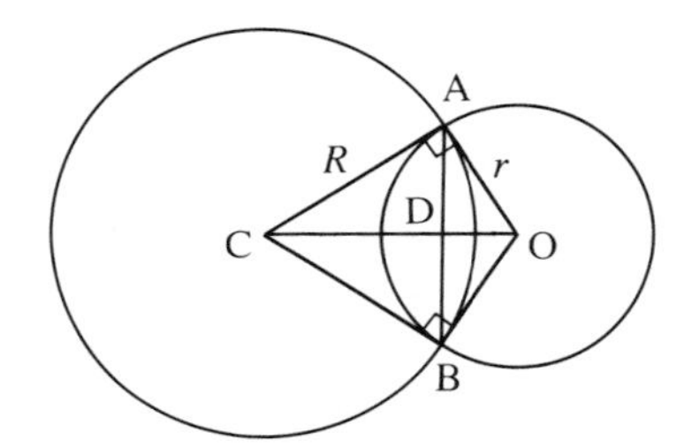

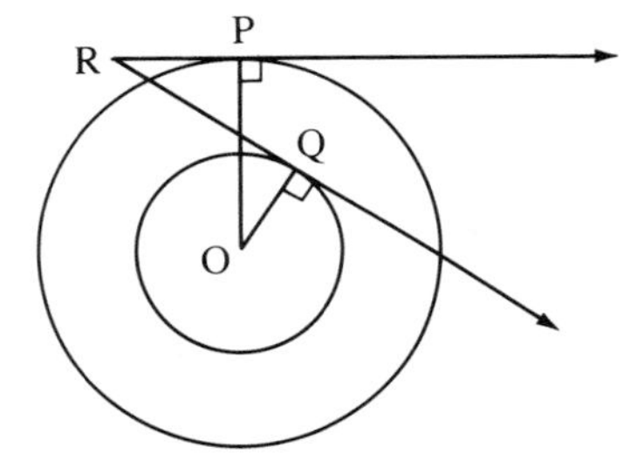

13. A tangent is drawn to each of two concentric circles with centre O (above right). If P and Q are the points of tangency and R is the point of intersection of the tangents, prove that $\angle$PRQ = $\angle$POQ.

Ⓒ

14. AB is any diameter of a circle and $\overleftrightarrow{PQ}$ is a tangent to that circle. Prove that the sum of the distances of A and B from $\overleftrightarrow{PQ}$ is a constant.

15. Prove that if the centre of a circle inscribed in a triangle is also the centre of the circumscribed circle, then the triangle is equilateral.

16. a) A right triangle has one side of length 8 cm and hypotenuse 17 cm. Find the radius of its inscribed circle.
    b) Prove that the diameter of the inscribed circle of a right triangle is the sum of the lengths of the two shorter sides less the length of the hypotenuse.

17. PQ is a tangent to the circles with centres O and C at points P and Q respectively. Also, RS is a tangent to those circles at R and S. If T is the point of intersection of PQ and RS, prove that O, T, and C are collinear.

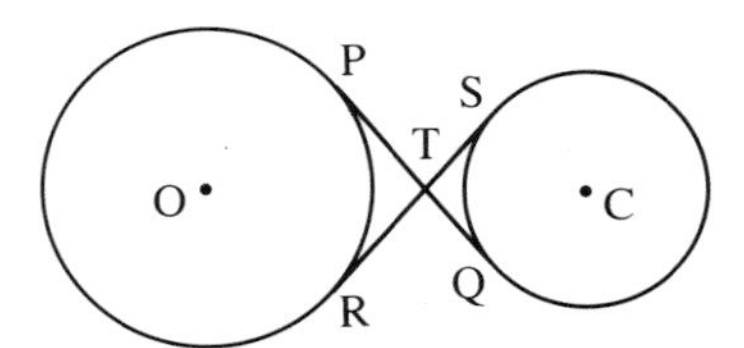

6-7 THE TANGENT-CHORD THEOREM

In the previous section we discovered that the angle between a tangent and the diameter (or radius) at the point of tangency is always 90°. In this section we extend our investigation to the angle between a tangent and *any* chord at the point of tangency. The following Tangent-Chord Theorem may be regarded as a generalization of the Tangent-Radius Theorem.

> **Tangent-Chord Theorem**
> The angle between a tangent to a circle and a chord of the circle is equal to one-half the angle subtended by the chord at the centre of the circle.

Given: A circle with centre O, a line $\overleftrightarrow{AC}$ which is tangent to the circle at point A, and a chord AB

Required to Prove: $\angle BAC = \frac{1}{2}\angle BOA$

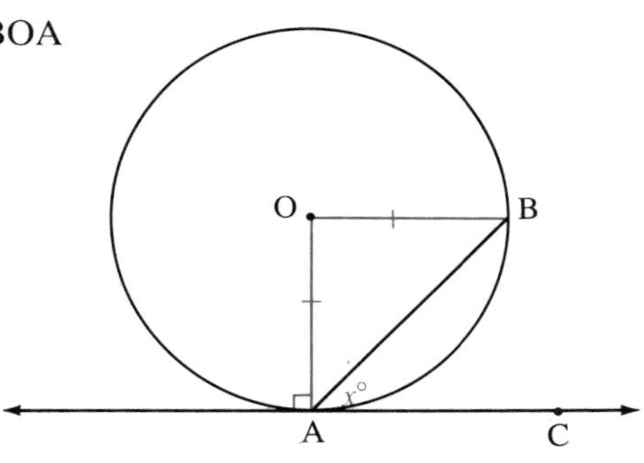

Proof:

Statement	Reason
Let $\angle BAC = x°$	
$\angle OAC = 90°$	Tangent-Radius Theorem
$\angle OAB = \angle OAC - \angle BAC$	Complementary angles
Therefore, $\angle OAB = (90 - x)°$	
$OA = OB$	Radii
$\angle OBA = \angle OAB$	Isosceles Triangle Theorem
Therefore, $\angle OBA = (90 - x)°$	
$\angle BOA = 180° - \angle OAB - \angle OBA$ $= 180° - (90 - x)° - (90 - x)°$ $= 2x°$ $= 2\angle BAC$	Sum of the Angles Theorem
Therefore, $\angle BAC = \frac{1}{2}\angle BOA$	

> **Corollary of the Tangent-Chord Theorem**
> The angle between a tangent to a circle and a chord is equal to the angle subtended on the opposite side of the chord.

In the diagram
$\overleftrightarrow{DC}$ is a tangent to the circle at A, with chords AE and AB.
∠EAD = ∠EBA
∠BAC = ∠BEA

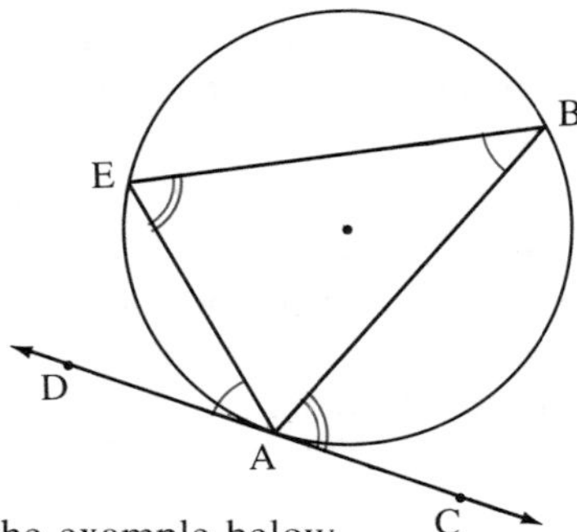

The following definition will be required in the example below.

Definition: The *angle of elevation* of an object is the angle (up to 90° maximum) between the horizontal plane and the line segment joining the observer's eye to the object.

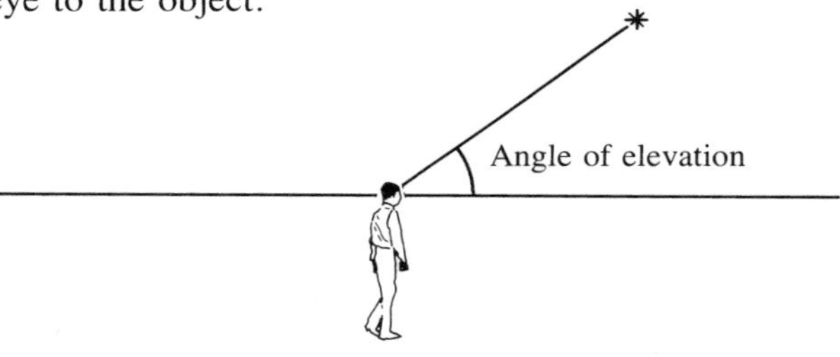

Example. Andy and Brinkley are seated at opposite ends of a diameter of a Ferris wheel. What is Andy's angle of elevation as seen from the bottom of the Ferris wheel when his angle of elevation as seen by Brinkley is $x°$? (Assume the ground is a tangent to the Ferris wheel.)

Solution. Let A and B denote Andy's and Brinkley's positions respectively and let O denote the centre of the Ferris wheel.
$x°$ is the angle of elevation of A from B.
G marks the position of the Ferris wheel where it is tangent to the ground, $\overleftrightarrow{GE}$.
Let $\overleftrightarrow{OC}$ and $\overleftrightarrow{BD}$ be lines parallel to the ground.
We want an expression for ∠AGE, the angle of elevation of A from G.

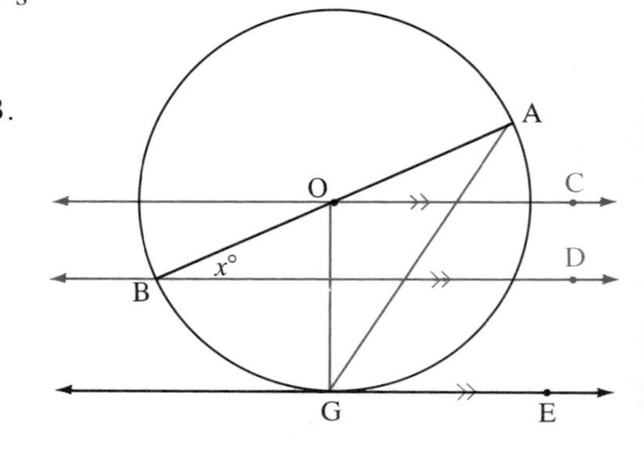

From the Parallel Lines Theorem
$\angle AOC = \angle ABD = x^\circ$
$\angle COG + \angle OGE = 180^\circ$
From the Tangent-Radius Theorem
$\angle OGE = 90^\circ$
Therefore, $\angle COG = 90^\circ$
$\angle AOG = \angle COG + \angle AOC$
$= (90 + x)^\circ$
From the Tangent-Chord Theorem
$\angle AGE = \frac{1}{2}\angle AOG$
$= 45^\circ + \frac{1}{2}x^\circ$
Andy's angle of elevation from the bottom
of the Ferris wheel is $45^\circ + \frac{1}{2}x^\circ$.

This *Example* shows the power of the Tangent-Chord Theorem in finding angles in a circle. For an observer at position G, what is the angle between the positions of Andy and Brinkley?

EXERCISES 6-7

Ⓐ

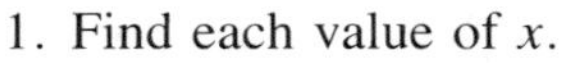

1. Find each value of x.

a)

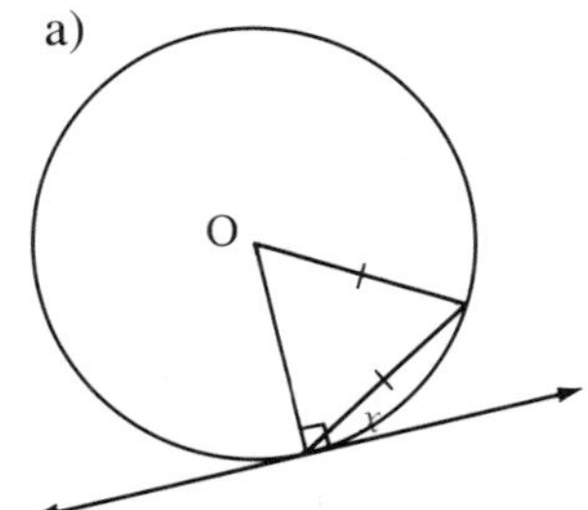

b)

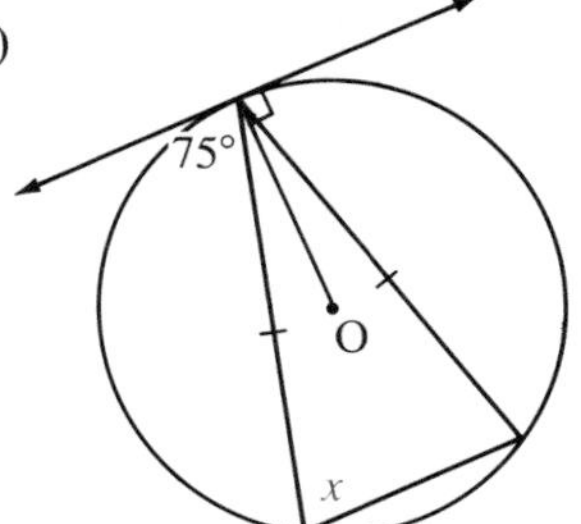

c)

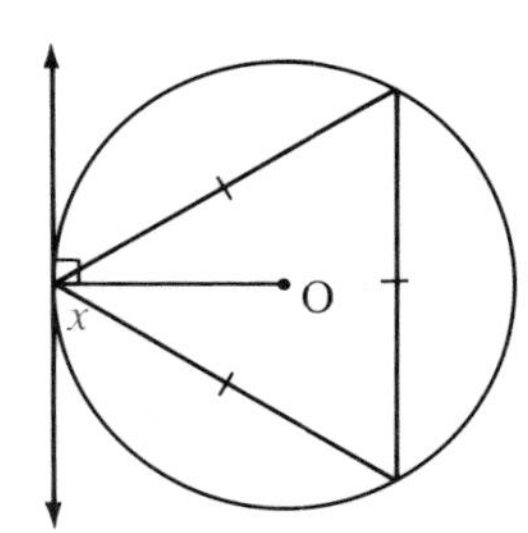

2. Find the values of x and y.

a)

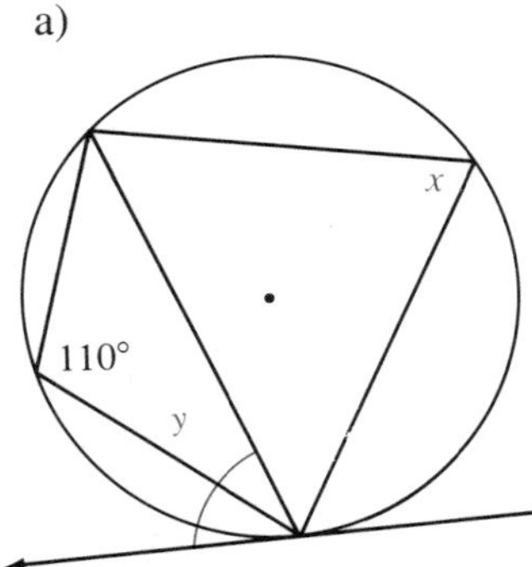

b)

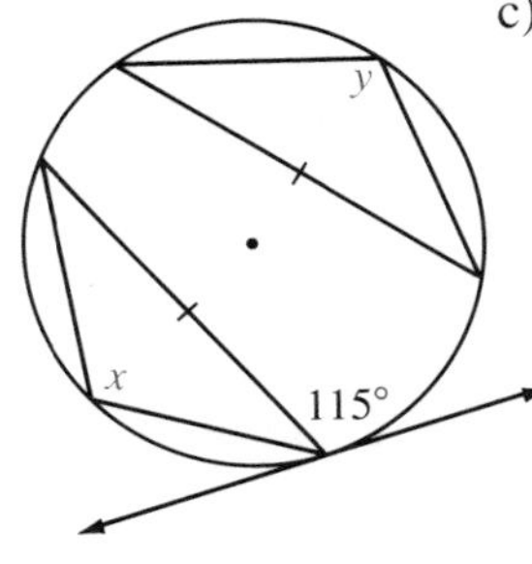

c)

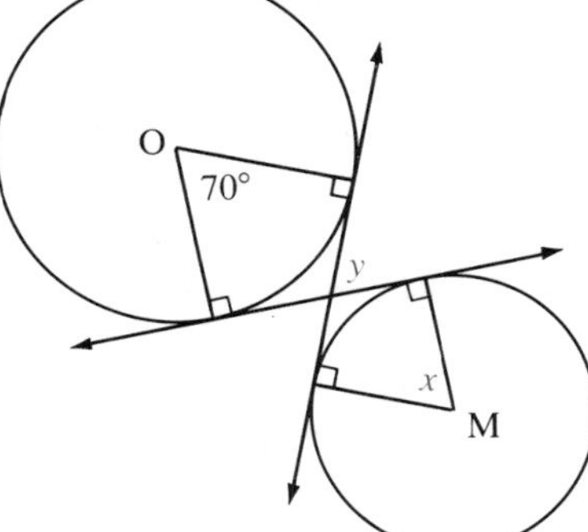

(B)

3. Tangents are drawn from an external point P to points A and B on a circle (below left). AD is a chord parallel to tangent PB. If $\angle PAB = 60°$ and $AP = 7$ cm, find:
   a) the measure of $\angle ADB$ b) the measure of $\angle BAD$ c) the length of AD.

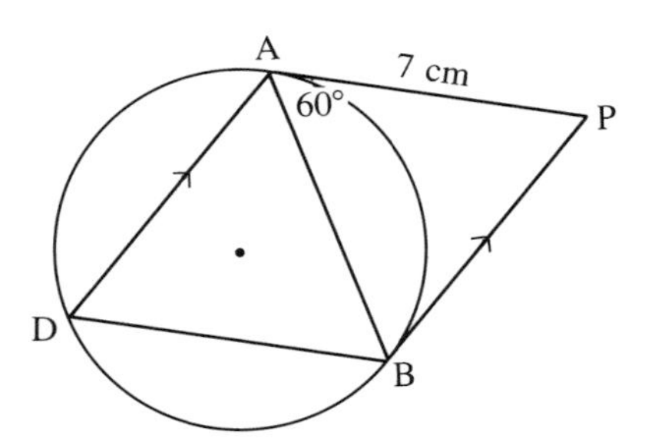

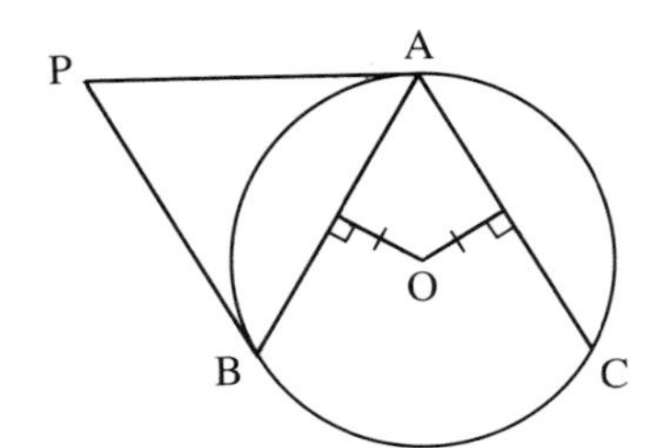

4. AB and AC are two chords which are equidistant from the centre of a circle (above right). P is any point external to the circle, such that PA and PB are tangent to the circle at points A and B. Prove that $\angle APB = \angle BAC$.

5. Tangents PA and PB are drawn from an external point P to points A and B on a circle. If secant PQC intersects the circle at points Q and C and bisects $\angle APB$, prove that $\angle CAQ = 90°$.

6. In the diagram (below left), D, E, and F are the points at which the sides of $\triangle PQR$ are tangent to its inscribed circle. Use the Tangent-Chord Theorem to deduce that the two tangents from each vertex of $\triangle PQR$ are equal in length.

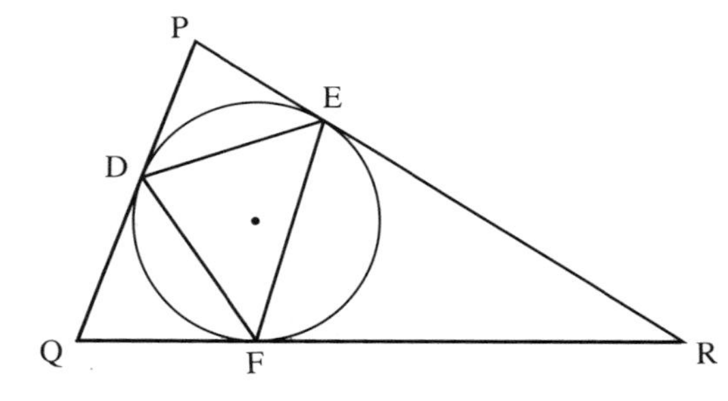

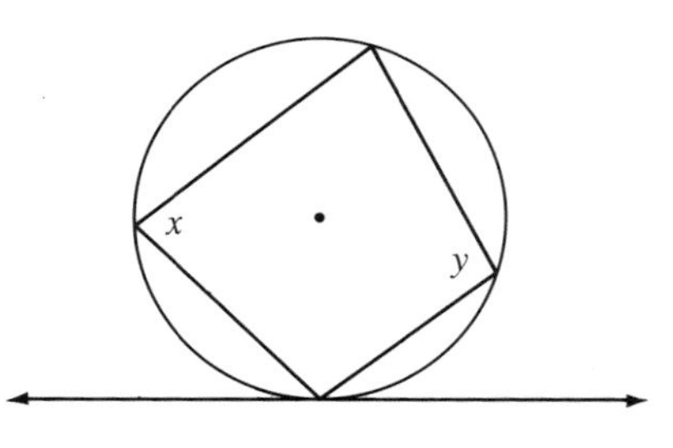

7. a) For x and y defined as in the diagram (above right), use the Tangent-Chord Theorem to deduce that $x + y = 180°$.
   b) Use the Tangent-Chord Theorem to deduce that opposite angles of a cyclic quadrilateral are supplementary.

(C)

8. One leg of a right triangle is the diameter of a circle. Prove that the tangent drawn from the point of intersection of the circle with the hypotenuse bisects the other leg of the triangle.

9. State and prove the converse of the Tangent-Chord Theorem.

6-8 PRODUCT THEOREMS OF CHORDS AND SECANTS

When two chords of a circle intersect inside the circle, they form the diagonals of a cyclic quadrilateral.

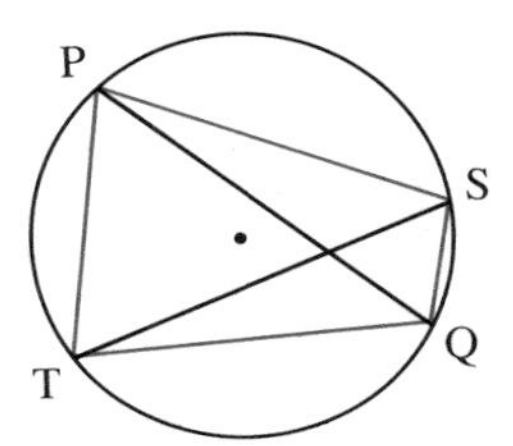

The diagonals divide the quadrilateral into two pairs of similar triangles.

When two non-parallel chords of a circle do not intersect inside the circle, they can be extended until they meet at a point outside the circle.

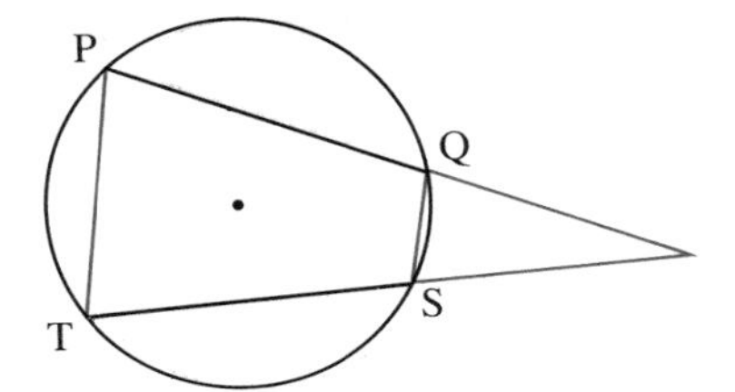

The extended chords or secants define a pair of similar triangles.

Using the properties of similar triangles, we can derive the following theorems.

Chord Product Theorem
If two chords intersect, then the product of the lengths into which each chord is divided is the same for both chords.

Given: PQ and ST are two chords of a circle, which intersect at a point R inside the circle.
Required to Prove: RP × RQ = RS × RT

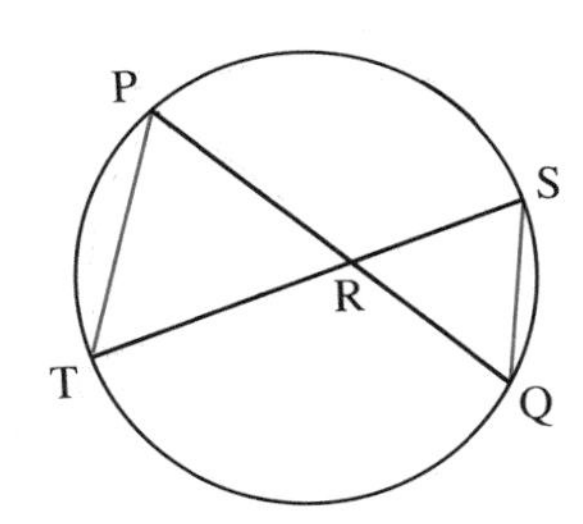

Proof:

Statement	Reason
In △PRT and △SRQ	
∠PRT = ∠SRQ	Opposite Angles Theorem
∠TPQ = ∠TSQ	Corollary 1, Angles in a Circle Theorem
∠PTR = ∠PQS	Corollary 1, Angles in a Circle Theorem
Therefore, △PRT ~ △SRQ	AAA~
$\frac{RP}{RT} = \frac{RS}{RQ}$	Similar triangles
RP × RQ = RS × RT	Cross-multiplying

Secant Product Theorem
If two secants are drawn to a circle from an external point, then the product of the distances from that point to the two points of intersection with the circle is the same for both secants.

Given: Two secants RP and RT are drawn to a circle from a point R outside the circle. The secants intersect the circle in the points Q and S respectively.

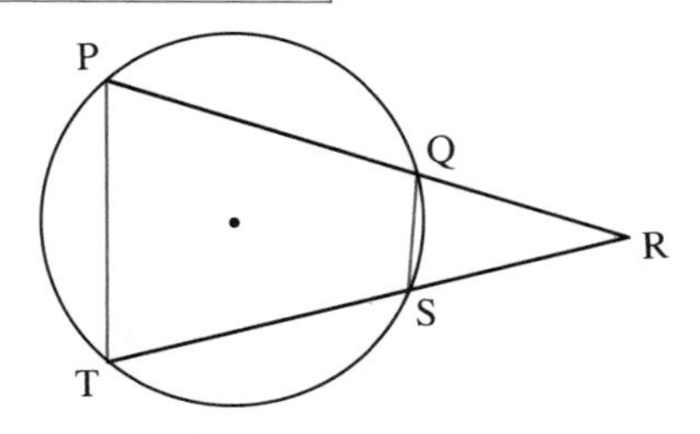

Required to Prove: $RP \times RQ = RS \times RT$
Proof:

Statement	Reason
In $\triangle RQS$ and $\triangle RTP$	
$\angle R$ is common	
$\angle RSQ = \angle RPT$	Corollary of Cyclic Quadrilateral Theorem
$\angle RQS = \angle RTP$	Corollary of Cyclic Quadrilateral Theorem
Therefore, $\triangle RQS \sim \triangle RTP$	AAA~
$\frac{RQ}{RS} = \frac{RT}{RP}$	Similar triangles
$RP \times RQ = RS \times RT$	Cross-multiplying

The Chord Product Theorem and the Secant Product Theorem are special cases of a more general result.

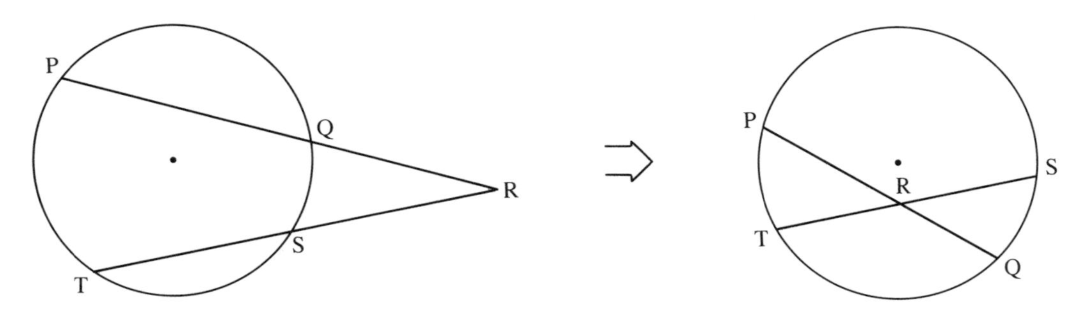

As R moves from outside to inside the circle, the relation $RP \times RQ = RS \times RT$ continues to hold. That is, if PQ and TS are any two chords of a circle intersecting at R, then $RP \times RQ = RS \times RT$ regardless of whether the chords intersect inside or outside the circle.

Since a tangent is merely a special secant for which the two points of intersection with the circle are coincident, we may regard the following theorem as a special case of the Secant Product Theorem.

> **Tangent-Secant Product Theorem**
> If, from an external point R, a tangent RP and a secant RST are drawn (where S and T are the points of intersection with the circle), then $RP^2 = RS \times RT$.

Given: Secant RT which intersects a circle at points S and T, and a tangent RP which touches the circle at P

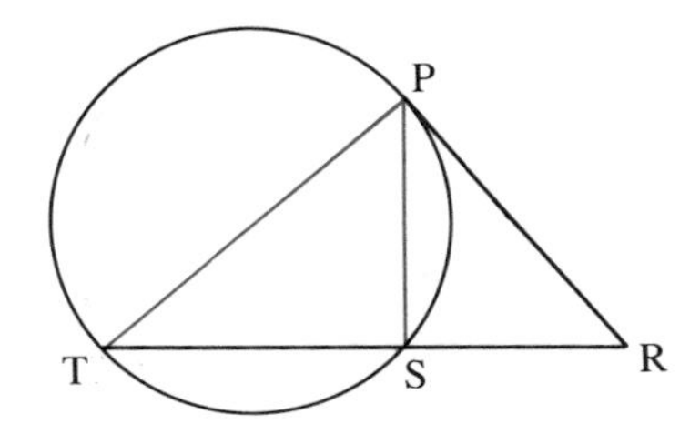

Required to Prove: $RP^2 = RS \times RT$
Analysis: Join PS and PT, and consider similar triangles.
Proof:

Statement	Reason
In △RPS and △RTP	
∠R is common	
∠RPS = ∠RTP	Corollary of Tangent-Chord Theorem
Therefore, △RPS ~ △RTP	AA~
$\frac{RP}{RS} = \frac{RT}{RP}$	Similar triangles
$RP^2 = RS \times RT$	Cross-multiplying

Example. Find each value of x.

a)

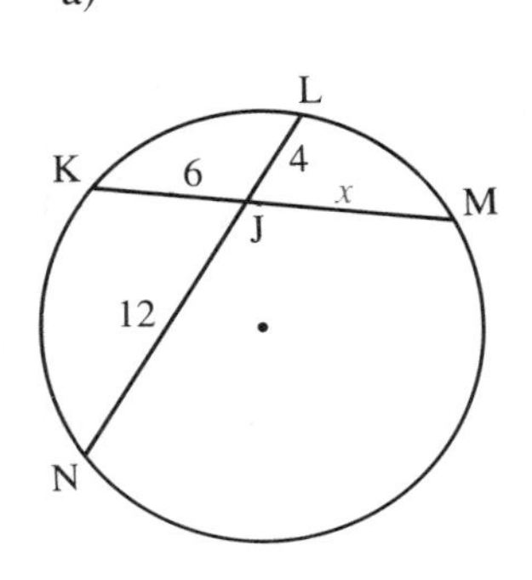

b) c)

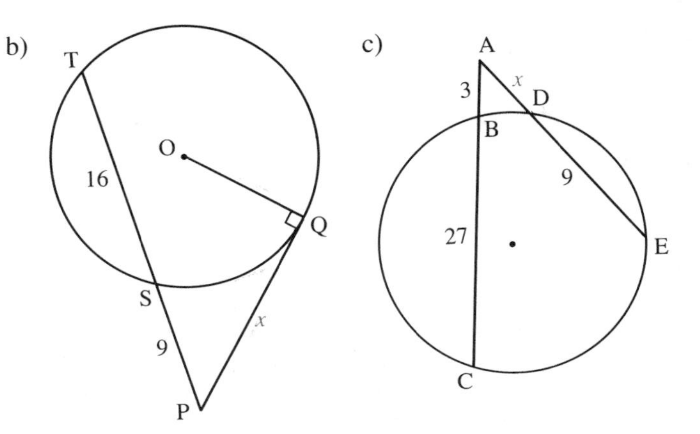

Solution. a) From the Chord Product Theorem

$JK \times JM = JL \times JN$
$6x = (4)(12)$
$x = 8$

b) From the Tangent-Secant Product Theorem

$PQ^2 = PS \times PT$
$x^2 = (25)(9)$
$= 225$
$x = 15$

c) From the Secant Product Theorem

$$AE \times AD = AC \times AB$$
$$(9 + x)x = (30)(3)$$
$$x^2 + 9x = 90$$
$$x^2 + 9x - 90 = 0$$
$$(x - 6)(x + 15) = 0$$
$$x = 6 \text{ or } x = -15$$

Since a length cannot be negative, $x = 6$

EXERCISES 6-8

Ⓐ

1. Find each value of x.

a)

b)

c)

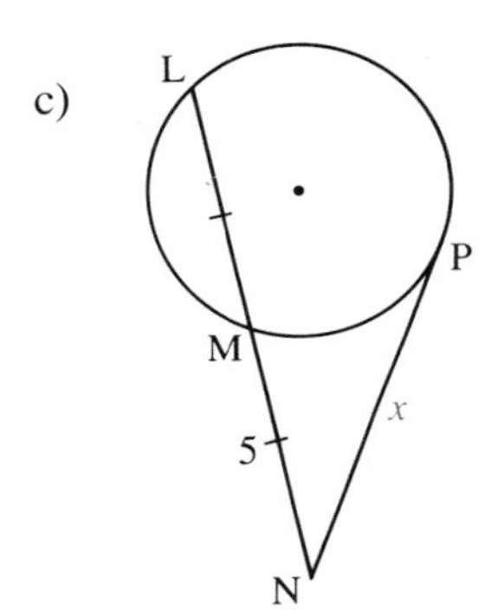

2. Find each value of x.

a)

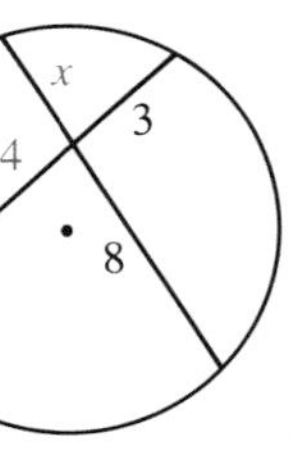

b)

c)

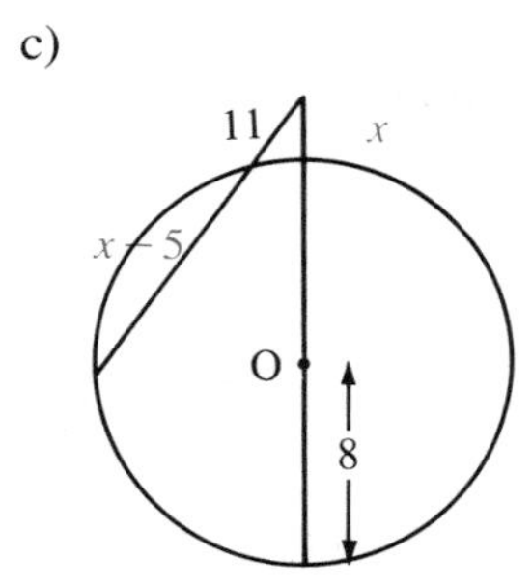

3. Two chords intersect in a circle. The point of intersection divides one chord into segments of length 1 cm and 6 cm. What are the lengths of the segments of the other chord if its total length is 5 cm?

Ⓑ

4. PAB and PCD are secants to a circle from an external point P such that PA = AB. If CD is 7 cm and PD is 16 cm, what is the length of PB?

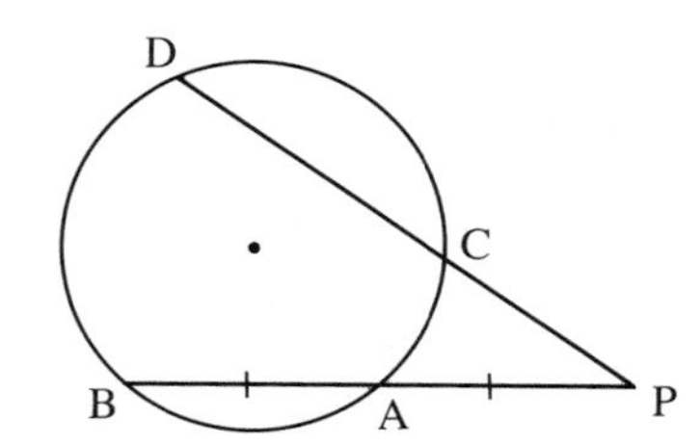

5. A tangent and a secant are drawn from an external point P to a circle. The tangent is 8 m long and the part of the secant inside the circle is 12 m long. How long is the secant?

6. Use the Chord Product Theorem to prove that a chord of length $2l$ units is located $\sqrt{R^2 - l^2}$ units from the centre of a circle of radius R.

7. The shortest distance from an external point to a circle is 5 cm. The greatest distance from that point to the circle is 20 cm. What is the length of the tangent from that point to the circle?

8. In the diagram (below left), AD, BE, and CF are the altitudes of $\triangle$ABC. They intersect at G. Prove that AG $\times$ GD $=$ BG $\times$ GE $=$ CG $\times$ GF.

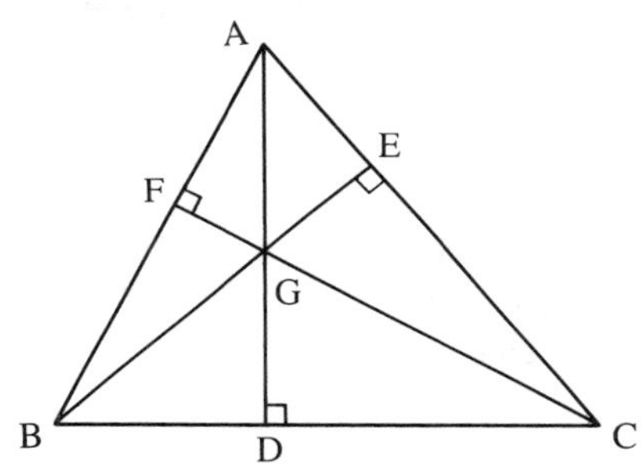

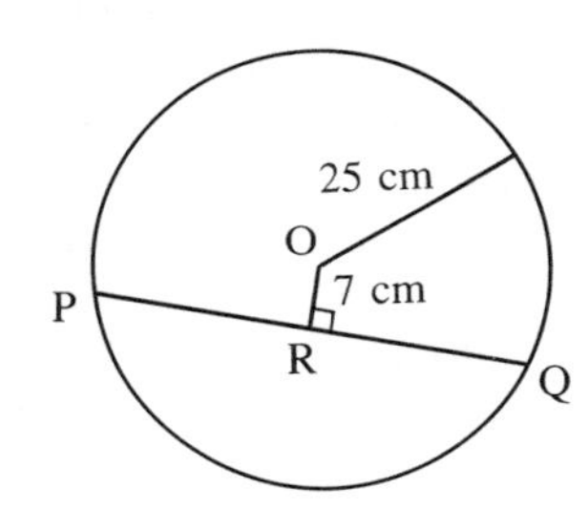

9. In the diagram (above right), a chord PQ is drawn through a point R, 7 cm from the centre of a circle. The circle has a radius of 25 cm.
   a) What is the product of the segments of PQ?
   b) What is the length of the shortest chord through R?

10. Two tangents, each 13 cm long, are drawn from an external point to a circle. The chord joining the points of tangency is 10 cm long. What is the radius of the circle to the nearest tenth of a centimetre?

11. Prove that the shortest distance from an external point P to a circle is the length PQ of secant PQR where QR is a diameter of the circle.

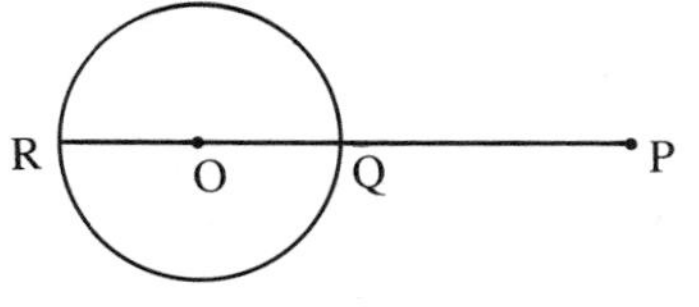

12. Prove that the longest secant from an external point P is the secant PQR where QR is a diameter of the circle.

Ⓒ

13. Prove that if a chord is drawn from point P on a circle and it is intersected by a secant parallel to the tangent at P, then the product of the chord length and its segment between the parallel lines is constant.

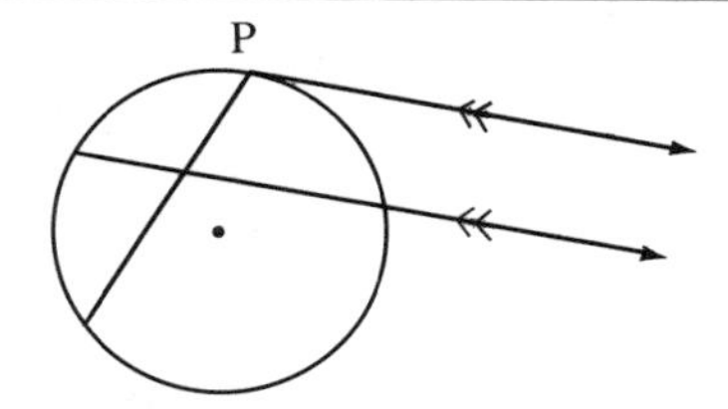

14. Prove that the length of the shortest chord which passes through a point x units from the centre of a circle is $2\sqrt{r^2 - x^2}$ units where r is the radius of the circle.

THE MATHEMATICAL MIND

The Mystic Hexagram

The great French mathematician, Blaise Pascal, was a child prodigy. His father realized that he was bright, and taught him languages with great care. Since Blaise was of frail health, his father did not permit him to study mathematics. He thought that Blaise needed to conserve his energy, and that the strain would be too great if he studied mathematics as well.

But the ban on mathematics naturally aroused the boy's curiosity, and when he was 12 years old he asked what geometry was. His father told him, and Blaise immediately became very interested. Without assistance from anyone, he soon discovered many theorems of elementary geometry. By age 16 he had discovered and proved many original results. His work astonished some of the leading mathematicians of the time, who could not believe that it had been done by a teenager.

One of these results concerns a pattern formed when any six points on a circle are joined in a certain way.

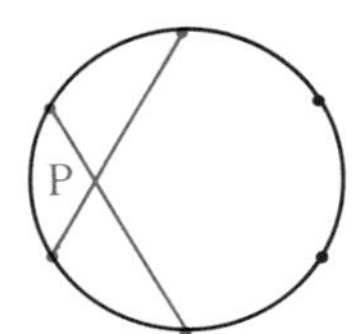

Step 1. Draw a circle and mark any six points on it. Make an X using the four points on the left. This locates point P.

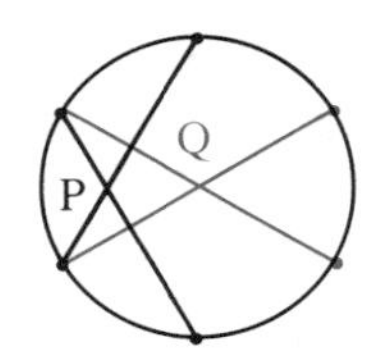

Step 2. Make an X using the two points on the left and the two on the right. This locates point Q.

Step 3. Make an X using the four points on the right. This locates point R. Join P, Q, and R.

When he was only 15 years old, Blaise discovered and proved the remarkable fact that no matter where the six points are marked on the circle, P, Q, and R will always lie on a straight line. For this reason, he called the figure formed by joining the six points the *mystic hexagram*. Blaise also proved that the same result occurs when six points are marked on certain figures other than circles.

1. Construct a circle and follow the steps described above. Do P, Q, and R lie on the same line?
2. Construct a circle and locate any three points P, Q, and R inside it which lie on a straight line. Can you find the six points on the circle which form the mystic hexagram?

6-9 AREAS OF SECTORS AND LENGTHS OF ARCS

When we construct a circle graph, we assume implicitly that the area of a sector of a circle is proportional to the sector angle. This fact enables us to calculate the area of a sector as a fraction of the area of a circle.

Example 1. Calculate the area of the sector of a circle of radius 10 cm if the sector angle is 30°.

Solution. Since the full-turn angle at the centre of a circle is 360°, the sector shown is $\frac{30}{360}$ of the entire circle. We write

$$\frac{\text{Area of sector}}{\text{Area of circle}} = \frac{30}{360}, \text{ or } \frac{1}{12}$$

The area of the circle is $\pi(10)^2$, or 100π.

$$\text{Therefore, area of sector } = \frac{1}{12}(100\pi)$$
$$\doteq 26.18$$

The area of the sector is about 26 cm^2.

Example 1 illustrates the following relationship.

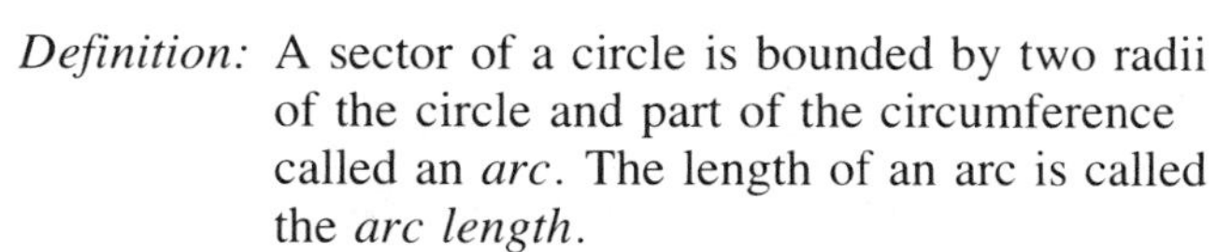

$$\frac{\text{Area of a sector}}{\text{Area of a circle}} = \frac{\text{Sector angle}}{\text{Full-turn angle}}$$

Definition: A sector of a circle is bounded by two radii of the circle and part of the circumference called an *arc*. The length of an arc is called the *arc length*.

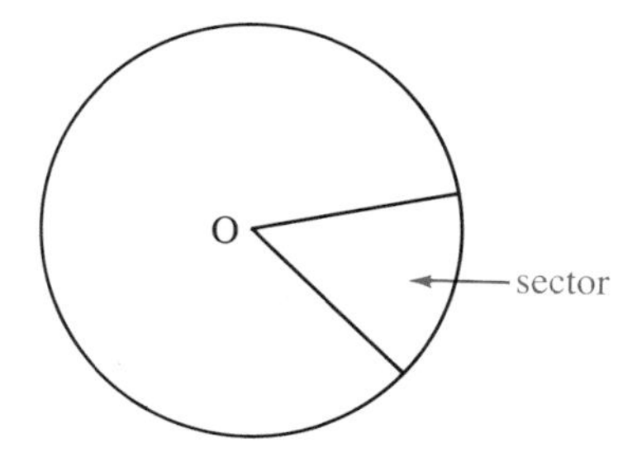

Just as the area of a sector is proportional to the sector angle, so the arc length of a sector is proportional to the sector angle. This fact enables us to calculate the arc length of a sector as a fraction of the circumference of the circle.

Example 2. Calculate the arc length of a sector of a circle of radius 20 cm if the sector angle is 140°.

Solution. Since the angle subtended at the centre of the circle by the circumference is 360°, the arc length of the sector shown is $\frac{140}{360}$ of the circumference.

$$\frac{\text{Arc length}}{\text{Circumference}} = \frac{140}{360}, \text{ or } \frac{7}{18}$$

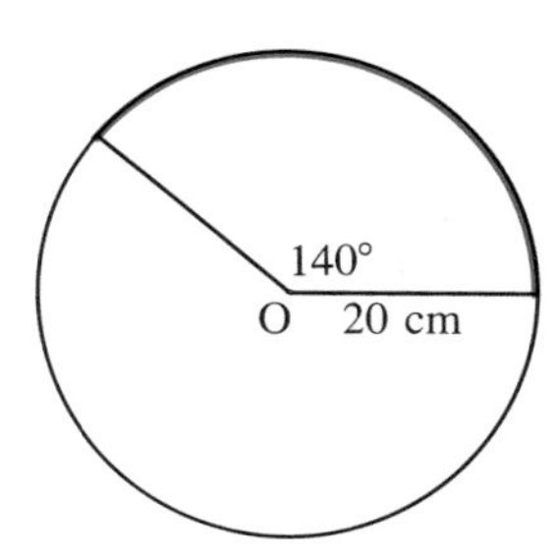

The circumference of the circle is $2\pi(20)$, or 40π.

Therefore, arc length $= \frac{7}{18}(40\pi)$

$\doteq 48.9$

The arc length is about 49 cm.

Example 2 illustrates the following relationship.

$$\frac{\text{Arc length of a sector}}{\text{Circumference}} = \frac{\text{Sector angle}}{\text{Full-turn angle}}$$

Using this relationship, we can calculate the sector angle that corresponds to a given arc length.

Example 3. Find the measure of the angle, to the nearest tenth of a degree, subtended at the centre of a circle, radius R, by an arc of each length.

a) R b) $2R$ c) $3R$

Solution. a) Rewrite the proportion above.

$$\frac{\text{Sector angle}}{\text{Full-turn angle}} = \frac{\text{Arc length}}{\text{Circumference}}$$

For an arc length R

$$\frac{\text{Sector angle}}{360°} = \frac{R}{2\pi R}$$

Therefore, sector angle $= \frac{360°}{2\pi}$

$= \frac{180°}{\pi}$

$\doteq 57.3°$

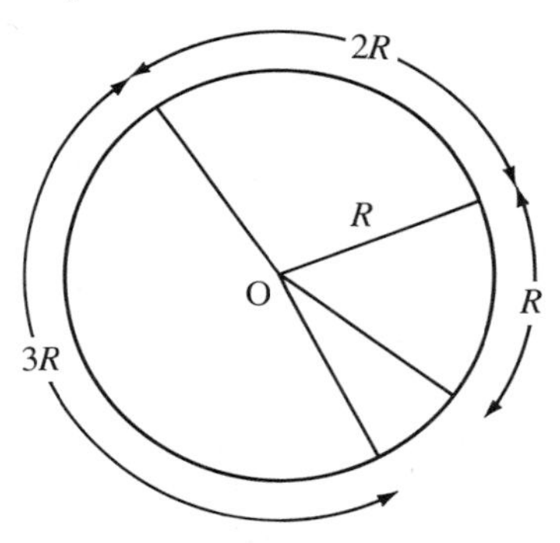

b) Since the sector angle is proportional to the arc length, for an arc length $2R$ the sector angle is twice as large as in part a).

Sector angle $= 2\left(\frac{180°}{\pi}\right)$

$\doteq 114.6°$

c) Similarly, for an arc length $3R$

Sector angle $= 3\left(\frac{180°}{\pi}\right)$

$\doteq 171.9°$

In *Example 3*, we discovered that an angle of $\frac{180°}{\pi}$ (approximately 57°) is subtended at the centre of a circle by an arc of length R, where R is the radius.

Definition: One *radian* is the measure of an angle which is subtended at the centre of a circle by an arc equal in length to the radius of the circle.

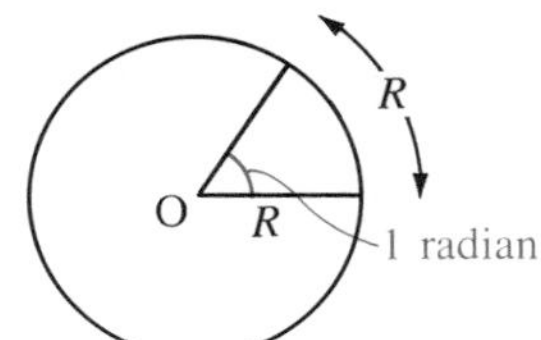

From this definition, $\quad 1 \text{ radian} = \frac{180°}{\pi}$

Multiply both sides by π, to get the following result.

$\pi \text{ radians} = 180°$

Hence, a full-turn angle, 360°, is equal to 2π radians.

We can use this result to derive a simple relation between the arc length, the radius, and the sector angle measured in radians. Let a represent the arc length which subtends an angle θ radians at the centre of a circle, radius R.

Substitute in this proportion.

$$\frac{\text{Arc length of a sector}}{\text{Circumference}} = \frac{\text{Sector angle}}{\text{Full-turn angle}}$$

$$\frac{a}{2\pi R} = \frac{\theta}{2\pi}$$

$$a = R\theta$$

This formula can be used to find an arc length if the angle it subtends at the centre of the circle is measured in radians.

The fact that π radians is equal to 180° can be used to convert from radians to degrees, and vice versa.

Example 4. Express each angle to 2 decimal places.

a) 4 radians in degrees $\qquad$ b) 138° in radians

Solution. a)

$$\pi \text{ radians} = 180°$$

$$1 \text{ radian} = \frac{180°}{\pi}$$

$$4 \text{ radians} = 4\left(\frac{180°}{\pi}\right)$$

$$\doteq 229.18°$$

b)

$$180° = \pi \text{ radians}$$

$$1° = \frac{\pi}{180} \text{ radians}$$

$$138° = 138\left(\frac{\pi}{180}\right) \text{ radians}$$

$$\doteq 2.41 \text{ radians}$$

Most scientific calculators have keys which enable you to convert from radians to degrees, and vice versa. Read your calculator manual to determine how to make these conversions. Verify the answers in *Example 4*.

EXERCISES 6-9

Ⓐ

1. Convert from degrees to radians. Express the answer in terms of π.

a) 30°	b) 45°	c) 60°	d) 90°	e) 120°	f) 135°
g) 150°	h) 180°	i) 210°	j) 225°	k) 240°	l) 270°
m) 300°	n) 315°	o) 330°	p) 360°	q) 390°	r) 405°

2. Convert from radians to degrees.
   a) $\frac{\pi}{2}$ radians b) $\frac{3\pi}{4}$ radians c) $-\frac{2\pi}{3}$ radians d) $\frac{7\pi}{6}$ radians
   e) $\frac{\pi}{4}$ radians f) $-\frac{3\pi}{2}$ radians g) $\frac{7\pi}{4}$ radians h) 2π radians
   i) $-\frac{5\pi}{3}$ radians j) $\frac{5\pi}{4}$ radians k) $\frac{\pi}{6}$ radians l) $-\frac{11\pi}{6}$ radians

3. Convert from degrees to radians. Give the answers to 2 decimal places.
   a) $100°$ b) $225°$ c) $57.3°$ d) $-125°$ e) $75x°$ f) $\frac{60°}{\pi}$
   g) $-65°$ h) $24.5x°$ i) $150°$ j) $30°$ k) $\frac{180°}{\pi}$ l) $-90x°$

4. Convert from radians to degrees. Give the answers to 1 decimal place.
   a) 2 radians b) -5 radians c) 3.2 radians d) 1.8 radians
   e) -0.7 radians f) 1.4θ radians g) 6.7 radians h) $-2\pi x$ radians

5. Find the length of the arc which subtends each angle at the centre of a circle of radius 5 cm. Give the answers to 1 decimal place.
   a) 2.0 radians b) 3.0 radians c) 1.8 radians
   d) 6.1 radians e) 4.2 radians f) 0.6 radians

6. Find the length of the arc of a circle with radius 12 cm that subtends each sector angle. Give the answers to 1 decimal place where necessary.
   a) $135°$ b) $75°$ c) $105°$ d) $165°$
   e) $240°$ f) $180°$ g) $310°$ h) $200°$

7. Find the area to the nearest square centimetre of the sector of a circle with radius:
   a) 20 cm, if the sector angle is i) $45°$ ii) $120°$
   b) 12 cm, if the sector angle is i) $90°$ ii) $225°$
   c) 25 cm, if the sector angle is i) $150°$ ii) $240°$.

8. Find the arc length to the nearest centimetre of the sector of a circle with radius:
   a) 7 m, if the sector angle is i) $120°$ ii) $210°$
   b) 90 cm, if the sector angle is i) $30°$ ii) $225°$
   c) 216 mm, if the sector angle is i) $135°$ ii) $300°$.

(B)

9. How many radians in:
   a) a full turn b) a half turn c) a quarter turn?

10. What is the area to the nearest square centimetre of the sector of a circle with radius 25 cm if the sector angle is $115°$?

11. Calculate the arc length to the nearest metre of a sector of a circle with radius 6 m if the sector angle is $140°$.

12. Two sectors of the same circle have sector angles of $35°$ and $105°$ respectively. The arc length of the smaller sector is 17 cm. What is the arc length of the larger sector?

13. A sector with sector angle 100° has an area of 25 cm^2. What is the area of the circle?

14. A sector bounded by an arc of length 48 cm has a sector angle of 2.4 radians. What is the radius of the circle?

15. A circle of radius R is divided into n equal sectors by radii. Write an algebraic expression for:
    a) the area of each sector
    b) the sector angle in degrees
    c) the arc length of each sector
    d) the sector angle in radians.

16. a) Through how many radians per minute does the minute hand on a clock turn?
    b) Through how many radians per minute does the hour hand turn?
    c) How many times as fast as the hour hand does the minute hand turn?

17. Write an expression for the measure in radians of the sector angle of a sector, in a circle graph with radius r, which represents $x\%$ of the total area.

18. The Earth travels in a nearly circular orbit around the sun. The radius of the orbit is about 149 000 000 km.
    a) What is the measure in radians of the angle subtended at the sun by the positions of the Earth at two different times 24 h apart?
    b) About how far does the Earth travel in one day in its orbit around the sun?

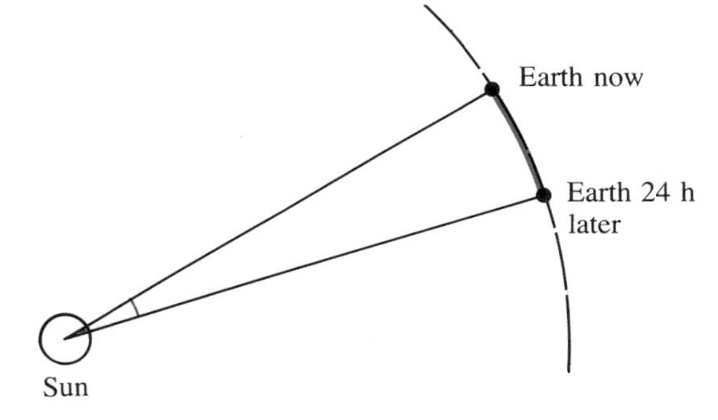

Ⓒ

19. The *angular velocity* of an object is the angle per unit time through which an object rotates about a rotation centre.
    a) What is the angular velocity in radians per second of a car tire of diameter 64 cm when the car is travelling at 100 km/h?
    b) Write an expression for the angular velocity in radians per second for a car tire of diameter d centimetres when the car is travelling at x kilometres per hour?

20. a) Write expressions for the distance from A to B:
    i) along the line segment AB
    ii) along the circular arc from A to B.
    b) How many times as long as the straight-line distance is the distance along the circular arc from A to B?
    c) Write an expression for the area of the shaded segment of the circle.
    d) Write an expression for the shortest distance from the vertex of the right angle to the line segment AB.

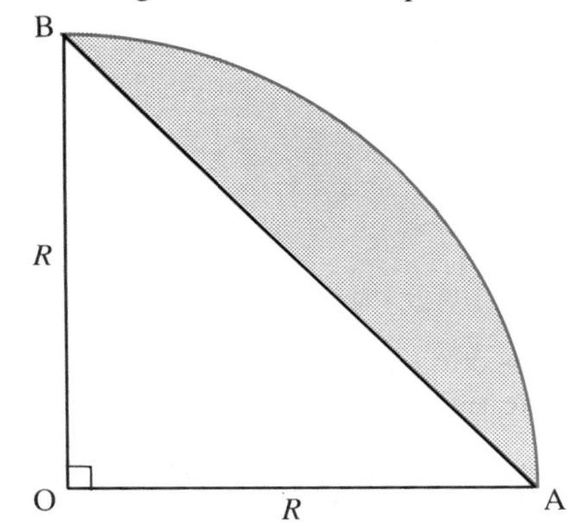

Review Exercises

1. Calculate each value of x.

a) 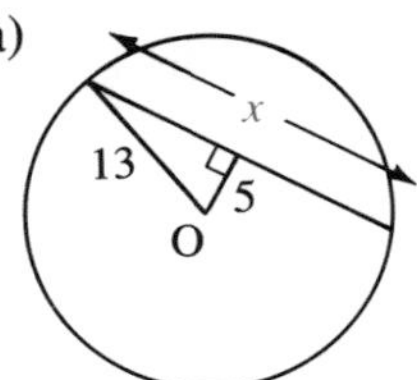

b) 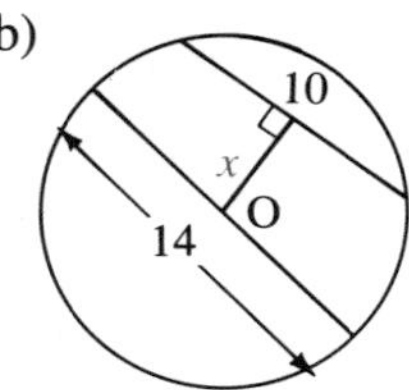

c) 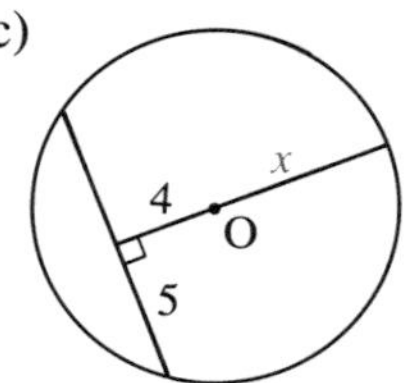

2. PQRS is a cyclic quadrilateral and ∠P is an acute angle. Is ∠R acute or obtuse? Explain your answer.

3. Prove that if the diagonals of a cyclic quadrilateral bisect each other, then the quadrilateral is a rectangle.

4. In △ABC (below left), altitudes BE and CD are drawn. Prove that DAEF is a cyclic quadrilateral.

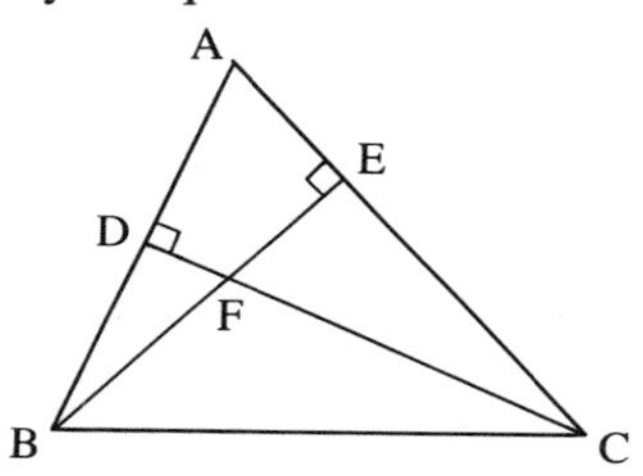

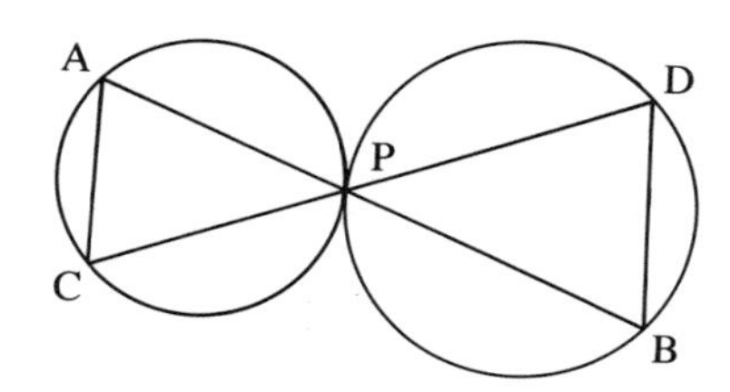

5. In the diagram (above right), P is the point of tangency of the two circles. Line segments AB and CD contain P. Prove that AC is parallel to DB.

6. L and M are the points of intersection of two circles (below left). Through a point P in the common chord LM, chords AB and CD are drawn. Prove that $AP \times PB = CP \times PD$.

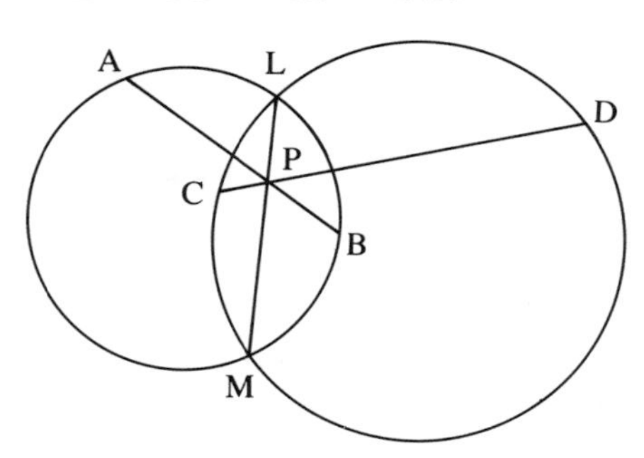

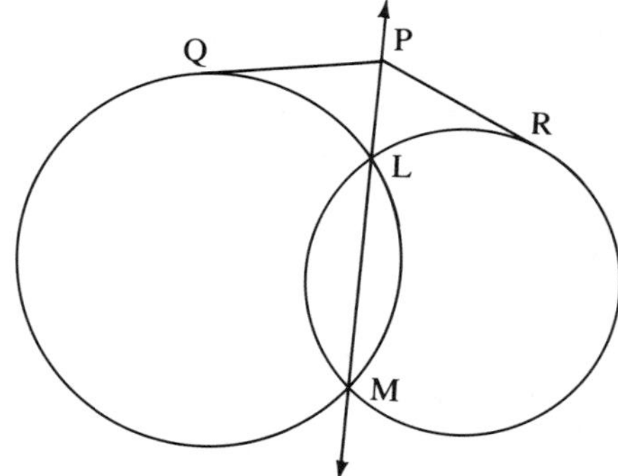

7. In the diagram (above right), prove that if LM is the common chord of two intersecting circles, then the tangents PQ and PR from any point P on the line $\overleftrightarrow{LM}$ to the two circles are equal.

8. What is the measure in radians of the angle between the minute hand and the hour hand at: a) 3:00 b) 4:00?

1. Define each term. Draw a sketch to illustrate each definition.
   a) transversal b) concyclic points c) opposite angles
   d) cyclic quadrilateral e) corresponding angles f) secant
   g) tangent h) circumcircle i) alternate angles

2. a) If you knew each value of x, how could you find a corresponding value of y?
   b) Write an equation relating x and y.
   i) ii) iii)

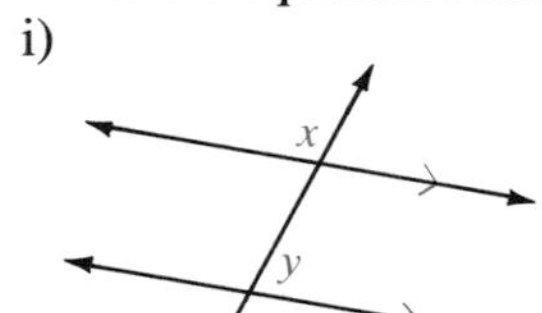

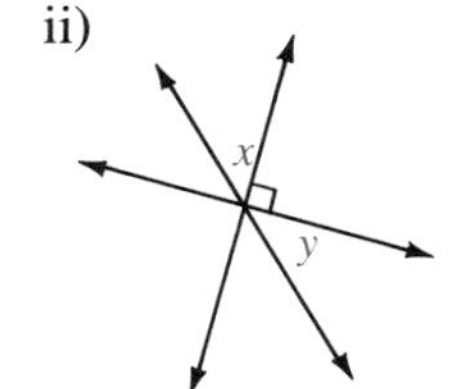

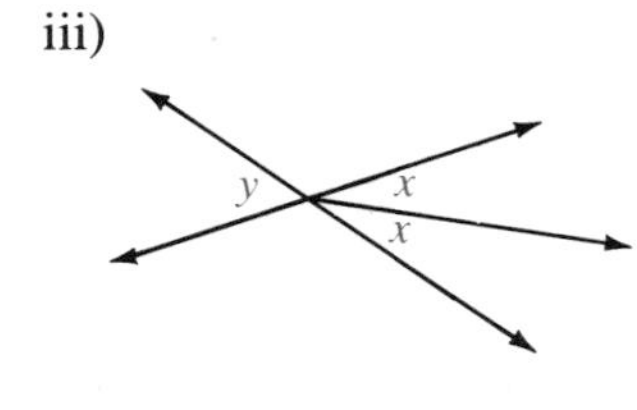

3. In quadrilateral ABCD (below left), AE = EB and DF = FC. Also EF is perpendicular to AB and to DC. Prove that: a) $\angle C = \angle D$ b) AD = BC.

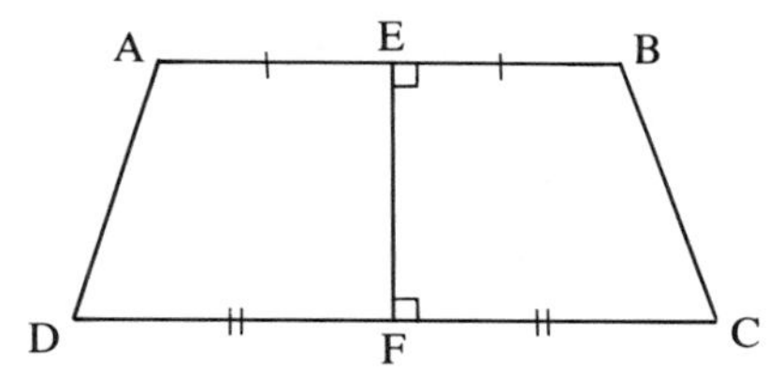

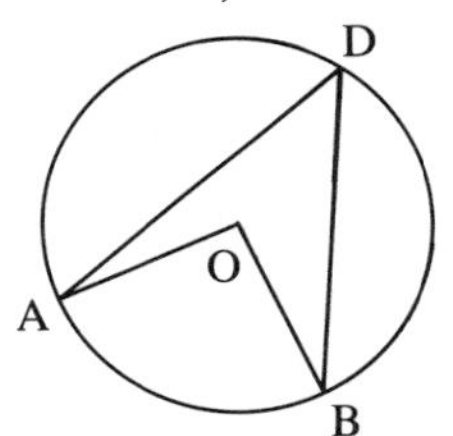

4. If O is the centre of the circle shown in the diagram (above right), prove that $\angle AOB$ has twice the measure of $\angle ADB$.

5. a) $\overleftrightarrow{EH}$ is a transversal which intersects parallel lines $\overleftrightarrow{AB}$ and $\overleftrightarrow{CD}$. Use the properties of a 180° rotation to deduce that $\angle BFG = \angle FGC$.
   b) Use part a) to deduce the Parallel Lines Theorem.

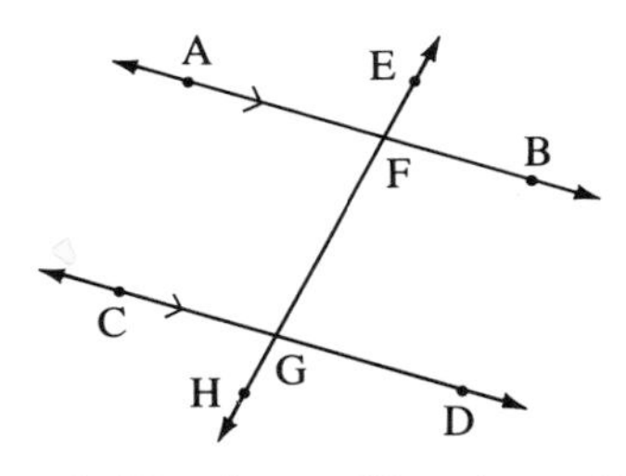

6. Construct a triangle similar to $\triangle ABC$ (below left) using a dilatation with each scale factor. a) 2 b) 1.6 c) 0.85

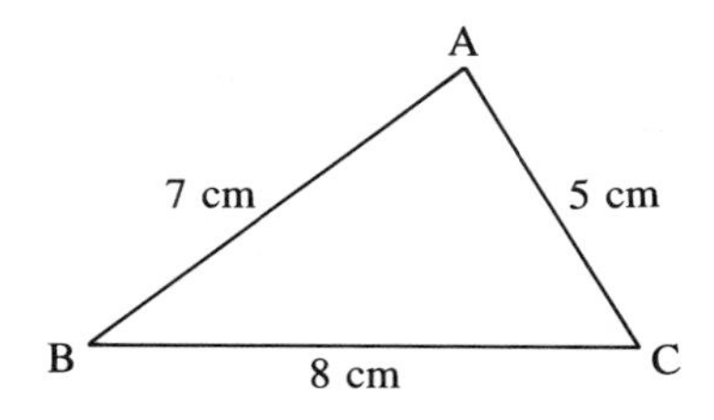

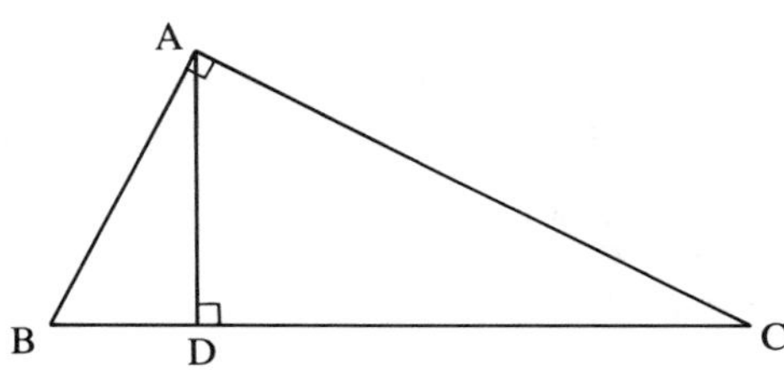

7. If $\triangle ABC \sim \triangle DBA \sim \triangle DAC$ (above right), name the congruent angles and the corresponding sides.

8. Perpendiculars WU and YV are drawn to the diagonal ZX of parallelogram WXYZ. Prove that WU = YV.

9. Prove that each side of a triangle is less than half the perimeter of that triangle.

10. To find the width AB of a river (below left), points C, D, and E were located as shown. If BD and AE are line segments, find the length of AB.

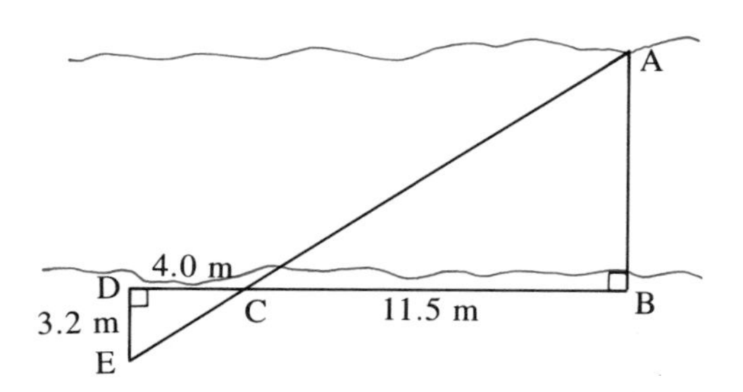

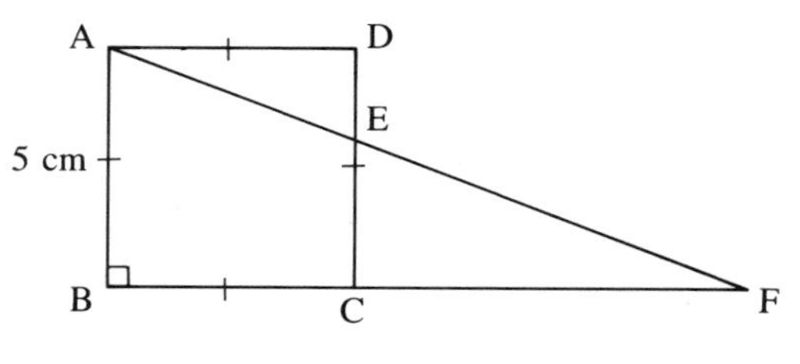

11. ABCD is a square of side length 5 cm (above right). BC is produced to F so that BF = 13 cm. Find the length of CE to 1 decimal place.

12. In the diagram (below left), prove that:

a) $\frac{BD}{AD} = \frac{AD}{DC}$ b) $\frac{BD}{BA} = \frac{BA}{BC}$ c) $\frac{CD}{CA} = \frac{CA}{CB}$.

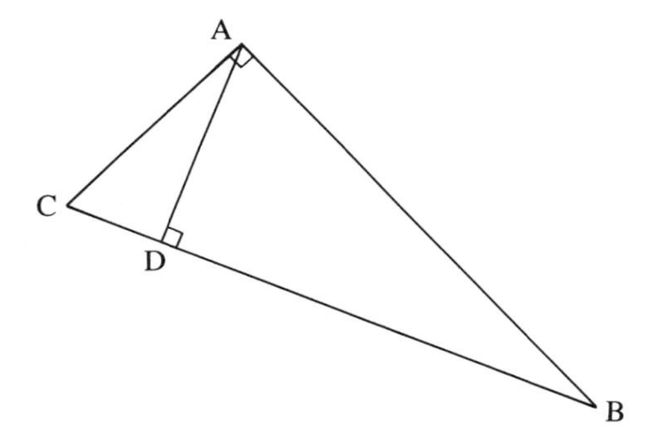

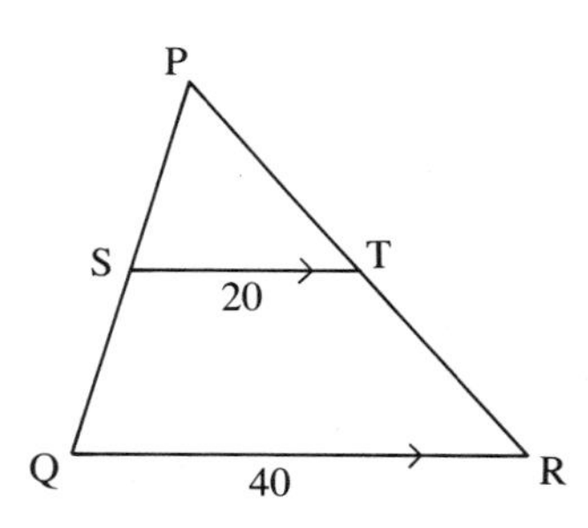

13. In $\triangle$PQR (above right), ST is parallel to QR. Prove that S and T are the midpoints of PQ and PR respectively.

14. PQ and PR are respectively a diameter and a chord of a circle. If PS is the perpendicular from P to the tangent at R, prove that $\angle$SPR = $\angle$RPQ.

15. Two circles C_1 and C_2 intersect at points P and Q. Let PA be a chord of C_1 which is tangent to C_2. Let PB be a chord of C_2 which is tangent to C_1 at point P. Prove that PQ bisects $\angle$AQB.

16. A sector of a circular pie with sector angle $\frac{\pi}{6}$ radians has an area of 42 cm^2. What is the diameter of the pie?

7 Trigonometric Ratios

The Simplon tunnel joining Italy and Switzerland was constructed by boring from both ends. When they met, in 1906, the engineers found that the two parts of the tunnel were exactly in line. How was this done? (See Section 7-9 *Example 4*.)

7-1 THE TANGENT RATIO

We often talk about the steepness of a roof, a hill, or a cable car ride. This steepness can be measured in at least two ways.

The *slope* of an incline is the ratio of the *rise* to the *run*.

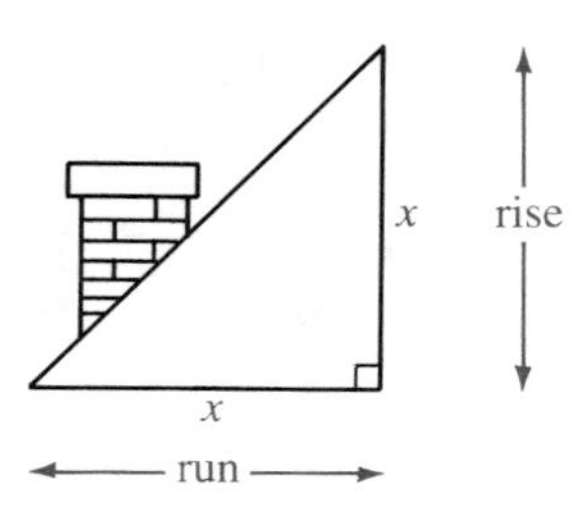

$$\text{Slope} = \frac{\text{rise}}{\text{run}}$$
$$= \frac{x}{x}, \text{ or } 1$$

The *angle of inclination* of a line is the angle between the line and the horizontal line which it intersects.

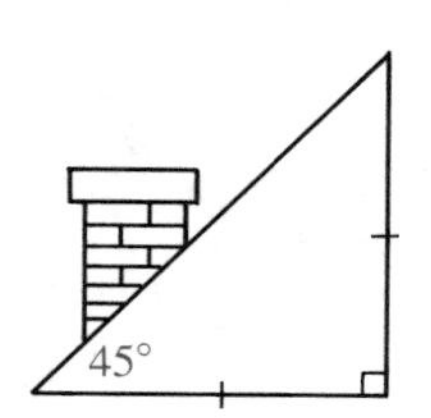

The angle of inclination is 45°.

All roofs inclined at 45° have a slope of 1 no matter how high or how wide they are. This suggests that for any angle of inclination θ there is a unique slope, which we call the *tangent of* θ. We use the symbol *tan* θ to denote this slope. The relationship between θ and tan θ is shown in the diagram below.

$$\tan\theta = \frac{y}{x}$$

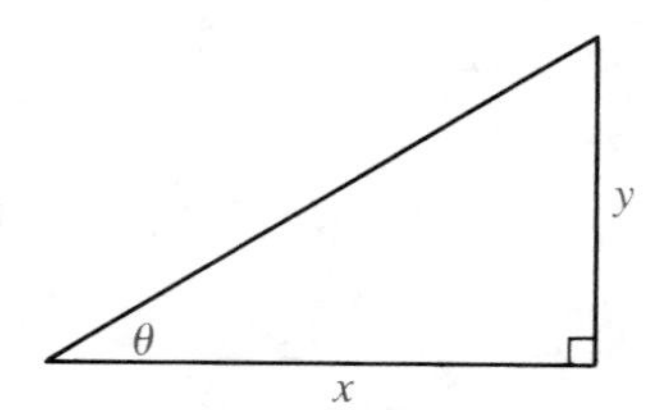

If we know the value of θ, then tan θ can be found by drawing and measuring.

Example 1. Construct an angle of 20° and determine tan 20° by measuring.

Solution. Construct an angle of 20° using a protractor.

Since tan 20° is the ratio $\frac{\text{BC}}{\text{AB}}$, we measure these segments.

We find BC $\doteq$ 1.8 cm and AB $\doteq$ 5.0 cm.

$$\tan 20° \doteq \frac{1.8}{5}$$
$$= 0.36$$

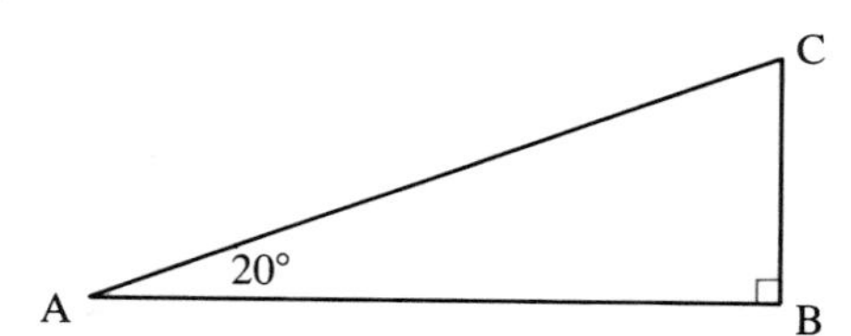

To determine tan 20° we drew a right triangle. This right triangle can be any size so long as the hypotenuse is inclined at 20°. The slope (or tangent ratio) will be the same for all such triangles since all such triangles are similar.

If we know tan θ, we can find θ by drawing and measuring.

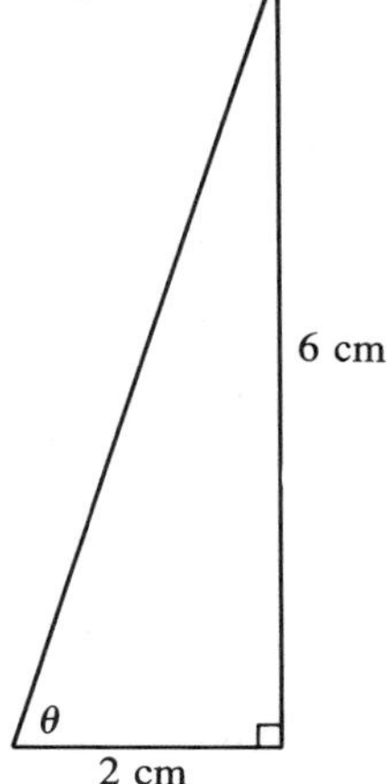

Example 2. Given $\tan \theta = 3$, find θ by measuring.

Solution. Construct a line of slope 3 by constructing a right triangle with a vertical side 6 cm and a horizontal side 2 cm.

Then, $\tan \theta = \frac{6}{2}$

$= 3$

Measure the angle θ with a protractor.

$\theta \doteq 72°$

An angle of 72° has a tangent of about 3.

Precise values of tan θ for various angles θ have been generated by computer and are recorded in published trigonometric tables.

Scientific calculators have a [tan] key. To find, for example, tan 72°, key in: 72 [tan] to display 3.0776835.

Example 3. A ski tow is inclined at an angle of 24°. What is the slope of the ski tow, to 3 decimal places?

Solution. The slope of the ski tow is tan 24°.

Key in: 24 [tan] to display 0.4452287

The slope of the tow is about 0.445.

Example 4. A guy wire is to be connected to the top of a rocket to hold it in place. What angle of inclination must the wire have if the slope of the wire is to be 3.5?

Solution. If θ is the angle of inclination, then $\tan \theta = 3.5$.

To find the value of θ, key in: 3.5 [$\tan^{-1}$] to display 74.054604.

An alternative keying sequence is 3.5 [INV] [tan].

The wire should be inclined at an angle of 74°.

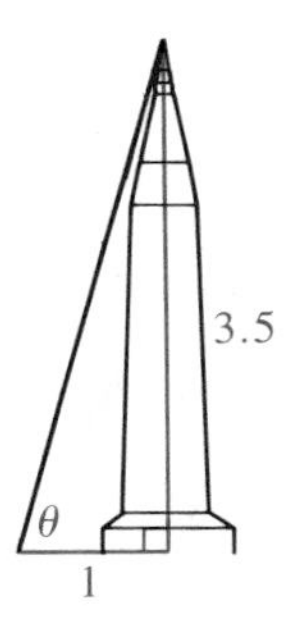

The angle of inclination is sometimes described as the *angle of elevation*.

EXERCISES 7-1

Ⓐ

1. Construct each angle and determine its tangent to 2 decimal places by measuring.
   a) 15° b) 35° c) 60° d) 75°

2. For each value of tan θ, find θ to the nearest degree by drawing and measuring.
   a) $\tan\theta = \frac{1}{2}$ b) $\tan\theta = 1$ c) $\tan\theta = 1.6$ d) $\tan\theta = 2.5$

3. Find tan θ to 3 decimal places for each value of θ.
   a) 23° b) 47° c) 62° d) 7° e) 38°
   f) 82° g) 51° h) 17° i) 70° j) 88°

4. Find θ to the nearest degree for each value of tan θ.
   a) 0.839 b) 2.145 c) 0.532 d) 1.540 e) 5.145
   f) 0.087 g) 0.344 h) 0.649 i) 11.430 j) 2.356

Ⓑ

5. Large shopping malls make use of ramps, steps, and escalators to move people from one level to another. Find the angle of inclination to the nearest degree and the slope to 1 decimal place of each conveyor.

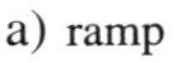

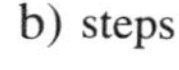

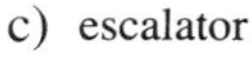

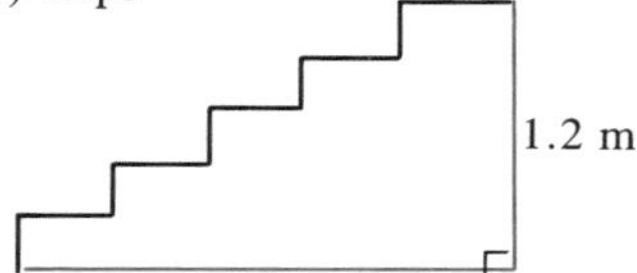

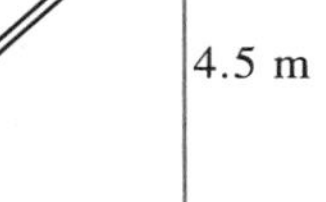

6. The back of a chaise lounge is adjustable. Find the slope of the back for each angle of inclination. Give the answers to 3 decimal places.
   a) 5° b) 35° c) 60° d) 80°

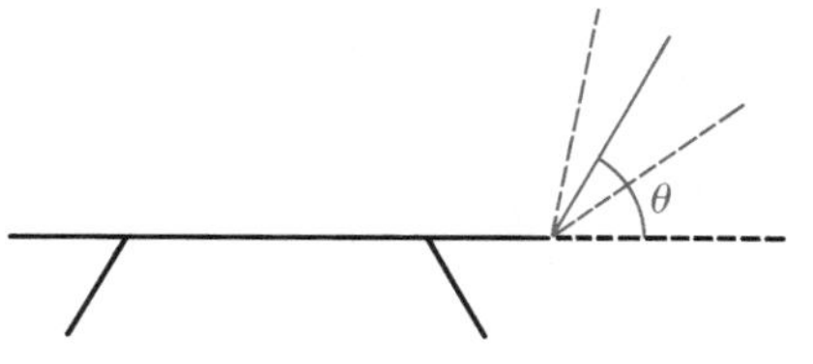

7. A TV tower is supported by guy wires (below left). Find the angle of inclination to 1 decimal place and the slope to 3 decimal places of each wire.

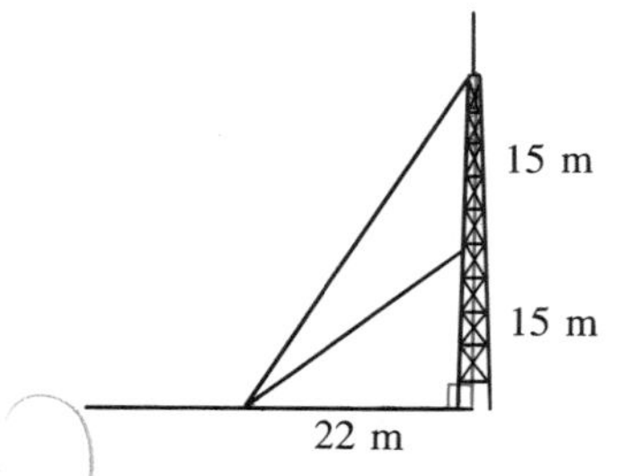

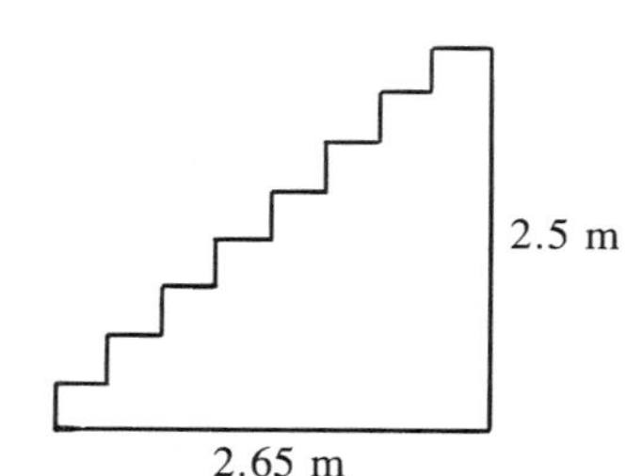

8. The distance between floors in a new home is 2.5 m (above right). If the stairs require 2.65 m measured along the floor, find their slope to 3 decimal places, and the angle of inclination to 1 decimal place.

9. In a large ship the stairs between decks are much steeper than in your home. If the decks are 2.5 m apart and 0.9 m of floor space are required, find the slope of the stairs to 3 decimal places and the angle of inclination to 1 decimal place.

10. When trees are used as a windbreak the approximate path of the wind is as shown in the diagram below. Find the measures of the angles at A and at B to the nearest degree.

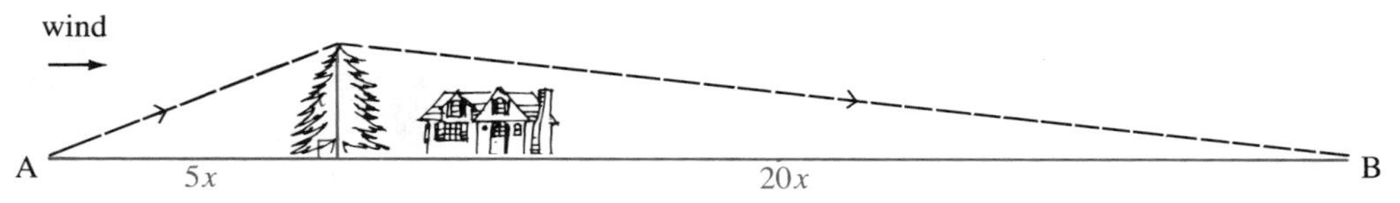

11. The seats in the balcony of a theatre are as shown in the diagram. Each seat is 40 cm above the one in front. There are 90 cm for each seat and the accompanying leg room. Find the angle of inclination of the balcony to the nearest degree.

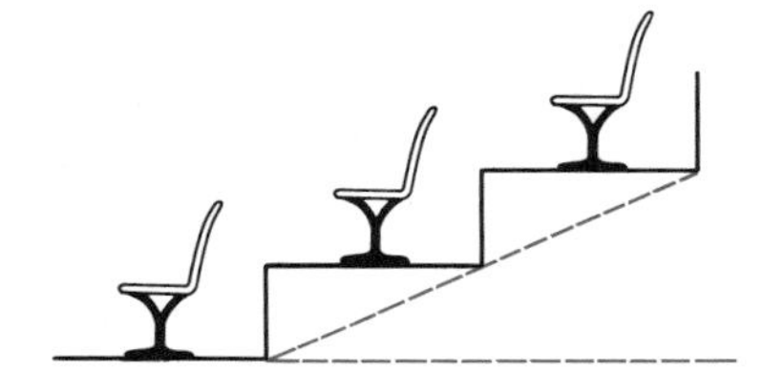

Ⓒ

12. A conveyor belt rises 2.40 m. What is the horizontal distance between the ends of the belt for each angle of inclination?
   a) 32° b) 55°

INVESTIGATE

An 8 cm by 8 cm square is cut into 4 pieces, as shown. The pieces are then rearranged to form a 5 cm by 13 cm rectangle.

a) Are the areas of the figures equal? b) Explain where the error is.

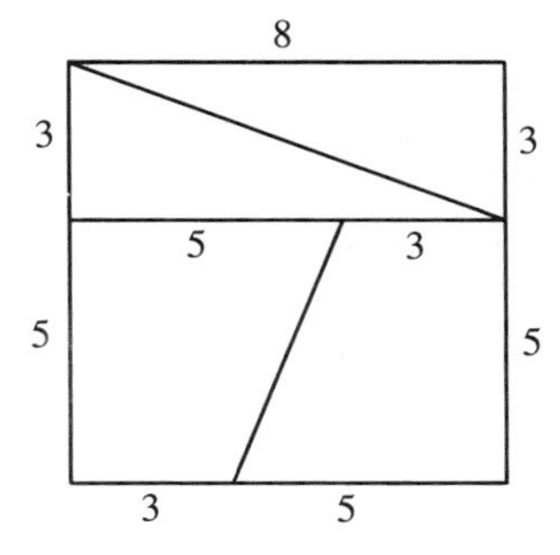

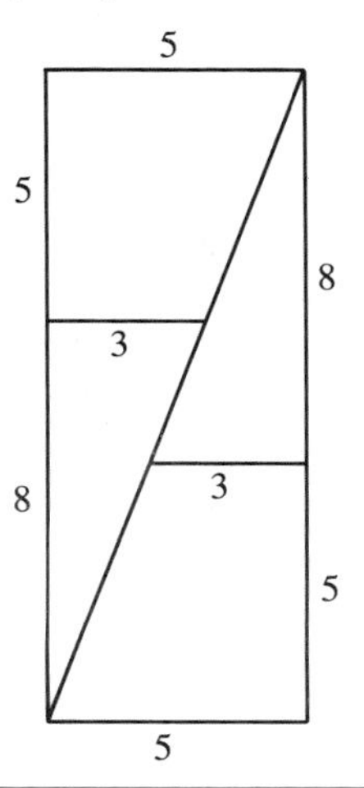

7-2 THE PRIMARY TRIGONOMETRIC RATIOS

In the previous section we learned that the slope of a line can be expressed as a ratio of two sides of a right triangle, or in terms of an angle of inclination. When the angle of inclination is θ, the slope is $\tan \theta$.

The next example shows how we can use the relationship between $\tan \theta$ and θ to find the height of an inaccessible cliff.

Example 1. The top of a cliff has an angle of elevation of 36° when measured from a point 175 m away from its base. How high is the cliff?

Solution. Let h metres represent the height of the cliff.

Then, $\tan 36° = \frac{h}{175}$

$h = 175 \tan 36°$

Key in: 36 [tan] [×] 175 [=] to display 127.14494

The cliff is about 127 m high.

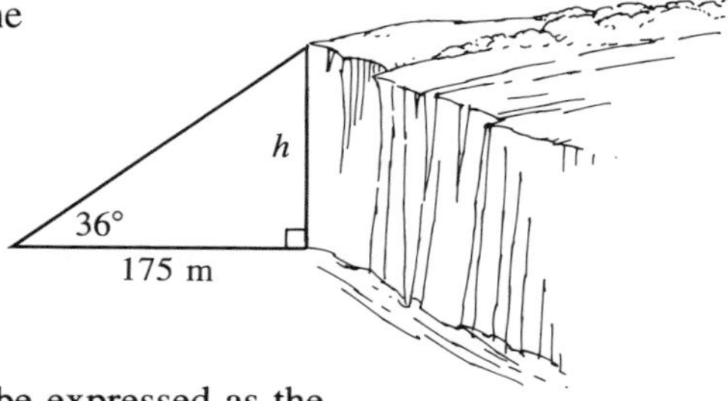

The tangent of an angle in a right triangle can be expressed as the ratio of the side *opposite* the angle to the side *adjacent* to the angle.

We write $\tan \theta = \frac{\text{opposite}}{\text{adjacent}}$

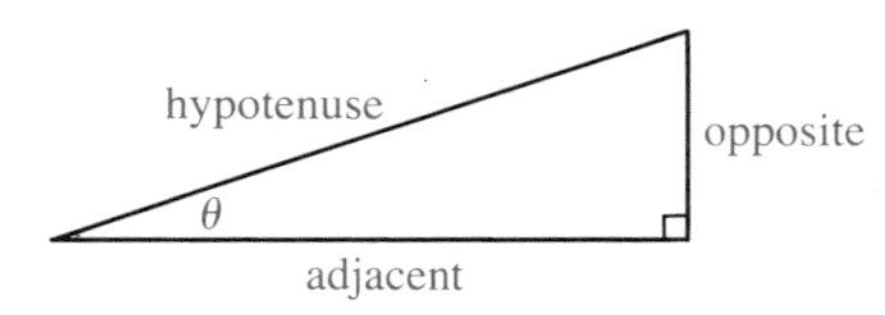

Example 1 demonstrated how we use the tangent ratio to calculate the length of the side opposite a given angle, given the length of the adjacent side. We could not use this ratio if we were given instead the length of the hypotenuse.

To remove this limitation we define two additional ratios called the sine and cosine ratios. The *sine ratio* for an angle θ is written *sin* θ and the *cosine ratio* is written *cos* θ. We define the sine and cosine ratios as follows.

$$\sin \theta = \frac{\text{opposite}}{\text{hypotenuse}}$$

$$\cos \theta = \frac{\text{adjacent}}{\text{hypotenuse}}$$

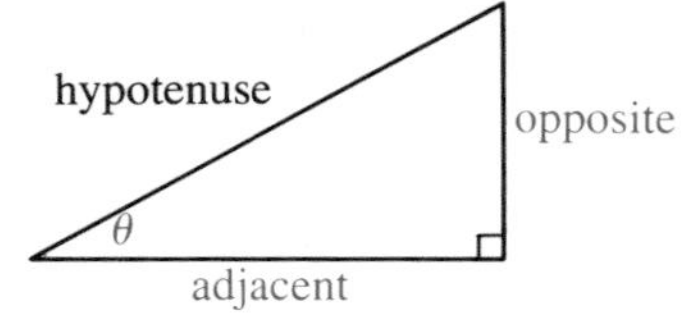

The ratios $\sin \theta$, $\cos \theta$, and $\tan \theta$ are called the *primary trigonometric ratios*.

Example 2. a) Find to 4 decimal places.
i) $\sin 68°$ ii) $\cos 47°$
b) Find to the nearest degree.
i) the angle θ for which $\sin \theta = 0.47$
ii) the angle ϕ for which $\cos \phi = 0.39$

Solution. a) i) For $\sin 68°$, key in: 68 [sin] to display 0.9271839
$\sin 68° \doteq 0.9272$
ii) For $\cos 47°$, key in: 47 [cos] to display 0.6819984
$\cos 47° \doteq 0.6820$
b) i) If $\sin \theta = 0.47$, to find θ
key in: .47 [$\sin^{-1}$] to display 28.034297
$\theta \doteq 28°$
ii) If $\cos \phi = 0.39$, to find ϕ
key in: .39 [$\cos^{-1}$] to display 67.045501
$\phi \doteq 67°$

We could have determined $\sin 68°$ and $\cos 47°$ by drawing each angle with a protractor and forming the corresponding right triangle. By measuring the sides of the triangles we could calculate the sine and cosine ratios, but these results would not be precise.

Example 3. Given $\triangle ABC$ with sides of lengths 3, 4, and 5 units
a) Write the ratios $\sin A$, $\cos A$, and $\tan A$, where $\angle A$ is opposite the side of length 3 units.
b) Find the measures of the two acute angles to the nearest degree.

Solution. From the converse of the Pythagorean Theorem, $\triangle ABC$ is a right triangle. Draw $\triangle ABC$ with $\angle C = 90°$.

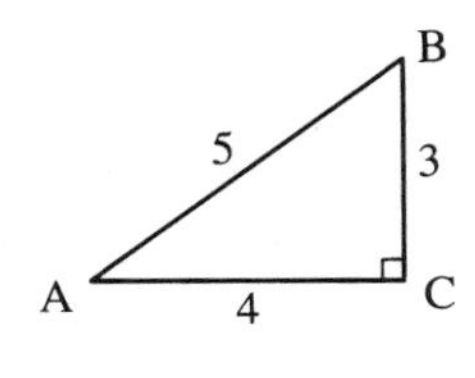

a) From the definitions of the trigonometric ratios

$$\sin A = \frac{3}{5} \quad \cos A = \frac{4}{5} \quad \tan A = \frac{3}{4}$$

b) Since $\sin A = \frac{3}{5}$ or 0.6, we can use a calculator to find $\angle A$.
Key in: .6 [$\sin^{-1}$] to display 36.869898
$\angle A \doteq 37°$
Since $\angle A + \angle B = 90°$, then $\angle B \doteq 53°$.

Example 4. A 35 m cable is attached to a TV tower at a height of 30 m. What is the angle of elevation of the cable?

Solution. Let θ be the angle of elevation.

Then, $\sin \theta = \frac{30}{35}$

To find θ, key in: 30 [÷] 35 [=] [$\sin^{-1}$] to display 58.997281.
The angle of elevation is about 59°.

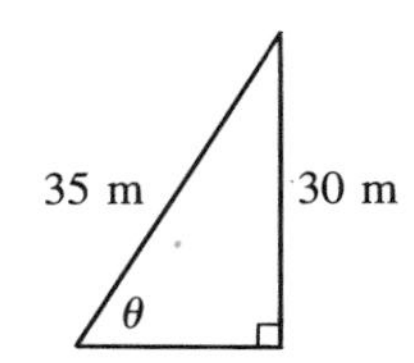

EXERCISES 7-2

Ⓐ

1. Find each ratio to 4 decimal places.
   a) sin 30° b) cos 78° c) cos 52° d) sin 16° e) cos 28°
   f) sin 40° g) sin 82° h) cos 9° i) sin 59° j) cos 37°

2. Find θ to the nearest degree if each given value is: a) sin θ b) cos θ.
   i) 0.2079 ii) 0.4384 iii) 0.7431 iv) 0.9063 v) 0.9945

3. Write the ratios sin θ, cos θ, and tan θ for each triangle.

a)

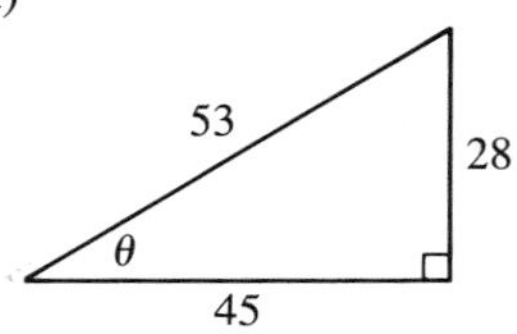

b)

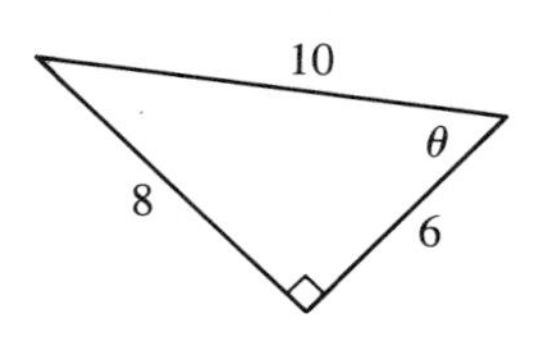

c)

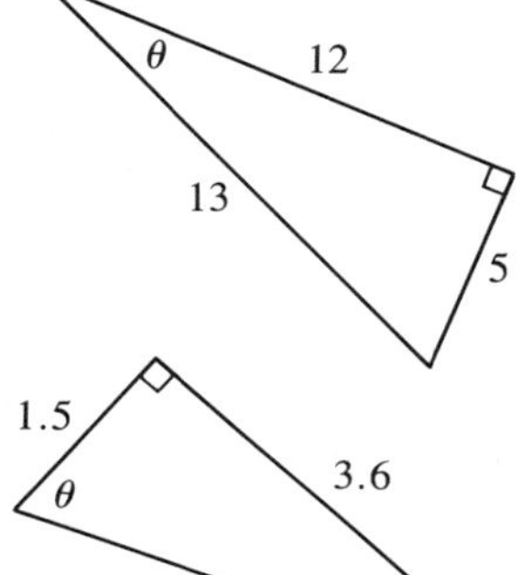

d)

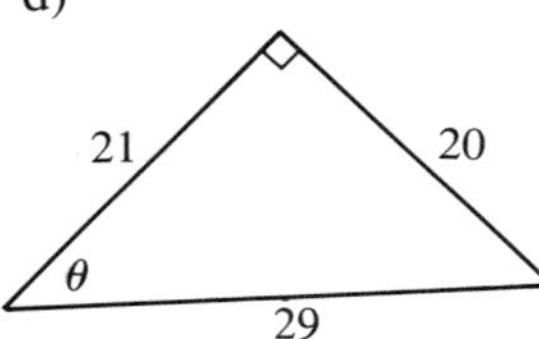

e)

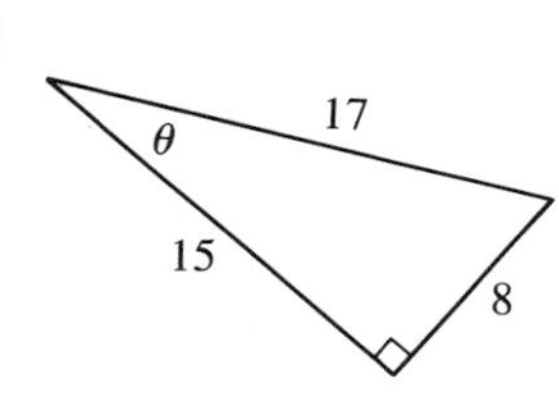

f)

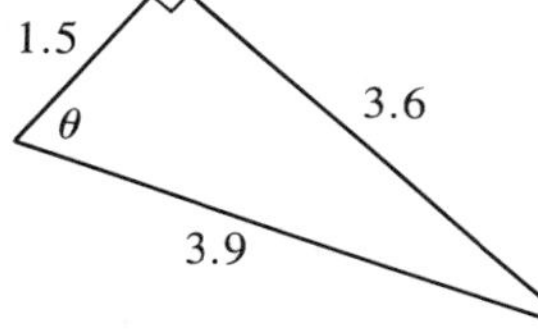

4. The lengths of the sides of $\triangle$PQR are 9, 40, and 41 units. If $\angle$Q = 90°, find:
   a) the primary trigonometric ratios for the smallest angle
   b) the measures of the two smaller angles to 1 decimal place.

Ⓑ

5. A wheelchair ramp (below left) is 4.2 m long and rises 0.7 m. What is its angle of inclination to 1 decimal place?

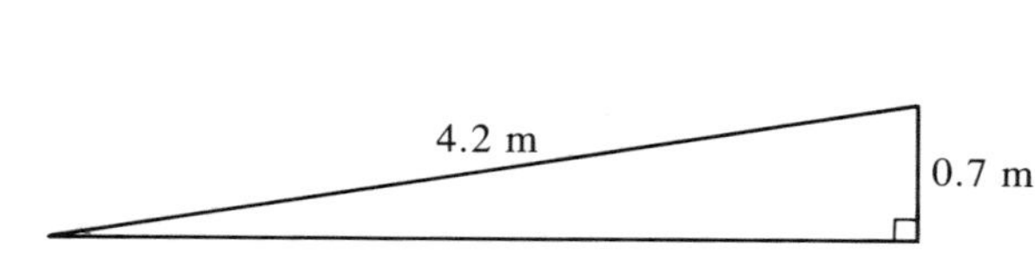

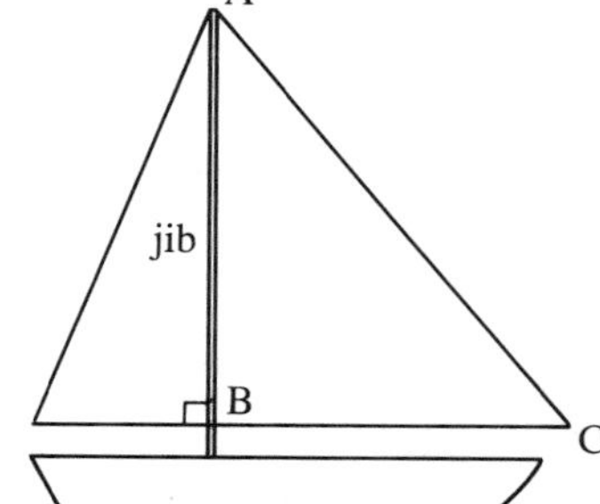

6. The guy wire for a jib sail (above right) is 3.7 m in length. It is attached at point A. The foot of the guy wire is 1.1 m from the mast AB. What is the angle of elevation of the guy wire to 1 decimal place?

7. In *Exercise 6*, the mast AB is 3.53 m long and the boom BC is 3.20 m. Find the measure of $\angle$C to 1 decimal place.

8. The Cinesphere at Ontario Place shows world class films on a huge curved screen. To gain access to the theatre, people walk up a series of five ramps, with the dimensions shown (below left).
   a) Find the angle of inclination of each ramp.
   b) Find the slope and the angle of inclination if only one set of steps had been built instead.

   Give the answers to 1 decimal place.

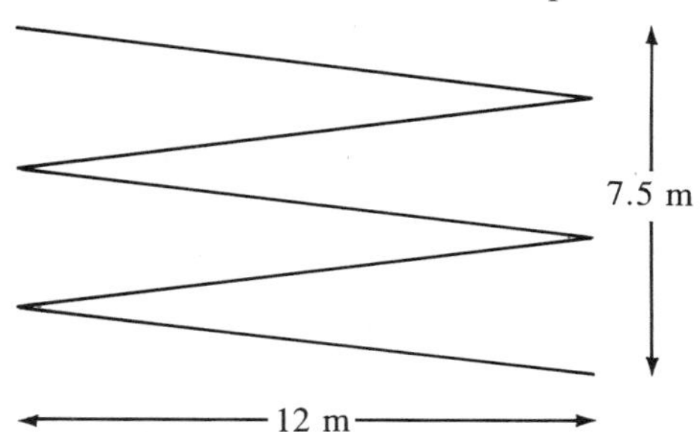

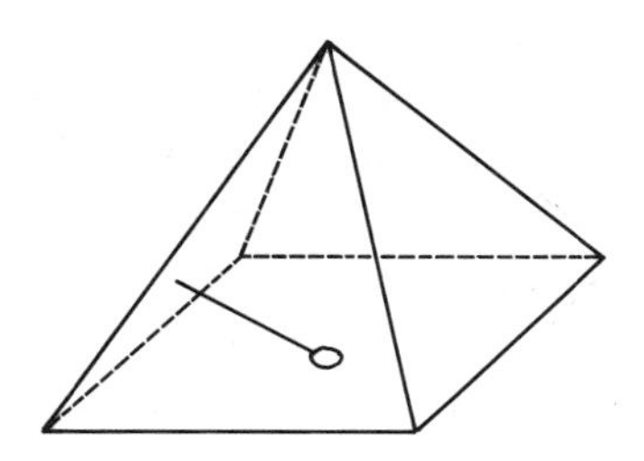

9. In the Great Pyramid at Giza (above right) there is a 115 m long passage that leads from the northern face to an interior chamber. If the chamber is 50 m below the opening of the passage, find the angle of inclination of the passage to 1 decimal place.

10. The largest slide in the world drops 220 m in a horizontal distance of 1203 m.
    a) How long is the slide to the nearest metre?
    b) What is its angle of inclination to the nearest degree?

11. If AB is a diameter of a circle of radius 2 units (below left), determine these values.
    a) $\sin\theta$ b) $\cos\theta$ c) $\tan\theta$

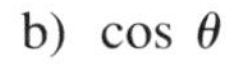

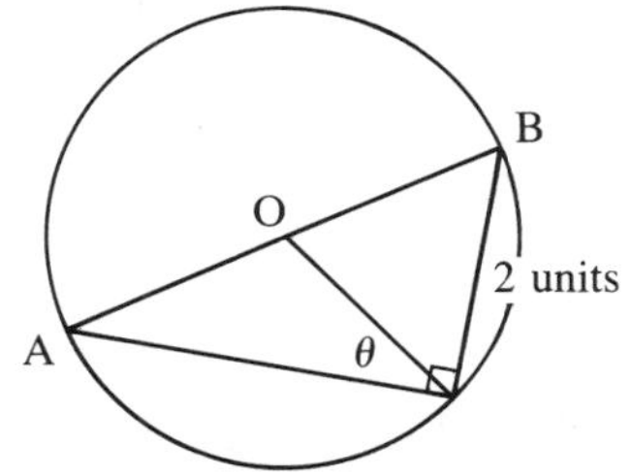

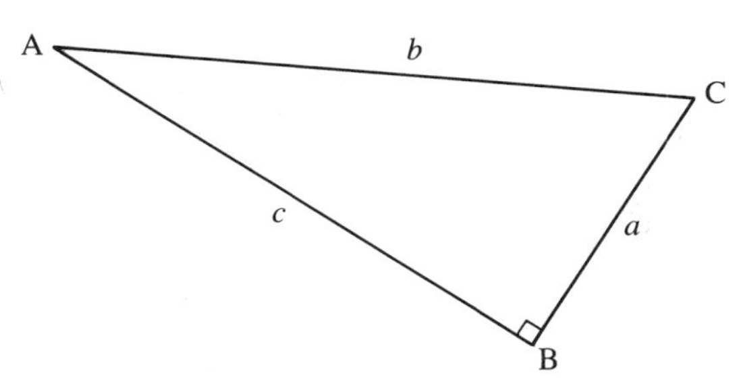

12. For the diagram (above right)
    a) State the primary trigonometric ratios for $\angle A$.
    b) State the primary trigonometric ratios for $\angle C$. What can you conclude?

Ⓒ

13. Find the measures of the acute angles to 1 decimal place in a right triangle if its sides have lengths a, $a + d$, $a + 2d$.

14. The volume V of a right square-based pyramid is given by the formula $V = \frac{1}{3}Bh$, where B is the area of the base and h is the height. Express V in terms of the length l along an inclined edge and the angle of inclination θ of the edge.

7-3 SOLVING RIGHT TRIANGLES

We have learned how to find the height of a cliff given the angle of inclination of the cliff at a given distance. This amounted to finding the length of one side of a right triangle given the length of another side and the measure of an angle. Finding all the unknown sides and angles of a triangle is called *solving the triangle*. We can solve a right triangle if we know either:

- the lengths of any two sides, or
- the length of one side and the measure of an acute angle.

The following example shows how we solve a right triangle given the lengths of two sides.

Example 1. Solve $\triangle ABC$ given $AB = 25$, $AC = 18$, and $\angle C = 90°$. Give the answers to 1 decimal place.

Solution. From the Pythagorean Theorem

$$\begin{aligned} BC^2 &= AB^2 - AC^2 \\ &= 25^2 - 18^2 \\ &= 301 \\ BC &= \sqrt{301} \\ &\doteq 17.349 \end{aligned}$$

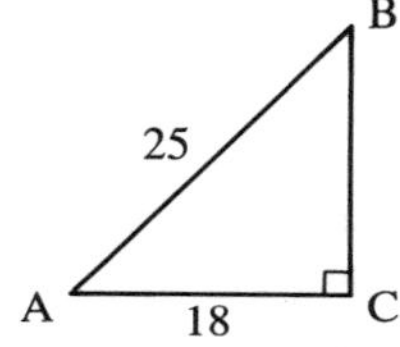

To find $\angle A$, we write $\cos A = \frac{18}{25}$ Use a calculator.

$$\angle A \doteq 43.9°$$

Since $\angle A + \angle B = 90°$, then $\angle B \doteq 46.1°$

We summarize these results in a table.

AB	AC	BC	∠A	∠B	∠C
25	18	17.3	43.9°	46.1°	90°

In *Example 1*, we used the Pythagorean Theorem to calculate the unknown side, and then the ratio of any two sides to determine an unknown angle. The next example shows how we can solve a right triangle given only the length of one side and the measure of an acute angle.

Example 2. Solve $\triangle DEF$ given that $\angle E = 90°$, $\angle D = 37°$, and $EF = 12$. Give the answers to the nearest whole number.

Solution. By definition of the tangent and sine ratios

$$\tan 37° = \frac{12}{DE}$$

$$DE = \frac{12}{\tan 37°}$$ Use a calculator.

$$\doteq 15.92$$

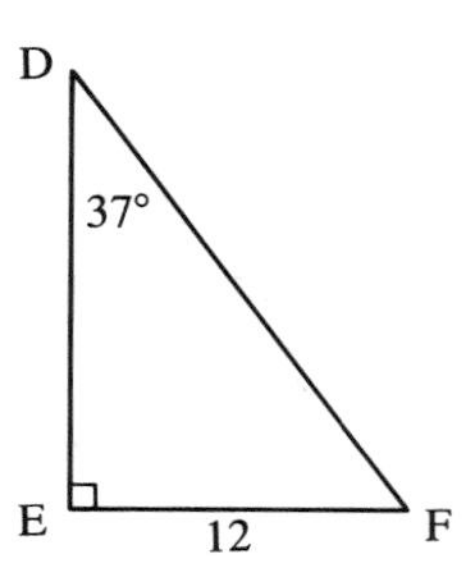

$$\sin 37° = \frac{12}{DF}$$

$$DF = \frac{12}{\sin 37°}$$

$$\doteq 19.94$$

Since $\angle D = 37°$, then $\angle F = 90° - 37°$, or $53°$

We summarize these results in a table.

EF	DE	DF	$\angle$D	$\angle$E	$\angle$F
12	16	20	37°	90°	53°

In *Example 2*, once we found DE we could have used the fact that EF = 12 and applied the Pythagorean Theorem to calculate DF.

The next examples show how we can find all the primary trigonometric ratios, given only one of them.

Example 3. If $\tan \theta = \frac{5}{12}$, find $\cos \theta$ and $\sin \theta$.

Solution. Sketch a right triangle with shorter sides 5 and 12, and hypotenuse h. Label the angle θ.

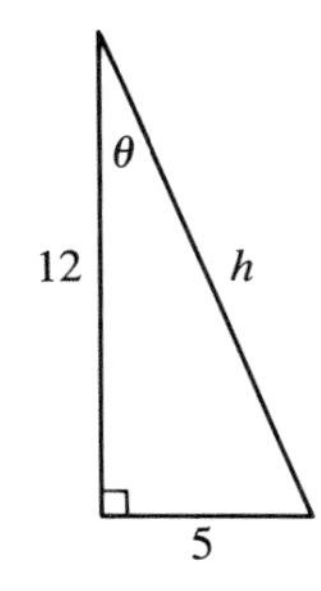

Using the Pythagorean Theorem

$$h = \sqrt{5^2 + 12^2}$$

$$= \sqrt{169}$$

$$= 13$$

Then, $\cos \theta = \frac{12}{13}$ and $\sin \theta = \frac{5}{13}$

Example 4. If $\sin \theta = \frac{a}{b}$, find expressions for $\cos \theta$ and $\tan \theta$.

Solution. Sketch a right triangle with side a opposite θ, and hypotenuse b.

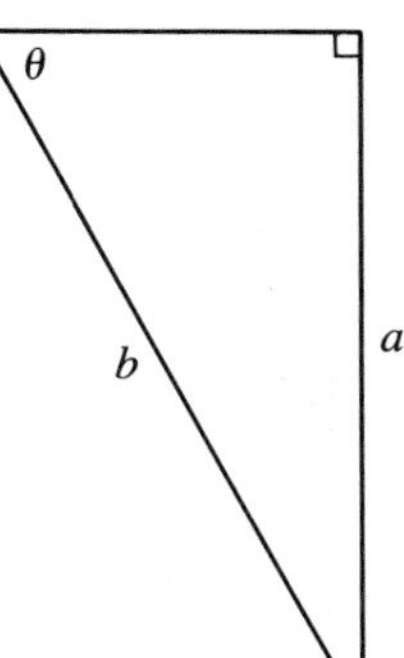

It follows from the Pythagorean Theorem that the third side has length $\sqrt{b^2 - a^2}$.

So, $\cos \theta = \frac{\sqrt{b^2 - a^2}}{b}$ and

$$\tan \theta = \frac{a}{\sqrt{b^2 - a^2}}$$

EXERCISES 7-3

Ⓐ

1. Solve each triangle. Give the answers to 1 decimal place.

a)

C
30
18
A
B

b)

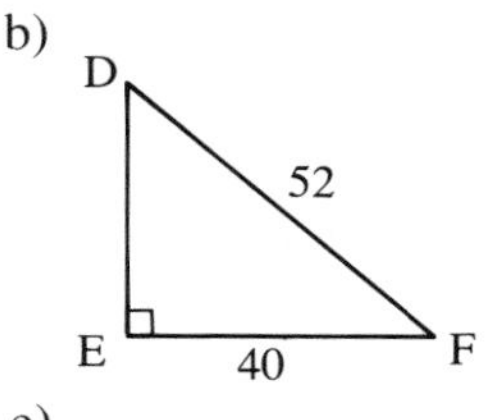

c)

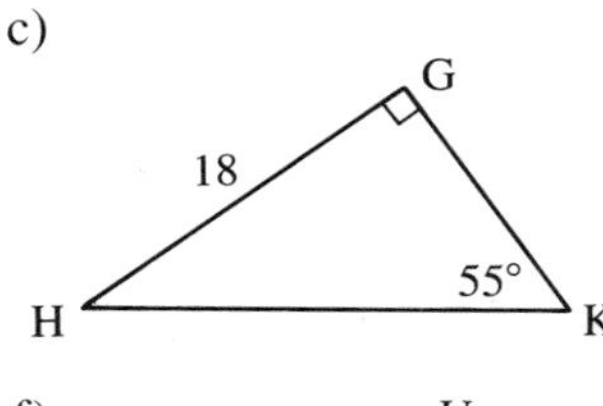

d)

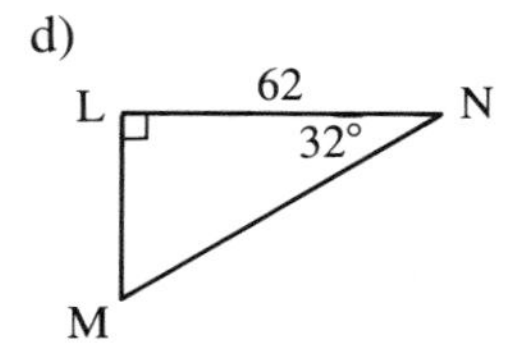

e)

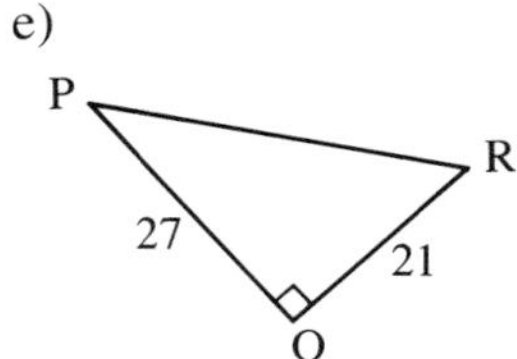

f)

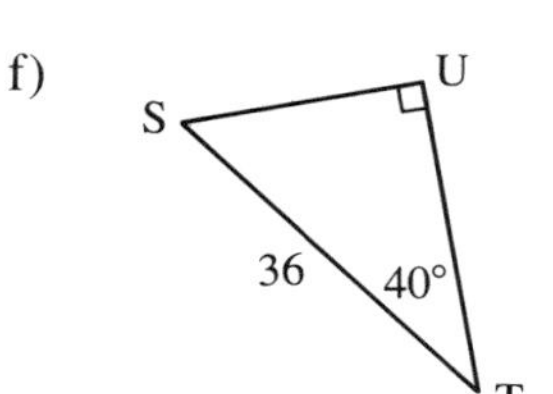

2. Solve △XYZ if ∠Y = 90° and:
   a) XY = 24, XZ = 35
   b) XY = 16, ∠X = 27°
   c) XZ = 51, YZ = 13
   d) XZ = 72, ∠Z = 52°
   e) YZ = 32, ∠X = 64°
   f) XY = 45, YZ = 20.

   Give the answers to 1 decimal place.

3. Find the other two primary trigonometric ratios for each value of θ.
   a) $\sin \theta = \frac{8}{17}$
   b) $\cos \theta = \frac{7}{25}$
   c) $\tan \theta = \frac{20}{21}$
   d) $\sin \theta = \frac{15}{32}$
   e) $\cos \theta = \frac{19}{23}$
   f) $\tan \theta = \frac{43}{112}$

Ⓑ

4. Find expressions for the other primary trigonometric ratios for each value of θ.
   a) $\sin \theta = \frac{p}{q}$
   b) $\cos \theta = \frac{a}{a + 2}$
   c) $\tan \theta = \frac{x - y}{x + y}$

5. At a point 28 m away, the angle of elevation of a building is 65° (below left).
   a) How tall is the building?
   b) How far is the observer's eye from the top of the building?

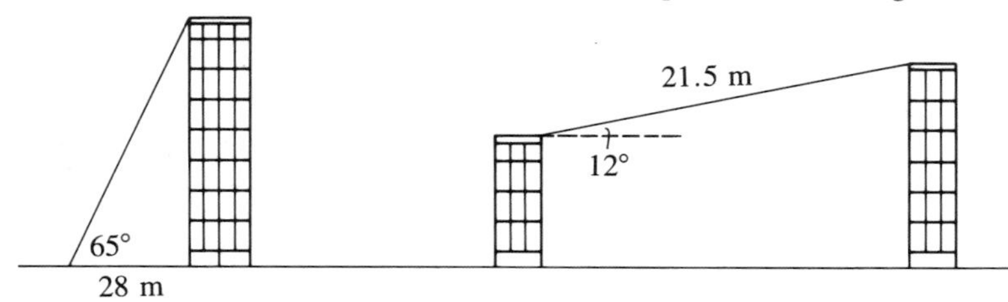

6. A tightrope walker attaches a cable to the roofs of two adjacent buildings (above right). The cable is 21.5 m long and the angle of inclination is 12°.
   a) How far apart are the buildings?
   b) What is the difference in their heights?

7. A rectangle has length 10 cm and width 6 cm. Find the acute angle to the nearest degree between the diagonals.

8. The length of rectangle ABCD is three times its width. Points M and N are the midpoints of the longer sides AB and DC.
   a) Find ∠MAN.
   b) If P is the midpoint of AD, find ∠MPN.
   Give the answers to the nearest degree.

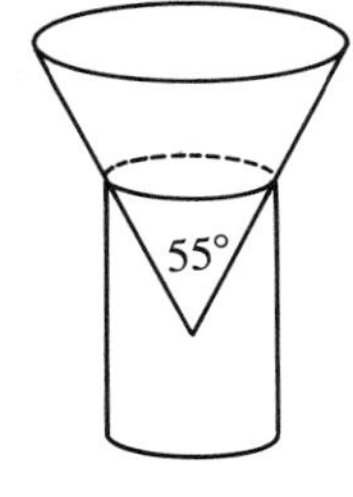

9. A funnel is placed in a glass, as shown. If the glass is 14.5 cm tall and 7.6 cm in diameter, how high is the vertex of the funnel above the bottom of the glass?

10. Prior to 1982, visitors to the observation deck of the Peace Tower in Ottawa had to ride two elevators. The Memorial Chamber at the base of the tower made a vertical assent impossible. A new elevator system carries visitors up the first 24.2 m by travelling a path inclined at 10° to the vertical. It then rises vertically for the balance of the trip.
    a) How long is the elevator shaft that runs on the incline?
    b) By how far is the elevator displaced horizontally by the incline?
    c) What is the slope of the incline to 2 decimal places?

11. Two office towers are 31.7 m apart. From the shorter one, the angle of elevation to the top of the other is 27.5°, while the angle of depression to the base is 78.2°. Find the height of each tower.

Ⓒ

12. The diagram (below left) shows how the ancient Greeks constructed line segments of lengths $\sqrt{2}$, $\sqrt{3}$, $\sqrt{4}$, $\sqrt{5}$, . . . As the process continues, the triangles turn about point A, as shown.
    a) Find these angles to 1 decimal place.
       i) ∠CAB ii) ∠DAB iii) ∠EAB iv) ∠FAB
    b) How many triangles can be drawn without overlapping?

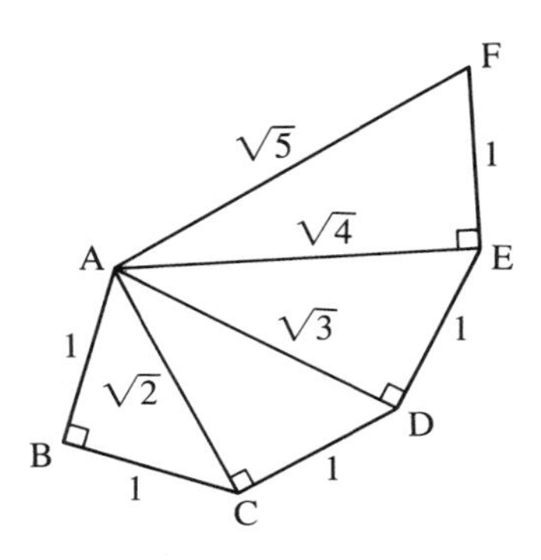

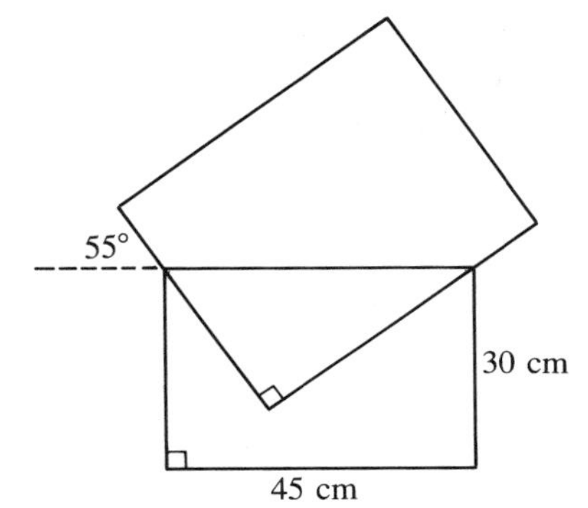

13. A box is resting inside a second box (above right). How high is the lowest corner of the first box above the bottom of the second box?

7-4 THE RECIPROCAL TRIGONOMETRIC RATIOS

To this point, we have defined the three primary trigonometric ratios of an angle θ.

$$\sin\theta = \frac{\text{opposite}}{\text{hypotenuse}} \qquad \cos\theta = \frac{\text{adjacent}}{\text{hypotenuse}} \qquad \tan\theta = \frac{\text{opposite}}{\text{adjacent}}$$

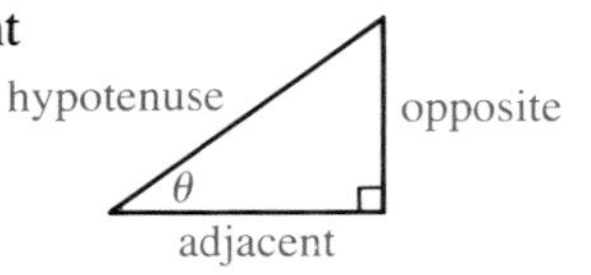

The reciprocals of these ratios are respectively called the *cosecant*, *secant*, and *cotangent ratios* and are abbreviated as *csc*, *sec*, and *cot*. These *reciprocal trigonometric ratios* are defined as follows.

$$\csc\theta = \frac{\text{hypotenuse}}{\text{opposite}} \qquad \sec\theta = \frac{\text{hypotenuse}}{\text{adjacent}} \qquad \cot\theta = \frac{\text{adjacent}}{\text{opposite}}$$

It follows from these definitions that:

$$\csc\theta = \frac{1}{\sin\theta} \qquad \sec\theta = \frac{1}{\cos\theta} \qquad \cot\theta = \frac{1}{\tan\theta}.$$

Since we can readily compute the value of a reciprocal ratio by taking the reciprocal of a primary ratio, most scientific calculators have keys for only the primary trigonometric ratios. For example, to obtain csc 36° on a calculator, we find sin 36° and press the reciprocal key [1/x].

Example 1. Find the values of the six trigonometric ratios for 47°.

Solution. Use a calculator.
For sin 47°, key in: 47 [sin] to display 0.7313537
For csc 47°, continue and key in: [1/x] to display 1.3673275
For cos 47°, key in: 47 [cos] to display 0.6819984
For sec 47°, continue and key in: [1/x] to display 1.4662792
For tan 47°, key in: 47 [tan] to display 1.0723687
For cot 47°, continue and key in: [1/x] to display 0.9325151

Example 2. Write the six trigonometric ratios for the two acute angles in the right triangle with sides of length 12, 35, and 37 units.

Solution. Let α and β represent the acute angles.
From the definition of the trigonometric ratios

$$\sin\alpha = \frac{12}{37} \quad \cos\alpha = \frac{35}{37} \quad \tan\alpha = \frac{12}{35}$$

$$\csc\alpha = \frac{37}{12} \quad \sec\alpha = \frac{37}{35} \quad \cot\alpha = \frac{35}{12}$$

$$\sin\beta = \frac{35}{37} \quad \cos\beta = \frac{12}{37} \quad \tan\beta = \frac{35}{12}$$

$$\csc\beta = \frac{37}{35} \quad \sec\beta = \frac{37}{12} \quad \cot\beta = \frac{12}{35}$$

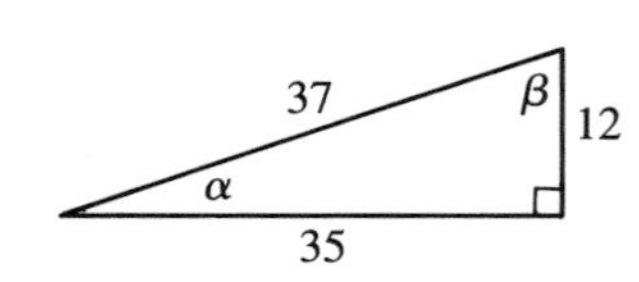

Example 2 not only shows the relationship between the primary and reciprocal ratios, but the diagram suggests a relationship between the trigonometric ratios of two angles which total 90°.

Since $\sin \alpha = \cos \beta = \frac{12}{37}$, and $\beta = 90° - \alpha$

then $\sin \alpha = \cos (90° - \alpha)$

Similarly, $\cos \alpha = \sin (90° - \alpha)$ and $\tan \alpha = \cot (90° - \alpha)$

Just as we can calculate all primary trigonometric ratios given any one primary trigonometric ratio, so also we can calculate all trigonometric ratios given any one trigonometric ratio.

Example 3. If $\cot \theta = \frac{b}{a}$, write expressions for the six trigonometric ratios for θ.

Solution. Sketch a right triangle with side a opposite θ and side b adjacent θ.
From the Pythagorean Theorem, the hypotenuse has length $\sqrt{a^2 + b^2}$.
From the definition of the trigonometric ratios

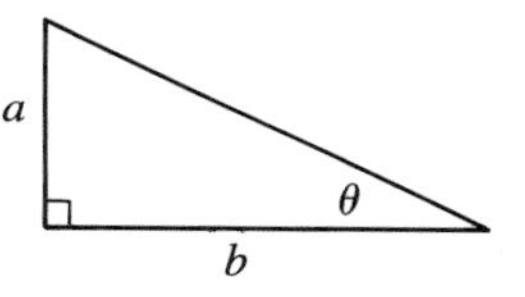

$$\sin \theta = \frac{a}{\sqrt{a^2 + b^2}} \qquad \cos \theta = \frac{b}{\sqrt{a^2 + b^2}} \qquad \tan \theta = \frac{a}{b}$$

$$\csc \theta = \frac{\sqrt{a^2 + b^2}}{a} \qquad \sec \theta = \frac{\sqrt{a^2 + b^2}}{b} \qquad \cot \theta = \frac{b}{a}$$

Example 4. Find each value of θ to the nearest degree.
a) $\cot \theta = 1.234$ b) $\sec \theta = 2.561$ c) $\csc \theta = 4.032$

Solution. a) Since $\tan \theta = \frac{1}{\cot \theta}$

$$\tan \theta = \frac{1}{1.234}$$

Key in: 1.234 [1/x] [tan⁻¹] to display 39.020367

$\theta \doteq 39°$

b) Since $\cos \theta = \frac{1}{\sec \theta}$

$$\cos \theta = \frac{1}{2.561}$$

Key in: 2.561 [1/x] [cos⁻¹] to display 67.016099

$\theta \doteq 67°$

c) Since $\sin \theta = \frac{1}{\csc \theta}$

$$\sin \theta = \frac{1}{4.032}$$

Key in: 4.032 [1/x] [sin⁻¹] to display 14.360133

$\theta \doteq 14°$

EXERCISES 7-4

(A)

1. Find the value to 3 decimal places of each trigonometric ratio.
   a) csc 17° b) cot 29° c) sec 64° d) cot 81° e) sec 57° f) csc 71°
   g) cot 11° h) sec 9° i) cot 53° j) csc 39° k) sec 23° l) csc 84°

2. Find the values to 3 decimal places of the six trigonometric ratios for each angle.
   a) 25° b) 50° c) 75° d) 30° e) 45° f) 60°

3. Find each value of θ to the nearest degree.
   a) $\csc \theta = 1.624$ b) $\cot \theta = 0.675$ c) $\sec \theta = 1.058$ d) $\cot \theta = 0.554$
   e) $\sec \theta = 1.325$ f) $\csc \theta = 1.305$ g) $\cot \theta = 3.732$ h) $\sec \theta = 3.628$
   i) $\csc \theta = 2.591$ j) $\sec \theta = 2.591$ k) $\cot \theta = 4.915$ l) $\csc \theta = 1.267$

(B)

4. Write expressions for the six trigonometric ratios of each angle.
   a) ∠A b) ∠B

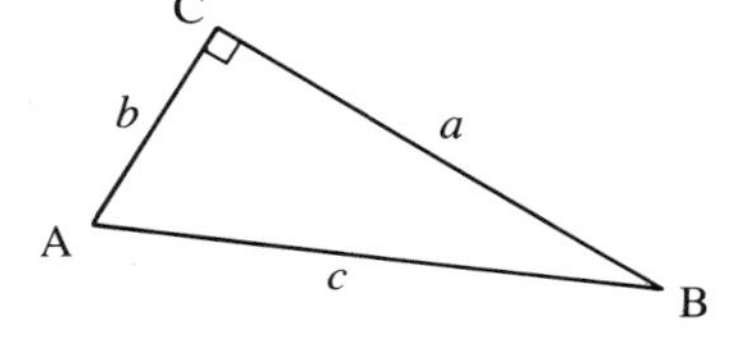

5. Match each ratio in the first row with an equivalent ratio from the second row if ∠A + ∠B = 90°.
   sin *A* cos *A* tan *A* csc *A* sec *A* cot *A*
   sin *B* cos *B* tan *B* csc *B* sec *B* cot *B*

6. Solve each triangle. Give the answers to 1 decimal place.
   a) b) c)

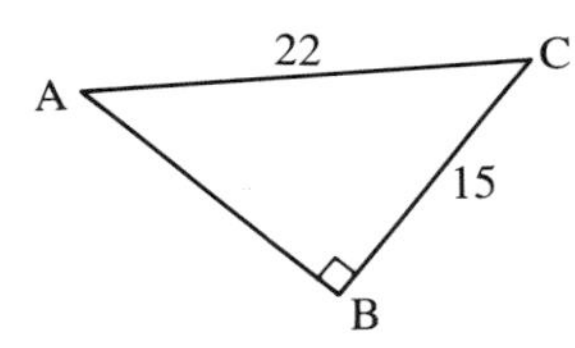

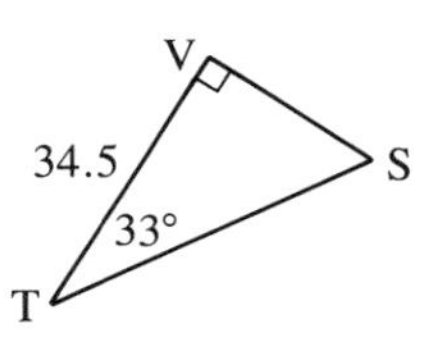

V
34.5
S
33°
T

7. Write expressions for the other five trigonometric ratios for each acute angle.
   a) $\csc \theta = \frac{p}{q}$ b) $\sec \phi = \frac{x+1}{x-1}, x \neq 1$ c) $\cot \alpha = \frac{2a}{a+1}, a \neq -1$

(C)

8. The departure *d* kilometres of the Earth's surface from the line of sight is approximated by this formula.
   $d = 6370\left(1 - \cos\left(\frac{18a}{637\pi}\right)\right)$ where *a* kilometres is the distance measured along the Earth's surface
   Find the value of *d* for each given value of *a*.
   a) 2 km b) 10 km c) 50 km d) 350 km

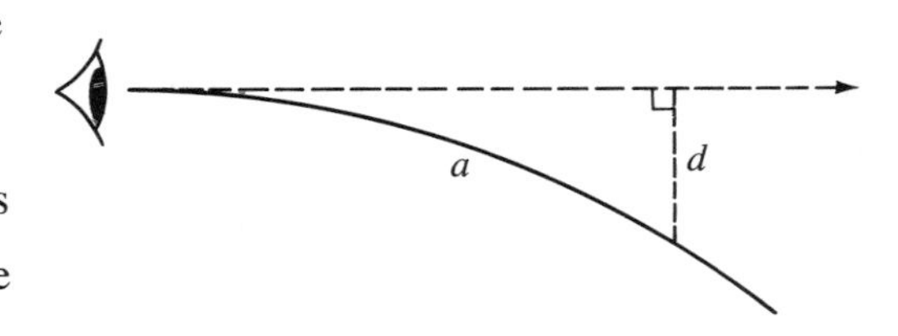

7-5 APPLICATIONS OF THE TRIGONOMETRIC RATIOS

In *Section 7-3* we learned how to solve a right triangle given either:

- the lengths of any two sides; or
- the length of one side and the measure of an acute angle.

In this section we apply these techniques to the solutions of various problems. In each case we solve for an unknown side or an unknown angle rather than solving for all sides and angles.

Example 1. The Great Pyramid in Egypt has a square base of side length 230 m. If the angle of elevation of the sides is 52°, what is the height of the pyramid?

Solution. Let h metres represent the height.
Then, in △ABC

$$\frac{h}{115} = \tan 52°$$

$$h = 115 \tan 52°$$

Key in: 52 [tan] [×] 115 [=] to display 147.19329

The pyramid is about 147 m high.

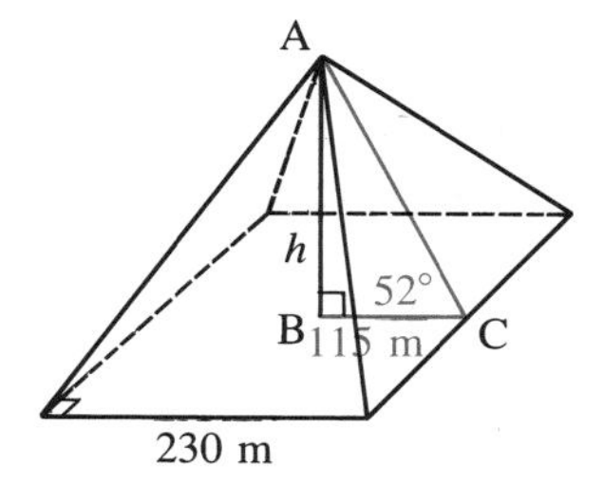

Example 2. A fireman's ladder is inclined at an angle of 58°. The ladder is 10 m long measured from the foot to the top rung, where a fireman is standing. How high is the fireman above the ground?

Solution. Let h metres represent the height of the top rung.

Then, $\frac{h}{10} = \sin 58°$

$$h = 10 \sin 58°$$

$$\doteq 8.48$$

The fireman is about 8.5 m above the ground.

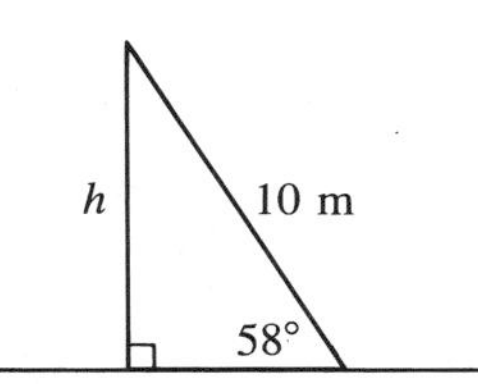

Example 3. The world's longest suspension bridge is across the Humber Estuary in England. The towers of this bridge reach about 135 m above the level of the bridge. The angles of elevation of the towers seen from the centre of the bridge and either end are 10.80° and 18.65° respectively. How long is the Humber Estuary Bridge?

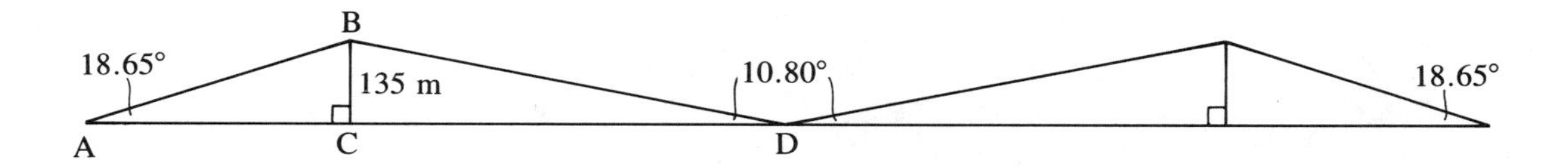

Solution. The length of the bridge is double the length of AD.

$$\frac{AC}{135} = \cot 18.65^\circ \quad \text{and} \quad \frac{CD}{135} = \cot 10.8^\circ$$

$$AC = 135 \cot 18.65^\circ \qquad CD = 135 \cot 10.8^\circ$$

$$\begin{aligned} AD &= AC + CD \\ &= 135 \cot 18.65^\circ + 135 \cot 10.8^\circ \\ &= 135(\cot 18.65^\circ + \cot 10.8^\circ) \\ &\doteq 1107.68 \end{aligned}$$

The length of the bridge is about 2(1107.68 m), or about 2215 m.

Example 3 could have been solved using the tangent ratio instead of the cotangent ratio. Then, the computations would have involved divisions by the tangent ratios instead of multiplications by the cotangent ratios. The reciprocal trigonometric ratios were originally introduced to simplify these types of calculations, but the use of calculators and computers has removed this need. The main use of the reciprocal trigonometric ratios lies in their behaviour as functions, which will be illustrated in Chapter 9.

EXERCISES 7-5

(B)

1. When spraying a crop with pesticides, a farmer uses a boom sprayer pulled by a tractor. The nozzles are 50 cm apart and spray at an angle of 70°. How high should the sprayer be set above the top of the crop to provide an even distribution of the pesticide?

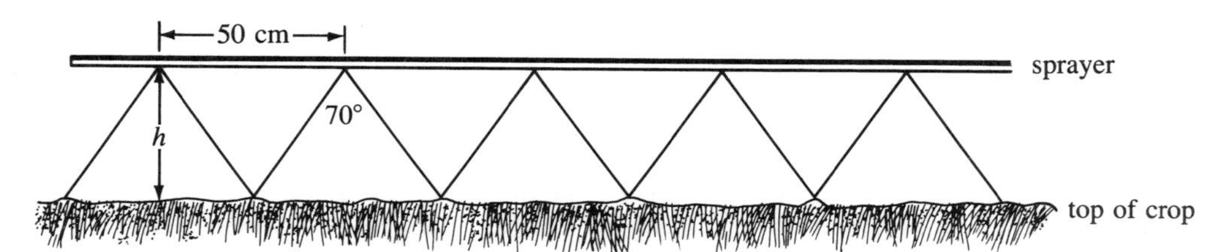

2. A hemispherical bowl of diameter 20 cm contains some liquid with a depth of 4 cm. Through what angle with the horizontal may the bowl be tipped before the liquid begins to spill out?

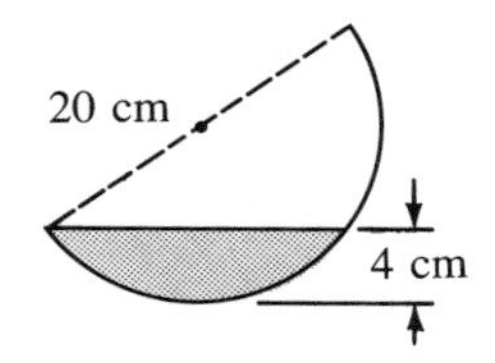

3. The Calgary Tower is 190 m high and casts a shadow 84 m long. Find the angle to the nearest degree which the sun's rays make with the ground.

4. A television antenna is supported by a guy wire connected to the mast. The angle of elevation of the guy wire is 39°, and the angle of elevation of the top of the antenna is 53°. If the guy wire is fixed to the ground 7 m from the base of the mast, find to the nearest tenth of a metre:
   a) the height of the antenna
   b) the distance from the top of the antenna to where the guy wire is connected.

5. The picture tube in a color television set is 50 cm wide, and has a deflection angle of 90° (below left).
   a) Calculate the least possible depth of a cabinet that could hold the tube.
   b) The manufacturer advertises that by increasing the deflection angle to 100°, the cabinet can be made smaller. Find the decrease in depth of the cabinet allowed by the larger deflection angle.

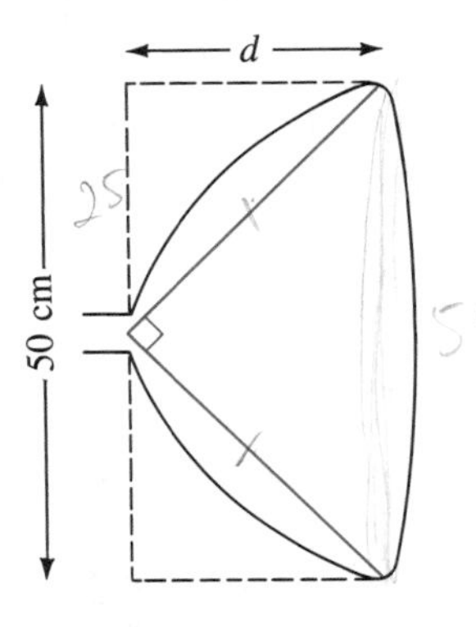

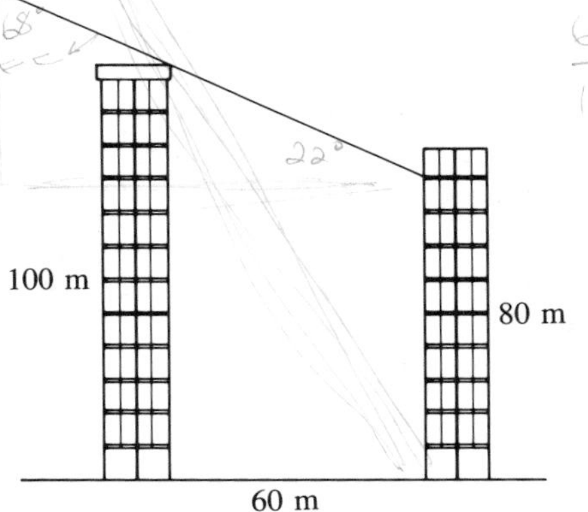

6. Two apartment buildings 100 m and 80 m high are 60 m apart (above right). The sun casts a shadow of the 100 m building on the 80 m building.
   a) If the angle of elevation of the sun is 22°, calculate the height of the shadow on the 80 m building to the nearest metre.
   b) If the angle of elevation of the sun changes at a constant rate of 15°/h, calculate the total time that the 80 m building is partly in the shadow of the 100 m building.

7. Donna measured the angle of elevation of a church steeple and found it to be 10°. Then she walked 100 m towards the steeple and measured the angle of elevation again; this time it was 20°. Find the height of the steeple, assuming that the ground is level.

8. Trigonometry can be used to find the circumference of the Earth. From the top of a mountain 5 km high the angle between the horizon and the true vertical is 87.73°. Use the diagram to calculate:
   a) the radius
   b) the circumference of the Earth.

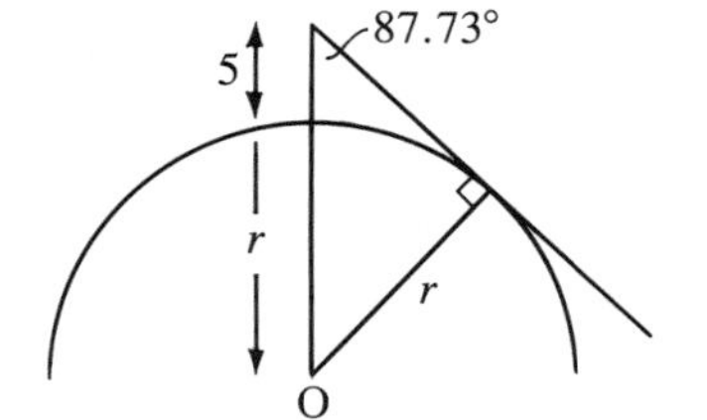

9. Assume that the method of *Exercise 8* is used with measurements taken from a satellite at an altitude of 200 km. If the Earth's radius is 6370 km, find the angle between the horizon and the true vertical to 2 decimal places.

10. Angle parking allows more cars to park along a given street than does parallel parking. However, the cars use more of the street width when angle parked.

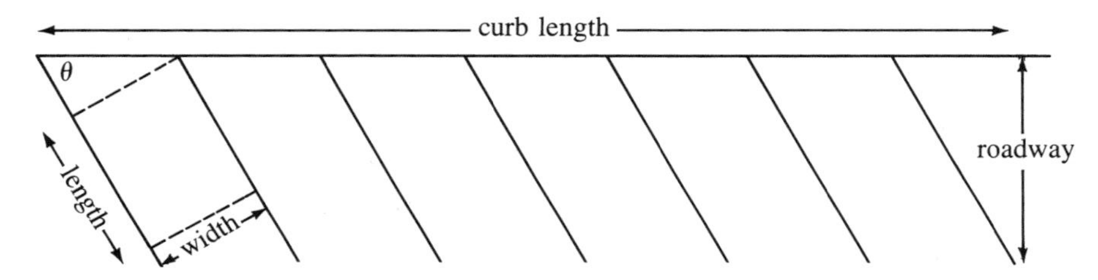

   a) If each car requires a space 2.7 m wide, how much curb length would be required to park 20 cars if θ is: i) 30° ii) 50° iii) 60°?
   b) If 20 cars had to be parked in 60 m of curb length, what would be the value of θ?
   c) If each car requires a space 6.5 m long, how much of the roadway is given up for parking if θ is: i) 30° ii) 50° iii) 60°?

Ⓒ

11. The measure of angle θ in *Exercise 10* depends upon the amount of roadway K that can be used for parking. The relationship between θ and K is given by $\frac{2.7 \cos \theta}{K - 6.5 \sin \theta} = 1$. If $K = 6.9$ m, find the value of θ to the nearest degree.

12. On a sunny day, the shadows of stationary objects move slowly across the ground. This is caused by the apparent motion of the sun across the sky, due to the rotation of the Earth. Assume that the sun rises due east at 6 A.M., and sets due west at 6 P.M.
   a) Find the length of the shadow of a 150 m building at:
      i) 8 A.M. ii) 10:30 A.M. iii) 2 P.M. iv) 5:30 P.M.
   b) At what times during the day is the shadow of a 150-m building 90 m long?
   c) Directly to the west of a 400-m building there is a 300-m building a distance of 200 m away. Calculate the total time during the day that the space between the buildings is entirely in shadow.

13. The top of a cylindrical oil storage tank, 55.3 m high and 28.4 m in diameter, is reached by a spiral stairway that circles the tank exactly once. Calculate the angle of inclination of the stairway to the nearest degree.

7-6 TRIGONOMETRIC RATIOS OF SPECIAL ANGLES

For angles such as 45°, 30°, and 60°, the trigonometric ratios can be calculated using an isosceles right triangle and an equilateral triangle.

Trigonometric Ratios of 45°

If the equal sides of an isosceles right triangle are 1 unit long, then from the Pythagorean Theorem, the length of the hypotenuse is $\sqrt{1^2 + 1^2}$, or $\sqrt{2}$.
Furthermore, the two acute angles are equal and since they total 90°, each angle is 45°. Therefore,

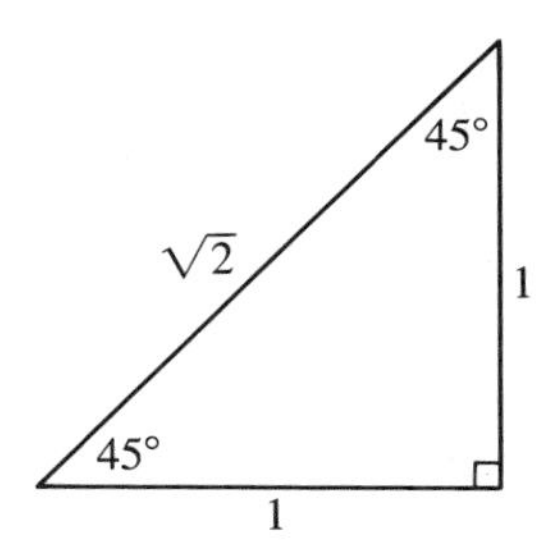

$\sin 45° = \frac{1}{\sqrt{2}}$ $\quad\cos 45° = \frac{1}{\sqrt{2}}$ $\quad\tan 45° = \frac{1}{1}$, or 1

$\csc 45° = \sqrt{2}$ $\quad\sec 45° = \sqrt{2}$ $\quad\cot 45° = 1$

Trigonometric Ratios of 30° and 60°

If the sides of an equilateral $\triangle ABC$ are 2 units long, then from the Pythagorean Theorem, the length of the altitude AD is $\sqrt{2^2 - 1^2}$, or $\sqrt{3}$.
Furthermore, $\angle A = \angle B = \angle C = 60°$
Therefore,

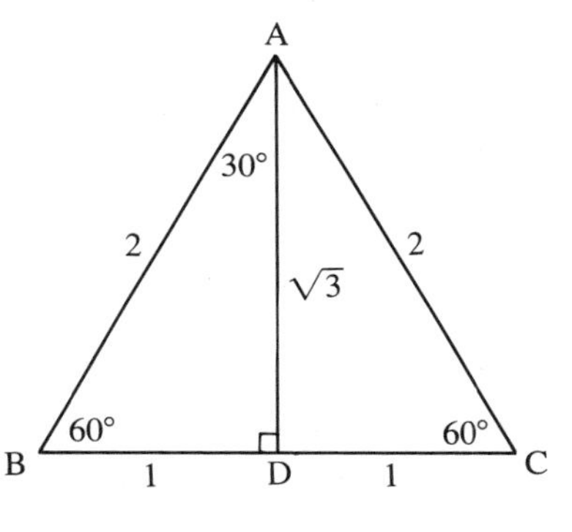

$\sin 60° = \frac{\sqrt{3}}{2}$ $\quad\cos 60° = \frac{1}{2}$ $\quad\tan 60° = \frac{\sqrt{3}}{1}$, or $\sqrt{3}$

$\csc 60° = \frac{2}{\sqrt{3}}$ $\quad\sec 60° = 2$ $\quad\cot 60° = \frac{1}{\sqrt{3}}$

Also, $\angle BAD = 180° - 90° - 60°$, or 30°
Therefore,

$\sin 30° = \frac{1}{2}$ $\quad\cos 30° = \frac{\sqrt{3}}{2}$ $\quad\tan 30° = \frac{1}{\sqrt{3}}$

$\csc 30° = 2$ $\quad\sec 30° = \frac{2}{\sqrt{3}}$ $\quad\cot 30° = \sqrt{3}$

We summarize these trigonometric ratios for angles of 30°, 45° and 60° in a table.

	sin	**cos**	**tan**	**csc**	**sec**	**cot**
30°	$\frac{1}{2}$	$\frac{\sqrt{3}}{2}$	$\frac{1}{\sqrt{3}}$	2	$\frac{2}{\sqrt{3}}$	$\sqrt{3}$
45°	$\frac{1}{\sqrt{2}}$	$\frac{1}{\sqrt{2}}$	1	$\sqrt{2}$	$\sqrt{2}$	1
60°	$\frac{\sqrt{3}}{2}$	$\frac{1}{2}$	$\sqrt{3}$	$\frac{2}{\sqrt{3}}$	2	$\frac{1}{\sqrt{3}}$

To determine the trigonometric ratios of 0° and 90°, we consider the ratios as θ decreases to 0° and as θ increases to 90°.

Trigonometric Ratios of 0°

Consider $\triangle$ABC as AB rotates to AC, and $\angle$BAC decreases to 0°. AB approaches AC in length and BC approaches 0 in length.
So, as θ approaches 0°

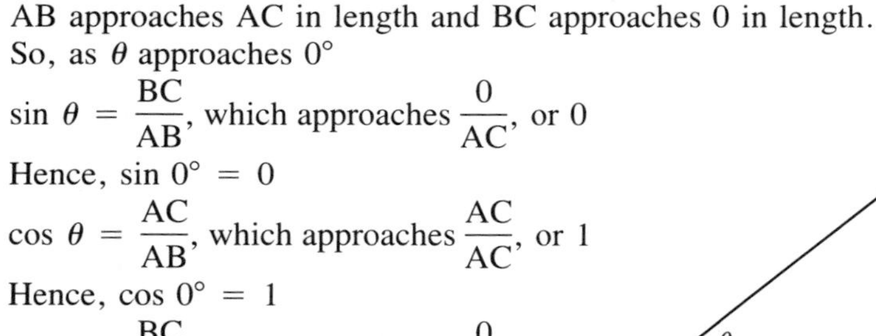

$\sin\theta = \frac{BC}{AB}$, which approaches $\frac{0}{AC}$, or 0

Hence, $\sin 0° = 0$

$\cos\theta = \frac{AC}{AB}$, which approaches $\frac{AC}{AC}$, or 1

Hence, $\cos 0° = 1$

$\tan\theta = \frac{BC}{AC}$, which approaches $\frac{0}{AC}$, or 0

Hence, $\tan 0° = 0$

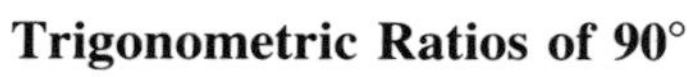

Trigonometric Ratios of 90°

Consider $\triangle$ABC as C moves along CA to A, and $\angle$CAB increases to 90°.
AC approaches 0 in length, and BC approaches BA in length.
So, as θ approaches 90°

$\sin\theta = \frac{BC}{BA}$, which approaches $\frac{BA}{BA}$, or 1

Hence, $\sin 90° = 1$

$\cos\theta = \frac{AC}{AB}$, which approaches $\frac{0}{AB}$, or 0

Hence, $\cos 90° = 0$

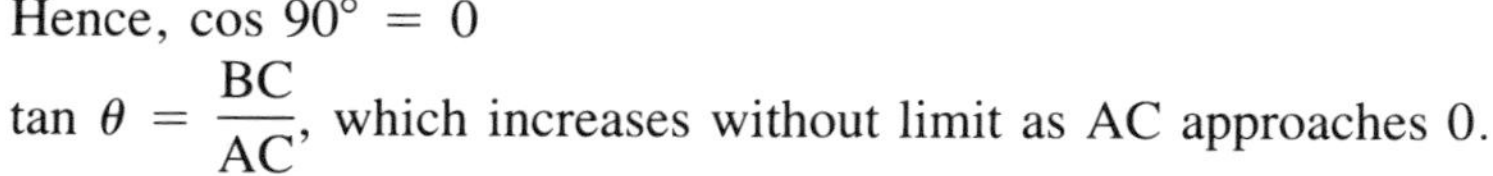

$\tan\theta = \frac{BC}{AC}$, which increases without limit as AC approaches 0.

tan 90° is undefined and we use the symbol ∞ to represent a quantity which is not finite.

The trigonometric ratios for 0° and 90° are summarized in the following table.

	sin	cos	tan	csc	sec	cot
0°	0	1	0	∞	1	∞
90°	1	0	∞	1	∞	0

We can use the values of the trigonometric ratios of these special angles to calculate exact answers to problems.

Example 1. A ladder is inclined at an angle of 60° against a wall. If the foot of the ladder is 6 m from the wall, how long is the ladder?

Solution. Let the length of the ladder be x metres.

$$\text{Then, } \frac{x}{6} = \sec 60^\circ$$
$$\begin{aligned} x &= 6 \sec 60^\circ \\ &= 6(2) \\ &= 12 \end{aligned}$$

The ladder is 12 m long.

Example 2. A tiling company wants to develop a hexagonal tile with area A square centimetres. Find a formula for the edge length x centimetres of the hexagonal tile.

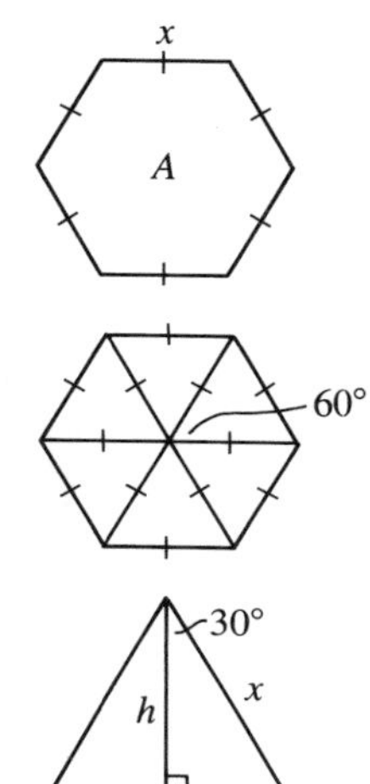

Solution. Divide the regular hexagon into 6 congruent triangles. Since 6 equal angles at the centre of the hexagon have total measure 360°, each angle at the centre is 60°. Furthermore the triangles are isosceles (by symmetry). So, the other two angles in each triangle are 60°. That is, the 6 triangles are equilateral with sides x centimetres long.

To relate x and A, we need to find the area in terms of x. To find the area of an equilateral triangle with sides of length x, let h denote the height. Then

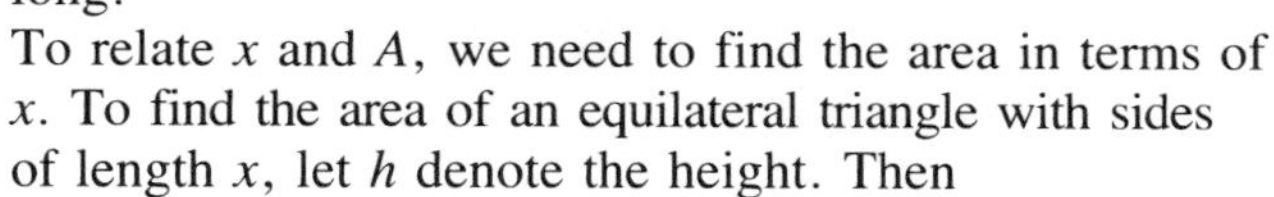

$$\frac{h}{x} = \cos 30^\circ$$
$$\begin{aligned} h &= x \cos 30^\circ \\ &= \frac{\sqrt{3}}{2}x \end{aligned}$$

$$\begin{aligned} \text{Area of triangle} &= \frac{1}{2}(\text{base})(\text{height}) \\ &= \frac{1}{2}(x)\left(\frac{\sqrt{3}}{2}x\right) \\ &= \frac{\sqrt{3}}{4}x^2 \end{aligned}$$

$$\begin{aligned} \text{Area of hexagon} &= 6\left(\frac{\sqrt{3}}{4}x^2\right) \\ &= \frac{3\sqrt{3}}{2}x^2 \end{aligned}$$

$$\text{Hence, } A = \frac{3\sqrt{3}}{2}x^2$$

$$\text{Rearrange, } x^2 = \frac{2A}{3\sqrt{3}}$$

$$x = \sqrt{\frac{2A}{3\sqrt{3}}}$$

Example 3. H.M.S. Napier observes a second ship 24 km due east. The first ship sights a lighthouse at E 30° S. For the second ship the lighthouse is at W 60° S. How far is each ship from the lighthouse?

Solution. Draw a diagram, with A, B, and L representing the positions of the ships and the lighthouse.
We need to find AL and BL.
In $\triangle ABL$
Since $\angle A = 30°$ and $\angle B = 60°$,
then $\angle L = 90°$

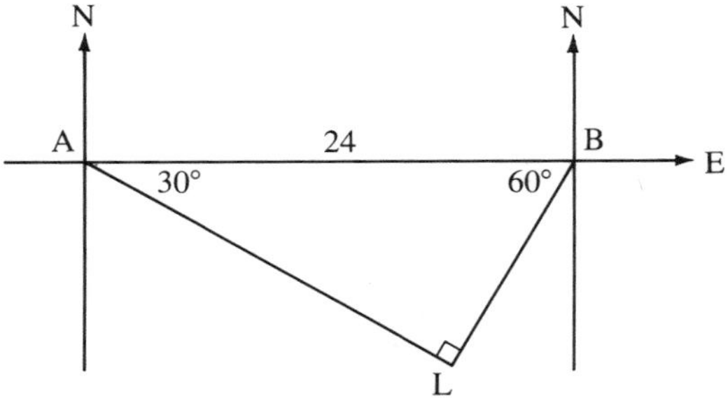

Hence, $\frac{BL}{24} = \sin 30°$

$$BL = 24\left(\frac{1}{2}\right)$$
$$= 12$$

$$\frac{AL}{24} = \cos 30°$$

$$AL = 24\left(\frac{\sqrt{3}}{2}\right)$$
$$= 12\sqrt{3}$$

The ships are 12 km and $12\sqrt{3}$ km from the lighthouse.

EXERCISES 7-6

Ⓐ

1. State the value of each ratio.
   a) sin 30° b) cos 60° c) sec 30° d) tan 45° e) csc 60° f) cot 30°
   g) sin 45° h) cot 60° i) cos 45° j) tan 30° k) csc 45° l) sec 45°

2. State the value of each ratio.
   a) csc 30° b) tan 60° c) sin 0° d) sec 90° e) cos 30° f) cot 45°
   g) tan 90° h) cos 0° i) sec 60° j) csc 0° k) cot 0° l) sin 90°

3. Find each value of θ.
   a) $\tan\theta = 1$ b) $\sin\theta = 0$ c) $\sec\theta = 2$ d) $\cos\theta = \frac{1}{2}$
   e) $\csc\theta = 2$ f) $\cos\theta = \frac{1}{\sqrt{2}}$ g) $\tan\theta = 0$ h) $\cot\theta = 1$
   i) $\sin\theta = \frac{\sqrt{3}}{2}$ j) $\csc\theta = \sqrt{2}$ k) $\cot\theta = \infty$ l) $\sec\theta = 1$

4. Find each value of θ.
   a) $\sin\theta = \frac{1}{\sqrt{2}}$ b) $\cot\theta = \frac{1}{\sqrt{3}}$ c) $\cos\theta = 0$ d) $\sec\theta = \sqrt{2}$
   e) $\csc\theta = 1$ f) $\sec\theta = \frac{2}{\sqrt{3}}$ g) $\tan\theta = \infty$ h) $\cot\theta = \sqrt{3}$
   i) $\sin\theta = \frac{1}{2}$ j) $\tan\theta = \sqrt{3}$ k) $\csc\theta = \infty$ l) $\cos\theta = 1$

(B)

5. One ship observes a second ship 6 km away and in the north-east direction. The first ship sights a flare due east. For the second ship the flare is due south. How far is each ship from the distress signal?

6. In a baseball diamond, each baseline is 27.4 m long. If the pitcher stands at the centre of the diamond how far is she from each base?

7. A guy wire is fastened 6.2 m from the base of a hydro pole. Find the length of the guy wire and how far up the pole it is fastened for each angle of elevation.
   a) 45° b) 30° c) 60°

8. A steel bridge is constructed, as shown. If the supporting towers are 12.6 m tall, how long is the bridge?

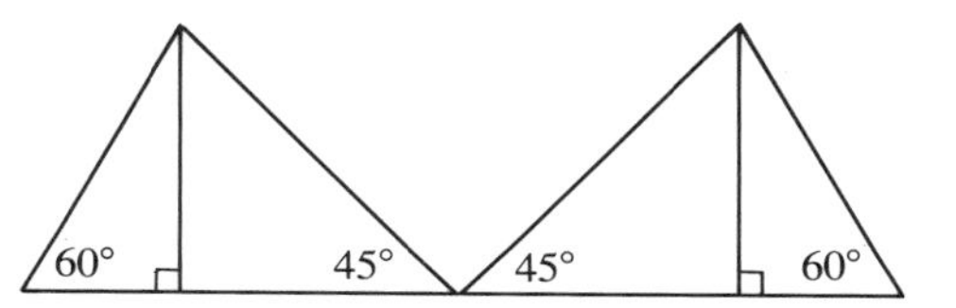

9. Rhombus ABCD has sides of length 10 cm. If the length of the diagonal AC is also 10 cm, find the length of the diagonal BD.

10. Triangle ABC is equilateral with sides of length s units.
    a) A segment of length x units is drawn parallel to BC so that △ABC is divided into two equal areas. Find an expression for x in terms of s.
    b) Two segments of lengths y and z units ($y < z$) are drawn parallel to BC so that △ABC is divided into 3 equal areas. Find expressions for y and z in terms of s.

11. The length of one diagonal of a rhombus is equal to the length of one of its sides. Find the length of the other diagonal in terms of the length l of its sides.

12. Right △ABC has ∠B = 60° and ∠C = 90°. The bisector of ∠B meets AC at D. Find the ratio AD : DC.

13. An equilateral triangle (below left) of side s is divided into three triangles of equal area by two line segments of length x passing through a vertex. Find x in terms of s.

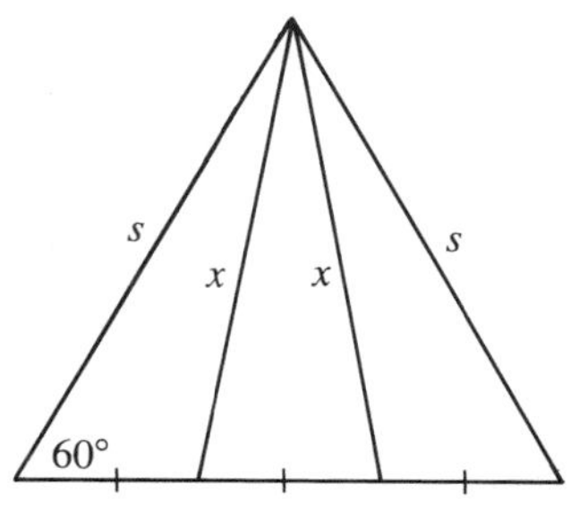

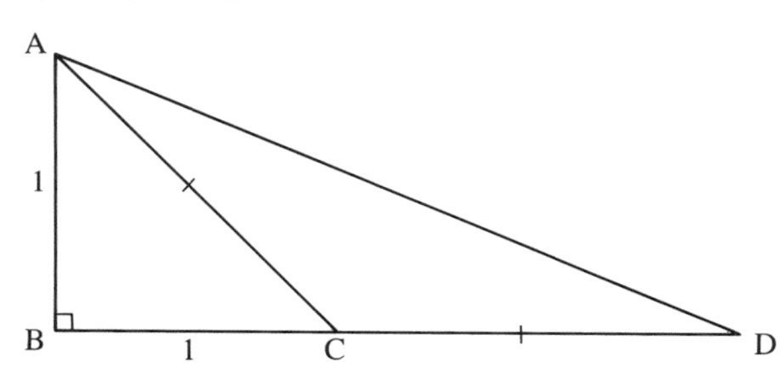

14. Right isosceles △ABC (above right) has AB = BC = 1 unit, and ∠B = 90°. Side BC is extended to D such that CD = CA. Use the diagram to find an expression for each trigonometric ratio.
    a) tan 22.5° b) sin 22.5° c) cos 22.5°

15. a) Derive a formula for the area A of a regular polygon of n sides in terms of its side length x.
    b) By using the trigonometric ratios of the special angles, show how the result of part a) reduces to a formula for the area of each regular polygon.
       i) square ii) hexagon iii) equilateral triangle

16. The perpendicular bisectors of the sides of an equilateral triangle meet at the centroid. If each side is 20 cm, how far is the centroid from each side?

17. An equilateral triangle is inscribed in a circle. Find the ratio of the area of the circle to the area of the triangle.

18. The vertical angle of a cone (below left) is 60°. A sphere of radius 5 cm is dropped into the cone. How far is the centre of the sphere from the vertex of the cone?

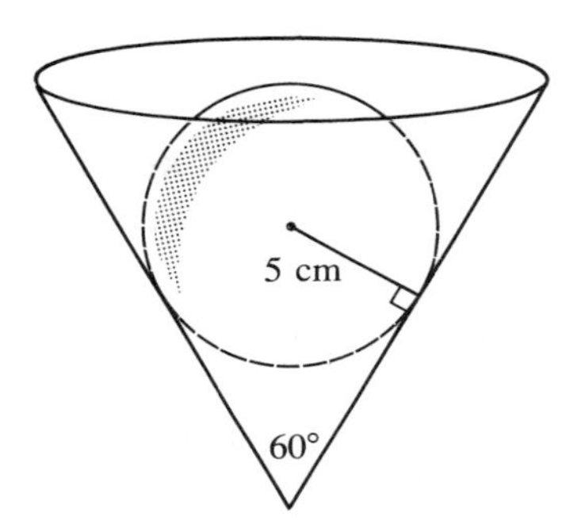

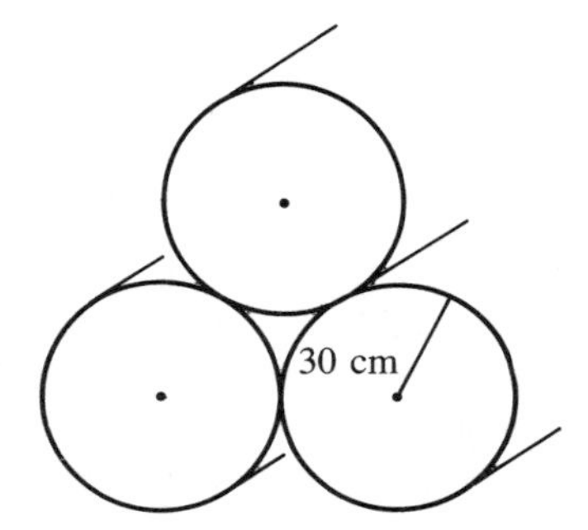

19. Three cylindrical logs of radius 30 cm are piled as shown (above right). How far is the top of the upper log from the ground?

20. From a position 10 m above the ground, the angle of elevation of the top of a tower is 45°. From a position 20 m higher up, the angle of elevation is 30°. How tall is the tower?

21. The angle of elevation of a church steeple is 45°. If the observer moves 10 m closer (on level ground) the angle of elevation is 60°. How tall is the steeple?

Ⓒ

22. In rectangle ABCD, points E and F are located on AB and BC so that △EBF and △FCD are congruent 30°-60°-90° triangles. EB = FC = 1 unit
    a) Find the lengths of the unmarked sides.
    b) Use the diagram to obtain an expression for each trigonometric ratio.
       i) sin 15° ii) cos 15°
       iii) tan 15° iv) sin 75°
       v) cos 75° vi) tan 75°

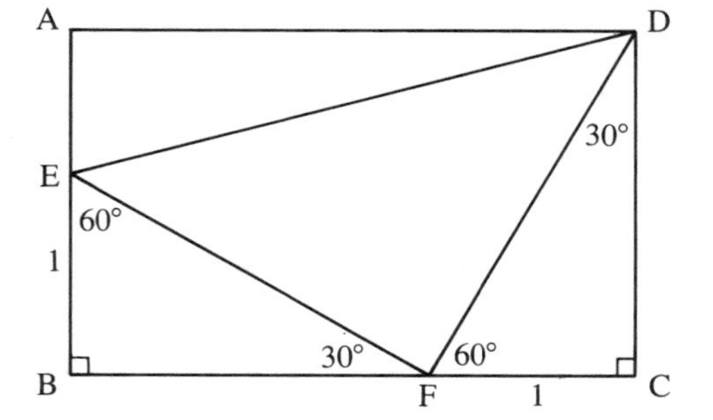

7-7 TRIGONOMETRIC RATIOS FOR OBTUSE ANGLES

In the following sections, we will be solving triangles other than right triangles. In this section, we extend the definitions of trigonometric ratios to include obtuse angles.

The trigonometric ratios of an acute angle θ can be defined in terms of the coordinates (x,y) of a point P on a grid, where θ is the measure of the angle between the positive x-axis and the line segment OP. The length of OP is r.

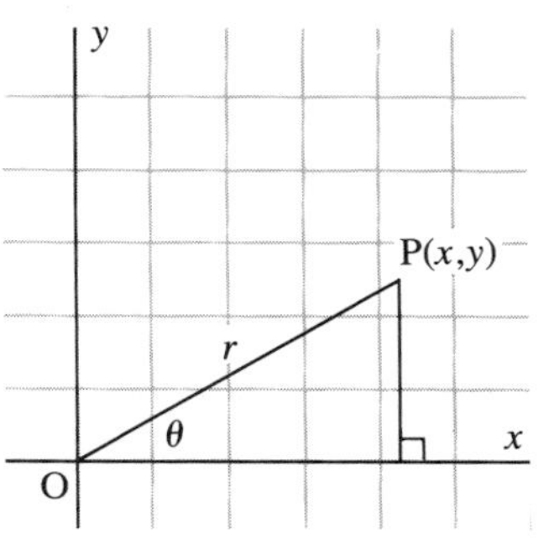

Then, $\sin\theta = \frac{y}{r}$ $\quad\csc\theta = \frac{r}{y}$

$\cos\theta = \frac{x}{r}$ $\quad\sec\theta = \frac{r}{x}$

$\tan\theta = \frac{y}{x}$ $\quad\cot\theta = \frac{x}{y}$

Since $P(x,y)$ is in the first quadrant for $\theta < 90°$, where x and y are positive, then all the trigonometric ratios of acute angles are positive.

The above definitions can be extended to obtuse angles. If $90° < \theta < 180°$, then $P(x,y)$ is in the second quadrant, where x is negative. Hence, any trigonometric ratio of an obtuse angle whose ratio is described using x will be negative.

For $90° < \theta < 180°$, $x < 0$ and $y > 0$

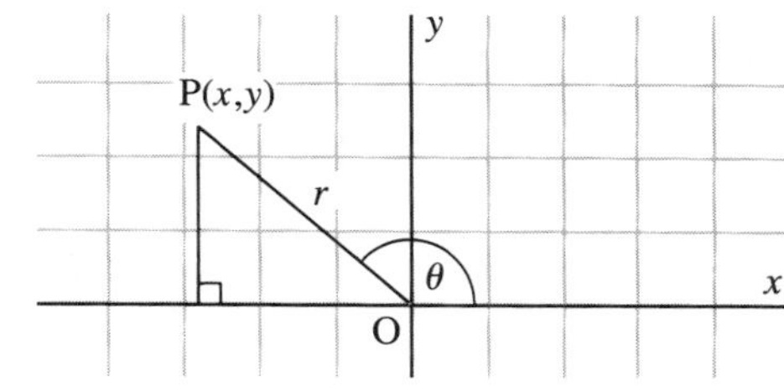

$\sin\theta = \frac{y}{r}$ which is positive

$\cos\theta = \frac{x}{r}$ which is negative

$\tan\theta = \frac{y}{x}$ which is negative

Example 1. a) Use a calculator to find each value.

i) $\sin 130°$ and $\sin 50°$

ii) $\cos 130°$ and $\cos 50°$

b) Explain the patterns in the results in part a).

Solution. a) i) For $\sin 130°$, key in: 130 [sin] to display 0.7660444

For $\sin 50°$, key in: 50 [sin] to display 0.7660444

ii) For $\cos 130°$, key in: 130 [cos] to display -0.6427876

For $\cos 50°$, key in: 50 [cos] to display 0.6427876

b) Draw a diagram showing 50° in the first quadrant and 130° in the second quadrant. Since 50° and 130° are supplementary angles, and $OP' = OP$, then the coordinates of P and P′ can be represented by (x,y) and $(-x,y)$ respectively.

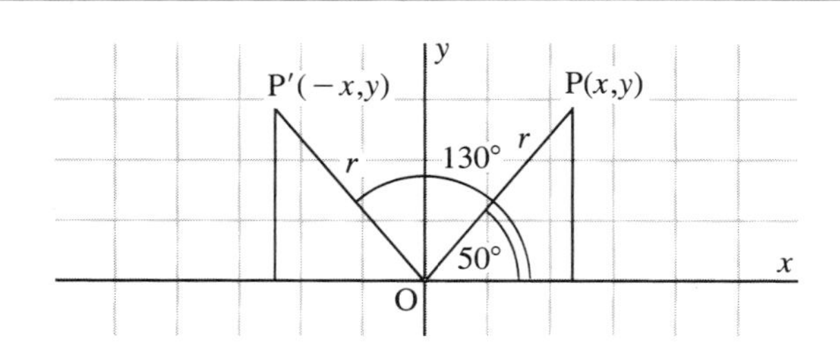

$\sin 130° = \frac{y}{r}$ and $\sin 50° = \frac{y}{r}$

Hence, $\sin 130° = \sin 50°$

$\cos 130° = \frac{-x}{r}$ and $\cos 50° = \frac{x}{r}$

Hence, $\cos 130° = -\cos 50°$

Example 1 suggests that the trigonometric ratios of any obtuse angle $180° - \theta$ are related to those of the supplementary acute angle θ.

Supplementary Angle Relations

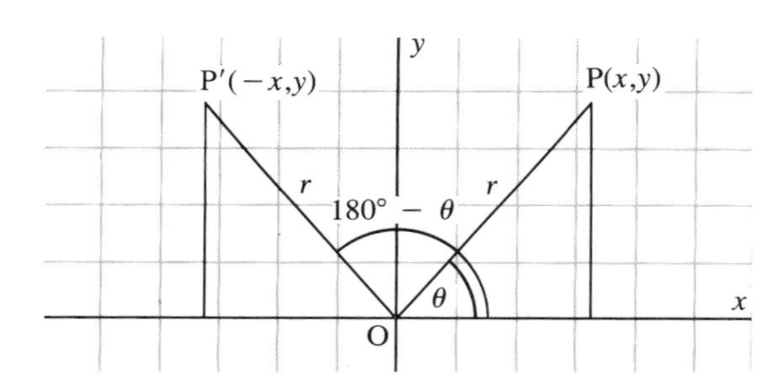

$\sin (180° - \theta) = \frac{y}{r}$

$\sin \theta = \frac{y}{r}$

Hence,
$\sin (180° - \theta) = \sin \theta$

$\cos (180° - \theta) = \frac{-x}{r}$

$\cos \theta = \frac{x}{r}$

Hence,
$\cos (180° - \theta) = -\cos \theta$

$\tan (180° - \theta) = \frac{y}{-x}$

$\tan \theta = \frac{y}{x}$

Hence,
$\tan (180° - \theta) = -\tan \theta$

Example 2. Evaluate each trigonometric ratio. Give exact answers.
a) $\cos 150°$ b) $\tan 135°$ c) $\csc 120°$

Solution. a) $\cos 150° = \cos (180° - 30°)$
$= -\cos 30°$
$= -\frac{\sqrt{3}}{2}$

b) $\tan 135° = \tan (180° - 45°)$
$= -\tan 45°$
$= -1$

c) For csc 120°, find sin 120° and then take the reciprocal.

$$\begin{aligned} \sin 120^\circ &= \sin(180^\circ - 60^\circ) \\ &= \sin 60^\circ \\ &= \frac{\sqrt{3}}{2} \\ \csc 120^\circ &= \frac{2}{\sqrt{3}} \end{aligned}$$

Example 3. If θ is an obtuse angle with $\cot \theta = -\frac{3}{4}$, find $\sin \theta$ and $\cos \theta$.

Solution. Since θ is obtuse, the point P lies in the second quadrant where $x < 0$ and $y > 0$.

Compare the general value of $\cot \theta = \frac{x}{y}$

with the given value of $\cot \theta = -\frac{3}{4}$.

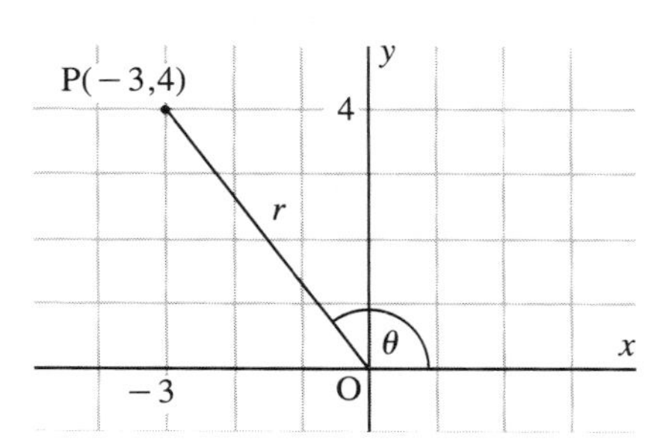

P has coordinates (−3,4).
From the Pythagorean Theorem

$$\begin{aligned} r &= \sqrt{x^2 + y^2} \\ &= 5 \end{aligned}$$

So, $\sin \theta = \frac{y}{r} = \frac{4}{5}$ and $\cos \theta = \frac{x}{r} = -\frac{3}{5}$

EXERCISES 7-7

Ⓐ

1. Use a calculator to find the value of each trigonometric ratio to 3 decimal places.
   a) sin 98° b) tan 113° c) cos 124° d) sec 174° e) csc 161° f) cot 143°

2. For each obtuse angle θ, state the six trigonometric ratios.

a)

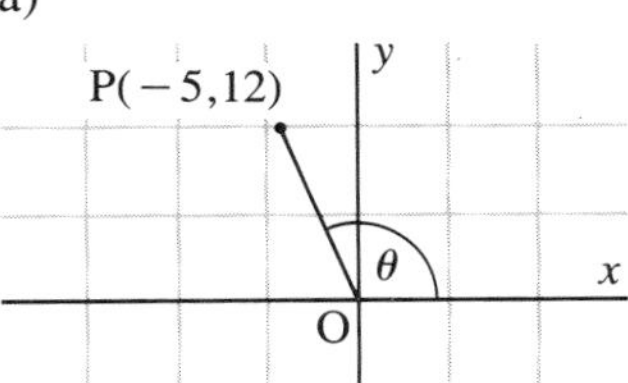

b)

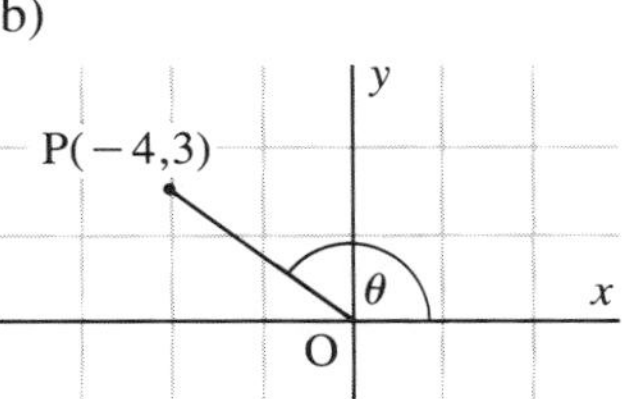

c)

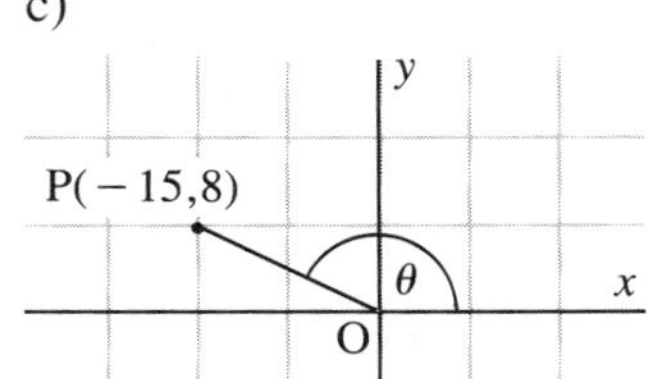

3. Evaluate each trigonometric ratio. Give exact answers.
   a) cos 120° b) sin 150° c) cot 135° d) csc 150° e) sec 135° f) sin 135°
   g) tan 120° h) cot 120° i) sin 120° j) cot 150° k) csc 135° l) sec 120°

4. Evaluate each trigonometric ratio to 2 decimal places.
   a) cos 110° b) cot 95° c) csc 138° d) tan 108° e) sin 142° f) tan 170°
   g) sec 115° h) cot 130° i) csc 165° j) cos 140° k) sec 175° l) sin 100°

5. Given θ is an obtuse angle and the value of one trigonometric ratio, find the other trigonometric ratios.

   a) $\sin\theta = \frac{15}{17}$; find $\tan\theta$ and $\sec\theta$ b) $\tan\theta = -\frac{7}{24}$; find $\cos\theta$ and $\csc\theta$

   c) $\sec\theta = -\frac{13}{5}$; find $\sin\theta$ and $\cot\theta$ d) $\cot\theta = -\frac{20}{21}$; find $\cos\theta$ and $\csc\theta$

   e) $\cos\theta = -\frac{40}{41}$; find $\sin\theta$ and $\cot\theta$ f) $\csc\theta = \frac{5}{4}$; find $\tan\theta$ and $\sec\theta$

Ⓑ

6. Find each value of θ if θ is obtuse.

   a) $\sin\theta = \frac{1}{\sqrt{2}}$ b) $\sec\theta = -2$ c) $\tan\theta = -\sqrt{3}$ d) $\cos\theta = -\frac{1}{\sqrt{2}}$

   e) $\csc\theta = 2$ f) $\cot\theta = -\sqrt{3}$ g) $\cot\theta = -1$ h) $\sin\theta = \frac{\sqrt{3}}{2}$

   i) $\cos\theta = -\frac{\sqrt{3}}{2}$ j) $\sec\theta = -\frac{2}{\sqrt{3}}$ k) $\tan\theta = -1$ l) $\csc\theta = \sqrt{2}$

7. Find each value of θ to the nearest degree if θ is obtuse.

   a) $\sin\theta = 0.906$ b) $\cos\theta = -0.574$ c) $\tan\theta = -3.732$
   d) $\cot\theta = -1.428$ e) $\csc\theta = 1.743$ f) $\sec\theta = -2.669$
   g) $\tan\theta = -0.532$ h) $\sin\theta = 0.978$ i) $\cot\theta = -0.123$
   j) $\csc\theta = 1.086$ k) $\cos\theta = -0.777$ l) $\sec\theta = -1.010$

8. Given θ is an obtuse angle and the value of one trigonometric ratio, find the other trigonometric ratio, and θ to the nearest degree.

   a) $\sin\theta = \frac{3}{\sqrt{13}}$; find $\sec\theta$ and θ b) $\cot\theta = -\frac{3}{7}$; find $\cos\theta$ and θ

   c) $\cos\theta = -\frac{2}{9}$; find $\cot\theta$ and θ d) $\csc\theta = \frac{\sqrt{5}}{2}$; find $\tan\theta$ and θ

   e) $\tan\theta = -3$; find $\csc\theta$ and θ f) $\sec\theta = -\frac{53}{45}$; find $\sin\theta$ and θ

Ⓒ

9. If θ is an acute angle defined by $P(x,y)$, use x, y, and r to define the six trigonometric ratios of: a) $(180° + \theta)$ b) $(360° - \theta)$.

10. State the value of each ratio exactly. Draw a diagram to illustrate each angle.

    a) sin 225° b) cos 240° c) cot 210°
    d) sin 270° e) tan 300° f) sec 315°
    g) cos 180° h) csc 330° i) sec 360°

11. State two values of θ to the nearest degree for each trigonometric ratio.

    a) $\sin\theta = 0.906$ b) $\cos\theta = -0.616$ c) $\tan\theta = -5.671$
    d) $\csc\theta = -2.924$ e) $\sec\theta = 1.743$ f) $\cot\theta = 2.145$
    g) $\tan\theta = -0.700$ h) $\sec\theta = -1.155$ i) $\sin\theta = -0.966$
    j) $\cos\theta = -0.423$ k) $\csc\theta = 1.035$ l) $\cot\theta = -2.747$

12. State the values of the six trigonometric ratios of each angle.

    a) 0° b) 90° c) 180° d) 270° e) 360°

7-8 THE COSINE LAW

Previously in this chapter we solved right triangles given the lengths of any two sides, or the length of one side and the measure of an acute angle. In this section, we will study the Cosine Law which will enable us to solve certain oblique triangles; that is, triangles which contain no right angles.

A triangle is uniquely determined by two sides and the contained angle. The following example shows how to calculate the remaining side.

Example 1. In △ABC, AB = 8, AC = 5, and ∠A = 35°; find the length of BC to 1 decimal place.

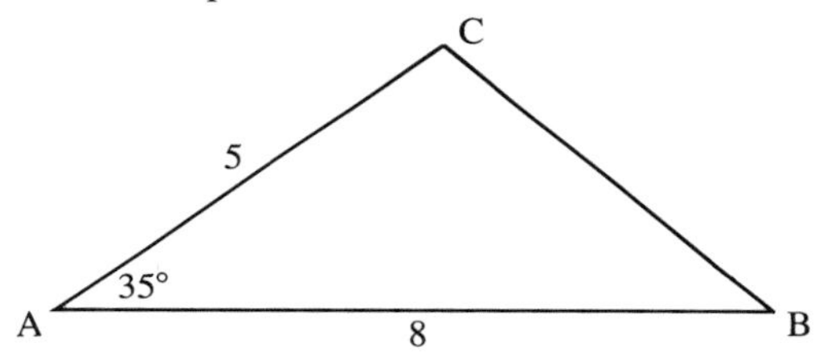

Solution. Construct CN perpendicular to AB and let BC = a, CN = h, and AN = x.

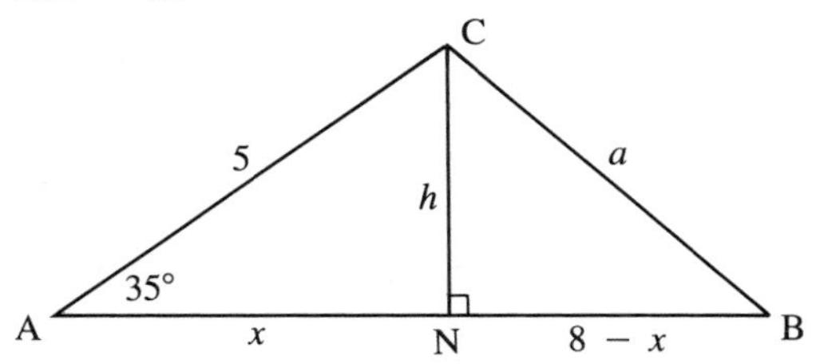

Apply the Pythagorean Theorem to △CNB and △CNA.

$a^2 = h^2 + (8 - x)^2$ . . . ①

$5^2 = h^2 + x^2$ . . . ②

Subtract ② from ①.

$a^2 - 5^2 = 64 - 16x$

$a^2 = 89 - 16x$

$= 89 - 16(5 \cos 35°)$ Since $\frac{x}{5} = \cos 35°$

Key in:

35 [cos] [×] 5 [×] 16 [+/−] [+] 89 [=] to display 23.467836

Hence, $a^2 \doteq 23.4678$

$a \doteq 4.844$

The length of BC is approximately 4.8.

Now we consider the general cases of △ABC where ∠A is acute and where ∠A is obtuse.

In both cases, construct CN perpendicular to AB or AB extended; let CN $= h$, and AN $= x$. Apply the Pythagorean Theorem to $\triangle$CNB and $\triangle$CNA.

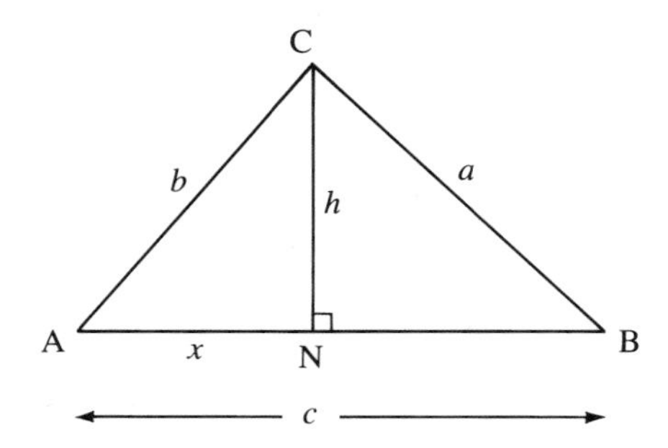

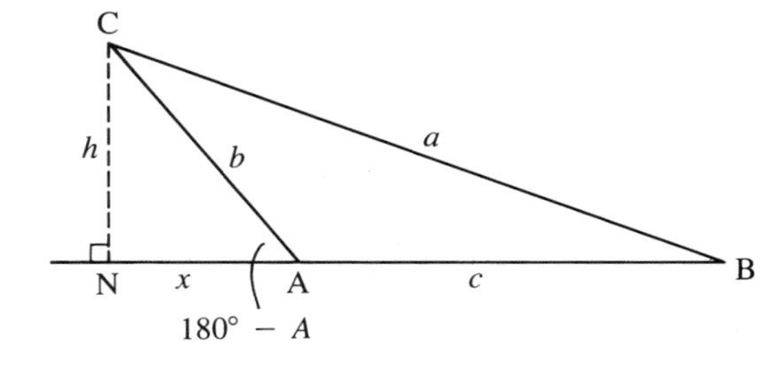

For the acute triangle

$$a^2 = h^2 + (c - x)^2$$
$$b^2 = h^2 + x^2$$

Subtract.

$$a^2 - b^2 = c^2 - 2cx$$
$$a^2 = b^2 + c^2 - 2cx$$
$$= b^2 + c^2 - 2c(b \cos A)$$
$$= b^2 + c^2 - 2bc \cos A$$

For the obtuse triangle

$$a^2 = h^2 + (c + x)^2$$
$$b^2 = h^2 + x^2$$

Subtract.

$$a^2 - b^2 = c^2 + 2cx$$
$$a^2 = b^2 + c^2 + 2cx$$
$$= b^2 + c^2 + 2c(b \cos (180° - A))$$
$$= b^2 + c^2 - 2bc \cos A$$

In both cases, $a^2 = b^2 + c^2 - 2bc \cos A$

Similarly, by letting BN $= x$ we can prove that $b^2 = a^2 + c^2 - 2ac \cos B$, and by constructing a perpendicular from A to BC we can prove that $c^2 = a^2 + b^2 - 2ab \cos C$.

The Cosine Law

In any $\triangle$ABC

$$a^2 = b^2 + c^2 - 2bc \cos A$$
$$b^2 = a^2 + c^2 - 2ac \cos B$$
$$c^2 = a^2 + b^2 - 2ab \cos C$$

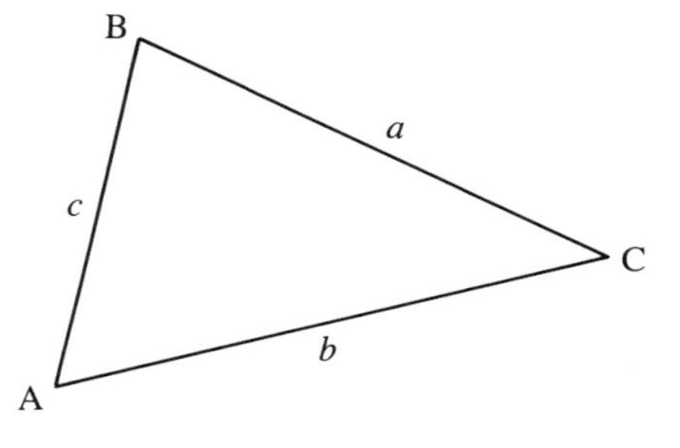

We can use the Cosine Law to find the third side of a triangle when two sides and the contained angle are given.

Example 2. In $\triangle$ABC, AB $= 10$ and AC $= 8$; find the length of BC to 1 decimal place for each value of $\angle$A.

a) $\angle A = 50°$ b) $\angle A = 130°$

Solution. In each case we use the Cosine Law in the form $a^2 = b^2 + c^2 - 2bc \cos A$.

a)

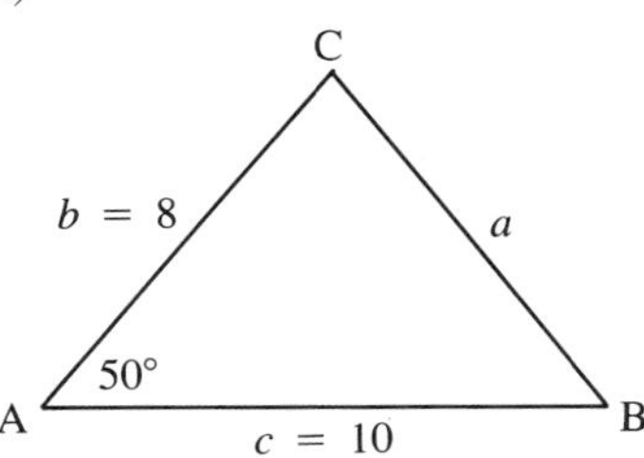

b)

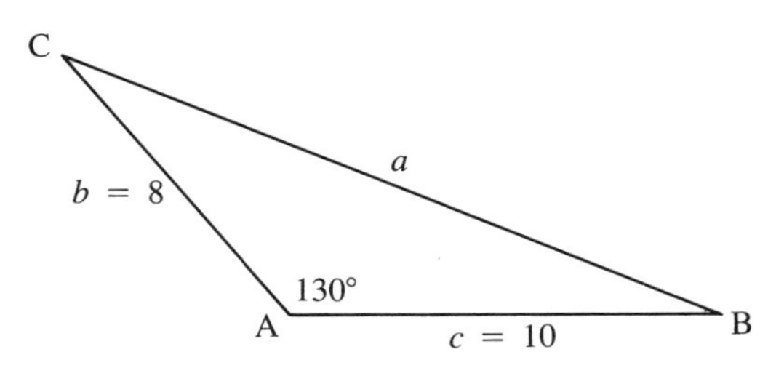

For the acute triangle

$a^2 = 8^2 + 10^2 - 2(8)(10)(\cos 50°)$

$\doteq 61.153\ 982$

$a \doteq 7.8201$

The length of BC is about 7.8.

For the obtuse triangle

$a^2 = 8^2 + 10^2 - 2(8)(10)(\cos 130°)$

$\doteq 266.846\ 02$

$a \doteq 16.3354$

The length of BC is about 16.3.

Example 2 and the diagrams below suggest that the Pythagorean Theorem is a special case of the Cosine Law.

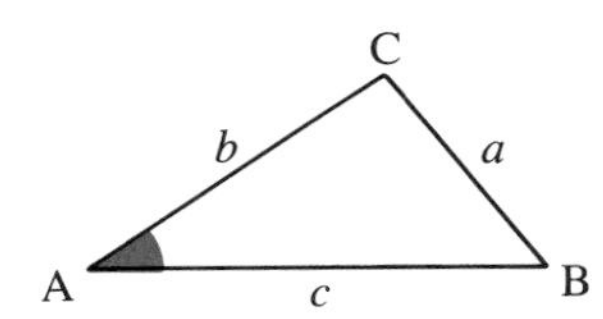

If $\angle A < 90°$, $\cos A > 0$ and $a^2 < b^2 + c^2$

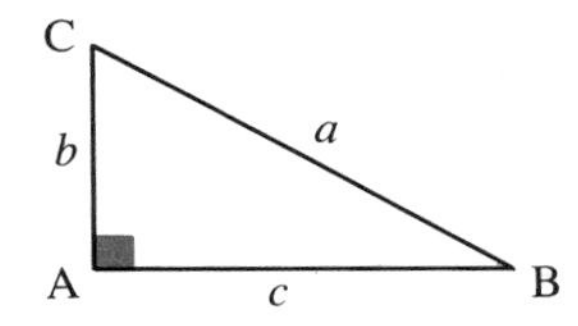

If $\angle A = 90°$, $\cos A = 0$ and $a^2 = b^2 + c^2$

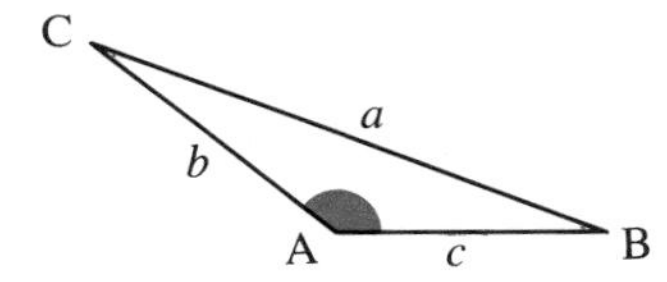

If $\angle A > 90°$, $\cos A < 0$ and $a^2 > b^2 + c^2$

The Cosine Law can also be used to find any angle of a triangle when its three sides are given.

Example 3. In $\triangle$PQR, PQ = 7, QR = 8, and RP = 10; find the measure of $\angle$R to the nearest degree.

Solution. To find $\angle$R, use the Cosine Law in this form.

$$r^2 = p^2 + q^2 - 2pq \cos R$$
$$7^2 = 8^2 + 10^2 - 2(8)(10) \cos R$$
$$49 = 164 - 160 \cos R$$
$$160 \cos R = 115$$
$$\cos R = \frac{115}{160}$$
$$\angle R \doteq 44.0486$$

To the nearest degree, $\angle R = 44°$

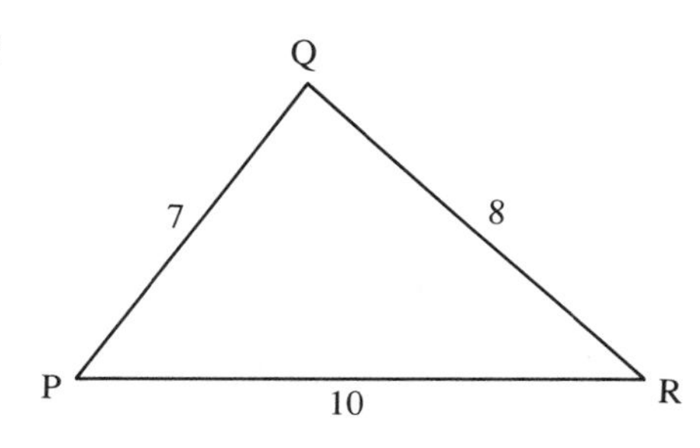

Example 4. A tunnel is to be built through a hill to connect points A and B in a straight line. Point C is chosen so that it is visible from both A and B, and measurement shows that $\angle C = 63°$, CA = 2 km, and CB = 5 km.
Find the length of AB to 2 decimal places and the measure of $\angle A$ to 1 decimal place.

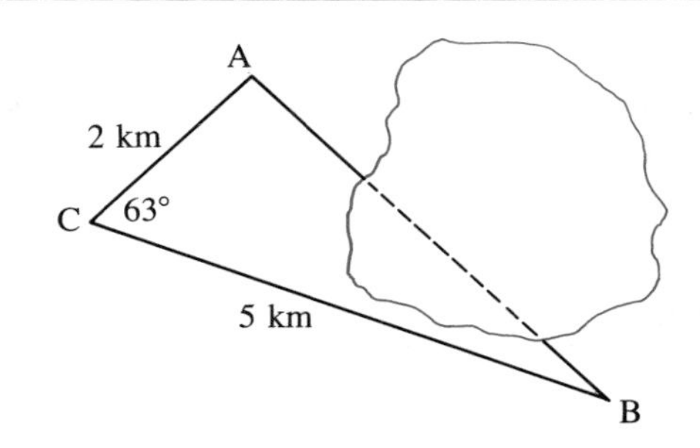

Solution. By the Cosine Law

$c^2 = a^2 + b^2 - 2ab \cos C$
$= 5^2 + 2^2 - 2(5)(2)(\cos 63°)$
$\doteq 19.920\ 19$
$c \doteq 4.4632$

The distance from A to B, through the hill, is approximately 4.46 km.
To find $\angle A$, we use the Cosine Law in this form.
$a^2 = b^2 + c^2 - 2bc \cos A$
Substitute the given values of a and b, and the (non-rounded) values of c and c^2.
$5^2 \doteq 2^2 + 19.920\ 19 - 2(2)(4.463\ 204) \cos A$
Solve for $\cos A$.

$$\cos A \doteq -\frac{1.079\ 81}{17.853\ 216}$$

Since $\cos A$ is negative, $\angle A$ is obtuse.
$\angle A \doteq 93.5°$

EXERCISES 7-8

Ⓐ

1. Find the third side of each triangle to 1 decimal place.

a)

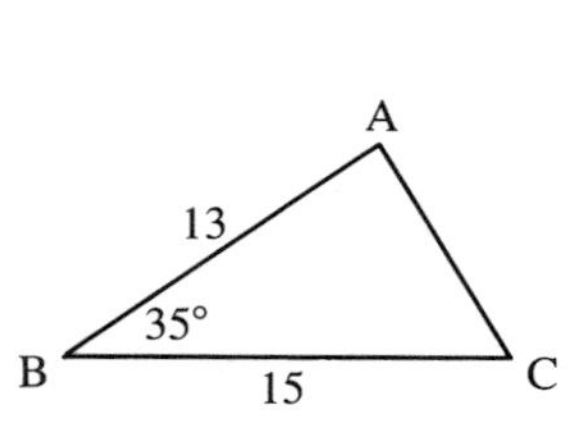

b)

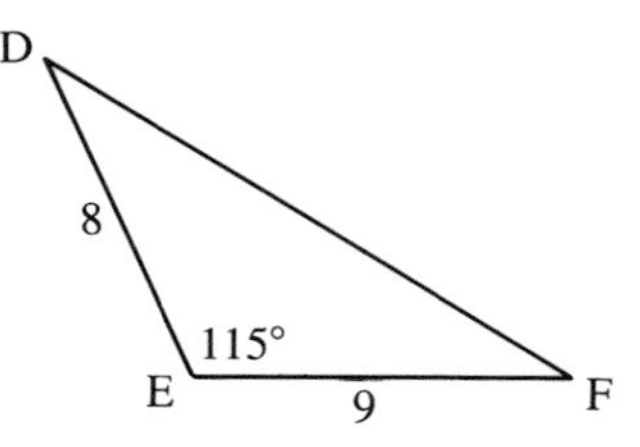

c)

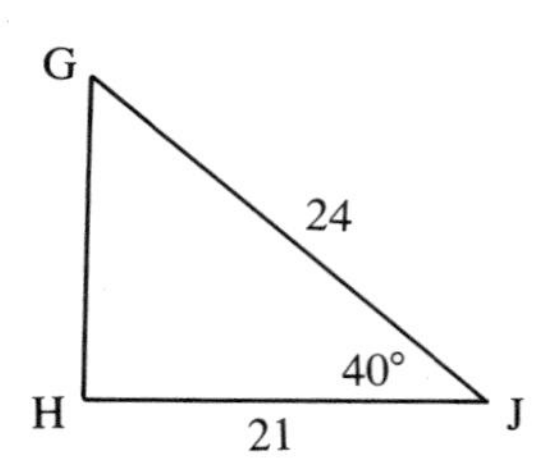

2. Use the given information to find the third side of $\triangle ABC$ to 1 decimal place.
   a) $\angle B = 42°$, $a = 6$, $c = 4$
   b) $\angle A = 130°$, $b = 15$, $c = 11$
   c) $\angle C = 95°$, $a = 18$, $b = 27$
   d) $\angle B = 28°$, $a = 17$, $c = 15$
   e) $\angle A = 105°$, $b = 7.4$, $c = 10.2$

3. Find θ to 1 decimal place.

a)

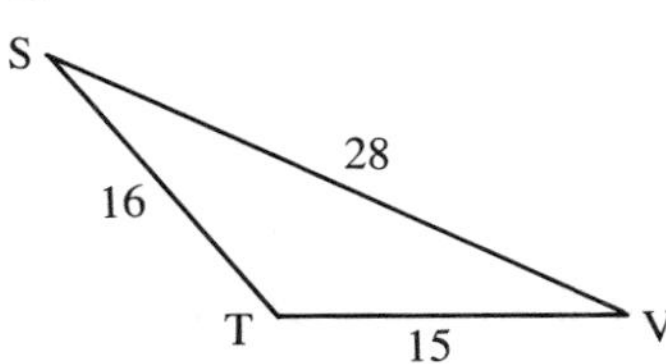

b)

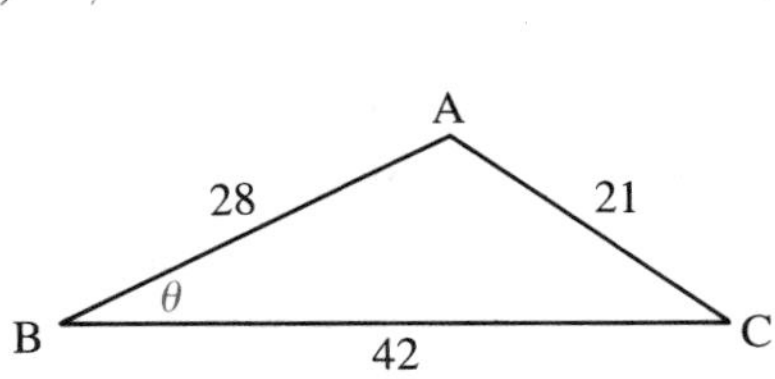

c)

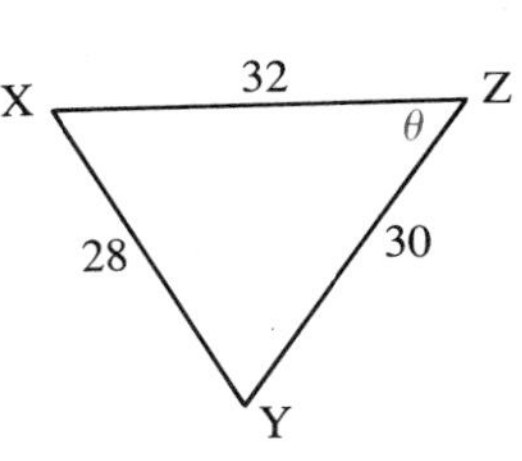

4. For a triangle with sides of the given lengths, find to 1 decimal place the measure of: i) the smallest angle ii) the largest angle.

a) 7, 9, 14 b) 6, 11, 15 c) 23, 31, 52
d) 28, 45, 53 e) 8.3, 9.7, 12.5 f) 14, 55, 61

Ⓑ

5. Use the given information to find the third side of $\triangle PQR$.

a) $\angle Q = 72°$, $p = 4.3$, $r = 2.9$
b) $\angle P = 112°$, $PQ = 25$, $PR = 33$
c) $\angle R = 98°$, $PR = 17.4$, $QR = 21.3$

6. A roof truss (below left) is to span 8.2 m. One piece of the truss is 6.8 m in length and set at an angle of 35°. How long is the other piece of the truss?

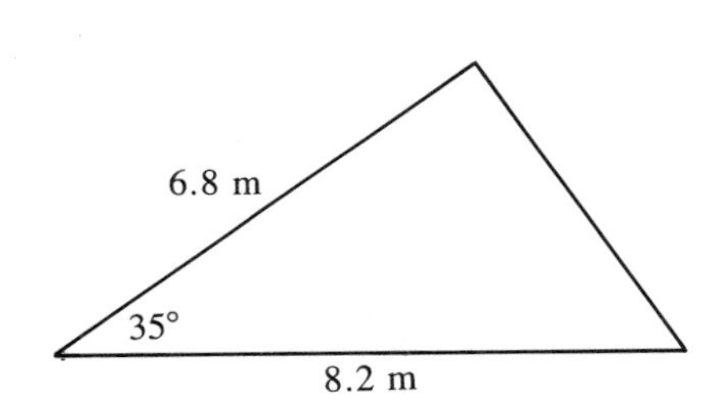

C B
4.5 km
3.3 km
100°
A

7. A radar station at A (above right) is tracking ships at B and C. How far apart are the two ships?

8. In parallelogram ABCD, AB = 4 cm and BC = 7 cm. If $\angle B = 65°$, how long is each diagonal to 1 decimal place?

9. Given the points P(5,8), Q(3,2), and R(7,5), calculate $\angle PQR$ to the nearest degree.

10. Calculate, to the nearest degree, the smallest angle in the triangle formed by the points O(0,0), A(4,3), and B(3,4).

11. In a circle of radius 10 cm, AB is an arc of length 10 cm. How long is the chord AB to 1 decimal place?

12. Find the area of each $\triangle ABC$ with the given lengths of sides.

a) 17 cm, 29 cm, 23 cm
b) 32 cm, 19 cm, 15 cm
c) 12 cm, 35 cm, 37 cm

13. Twelve points are equally spaced around a circle of radius r. Express these lengths in terms of r.
    a) AB b) AC c) AD
    d) AE e) AF f) AG

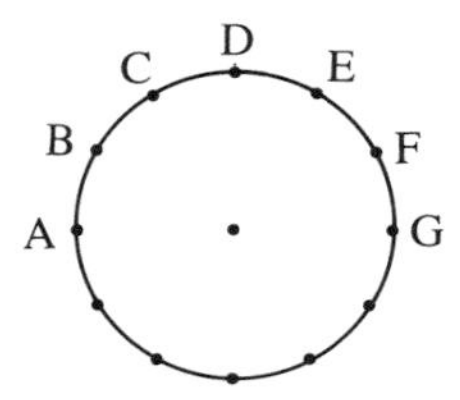

14. In the diagrams below, ABCD is a square with side length 3 cm and $\triangle$PBC is equilateral. Find the length of AP.

a)

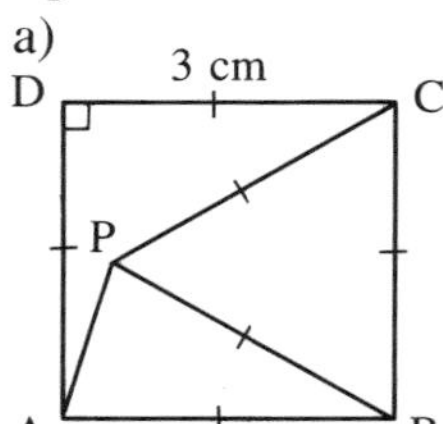

b) D 3 cm C P A B

15. ABCD is a square of side 1 unit. Equilateral triangles are constructed on the sides of the square.
    a) Find the length of EH.
    b) Find the area of $\triangle$EDH.

E H D A C B

16. Find the values of x and y.

a)

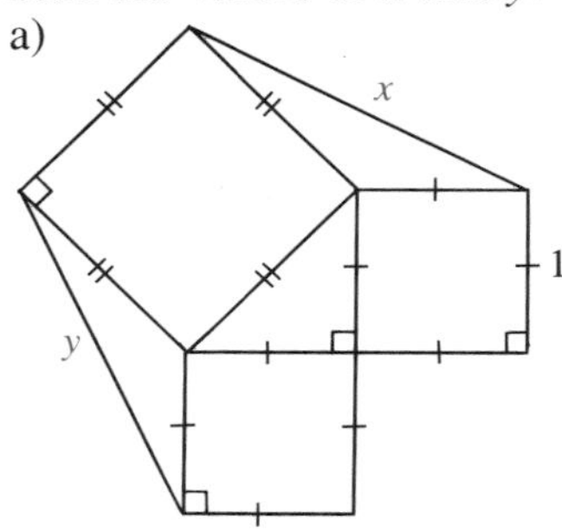

b)

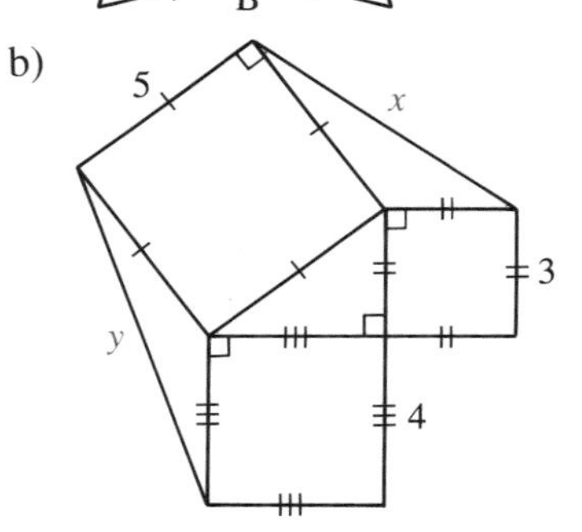

Ⓒ

17. For the diagram (below left), show that $x^2 + y^2 = 5c^2$.

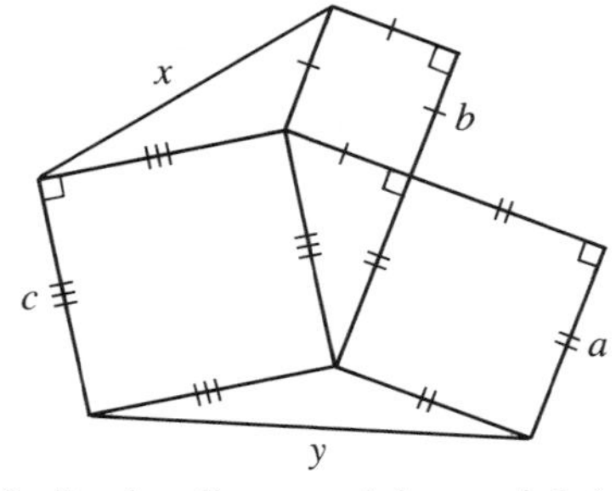

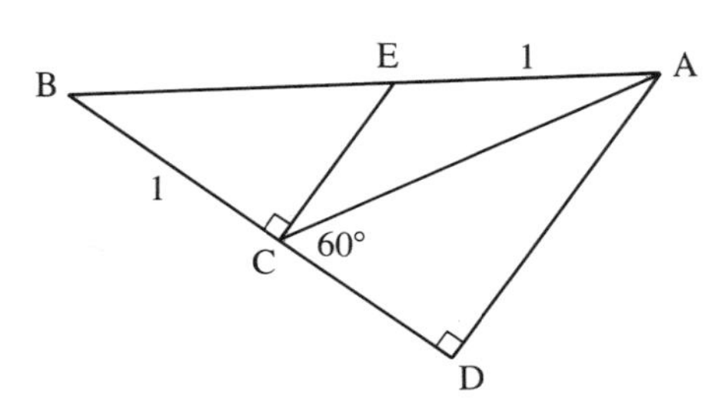

18. In the diagram (above right), EC is perpendicular to BD, $\angle$ACD = 60°, and AE = BC = 1 unit. Find the lengths of BE and CA.

7-9 THE SINE LAW

There are some triangles which cannot be solved using the Cosine Law; that is, triangles for which only one side is known.

A triangle is uniquely determined by two angles and a particular side. The following example shows how to find the other sides of such a triangle.

Example 1. In $\triangle ABC$, $\angle A = 30°$, $BC = 5$, and $\angle B = 65°$; find the length of AC to 1 decimal place.

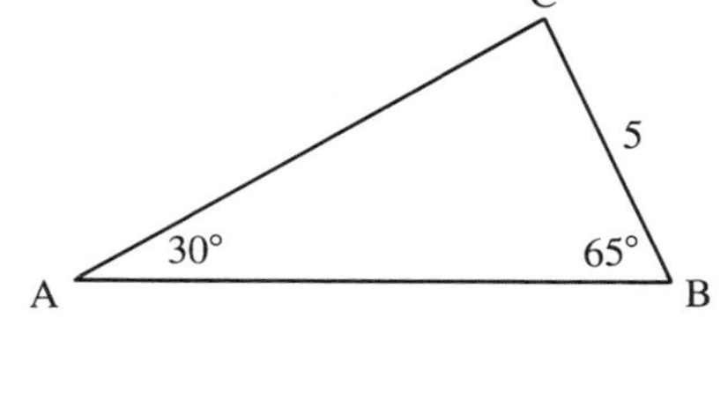

Solution. Construct CN perpendicular to AB, and let $CN = h$ and $AC = b$.

In right $\triangle ANC$

$$\frac{h}{b} = \sin 30°, \text{ or } h = b \sin 30°$$

In right $\triangle BNC$

$$\frac{h}{5} = \sin 65°, \text{ or } h = 5 \sin 65°$$

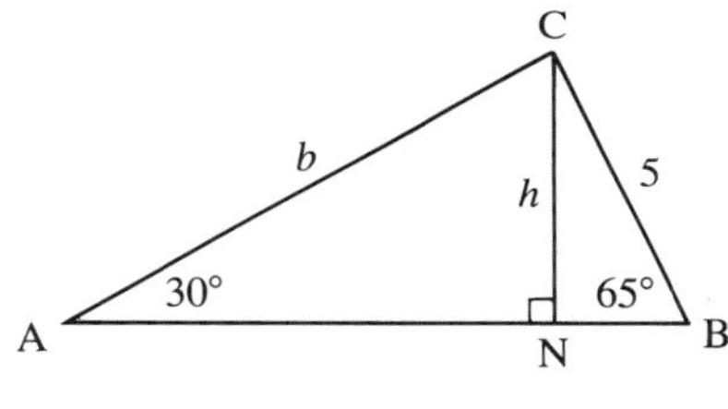

That is, $b \sin 30° = 5 \sin 65°$

$$b = \frac{5 \sin 65°}{\sin 30°}$$

$$\doteq 9.063$$

The length of AC is approximately 9.1.

Now we consider the general cases of $\triangle ABC$ where $\angle A$ is acute and $\angle A$ is obtuse. In both cases, construct CN perpendicular to AB or AB extended, and let $CN = h$.

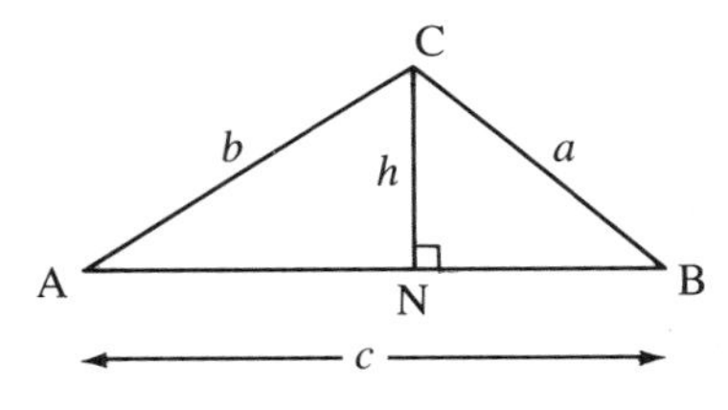

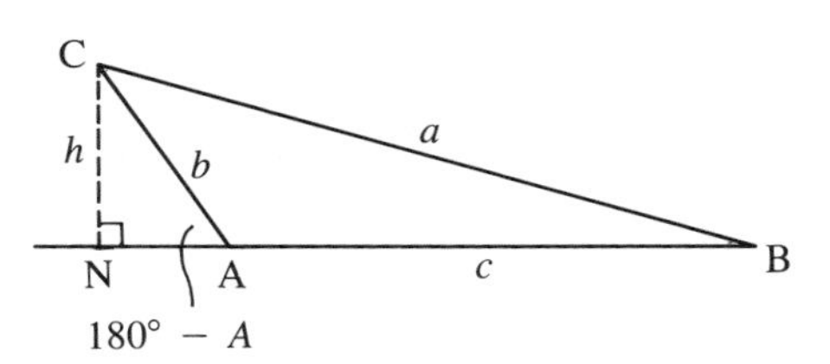

For the acute triangle

$h = b \sin A$

and $h = a \sin B$

For the obtuse triangle

$h = b \sin (180° - A)$

$= b \sin A$

and $h = a \sin B$

In both cases, $b \sin A = a \sin B$

$$\frac{\sin A}{a} = \frac{\sin B}{b}$$

Similarly, by constructing a perpendicular from A to BC, we can show that $\dfrac{\sin B}{b} = \dfrac{\sin C}{c}$.

The Sine Law
In any $\triangle ABC$
$$\frac{\sin A}{a} = \frac{\sin B}{b} = \frac{\sin C}{c}$$

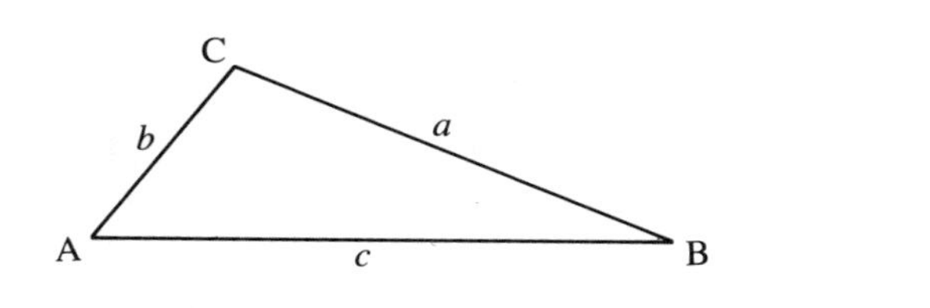

We can use the Sine Law to find the remaining sides of a triangle when two angles and one side are given.

Example 2. Solve $\triangle PQR$, given that $\angle P = 57°$, $\angle Q = 73°$, and $QR = 24$. Give the answers to 1 decimal place.

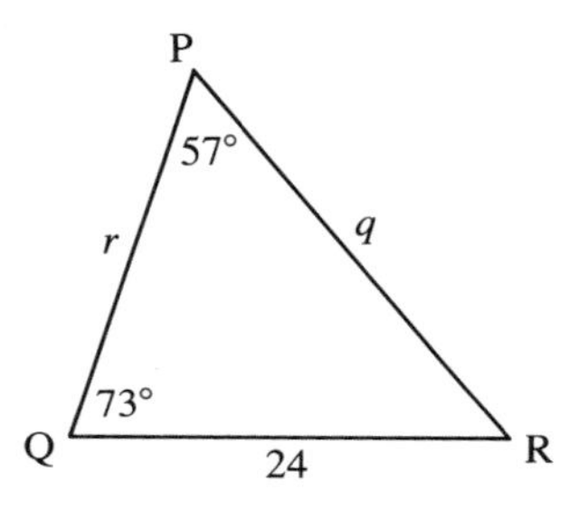

Solution.
$$\angle R = 180° - (73° + 57°)$$
$$= 50°$$
By the Sine Law
$$\frac{\sin P}{p} = \frac{\sin Q}{q} = \frac{\sin R}{r}$$
$$\frac{\sin 57°}{24} = \frac{\sin 73°}{q} = \frac{\sin 50°}{r}$$

To find q
$$\frac{\sin 57°}{24} = \frac{\sin 73°}{q}$$
$$q = \frac{24 \sin 73°}{\sin 57°}$$
$$\doteq 27.366\ 304$$
$$\doteq 27.4$$

To find r
$$\frac{\sin 57°}{24} = \frac{\sin 50°}{r}$$
$$r = \frac{24 \sin 50°}{\sin 57°}$$
$$\doteq 21.921\ 679$$
$$\doteq 21.9$$

We summarize these results in a table.

$\angle P$	$\angle Q$	$\angle R$	p	q	r
57°	73°	50°	24	27.4	21.9

The Sine Law actually represent three equations. Each equation relates four variables.
$$\frac{\sin A}{a} = \frac{\sin B}{b} \qquad \frac{\sin B}{b} = \frac{\sin C}{c} \qquad \frac{\sin A}{a} = \frac{\sin C}{c}$$

To use the Sine Law, we must know the values of three of the four variables in any equation. Then, we select the equation relating these three variables and solve for the unknown variable.

Since no single equation above contains the three variables a, b, and C we cannot use the Sine Law to solve a triangle given only that information. As explained in *Section 7-8*, the Cosine Law is used in this situation.

To apply the Sine Law to solve a triangle we must know the measure of one angle and the length of the opposite side, plus one other angle or side.

Example 3. Solve $\triangle ABC$ given $\angle B = 48°$, $b = 9$, and $c = 11$. Give the answers to 1 decimal place.

Solution. Use the Sine Law to find $\angle C$.

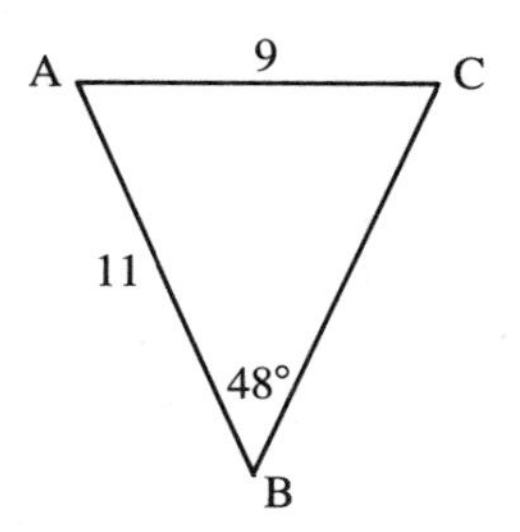

$$\frac{\sin C}{c} = \frac{\sin B}{b}$$

$$\sin C = \frac{11 \sin 48°}{9}$$

$$\doteq 0.908\ 288\ 1$$

$$\angle C \doteq 65.3°$$

Since $\sin C = \sin (180° - C)$, $\angle C$ could be 114.7°.

That is, there are two different triangles which satisfy the given conditions.

We proceed to solve the triangle for both values of $\angle C$.

If $\angle C = 65.3°$

Then $\angle A = 180° - 48° - 65.3°$
$= 66.7°$

To find a

$$\frac{a}{\sin A} = \frac{c}{\sin C}$$

$$a = \frac{11 \sin 66.7°}{\sin 65.3°}$$

$$\doteq 11.120\ 329$$

$$\doteq 11.1$$

If $\angle C = 114.7°$

Then $\angle A = 180° - 48° - 114.7°$
$= 17.3°$

To find a

$$\frac{a}{\sin A} = \frac{c}{\sin C}$$

$$a = \frac{11 \sin 17.3°}{\sin 65.3°}$$

$$\doteq 3.600\ 544$$

$$\doteq 3.6$$

We summarize these results in tables and draw a triangle to illustrate each case.

∠A	∠B	∠C	a	b	c
66.7°	48°	65.3°	11.1	9	11

∠A	∠B	∠C	a	b	c
17.3°	48°	114.7°	3.6	9	11

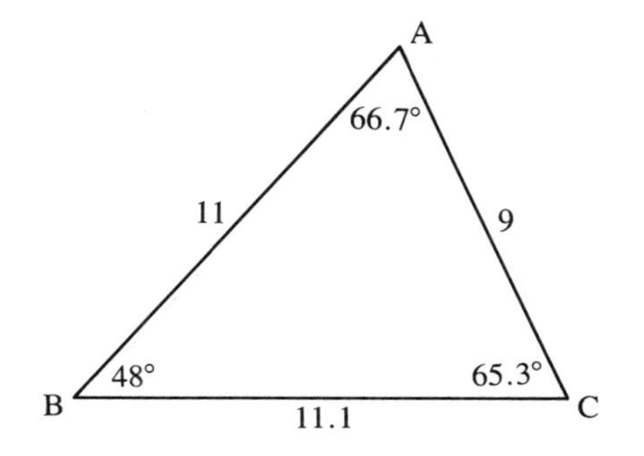

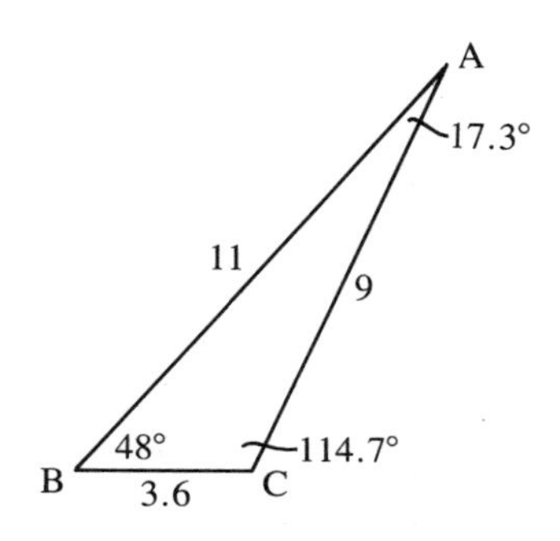

The Ambiguous Case

If we superimpose the two triangles obtained in *Example 3*, we discover why, given two sides and an angle other than the contained angle, there are two solutions.

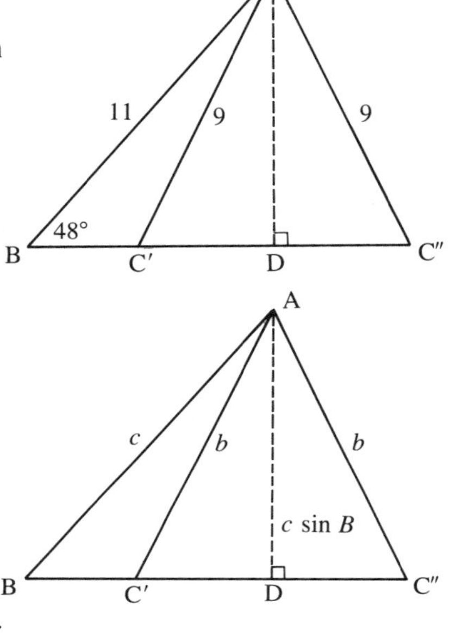

The vertex C of △ABC can be placed in position C′ or its mirror image in AD, C″ without affecting the given values; that is, ∠B and the lengths b and c.

The case in which two triangles are possible is called the *ambiguous case*.

How can we tell when we have an ambiguous case; that is, two solutions?

Consider △ABC where ∠B, b, and c are given. The length of AD, the perpendicular from A to BC, is $c \sin B$.

Case I If $b < c \sin B$, then there is no triangle possible because AD is the shortest distance from A to BC″.

Case II If $b = c \sin B$, then b is the length of AD; that is, △ABC is the right triangle △ABD.

Case III If $b > c \sin B$, then there are two triangles provided $b < c$. If $b > c$, then C can be only in position C″ and not C′.

These cases are summarized in the following statement.

> If △ABC is known to exist; and the measure of ∠B, the length b, and the length c are given, then there are exactly two different triangles which satisfy these conditions provided $c \sin B < b < c$. Otherwise, there is exactly one triangle.

Example 4. A tunnel through the mountains is to be constructed to join A and B. Point C is 12.6 km from B. A cannot be seen from B or from C. Point D is 10.3 km from C and 6.7 km from A; ∠ADC = 125° and ∠DCB = 142°.

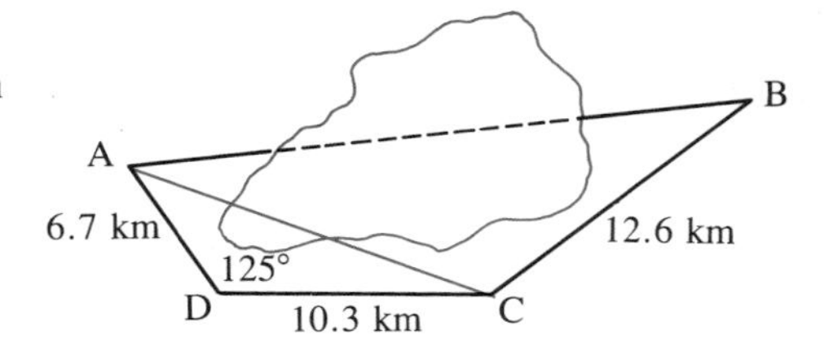

a) Find the length of the tunnel AB.

b) Find the angle between:

i) AB and AD ii) AB and CB.

Solution. a) First, use the Cosine Law in △ACD to find AC.

$$\begin{aligned} d^2 &= a^2 + c^2 - 2ac \cos D \\ &= 10.3^2 + 6.7^2 - 2(6.7)(10.3)(\cos 125°) \\ &\doteq 230.145\,02 \\ d &\doteq 15.1705 \end{aligned}$$

Then, use the Sine Law in △ACD to find ∠C.

$$\frac{\sin C}{c} = \frac{\sin D}{d}$$

$$\sin C = \frac{6.7 \sin 125°}{15.1705}$$

$$\doteq 0.361\ 775\ 7$$

$$\angle C \doteq 21.2°$$

Subtract to find ∠ACB.

$$\angle ACB = 142° - 21.2°$$
$$= 120.8°$$

Use the Cosine Law in △ABC to find AB.

$$c^2 = a^2 + b^2 - 2ab \cos C$$
$$= 12.6^2 + 15.1705^2 - 2(15.1705)(12.6)(\cos 120.8°)$$
$$\doteq 584.6563$$
$$c \doteq 24.180$$

The tunnel is approximately 24.2 km in length.

b) Use the Sine Law in △ABC to find ∠A.

$$\frac{\sin A}{a} = \frac{\sin C}{c}$$

$$\sin A = \frac{12.6 \sin 120.8°}{24.180}$$

$$\doteq 0.447\ 597$$

$$\angle A \doteq 26.6°$$

i) The angle between AB and AD is ∠DAB.

$$\angle DAB = \angle BAC + \angle DAC$$
$$\angle BAC = 26.6°$$

In △ADC

$$\angle DAC = 180° - 125° - 21.2°$$
$$= 33.8°$$
$$\angle DAB = 26.6° + 33.8°$$
$$= 60.4°$$

ii) The angle between AB and CB is ∠ABC.

In △ABC, $\angle ABC = 180° - 120.8° - 26.6°$
$$= 32.6°$$

These examples show that we can solve any triangle using the Sine and/or Cosine Laws given:

- the length of one side and the measures of any two angles; or
- the lengths of two sides and the measure of any one angle; or
- the lengths of three sides.

If we are given only the measures of 3 angles, then there is an infinite number of similar triangles with this shape; the lengths of the sides of the triangles can be expressed only in terms of one of the sides of the triangle. That is, the Sine and Cosine Laws enable us to solve any triangle given any three pieces of data except the measures of the three angles. In all but the ambiguous case, the solution is unique.

The fact that the sets of conditions SSS, AAS, and SAS determine unique triangles is a direct consequence of the corresponding congruence theorems. That is, if there were another triangle satisfying any of these three conditions (such as SSS) it would be congruent to any triangle satisfying these conditions. The SSA condition is not a congruence condition and, as shown in the ambiguous case above, does not guarantee a unique solution.

These results are summarized below.

Number of Sides Given	Number of Angles Given	Method of Solution of the Triangle
1	2	Sine Law
2	1 not contained	Sine Law—ambiguous case
2	1 contained	Cosine Law
3	0	Cosine Law

EXERCISES 7-9

(A)

1. Find the length of AB to 1 decimal place.

a)

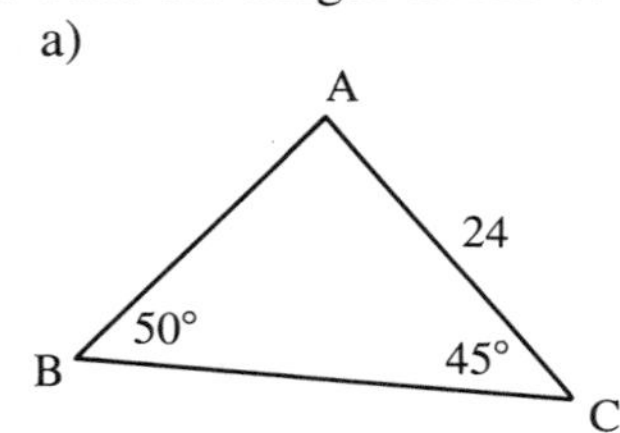

b)

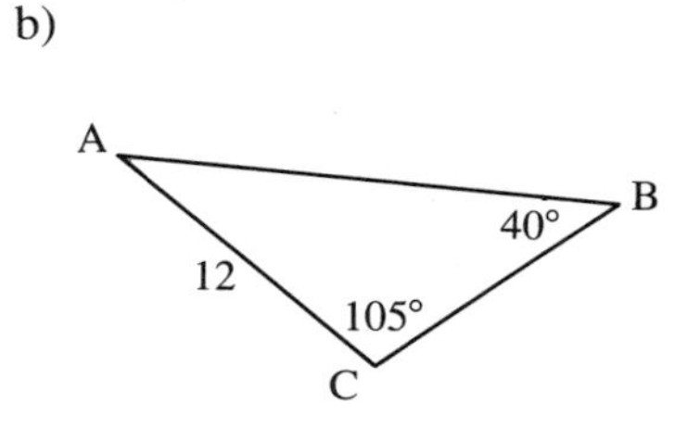

c)

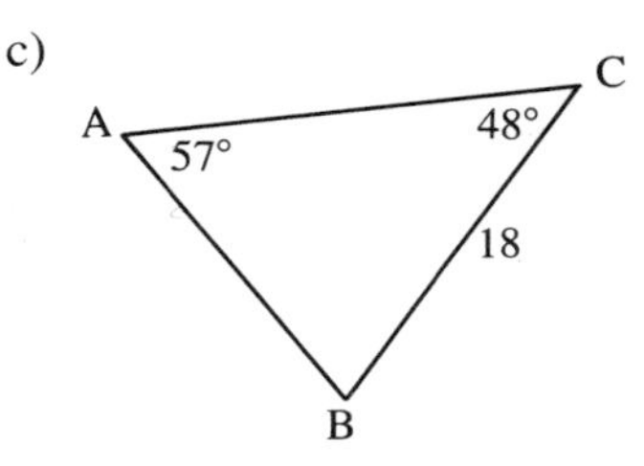

2. Find θ to 1 decimal place.

a)

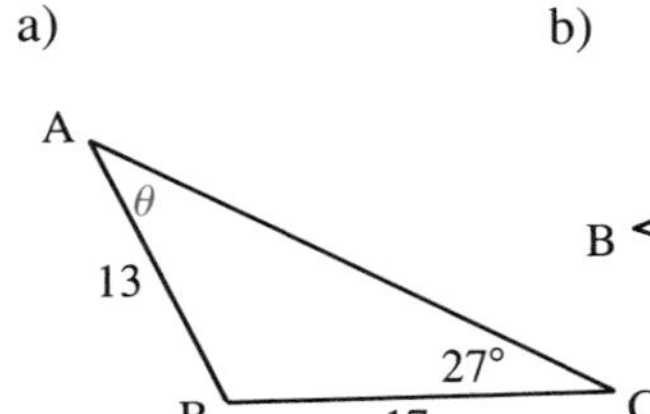

b)

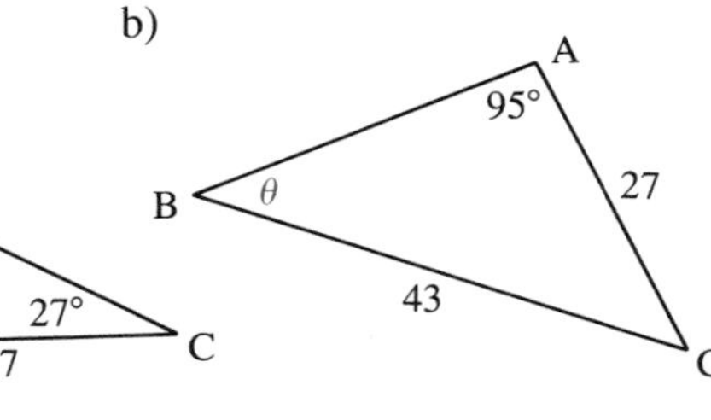

c)

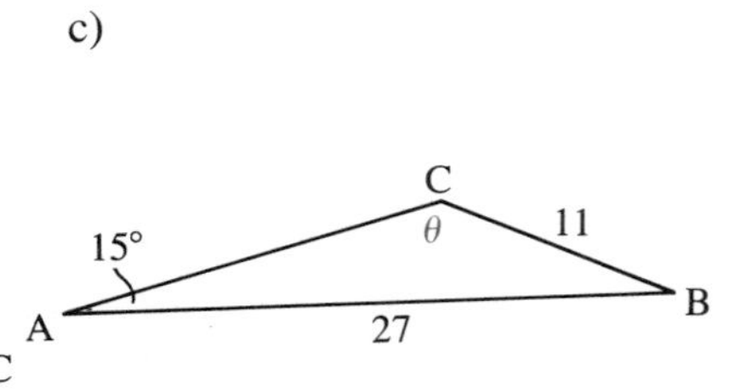

3. a) In $\triangle ABC$, $\angle A = 65°$, $\angle B = 40°$, and $a = 15$; find b.
   b) In $\triangle PQR$, $\angle P = 52°$, $\angle Q = 73°$, and $q = 27$; find p.
   c) In $\triangle ABC$, $\angle B = 27°$, $\angle C = 64°$, and $b = 14$; find c.
   d) In $\triangle ABC$, $\angle A = 38°$, $\angle B = 77°$, and $b = 16.5$; find c.
   e) In $\triangle XYZ$, $\angle Y = 84°$, $\angle Z = 33°$, and $z = 9.2$; find x.
   Give the answers to 1 decimal place.

Ⓑ

4. Solve each $\triangle PQR$. Give the answers to 1 decimal place.
   a) $\angle P = 105°, p = 12, q = 9$
   b) $\angle Q = 63°, q = 20, r = 17$
   c) $\angle P = 112°, p = 32, r = 25$
   d) $\angle R = 78°, r = 42, p = 28$

5. Solve each $\triangle ABC$. Give the answers to 1 decimal place.
   a) $\angle A = 35°, a = 12, b = 15$
   b) $\angle B = 55°, b = 11, c = 13$
   c) $\angle C = 78°, b = 19, a = 24$
   d) $\angle B = 42°, b = 22, c = 27$
   e) $\angle A = 39°, c = 32, b = 45$
   f) $\angle B = 124°, b = 27, a = 13$

6. Solve each $\triangle XYZ$. Give the answers to 1 decimal place.
   a) $\angle X = 72°, \angle Z = 50°, x = 34$
   b) $\angle X = 46.4°, y = 21, z = 29$
   c) $\angle Y = 54°, x = 22, y = 19$
   d) $\angle Z = 61°, y = 6.3, x = 7.8$

7. A bridge AB (below left) is to be built across a river. The point C is located 62.0 m from B, and $\angle ABC = 74°$ while $\angle ACB = 48°$. How long will the bridge be?

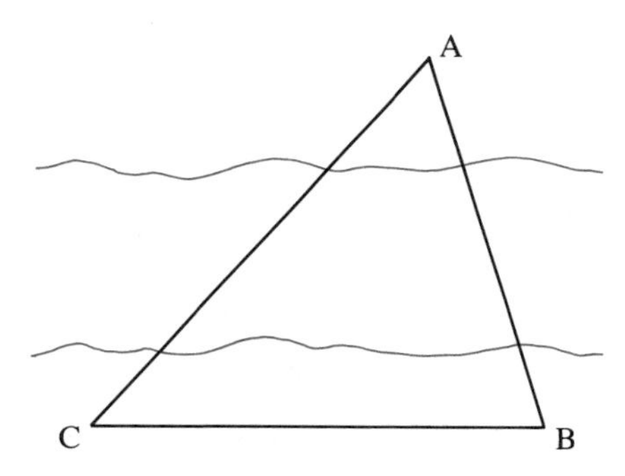

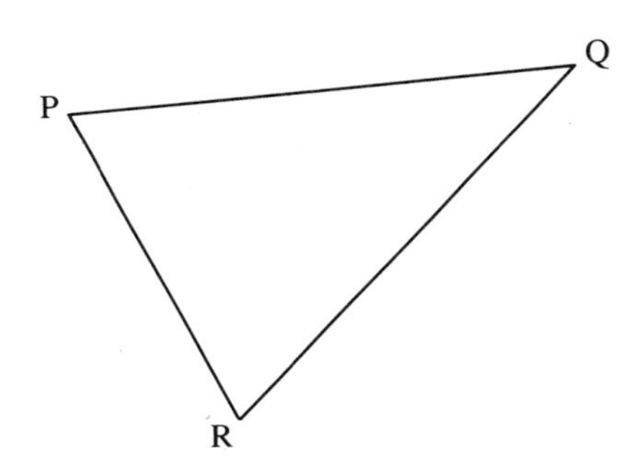

8. Two ships at P and Q (above right) are 32.0 km apart. How far is each ship from a lighthouse at R if $\angle P = 68°$ and $\angle Q = 42°$?

9. Two guy wires 17.0 m and 10.0 m in length are fastened to the top of a TV tower from two points M and N on level ground. The angle of elevation of the longer wire is 28.1°.
   a) How far apart are M and N?
   b) How tall is the tower?

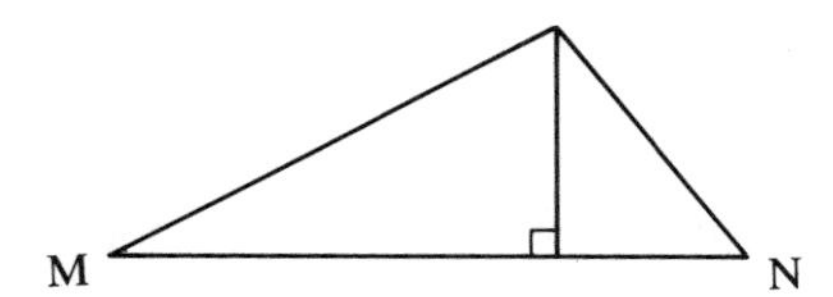

10. Bijan observes the angle of elevation of an ultra-light airplane to be 52°. At the same instant the angle of elevation for Therese is 36°. Bijan and Therese are 325 m apart on level ground and in the same vertical plane as the ultra-light.
    a) How far is each person from the ultra-light?
    b) How high is the ultra-light?

11. From one end of the Prince Edward Viaduct over the Don River the angle of depression of a particular point on the railroad track is 37°. If that point is 112 m from the observer and 75 m from the other end of the viaduct, how long is the viaduct?

12. In the diagram (below left), ABCD is a square of side 1 unit. Point P is such that $\angle PAD = 30° = \angle PCD$. Find the length to 1 decimal place of: a) PD b) PC.

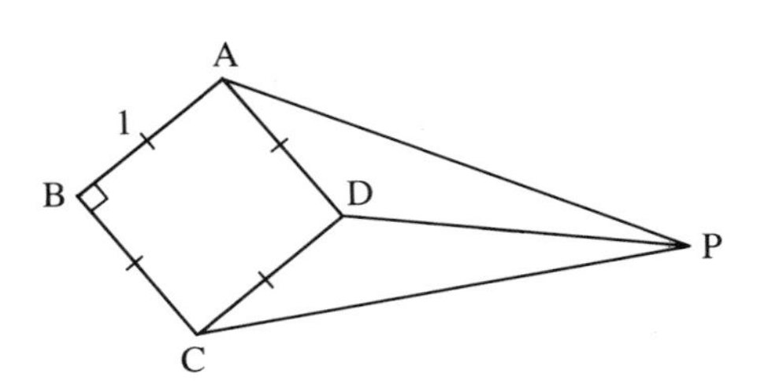

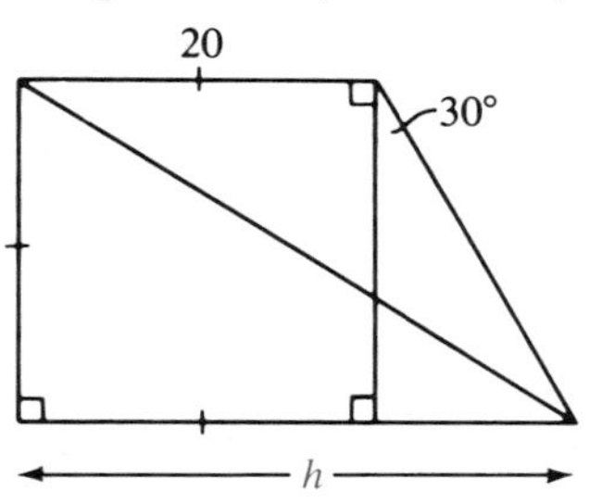

13. In the diagram (above right), find the value of h.

14. In a molecule of water (below left), the two hydrogen atoms and one oxygen atom are bonded in the shape of a triangle. The nuclei of the atoms are separated by the distances shown. Calculate the bond angles.

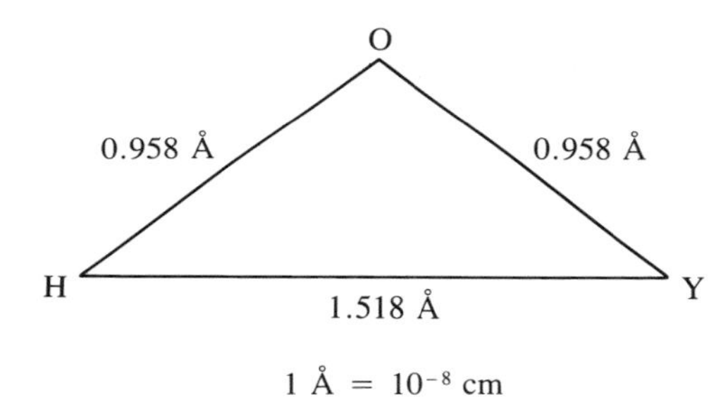

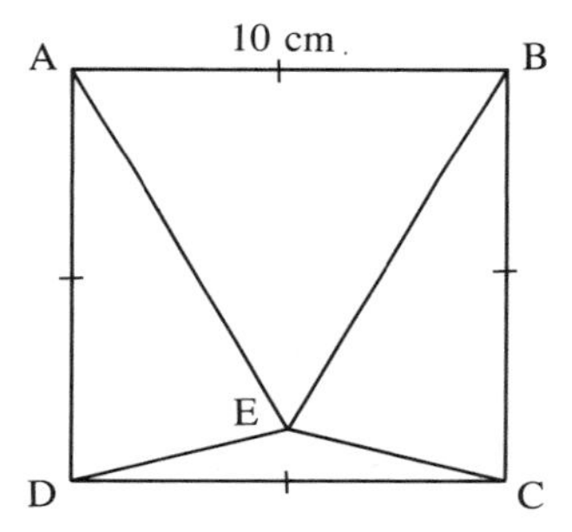

15. Square ABCD (above right) has sides of length 10 cm. Point E is inside the square so that $\angle CDE = \angle DCE = 15°$. Find the length of AE.

Ⓒ

16. In $\triangle ABC$, $AC = 2$, $AB = 3$, and $BC = 4$. Prove that:

    a) $\sin B = \frac{1}{2} \sin A$ b) $\sin C = \frac{3}{4} \sin A$.

17. Prove that in any $\triangle ABC$ the constant of proportionality for the Sine Law is the diameter of the circumscribing circle.

18. An isosceles $\triangle ABC$ has vertical $\angle C = 20°$. Points M and N are taken on AC and BC so that $\angle ABM = 60°$ and $\angle BAN = 50°$. Prove that $\angle BMN = 30°$.

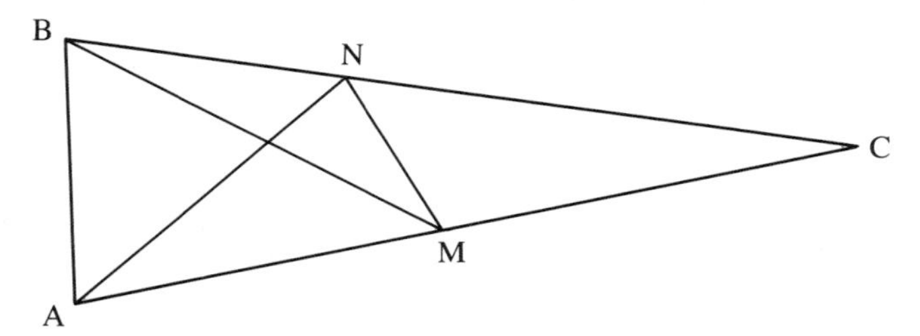

COMPUTER POWER

Solving Triangles

You can use the program on page 301 to solve any triangle when sufficient information to define the triangle is given. When the program is run, the computer displays a menu showing the various possibilities: SAS, SSS, ASA, AAS, or SSA. When you enter the data, enter the three numbers (in the order specified), separated by commas. The computer then uses the Cosine and Sine Laws to solve the triangle.

The output generated by the program for four examples studied earlier in this chapter is shown below. Notice that in each row of each table the angle and the side are opposite each other in the triangle.

SAS Example 2a, page 286

```
ENTER DATA: SIDE, ANGLE, SIDE:
8,50,10
```

SIDES	ANGLES
8	51.5975633
10	78.4024368
7.82010118	50

SSS Example 3, page 287

```
ENTER DATA: SIDE, SIDE, SIDE:
7,8,10
```

SIDES	ANGLES
7	44.0486257
8	52.6168016
10	83.3345728

AAS Example 2, page 292

```
ENTER DATA IN THIS ORDER AROUND
THE TRIANGLE: ANGLE, ANGLE,
SIDE: 57,73,24
```

SIDES	ANGLES
27.3663045	73
21.9216786	50
24	57

SSA Example 3, page 293

```
ENTER DATA IN THIS ORDER AROUND
THE TRIANGLE: SIDE, SIDE,
ANGLE: 9,11,48
```

SIDES	ANGLES
11.1255433	66.7301559
9	48
11	65.2698441

SIDES	ANGLES
3.59533003	17.2698441
9	48
11	114.730156

QUESTIONS

1. Solve $\triangle ABC$ given that:
   a) $\angle B = 126°$, $a = 17.6$, $c = 24.2$ b) $a = 36$, $b = 27$, $c = 17$
   c) $\angle A = 40°$, $\angle B = 70°$, $c = 21$ d) $\angle B = 17.3°$, $b = 6.94$, $c = 18.3$
   e) $\angle B = 72°$, $\angle C = 48°$, $b = 17$ f) $\angle C = 67.8°$, $a = 41.5$, $c = 59.2$.

2. The moon subtends an angle of 0.518° when viewed from the surface of the Earth (below left). If the distance from the Earth to points A and B on the surface of the moon is 384 390 km, what is the diameter of the moon?

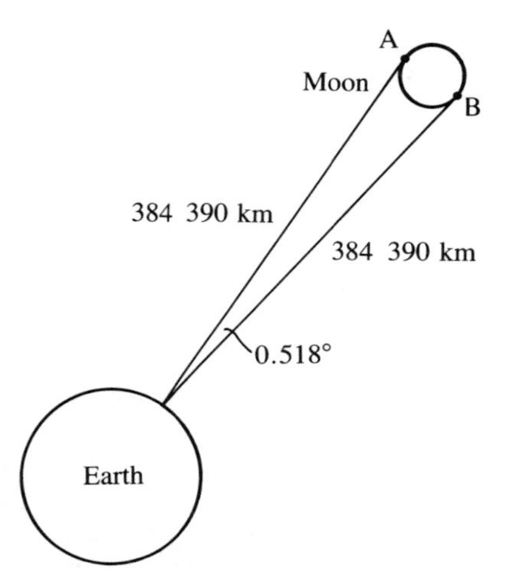

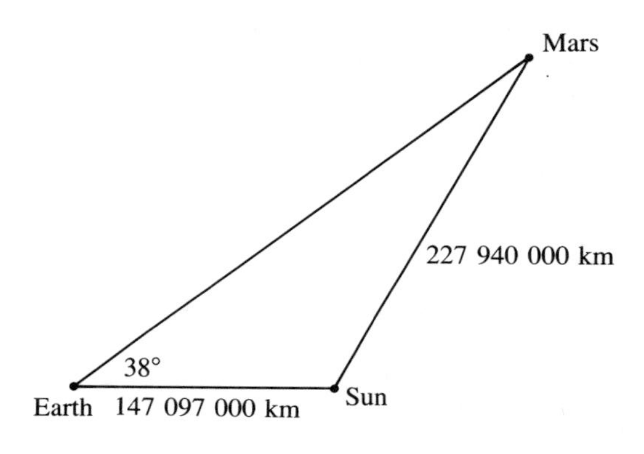

3. What is the distance between the Earth and Mars when the angle between Mars and the sun is observed to be 38° (above right). The distances to the sun from Earth and Mars are 147 097 000 km and 227 940 000 km respectively.

4. When the Earth is at point A the angle between the plane of its orbit and a star at S is 83.903 224 5°. Six months later the Earth is at point B and the angle between the plane of its orbit and the star is 96.096 361 1°. How far away is the star if the distance from the Earth to the sun is about 1.50×10^8 km?

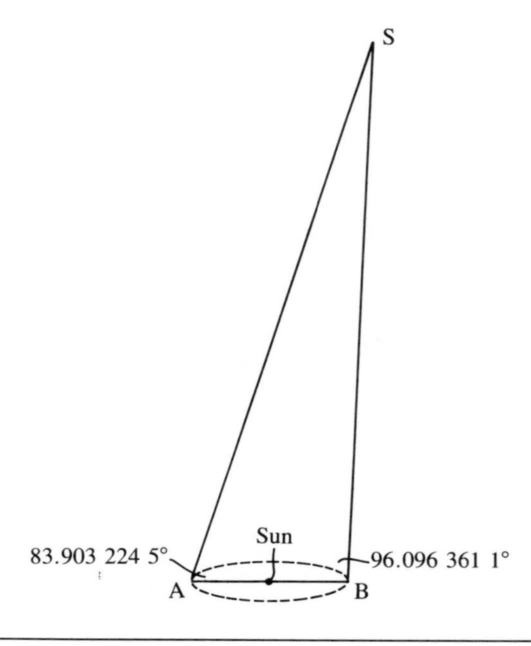

```
100 REM *** TRIANGLE SOLVER ***
110 P=3.14159265359/180
120 HOME:PRINT "SELECT 1, 2, 3, 4, OR 5"
130 PRINT:PRINT "1 - SAS":PRINT:PRINT "2 - SSS"
140 PRINT:PRINT "3 - ASA":PRINT:PRINT "4 - AAS"
150 PRINT:PRINT "5 - SSA":PRINT:INPUT Q:PRINT
160 ON Q GOTO 170,230,340,370,400
170 PRINT "ENTER DATA: SIDE, ANGLE, SIDE:
    ";S1,A3,S2:REM *** SAS ***
180 S3=SQR(S1*S1+S2*S2-2*S1*S2*COS(P*A3))
190 T=S1*SIN(P*A3)/S3
200 IF T=1 THEN A1=90:A2=90-A1:GOTO 510
210 A1=1/P*ATN(T/SQR(1-T*T)):A2=180-A1-A3
220 GOTO 510
230 INPUT "ENTER DATA: SIDE, SIDE, SIDE:
    ";S1,S2,S3:REM *** SSS ***
240 IF S1>S2 THEN S=S1:S1=S2:S2=S
250 IF S2>S3 THEN S=S2:S2=S3:S3=S
260 Z1=(S2*S2+S3*S3-S1*S1)/(2*S2*S3)
270 Z2=(S3*S3+S1*S1-S2*S2)/(2*S3*S1)
280 Z3=(S1*S1+S2*S2-S3*S3)/(2*S1*S2)
290 A1=1/P*ATN(SQR(1-Z1*Z1)/Z1)
    :A2=1/P*ATN(SQR(1-Z2*Z2)/Z2)
300 IF Z3=0 THEN A3=90
310 IF Z3<>0 THEN A3=1/P*ATN(SQR(1-Z3*Z3)/Z3)
320 IF A3<0 THEN A3=180+A3
330 GOTO 510
340 PRINT "ENTER DATA: ANGLE, SIDE, ANGLE:
    ";A1,S3,A2:REM *** ASA ***
350 A3=180-A1-A2:C=S3/SIN(P*A3):S1=C*SIN(P*A1)
    :S2=C*SIN(P*A2)
360 GOTO 510
370 PRINT "ENTER DATA IN THIS ORDER AROUND THE":REM
    *** AAS ***
380 INPUT "TRIANGLE: ANGLE, ANGLE, SIDE:
    ";A3,A1,S3:A2=180-A1-A3
390 GOTO 350
400 PRINT "ENTER DATA IN THIS ORDER AROUND THE":REM
    *** SSA ***
410 INPUT "TRIANGLE: SIDE, SIDE, ANGLE: ";S2,S3,A2
420 IF S2<S3*SIN(P*A2) THEN PRINT "THERE IS NO
    TRIANGLE":END
430 IF ABS(S2-S3*SIN(P*A2))<1E-8 THEN GOTO 500
440 Z3=S3*SIN(P*A2)/S2:A3=1/P*ATN(Z3/SQR(1-Z3*Z3))
450 A1=180-A2-A3:S1=S3*SIN(P*A1)/SIN(P*A3)
460 PRINT:PRINT "SIDES","ANGLES"
470 PRINT S1,A1:PRINT S2,A2:PRINT S3,A3:IF S2>=S3 THEN END
480 A3=180-A3:A1=180-A2-A3:S1=S3*SIN(P*A1)/SIN(P*A3)
490 GOTO 510
500 A3=90:A1=90-A2:S1=SQR(S3*S3-S2*S2)
510 PRINT:PRINT "SIDES","ANGLES":REM *** PRINT RESULTS ***
520 PRINT S1,A1:PRINT S2,A2:PRINT S3,A3
530 END
```

Review Exercises

1. Evaluate each trigonometric ratio to 3 decimal places.
   a) sin 55° b) tan 27° c) sec 81° d) cot 37° e) cos 65° f) csc 22°
   g) tan 138° h) sin 102° i) csc 95° j) cot 107° k) cos 141° l) sec 170°

2. Find each value of θ to the nearest degree if $0° < \theta < 180°$.
   a) $\cos \theta = 0.274$ b) $\cot \theta = 1.912$ c) $\sec \theta = 1.125$
   d) $\sin \theta = 0.469$ e) $\csc \theta = 3.150$ f) $\tan \theta = 2.247$

3. State the exact values of the six trigonometric ratios of each angle.
   a) 0° b) 30° c) 45° d) 60° e) 90°
   f) 120° g) 135° h) 150° i) 180°

4. Given θ is an acute angle, find the values of the other five trigonometric ratios.
   a) $\cos \theta = \frac{8}{17}$ b) $\tan \theta = \frac{12}{5}$ c) $\sec \theta = \frac{21}{11}$ d) $\sin \theta = \frac{5}{9}$

5. Given θ is an acute angle, find expressions for the other five trigonometric ratios.
   a) $\sin \theta = \frac{a}{b}$ b) $\tan \theta = \frac{p}{p + q}$ c) $\sec \theta = \frac{2m - 1}{m + 3}$

6. Solve $\triangle$ABC, if $\angle$B = 90°, and:
   a) AB = 15, BC = 27 b) AC = 18, BC = 10
   c) AB = 42, $\angle$C = 72° d) AC = 12, $\angle$A = 35°.
   Give the answers to 1 decimal place where necessary.

7. Solve each $\triangle$PQR. Give the answers to 1 decimal place.
   a) $\angle Q = 75°$, $r = 8$, $p = 11$ b) $\angle R = 52°$, $r = 28$, $q = 25$
   c) $\angle P = 38°$, $\angle Q = 105°$, $p = 32$ d) $r = 17$, $p = 14$, $q = 26$
   e) $\angle Q = 57°$, $q = 42$, $r = 45$ f) $\angle R = 33°$, $p = 14$, $q = 24$

8. A wheelchair ramp 8.2 m long rises 94 cm. Find its angle of inclination to 1 decimal place.

9. The angle of elevation of the sun is 68° when a tree casts a shadow 14.3 m long. How tall is the tree?

10. A cable car rises 762 m as it moves a horizontal distance of 628 m.
    a) How long is the ride?
    b) What is the angle of inclination of the cable to the nearest degree?

11. Two identical apartment buildings are 41.3 m apart. From her balcony, Kudo notices that the angle of elevation to the top of the adjacent building is 57°. The angle of depression to the base of the building is 28°. Find the height of the buildings.

12. Rectangle PQRS has sides whose lengths are in the ratio of 3 : 2. Points A and B are the midpoints of PQ and PS respectively. Find the measure of $\angle$BAR to 1 decimal place.

13. When watching a rocket launch, Nema is 0.8 km closer to the launching pad than Joel is. When the rocket disappears from view, its angle of elevation for Nema is 36.5° and for Joel is 31.9°. How high is the rocket at this point?

8 Trigonometric Functions

The tides in the Bay of Fundy are among the highest in the world. Suppose you know how high the water is at high tide, and the time of day this occurs, and also how high it is at low tide, and the time it occurs. How can you determine the height of the water at any other time of the day? (See Section 8-12 *Example 1*.)

8-1 INTRODUCTION TO PERIODIC FUNCTIONS

In this chapter we will describe many applications of mathematics involving quantities that change in a regular way. Applications concerned with the sun and human physiology are shown on these pages.

The time of the sunset
In summer, the sun sets later than it does in winter. The graph below shows how the time of the sunset at Ottawa varies during a two-year period. The times are given on a 24 h clock in hours and decimals of hours. For example, on June 21 the sun sets at 20.3 h. This means 20 h and 0.3×60 min, or 20 h 18 min.

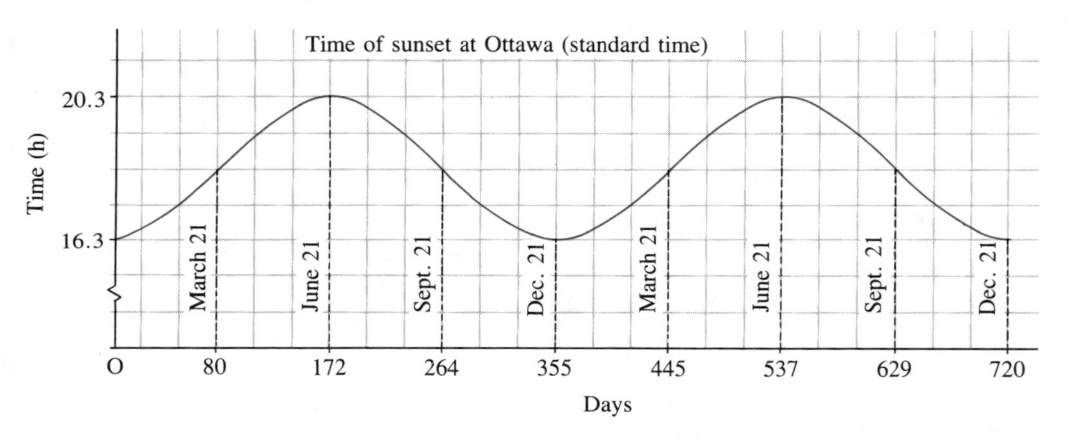

1. a) Estimate the time of the sunset at Ottawa on these dates.
   i) February 2 ii) July 25 iii) October 30
   b) Estimate the dates when the sun sets at these times.
   i) 8 P.M. ii) 7 P.M. iii) 6 P.M. iv) 5 P.M.

2. Suppose similar graphs were drawn for Yellowknife and Mexico City. In what ways would the graphs for these cities differ from the graph above? In what ways would they be similar?

	Approximate time of sunset on			
	March 21	June 21	September 21	December 21
Mexico City	18.8 h	19.3 h	18.6 h	17.9 h
Yellowknife	18.9 h	22.4 h	18.7 h	15.2 h

Sunspots
Sunspots are dark spots that appear from time to time on the surface of the sun. The periodic variation in the number of sunspots has been recorded for hundreds of years. The following graph shows how the number of sunspots varied from 1944 to 1986.

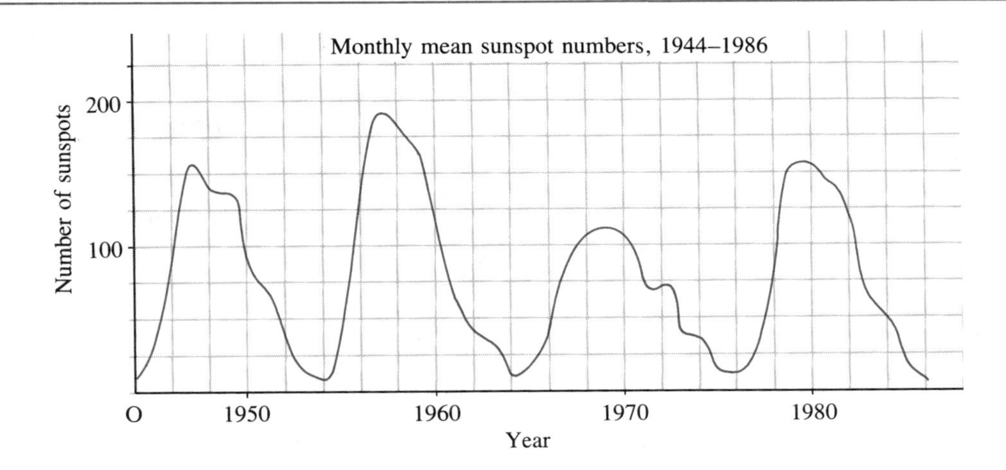

3. The graph shows that sunspot activity increases and decreases at fairly regular intervals. Estimate the number of years, on the average, between the times when there is a maximum number of sunspots.

Lengths of shadows

The graph below shows how the length of the shadow of a 100-m building varies during a three-day period. It is assumed that the sun is directly overhead at noon.

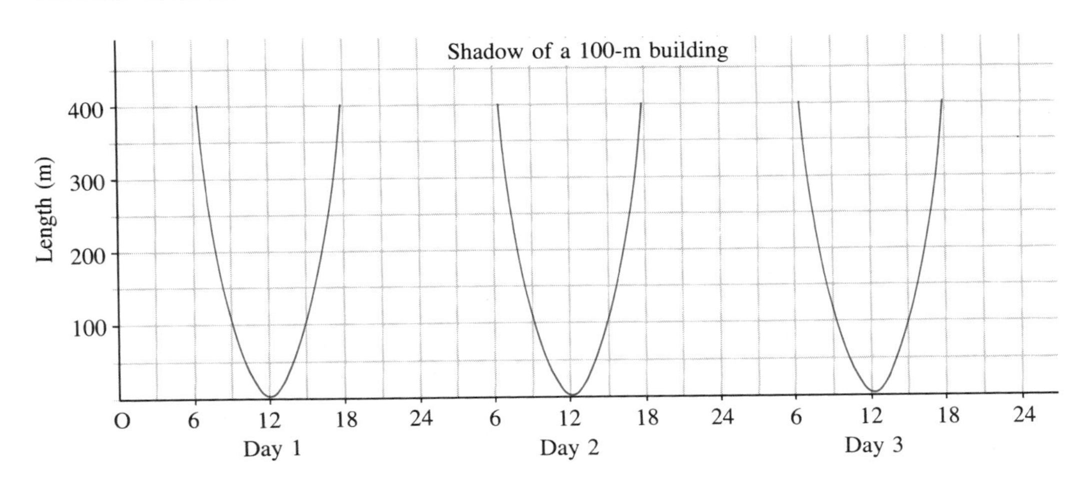

4. a) How long is the shadow at 8 A.M.? at 2 P.M.?
   b) For about how many hours during the day is the shadow longer than 100 m?

5. In many localities the sun is never directly overhead. What change would be needed in the graph if it were drawn for such a locality?

Blood pressure and volume

There are two significant phases to a heartbeat. During the systolic phase, the heart contracts, and pumps blood into the arteries. This phase is marked by a sudden increase in the pressure and a decrease in the volume of blood in the heart. The second phase is the diastolic phase, when the heart relaxes. The pressure decreases and the volume increases as more blood is drawn into the heart from the veins.

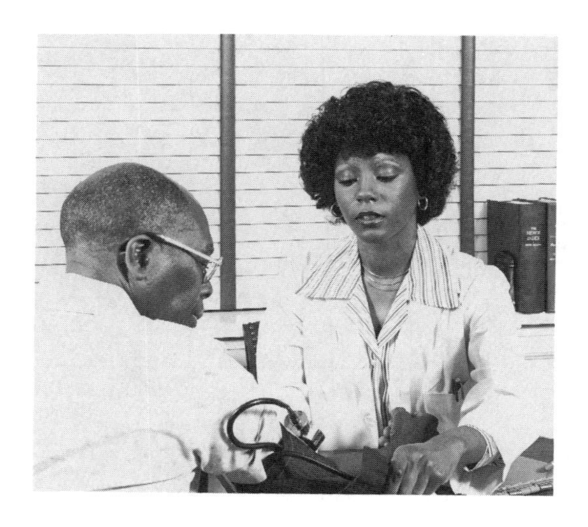

Graphs showing how the pressure and volume of blood in the left ventricle of the heart vary during five consecutive heartbeats are shown below. The time scale is the same for both graphs.

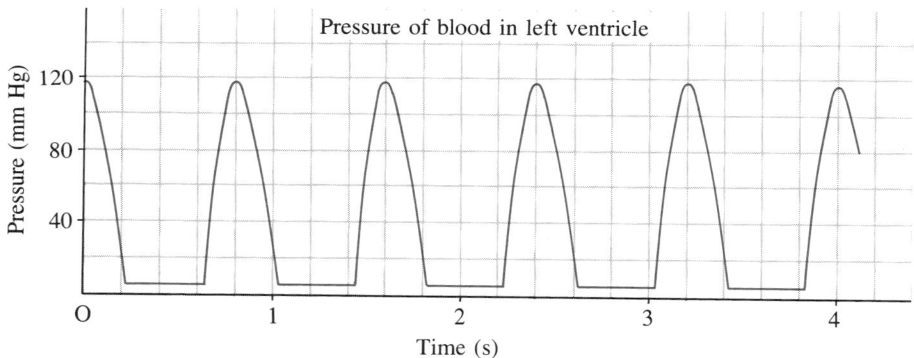

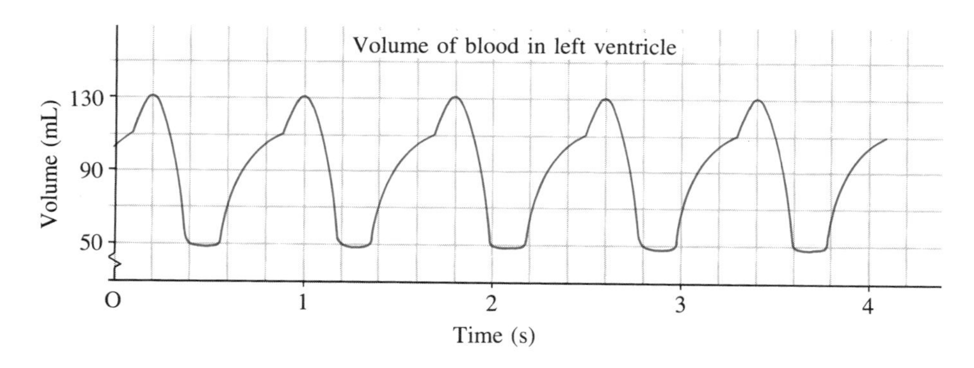

6. During intense physical activity the heart beats faster to satisfy the body's demand for more oxygen. Suppose graphs showing the variation of blood pressure and volume were drawn in this situation. How would the graphs differ from those above? In what ways would they be similar?

Volume of air in the lungs

The volume of air in your lungs is a periodic function of time. This graph shows how the volume of air in the lungs varies during normal breathing.

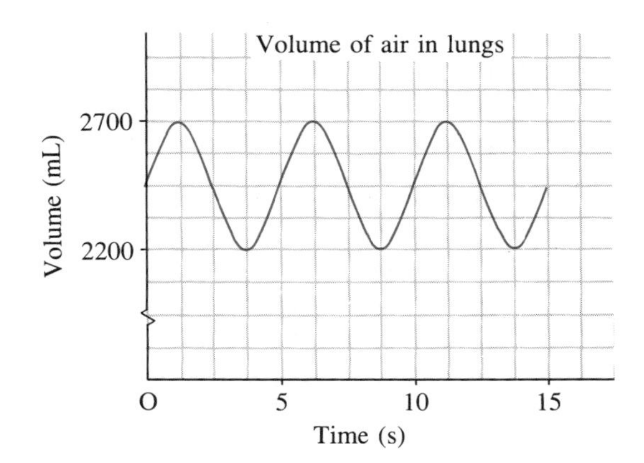

7. According to the graph, how long does it take to inhale and exhale once?

8. When the average person takes a deep breath, about 5000 mL of air can be inhaled. But only about 4000 mL of this air can be exhaled. Suppose that such a breath takes twice as much time as a normal breath. If a graph similar to the one shown were drawn for deep breathing, in what ways would it differ?

Summary

The graphs in this section suggest what is meant by a *periodic function*. The graph of such a function repeats in a regular way. The length of the part that repeats, measured along the horizontal axis, is called the *period* of the function.

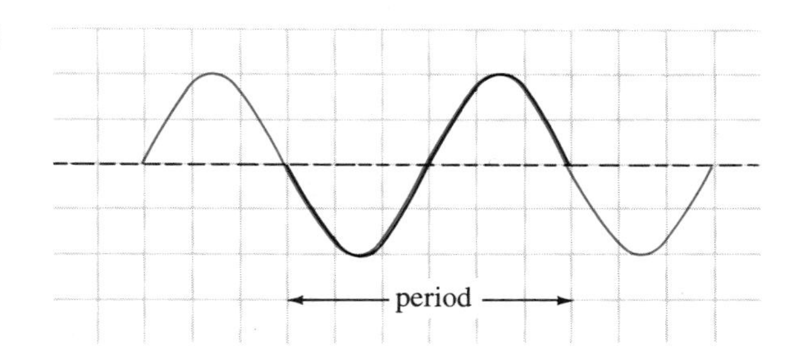

9. All periodic functions have a period. Estimate the period for the functions illustrated above.

10. State the period of this function.

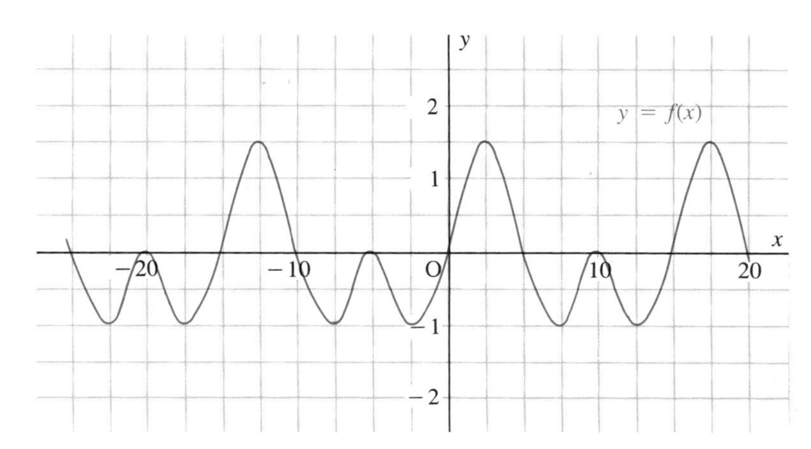

11. One of the examples in this section suggests a periodic function, but it is not a periodic function. Which example is this?

8-2 ANGLES IN STANDARD POSITION

Perhaps the simplest example of periodic motion is motion in a circle. To study motion in a circle, we need to define the standard position of an angle.

Let P(x,y) represent a point which moves around a circle with radius r and centre (0,0). P starts at the point A(r,0) on the x-axis. For any position of P, an angle θ is defined, which represents the amount of rotation about the origin. When the vertex of the angle is (0,0), the *initial arm* is OA, the *terminal arm* is OP, and we say that the angle θ is in *standard position*. The measure of the angle may be in degrees or in radians.

If $\theta > 0$, the rotation is counterclockwise. If $\theta < 0$, the rotation is clockwise.

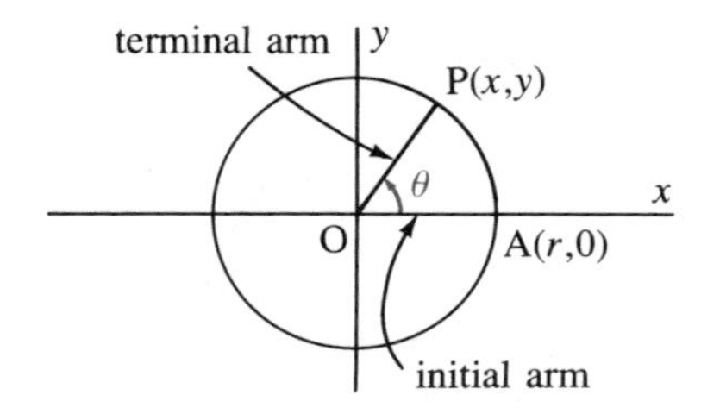

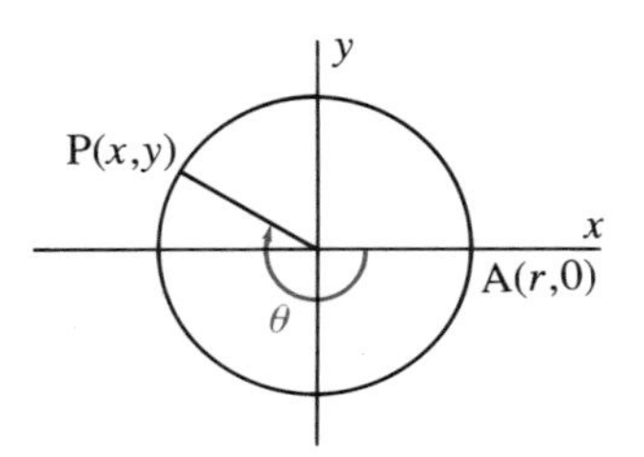

When P moves around the circle, the motion is repeated after P has rotated 360°, or 2π radians. If any angle θ is given, we can always determine other angles for which the position of P is the same. All these angles are in standard position.

Given an angle of 60°, or $\frac{\pi}{3}$

Add 360°, or 2π

$60° + 360° = 420°$

$\frac{\pi}{3} + 2\pi = \frac{7\pi}{3}$

Add 360°, or 2π again

$420° + 360° = 780°$

$\frac{7\pi}{3} + 2\pi = \frac{13\pi}{3}$

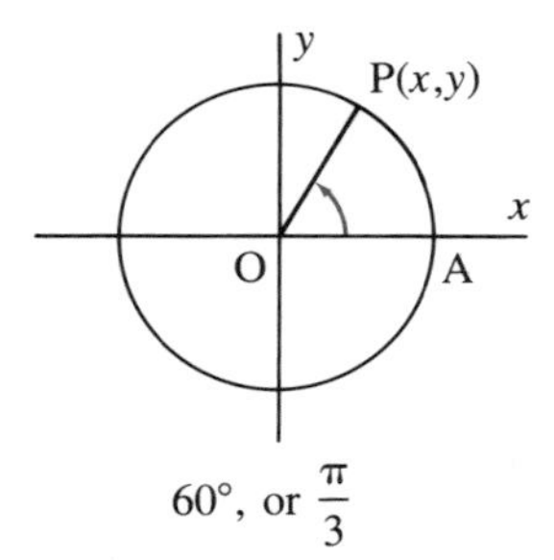

60°, or $\frac{\pi}{3}$

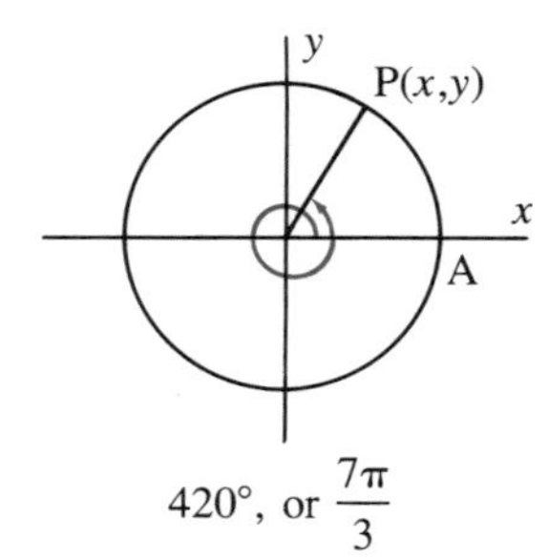

420°, or $\frac{7\pi}{3}$

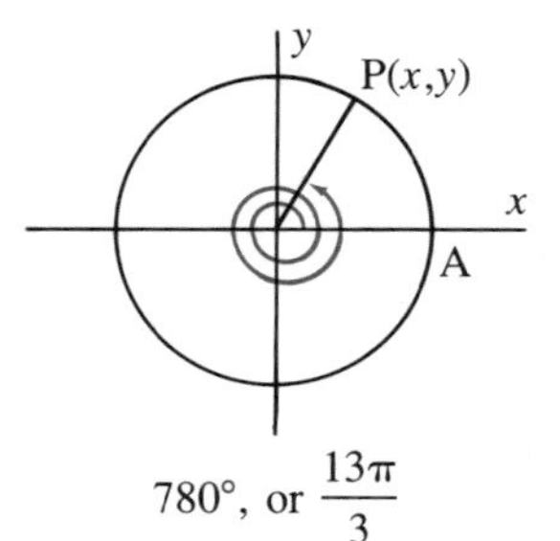

780°, or $\frac{13\pi}{3}$

The angles shown above are in standard position, and have the same terminal arm. For this reason, they are called coterminal angles. If θ is any angle in standard position, other angles which are coterminal with θ can be found by adding or subtracting multiples of 360° if θ is in degrees, or multiples of 2π if θ is in radians.

Coterminal Angles

- Two or more angles in standard position are *coterminal angles* if the position of P is the same for each angle.
- If θ represents any angle, then any angle coterminal with θ is represented by these expressions, where n is an integer.
  $\theta + n(360°)$, if θ is in degrees
  $\theta + 2\pi n$, if θ is in radians

Example 1. Given a) $\theta = 150°$ b) $\theta = \frac{\pi}{6}$

i) Draw the angle θ in standard position.
ii) Find two other angles which are coterminal with θ and illustrate them on diagrams.
iii) Write an expression to represent any angle coterminal with θ.

Solution. a) i)

ii) $150° + 360° = 510°$ $150° - 360° = -210°$

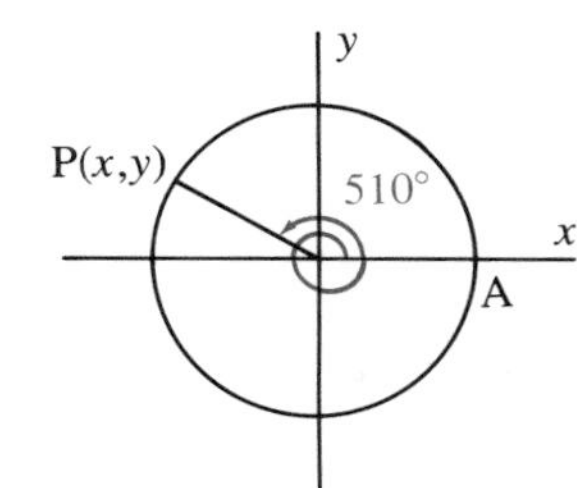

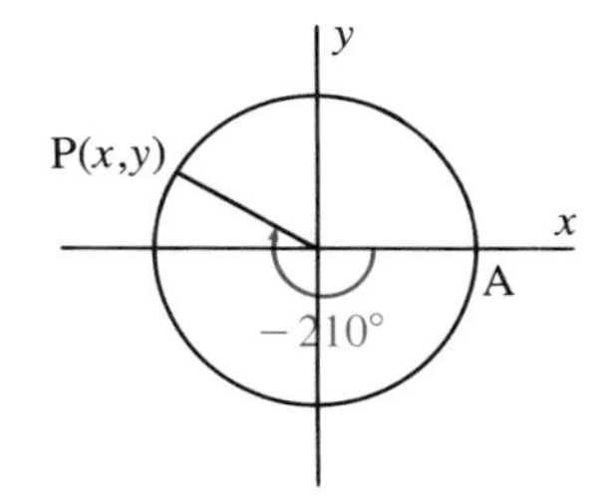

iii) Any angle coterminal with θ is represented by the expression $150° + n(360°)$, where n is an integer.

b) i)

ii) $\frac{\pi}{6} + 2\pi = \frac{13\pi}{6}$

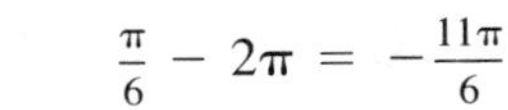
$\frac{\pi}{6} - 2\pi = -\frac{11\pi}{6}$

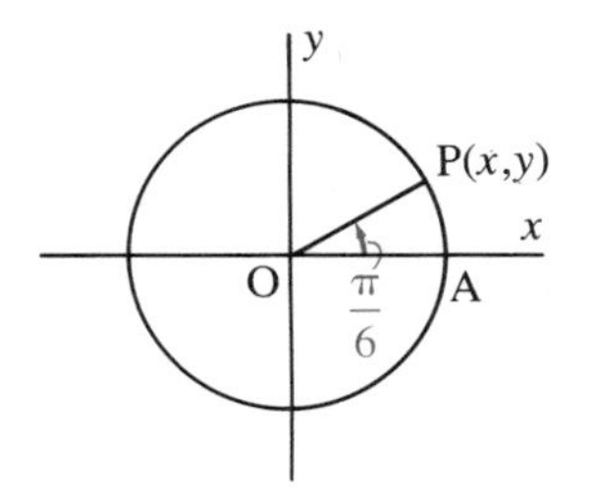

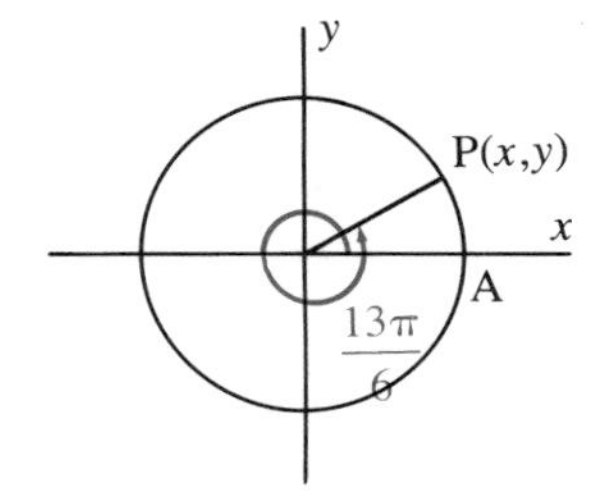

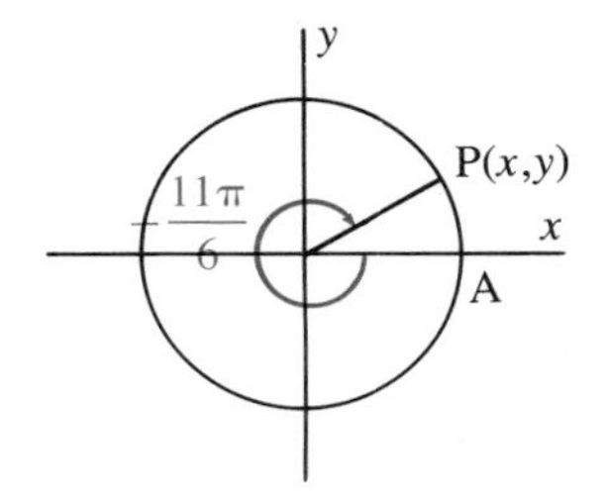

iii) Any angle coterminal with θ is represented by the expression $\frac{\pi}{6} + 2\pi n$, where n is an integer.

We can determine which quadrant P is in for any given angle expressed in degrees or in radians.

Example 2. Suppose P has rotated 830° about (0,0) from A.
a) How many complete rotations have been made?
b) In which quadrant is P located now?
c) Draw a diagram to show the position of P.

Solution. a) Since a complete rotation is 360°, divide 830 by 360.
$830 \div 360 \doteq 2.3056$
Since the result is between 2 and 3, P has made 2 complete rotations around the circle, and part of a third rotation.

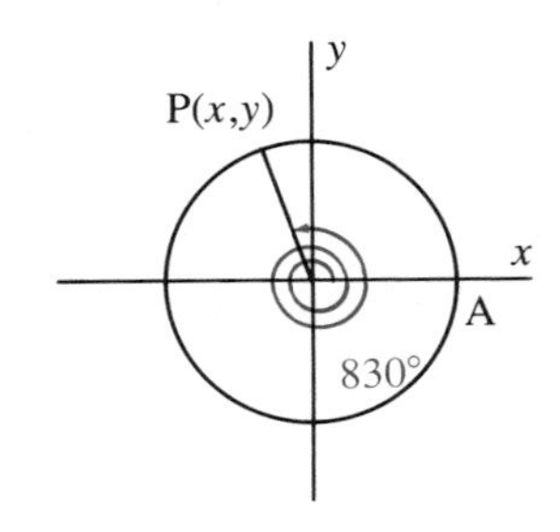

b) Two complete rotations amount to 2(360°), or 720°. The additional rotation beyond 720° is 830° − 720°, or 110°. Since $90° < 110° < 180°$, P is now in the second quadrant.

Example 3. Suppose P has rotated 3π radians about (0,0) from A.
a) How many complete rotations have been made?
b) In which quadrant is P located now?
c) Draw a diagram to show the position of P.

Solution. a) Since a complete rotation is 2π radians, divide 3π by 2π.
$3\pi \div 2\pi = 1.5$
P has made 1 complete rotation, and half of a second rotation.

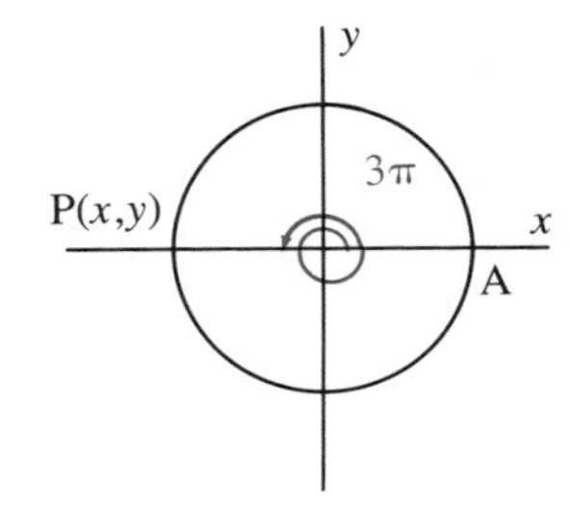

b) P is on the x-axis, between the second and third quadrants.

EXERCISES 8-2

Ⓐ

1. An angle in standard position is shown. What is the value of θ, in degrees and in radians?

a)

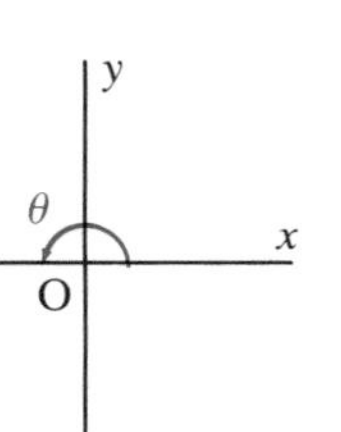

b)

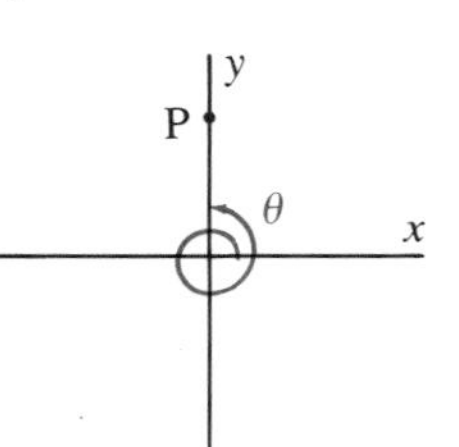

c)

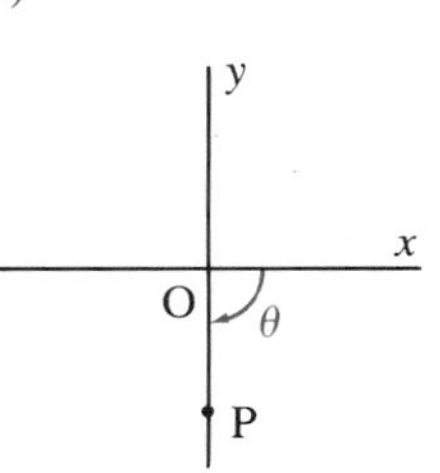

d)

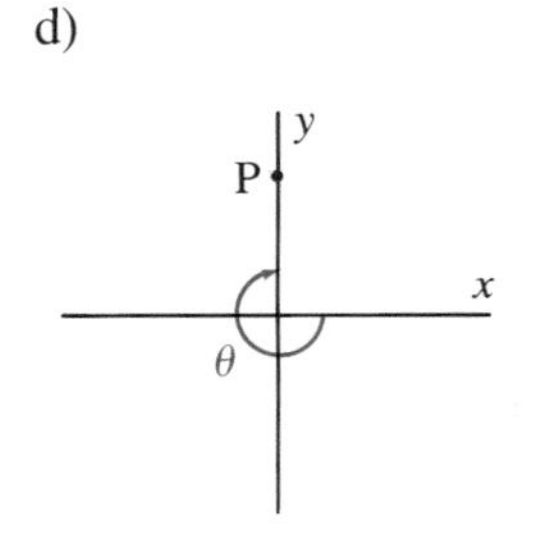

2. Draw each angle in standard position.

a) $\theta = 50°$ b) $\theta = 120°$ c) $\theta = 165°$ d) $\theta = 240°$

e) $\theta = \frac{\pi}{2}$ f) $\theta = \frac{\pi}{4}$ g) $\theta = \frac{2\pi}{3}$ h) $\theta = \frac{3\pi}{2}$

3. In *Exercise 2*, find two angles which are coterminal with θ.

4. An angle θ in standard position is shown. Find two other angles which are coterminal with θ.

a) b) 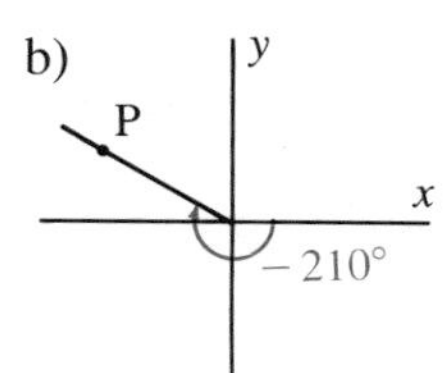

c) 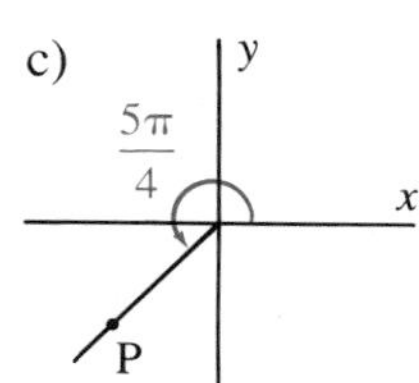

d) 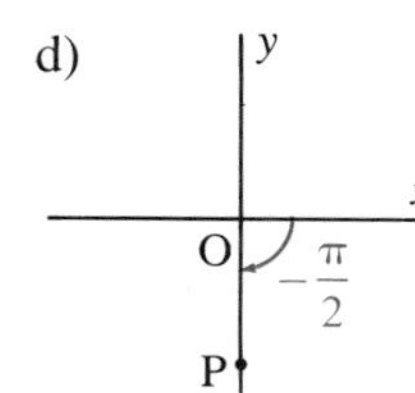

5. Find two angles which are coterminal with θ.

a) $\theta = \pi$ b) $\theta = \frac{\pi}{2}$ 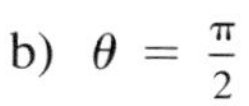 c) $\theta = -\frac{\pi}{3}$ d) $\theta = -2\pi$

---

6. P is a point on the terminal arm of an angle θ in standard position. Suppose P has rotated 420°.
   a) How many complete rotations have been made?
   b) In which quadrant is P located now?
   c) Draw a diagram to show the position of P.

7. Repeat *Exercise 6* if P has rotated:
   a) 480° b) 660° c) 870° d) 1000°.

8. Draw each angle in standard position.
   a) $\theta = 400°$ b) $\theta = 750°$ c) $\theta = -270°$ d) $\theta = -60°$

9. Repeat *Exercise 6* if P has rotated $\frac{7\pi}{3}$ radians.

10. Repeat *Exercise 6* if P has rotated:
    a) π b) $\frac{3\pi}{2}$ c) 2π d) $\frac{5\pi}{2}$.

11. Draw each angle in standard position.
    a) $\theta = \frac{9\pi}{2}$ b) $\theta = \frac{10\pi}{3}$ c) $\theta = -\frac{5\pi}{4}$ d) $\theta = -7\pi$

12. Write an expression to represent any angle coterminal with θ.
    a) $\theta = 45°$ b) $\theta = 150°$ c) $\theta = 240°$ d) $\theta = -30°$
    e) $\theta = \pi$ f) $\theta = -\frac{\pi}{4}$ g) $\theta = \frac{5\pi}{2}$ h) $\theta = 1$

(C)

---

13. P is a point on the terminal arm of an angle θ in standard position. Explain how you could determine the quadrant in which P is located, if you know the value of θ in:
    a) degrees b) radians.

14. Let θ represent any angle, where θ is in radians. Let α represent the angle which is coterminal with θ, where $0 \leqslant \alpha < 2\pi$.
    a) Draw a graph to represent α as a function of θ.
    b) What are the domain and the range of the function?

8-3 TRIGONOMETRIC FUNCTIONS OF ANGLES IN STANDARD POSITION: PART ONE

In the previous chapter we defined the trigonometric ratios of an angle in a right triangle, and we extended the definitions to obtuse angles. We can extend these definitions further to any angle in standard position.

Let P(x,y) represent any point in the first quadrant on a circle with radius r. Then P is on the terminal arm of an angle θ in standard position, as shown. Draw a right triangle $\triangle$PON by dropping a perpendicular from P to the x-axis. We can use $\triangle$PON to write trigonometric ratios in terms of the sides of $\triangle$PON.

$$\sin \angle \text{PON} = \frac{\text{PN}}{\text{OP}} \qquad \cos \angle \text{PON} = \frac{\text{ON}}{\text{OP}}$$

$$\tan \angle \text{PON} = \frac{\text{PN}}{\text{ON}}$$

Since the coordinates of P correspond to two sides of $\triangle$PON, and the radius of the circle corresponds to the third side, we can write the trigonometric ratios of θ in terms of x, y, and r, where $r = \sqrt{x^2 + y^2}$.

Let P(x,y) be any point on a circle of radius r. If θ represents the angle of rotation, then the *primary trigonometric functions* of θ are defined as follows.

$$\sin \theta = \frac{y}{r} \qquad \cos \theta = \frac{x}{r} \qquad \tan \theta = \frac{y}{x},\ x \neq 0 \quad \text{where } r = \sqrt{x^2 + y^2}$$

First Quadrant *Second Quadrant* *Third Quadrant* *Fourth Quadrant*

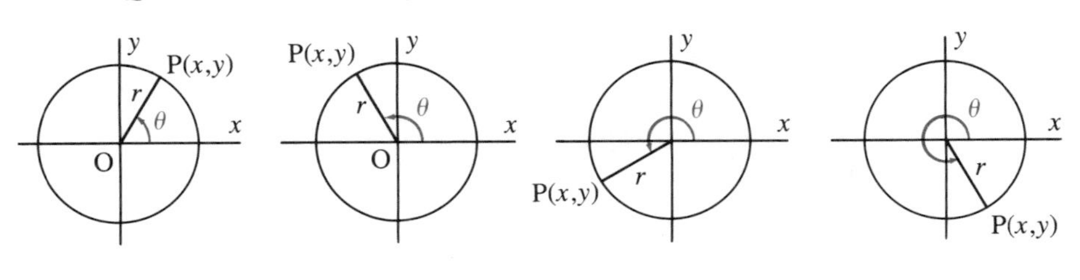

The definitions above are more general definitions of the sine, cosine, and tangent of an angle than those given in Chapter 7. Since these definitions are given in terms of the coordinates of P and the radius of the circle, they can be applied to any angle in standard position, and not just angles between 0 and π. However, when applied to angles in a right triangle, they reduce to the earlier definitions.

We can use these definitions to determine the sine, cosine, or tangent of any angle θ in standard position.

Example 1. The point P(4,3) is on the terminal arm of an angle θ.
a) Draw a diagram showing θ in standard position.
b) Calculate $\sin\theta$, $\cos\theta$, and $\tan\theta$.

Solution. a)

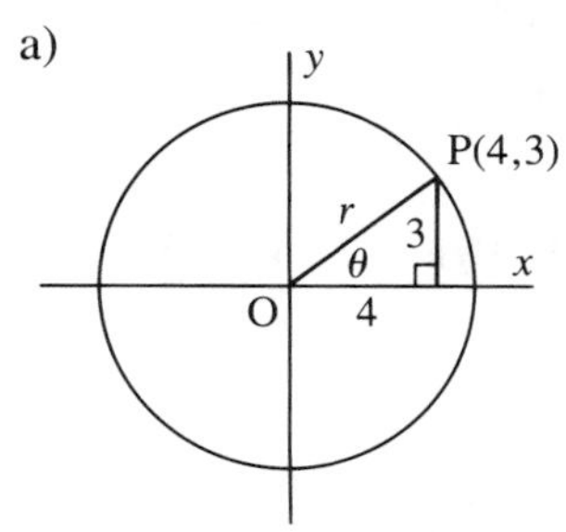

b) From the diagram,
$r = \sqrt{4^2 + 3^2}$
$= 5$
Therefore,

$\sin\theta = \frac{y}{r} = \frac{3}{5} = 0.6$ $\qquad \cos\theta = \frac{x}{r} = \frac{4}{5} = 0.8$ $\qquad \tan\theta = \frac{y}{x} = \frac{3}{4} = 0.75$

Example 2. The point P(−2,3) is on the terminal arm of an angle θ.
a) Draw a diagram showing θ in standard position.
b) Find expressions for $\sin\theta$, $\cos\theta$, and $\tan\theta$.
c) Calculate the values of $\sin\theta$, $\cos\theta$, and $\tan\theta$ to five decimal places.

Solution. a)

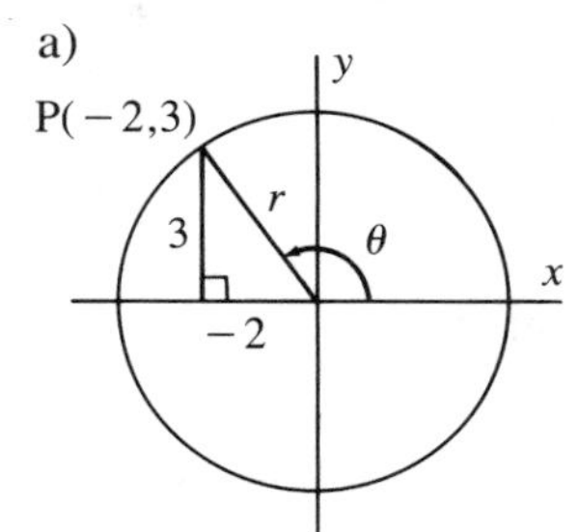

b) From the diagram,
$r = \sqrt{(-2)^2 + 3^2}$
$= \sqrt{13}$
Therefore,

$\sin\theta = \frac{y}{r} = \frac{3}{\sqrt{13}}$ $\qquad \cos\theta = \frac{x}{r} = -\frac{2}{\sqrt{13}}$ $\qquad \tan\theta = \frac{y}{x} = -\frac{3}{2}$

c) Use a scientific calculator. To find $\sin\theta$,
key in: 3 [÷] 13 [√] [=] to display 0.8320503
To five decimal places, $\sin\theta = 0.832\ 05$
Similarly, $\cos\theta = -0.554\ 70$ and $\tan\theta = -1.500\ 00$

A scientific calculator can be used to find the sine, cosine or tangent of any angle when its measure is given in degrees or radians. When the angle is in radians, it is customary to indicate no unit.

Example 3. Find each value to five decimal places.
a) $\cos 152°$ b) $\sin 3.5$

Solution. a) $\cos 152°$
First, be sure that the calculator is in *degree mode*. To find $\cos 152°$,
key in: 152 [cos] to display −0.8829476
To five decimal places, $\cos 152° = -0.882\ 95$

b) $\sin 3.5$
Since there is no unit for the angle, we assume that the angle is in radians. Be sure that the calculator is in *radian mode*. To find $\sin 3.5$,
key in: 3.5 [sin] to display −0.3507832
To five decimal places, $\sin 3.5 = -0.350\ 78$

There are infinitely many angles which have the same cosine as 152°, or the same sine as 3.5 radians. For example, use your calculator to verify that the following expressions are also equal to $-0.882\ 95$.

$\cos(152° + 360°)$, or $\cos 512°$ $\quad$ $\cos(152° - 360°)$, or $\cos(-208°)$
$\cos(152° + 720°)$, or $\cos 872°$ $\quad$ $\cos(152° - 720°)$, or $\cos(-568°)$

Use your calculator to verify that the following expressions are also equal to $-0.350\ 78$.

$\sin(3.5 + 2\pi)$ $\quad$ $\sin(3.5 - 2\pi)$ $\quad$ $\sin(3.5 + 4\pi)$ $\quad$ $\sin(3.5 - 4\pi)$

EXERCISES 8-3

Ⓐ

1. Determine $\sin \theta$, $\cos \theta$, and $\tan \theta$. Express your answers in decimal form, to 4 decimal places.

a) 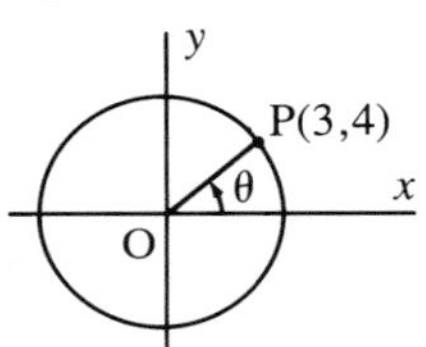

b) c) 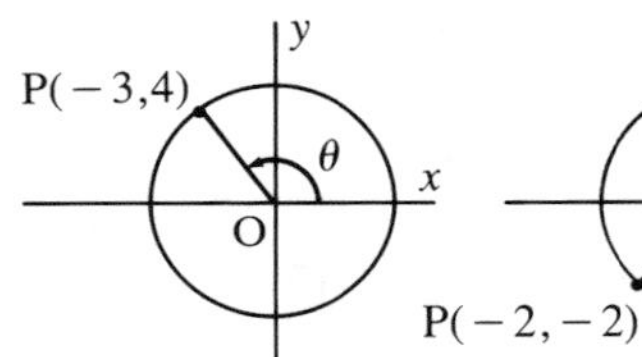

d) 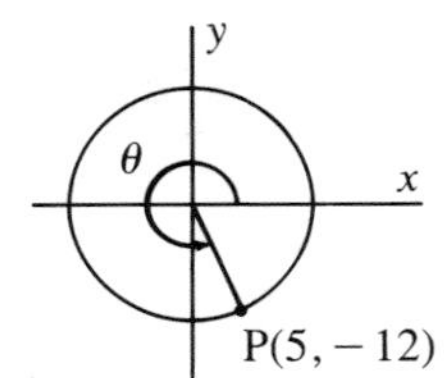

2. Determine $\sin \theta$, $\cos \theta$, and $\tan \theta$ to 4 decimal places.

a) 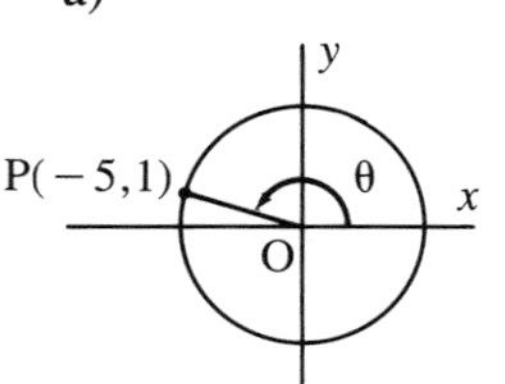

b) 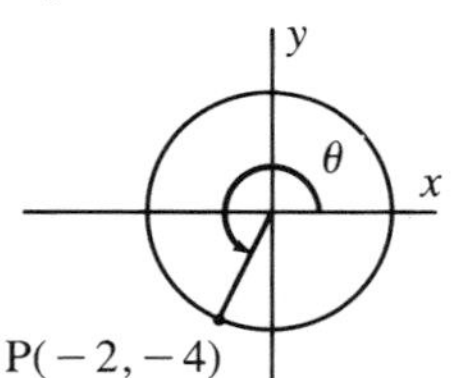

c) d) 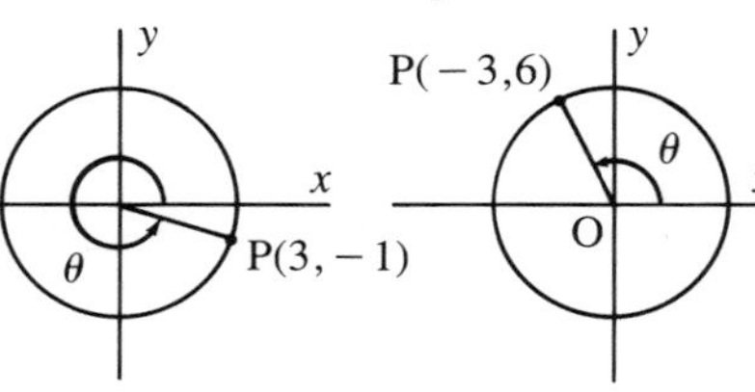

3. Use a scientific calculator in degree mode. Find each value to 3 decimal places.
   a) sin 130° b) cos 145° c) tan 130° d) sin 200°
   e) cos 260° f) sin 325° g) tan 347° h) cos 534°

4. Use a scientific calculator in radian mode. Find each value to 3 decimal places.
   a) sin 0.4 b) cos 0.6 c) tan 1.25 d) sin 1.8
   e) cos 3.0 f) tan 4.15 g) sin 5.39 h) cos 8.75

5. The point P(4, −3) is on the terminal arm of an angle θ.
   a) Draw a diagram showing θ in standard position.
   b) Calculate $\sin \theta$, $\cos \theta$, and $\tan \theta$.

6. The point P(−1,2) is on the terminal arm of an angle θ.
   a) Draw a diagram showing θ in standard position.
   b) Calculate $\sin \theta$, $\cos \theta$, and $\tan \theta$ to 3 decimal places.

Ⓑ

7. Each point P is on the terminal arm of an angle θ. Use a diagram to calculate $\sin\theta$, $\cos\theta$, and $\tan\theta$.
   a) $P(12,-5)$ b) $P(-4,-2)$ c) $P(-3,1)$ d) $P(-3,-4)$
   e) $P(6,-2)$ f) $P(2,9)$ g) $P(0,4)$ h) $P(-5,0)$

8. a) Find $\sin 125°$ to 5 decimal places.
   b) Find three other angles which have the same sine as $125°$, and verify with a calculator.

9. a) Find $\cos 220°$ to 5 decimal places.
   b) Find three other angles which have the same cosine as $220°$, and verify with a calculator.

10. a) Find $\sin 1.25$ to 5 decimal places.
    b) Find three other angles which have the same sine as 1.25 radians, and verify with a calculator.

11. a) Find $\tan 4.7$ to 5 decimal places.
    b) Find three other angles which have the same tangent as 4.7 radians, and verify with a calculator.

12. The angle θ is in the first quadrant, and $\tan\theta = \frac{2}{3}$.
    a) Draw a diagram showing the angle in standard position and a point P on its terminal arm.
    b) Determine possible coordinates for P.
    c) Find the other two primary trigonometric functions of θ.

13. Repeat *Exercise 12* if θ is in the second quadrant, and $\tan\theta = -\frac{5}{2}$.

14. Repeat *Exercise 12* if θ is in the second quadrant, and $\sin\theta = \frac{2}{\sqrt{5}}$.

Ⓒ

15. For each angle θ, find the other two primary trigonometric functions of θ.

	Quadrant	Given function
a)	Second	$\cos\theta = -\frac{5}{13}$
b)	Third	$\sin\theta = -\frac{1}{4}$
c)	Third	$\tan\theta = \frac{3}{2}$
d)	Fourth	$\sin\theta = -\frac{3}{4}$

16. Given the equation $\sin\theta = 0.5$
    a) Find three different roots for θ.
    b) How many different roots are there?

17. You can use a scientific calculator to find the sine, cosine or tangent of any angle in standard position.
    a) Determine the *largest* angle your calculator will accept: in degrees; in radians.
    b) Are these two angles equal?

8-4 TRIGONOMETRIC FUNCTIONS OF ANGLES IN STANDARD POSITION: PART TWO

In the preceding section we found how to determine the sine, cosine, or tangent of any angle in standard position. We now consider how to determine the angle if its sine, cosine, or tangent is given. For example, we can solve equations such as these, for θ.

$\sin\theta = 0.548 \qquad \cos\theta = -0.255 \qquad \tan\theta = 0.65$

Since the trigonometric functions are periodic, equations such as these have infinitely many roots. Each root is an angle in standard position with its terminal arm in one of the four quadrants. To help us determine the quadrants in which the roots occur for any given equation, the table below summarizes the possible combinations of signs for each function (the sign of r is always taken to be positive).

	Quadrant I 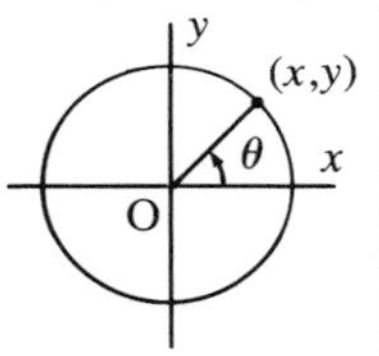	Quadrant II 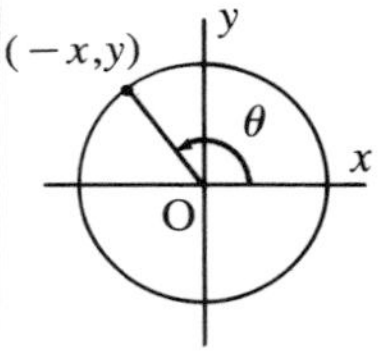	Quadrant III 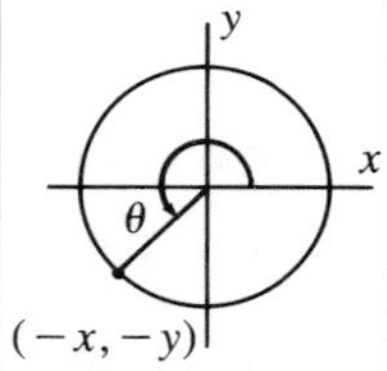	Quadrant IV 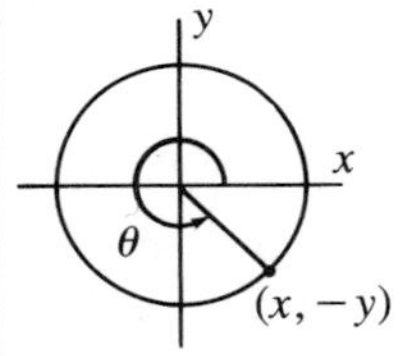
Sign of $\sin\theta = \frac{y}{r}$	+	+	−	−
Sign of $\cos\theta = \frac{x}{r}$	+	−	−	+
Sign of $\tan\theta = \frac{y}{x}$	+	−	+	−

Example 1. Solve the equation $\sin\theta = 0.65$ for θ:
a) to the nearest degree, where $0° \leqslant \theta \leqslant 360°$
b) in radians, to two decimal places, where $0 \leqslant \theta \leqslant 2\pi$.

Solution. Since $\sin\theta$ is positive, and $\sin\theta = \frac{y}{r}$, θ lies in the quadrants in which $y > 0$, namely, Quadrants I and II.

a) Be sure your calculator is in degree mode.
Key in: 0.65 [INV] [sin] to display 40.541602
On some calculators, key in: 0.65 [$\sin^{-1}$]
Hence, one value of θ is 41°, which is in Quadrant I.

To find the root in Quadrant II, consider the diagram. $P'(-x,y)$ is the image of $P(x,y)$ under a reflection in the y-axis.
If $\angle POA = 41°$, then by the properties of a reflection,
$\angle P'OB = 41°$
Hence, $\angle P'OA = 180° - 41°$
$= 139°$

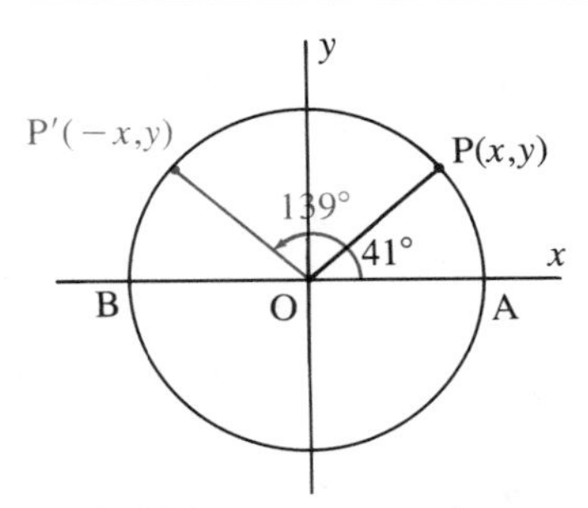

To the nearest degree, the equation $\sin\theta = 0.65$ has two roots between $0°$ and $360°$: $\theta_1 = 41°$, and $\theta_2 = 139°$.

Check. Key in: 40.541602 [sin] to display 0.6500000
Key in: 180 [−] 40.541602 [=] [sin] to display 0.6500000

b) Be sure your calculator is in radian mode.
Key in: 0.65 [INV] [sin] to display 0.7075844
Hence, one value of θ is 0.71, which is in Quadrant I.
Using the diagram in part a), the value of θ in Quadrant II is $\pi - 0.7075844$, or 2.4340082.
To two decimal places, the equation $\sin\theta = 0.65$ has two roots between 0 and 2π: $\theta_1 = 0.71$ and $\theta_2 = 2.43$.

Check. Key in: 0.7075844 [sin] to display 0.6500000
Key in: 2.4340082 [sin] to display 0.6499999

Example 1 illustrates the following general result.

Property of sine functions
If θ_1 is any value of θ such that $\sin\theta = k$, then another value of θ which satisfies this equation is:
$\theta_2 = 180° - \theta_1$ (in degrees)
or $\theta_2 = \pi - \theta_1$ (in radians)
All other values of θ can be found by adding multiples of $360°$ or 2π to θ_1 and θ_2.

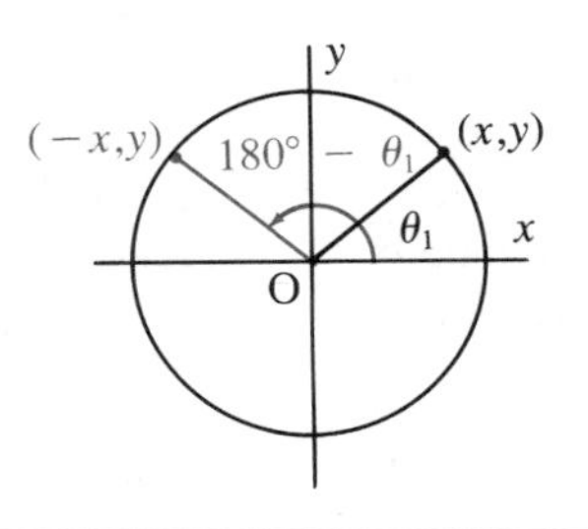

Example 2. Solve the equation $\sin\theta = -0.8974$ to the nearest degree, where $0° \leqslant \theta \leqslant 360°$.

Solution. Since $\sin\theta$ is negative, and $\sin\theta = \frac{y}{r}$, θ lies in the quadrants in which $y < 0$, namely, Quadrants III and IV.
In degree mode, key in: 0.8974 [+/−] [INV] [sin] to display −63.818386.
Hence, one value of θ which satisfies the equation is $-64°$. Although this root is not between $0°$ and $360°$, we can use it to obtain two roots which are between $0°$ and $360°$.

To obtain one root, add 360°: $-64° + 360°$, or 296°. This is the root in Quadrant IV.
To obtain the other root, use the property of sine functions. Another angle that satisfies the equation is:
$180° - (-64°)$, or 244°. This is the root in Quadrant III.
To the nearest degree, the equation $\sin \theta = -0.8974$ has two roots between 0° and 360°: $\theta_1 = 296°$ and $\theta_2 = 244°$.
Check these results with your calculator.

Example 3. Solve the equation $\cos \theta = 0.4138$ to the nearest degree, where $0° \leqslant \theta \leqslant 360°$.

Solution. Since $\cos \theta$ is positive, and $\cos \theta = \frac{x}{r}$, θ lies in the quadrants in which $x > 0$, namely, Quadrants I and IV.
In degree mode, key in: 0.4138 [INV] [cos] to display 65.556231
Hence, one value of θ is 66°, which is in Quadrant I.
To find the root in Quadrant IV, consider the diagram.
$P'(x, -y)$ is the image of $P(x,y)$ under a reflection in the x-axis.
By the properties of a reflection,
$\angle P'OA = \angle POA$
Hence, as an angle in standard position,
$\angle P'OA = 360° - 66°$, or 294°
To the nearest degree, the equation $\cos \theta = 0.4138$ has two roots between 0° and 360°:
$\theta_1 = 66°$ and $\theta_2 = 294°$.
Check these results with your calculator.

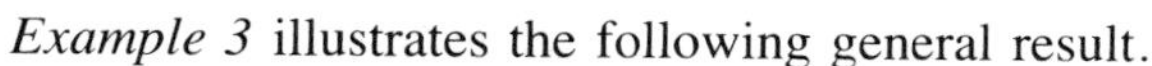
Example 3 illustrates the following general result.

Property of cosine functions
If θ_1 is any value of θ such that $\cos \theta = k$, then another value of θ which satisfies this equation is:
$\theta_2 = 360° - \theta_1$ (in degrees)
or $\theta_2 = 2\pi - \theta_1$ (in radians)
All other values of θ can be found by adding multiples of 360° or 2π to θ_1 and θ_2.

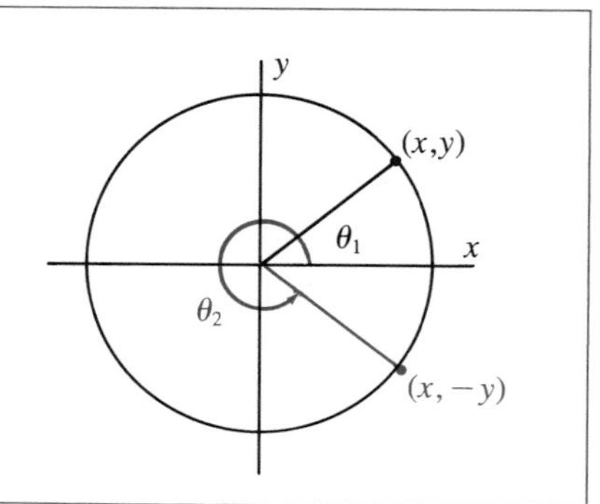

Remember, when working with trigonometric functions using a scientific calculator, you must always know whether your calculator is in degree mode or in radian mode.

Example 4. Solve the equation $3\cos^2\theta + \cos\theta - 1 = 0$ for θ in radians to two decimal places, where $0 \leq \theta \leq 2\pi$.

Solution. $3\cos^2\theta + \cos\theta - 1 = 0$ is a quadratic equation in $\cos\theta$.
Use the quadratic formula.

$$\cos\theta = \frac{-b \pm \sqrt{b^2 - 4ac}}{2a}$$

$$= \frac{-1 \pm \sqrt{1^2 - 4(3)(-1)}}{2(3)}$$

$$= \frac{-1 \pm \sqrt{13}}{6}$$

$$= 0.434\ 258\ 5 \text{ or } -0.767\ 591\ 9$$

In radian mode, key in: 0.4342585 [INV] [cos] to display 1.1215813, which is one root of the equation.
Another root is $2\pi - 1.1215813$. Continue and key in:
[+/−] [+] 2 [×] [π] [=] to display 5.161604.
Key in: 0.7675919 [+/−] [INV] [cos] to display 2.4458718, which is a root of the equation.
Another root is $2\pi - 2.4458718$. Continue and key in:
[+/−] [+] 2 [×] [π] [=] to display 3.8373135.
Hence, the given equation has four roots between 0 and 2π. To two decimal places, these roots are 1.12, 2.45, 3.84, and 5.16.

In *Example 4,* notice that when the values of θ are subtracted from 2π, more than two decimal places are used. This avoids rounding errors. For example, if the root 2.445 871 8 had been rounded to two decimal places as 2.45 and then subtracted from 2π, the result would have been 3.83. This value is not correct to two decimal places.

EXERCISES 8-4

Ⓐ

1. Solve for θ to the nearest degree, $0° \leq \theta \leq 90°$.
   a) $\sin\theta = 0.35$ b) $\cos\theta = 0.112$ c) $\tan\theta = 0.485$
   d) $\cos\theta = 0.8492$ e) $\sin\theta = 0.9044$ f) $\tan\theta = 2.058$

2. Solve for θ in radians to 2 decimal places, $0 \leq \theta \leq \frac{\pi}{2}$.
   a) $\sin\theta = 0.82$ b) $\cos\theta = 0.75$ c) $\tan\theta = 0.685$
   d) $\cos\theta = 0.1123$ e) $\sin\theta = 0.2552$ f) $\tan\theta = 3.158$

Ⓑ

3. Solve for θ to the nearest degree, $0° \leq \theta \leq 360°$.
   a) $\sin\theta = 0.75$ b) $\cos\theta = 0.0965$ c) $\sin\theta = 0.1392$
   d) $\cos\theta = 0.3558$ e) $\sin\theta = 0.6666$ f) $\cos\theta = 0.9876$

4. Solve for θ in radians to 2 decimal places, $0 \leqslant \theta \leqslant 2\pi$.
   a) $\cos \theta = 0.44$
   b) $\sin \theta = 0.6805$
   c) $\cos \theta = 0.8923$
   d) $\sin \theta = 0.2671$
   e) $\tan \theta = 2.671$
   f) $\cos \theta = 0.3498$

5. Solve for θ to the nearest degree, $0° \leqslant \theta \leqslant 360°$.
   a) $\sin \theta = -0.6855$
   b) $\cos \theta = -0.1881$
   c) $\sin \theta = -0.2550$

6. Solve for θ in radians to 2 decimal places, $0 \leqslant \theta \leqslant 2\pi$.
   a) $\cos \theta = 0.8245$
   b) $\cos \theta = -0.1067$
   c) $\sin \theta = -0.8040$

7. a) Explain why the property of sine functions is another way of stating the identity $\sin (180° - \theta) = \sin \theta$.
   b) Explain why the property of cosine functions is another way of stating the identity $\cos (360° - \theta) = \cos \theta$.

8. The point $P(-2, -6)$ is on the terminal arm of an angle θ in standard position. Find a value of θ to the nearest degree.

9. The point given is on the terminal arm of an angle θ in standard position. Find a value of θ to the nearest degree.
   a) $P(-1, -4)$
   b) $Q(3, -4)$
   c) $R(2, -3)$
   d) $S(-1, 2)$

10. Solve for θ to the nearest degree, $0° \leqslant \theta \leqslant 360°$.
    a) $4 \sin \theta - 1 = 0$
    b) $3 \cos \theta + 2 = 0$
    c) $\cos^2\theta + \cos \theta - 1 = 0$
    d) $3 \sin^2\theta + \sin \theta - 1 = 0$
    e) $6 \sin^2\theta - 5 \sin \theta + 1 = 0$
    f) $3 \cos^2\theta + 5 \cos \theta - 2 = 0$

11. Solve for θ in radians to 2 decimal places, $0 \leqslant \theta \leqslant 2\pi$.
    a) $6 \cos \theta + 1 = 0$
    b) $3 \sin \theta + 1 = 2$
    c) $2 \cos^2\theta + 3 \cos \theta - 1 = 0$
    d) $\sin^2\theta + 3 \sin \theta + 1 = 0$
    e) $6 \sin^2\theta + 5 \sin \theta - 6 = 0$
    f) $4 \cos^2\theta + 5 \cos \theta - 6 = 0$

Ⓒ

12. Solve for θ to the nearest tenth of a degree, $0° \leqslant \theta \leqslant 90°$.
    a) $\sin 2\theta = 0.75$
    b) $4 \cos 2\theta - 3 = 0$
    c) $3 \sin^2 2\theta - 10 \sin 2\theta + 3 = 0$
    d) $8 \cos^2 2\theta + 2 \cos 2\theta - 1 = 0$

13. Write a property of the tangent function which is similar to the properties of sine and cosine functions which were developed in this section.

14. Solve for θ to the nearest degree, $0° \leqslant \theta \leqslant 360°$.
    a) $3 \tan \theta - 2 = 0$
    b) $2 \tan \theta + 7 = 0$
    c) $2 \tan^2\theta - 3 \tan \theta + 1 = 0$
    d) $3 \tan^2\theta - 2 \tan \theta - 4 = 0$

15. Solve for θ to the nearest tenth of a degree, $0° \leqslant \theta \leqslant 90°$.
    a) $\tan 3\theta = 0.5$
    b) $5 \tan 2\theta + 2 = 0$
    c) $3 \tan 2\theta - 1 = 4$
    d) $4 \tan \theta - 1 = 5$
    e) $2 \tan^2 2\theta + \tan 2\theta - 1 = 0$
    f) $\tan^2 2\theta - 5 \tan 2\theta + 6 = 0$

16. a) Find the smallest angle greater than 1000° whose cosine is 0.5.
    b) Find the greatest angle less than 2000° whose tangent is 2.5.

8-5 GRAPHING THE SINE AND COSINE FUNCTIONS

To draw graphs of the functions $y = \sin \theta$ and $y = \cos \theta$, recall their definitions. If $P(x,y)$ is any point on a circle of radius r and centre $(0,0)$, then

$\sin \theta = \frac{y}{r} \qquad \cos \theta = \frac{x}{r}$.

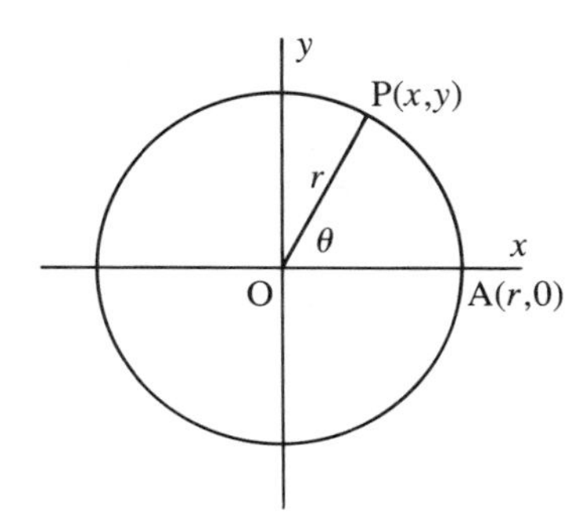

Imagine that P rotates around the circle counterclockwise starting at $A(r,0)$. As θ increases, the values of x and y change periodically. This causes a periodic change in the values of $\sin \theta$ and $\cos \theta$.

Graphing the function $y = \sin \theta$

The function values are independent of the radius of the circle. Therefore, for convenience, we assume that $r = 2$.

Suppose θ starts at 0° and increases to 180°. Then $\sin \theta$ changes as follows.

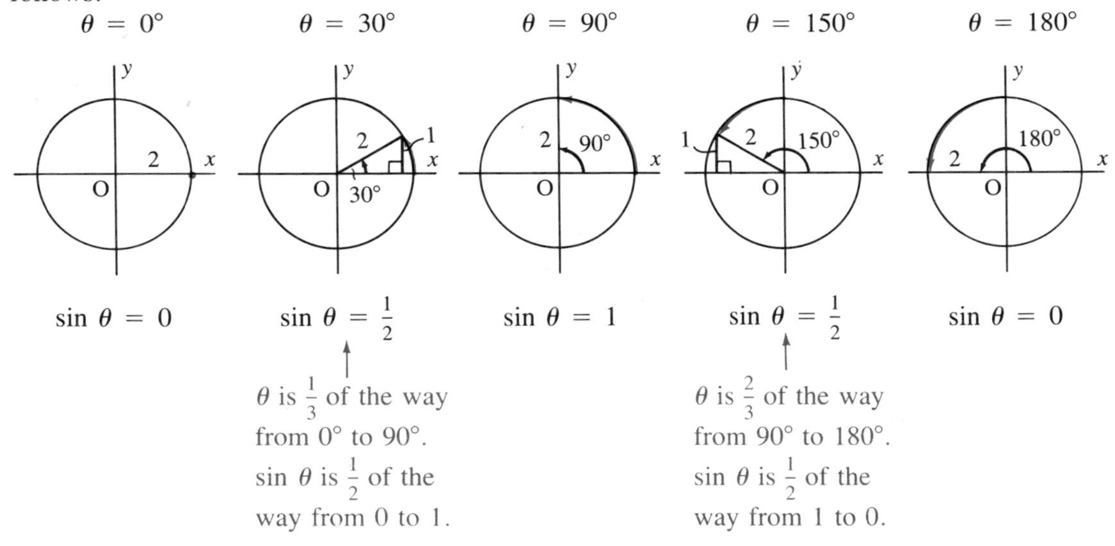

We use these results to sketch the graph for $0° \leqslant \theta \leqslant 180°$.

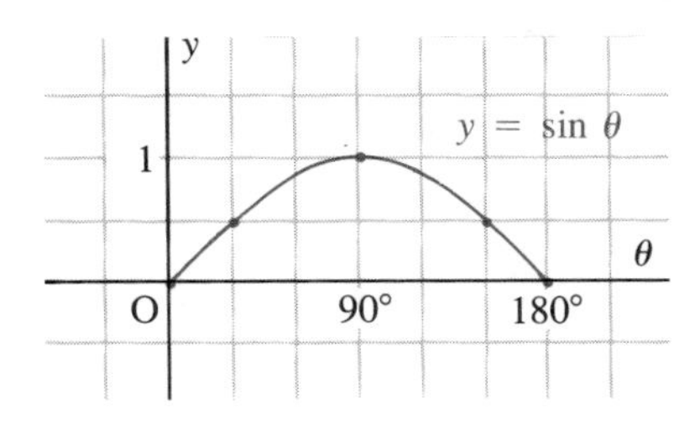

Suppose θ continues from 180° to 360°. Then $\sin\theta$ changes as follows.

$\theta = 180°$	$\theta = 210°$	$\theta = 270°$	$\theta = 330°$	$\theta = 360°$
$\sin\theta = 0$	$\sin\theta = -\frac{1}{2}$	$\sin\theta = -1$	$\sin\theta = -\frac{1}{2}$	$\sin\theta = 0$

For $\theta = 210°$: θ is $\frac{1}{3}$ of the way from 180° to 270°. $\sin\theta$ is $\frac{1}{2}$ of the way from 0 to -1.

For $\theta = 330°$: θ is $\frac{2}{3}$ of the way from 270° to 360°. $\sin\theta$ is $\frac{1}{2}$ of the way from -1 to 0.

We use these results to sketch the graph for $180° \leqslant \theta \leqslant 360°$.

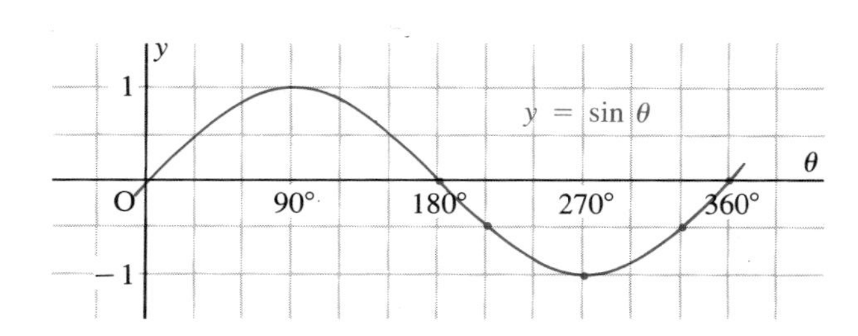

As θ continues beyond 360°, P rotates around the circle again, and the same values of $\sin\theta$ are encountered. Hence, the graph can be continued to the right. Similarly, the graph can be continued to the left, corresponding to a rotation in the opposite direction. Hence, the patterns in the graph repeat every 360° in both directions.

The graph on the next page shows two different cycles of the function $y = \sin\theta$.

A *cycle* of a periodic function is a part of its graph from any point to the first point where the graph starts repeating.

The *period* of a periodic function of θ may be expressed as the difference in the values of θ for the points at the ends of a cycle.

The graph shows that when θ is in degrees, the period of the function $y = \sin \theta$ is 360°.

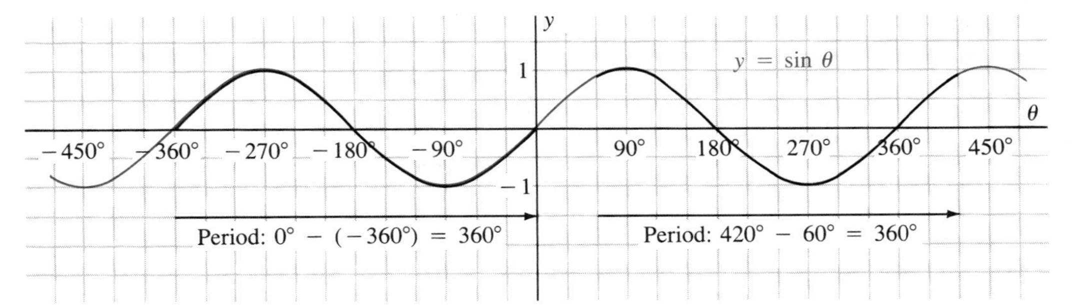

For θ in radians, the graph of $y = \sin \theta$ is shown below. It differs from the previous graph only in the scale on the θ-axis. When θ is in radians, the period of the function $y = \sin \theta$ is 2π.

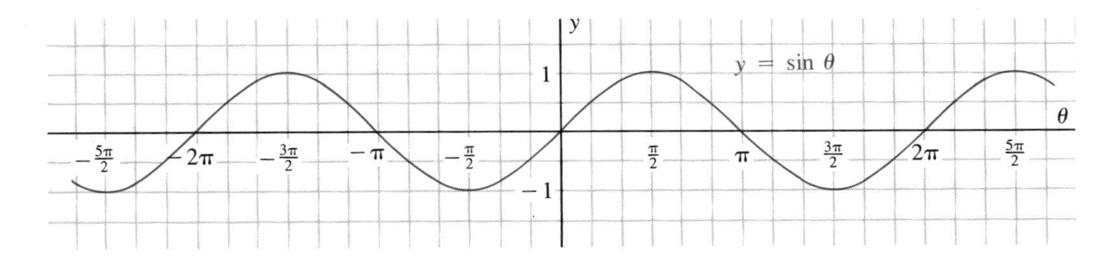

Graphing the function $y = \cos \theta$

We can graph the function $y = \cos \theta$ using the same method as we used to graph the function $y = \sin \theta$. The result is shown below.

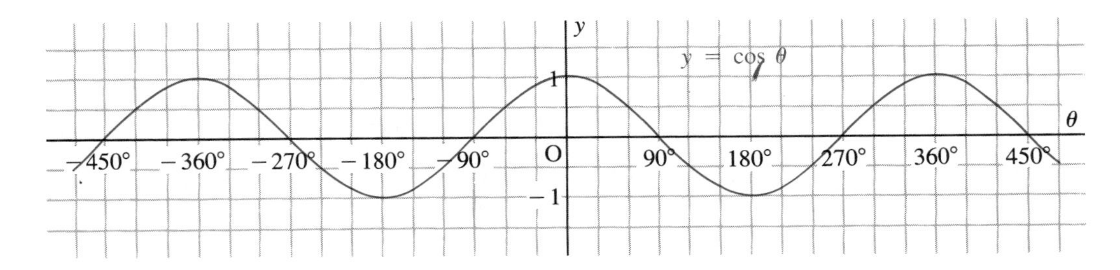

The function $y = \cos \theta$ has a period of 360°, or 2π. Its graph is congruent to the graph of $y = \sin \theta$, but it is shifted horizontally so that it intersects the y-axis at (0,1) instead of (0,0). These curves are called *sinusoids*, meaning "like sine curves".

The graphs of the sine and cosine functions illustrate many properties of these functions.

Properties of the function $y = \sin\theta$

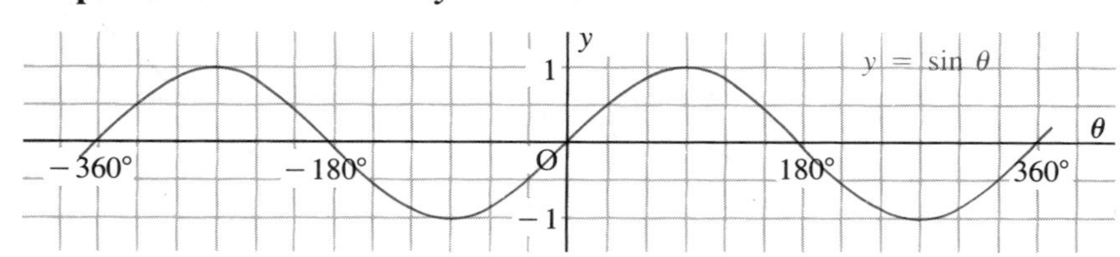

Period: 360°, or 2π
Maximum value of y: 1
Minimum value of y: -1
Domain: θ may represent any angle in standard position
Range: $\{y \mid -1 \leqslant y \leqslant 1\}$
θ-intercepts: $\ldots, -180°, 0°, 180°, 360°, \ldots$ or: $\ldots, -\pi, 0, \pi, 2\pi, \ldots$
y-intercept: 0

Properties of the function $y = \cos\theta$

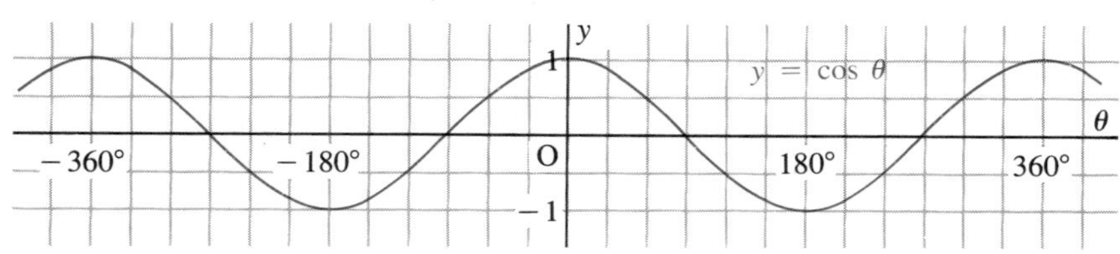

Period: 360°, or 2π
Maximum value of y: 1
Minimum value of y: -1
Domain: θ may represent any angle in standard position
Range: $\{y \mid -1 \leqslant y \leqslant 1\}$
θ-intercepts: $\ldots, -90°, 90°, 270°, 450°, \ldots$ or: $\ldots, -\frac{\pi}{2}, \frac{\pi}{2}, \frac{3\pi}{2}, \frac{5\pi}{2}, \ldots$
y-intercept: 1

To use sinusoidal functions in applications involving quantities that change periodically, we must be able to work with them when their maximum and minimum values are different from 1 and -1, and their periods are different from 360°, or 2π. This involves taking the basic graphs described in this section, and expanding or compressing them in the vertical or horizontal directions, as well as changing their positions relative to the axes. When changes such as these are made to the graphs of these functions, corresponding changes occur in the equations. In the following sections we will investigate how the changes in the equations are related to the changes in the graphs.

EXERCISES 8-5

(A)

1. In the following diagrams, graphs of $y = \sin \theta$ have been started using different scales. Copy each graph on graph paper, and then extend it for the number of cycles indicated.
   a) 2 cycles b) 2 cycles c) 1 cycle

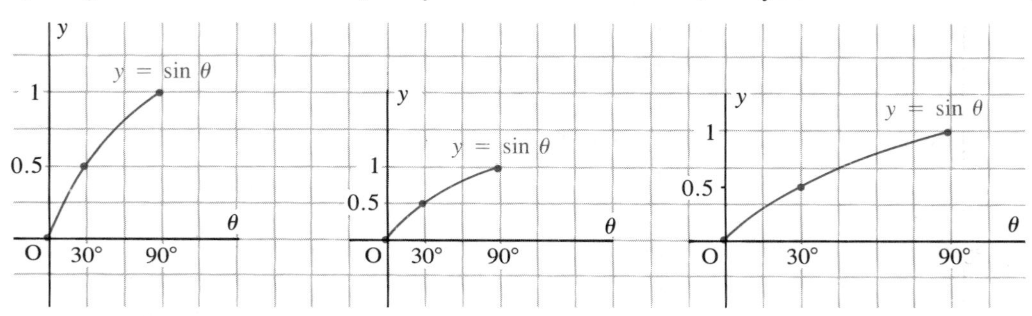

2. **Graphing the function $y = \cos \theta$**
   Let P be a point on the terminal arm of an angle θ in standard position on a circle with radius $r = 2$.
   a) Suppose θ starts at 0° and increases to 180°. Use diagrams like those on page 321 corresponding to $\theta = 0°, 60°, 90°, 120°$, and 180° to determine values of $\cos \theta$, and use the results to sketch the graph of $y = \cos \theta$ for $0° \leqslant \theta \leqslant 180°$
   b) Suppose θ continues from 180° to 360°. Determine values of $\cos \theta$ for $\theta = 240°, 270°, 300°$, and 360°, and use the results to continue the graph from 180° to 360°.
   c) Continue the graph of $y = \cos \theta$ for values of θ greater than 360° and less than 0°.

3. In the following diagrams, graphs of $y = \cos \theta$ have been started using different scales. Copy each graph on graph paper, and then extend it for the number of cycles indicated.
   a) 2 cycles b) 2 cycles c) 4 cycles

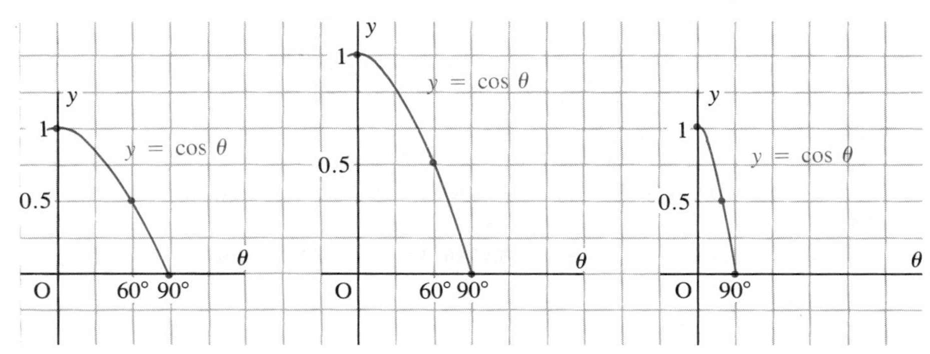

(B)

4. Without making a table of values, draw graphs of $y = \sin \theta$ and $y = \cos \theta$ for $-360° \leqslant \theta \leqslant 360°$.

5. For the graph of $y = \sin \theta$
   a) What is the maximum value of y? For what values of θ does this occur?
   b) What is the minimum value of y? For what values of θ does this occur?
   c) What is the range of the function?
   d) What is the y-intercept?
   e) What are the θ-intercepts?

6. Repeat *Exercise 5* for the graph of $y = \cos \theta$.

7. Compare the graphs of $y = \sin \theta$ and $y = \cos \theta$. In what ways are they alike? In what ways are they different?

(C)

8. A function $y = f(x)$ is defined to be *periodic* if there is a number p such that $f(x + p) = f(x)$ for all values of x in the domain. Use this definition to prove that the functions $y = \sin \theta$ and $y = \cos \theta$ are periodic.

9. **Graphing the function $y = \tan \theta$**
   Let P be a point on the terminal arm of an angle θ in standard position on a circle with radius $r = 2$.
   a) Suppose θ starts at 0° and increases to 90°. Use diagrams like those on page 321 corresponding to $\theta = 0°, 30°, 45°, 60°$, and 90° to determine values of $\tan \theta$, and use the results to sketch the graph of $y = \tan \theta$ for $0° \leqslant \theta < 90°$.
   b) Suppose θ continues from 90° to 180°. Determine values of $\tan \theta$ for $\theta = 120°$, 135°, 150°, and 180°, and use the results to continue the graph from 90° to 180°.
   c) Continue the graph of $y = \tan \theta$ for values of θ greater than 180° and less than 0°.
   d) Make a list of properties of the function $y = \tan \theta$ that are illustrated by the graph.

10. Compare the graph of $y = \tan \theta$ with the graphs of $y = \sin \theta$ and $y = \cos \theta$. In what ways are they alike? In what ways are they different?

11. a) A function $y = f(x)$ is defined to be an *even* function if $f(-x) = f(x)$ for all values of x in the domain. Use this definition to prove that $y = \cos \theta$ is an even function.
    b) A function $y = f(x)$ is defined to be an *odd* function if $f(-x) = -f(x)$ for all values of x in the domain. Use this definition to prove that $y = \sin \theta$ is an odd function.
    c) Is the tangent function an even function or an odd function? Explain.

12. Graph each function.
    a) $y = |\sin \theta|$ b) $y = \sin |\theta|$ c) $y = |\cos \theta|$ d) $y = \cos |\theta|$

INVESTIGATE

Graphing Sinusoids

There is a simple method of sketching the graph of a sinusoidal function without using graph paper. It involves locating nine points on the graph using a rectangle as a guide.

To graph the function $y = \sin\theta$

Step 1. Draw a rectangle divided into 8 congruent sections as shown. Mark the axes, showing their scales. Locate the points which correspond to multiples of 90°. Then identify the sections of the rectangle through which the curve will pass. Each section has points marked at the ends of one diagonal.

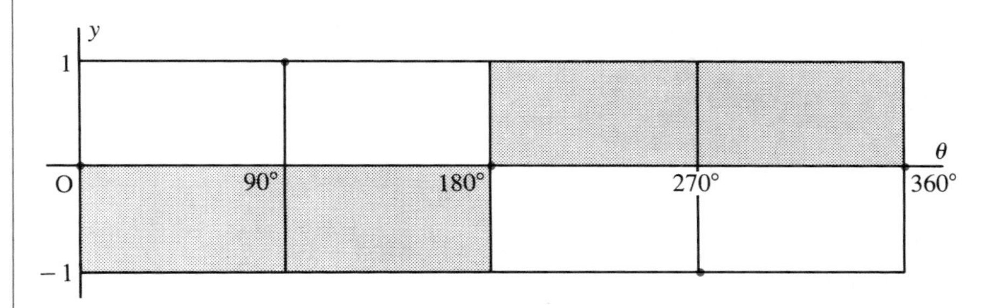

The curve will pass through the unshaded sections.

Step 2. Divide each section into 6 congruent rectangles, as shown. Locate the vertex in each section, which is closest to the point where the graph crosses the θ-axis. Draw a smooth curve through the marked points.

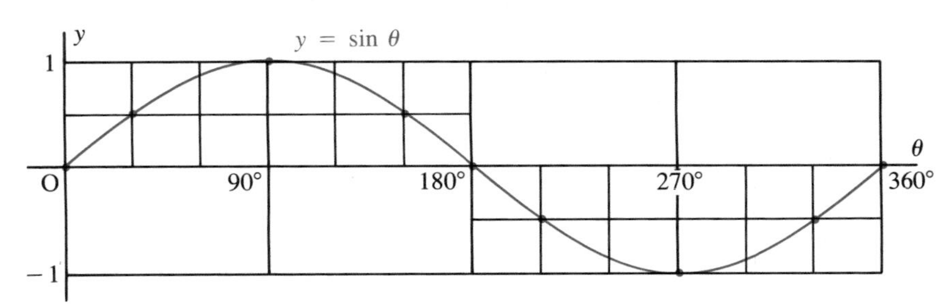

By extending the rectangles to the left or the right, we can sketch additional cycles of $y = \sin\theta$.

1. a) Use the above method to sketch the graph of $y = \sin\theta$ for $-360° \leqslant \theta \leqslant 360°$.

   b) Use the method to sketch the graph of $y = \cos\theta$ for $-360° \leqslant \theta \leqslant 360°$.

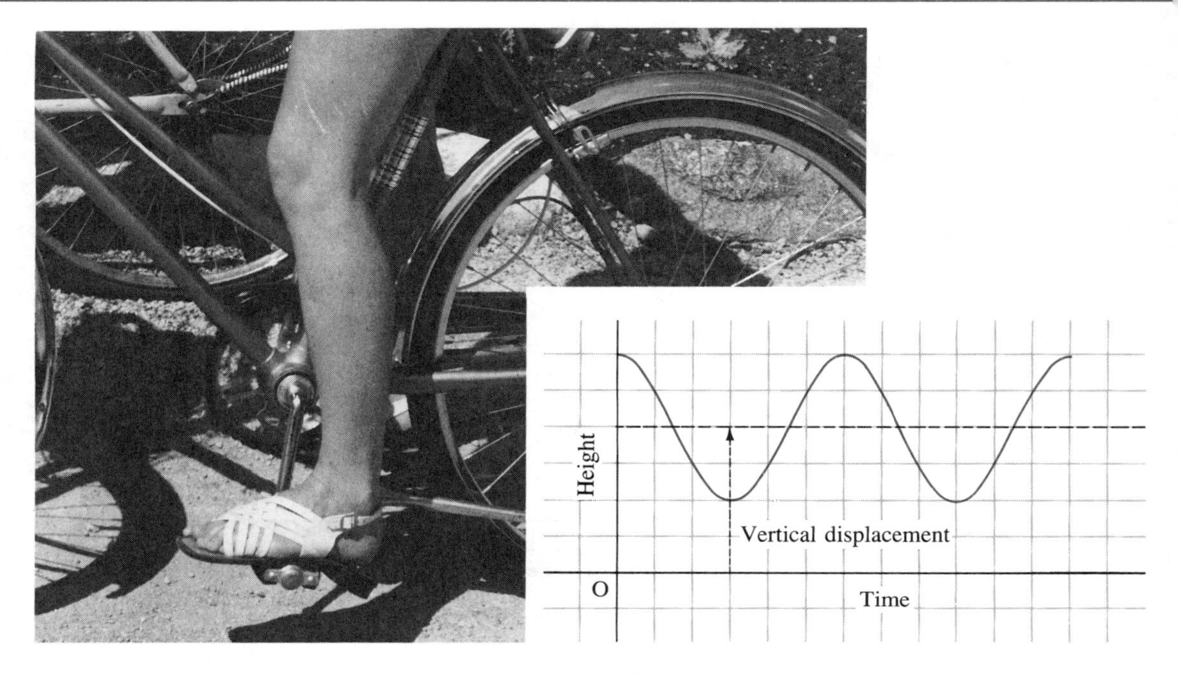

8-6 VARYING THE VERTICAL DISPLACEMENT OF SINE AND COSINE FUNCTIONS

As you pedal a bicycle, the heights of the pedals above the ground change periodically. A graph of the height of a pedal against time is a sinusoidal curve with a vertical displacement corresponding to the mean height of the pedal above the ground.

In this and the following sections, we shall develop a technique for graphing sinusoidal functions without making a table of values. The first step is to investigate the effect of q on the graph of the function $y = \cos \theta + q$. We substitute different values for q, and graph the resulting functions.

If $q = 0$, the equation is $y = \cos \theta$ ...... ①

If $q = 1$, the equation is $y = \cos \theta + 1$ ...... ②

If we were to graph this function using a table of values, we would start with values of θ, find the cosines, and then add 1. The values of y will all be 1 greater than those in ①. Hence, the y-coordinates of all points on the graph of ② are 1 *greater* than those on the graph of ①. Therefore, the graph of ② is 1 unit *above* the graph of ①. We say that the *vertical displacement* of the function $y = \cos \theta + 1$ is 1.

If $q = -0.5$, the equation is $y = \cos \theta - 0.5$ ...... ③

The values of y will all be 0.5 less than those in ①. Therefore, the graph of ③ is 0.5 units *below* the graph of ①. The vertical displacement is -0.5.

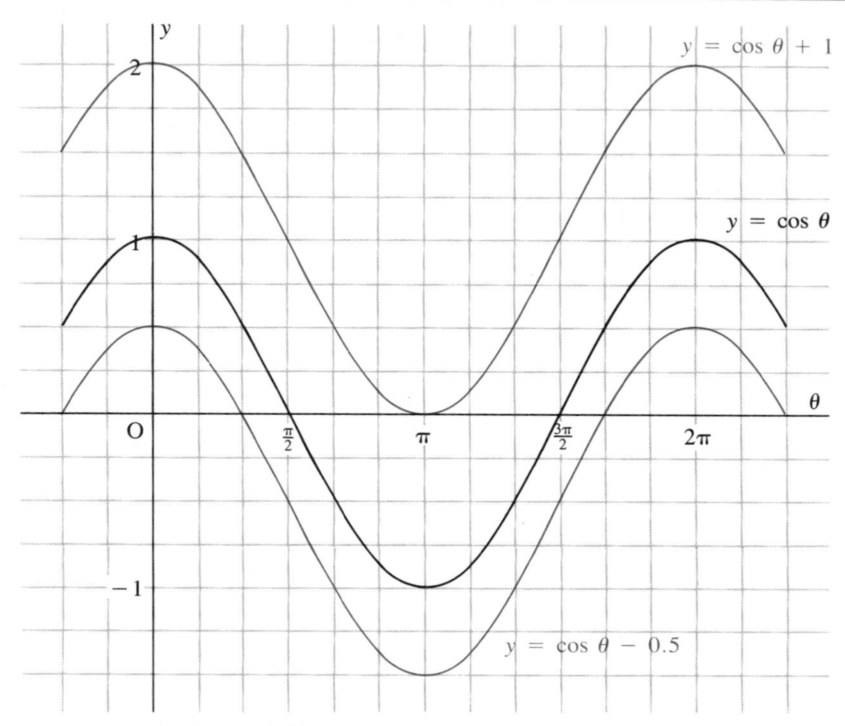

Similar results will be found for other values of q, and for sine functions.

In general, adding a constant to $\sin \theta$ or $\cos \theta$ in the equations of the functions $y = \sin \theta$ or $y = \cos \theta$ causes a vertical translation of the graph. The sign of the constant indicates whether the graph is translated up or down. A positive constant causes a translation up; a negative constant causes a translation down.

The graph of $y = \cos \theta + q$ is related to that of $y = \cos \theta$ by a vertical translation. The vertical displacement is q.

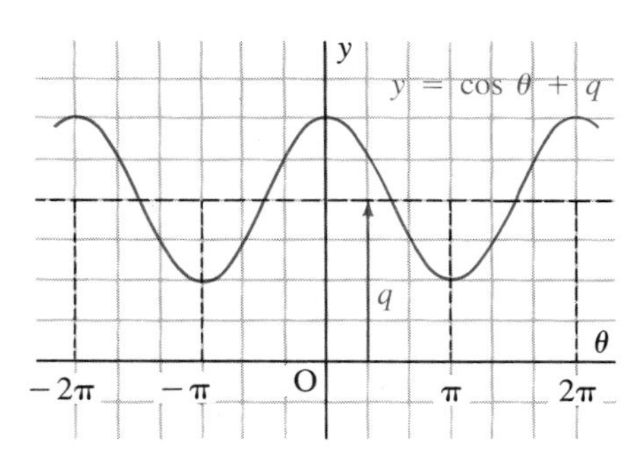

The graph of $y = \sin \theta + q$ is related to that of $y = \sin \theta$ by a vertical translation. The vertical displacement is q.

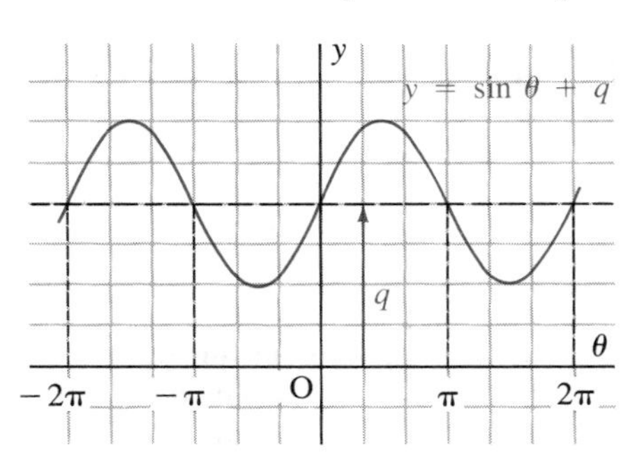

We can draw the graph of an equation in this form without making a table of values.

Example 1. State the vertical displacement for the function $y = \sin\theta + 2$, and draw its graph.

Solution. The vertical displacement is 2.
Draw a graph of $y = \sin\theta$, and then draw its image when translated 2 units up.

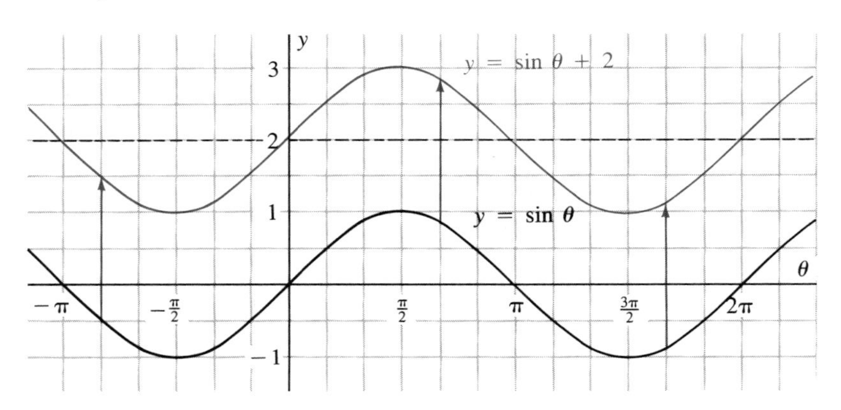

Example 2. Find an equation of a function of the form $y = \cos\theta + q$ whose graph passes through the point $A\left(\frac{\pi}{3}, -\frac{1}{2}\right)$.

Solution. Let the equation of the function be $y = \cos\theta + q$.
Since A lies on the graph, its coordinates satisfy the equation.
Substitute $\frac{\pi}{3}$ for θ, and $-\frac{1}{2}$ for y.

$$y = \cos\theta + q$$
$$-\frac{1}{2} = \cos\frac{\pi}{3} + q$$
$$-\frac{1}{2} = \frac{1}{2} + q$$
$$q = -1$$

An equation of the function is $y = \cos\theta - 1$.

EXERCISES 8-6

Ⓐ

1. a) Graph these functions on the same grid for $-\pi \leqslant \theta \leqslant \pi$.
   $y = \sin\theta$ $\quad y = \sin\theta + 1.5$ $\quad y = \sin\theta + 0.5$
   $y = \sin\theta - 1$ $\quad y = \sin\theta - 3$ $\quad y = \sin\theta + 4$
   b) Describe the effect on the graph of $y = \sin\theta + q$ as the value of q varies.

2. a) Graph these functions on the same grid for $-\pi \leqslant \theta \leqslant \pi$.
$y = \cos\theta$ $\quad$ $y = \cos\theta + 1$ $\quad$ $y = \cos\theta + 3$
$y = \cos\theta - 2$ $\quad$ $y = \cos\theta - 0.5$ $\quad$ $y = \cos\theta - 4$
b) Describe the effect on the graph of $y = \cos\theta + q$ as the value of q varies.

3. Write an equation to represent each function shown below. For each function, state the vertical displacement, the maximum value of y, the minimum value of y, and the y-intercept.
a)

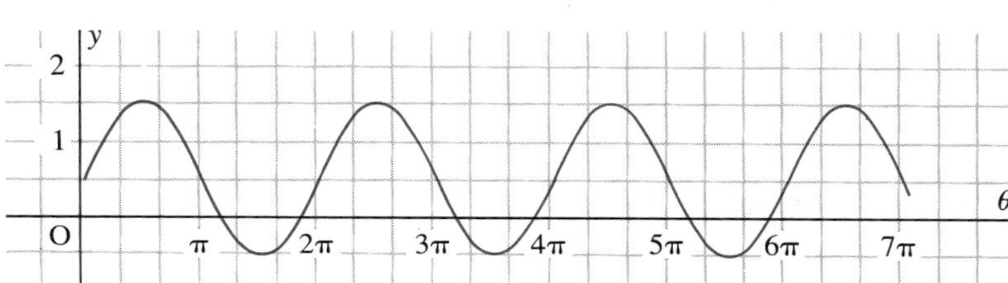

b)

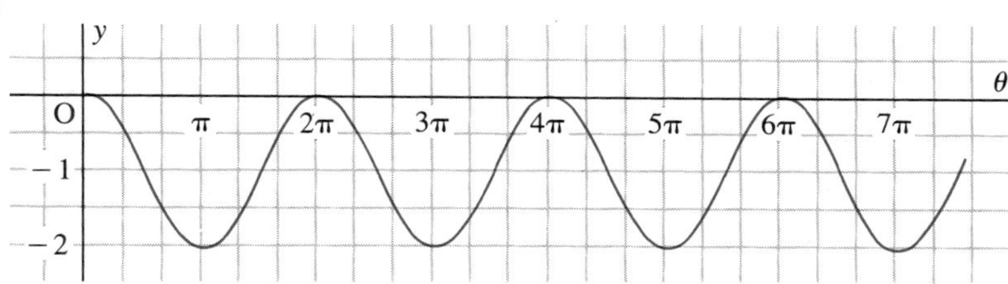

Ⓑ

4. a) For each function, determine the maximum value of y, the minimum value of y, and the y-intercept.
i) $y = \sin\theta + 5$ $\quad$ ii) $y = \cos\theta + 5$ $\quad$ iii) $y = \cos\theta - 2$
b) Determine the domain and the range of each function in part a).

5. Find an equation of a function of the form $y = \sin\theta + q$ whose graph passes through each point.
a) A(0,1) $\quad$ b) $B\left(\frac{\pi}{2},0\right)$ $\quad$ c) $C\left(\frac{\pi}{6},2\right)$ $\quad$ d) $D\left(\frac{\pi}{4},-\frac{1}{\sqrt{2}}\right)$

6. Find an equation of a function of the form $y = \cos\theta + q$ whose graph passes through each point.
a) O(0,0) $\quad$ b) $P(\pi,1)$ $\quad$ c) $Q\left(\frac{\pi}{3},-2\right)$ $\quad$ d) $R\left(\frac{4\pi}{3},2\right)$

7. Given the function $y = \sin\theta + q$
a) What is the maximum value of y? For what values of θ does this occur?
b) What is the minimum value of y? For what values of θ does this occur?

8. Repeat *Exercise 7* for the function $y = \cos\theta + q$.

Ⓒ

9. Find the equation of a function of the form $y = \sin\theta + p$ whose graph just touches the θ-axis. How many such functions are there?

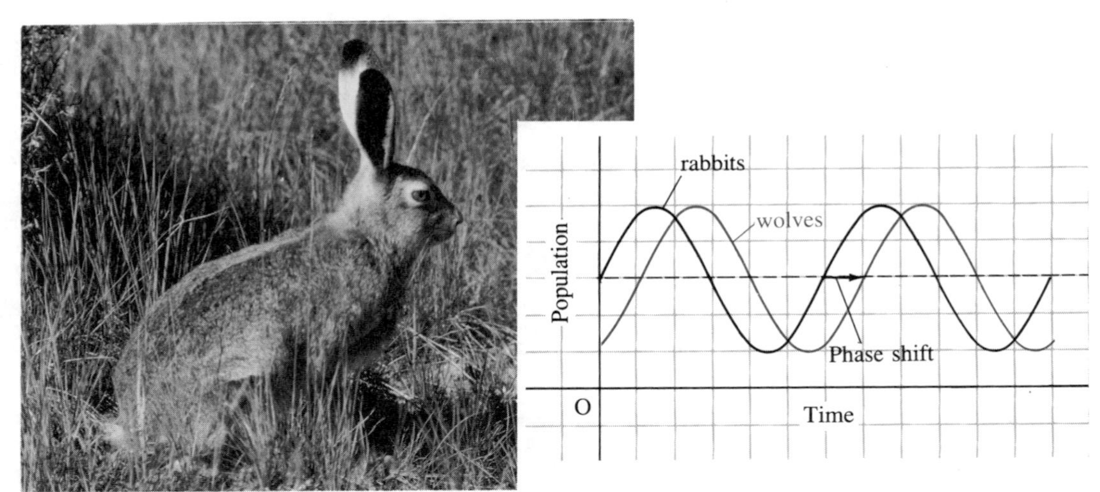

8-7 VARYING THE PHASE SHIFT OF SINE AND COSINE FUNCTIONS

In a certain region the number of rabbits increases and decreases periodically. This variation is caused by wolves which feed on the rabbits. If the number of wolves is small, the rabbits will flourish. But then the number of wolves will increase, since food is easy to find. This, in turn, causes a decrease in the number of rabbits, which causes the number of wolves to decrease, and the cycle begins all over again. The population graph for the wolves is shifted horizontally relative to the population graph for the rabbits.

In $y = \sin \theta$, if θ is replaced with $\theta - p$, we obtain $y = \sin (\theta - p)$. To investigate the effect of this on the graph of the function $y = \sin \theta$, we substitute different values for p, and graph the resulting functions.

If $p = 0$, the equation is $y = \sin \theta$ ...... ①

If $p = \frac{\pi}{2}$, the equation is $y = \sin \left(\theta - \frac{\pi}{2}\right)$ ...... ②

If we were to graph this function using a table of values, we would start with values of θ, subtract $\frac{\pi}{2}$, and then find the sines of the results. To give the same y-coordinates as in ①, the values of θ must be $\frac{\pi}{2}$ units greater than in ①. That is, the θ-coordinates of all points on the graph of ② are $\frac{\pi}{2}$ *greater* than those on the graph of ①. Therefore, the graph of ② is shifted $\frac{\pi}{2}$ units to the *right* relative to the graph of ①.

We say that the phase shift of the function $y = \sin \left(\theta - \frac{\pi}{2}\right)$ is $+\frac{\pi}{2}$.

If $p = -\frac{\pi}{3}$, the equation is $y = \sin\left(\theta + \frac{\pi}{3}\right)$ ...... ③

To give the same y-coordinates as in ①, the values of θ must be $\frac{\pi}{3}$ *less* than those in ①. Therefore, the graph of ③ is shifted $\frac{\pi}{3}$ units to the *left* relative to the graph of ①. The phase shift is $-\frac{\pi}{3}$.

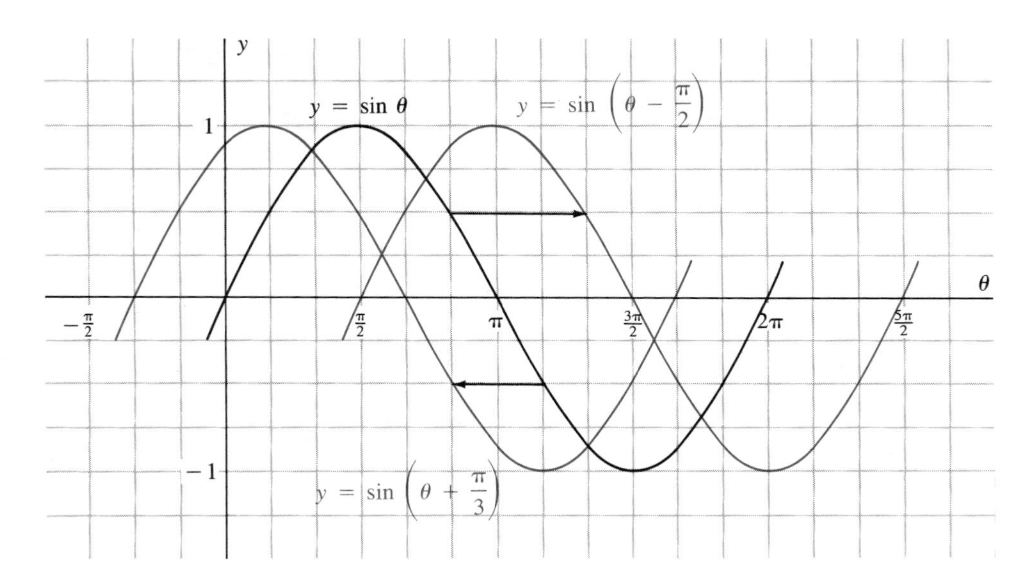

The graph of $y = \sin\left(\theta + \frac{\pi}{3}\right)$ is the image of the graph of $y = \sin\theta$, which has been translated $\frac{\pi}{3}$ to the *left*.

The graph of $y = \sin\left(\theta - \frac{\pi}{2}\right)$ is the image of the graph of $y = \sin\theta$, which has been translated $\frac{\pi}{2}$ to the *right*.

The *phase shift* of a periodic function is the amount by which the graph of the function is translated horizontally with respect to the basic function. A negative phase shift corresponds to a translation to the left. A positive phase shift corresponds to a translation to the right.

Similar results will be found for other values of θ, and for cosine functions. In general, adding a constant to the variable θ in the equations of the functions $y = \sin\theta$ or $y = \cos\theta$ causes a horizontal translation of the graph. A positive constant causes a translation to the left; a negative constant causes a translation to the right.

The graph of $y = \sin(\theta - p)$ is the image of the graph of $y = \sin\theta$ under a horizontal translation of p units.

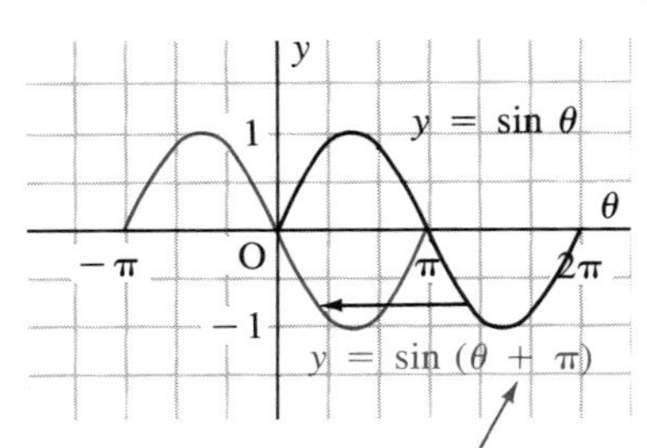

Positive sign, graph moved π units to the *left*

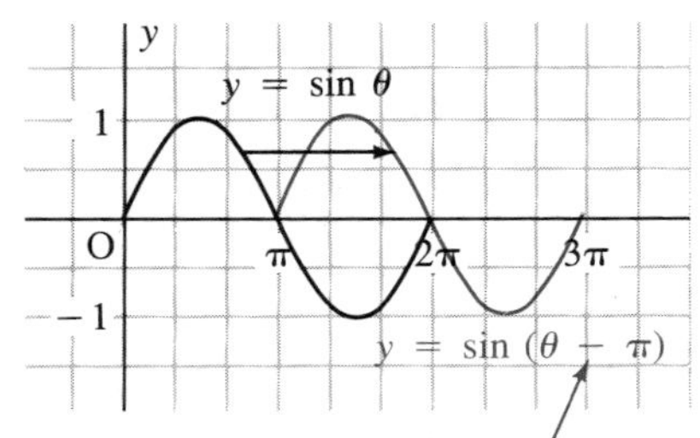

Negative sign, graph moved π units to the *right*

The graph of $y = \cos(\theta - p)$ is the image of the graph of $y = \cos\theta$ under a horizontal translation of p units.

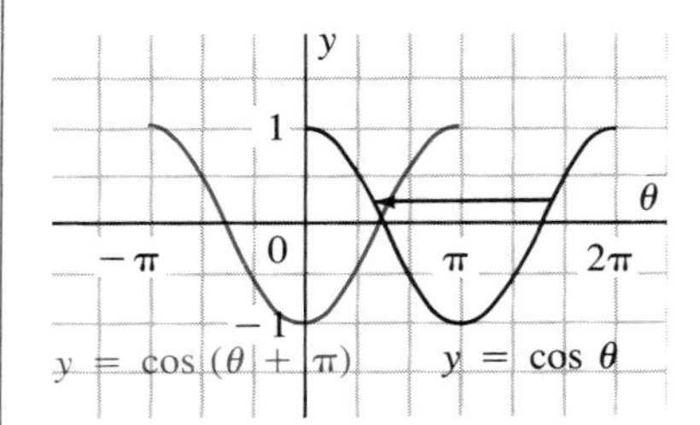

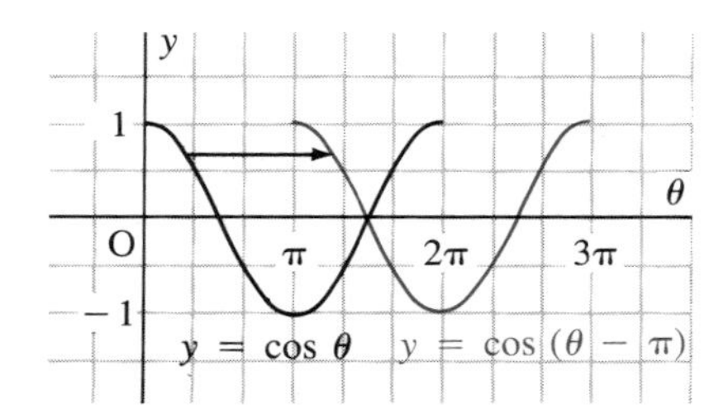

We can draw the graph of an equation in this form without making a table of values.

Example 1. Draw a graph of the function $y = \cos\left(\theta + \frac{2\pi}{3}\right)$ over two cycles, and state its phase shift.

Solution. Draw a graph of $y = \cos\theta$, then translate it $\frac{2\pi}{3}$ units to the left. The phase shift is $-\frac{2\pi}{3}$.

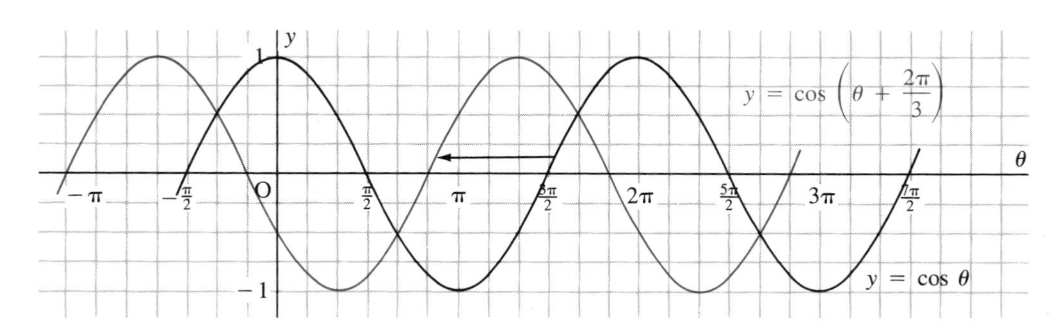

> In general, the phase shift of $y = \sin(\theta - p)$ or $y = \cos(\theta - p)$ is the value of θ for which $\theta - p = 0$; that is, p.

Since sinusoidal functions are periodic, a graph of a sinusoidal function has more than one equation. In fact, it has infinitely many equations.

Example 2. A sinusoidal function is graphed below. Find four possible equations for the function.

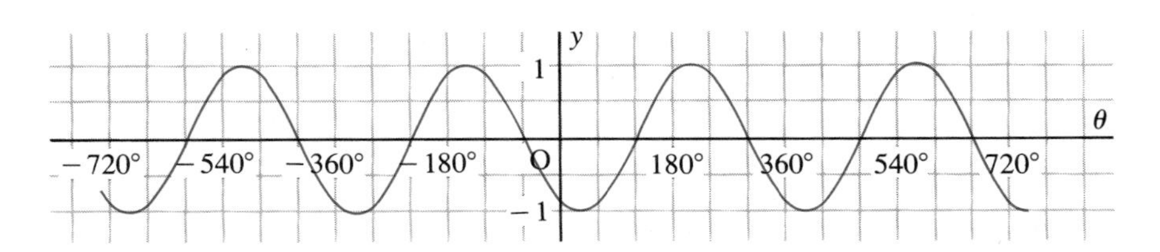

Solution. We can consider the function to be a sine function. Copy the graph and draw the graph of $y = \sin\theta$ on the same grid.

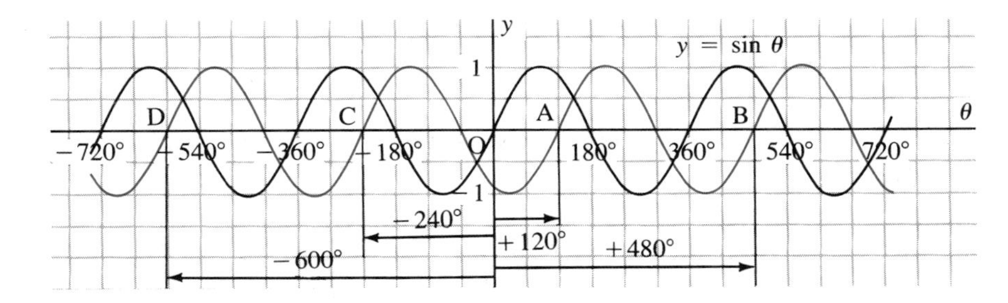

The given graph is the image of the graph of $y = \sin\theta$ under a translation from the origin to any of the points marked A, B, C, and D on the graph. Hence, four possible values for the phase shift are the θ-coordinates of these points. We can write an equation of the function for each phase shift.

Using A and its θ-coordinate 120° as the phase shift, the equation of the function can be written as $y = \sin(\theta - 120°)$.

Since the graph of $y = \sin\theta$ cuts the θ-axis at (0,0), and the corresponding point A on $y = \sin(\theta - 120°)$ has coordinates (120°,0), the phase shift can be considered as the θ-coordinate of this point. That is, the θ-coordinate of a point that is halfway between a maximum and a minimum, and precedes a maximum can be considered as the phase shift.

Similarly, using B, C, and D, other possible equations are $y = \sin(\theta - 480°)$, $y = \sin(\theta + 240°)$, and $y = \sin(\theta + 600°)$, respectively.

In *Example 2*, by considering the function to be a cosine function, we can obtain other possible equations.

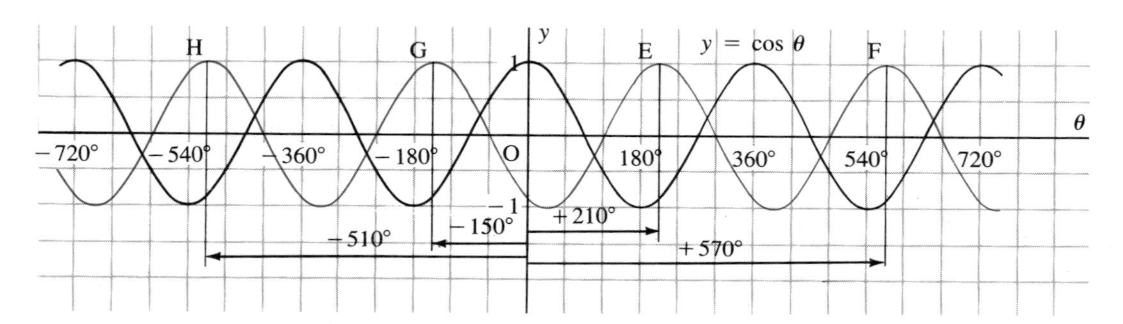

Using E and its θ-coordinate 210° as the phase shift, the equation of the graph can be written as $y = \cos(\theta - 210°)$.

Since a maximum of $y = \cos\theta$ has coordinates (0°,1) and the corresponding maximum of $y = \cos(\theta - 210°)$ has coordinates (210°,1), the phase shift can be considered as the θ-coordinate of a maximum point.

Similarly, using F, G, and H, other possible equations are $y = \cos(\theta - 570°)$, $y = \cos(\theta + 150°)$, and $y = \cos(\theta + 510°)$, respectively.

Frequently, a vertical displacement and a phase shift are combined in one function.

Example 3. Draw a graph of the function $y = \sin\left(\theta - \frac{3\pi}{4}\right) + 2$ over two cycles.

a) State the vertical displacement and the phase shift.
b) State the domain and the range.

Solution. Draw a graph of $y = \sin\theta$, then translate it $\frac{3\pi}{4}$ units to the right. Then translate the image 2 units up.

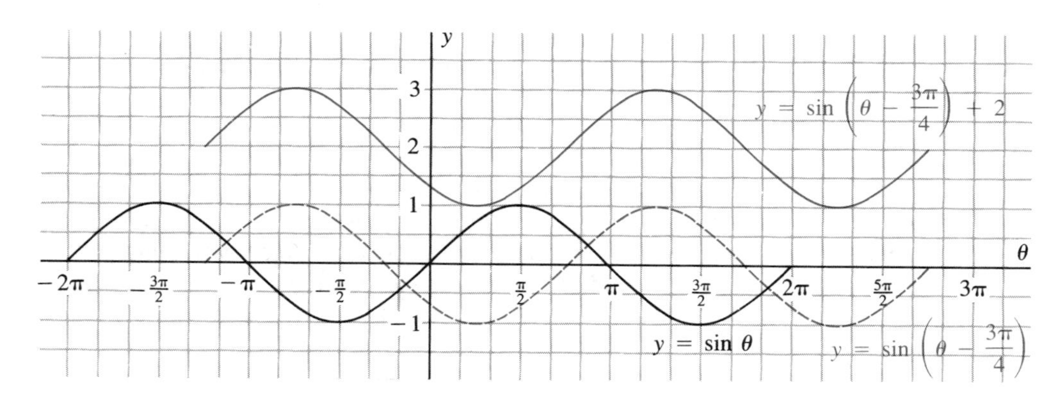

a) The vertical displacement is 2, and the phase shift is $\frac{3\pi}{4}$.

b) The domain is R.
The range is $\{y \mid 1 \leqslant y \leqslant 3,\ y \in R\}$.

EXERCISES 8-7

Ⓐ

1. a) Graph these functions on the same grid for $-\pi \leqslant \theta \leqslant \pi$.

$y = \sin \theta \qquad y = \sin\left(\theta - \frac{\pi}{6}\right) \qquad y = \sin\left(\theta - \frac{\pi}{3}\right) \qquad y = \sin\left(\theta + \frac{\pi}{4}\right)$

b) Describe the effect on the graph of $y = \sin(\theta - p)$ as the value of p varies.

2. a) Graph these functions on the same grid for $-\pi \leqslant \theta \leqslant \pi$.

$y = \cos \theta \qquad y = \cos\left(\theta + \frac{\pi}{3}\right) \qquad y = \cos\left(\theta - \frac{\pi}{3}\right) \qquad y = \cos\left(\theta - \frac{\pi}{4}\right)$

b) Describe the effect on the graph of $y = \cos(\theta - p)$ as the value of p varies.

3. Each function graphed below can be considered as a sine function. Find two possible values for the phase shift. What is the equation of the function for each phase shift?

a)

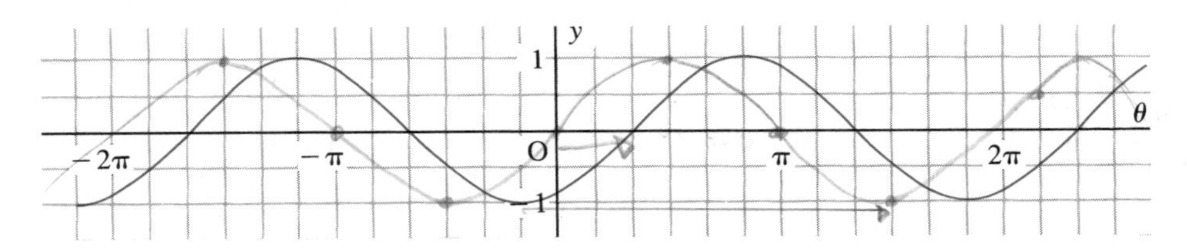

b)

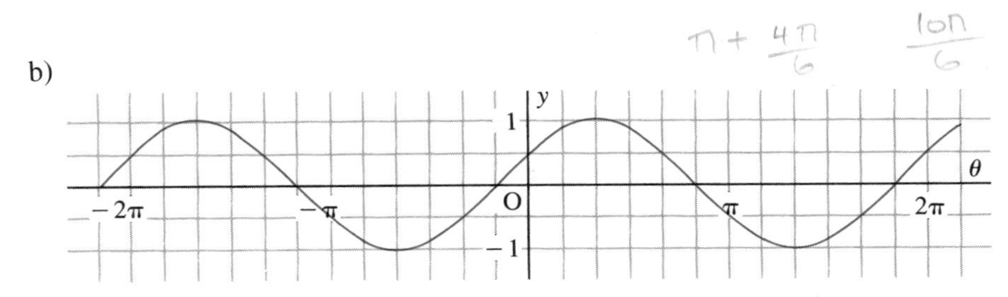

4. Each function in *Exercise 3* can also be considered as a cosine function. Find two possible values for the phase shift. What is the equation of the function for each phase shift?

Ⓑ

5. Graph each sinusoidal function over two cycles.

a) $y = \sin\left(\theta - \frac{\pi}{4}\right)$ b) $y = \sin\left(\theta - \frac{4\pi}{3}\right)$ c) $y = \sin\left(\theta + \frac{5\pi}{6}\right)$

d) $y = \cos\left(\theta - \frac{\pi}{6}\right)$ e) $y = \cos\left(\theta + \frac{5\pi}{3}\right)$ f) $y = \cos\left(\theta - \frac{7\pi}{6}\right)$

6. Graph each sinusoidal function, and determine its domain and range.
   a) $y = \sin\left(\theta - \frac{\pi}{4}\right) + 3$
   b) $y = \cos\left(\theta + \frac{\pi}{3}\right) + 1$
   c) $y = \cos\left(\theta - \frac{4\pi}{3}\right) - 1$
   d) $y = \sin\left(\theta - \frac{3\pi}{2}\right) + 2$

7. a) Graph the function $y = \sin\left(\theta + \frac{\pi}{2}\right)$. What conclusion can you make?
   b) Graph the function $y = \cos\left(\theta - \frac{\pi}{2}\right)$. What conclusion can you make?

8. Find an equation of the form $y = \sin(\theta - p)$ whose graph passes through:
   a) $A\left(\frac{\pi}{6}, 0\right)$
   b) $B\left(\pi, \frac{1}{2}\right)$
   c) $C\left(\frac{\pi}{4}, -\frac{1}{\sqrt{2}}\right)$
   d) $D\left(-\frac{\pi}{3}, \frac{1}{\sqrt{2}}\right)$.

9. Find an equation of the form $y = \cos(\theta - p)$ whose graph passes through:
   a) $E\left(-\frac{\pi}{4}, 0\right)$
   b) $F\left(\frac{\pi}{2}, \frac{1}{2}\right)$.
   c) $G\left(2\pi, \frac{\sqrt{3}}{2}\right)$
   d) $H\left(-\pi, -\frac{1}{\sqrt{2}}\right)$.

10. If $A(k, 1)$ is a point on the graph of $y = \sin\left(\theta - \frac{\pi}{4}\right)$, find a possible value of k.

11. If $A\left(k, -\frac{\sqrt{3}}{2}\right)$ is on the graph of $y = \cos\left(\theta + \frac{\pi}{6}\right)$, find a possible value of k.

Ⓒ

12. Given the function $y = \sin(\theta - p) + q$
    a) What is the maximum value of y? For what values of θ does this occur?
    b) What is the minimum value of y? For what values of θ does this occur?

13. Repeat *Exercise 12* for the function $y = \cos(\theta - p) + q$.

14. Find an equation of a function of the form $y = \sin(\theta - p) + q$ which has a maximum value of 3 when $\theta = 0$.

15. Find an equation of a function of the form $y = \cos(\theta - p) + q$ which has a minimum value of -5 when $\theta = 0$.

INVESTIGATE

1. When a sine curve is translated horizontally, it will coincide with itself for certain phase shifts. Investigate this, and find values of p for which the graph of $y = \sin(\theta - p)$ coincides with the graph of $y = \sin\theta$.

2. Also, when a sine curve is translated horizontally, it will coincide with a cosine curve for certain phase shifts. Find values of p for which the graph of $y = \sin(\theta - p)$ coincides with the graph of $y = \cos\theta$.

3. Find values of p for which the graph of $y = \cos(\theta - p)$ coincides with the graph of $y = \sin\theta$.

4. Write a report of your findings.

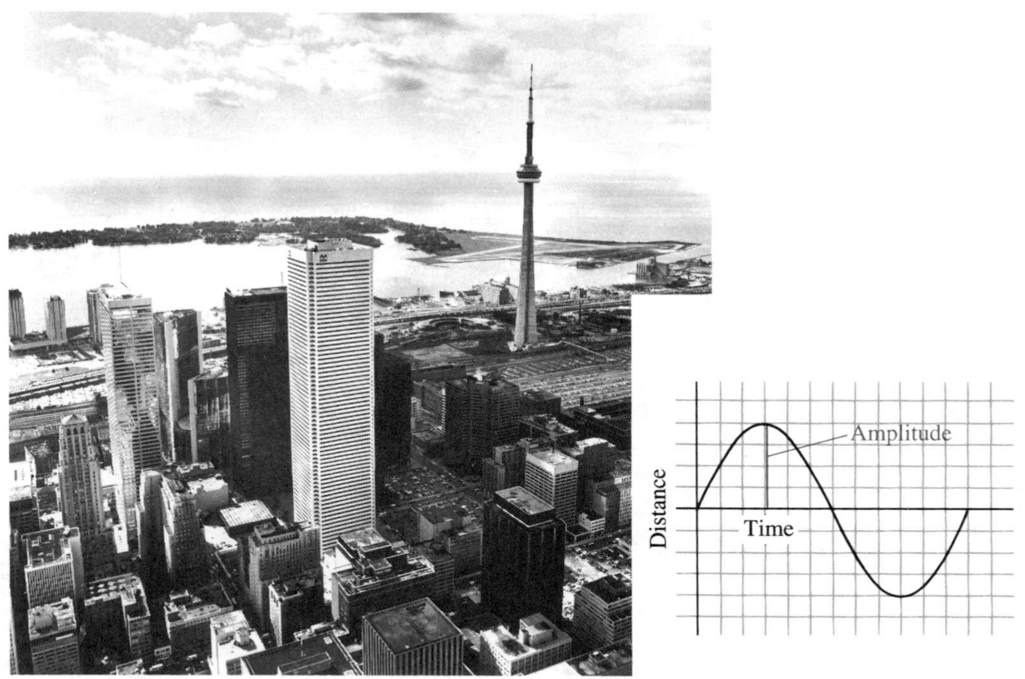

8-8 VARYING THE AMPLITUDE OF SINE AND COSINE FUNCTIONS

The graph above shows how the top of a building sways in a high wind. The distance the building sways from the centre is called the amplitude of the vibration.

In this section we investigate the effect on the graph of $y = \sin \theta$ of multiplying $\sin \theta$ by a constant a to get $y = a \sin \theta$. We substitute different values for a, and graph the resulting functions. We will assume that a is positive, since there is no need to consider negative values of a in applications.

If $a = 1$, the equation is $y = \sin \theta$ ...... ①

If $a = 2$, the equation is $y = 2 \sin \theta$ ...... ②

If we were to graph this function using a table of values, we would start with values of θ, find the sines, and then multiply by 2. The values of y will all be two times those in ①. That is, the y-coordinates of all points on the graph of ② are *two times* those on the graph of ①. Therefore, the graph of ② is *expanded* vertically relative to the graph of ①. The factor 2 is called the amplitude of the function.

If $a = \frac{1}{2}$, the equation is $y = \frac{1}{2} \sin \theta$ ...... ③

The values of y will all be one-half of those in ①. Therefore, the graph of ③ is *compressed* vertically relative to the graph of ①.

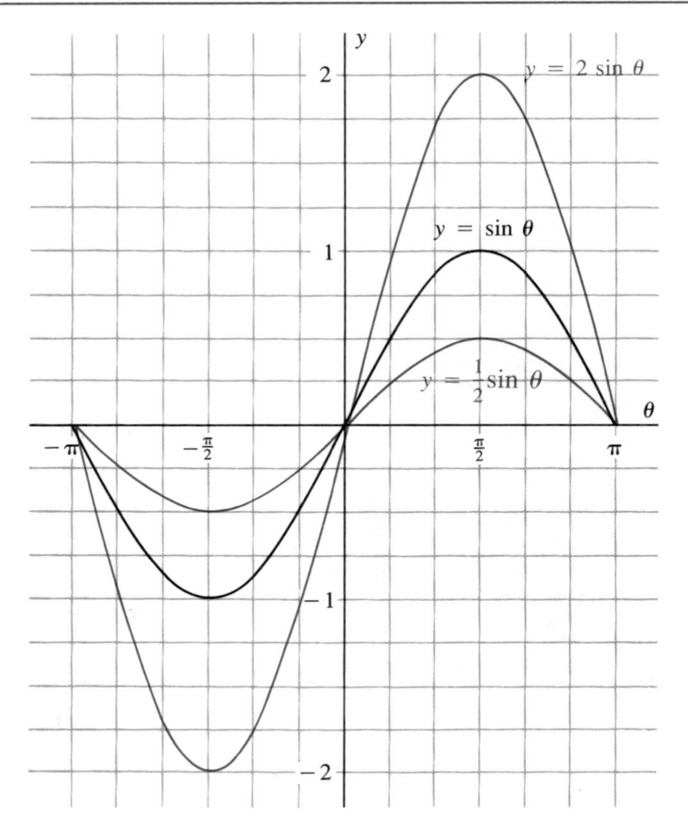

Similar results will be found for other positive values of a, and for cosine functions.

In general, multiplying $\sin \theta$ or $\cos \theta$ by a positive constant a causes a vertical expansion or compression of the graphs of $y = \sin \theta$ or $y = \cos \theta$. That is, for $0 < a < 1$, there is a compression; for $a > 1$, there is an expansion.

$y = a \sin \theta$ $(a > 0)$ represents a sine function with amplitude a.

$y = a \cos \theta$ $(a > 0)$ represents a cosine function with amplitude a.

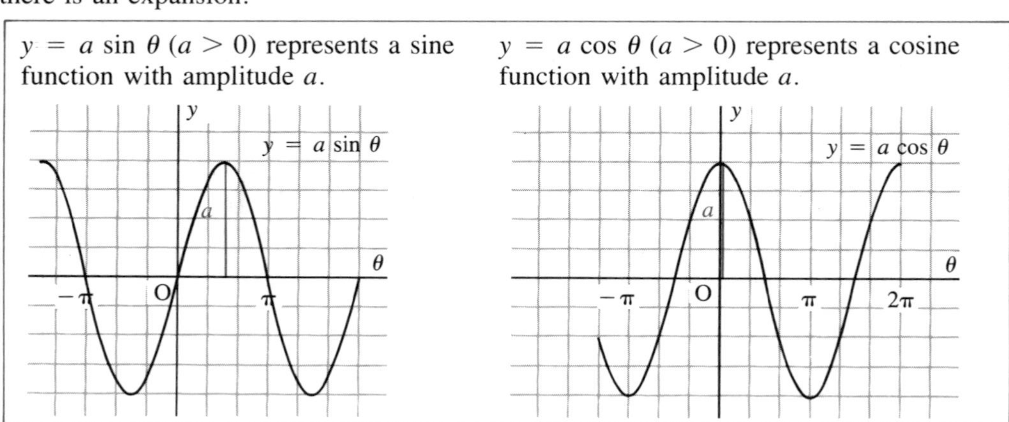

Since we know that $y = a \sin \theta$ and $y = a \cos \theta$ represent sinusoidal functions with the above properties, we can draw the graph of an equation in this form without making a table of values.

Example 1. Draw a graph of the function $y = 0.75 \cos \theta$, and state its amplitude.

Solution. Draw a graph of $y = \cos \theta$, then compress it vertically by a factor of 0.75. This means that the y-coordinate of each point on the image is 0.75 times the y-coordinate of the corresponding point on the graph of $y = \cos \theta$.

The amplitude of $y = 0.75 \cos \theta$ is 0.75.

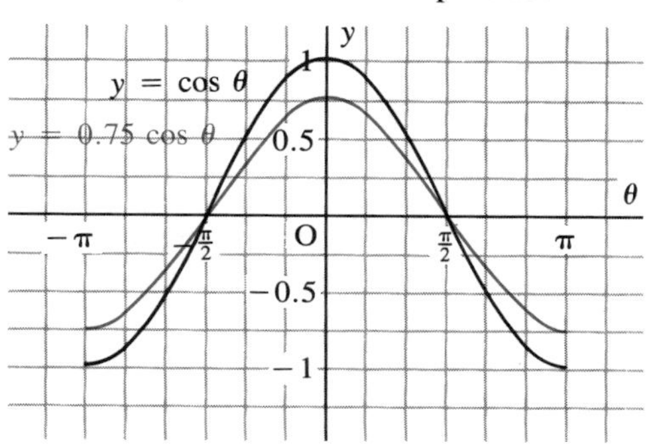

Vertical displacement, phase shift, and amplitude are often combined in the same function.

Example 2. Draw a graph of the function $y = 3 \sin \left(\theta - \frac{2\pi}{3}\right) + 2$ over two cycles. State the vertical displacement, the phase shift, and the amplitude.

Solution. Draw a graph of $y = \sin \theta$, and expand it vertically by a factor of 3. Then translate the image $\frac{2\pi}{3}$ units to the right and 2 units up.

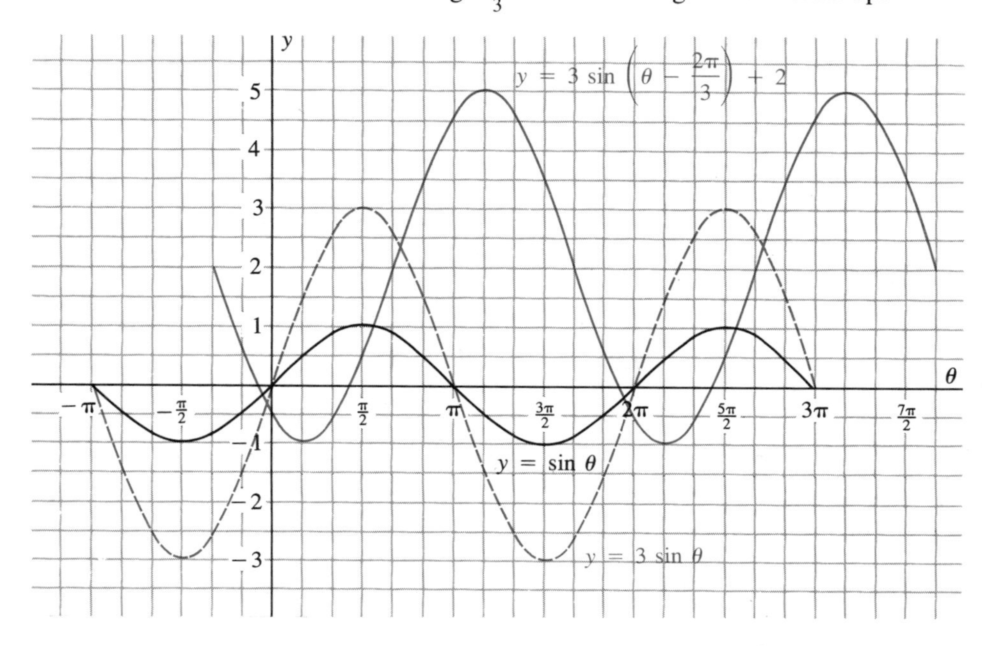

The vertical displacement is 2, the phase shift is $\frac{2\pi}{3}$, and the amplitude is 3.

We can use the graph in *Example 2* to derive a definition for the amplitude of a periodic function. In this graph, the maximum value of the function is 5, and the minimum value is -1. The amplitude is one-half the way from the minimum to the maximum, measured in the vertical direction. For this function, the amplitude is $\frac{1}{2}(5 - (-1))$, or 3.

If M represents the maximum value of a periodic function in any cycle, and m represents the minimum value in that cycle, then the *amplitude A* of the function is

$$A = \frac{M - m}{2}$$

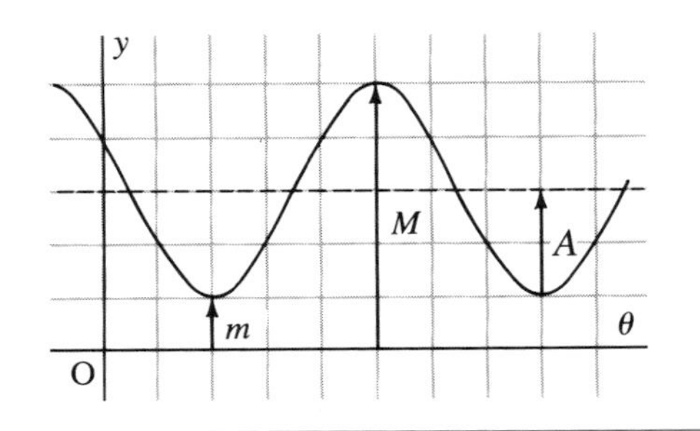

EXERCISES 8-8

Ⓐ

1. a) Graph these functions on the same grid for $-\pi \leqslant \theta \leqslant \pi$.

   $y = 2 \cos \theta \qquad y = \cos \theta \qquad y = \frac{1}{2} \cos \theta$

   b) Graph these functions on the same grid for $-\pi \leqslant \theta \leqslant \pi$.

   $y = 3 \sin \theta \qquad y = \sin \theta \qquad y = \frac{1}{4} \sin \theta$

   c) Describe the effect on the graphs of $y = a \cos \theta$ and $y = a \sin \theta$ as the value of a varies.

2. Each function graphed below is sinusoidal. Write an equation for each function. State the maximum and minimum values of y, and the amplitude.

a)

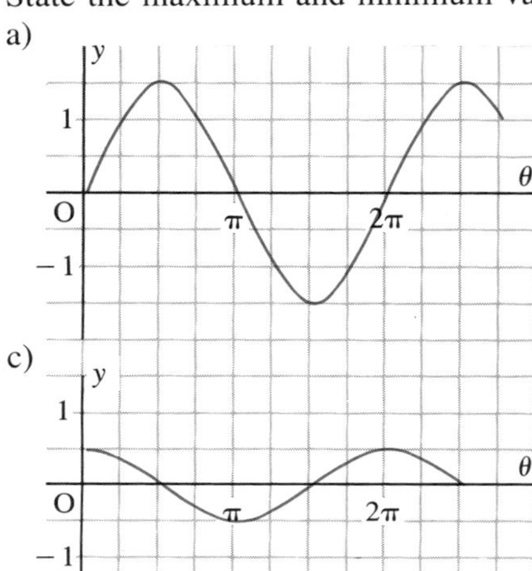

b)

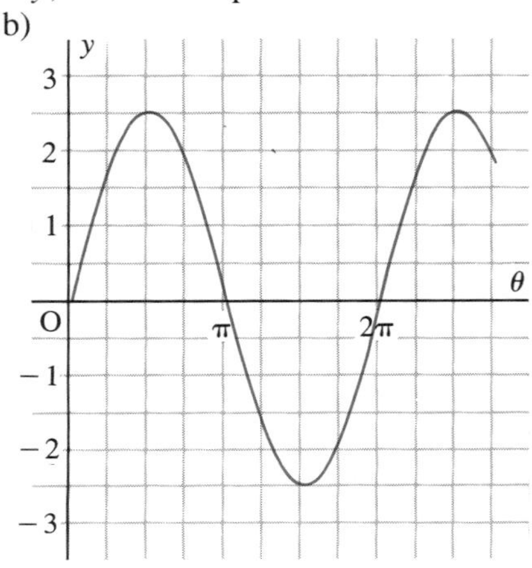

(B)

3. Graph each sinusoidal function.
   a) $y = 10 \sin \theta$ b) $y = 25 \cos \theta$ c) $y = 0.1 \cos \theta$

4. Find an equation of a function of the form $y = a \sin \theta$ whose graph passes through:
   a) $A\left(\frac{\pi}{6},1\right)$ b) $B\left(\frac{\pi}{2},3\right)$ c) $C\left(\frac{\pi}{3},\sqrt{3}\right)$ d) $D\left(\frac{\pi}{4},\sqrt{2}\right)$.

5. Find an equation of a function of the form $y = a \cos \theta$ whose graph passes through:
   a) $E(0,3)$ b) $F\left(\frac{\pi}{4},1\right)$ c) $G(\pi,-2)$ d) $H\left(\frac{\pi}{6},\sqrt{3}\right)$.

6. a) Graph each sinusoidal function.
   i) $y = 2 \sin\left(\theta - \frac{\pi}{3}\right)$ ii) $y = 3 \cos\left(\theta + \frac{\pi}{4}\right)$
   iii) $y = 2 \cos\left(\theta - \frac{\pi}{6}\right) + 2$ iv) $y = 4 \sin\left(\theta + \frac{2\pi}{3}\right) - 2$
   b) Determine the amplitude and the phase shift for each function in part a).
   c) Determine the domain and the range for each function in part a).

7. Find an equation of a function of the form $y = 4 \sin(\theta - p)$ if its graph passes through the point $R\left(\frac{\pi}{4},4\right)$.

8. Find an equation of a function of the form $y = 4 \cos(\theta - p)$ if its graph passes through the point $S\left(\frac{\pi}{6},2\right)$.

9. A sinusoidal function has an amplitude of 4. Its graph passes through the point $T\left(\frac{\pi}{3},2\right)$. Find two possible equations of the function, one involving a sine function, and the other involving a cosine function.

10. **Negative values of a in $y = a \sin \theta$ and $y = a \cos \theta$**
    a) Draw graphs of these functions.
    i) $y = -\sin \theta$ ii) $y = -2 \sin \theta$ iii) $y = -\frac{1}{2} \sin \theta$
    b) How are the graphs of the functions in part a) related to the graph of the function $y = \sin \theta$?
    c) Draw diagrams to illustrate how the graphs of $y = a \sin \theta$ and $y = a \cos \theta$ are related to the graphs of $y = \sin \theta$ and $y = \cos \theta$ if $a < 0$.
    d) Do negative values of a affect the amplitude? In what way?

11. Graph each function over two cycles, and state the amplitude.
    a) $y = -4 \sin \theta$ b) $y = -0.2 \sin \theta$ c) $y = -9 \cos \theta$

(C)

12. a) Given the function $y = a \sin(\theta - p) + q$, where $a > 0$
    i) What is the maximum value of y? For what values of θ does this occur?
    ii) What is the minimum value of y? For what values of θ does this occur?
    b) Repeat part a) for the function $y = a \cos(\theta - p) + q$, where $a > 0$.

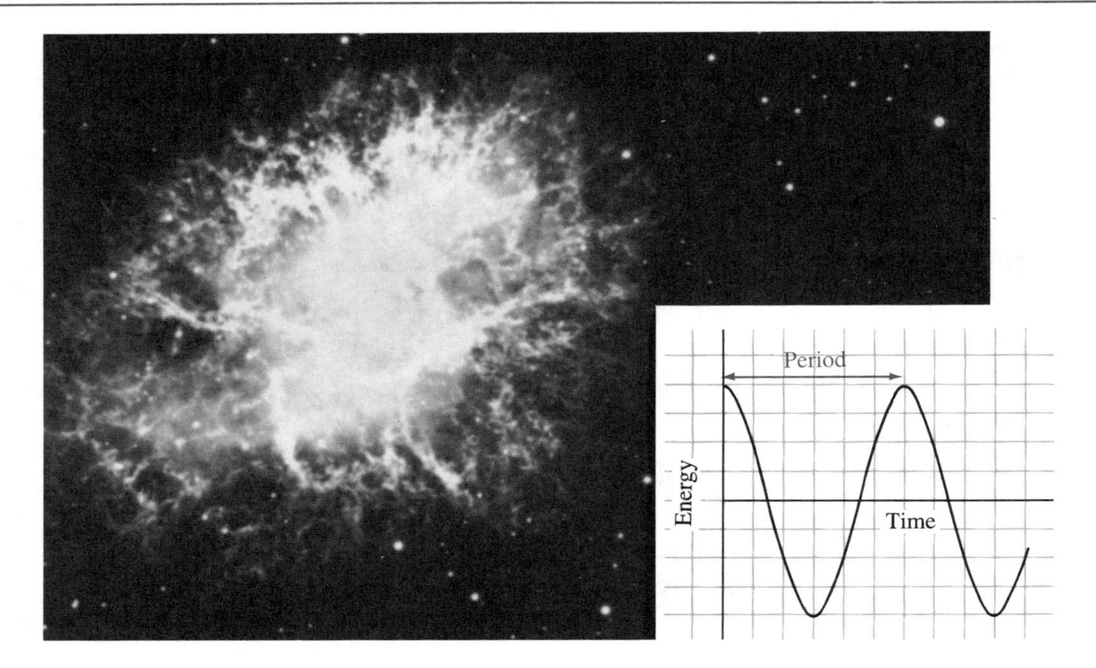

8-9 VARYING THE PERIOD OF SINE AND COSINE FUNCTIONS

In 1968 the scientific world was astonished when two astronomers detected extremely massive stars which spin on their axes in a fraction of a second. Since a pulse of radio energy is sent out on each rotation, these stars are called pulsating stars, or pulsars. One pulsar, in the Crab Nebula, pulses every 0.033 s. This time is called the period.

In $y = \cos \theta$, if θ is replaced with $k\theta$, we obtain $y = \cos k\theta$. To investigate the effect of this on the graph of the function $y = \cos \theta$, we substitute different values for k, and graph the resulting functions. We will assume that k is positive, since there is no need to consider negative values of k in applications.

If $k = 1$, the equation is $y = \cos \theta$ ...... ①
Since one cycle is completed in 2π units along the θ-axis, the period of $y = \cos \theta$ is 2π.

If $k = 2$, the equation is $y = \cos 2\theta$ ...... ②
If we were to graph this function using a table of values, we would start with values of θ, multiply by 2, and then find the cosines of the results. To give the same y-coordinates as in ①, the values of θ must be one-half of those in ①. That is, the θ-coordinates of all points on the graph of ② are *one-half* of those on the graph of ①. Therefore, the graph of ② is *compressed* horizontally relative to the graph of ①. The period of $y = \cos 2\theta$ is π, since one cycle is completed in π units along the θ-axis.

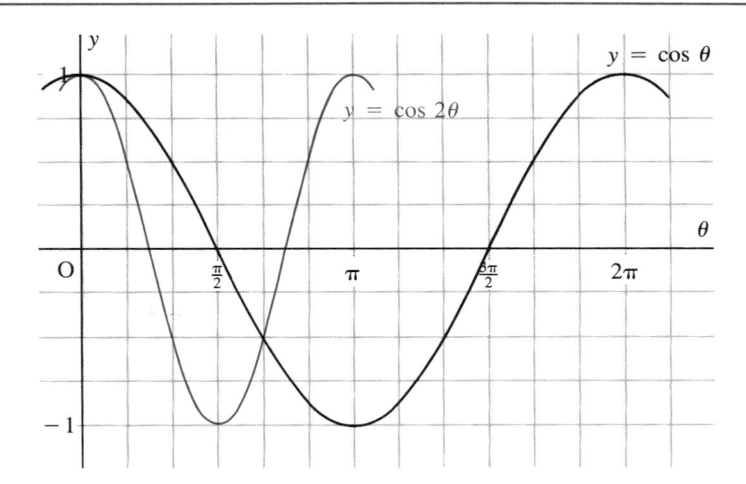

The graph of $y = \cos 2\theta$ is the image of the graph of $y = \cos \theta$ which has been compressed horizontally by a factor of $\frac{1}{2}$.

If $k = \frac{1}{2}$, the equation is $y = \cos \frac{1}{2}\theta$ ...... ③

To give the same y-coordinates as in ①, the values of θ must be *two times* those in ①. Therefore, the graph of ③ is *expanded* horizontally relative to the graph of ①. The period of $y = \cos \frac{1}{2}\theta$ is 4π.

The graph of $y = \cos \frac{1}{2}\theta$ is the image of the graph of $y = \cos \theta$ which has been expanded horizontally by a factor of 2.

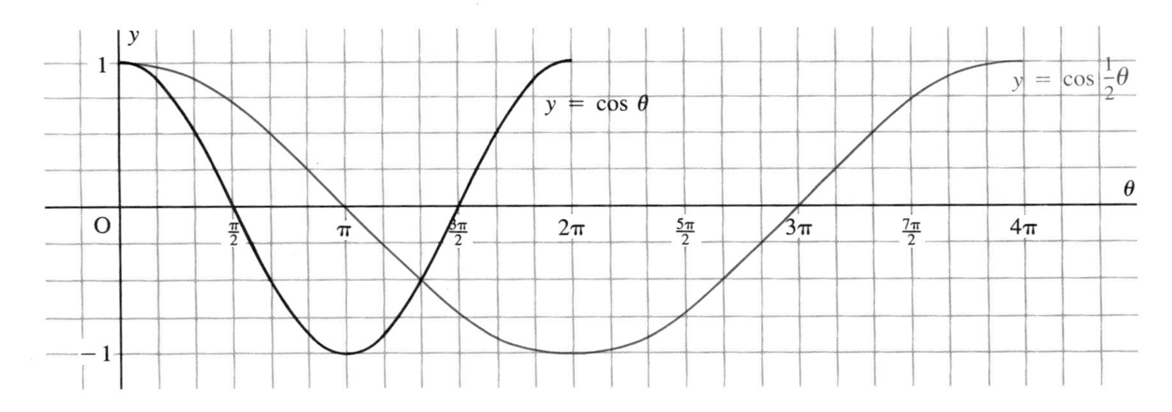

Similar results will be found for other positive values of k, and for sine functions.

In general, multiplying the variable θ in the equations of the functions $y = \cos\theta$ or $y = \sin\theta$ by a positive constant k affects the period and causes a horizontal expansion or compression of its graph. If $0 < k < 1$, there is an expansion; if $k > 1$, there is a compression.

To discover how k is related to the period, we compare the three functions graphed on the previous page with their periods.

Function	Value of k	Period
$y = \cos\theta$	1	2π
$y = \cos 2\theta$	2	π
$y = \cos \frac{1}{2}\theta$	$\frac{1}{2}$	4π

In each case, if we multiply the value of k by the period, the product is 2π.

$$(k)(\text{period}) = 2\pi$$

$$\text{period} = \frac{2\pi}{k}$$

The graphs of $y = \cos k\theta$ and $y = \sin k\theta$ $(k > 0)$ are related to the graphs of $y = \cos\theta$ and $y = \sin\theta$ by a horizontal expansion or compression. The period of each function is $\frac{2\pi}{k}$.

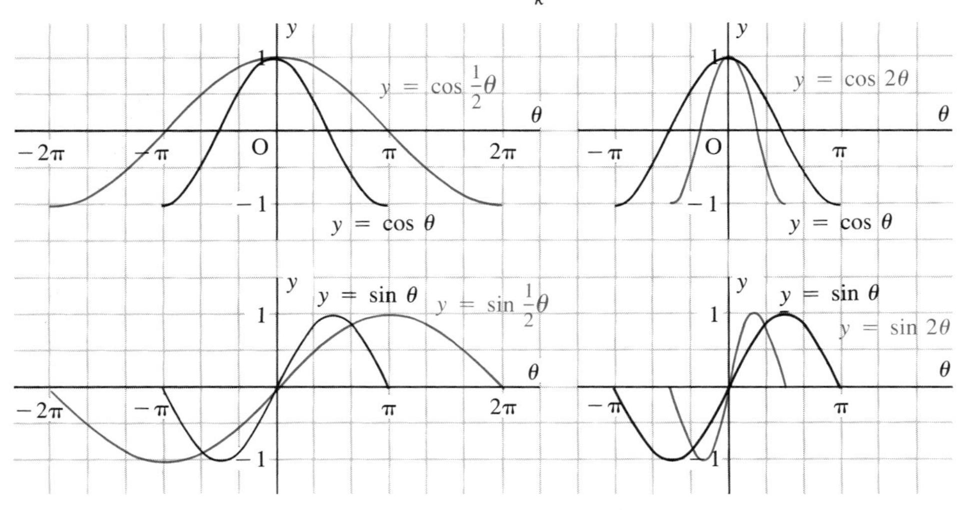

If $0 < k < 1$, there is a horizontal expansion.

If $k > 1$, there is a horizontal compression.

Since we know that $y = \sin k\theta$ and $y = \cos k\theta$ represent sinusoidal functions with the above properties, we can draw the graph of an equation in this form without making a table of values.

Example 1. Draw a graph of the function $y = \sin 3\theta$ over two cycles, and state its period.

Solution. Graph $y = \sin \theta$, then compress horizontally by a factor of $\frac{1}{3}$.

If (θ,y) is any point on the graph of $y = \sin \theta$, then $\left(\frac{1}{3}\theta,y\right)$ is the image point on the graph of $y = \sin 3\theta$. For example, the image of $A(2\pi,0)$ is $A'\left(\frac{2\pi}{3},0\right)$.

The period of this function is $\frac{2\pi}{3}$.

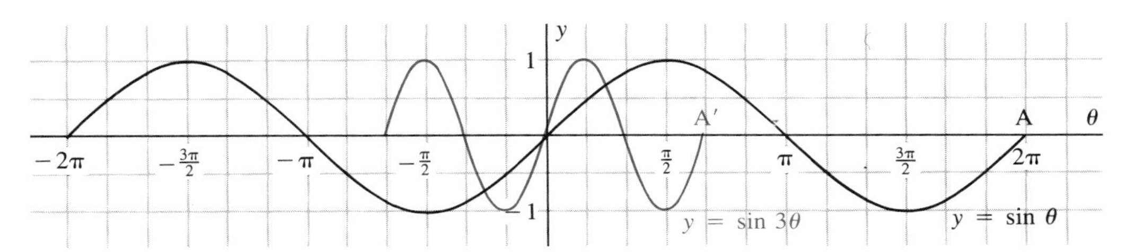

Very often, horizontal expansions or compressions are combined with horizontal translations. The result depends on the order in which these two transformations are applied. With sinusoidal functions we will assume that the expansion or compression is applied first, since there is no need to consider the reverse order in applications.

Suppose the graph of the function $y = \cos \theta$ is compressed horizontally by a factor of $\frac{1}{2}$. To find the equation of the image, replace θ with 2θ. The equation becomes $y = \cos 2\theta$.

Now suppose the resulting graph is translated $\frac{\pi}{3}$ units to the right. To find the image equation after the translation, replace θ with $\left(\theta - \frac{\pi}{3}\right)$.

The equation becomes $y = \cos 2\left(\theta - \frac{\pi}{3}\right)$.

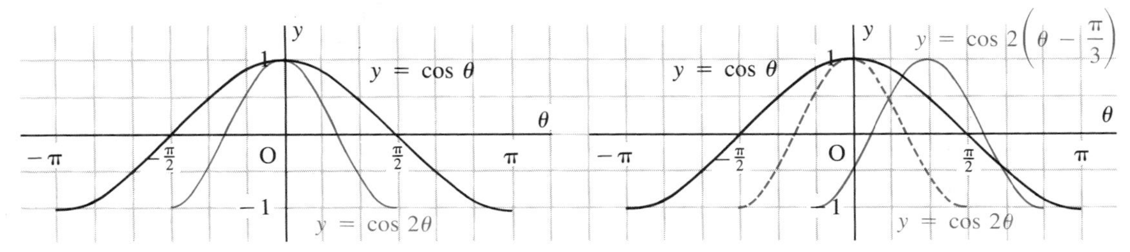

In the above example, the magnitude and direction of the translation give the phase shift. Also, the translation does not affect the period.

The phase shift of $y = \cos 2\left(\theta - \frac{\pi}{3}\right)$ is $\frac{\pi}{3}$. The period of $y = \cos 2\left(\theta - \frac{\pi}{3}\right)$ is $\frac{2\pi}{2}$, or π.

Similar results will be found for other functions.

> The graphs of $y = \cos k(\theta - p)$ and $y = \sin k(\theta - p)$ are related to the graphs of $y = \cos\theta$ and $y = \sin\theta$ by a horizontal expansion or compression followed by a horizontal translation. For $y = \cos k(\theta - p)$ and $y = \sin k(\theta - p)$:
>
> - the phase shift is p
> - the period is $\frac{2\pi}{k}$.

Example 2. Graph the function $y = 2\cos 3\left(\theta - \frac{\pi}{2}\right)$ over two cycles, and state its amplitude, phase shift, and period.

Solution. Graph $y = 2\cos\theta$, then compress horizontally by a factor of $\frac{1}{3}$. At this point, the equation of the curve is $y = 2\cos 3\theta$.

Then translate the image $\frac{\pi}{2}$ units to the right.

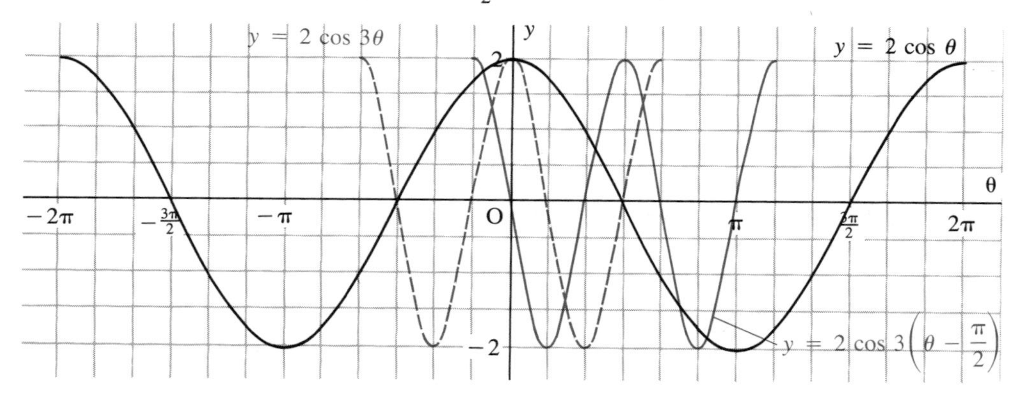

The amplitude of the function is 2.

The phase shift is $\frac{\pi}{2}$.

The period is $\frac{2\pi}{3}$.

EXERCISES 8-9

1. a) Graph these functions on the same grid for $-\pi \leqslant \theta \leqslant \pi$.

   $y = \sin 2\theta \qquad y = \sin\theta \qquad y = \sin\frac{1}{2}\theta$

   b) Graph these functions on the same grid for $-\pi \leqslant \theta \leqslant \pi$.

   $y = \cos 3\theta \qquad y = \cos\theta \qquad y = \cos\frac{1}{3}\theta$

   c) Describe the effect on the graphs of $y = \sin k\theta$ and $y = \cos k\theta$ as the value of k varies.

2. Each function graphed below is sinusoidal. Write an equation for each function.

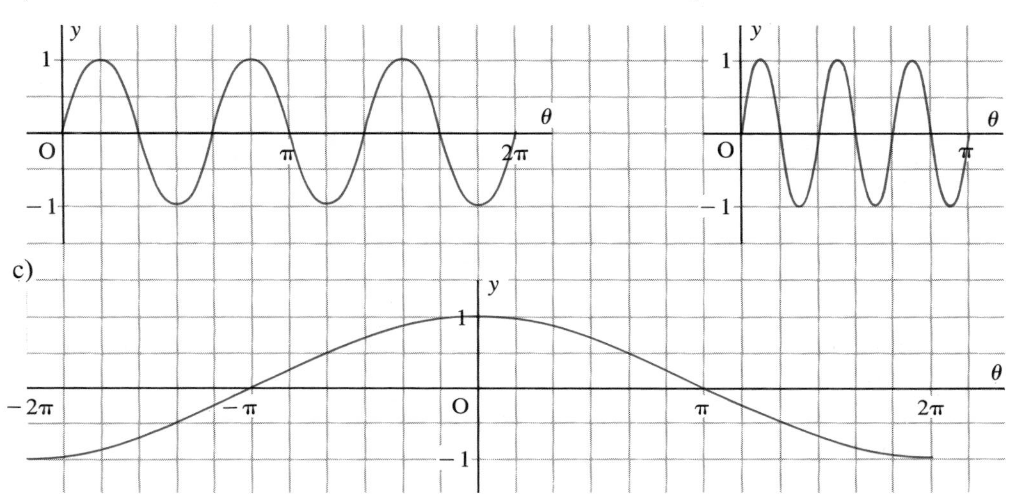

Ⓑ

3. Graph each sinusoidal function, and state its amplitude and period.

   a) $y = 2 \sin 2\theta$ b) $y = 3 \sin \frac{1}{2}\theta$ c) $y = 4 \sin 2\theta$

   d) $y = 4 \cos \frac{1}{2}\theta$ e) $y = 5 \cos 2\theta$ f) $y = -3 \cos 3\theta$

4. State the amplitude, the period, and the phase shift for each function.

   a) $y = 5 \cos 3(\theta - \pi)$ b) $y = 2 \sin 4\left(\theta + \frac{\pi}{2}\right)$

   c) $y = 2.5 \sin 6\left(\theta - \frac{2\pi}{3}\right)$ d) $y = 0.5 \cos 5\left(\theta + \frac{5\pi}{4}\right)$

5. Graph each function over two cycles, and state its amplitude, period, and phase shift.

   a) $y = \sin 2\left(\theta - \frac{\pi}{3}\right)$ b) $y = 2 \cos 3\left(\theta - \frac{\pi}{2}\right)$

   c) $y = 4 \cos \frac{1}{2}(\theta + \pi)$ d) $y = 0.5 \sin \frac{1}{2}\left(\theta - \frac{5\pi}{4}\right)$

6. Find an equation of a function of the form $y = \sin k\theta$ whose graph passes through each point.

   a) $A\left(\frac{\pi}{4},1\right)$ b) $B\left(\frac{\pi}{3},\frac{\sqrt{3}}{2}\right)$ c) $C\left(\frac{\pi}{6},\frac{\sqrt{3}}{2}\right)$ d) $D\left(\frac{\pi}{2},0\right)$

7. Find an equation of a function of the form $y = \cos k\theta$ whose graph passes through each point.

   a) $E(\pi,0)$ b) $F\left(\frac{\pi}{4},-1\right)$ c) $G\left(\frac{\pi}{6},\frac{1}{\sqrt{2}}\right)$ d) $H\left(\frac{2\pi}{3},-1\right)$

8. If $A(k,1)$ is a point on the graph of the function $y = \sin 2\theta$, find a possible value of k.

9. If $A\left(k,\frac{1}{\sqrt{2}}\right)$ is a point on the graph of the function $y = \cos 3\theta$, find a possible value of k.

Ⓒ

10. a) Draw graphs of the functions $f(\theta) = \sin \theta$ and $g(\theta) = \cos \theta$ on the same grid.
    b) Use the graphs in part a) to draw a graph of the function $y = f(\theta) + g(\theta)$.

11. Use the method of adding ordinates to draw a graph of each function.
    a) $y = \sin \theta + \sin 2\theta$ b) $y = \cos \theta + \sin 2\theta$

12. If the coordinates of any point are given, is it always possible to find the equation of a function of the form $y = \sin k\theta$ whose graph passes through the point? Illustrate your answer with examples and an explanation.

13. **Negative values of k in $y = \sin k\theta$ and $y = \cos k\theta$**
    a) Draw graphs of these functions.
       i) $y = \sin(-\theta)$ ii) $y = \sin(-2\theta)$ iii) $y = \sin\left(-\frac{1}{2}\theta\right)$
    b) How are the graphs of the functions in part a) related to the graph of the function $y = \sin \theta$?
    c) Draw diagrams to illustrate how the graphs of $y = \sin k\theta$ and $y = \cos k\theta$ are related to the graphs of $y = \sin \theta$ and $y = \cos \theta$ if $k < 0$.
    d) Do negative values of k affect the period? In what way?

14. Graph each function over two cycles, and state the period.
    a) $y = \sin(-3\theta)$ b) $y = 4 \cos\left(-\frac{1}{2}\theta\right)$ c) $y = 3 \sin(-2\theta) + 3$

15. a) Compare the graphs of each pair of functions.
       i) $y = \sin \theta$ and $y = \sin(-\theta)$
       ii) $y = \cos \theta$ and $y = \cos(-\theta)$
    b) What conclusions can you make?

INVESTIGATE

All the graphs in this section have θ-axes marked with intervals involving the irrational number π. Find an equation for each graph below, in which the θ-axes are marked with intervals of natural numbers.

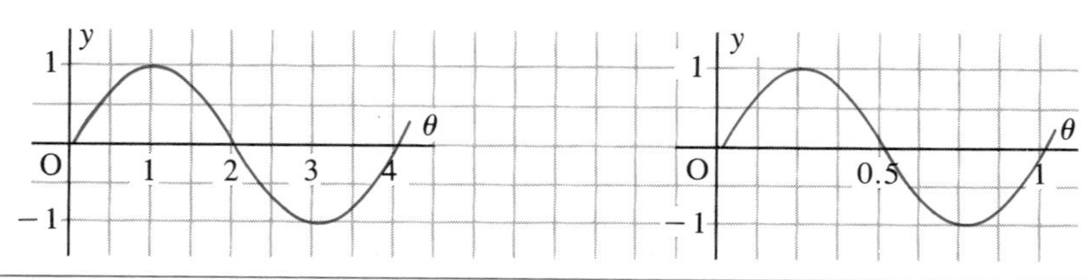

THE MATHEMATICAL MIND

Evaluating Trigonometric Functions

To keep pace with progress in navigation and astronomy in the 17th and 18th centuries, mathematicians required increasingly more accurate values of certain functions, including trigonometric functions. Credit goes to the Englishman, Brook Taylor (1685-1731) and the Scotsman, Colin Maclaurin (1698-1746) for showing that under certain conditions a function $f(x)$ can be expressed as an infinite series of powers of x. Two important series are the series for $\sin x$ and $\cos x$, where x is a real number.

$$\sin x = \frac{x}{1!} - \frac{x^3}{3!} + \frac{x^5}{5!} - \frac{x^7}{7!} + \dots \qquad \cos x = 1 - \frac{x^2}{2!} + \frac{x^4}{4!} - \frac{x^6}{6!} + \dots$$

The denominators in these series use a special notation called *factorial notation*. The factorial sign ! following a number means the product of all natural numbers up to and including the number. For example, $4! = 4 \times 3 \times 2 \times 1$, or 24

We can regard these series as formulas for calculating values of the trigonometric functions for all real values of x. The formulas are valid only when x is in radians. Hence, to calculate $\cos 60°$, we substitute $\frac{\pi}{3}$ for x in the second formula. Taking the first four terms, we obtain:

$$\begin{aligned}\cos\frac{\pi}{3} &\doteq 1 - \frac{1}{2}\left(\frac{\pi}{3}\right)^2 + \frac{1}{24}\left(\frac{\pi}{3}\right)^4 - \frac{1}{720}\left(\frac{\pi}{3}\right)^6 \\ &\doteq 1 - 0.548\,311\,4 + 0.050\,107\,6 - 0.001\,831\,6 \\ &\doteq 0.499\,964\,6\end{aligned}$$

This is very close to the actual value of 0.5. For a more accurate result, additional terms of the series can be used.

QUESTIONS

1. Simplify each factorial.
   a) 3! b) 5! c) 7! d) 8! e) 9! f) 10!
2. Write the first six terms of the series for $\sin x$ and $\cos x$.
3. Use the result of *Question 2* to calculate each value. Check using the [sin] or [cos] key on your calculator.
   a) $\cos\frac{\pi}{6}$ b) $\sin\frac{\pi}{2}$ c) $\sin\frac{\pi}{5}$ d) $\cos\pi$
4. How many terms of the series are needed to obtain a value of $\cos\frac{\pi}{5}$:
   a) to 2 decimal places b) to 4 decimal places c) to 6 decimal places?

8-10 GRAPHING GENERAL SINUSOIDAL FUNCTIONS

When we graph a function, we customarily draw the axes before we draw the curve. Then we make the curve fit the scales on the axes we have already drawn. We have used this method in previous sections of this book. However, with sinusoidal functions, it is easier to draw the curve first and then add the axes later. In other words, we make the axes fit the curve.

For example, consider the function $y = 3 \cos 2\left(\theta - \frac{\pi}{3}\right) + 4$.

We can graph this function as follows.

Step 1. Draw a sinusoidal curve, without axes.

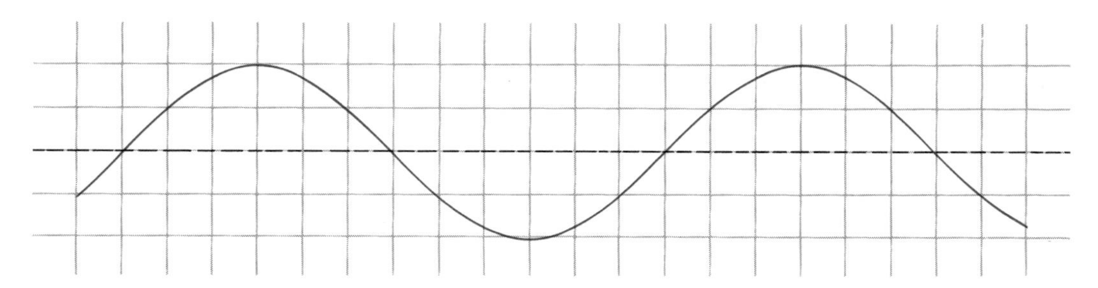

Step 2. Find the phase shift and the period, and use them to establish a horizontal scale.

The phase shift is $\frac{\pi}{3}$, and the period is $\frac{2\pi}{2}$, or π.

Since the function is a cosine function, the phase shift $\frac{\pi}{3}$ is the θ-coordinate of a maximum point. Since the period is π, the θ-coordinate of the next maximum point is $\frac{\pi}{3} + \pi$, or $\frac{4\pi}{3}$. Label these points.

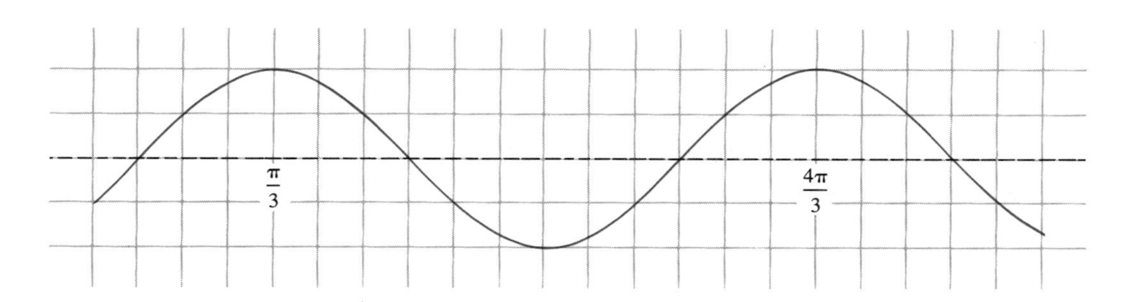

Step 3. Complete the graph by drawing the axes and their scales.
The graph was drawn such that the period corresponds to 12 squares. Therefore, the horizontal scale is:
12 squares correspond to π
4 squares correspond to $\frac{\pi}{3}$.
The position of O is 4 squares to the left of the first maximum point. Draw the y-axis through this point.

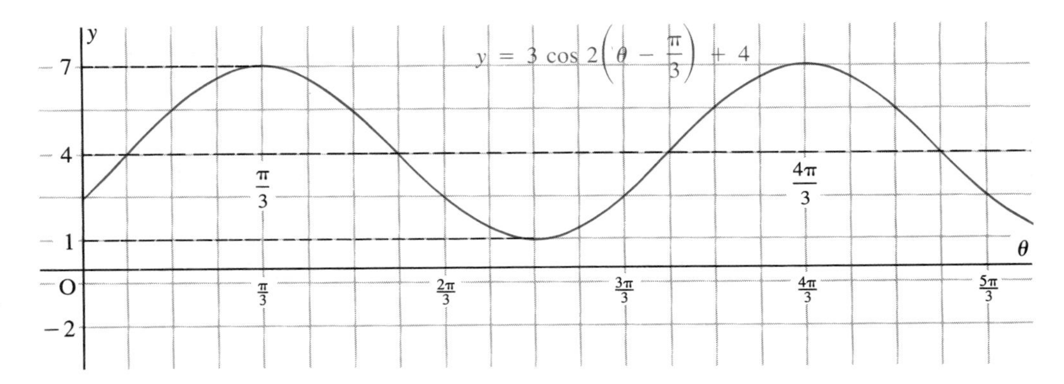

The vertical displacement is 4. Since the amplitude is 3, the maximum value of y is 7 and the minimum value is 1. Use these values to mark the vertical scale. Draw the θ-axis and mark its scale.

The method illustrated above may be used to graph any sinusoidal function.

Example 1. Draw a graph of the function $y = 5 \sin 3(\theta + 45°) + 3$ over two cycles.

Solution. *Step 1.*

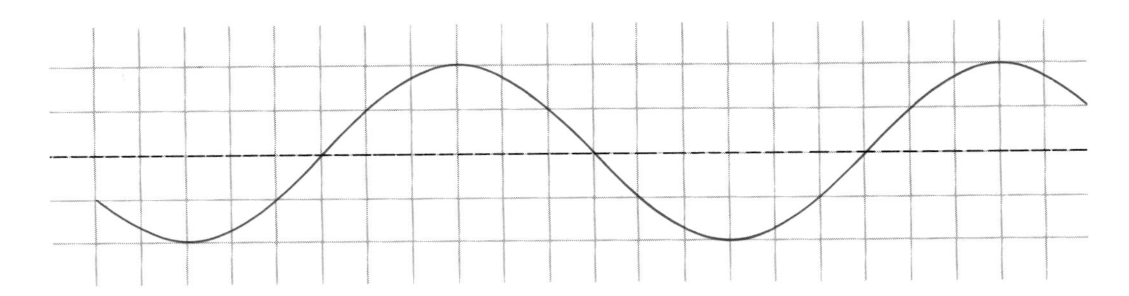

Step 2. The phase shift is $-45°$, and the period is 120°. Since the function is a sine function, the phase shift $-45°$ is the θ-coordinate of a point on the axis preceding a maximum point. Then, since the period is 120°, the θ-coordinate of the next point preceding a maximum point is $-45° + 120°$, or 75°.

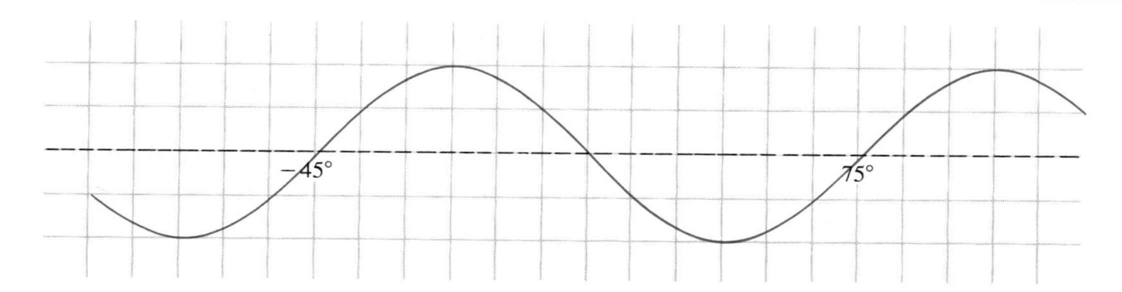

Step 3. The graph was drawn such that the period corresponds to 12 squares. Therefore, the horizontal scale is:
12 squares correspond to 120°
 1 square corresponds to 10°.
Mark the horizontal scale as shown. The position of O is halfway between − 15° and 15°. Draw the y-axis through this point.

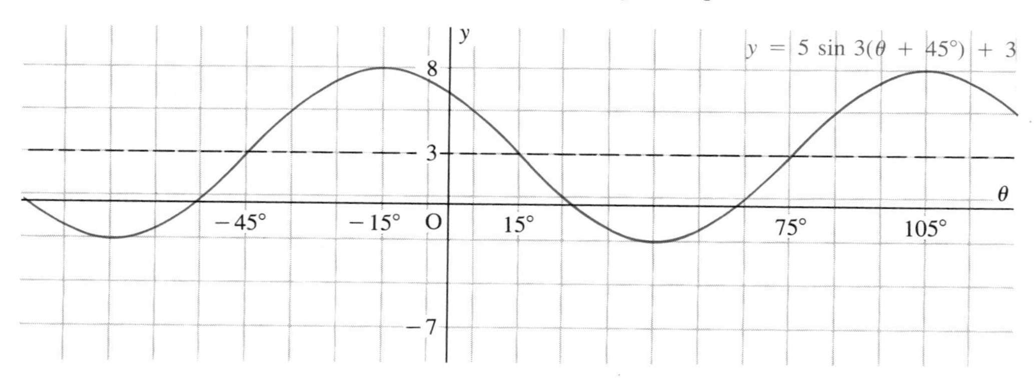

The vertical displacement is 3. Since the amplitude is 5, the maximum value of y is 8 and the minimum value is -2. Use these values to mark the vertical scale.

We can also find an equation of a sinusoidal function from its graph.

Example 2. A sinusoidal function is shown in the graph below.
a) Determine the vertical displacement and the amplitude.
b) Determine a possible phase shift, and the period.
c) Write an equation of the function.

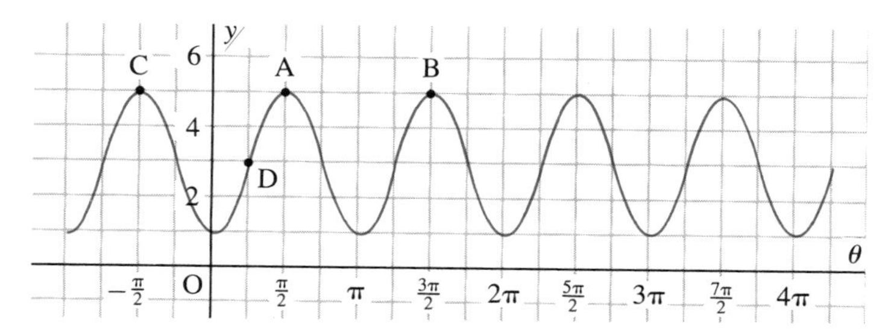

Solution. a) The vertical displacement is 3.
The amplitude is 2.

b) There are many possible phase shifts, depending on whether we regard the function as a cosine function or a sine function, and on which point is taken to correspond to the phase shift.

For example, if we consider the function to be a cosine function, the phase shift is the θ-coordinate of any maximum point. Using point A, the phase shift is $\frac{\pi}{2}$.

The period is the difference in the values of θ for two consecutive maximum points. Using points A and B, the period is $\frac{3\pi}{2} - \frac{\pi}{2}$, or π.

c) An equation of the function is $y = 2 \cos 2\left(\theta - \frac{\pi}{2}\right) + 3$.

In *Example 2*, there are other functions with the same graph.

Using point B and its θ-coordinate $\frac{3\pi}{2}$ as the phase shift: $y = 2 \cos 2\left(\theta - \frac{3\pi}{2}\right) + 3$

Using point C and its θ-coordinate $-\frac{\pi}{2}$ as the phase shift: $y = 2 \cos 2\left(\theta + \frac{\pi}{2}\right) + 3$

Considering the function as a sine function, and using point D and its θ-coordinate $\frac{\pi}{4}$ as the phase shift: $y = 2 \sin 2\left(\theta - \frac{\pi}{4}\right) + 3$

EXERCISES 8-10

(A)

1. For each graph below, state:
   i) the amplitude ii) the period iii) a possible phase shift
   iv) the maximum value of y, and the values of θ for which it occurs
   v) the minimum value of y, and the values of θ for which it occurs
   vi) the vertical displacement.

   a) b)

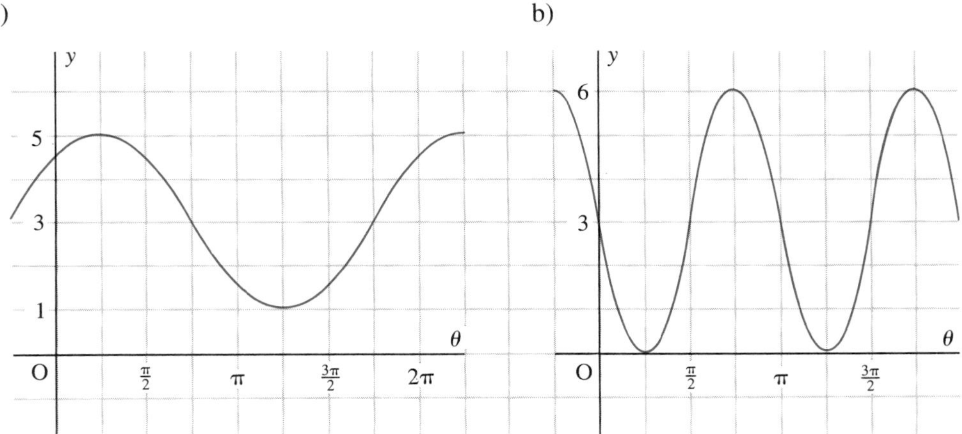

c)

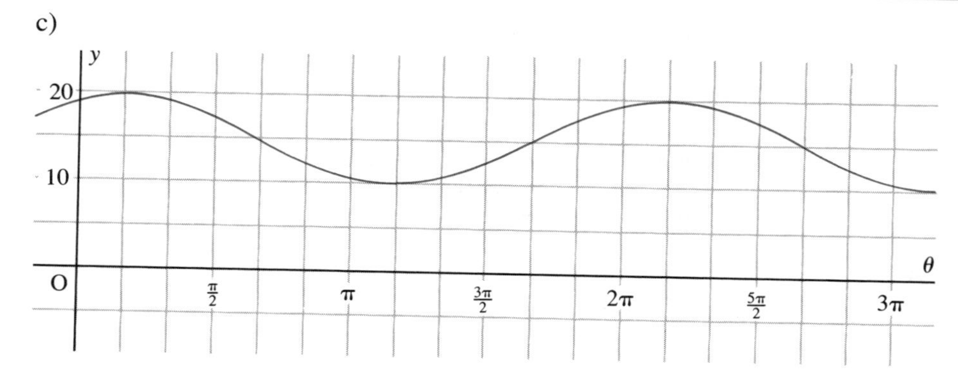

2. Write an equation to represent each function in *Exercise 1*.

(B)

3. Given the function $y = 2 \cos 2(\theta - 60°) + 4$
   a) Find the phase shift and the period.
   b) Determine the vertical displacement and the amplitude.
   c) Graph the function by graphing a sinusoidal curve first, and making the axes fit the curve.

4. Given the function $y = 3 \sin 2\left(\theta - \frac{\pi}{4}\right) + 3$
   a) Find the phase shift and the period.
   b) Determine the vertical displacement and the amplitude.
   c) Graph the function by graphing a sinusoidal curve first, and making the axes fit the curve.

5. Determine the phase shift and the period for each function. Then graph the function by graphing a sinusoidal curve first, and making the axes fit the curve.
   a) $y = 4 \cos 3\left(\theta - \frac{\pi}{2}\right) + 4$
   b) $y = 2 \cos 4(\theta + 180°) + 3$
   c) $y = 3 \sin 2\left(\theta + \frac{\pi}{6}\right) + 6$
   d) $y = 4 \sin 3(\theta - 30°) + 2$

6. Graph each function.
   a) $y = \sin 2(\theta - 90°)$
   b) $y = 2 \sin 3\left(\theta - \frac{\pi}{3}\right) + 5$
   c) $y = 3 \cos 2(\theta + 45°) + 1$
   d) $y = 3 \cos 3\left(\theta - \frac{2\pi}{3}\right) + 4$

7. Describe what happens to each graph.
   a) $y = a \sin 2\left(\theta - \frac{\pi}{6}\right) + 5$ as a varies
   b) $y = 3 \sin k\left(\theta - \frac{\pi}{6}\right) + 5$ as k varies
   c) $y = 3 \sin 2(\theta - p) + 5$ as p varies
   d) $y = 3 \sin 2\left(\theta - \frac{\pi}{3}\right) + q$ as q varies

8. Determine the phase shift and the period of each function, and draw the graph.
   a) $y = \sin(2\theta - \pi)$ b) $y = 2\cos(3\theta - \pi) + 1$
   c) $y = 2\cos(3\theta - \pi) + 4$ d) $y = 5\sin(4\theta + \pi) - 3$

9. Graph each function.
   a) $y = 2\sin\left(2\theta + \frac{\pi}{3}\right)$ b) $y = 5\cos\left(2\theta - \frac{\pi}{2}\right)$
   c) $y = -3\cos\left(2\theta - \frac{\pi}{2}\right)$ d) $y = 5\sin\left(2\theta + \frac{\pi}{3}\right)$

Ⓒ

10. Two of these equations represent the same function. Which two are they?
    a) $y = 3\sin 2\left(\theta + \frac{\pi}{2}\right)$ b) $y = 3\cos 2\theta$
    c) $y = 3\cos 2\left(\theta + \frac{\pi}{4}\right)$ d) $y = 3\sin 2(\theta + \pi)$

11. Two of these equations represent the same function. Which two are they?
    a) $y = 3\sin(2\theta + \pi)$ b) $y = 3\cos\left(2\theta + \frac{\pi}{2}\right)$
    c) $y = 3\cos 2\theta$ d) $y = 3\sin(2\theta + 2\pi)$

12. a) Find three different roots of the equation $2\cos\left(\theta + \frac{\pi}{2}\right) = 0$.
    b) Write a general expression which could be used to represent all the roots of the equation in part a).

13. a) Find three different roots of the equation $3\sin 2\left(\theta - \frac{\pi}{4}\right) = 0$.
    b) Write a general expression which could be used to represent all the roots of the equation in part a).

14. Two students discussed their methods of graphing sinusoidal functions. Their discussion went as follows.
    Kwan: "I always draw the curve first and make the axes fit the curve. That method is very easy."
    Marc: "But then all your graphs are going to look the same, even if they have different amplitudes and different periods."
    Kwan: "Not really. I have two different ways of getting around that problem."
    What methods might Kwan have been using so that her graphs do not all look like they have the same amplitude and the same period?

15. Given the function $y = \cos 2\pi\theta$
    a) Find the phase shift and the period.
    b) Graph the function.

16. Repeat *Exercise 15* for these functions.
    a) $y = \sin 2\pi\theta$ b) $y = \cos\frac{\pi}{2}\theta$ c) $y = \sin\frac{\pi}{2}\theta$

8-11 SCALING THE HORIZONTAL AXIS

In the first section of this chapter several graphs were shown illustrating some examples of sinusoidal functions.

- time of the sunset
- number of sunspots
- lengths of shadows
- blood pressure
- volume of blood in the heart
- volume of air in the lungs

These graphs differ from the trigonometric graphs we studied in the preceding sections in one major way. They show periodic functions without the use of angles.

Up to now the horizontal axis has been scaled in degrees or in radians. These scales are not very useful in applications such as those above, where the horizontal axis is usually marked in time intervals. To use sinusoidal functions in applications we must change their graphs in two ways.

- We will no longer use θ as the variable on the horizontal axis. Instead, we will use t to indicate time. This involves nothing more than changing the letter on the axis and in the equations.
- We will scale the horizontal axis with whole numbers such as 1, 2, 3, or their multiples. We do this by adjusting the period of the functions.

For example, the graphs below show cosine and sine functions with period 1. Their equations can be written in the form $y = \cos kt$ and $y = \sin kt$. Since the period of each function is $\frac{2\pi}{k}$, we can write

$$\frac{2\pi}{k} = 1$$

$$k = 2\pi$$

The equations of the functions are $y = \cos 2\pi t$ and $y = \sin 2\pi t$.

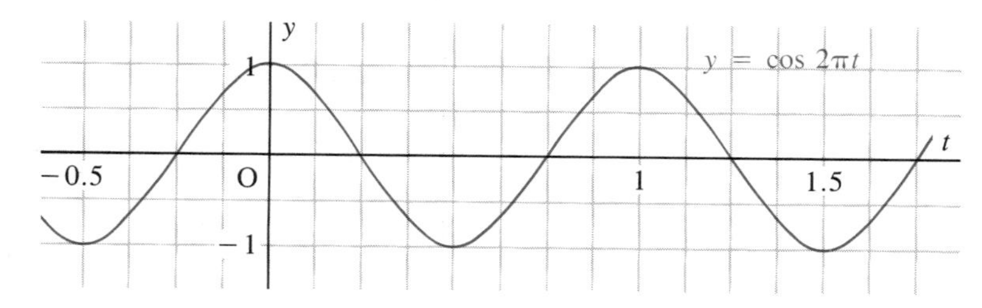

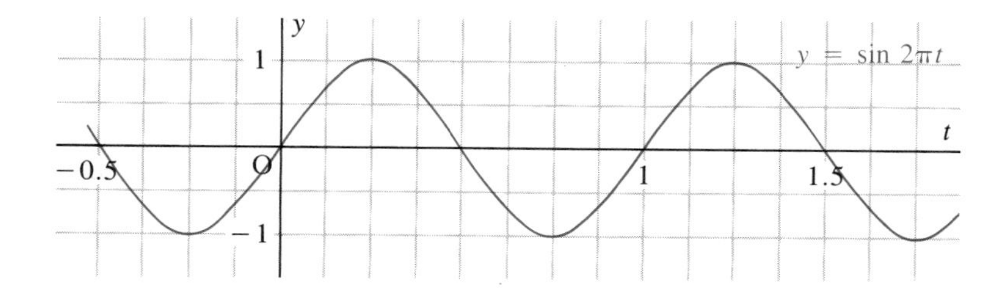

The examples on the previous page show that if π occurs in the equation as a factor of the quantity whose sine or cosine is to be found, then it does not appear on the horizontal axis. The fact that π does not occur on the axis means that it must occur in the equation.

Example 1. a) Find the period of the function $y = \sin \frac{2\pi t}{5}$.

b) Graph the function in part a).

Solution. a) The equation is in the form $y = \sin kt$, which has period $\frac{2\pi}{k}$.

Since $k = \frac{2\pi}{5}$, we see that the period of the function is $\frac{2\pi}{\frac{2\pi}{5}}$, or 5.

b) Draw the graph of a sine function with period 5.

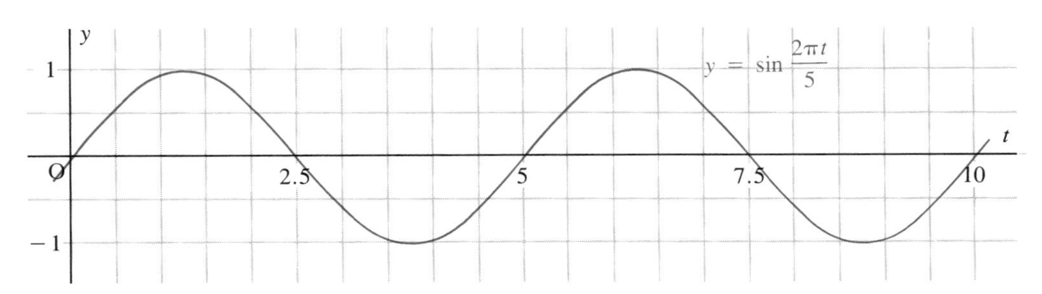

In *Example 1*, notice that the coefficient of t in the equation can be expressed in the form of a fraction, $\frac{2\pi}{k}$. When the coefficient is written in this form, the denominator is the period of the function.

$y = \cos \frac{2\pi t}{k}$ represents a cosine function with period k.

$y = \sin \frac{2\pi t}{k}$ represents a sine function with period k.

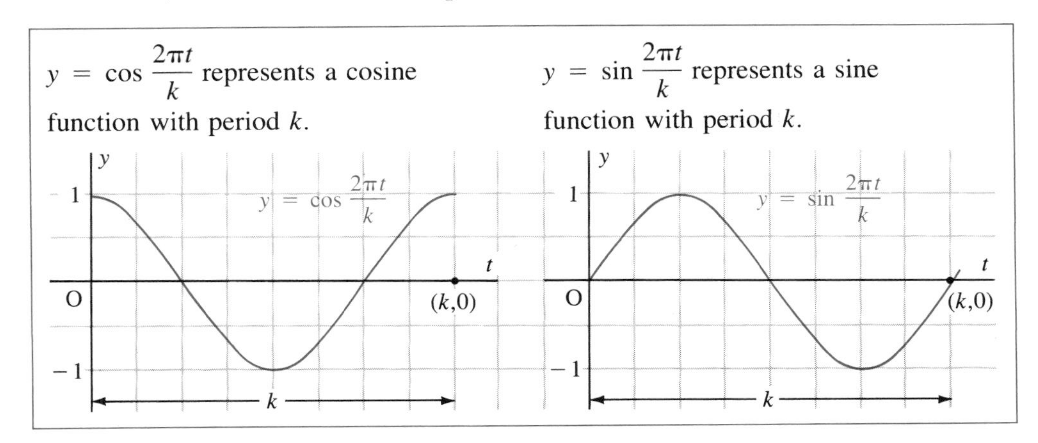

This scaling of the horizontal axis affects only the period, as shown above. It does not affect the vertical displacement, amplitude or how the phase shift is found.

Example 2. Graph the function $y = 3 \sin 2\pi\frac{(t - 2)}{4} + 6$.

Solution. *Step 1*. Draw a sinusoidal curve.

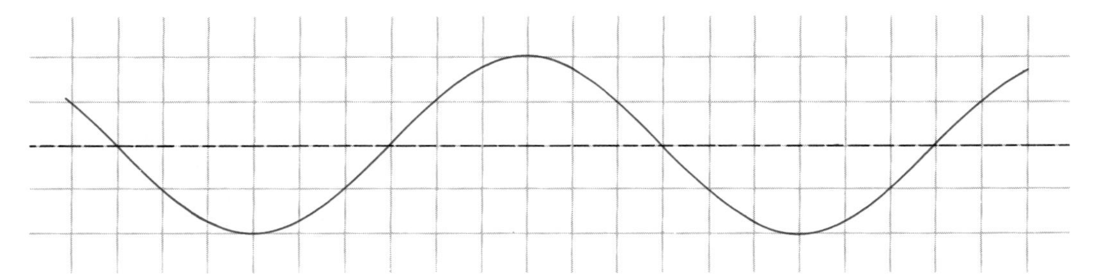

Step 2. Find the phase shift and the period, and use them to establish a horizontal scale.
The phase shift is 2. The period is 4.

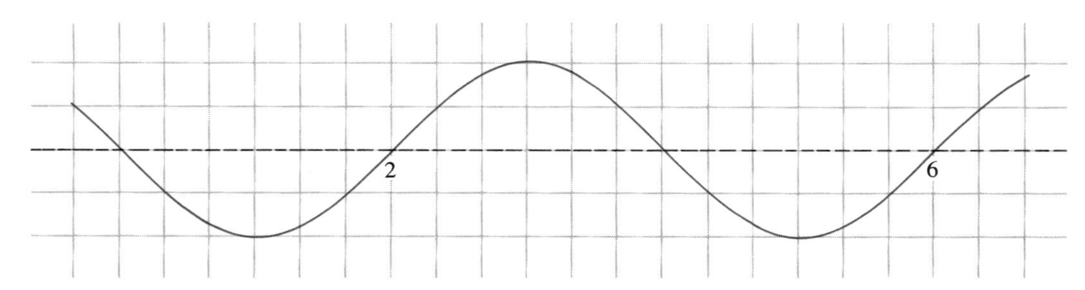

Step 3. Complete the graph by drawing the axes and their scales.
We use the fact that the amplitude is 3 and the vertical displacement is 6.

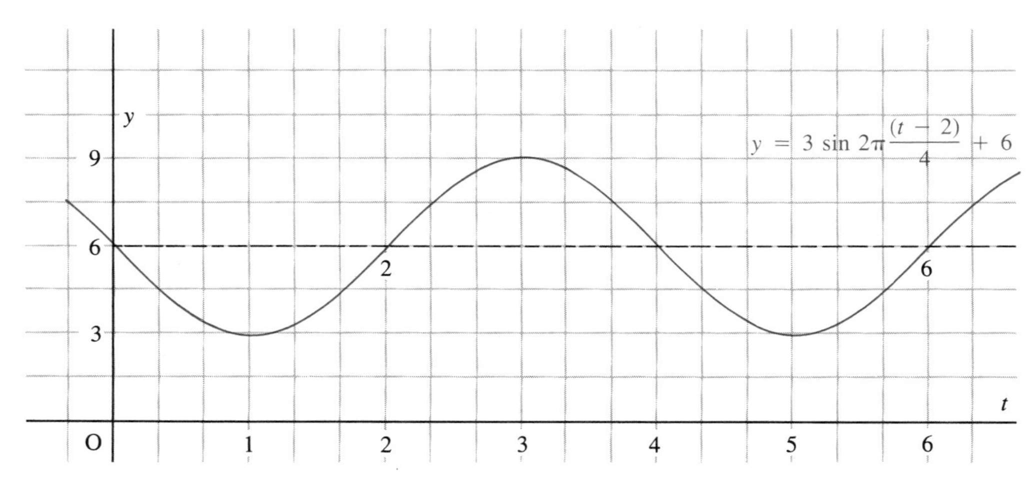

In *Example 2*, the period, amplitude, phase shift, and vertical displacement are all represented by numbers in the equation.

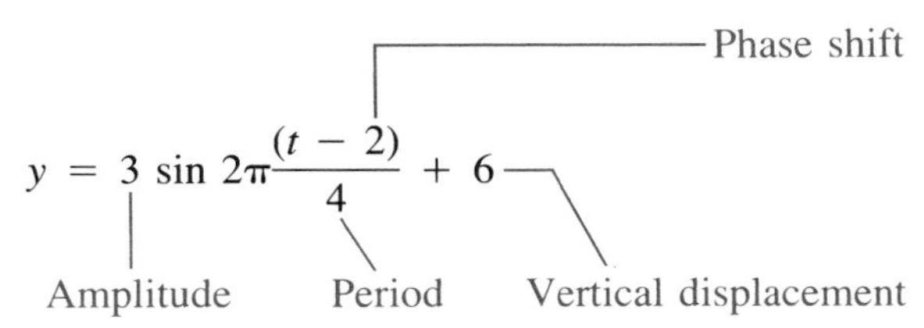

Notice the factor 2π in the equation. This factor must be present for the period to be as indicated. We can use this pattern to write the equation when these data are given or when they can be read from a graph.

Example 3. Write an equation of this sinusoidal function.

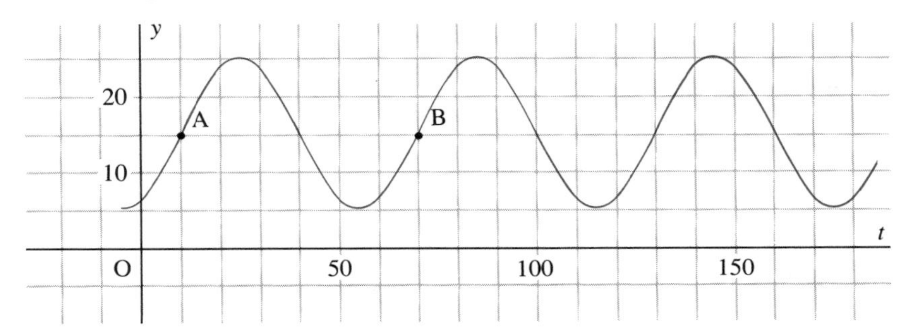

Solution. The vertical displacement is 15.
The amplitude is 10.
For a sine function, the phase shift is the horizontal coordinate of A: 10.
The period is the difference between the horizontal coordinates of A and B: 70 − 10, or 60.

An equation of the function is $y = 10 \sin 2\pi\frac{(t-10)}{60} + 15$.

In *Example 3*, the function can also be expressed as a cosine function. The only difference is the phase shift. Since the first maximum occurs when $t = 25$, the phase shift is 25. An equation of the function is $y = 10 \cos 2\pi\frac{(t-25)}{60} + 15$. What are other equations for this function?

Example 4. The volume of air in the lungs is a sinusoidal function of time. A graph illustrating this variation for normal breathing is shown on page 307. Write an equation for this function.

Solution. The vertical displacement is 2450 mL. The amplitude is 250 mL. The period is 5 s. If V millilitres represents the volume of air in the lungs at time t seconds, then an equation for the function is:

$$V = 250 \sin \frac{2\pi t}{5} + 2450.$$

EXERCISES 8-11

(A)

1. State the amplitude, period, phase shift, and vertical displacement for each function.

   a) $y = 3 \sin 2\pi\frac{(t-1)}{5} + 4$ b) $y = 2 \cos 2\pi\frac{(t-5)}{4} + 6$

2. For each graph, determine the amplitude, period, phase shift, and vertical displacement.

   a)

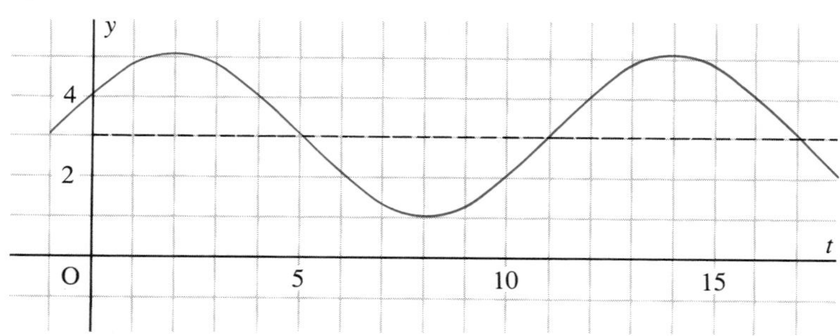

   b)

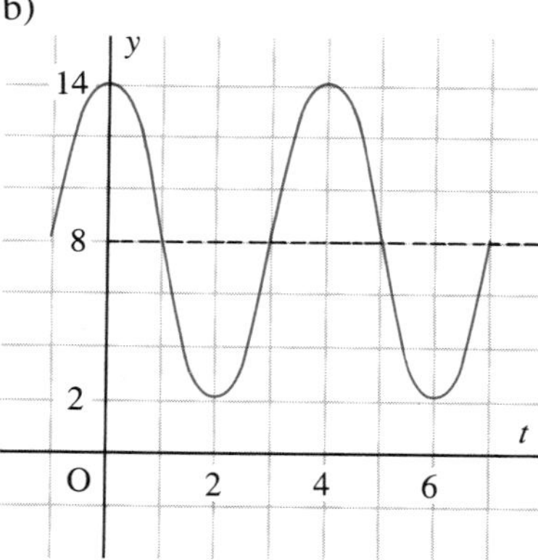

   c)

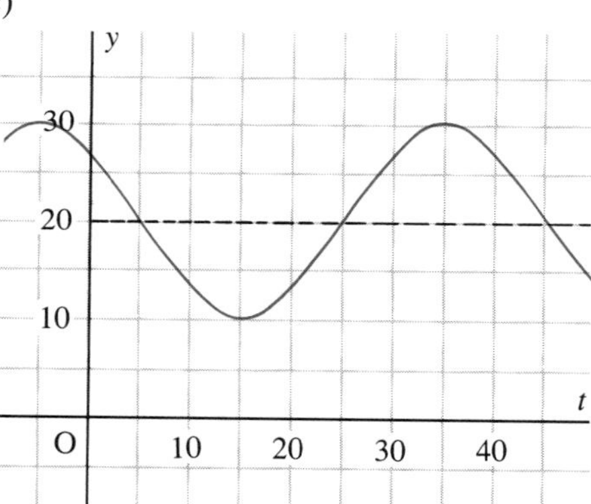

3. Write an equation to represent each function in *Exercise 2*.

4. Write an equation to represent each function.

   a)

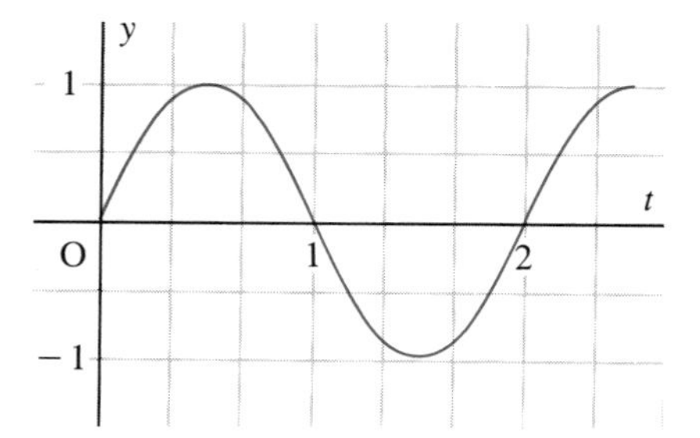

   b)

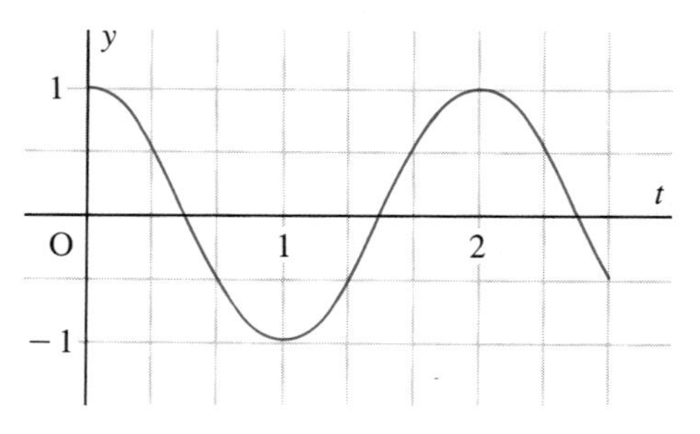

c)

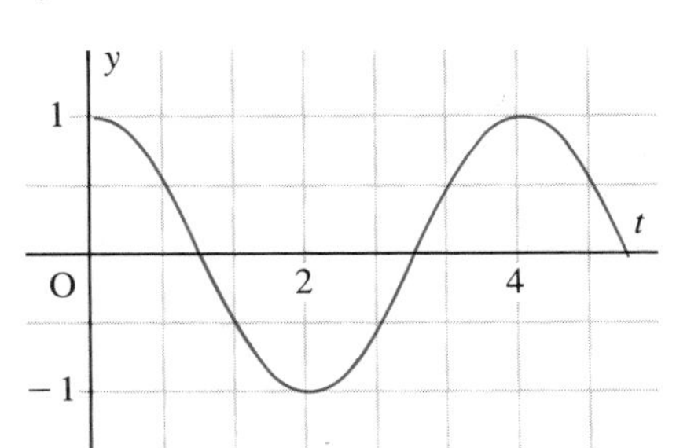

d)

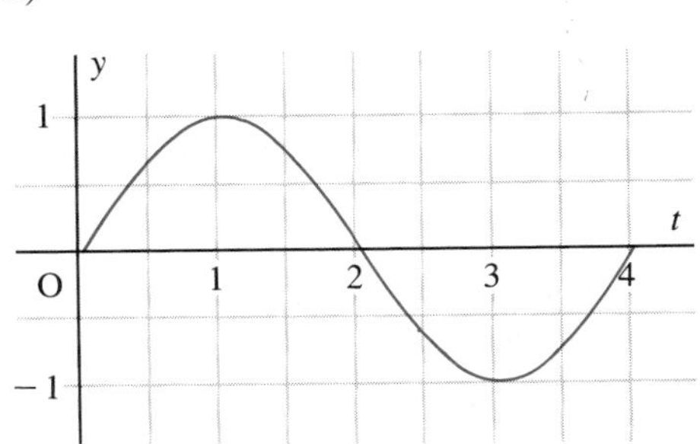

5. Write an equation for a cosine function with the following properties.
   a) amplitude: 5 period: 1 phase shift: 9 vertical displacement: 4
   b) amplitude: 12 period: $\frac{1}{2}$ phase shift: -3 vertical displacement: 1.5
   c) amplitude: 2.4 period: 27 phase shift: 19 vertical displacement: 15.1

(B)

6. Draw a graph of each function.
   a) $y = 2 \cos 2\pi \frac{(t - 1)}{3} + 4$
   b) $y = 3 \cos 2\pi \frac{(t - 4)}{2} + 3$
   c) $y = 2.4 \cos 2\pi \frac{(t + 3)}{12} + 3.6$
   d) $y = 3.5 \sin 2\pi \frac{(t - 8.4)}{9.2} + 10$

7. Draw a graph of each function.
   a) $y = \sin 2\pi t$
   b) $y = \sin \frac{2\pi t}{3}$
   c) $y = \sin 2\pi(t - 2)$
   d) $y = \sin 2\pi \frac{(t - 2)}{3}$
   e) $y = \cos 2\pi t$
   f) $y = \cos \frac{2\pi t}{3}$
   g) $y = \cos 2\pi(t - 2)$
   h) $y = \cos 2\pi \frac{(t - 2)}{3}$

8. State the maximum and minimum values of y, and the values of t for which they occur, where $-5 \leqslant t \leqslant 5$.
   a) $y = 2 \cos 2\pi \frac{(t - 1)}{3} + 3$
   b) $y = 4 \sin 2\pi \frac{(t + 2)}{5} - 4$
   c) $y = 2 \sin 2\pi \frac{(t - 1)}{3} + 6$
   d) $y = 5 \cos 2\pi \frac{(t + 3)}{6} + 2$

9. Write an equation to represent a sine function with the following properties.
   a) maximum: 23 minimum: 11 period: 5 phase shift: 9
   b) maximum: 17.2 minimum: 8.6 period: 3.9 phase shift: 4.7

10. Write an equation for the volume of air in the lungs during deep breathing, when the variation is from 1000 mL to 5000 mL. Assume that the period is 10 s.

11. The twin towers of the World Trade Center in New York were once the tallest buildings in the world. During a strong wind, the top of each tower swings back and forth as much as 80 cm, with a period of 10 s.
    a) Draw a graph showing the departure of the top of one of the buildings from the normal position as a function of time, for 20 s.
    b) Write an equation for the function in part a).

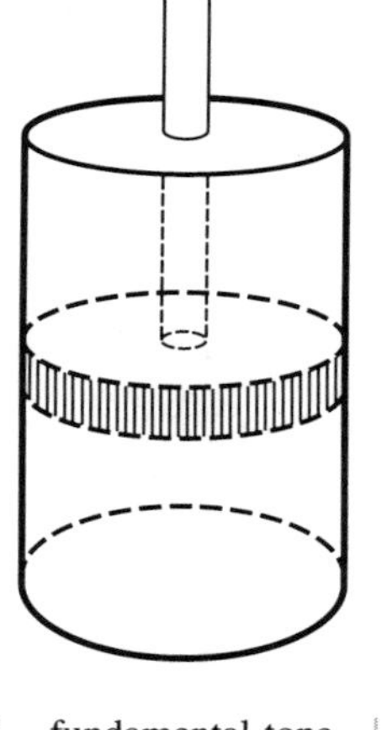

12. A piston in an engine moves up and down in the cylinder, as shown in the diagram. The height h centimetres of the piston at time t seconds is given by this formula.

    $$h = 20 \sin \frac{2\pi t}{0.05} + 20$$

    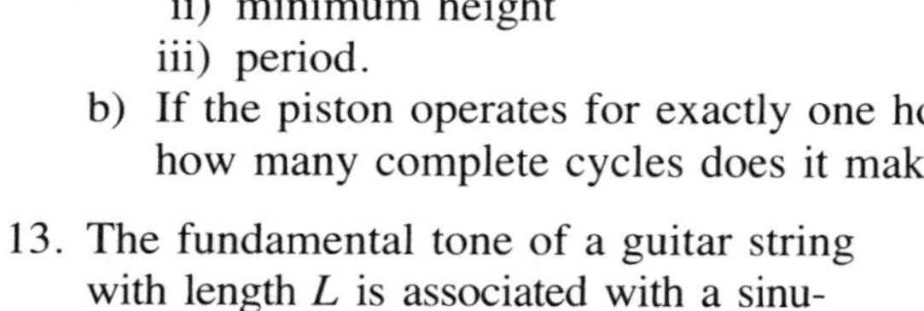

    a) State the piston's:
       i) maximum height
       ii) minimum height
       iii) period.
    b) If the piston operates for exactly one hour, how many complete cycles does it make?

13. The fundamental tone of a guitar string with length L is associated with a sinusoidal function with a period of $2L$.
    The period of the first overtone is $\frac{2L}{2}$;
    the period of the second overtone is $\frac{2L}{3}$;
    and so on.
    a) Assuming that the string is 50 cm long, and that the amplitude of the vibration is 0.5 cm, write the equations of the functions associated with the fundamental tone and the first three overtones.
    b) Draw the graphs of the functions in part a) on the same axes.

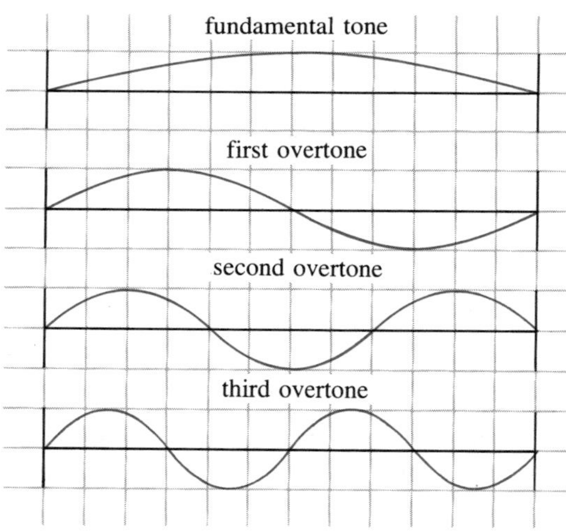

Ⓒ

14. Two of these equations represent the same function. Which two are they?

    a) $y = 3 \sin 2\pi\frac{(t - 1)}{8} + 2$
    b) $y = 3 \cos 2\pi\frac{(t - 5)}{8} + 2$
    c) $y = 3 \sin 2\pi\frac{(t - 3)}{8} + 2$
    d) $y = 3 \cos 2\pi\frac{(t + 1)}{8} + 2$

8-12 APPLYING GENERAL SINUSOIDAL FUNCTIONS

The tides are the periodic rise and fall of the water in the oceans, caused almost entirely by the gravitational attraction of the moon and the sun. An equation expressing the depth of the water as a function of time is extremely complicated, since the distances and relative positions of the moon and sun are constantly changing. However, the depth can be approximated by a sinusoidal function. The amplitude of the function depends on the location, and at any particular location it varies considerably at different times of the year.

Some of the highest tides in the world occur in the Bay of Fundy, where the Annapolis Tidal Generating Station has been in operation since 1984. The graph below shows how the depth of the water at the station varies during a typical day. Notice that times are given in decimal form using a 24 h clock.

When we work with sinusoidal functions involving time in hours, a fractional part of an hour must be expressed in decimal form. For example, the period of the tidal motion (below) is 12 h 25 min. Converting to decimal form,

$$\begin{aligned} 12 \text{ h } 25 \text{ min} &= \left(12 + \frac{25}{60}\right) \text{ h} \\ &\doteq 12.4 \text{ h} \end{aligned}$$

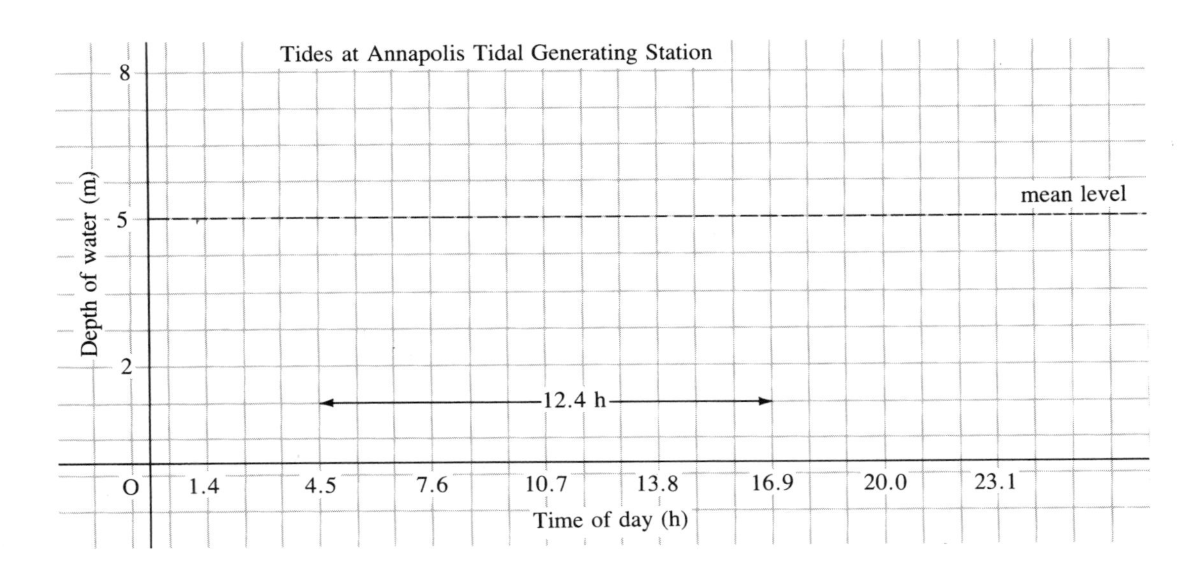

We can find the vertical displacement, the phase shift, the period, and the amplitude of the function from the graph, and use these to write an equation of the function.

Since the mean level is 5 m, the vertical displacement is 5 m.

The amplitude is the difference between high tide level and mean level, 3 m.

The first high tide occurs at 4.5 h. If we think of the function as a cosine function, then the phase shift is 4.5 h.

The period is the time between two high tides, 12.4 h.

Therefore, if h metres represents the depth, and t hours represents the time, an equation of the function is:

$$h = 3 \cos 2\pi\frac{(t - 4.5)}{12.4} + 5$$

Amplitude (3); Period (12.4); Mean level (5); Phase shift (time at first high tide) (4.5)

We can use this equation to calculate the depth of the water at any time during the day.

Example 1. Calculate the depth of the water to the nearest tenth of a metre at:
a) 9:30 A.M.   b) 6:45 P.M.

Solution. Convert the times to decimals of hours, on a 24 h clock.

9:30 A.M = 09.50 h

6:45 P.M. = (12 + 6.75) h
= 18.75 h

a) Substitute $t = 9.5$ in the above equation.

$$h = 3 \cos 2\pi\frac{(t - 4.5)}{12.4} + 5$$

$$= 3 \cos 2\pi\frac{(9.5 - 4.5)}{12.4} + 5$$

Use a scientific calculator in *radian mode* to evaluate this expression.

Key in:
9.5 [−] 4.5 [=] [÷] 12.4 [×] 2 [×] [π] [=] [cos] [×] 3 [+] 5 [=]
to display 2.5377097

At 9:30 A.M., the depth of the water is approximately 2.5 m.

b) Substitute $t = 18.75$ in the above equation.

$$h = 3 \cos 2\pi\frac{(t - 4.5)}{12.4} + 5$$

$$= 3 \cos 2\pi\frac{(18.75 - 4.5)}{12.4} + 5$$

$$\doteq 6.775\,631$$

At 6:45 P.M., the depth of the water is approximately 6.8 m.

If your calculator requires the function key to be pressed first you may need to use the memory or brackets to evaluate expressions such as those in *Example 1*.

The pattern suggested by *Example 1* can be used to solve other problems involving quantities which change periodically. In each case, we use a sinusoidal function to approximate the data. The general pattern in the equation of the function is shown below.

$$y = A \cos 2\pi\frac{(t - S)}{P} + M$$

- A: Amplitude
- P: Period
- S: Phase shift (value of t at first maximum)
- M: Mean value or vertical displacement

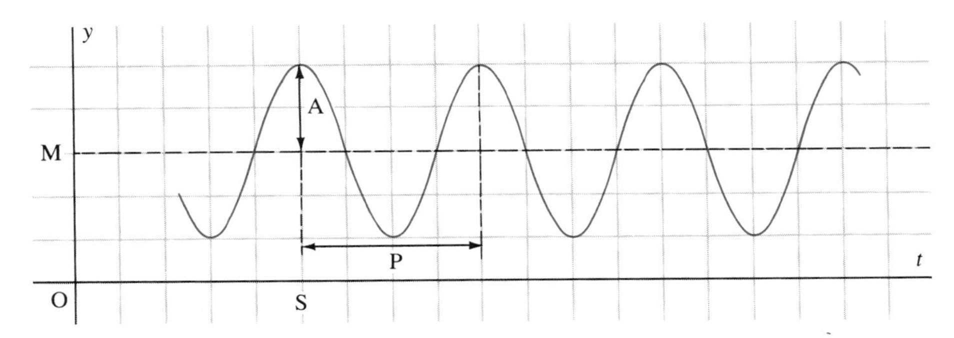

Example 2. A Ferris wheel with a radius of 20 m rotates once every 40 s. Passengers get on at point S, which is 1 m above level ground. Suppose you get on at S and the wheel starts to rotate.

a) Draw a graph showing how your height above the ground varies during the first two cycles.

b) Write an equation which expresses your height as a function of the elapsed time.

c) Calculate your height above the ground after 15 s.

Solution. a) *Step 1.* Draw a sinusoidal curve.

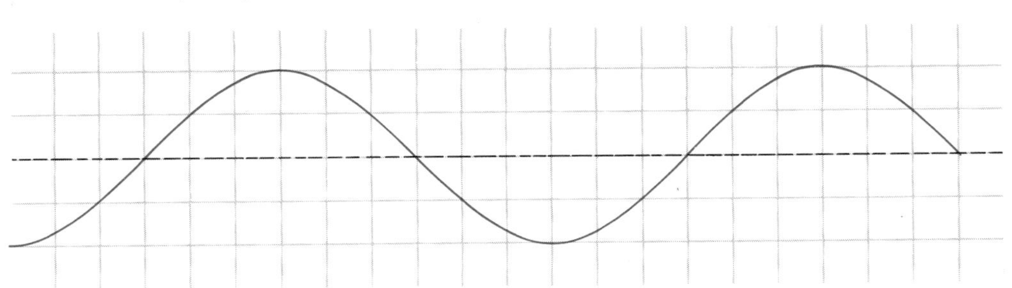

Step 2. Find the phase shift and the period, and use them to establish a horizontal scale.

For a cosine function, the phase shift is the t-coordinate of the first maximum, point A. Since you take 20 s to reach A, the phase shift is 20 s. Since the Ferris wheel rotates once every 40 s, the period is 40 s. Hence, the t-coordinates of two consecutive maximum points are 20 and 60.

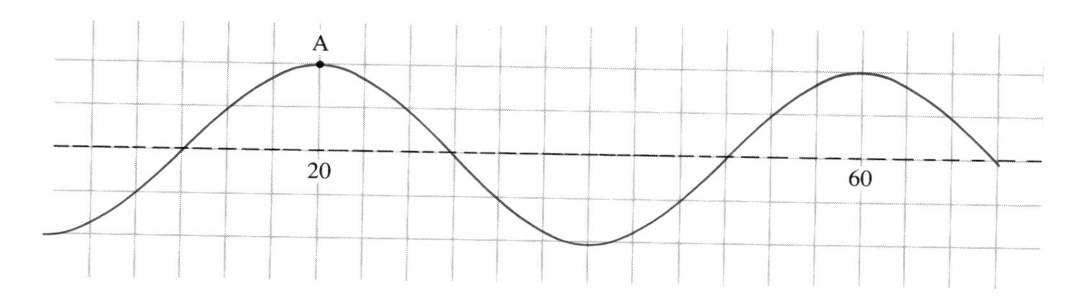

Step 3. Complete the graph by drawing the axes and their scales. The vertical displacement is 21 m, and the amplitude is 20 m. Since the people get on at the bottom, draw the vertical axis as shown.

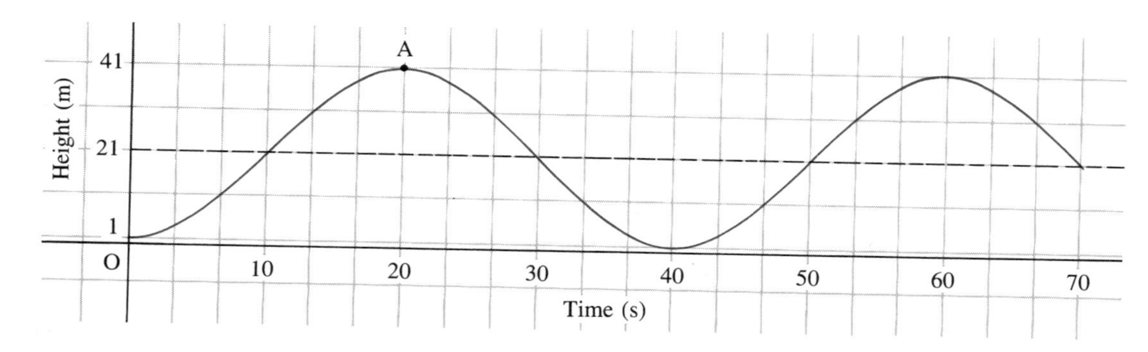

b) An equation which expresses your height as a function of time is:

$$h = 20 \cos 2\pi \frac{(t - 20)}{40} + 21.$$

c) To calculate your height above the ground after 15 s, substitute 15 for t in the above equation.

$$\begin{aligned} h &= 20 \cos 2\pi \frac{(t - 20)}{40} + 21 \\ &= 20 \cos 2\pi \frac{(15 - 20)}{40} + 21 \\ &\doteq 35.142\ 136 \end{aligned}$$

After 15 s you will be about 35 m above the ground.

EXERCISES 8-12

1. At a seaport, the depth of the water h metres at time t hours during a certain day is given by this formula.

$$h = 1.8 \sin 2\pi\frac{(t - 4.00)}{12.4} + 3.1$$

a) Calculate the depth of the water at 5 A.M. and at 12 noon.
b) What is the maximum depth of the water? When does it occur?

2. The equation below gives the depth of the water h metres at an ocean port at any time t hours during a certain day.

$$h = 2.5 \sin 2\pi\frac{(t - 1.5)}{12.4} + 4.3$$

Calculate the approximate depth of the water at 9:30 A.M.

(B)

3. At an ocean port, the water has a maximum depth of 4 m above the mean level at 8 A.M., and the period is 12.4 h.
   a) Assuming that the relation between the depth of the water and time is a sinusoidal function, write an equation for the depth of the water at any time t.
   b) Find the depth of the water at 10 A.M.

4. Tidal forces are greatest when the Earth, the sun, and the moon are in line. When this occurs at the Annapolis Tidal Generating Station, the water has a maximum depth of 9.6 m at 4:30 A.M. and a minimum depth of 0.4 m 6.2 h later.
   a) Write an equation for the depth of the water at any time t.
   b) Calculate the depth of the water at 9:30 A.M. and at 6:45 P.M.
   c) Compare the results of part b) with *Example 1*.

5. Repeat *Exercise 4* when the tidal forces are weakest. The maximum and minimum depths of the water at this time are 6.4 m and 3.6 m.

6. A certain mass is supported by a spring so that it is at rest 0.5 m above a table top. The mass is pulled down 0.4 m and released at time $t = 0$, creating a periodic up and down motion, called *simple harmonic motion*. It takes 1.2 s for the mass to return to the low position each time.
   a) Draw a graph showing the height of the mass above the table top as a function of time for the first 2.0 s.
   b) Write an equation for the function in part a).
   c) Use your equation to determine the height of the mass above the table top after: i) 0.3 s ii) 0.7 s iii) 1.2 s.

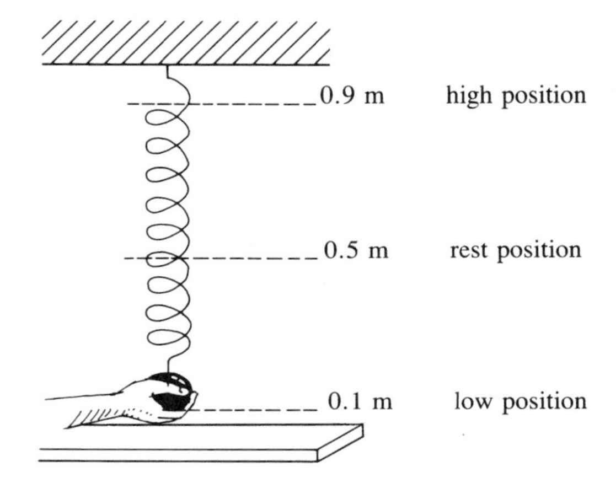

7. A Ferris wheel has a radius of 25 m, and its centre is 26 m above the ground. It rotates once every 50 s. Suppose you get on at the bottom at $t = 0$.
   a) Draw a graph showing how your height above the ground changes during the first two minutes.
   b) Write an equation for the function in part a).
   c) Use your equation to determine how high you will be above the ground after:
      i) 10 s   ii) 20 s   iii) 40 s   iv) 60 s.

8. The pedals of a bicycle are mounted on a bracket whose centre is 29.0 cm above the ground. Each pedal is 16.5 cm from the bracket. Assume that the bicycle is pedalled at the rate of 12 cycles per minute.

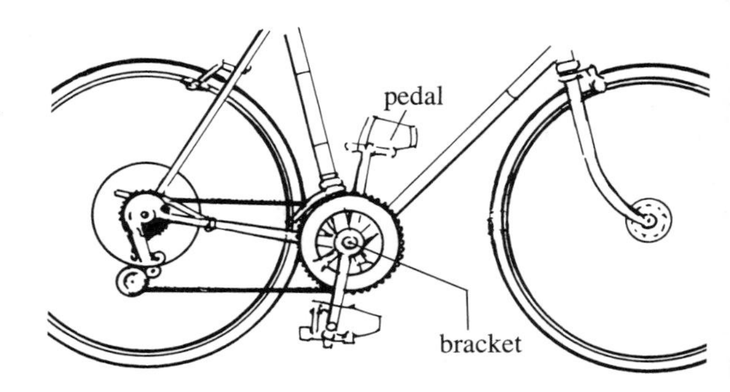

   a) Draw a graph showing the height of a pedal above the ground for the first few cycles. Assume that the pedal starts at the topmost position at $t = 0$.
   b) Write an equation for the function in part a).
   c) Use your equation to determine the height of the pedal after:
      i) 5 s   ii) 12 s   iii) 18 s.

9. The graph shows how the time of the sunset at Edmonton varies during the year.
   a) Write an equation which gives the time of the sunset on the nth day of the year.
   b) Use the equation found in part a) to calculate, to the nearest minute, the time of the sunset on:
      i) May 10 (day 130)
      ii) June 12 (day 163)
      iii) September 17 (day 260)
      iv) December 2 (day 336).

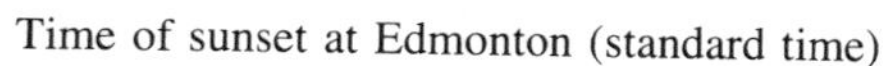
Time of sunset at Edmonton (standard time)

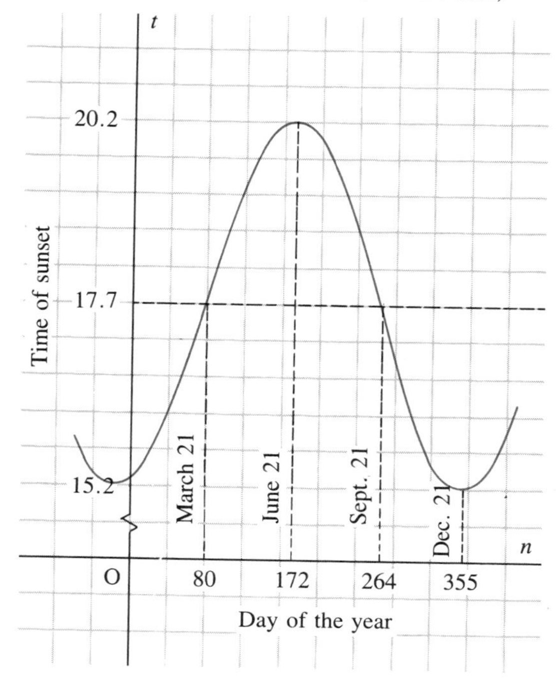

10. A graph showing the time of the sunset at Ottawa was shown on page 304.
    a) Write an equation which can be used to find the time of the sunset at Ottawa on the nth day of the year. (Assume it is not a leap year.)
    b) Use the equation to find the time of the sunset at Ottawa on:
       i) February 20   ii) April 14
       iii) July 25   iv) November 5.

11. At St. John's, the time of the sunrise on the nth day of the year is given by this formula.

$$t = 1.89 \sin 2\pi\frac{(n - 80)}{365} + 6.41$$

a) Calculate the time the sun rises on October 20 (day 293).
b) Give one significant reason why the actual time of the sunrise on October 20 may differ somewhat from your answer in part a).

12. On December 21 each year, the sun is closest to the Earth, at approximately 147.2 million kilometres. On June 21 the sun is at its greatest distance, approximately 152.2 million kilometres.

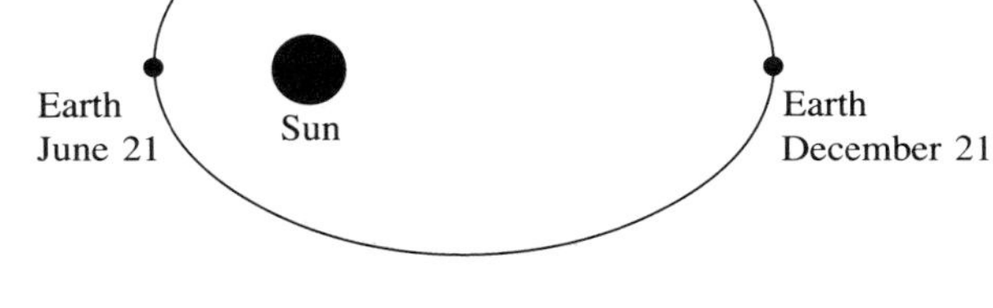

a) Express the distance d from the Earth to the sun as a sinusoidal function of the number of the day of the year.
b) Use the function to calculate the approximate distance from the Earth to the sun on:
i) March 1 ii) April 30 iii) September 2.

Ⓒ

13. a) In *Example 1*, if the calculator is in *degree mode*, what change would have to be made in the equation?
b) Solve *Example 1* using your calculator in degree mode.

14. In the solution of *Example 1*, a cosine function was used. Solve *Example 1* using a sine function.

15. On the nth day of the year, the number of hours of daylight at Victoria is given by this formula.

$$h = 3.98 \sin 2\pi\frac{(n - 80)}{365} + 12.16$$

a) About how many hours of daylight should there be today?
b) On what dates should there be about 10 h of daylight?

16. In *Example 1*, calculate to the nearest minute the first time after 4:30 A.M. when the depth of the water is: a) 6.0 m b) 3.0 m.

1. From an almanac or newspaper files, determine the approximate time the sun rises and sets in your locality on June 21 and December 21.
2. Determine equations which represent the time the sun rises and sets on the nth day of the year.
3. Use the equations to predict the time the sun rises and sets today, and check your results in the newspaper.

Review Exercises

1. Draw each angle in standard position, then find two angles which are coterminal with it.
   a) $65°$ b) $135°$ c) $200°$ d) $-450°$
   e) $\frac{\pi}{3}$ f) $\frac{5\pi}{4}$ g) $-\frac{\pi}{6}$ h) $\frac{8\pi}{3}$

2. Determine the sine, the cosine, and the tangent to 3 decimal places of each angle in *Exercise 1*.

3. Each point P is on the terminal arm of angle θ. Find $\sin \theta$, $\cos \theta$, and $\tan \theta$ to 3 decimal places.
   a) P(4,9) b) P(8, −15) c) P(−4,7) d) P(−6, −5)

4. Find each value of θ in *Exercise 3*:
   i) in degrees to 1 decimal place ii) in radians to 3 decimal places.

5. Solve for θ to the nearest degree, $0° \leqslant \theta \leqslant 360°$.
   a) $\sin \theta = 0.7295$ b) $\cos \theta = -0.3862$ c) $\tan \theta = -5.1730$

6. Solve for θ in radians to 2 decimal places, $0 \leqslant \theta \leqslant 2\pi$.
   a) $\cos \theta = 0.2681$ b) $\tan \theta = 1.0744$ c) $\sin \theta = -0.4683$

7. Solve for θ to the nearest degree, $0° \leqslant \theta \leqslant 360°$.
   a) $3 \sin \theta + 2 = 0$ b) $2 \tan \theta - 5 = 2$
   c) $12 \sin^2\theta - 11 \sin \theta + 2 = 0$ d) $3 \cos^2\theta + 4 \cos \theta - 2 = 0$
   e) $3 \cos^2\theta + 2 = 4$ f) $2 \sin^2\theta + 5 \sin \theta + 1 = 0$

8. Draw graphs of $y = \sin \theta$ and $y = \cos \theta$ for $-360° \leqslant \theta \leqslant 360°$. For each graph
   a) State the maximum value of y, and the values of θ for which it occurs.
   b) State the minimum value of y, and the values of θ for which it occurs.
   c) State the θ- and y-intercepts.

9. Find the amplitude, the period, the phase shift, and the vertical displacement for each function.
   a) $y = 3 \sin 2(\theta - 45°) - 4$ b) $y = -2 \cos 5\left(\theta + \frac{\pi}{3}\right) + 1$

10. Sketch the graphs of each set of functions on the same grid for $-2\pi \leqslant \theta \leqslant 2\pi$.
    a) $y = \sin \theta$ $y = 3 \sin \theta$ $y = 3 \sin \theta + 2$
    b) $y = \frac{1}{2} \cos \theta$ $y = \frac{1}{2} \cos \left(\theta + \frac{\pi}{3}\right)$ $y = \frac{1}{2} \cos \left(\theta + \frac{\pi}{3}\right) + 2$

11. Sketch the graph of each function.
    a) $y = \frac{1}{2} \sin 2\pi \frac{(t + 1)}{2} - 3$ b) $y = -3 \sin 2\pi \frac{(t - 2)}{5} + 2$

12. A Ferris wheel of radius 16 m rotates once every 48 s. The passengers get on at a point 1 m above ground level.
    a) Write an equation to express the height h metres of a passenger above the ground at any time t seconds.
    b) How high is a passenger after: i) 10 s ii) 25 s?

9 Transformations of Functions

The volume occupied by a gas is a function of its temperature. When it is heated it expands; conversely, when it is cooled, it contracts. Can a gas ever be cooled enough to have a volume of zero? (See Section 9-3 *Example 3*.)

9-1 SOME FUNCTIONS AND THEIR GRAPHS

In the preceding chapter we saw that the graphs of the trigonometric functions have characteristic shapes. In particular, the graphs of the sine and cosine functions are sinusoidal curves. In this chapter, we shall investigate other functions, some of which are illustrated in this section.

From studies of waves, oceanographers have learned that certain properties of waves are related. These relationships provide examples of some functions and the characteristic shapes of their graphs.

Linear Functions

As a general rule, the wavelength (distance between crests) is approximately 7 times the height. The equation expressing this relationship is $L = 7h$, where L is the wavelength and h is the height.

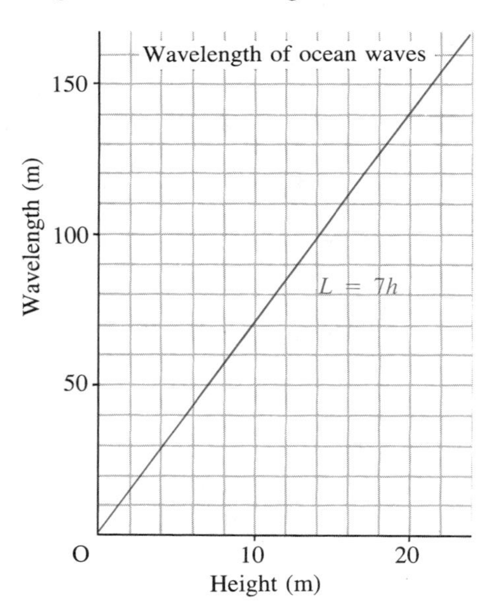

A simple linear function is $y = x$. Its graph is a straight line with slope 1, which passes through the origin. The graphs of other linear functions are also straight lines.

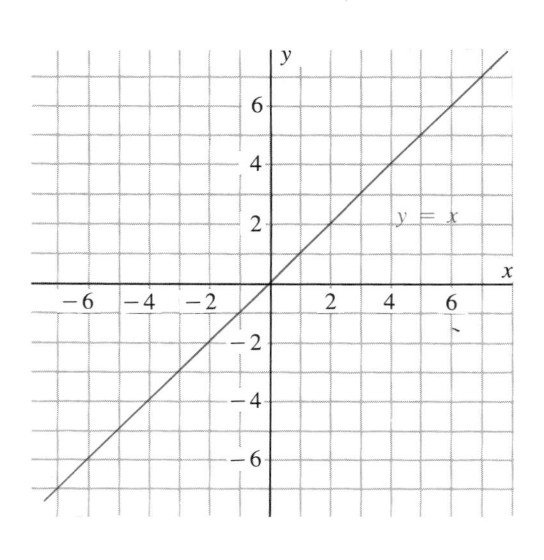

Examples of other linear functions are $y = 3x - 2$ and $f(x) = -5x + 1$. The slope and vertical intercept of each line are determined by the numbers in its equation.

Linear functions occur in a wide variety of applications such as commissions, sports records, taxi fares, and the temperature of the atmosphere.

Quadratic Functions

The length of a wave is also a function of its velocity. The equation $L = 0.64v^2$ expresses the wavelength L metres as a function of the velocity v metres per second.

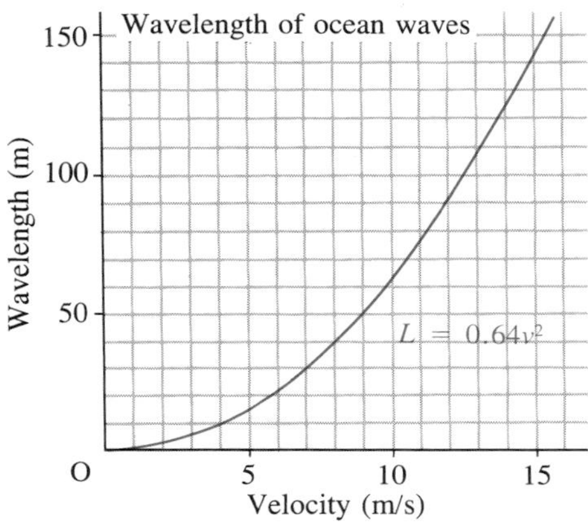

A simple quadratic function is $y = x^2$. Its graph is a parabola opening upwards, with vertex (0,0) and axis of symmetry the y-axis. The graphs of other quadratic functions are also parabolas, opening up or down.

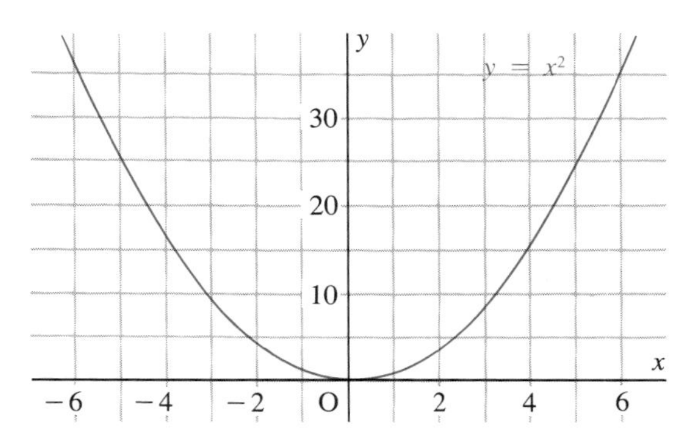

Examples of other quadratic functions are $y = 3x^2 - 5x$ and $f(x) = -2(x + 1)^2 + 4$. The position and appearance of a parabola depend on the numbers in its equation.

Applications of quadratic functions include ballistics, oceanography, electronics, and fuel economy.

Square-Root Functions

In shallow water, the velocity of a wave is a function of the depth of the water. The equation $v = 3.1\sqrt{d}$ expresses the velocity v metres per second as a function of the depth d metres.

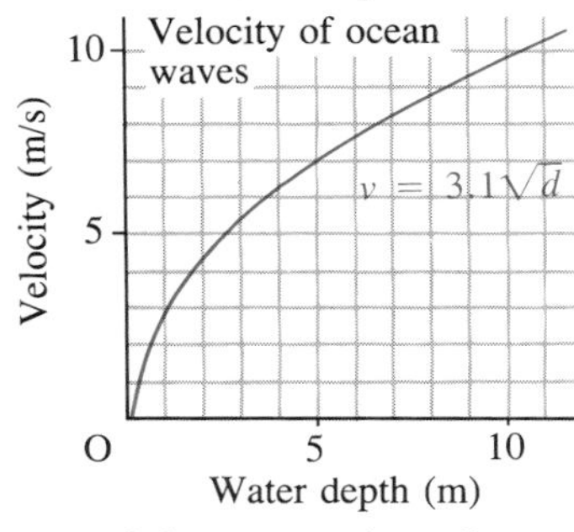

A simple square-root function is $y = \sqrt{x}$, where $x \geqslant 0$. The graph of a square-root function starts at a fixed point and extends in one direction only. The curve is part of a parabola.

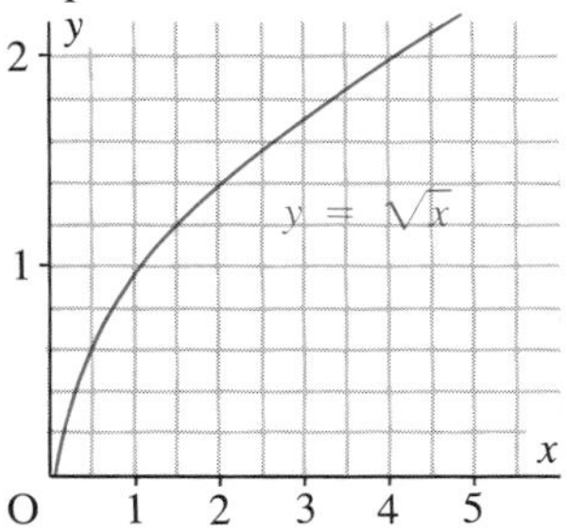

Other examples of square-root functions are $y = 2\sqrt{x - 5}$, $x \geqslant 5$ and $f(x) = 0.5\sqrt{3x + 1} + 2$, $x \geqslant -\frac{1}{3}$.

Applications of square-root functions include the motion of pendulums, the distance to the horizon, and inventory control.

The graphs of the above functions have characteristic shapes. Examples of three other functions with characteristic shapes are illustrated below.

Cubic Functions An example of a cubic function is $y = x^3$.

$y = x^3$

x	y
−3	−27
−2	−8
−1	−1
0	0
1	1
2	8
3	27

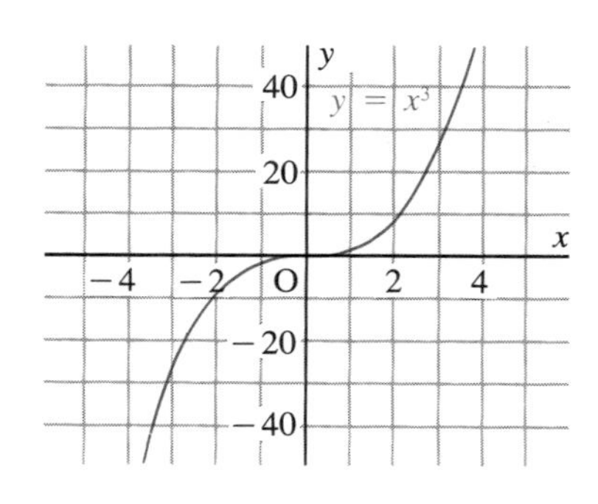

Cubic functions are examples of a large group of functions called *polynomial functions*. Other examples of polynomial functions are $f(x) = x^4 - x^2 + x$ and $y = x^2 - 5x + 2$.

Absolute-Value Functions An example of an absolute-value function is $y = |x|$.

$y = |x|$

x	y
−3	3
−2	2
−1	1
0	0
1	1
2	2
3	3

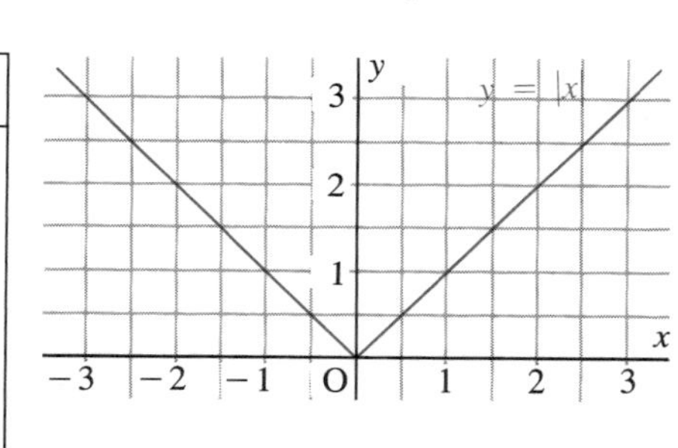

There are two parts to the graph, depending on whether x is positive or negative. If $x \geqslant 0$, the graph is the same as the graph of $y = x$. If $x < 0$, the graph is the same as the graph of $y = -x$.

Semicircle Functions An example of a semicircle function is $y = \sqrt{25 - x^2}$.

$y = \sqrt{25 - x^2}$

x	y
±5	0
±4	3
±3	4
0	5

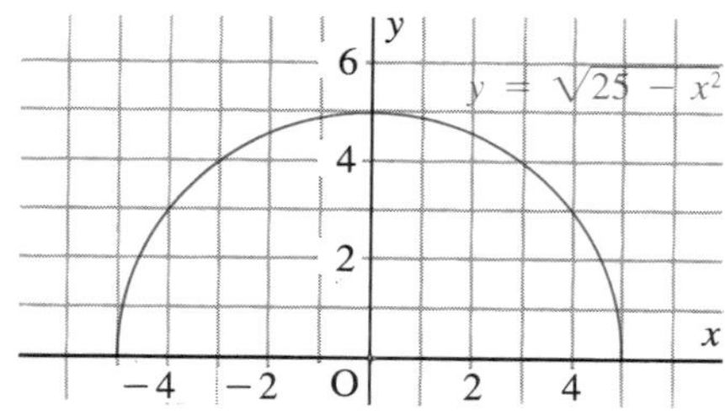

This is a semicircle with centre (0,0) and radius $\sqrt{25}$, or 5. Since the graphs of semicircle functions are semicircles, they are easy to sketch without making a table of values.

In Chapter 8, we saw how to transform the graphs of the sine and cosine functions so that they could be applied to problems involving quantities that change periodically. In other applications, such as those illustrated in this section, the equation and the graph of the corresponding functions are transformed in a similar way. In this chapter we will investigate how the changes in the equations are related to the changes in the graphs.

EXERCISES 9-1

(A)

1. Classify each function as linear, quadratic, square root, cubic, absolute value or semicircle.

a)

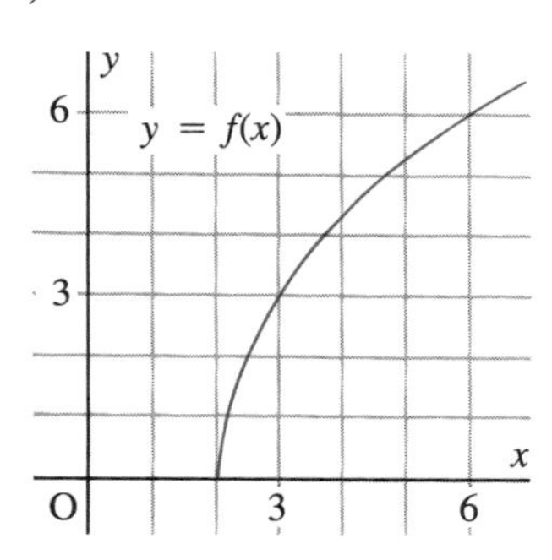

b)

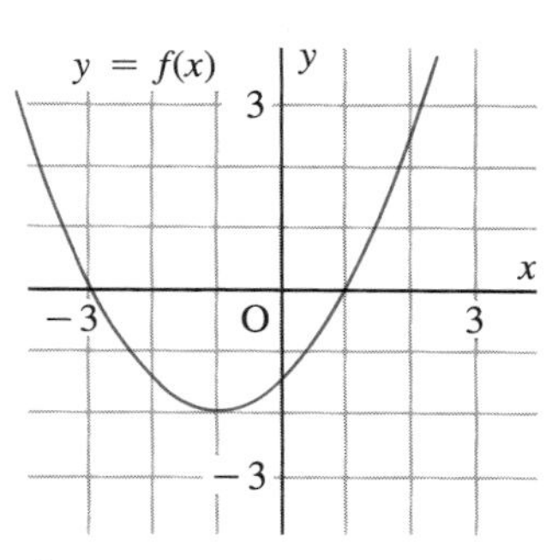

c)

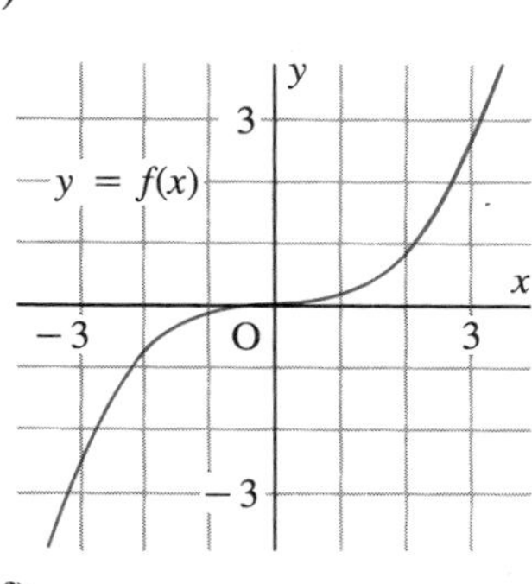

d)

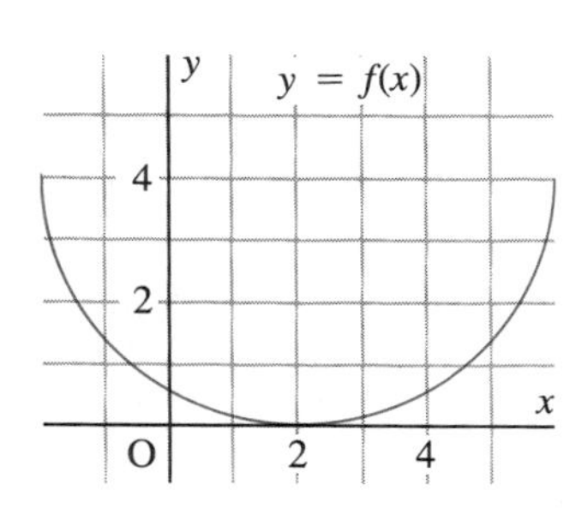

e)

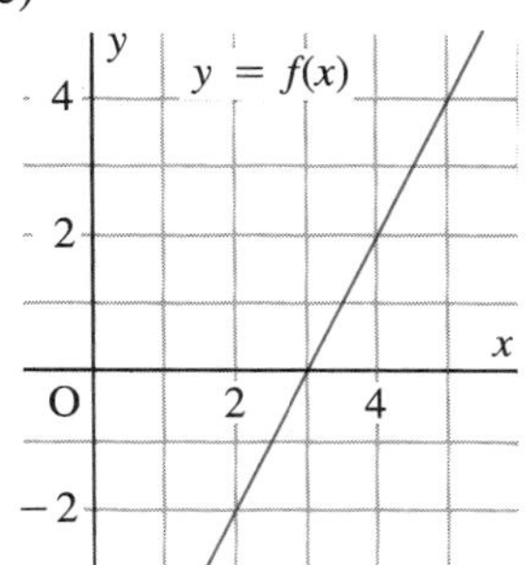

f)

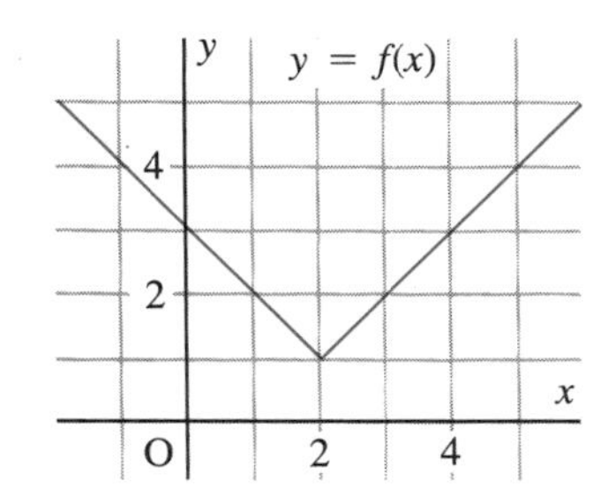

2. Classify each function.
   a) The area of a circle with diameter d is $A = 0.25\pi d^2$.
   b) The period T seconds of a pendulum with length l metres is $T \doteq 2\sqrt{l}$.
   c) If \$100 is invested at an annual interest rate i, the balance A after one year is given by $A = \$100(1 + i)$.
   d) If \$100 is invested at an annual interest rate i, the balance A after two years is given by $A = \$100(1 + i)^2$.
   e) In a certain tract of forest the value V dollars of lumber obtained from a tree x years old is estimated using the formula $V = 0.01x^3 - 5x^2 + 700x$.

(B)

3. a) Using a table of values, graph each absolute-value function.
 i) $y = |x - 4|$ ii) $y = |x - 2|$ iii) $y = |x + 3|$
 b) State the domain and the range of each function in part a).
 c) Describe how the graph of $y = |x - a|$ changes as a changes.

4. In each diagram, the shaded area is equal to the unshaded area. Express y as a function of x in each case. What kind of function is it?

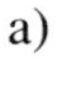

a)
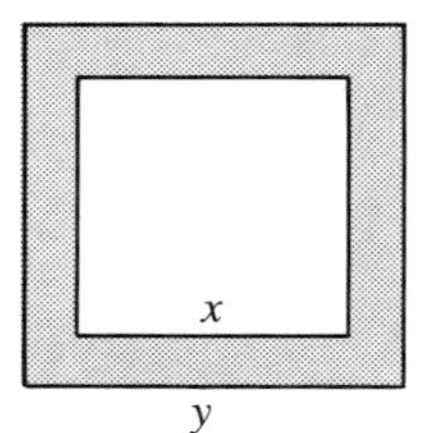

b)
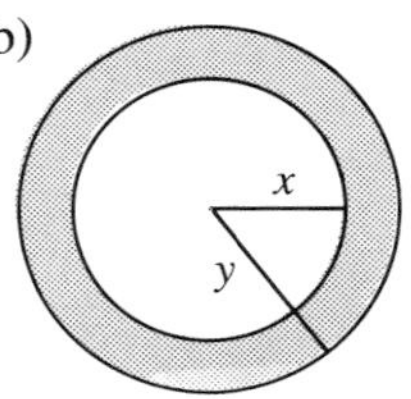

c)
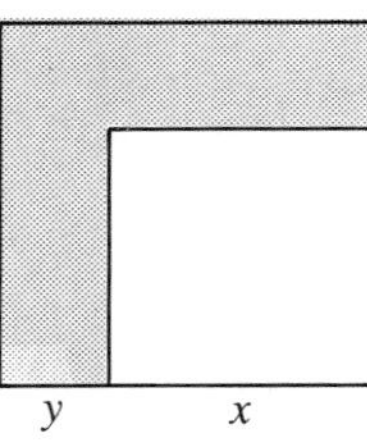

d)
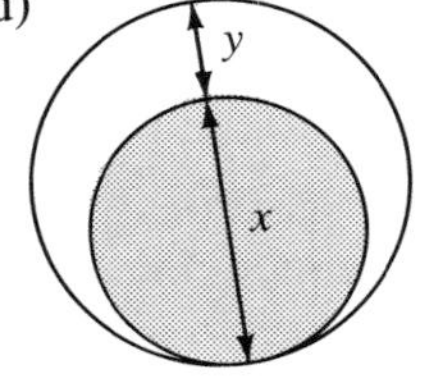

5. A square (below left) with sides of length s is divided into three regions with equal areas by two segments of length x passing through a vertex. Express:
 a) h as a function of s b) x as a function of s.

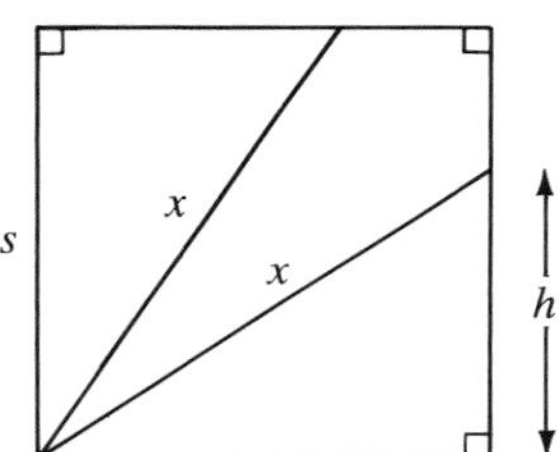

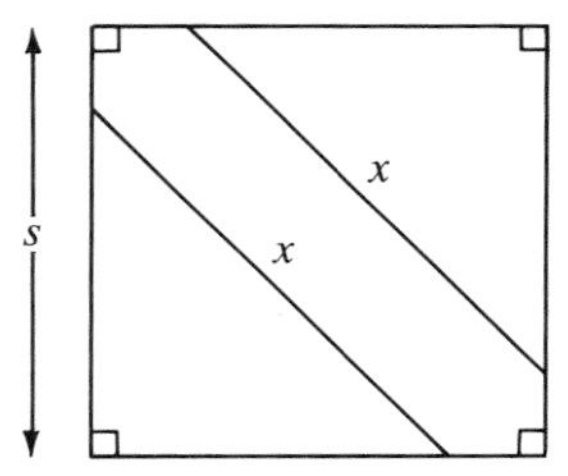

6. A square (above right) with sides of length s is divided into three regions with equal areas by two segments of length x parallel to a diagonal. Express x as a function of s.

7. The erosive power E of the wind is a cubic function of the wind velocity v. The equation is $E = kv^3$, where k is a constant.
 a) How does the erosive power of the wind change if the wind velocity changes from 3 m/s to: i) 6 m/s ii) 9 m/s iii) 12 m/s?
 b) Which of these graphs best represents the relation between the erosive power and the wind velocity?

i)
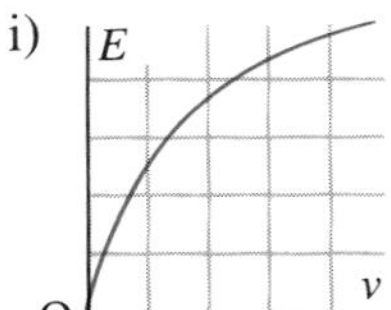

ii)
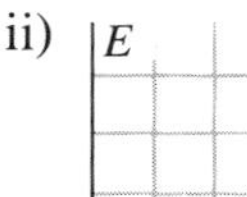
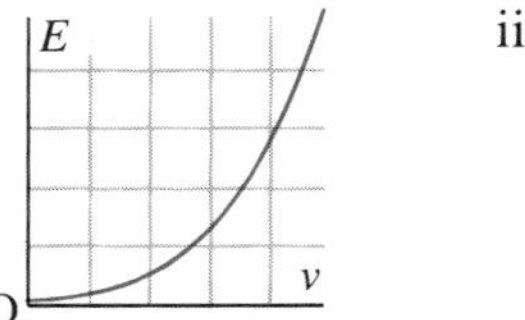

iii)
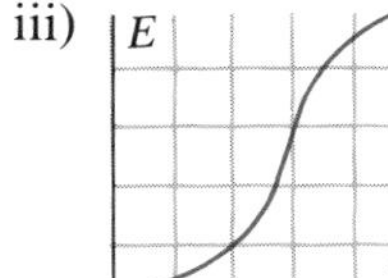

8. The amount of radiation a star emits is a function of its temperature. The total energy E radiated from a star varies as the fourth power of the Kelvin temperature T. The equation is $E = kT^4$, where k is a constant.

Star	Temperature
Sun	6 000°K
Sirius	10 000°K
Antares	3 600°K

a) How does the energy radiated from each star compare with the energy radiated from the sun?
i) Sirius ii) Antares

b) Which graph best represents the relation between energy radiated and Kelvin temperature?

i) 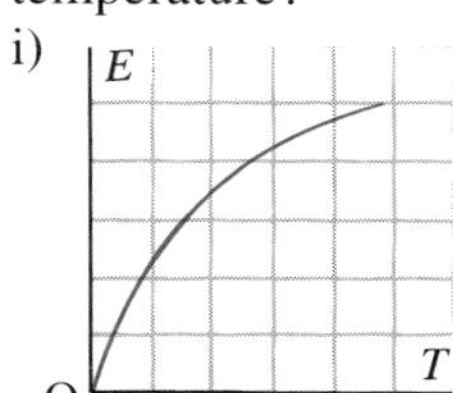

ii) 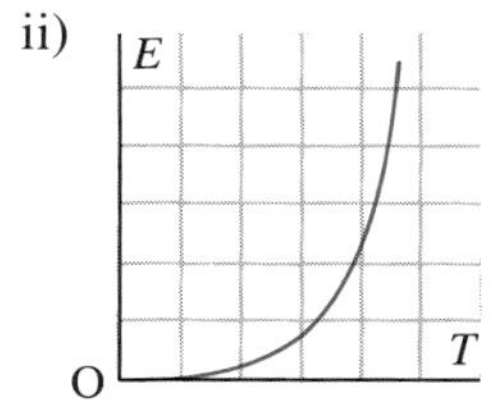

iii) 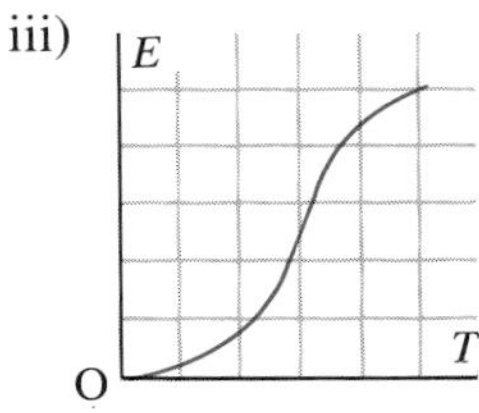

Ⓒ

9. *Power functions* have equations of the form $y = x^a$, where x is a real number, and a is a constant. The graphs of six typical power functions are shown. In each case, determine a reasonable value of a such that the graph represents the function $y = x^a$.

a) 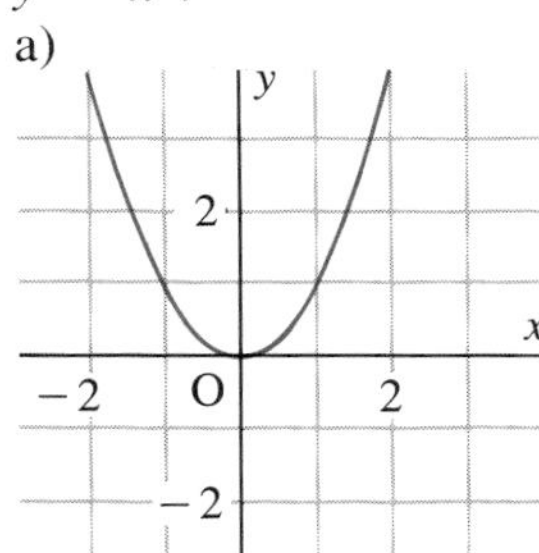

b) 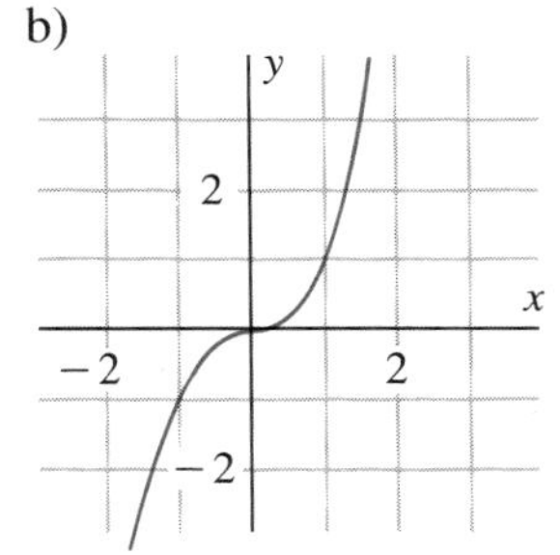

c) 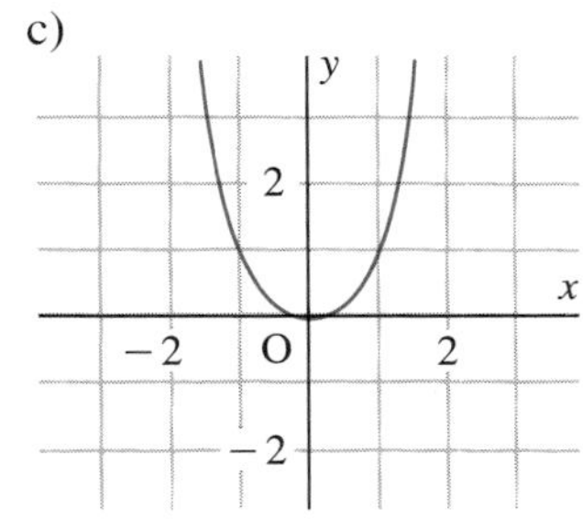

d) 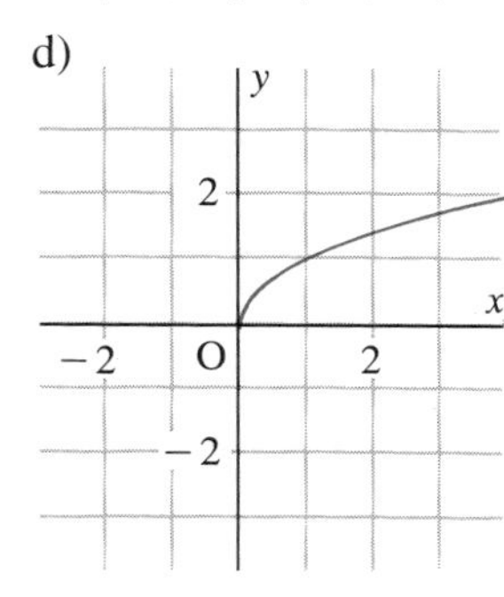

e) 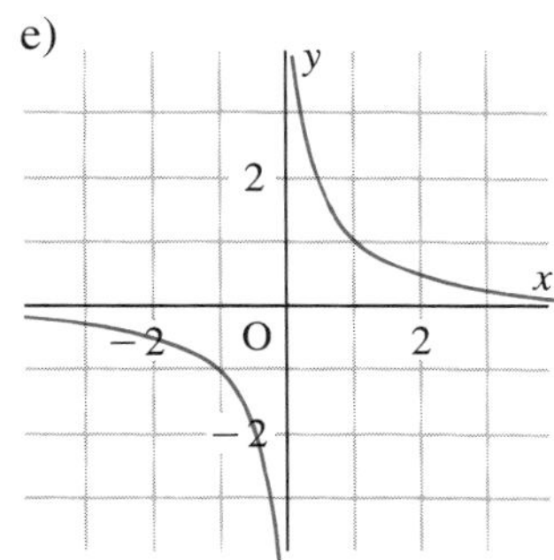

f) 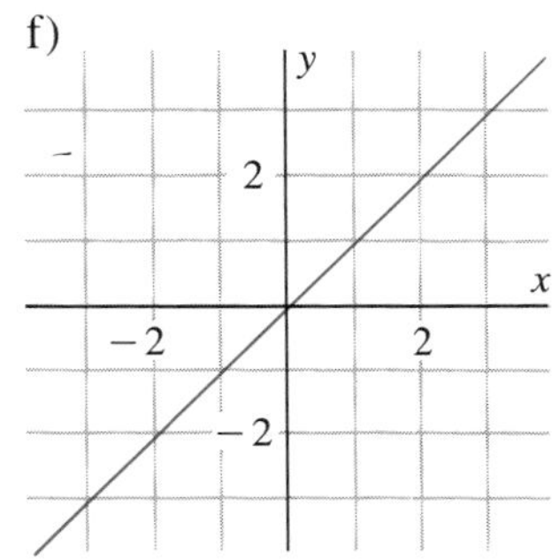

10. If several power functions were graphed on the same grid, would they have any points in common? Explain how you know.

11. A circle with radius R is inscribed in a square. A smaller circle with radius r touches two sides of the square and the larger circle as shown. Express r as a function of R.

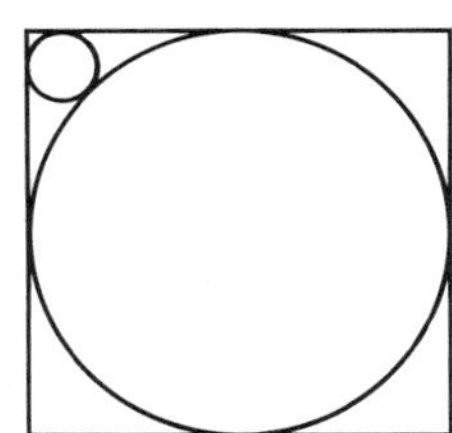

THE MATHEMATICAL MIND

Problems Computers Can't Solve

Even the world's fastest supercomputers have limitations. Some practical problems require so much computation that one would need a computer as large as the universe, operating for as long as the age of the universe.

The Travelling Salesman Problem
Bob sells farm machinery and lives in Goderich, Ontario. He must make calls in each town shown on the map. What is the shortest distance he could travel before returning home?

This problem can be solved by systematic trial. But for 100 towns it would take the world's fastest computers centuries to solve the problem. No one has yet been able to give a general solution for any number of cities.

If a solution is ever found, it could be applied to similar problems such as making deliveries, collecting money from vending machines, and routing telephone calls.

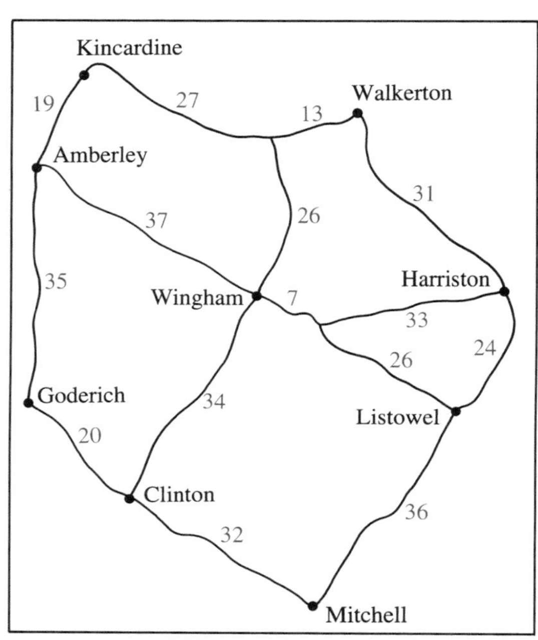

What is the shortest route which passes through each town?

The Bin-Packing Problem
A manufacturer has items with masses as indicated. What is the least number of bins needed to pack the items if each bin can hold no more than 1 kg?

For a small number of items this problem can also be solved by systematic trial. But for 100 items the number of possible packings is so great that even if all the computing power in the world were available, it is very unlikely that the problem would ever be solved.

If a general solution is found, it could be applied to similar problems such as cutting material with the least amount of waste, and scheduling television commercials.

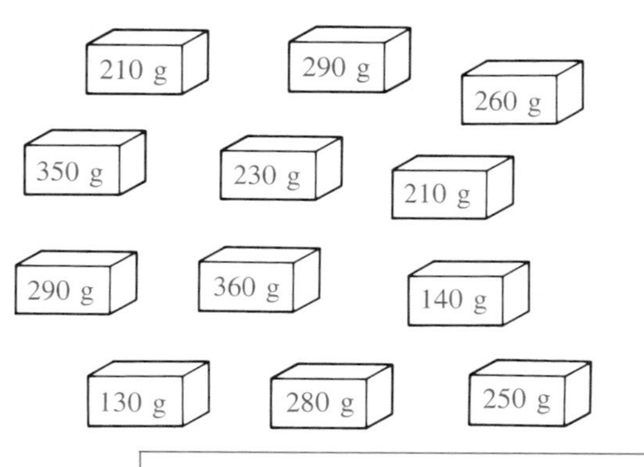

What is the least number of 1 kg bins needed to pack the items with masses indicated?

There are elaborate algorithms (step-by-step procedures) for solving these problems, but they are not much better than the simplest one: list all the possibilities and choose the best one. But it can be shown that the time required to do this is an exponential function of the size of the problem, n. For example, in the two problems on the opposite page, $n = 9$ (there are 9 towns) and $n = 12$ (there are 12 items). For larger values of n, say 100, this algorithm is far too slow, even for the world's fastest supercomputers.

The travelling salesman problem and the bin-packing problem are examples of what are known as *NP-complete* problems. This concept was introduced in 1971 by Stephen Cook of the University of Toronto. These are a certain kind of problem that some computer scientists think can never be solved. Since 1971, Stephen Cook has gained worldwide recognition for his work on the problem of showing what computers cannot do.

Mathematicians think that our inability to discover an efficient algorithm for such problems is inherent in the nature of the problems themselves, because the time required to solve the problem is an exponential function of the size of the problem.

QUESTIONS

1. Use systematic trial to solve the two problems on the opposite page.
2. A carpenter is making wooden inserts for windows. He needs pieces of trim as follows.
   44 cm (4 pieces)
   59 cm (6 pieces)
   74 cm (6 pieces)
   88 cm (4 pieces)
   145 cm (3 pieces)
   The total length of the pieces is less than 18 m. Determine if it is possible to cut them from six 3 m lengths of trim.
3. If the time required to solve a problem is a polynomial function of the size of the problem, then the problem can be solved by a computer in a reasonable time. To see why, compare polynomial and exponential functions as follows.
   A polynomial function $y = f(x)$ and an exponential function $y = g(x)$ are given. Use a calculator to evaluate each function for $x = 10$, 50, 100, and 300.
   a) $f(x) = x^2$ and $g(x) = 2^x$
   b) $f(x) = x^3$ and $g(x) = 1.5^x$
   c) $f(x) = x^{10}$ and $g(x) = 1.1^x$
4. Based on the results of *Question 3*, what conclusion might you make about how the values of exponential and polynomial functions compare for large values of the variable?

9-2 GRAPHING $y = f(x) + q$

In this and the following sections we shall develop a technique for sketching the graphs of functions without tables of values. The first step is to investigate the effect on the graph of $y = f(x)$ of adding some constant q to get $y = f(x) + q$.

The following example illustrates this effect for the quadratic function $y = x^2$. We substitute different values for q in $y = x^2 + q$, and graph the resulting functions. These graphs are images of $y = x^2$.

If $q = 0$, the equation is $y = x^2$.

If $q = 3$, the equation is $y = x^2 + 3$. If we were to graph this function using a table of values, we would start with values of x, square them, and then add 3. The values of y would all be 3 greater than those in $y = x^2$. Hence, the graph of $y = x^2 + 3$ is 3 units above the graph of $y = x^2$.

Similarly, if $q = -5$, the equation is $y = x^2 - 5$. The graph of this function is 5 units below the graph of $y = x^2$.

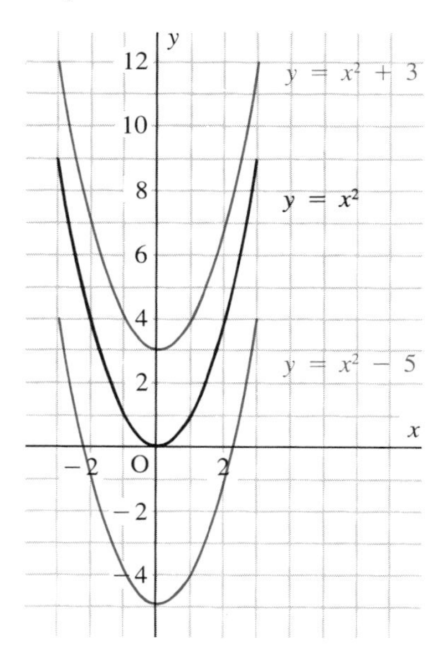

Similar results will be found using other values of q, and for functions other than quadratic functions.

In general, adding a positive or a negative constant to any function $y = f(x)$ causes a vertical translation of its graph.

The graph of $y = f(x) + q$ is related to that of $y = f(x)$ by a vertical translation.

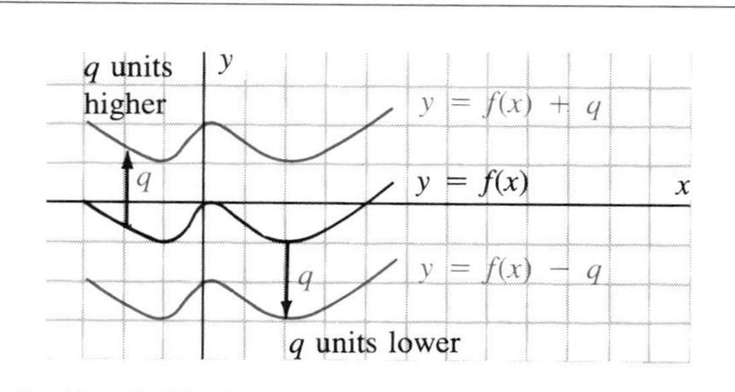

We can sketch graphs of equations in this form without making tables of values.

Example. a) Sketch the graph of $y = |x| - 4$ for $-5 \leqslant x \leqslant 5$.
b) What are the x- and y-intercepts of the graph?

Solution. a) Sketch the graph of $y = |x|$. The graph of $y = |x| - 4$ is then obtained by translating this graph 4 units down.

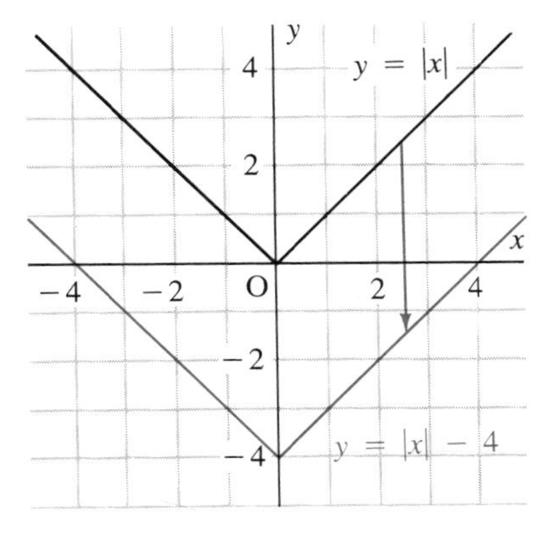

b) The intercepts may be found from the graph or from the equation.
From the graph, the x-intercepts are 4 and -4, and the y-intercept is -4.
To find the x-intercepts from the equation, let $y = 0$.

$|x| - 4 = 0$
$|x| = 4$
$x = \pm 4$

The x-intercepts are 4 and -4.
To find the y-intercept from the equation, let $x = 0$.

$y = |0| - 4$
$= -4$

The y-intercept is -4.

EXERCISES 9-2

Ⓐ

1. a) Graph these functions on the same grid for $-4 \leqslant x \leqslant 4$.
$y = x^2$ $\quad y = x^2 + 2$ $\quad y = x^2 + 6$
$y = x^2 - 2$ $\quad y = x^2 - 4$ $\quad y = x^2 - 7$
b) Describe the effect of various values of q on the graph of $y = x^2 + q$.

2. State which graph best represents each function.
a) $y = \sqrt{x} - 2$ b) $y = |x| + 3$ c) $y = 2x^2 + 1$

i)

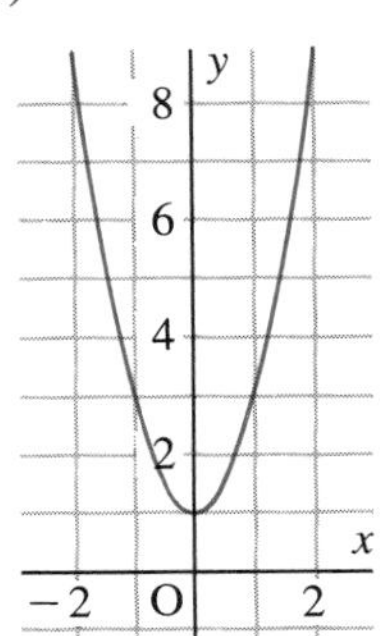

ii)

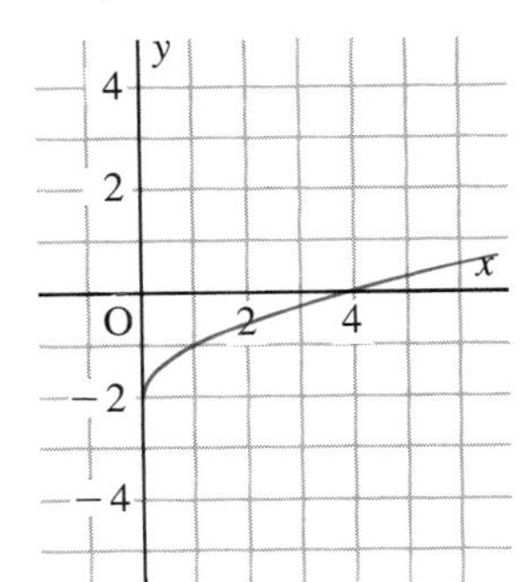

iii)

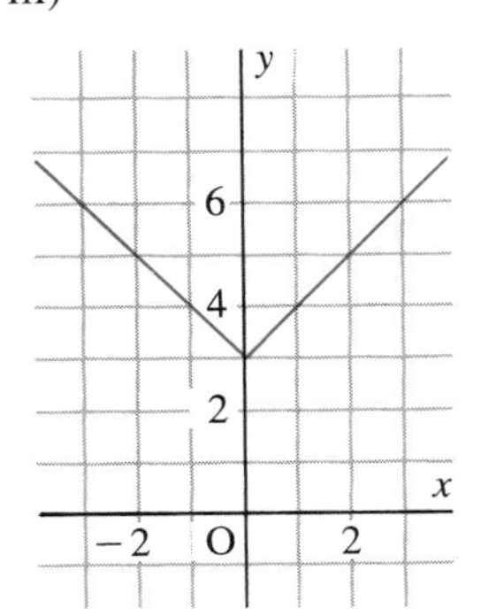

3. Write an equation that could describe each graph.

a) 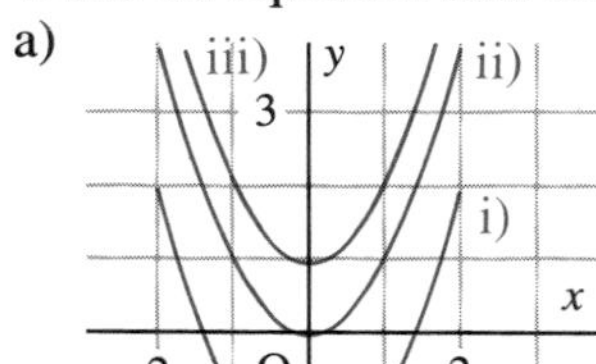

b) 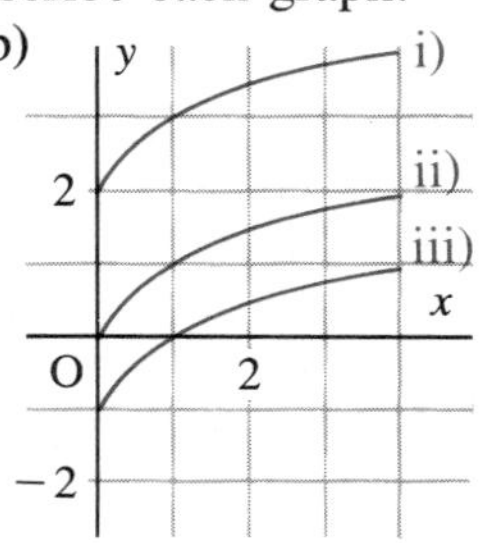

c) 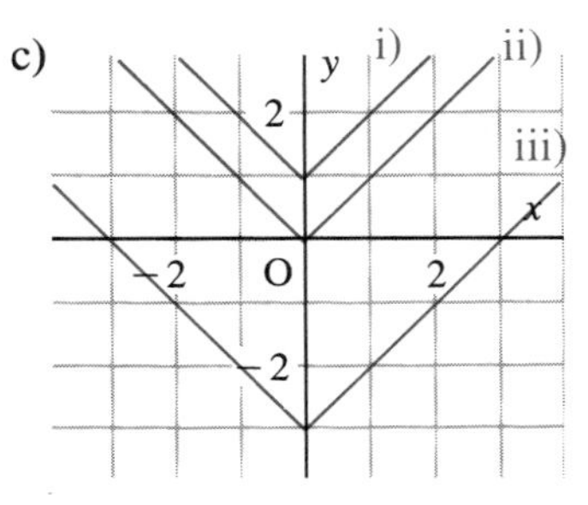

4. Sketch each set of graphs on the same grid without using a table of values.
   a) $y = 2x^2$ $\quad y = 2x^2 - 5$ $\quad y = 2x^2 + 3$
   b) $y = x^3$ $\quad y = x^3 - 5$ $\quad y = x^3 + 2$
   c) $y = \sqrt{x}$ $\quad y = \sqrt{x} - 3$ $\quad y = \sqrt{x} + 2$

Ⓑ

5. Select the function best represented by each graph.
   i) $y = \sqrt{9 - x^2} + 4$ $\quad$ ii) $y = \sqrt{9 - x^2} - 4$ $\quad$ iii) $y = x^3 + 4$
   iv) $y = x^3 - 4$ $\quad$ v) $y = |x| + 4$ $\quad$ vi) $y = |x| - 4$

a) 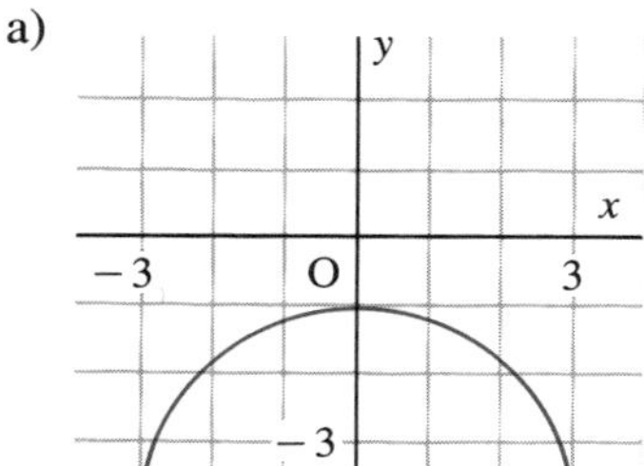

b) 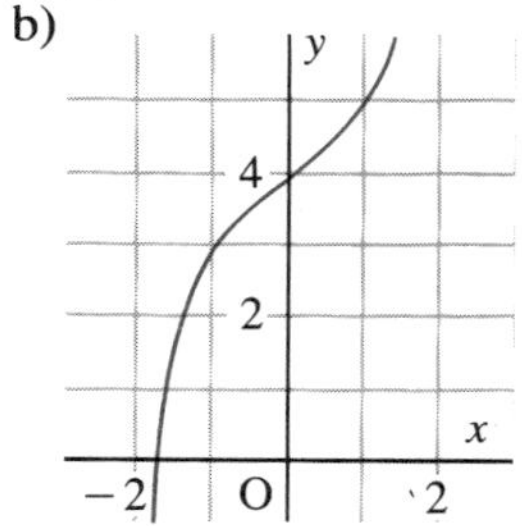

c) 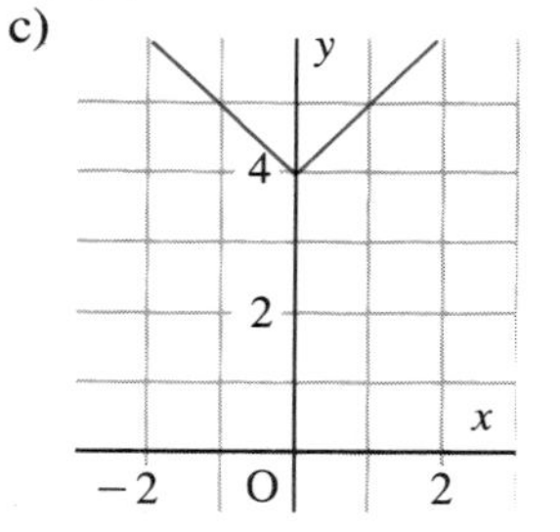

6. Sketch each set of graphs on the same grid.
   a) $y = -\sqrt{x}$ $\quad y = -\sqrt{x} + 4$ $\quad y = -\sqrt{x} - 2$
   b) $y = |x|$ $\quad y = |x| + 1$ $\quad y = |x| - 3$
   c) $y = \sin\theta$ $\quad y = \sin\theta + 2$ $\quad y = \sin\theta - 3$
   d) $y = \cos\theta$ $\quad y = \cos\theta - 1$ $\quad y = \cos\theta + 0.5$

7. Sketch each graph.
   a) $y = x^2 - 2.5$ $\quad$ b) $y = x^3 + 3$ $\quad$ c) $y = |x| - 1$
   d) $y = |x| + 2$ $\quad$ e) $y = \sqrt{25 - x^2} - 2$ $\quad$ f) $y = \sqrt{x} + 1$

Ⓒ

8. a) Copy the graph of $y = f(x)$. On the same grid, sketch the graphs of $y = f(x) + 2$ and $y = f(x) - 2$.
   b) The equation of the function given in part a) is $y = \dfrac{5x^2}{x^2 + 1}$. Write the equations of the images.

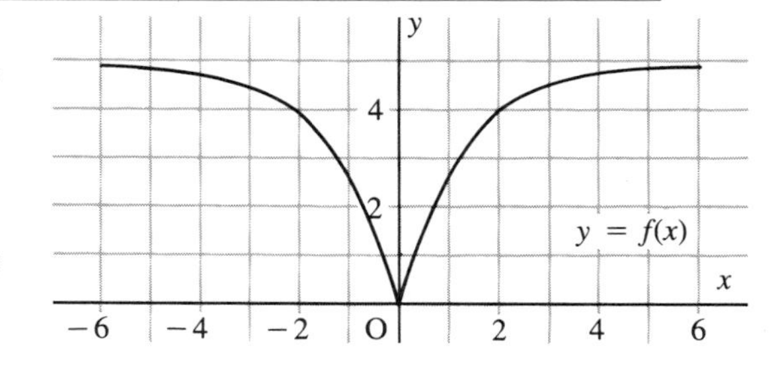

9-3 GRAPHING $y = f(x - p)$

In $y = f(x)$, if x is replaced by $x - p$, we obtain $y = f(x - p)$. To investigate the effect of this on the graph of a function such as $y = x^2$, we give different values to p in $y = (x - p)^2$ and graph the resulting functions.

If $p = 0$, the equation is $y = x^2$.

If $p = 5$, the equation is $y = (x - 5)^2$. If we were to graph this function using a table of values, we would start with values of x, subtract 5, and then square the results. To give the same y-coordinates as in $y = x^2$, the values of x must be 5 *greater* than those in $y = x^2$. Hence, the graph of $y = (x - 5)^2$ is 5 units to the *right* of the graph of $y = x^2$.

Similarly, if $p = -8$, the equation is $y = (x + 8)^2$. To give the same y-coordinates as in $y = x^2$, the values of x must be 8 *less* than those in $y = x^2$. The graph of $y = (x + 8)^2$ is 8 units to the *left* of the graph of $y = x^2$.

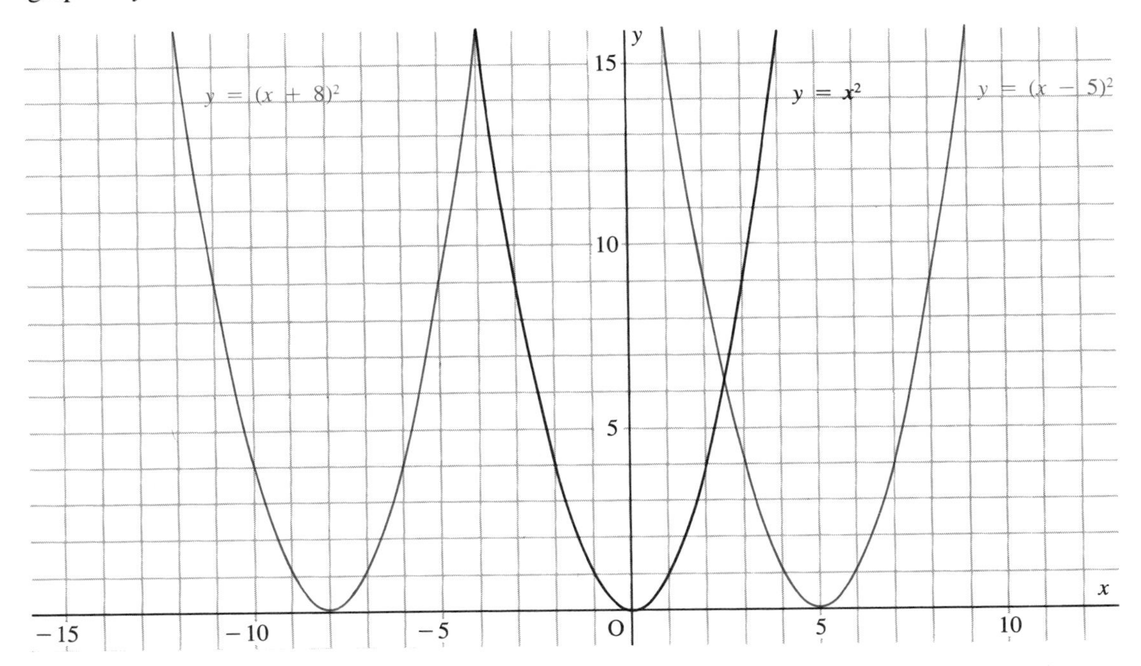

Similar results will be found for other values of p, and for functions other than quadratic functions.

In general, adding a constant to the variable x in the equation of any function $y = f(x)$ causes a horizontal translation of its graph. The sign inside the brackets indicates whether the graph is translated to the left or to the right.

The graph of $y = f(x - p)$ is related to the graph of $y = f(x)$ by a horizontal translation.

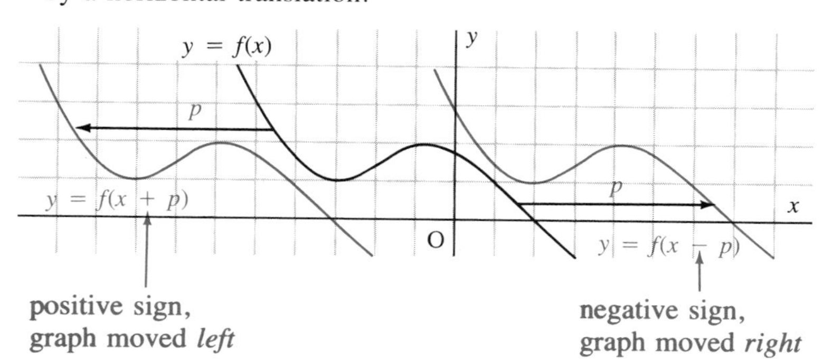

We can sketch graphs of equations in this form without making a table of values.

Example 1. Sketch the graph of $y = \sqrt{25 - (x + 2)^2}$.

Solution. Sketch the graph of $y = \sqrt{25 - x^2}$. This is a semicircle with radius 5 and centre (0,0). Translate this graph 2 units to the left to obtain the graph of $y = \sqrt{25 - (x + 2)^2}$.

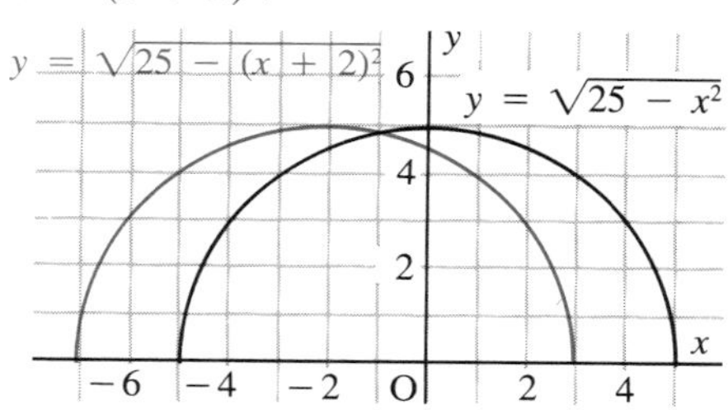

Frequently, both horizontal and vertical translations are combined in one example.

Example 2. Sketch the graph of each function.

a) $y = (x + 4)^2 - 3$ b) $y = \sqrt{x - 3} + 2$

Solution. a) Begin with the graph of $y = x^2$. The graph of $y = (x + 4)^2$ is obtained by translating this graph 4 units to the left. The graph of $y = (x + 4)^2 - 3$ is obtained by a further translation of 3 units down.

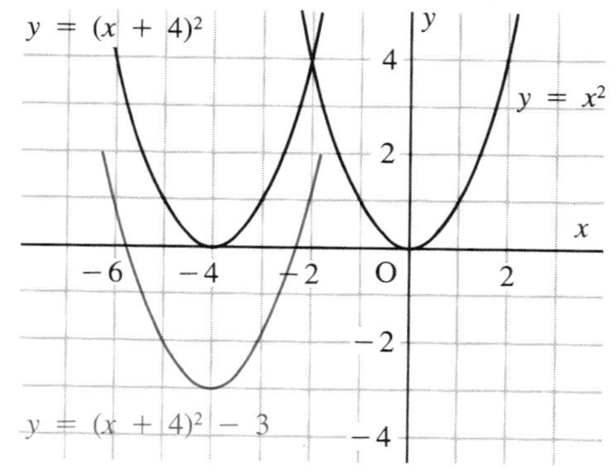

b) Begin with the graph of $y = \sqrt{x}$. The graph of $y = \sqrt{x - 3}$ is obtained by translating this graph 3 units to the right. The graph of $y = \sqrt{x - 3} + 2$ is obtained by a further translation of 2 units up.

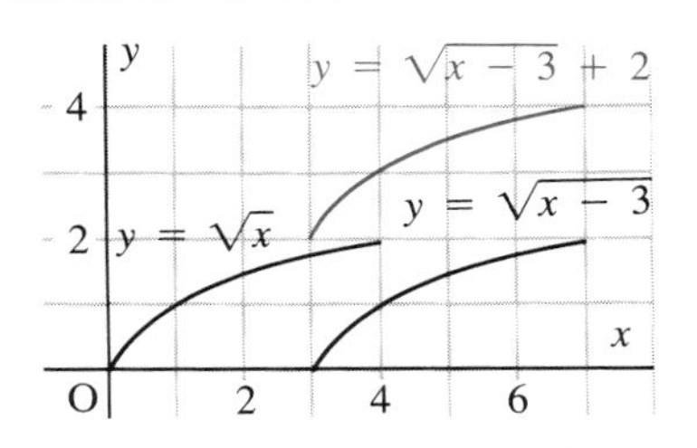

A famous example of the horizontal translation of a graph occurred in 1787 when the French chemist, Jacques Charles, investigated the effect of increasing the temperature on the volume of a gas (at constant pressure). The results for a sample of air are shown in the table and on the graph (below left).

Temperature (°C)	Volume (mL)
0	152
20.0	163
40.0	174
60.0	185
80.0	197
100.0	208

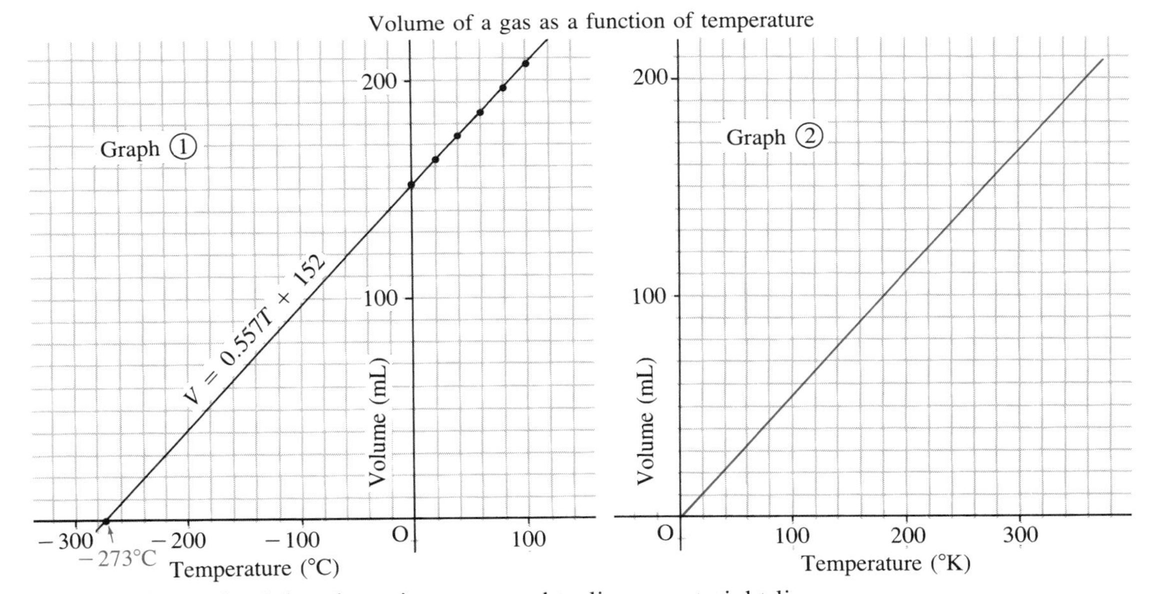

Charles noticed that the points appeared to lie on a straight line, which he extended to the left until it intersected the temperature axis. His graph showed that the volume should equal zero at a temperature of approximately −273°C. Since the sample of air can never disappear completely, this temperature is known as *absolute zero*.

On the Kelvin scale of temperatures, this is taken to be 0°K. If the graph is drawn on this scale (above right), the only difference is that it appears to be translated horizontally to the right. If we know the equation of the line on one graph, we can find the equation of the line on the other graph.

Example 3. The equation of the line on graph ① is $V \doteq 0.557T + 152$, where V is the volume in millilitres, and T is the Celsius temperature. Find the equation of the line on graph ②.

Solution. On graph ②, the line is translated 273 units to the right relative to its position on graph ①. The equation of the line is therefore

$$\begin{aligned} V &\doteq 0.557(T - 273) + 152 \\ &\doteq 0.557T - 152.061 + 152 \\ &\doteq 0.557T \end{aligned}$$

When the Kelvin scale of temperature is used, the equation of the line is $V \doteq 0.557T$

The result of *Example 3* is an example of Charles' Law in physics, which states that if the pressure is kept constant, the volume of a fixed mass of gas varies directly as the Kelvin temperature.

EXERCISES 9-3

Ⓐ

1. Sketch each set of graphs on the same grid.
   a) $y = x^2$ $\quad y = (x - 3)^2$ $\quad y = (x + 5)^2$
   b) $y = \sqrt{x}$ $\quad y = \sqrt{x + 2}$ $\quad y = \sqrt{x - 4}$
   c) $y = x^3$ $\quad y = (x - 1)^3$ $\quad y = (x + 3)^3$
   d) $y = |x|$ $\quad y = |x - 3|$ $\quad y = |x + 1|$

2. Describe the effect of various values of p on the graph of $y = f(x - p)$.

3. State which graph best represents each function.
   a) $y = (x - 3)^3$ b) $y = (x + 2)^3$ c) $y = (x + 1)^3$

i)

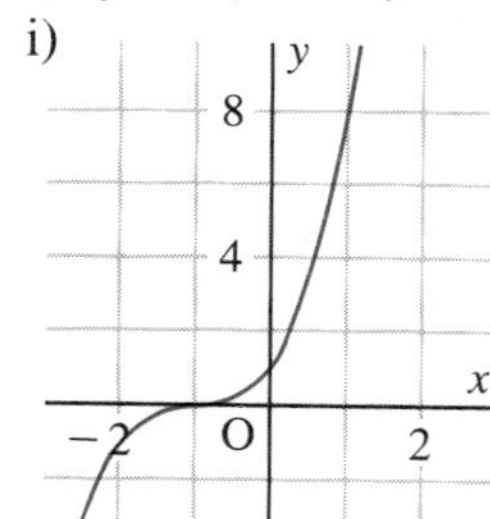

ii)

iii)

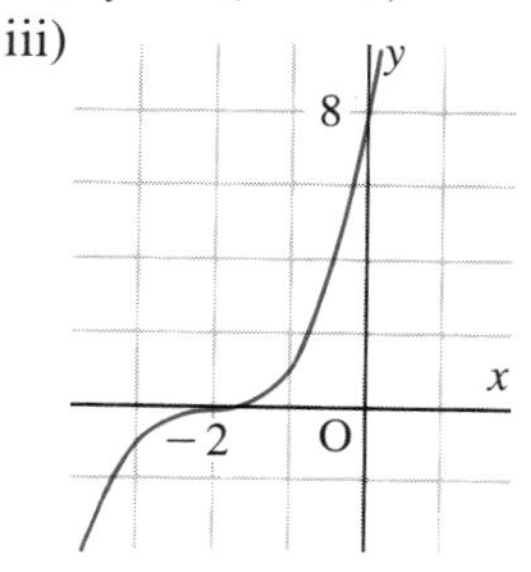

4. State which graph best represents each function.
   a) $y = \sqrt{x - 2}$ b) $y = \sqrt{4 - (x - 2)^2}$ c) $y = \sqrt{16 - (x + 1)^2}$

i)

ii)

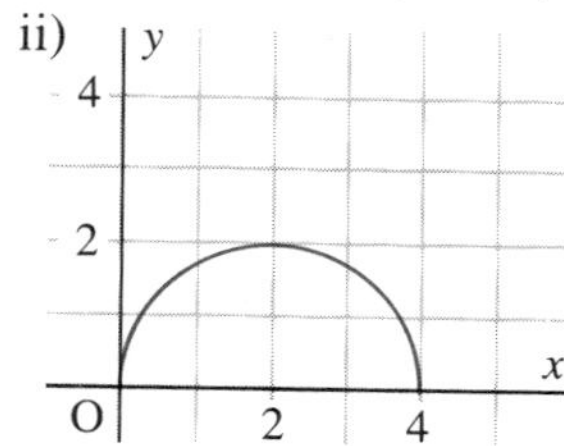

iii)

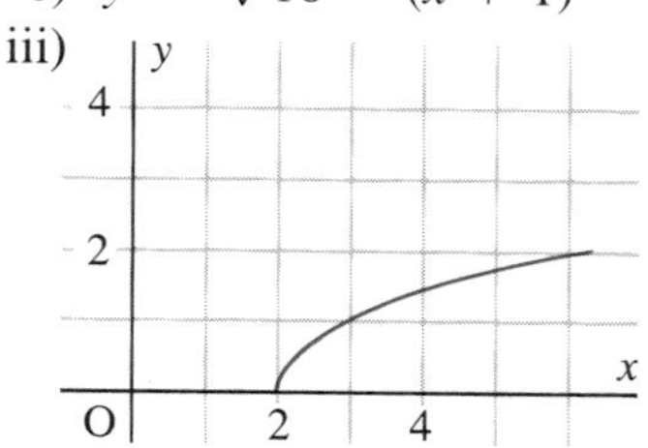

5. Write an equation that could describe each graph.

a)

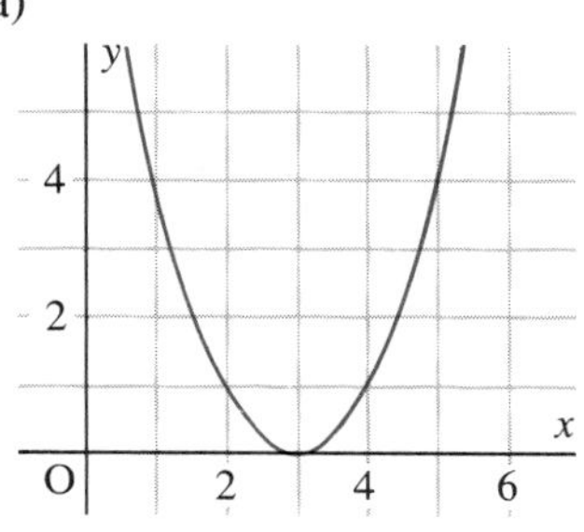

b)

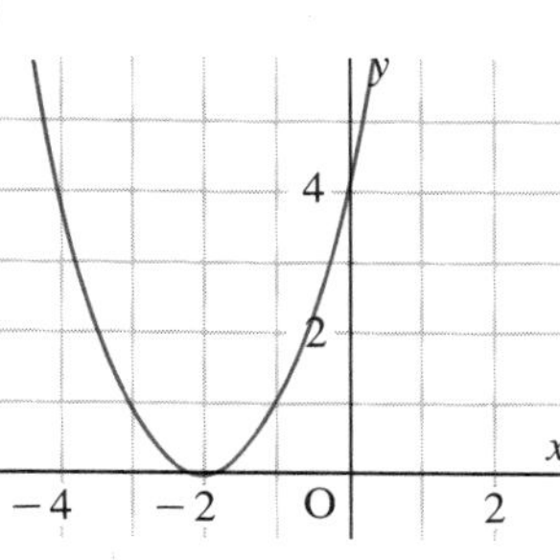

c)

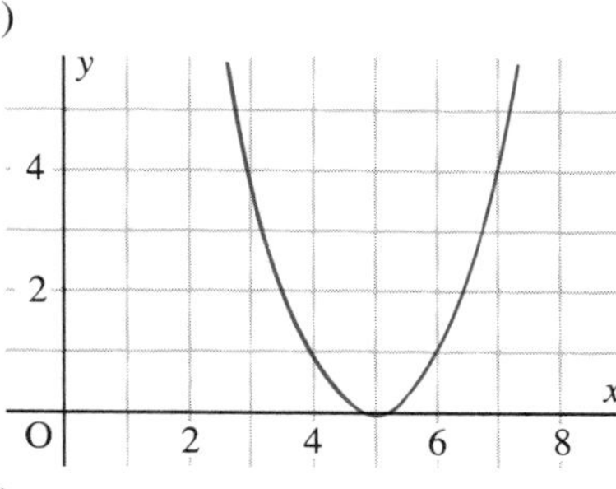

d)

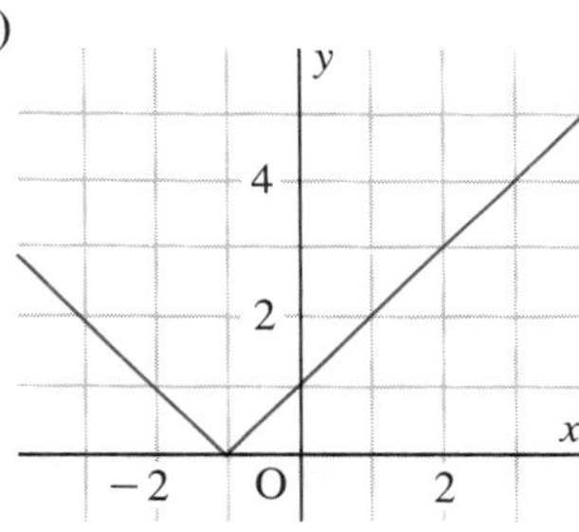

e)

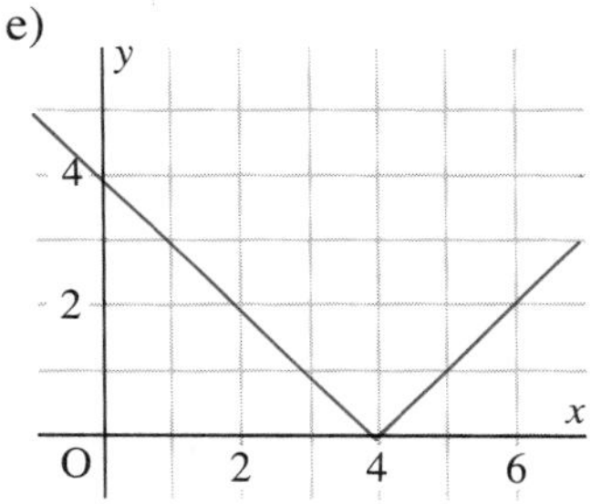

f)

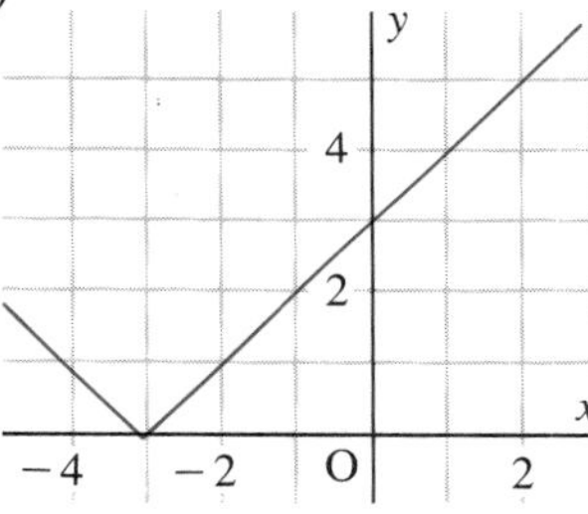

(B)

6. a) Graph the function $y = x^2$.
   b) Find the equation of the image of $y = x^2$ when it is translated:
      i) 5 units to the right
      ii) 2 units down
      iii) 5 units to the right, then 2 units down.

7. a) Graph the function $y = x^3$.
   b) Find the equation of the image of $y = x^3$ when it is translated:
      i) 3 units to the left
      ii) 2 units up
      iii) 3 units to the left, then 2 units up.

8. Select the function best represented by each graph.
   i) $y = \sqrt{x + 2}$
   ii) $y = \sqrt{x - 2}$
   iii) $y = \sqrt{16 - (x - 2)^2}$
   iv) $y = \sqrt{16 - (x + 2)^2}$
   v) $y = (x + 2)^2$
   vi) $y = (x - 2)^2$

a)

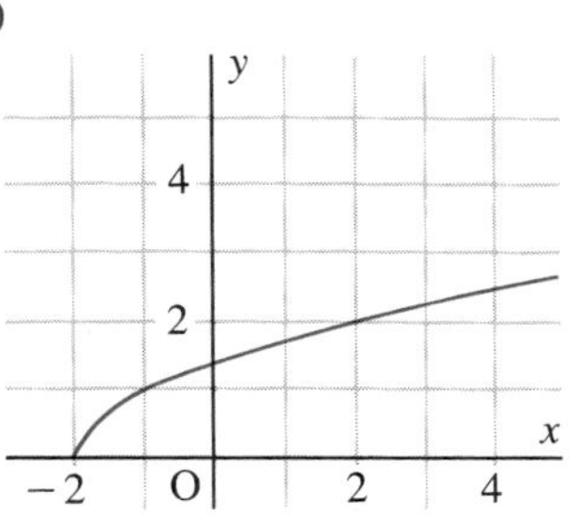

b)

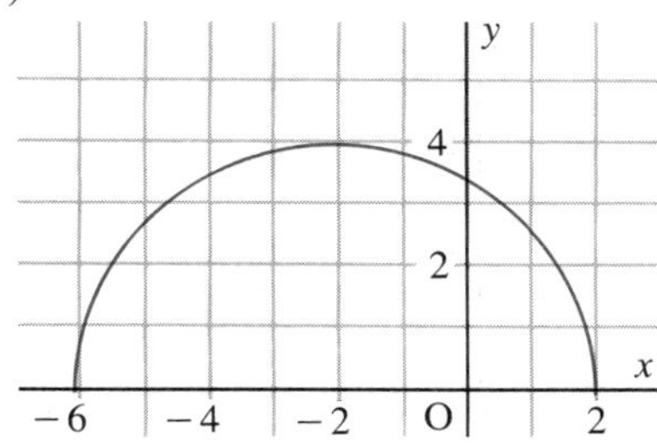

c)

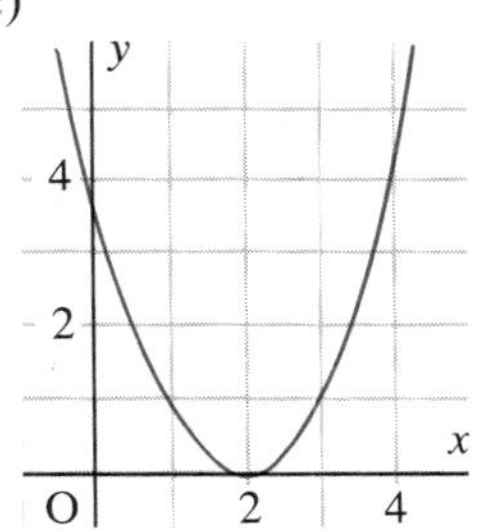

9. Sketch the graph of each function.
   a) $y = (x - 4)^2$ b) $y = (x + 3)^2$ c) $y = \sqrt{25 - (x + 3)^2}$
   d) $y = |x + 2|$ e) $y = (x - 2)^3$ f) $y = \sqrt{x - 3}$

10. Sketch the graph of each function.
   a) $y = (x + 2)^2 - 3$ b) $y = (x + 2)^3 - 4$ c) $y = |x - 3| + 2$
   d) $y = |x + 2| - 3$ e) $y = \sqrt{9 - (x + 4)^2} + 3$ f) $y = \sqrt{x - 5} + 3$

11. Sketch the graph of each function.
   a) $y = (x - 1)^3 + 3$ b) $y = \sqrt{x + 3} - 5$ c) $y = \sqrt{x - 1} + 1$
   d) $y = (x - 3)^2 + 1$ e) $y = \sqrt{49 - (x - 3)^2} - 2$ f) $y = |x + 3| - 7$

12. Sketch the graph of each function.
   a) $y = \sin(\theta + 60°)$ b) $y = \cos(\theta - 45°)$
   c) $y = \cos(\theta + 30°)$ d) $y = \sin(\theta - 90°)$

13. A sawmill receives a shipment of logs 4 m long. To estimate the volume, in cubic metres, of wood in a 4 m log, the following rule is used. Measure the diameter of the smaller end, in centimetres, subtract 10, square the result, and then multiply by 0.0003.
   a) If V cubic metres represents the volume, and d centimetres represents the diameter of the smaller end, write an equation which expresses V as a function of d.
   b) Graph the function for $10 \leqslant d \leqslant 100$.

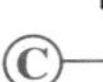

14. a) Copy the graph of $y = f(x)$. On the same grid, sketch the graphs of $y = f(x - 3)$ and $y = f(x + 5)$.
   b) The equation of the function given in part a) is $y = \dfrac{5\sqrt{x}}{x^2 + 1}$. Write the equations of the images.

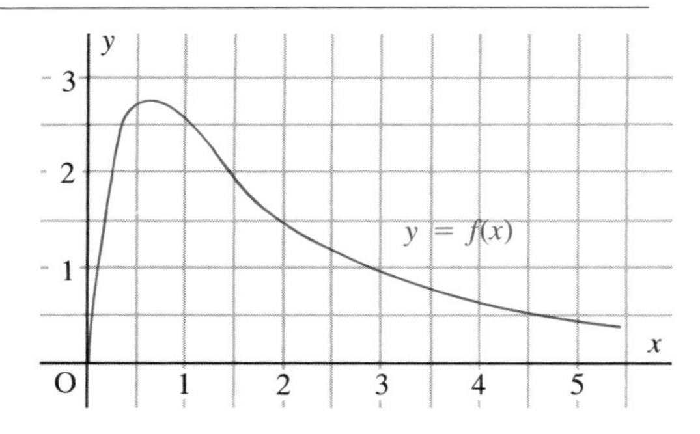

15. a) Using a table of values, graph $y = \dfrac{1}{x^2 - 4}$.
   b) Without using a table of values, sketch each graph.
   i) $y = \dfrac{1}{(x - 1)^2 - 4}$ ii) $y = \dfrac{1}{(x + 2)^2 - 4}$ iii) $y = \dfrac{1}{x^2 - 6x + 5}$

16. a) Sketch the graph of $x^2 + y^2 = 25$.
   b) Write the equation of the circle with the same radius, but with centre at:
   i) $(3,0)$ ii) $(0,2)$ iii) $(-2,-4)$ iv) $(1,5)$.

17. Sketch the graph of $y^2 - x = 0$. Write an equation of the image of this parabola if the vertex is at:
   a) $(-2,0)$ b) $(0,-3)$ c) $(3,4)$ d) $(-4,-2)$.

9-4 GRAPHING $y = af(x)$

In this section we investigate the effect on the graph of $y = f(x)$ of multiplying $f(x)$ by a constant a to get $y = af(x)$. We do this using the quadratic function $y = ax^2$ as an example, for different values of a, as shown in the graph.

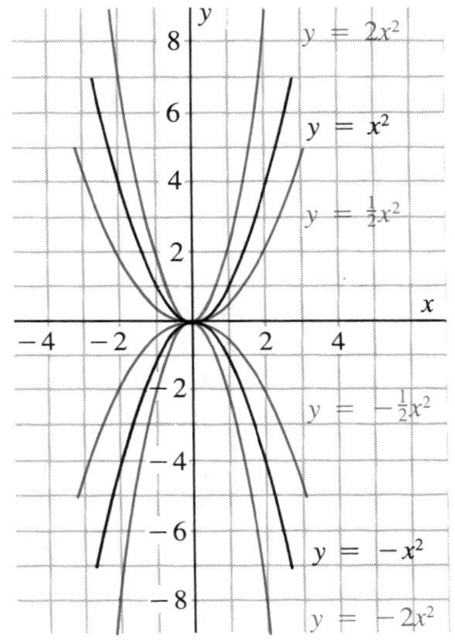

We observe the following results.

- **The graph of $y = 2x^2$ is expanded vertically relative to the graph of $y = x^2$.**
- **The graph of $y = \frac{1}{2}x^2$ is compressed vertically relative to the graph of $y = x^2$.**
- The graph of $y = -x^2$ is the image of the graph of $y = x^2$ under a reflection in the x-axis.
- The graph of $y = -2x^2$ is the image of the graph of $y = 2x^2$ under a reflection in the x-axis.
- The graph of $y = -\frac{1}{2}x^2$ is the image of the graph of $y = \frac{1}{2}x^2$ under a reflection in the x-axis.

Similar results will be found for other values of a ($a \neq 0$), and for functions other than quadratic functions.

In general, multiplying any function $y = f(x)$ by a non-zero constant a causes a vertical expansion or compression of its graph. If the constant is negative, the graph is also reflected in the x-axis.

The graph of $y = af(x)$ is related to that of $y = f(x)$ by a vertical expansion (if $|a| > 1$) or compression (if $0 < |a| < 1$). If $a < 0$, there is a reflection in the x-axis.

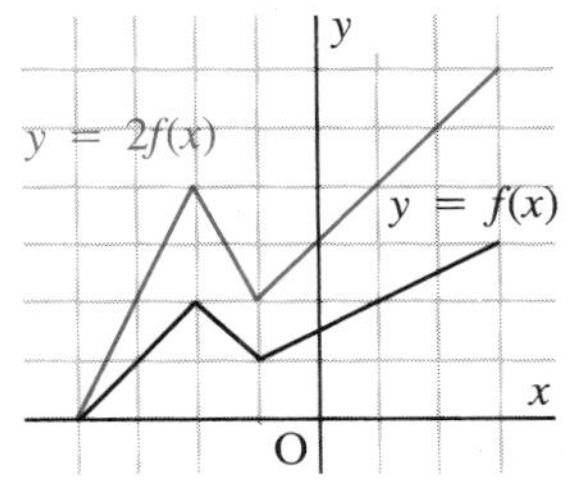

All vertical distances are doubled.

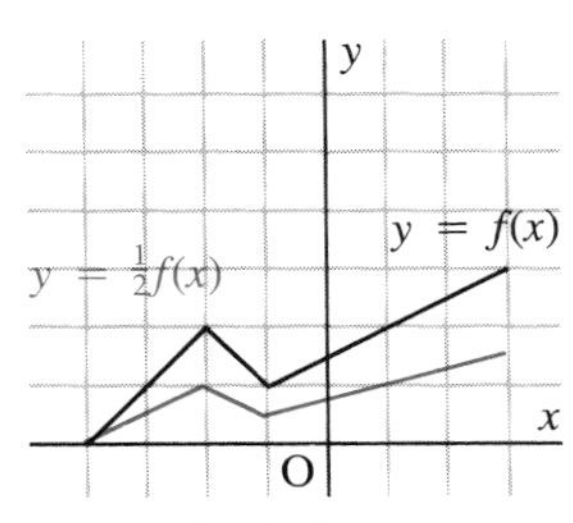

All vertical distances are halved.

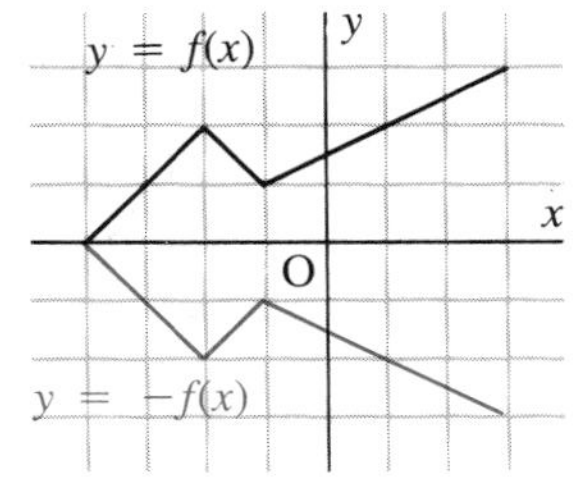

The graph is reflected in the x-axis.

We can use this property to sketch the graphs of certain functions without making a table of values.

Example 1. Sketch the graph of $y = 3\sqrt{x}$.

Solution. First sketch the graph of $y = \sqrt{x}$. The graph of $y = 3\sqrt{x}$ is obtained by a vertical expansion of factor 3.

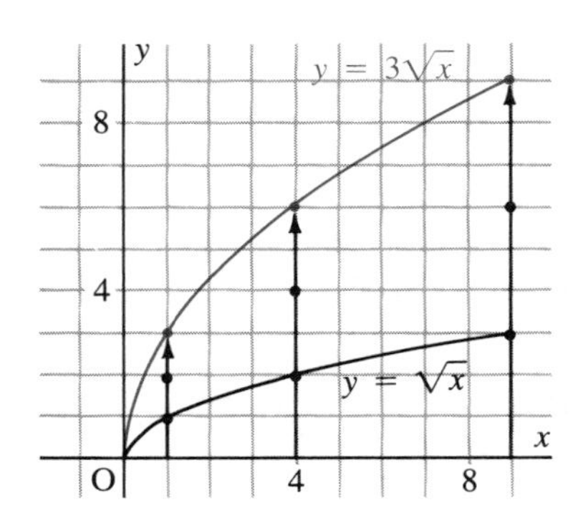

Translations and expansions or compressions are often combined in the same example.

Example 2. Sketch the graph of $y = -\frac{1}{2}(x + 3)^2 + 2$.

Solution. *Step 1*. Sketch the graph of $y = x^2$.
Step 2. Compress this graph by a factor $\frac{1}{2}$ and reflect in the x-axis. The result is the graph of $y = -\frac{1}{2}x^2$.

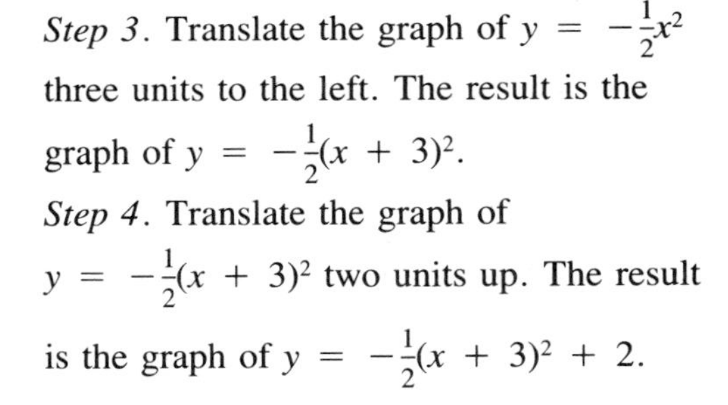
Step 3. Translate the graph of $y = -\frac{1}{2}x^2$ three units to the left. The result is the graph of $y = -\frac{1}{2}(x + 3)^2$.
Step 4. Translate the graph of $y = -\frac{1}{2}(x + 3)^2$ two units up. The result is the graph of $y = -\frac{1}{2}(x + 3)^2 + 2$.

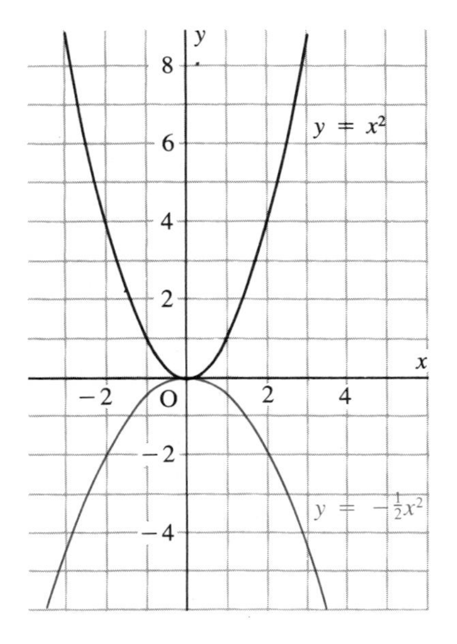

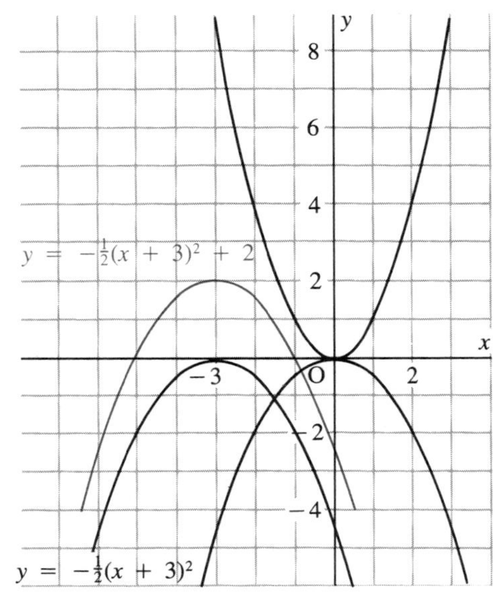

EXERCISES 9-4

(A)

1. a) Sketch graphs for these functions on the same grid, for $-4 \leqslant x \leqslant 4$.

$y = x^2 \qquad y = 3x^2 \qquad y = \frac{1}{2}x^2$

$y = -x^2 \quad y = -2x^2 \quad y = -\frac{1}{4}x^2$

b) Describe the effect of a on the graph of $y = ax^2$, as the value of a varies.

2. State which graph best represents each function.

a) $y = \frac{1}{5}x^3$ b) $y = -2\sqrt{x}$ c) $y = 0.5\sqrt{25 - x^2}$

i)

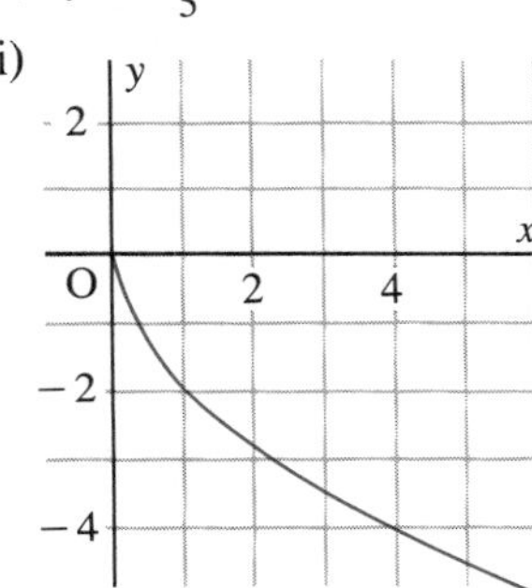

ii)

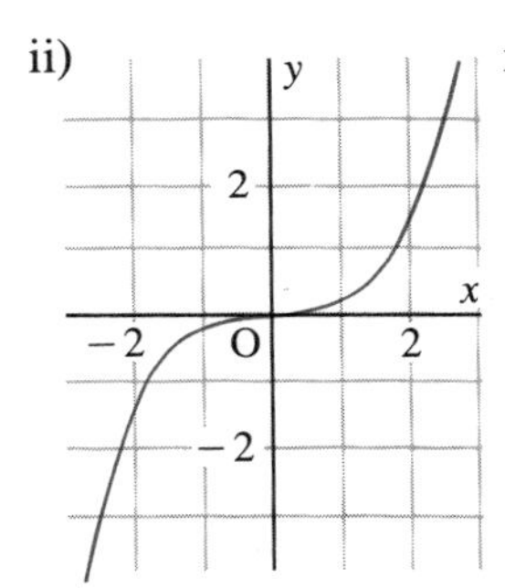

iii)

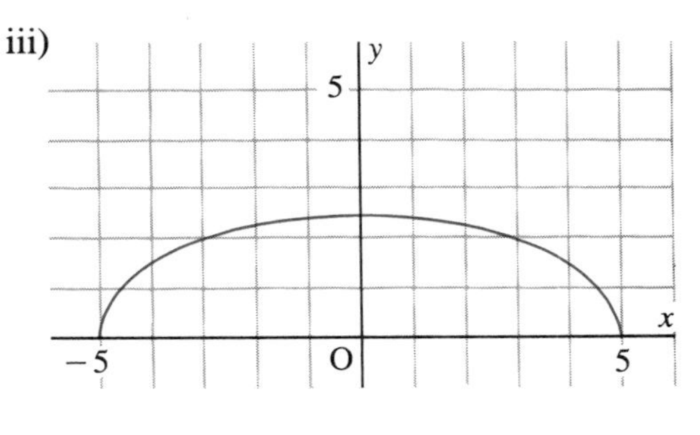

3. Without making tables of values, sketch each set of graphs on the same grid.

a) $y = \sqrt{x} \quad y = 2\sqrt{x} \quad y = \frac{1}{3}\sqrt{x}$ b) $y = -x^3 \quad y = -2x^3 \quad y = -\frac{1}{3}x^3$

4. The period T seconds of a pendulum is given approximately by the formula $T = 2\sqrt{l}$, where l metres is its length.
   a) Sketch a graph of the function for reasonable values of l.
   b) What are the domain and the range of the function graphed in part a)?

(B)

5. a) Graph the function $y = x^2$.
   b) Find the equation of the image of $y = x^2$ when:
      i) it is expanded by a factor 2
      ii) it is translated 3 units down
      iii) it is translated 4 units to the left
      iv) it is expanded by a factor 2, translated 3 units down, and then 4 units to the left.

6. a) Graph the function $y = \sqrt{16 - x^2}$.
   b) Find the equation of the image of $y = \sqrt{16 - x^2}$ when it is:
      i) compressed by a factor $\frac{1}{3}$
      ii) translated 4 units to the right
      iii) translated 1 unit up
      iv) compressed by a factor $\frac{1}{3}$, translated 4 units to the right, and then 1 unit up.

7. State which function best represents each graph.

a) $y = -4\sqrt{x}$ b) $y = 4\sqrt{x}$ c) $y = \frac{1}{2}x^3$

d) $y = -\frac{1}{2}x^3$ e) $y = \frac{3}{4}|x|$ f) $y = -\frac{3}{4}|x|$

i)

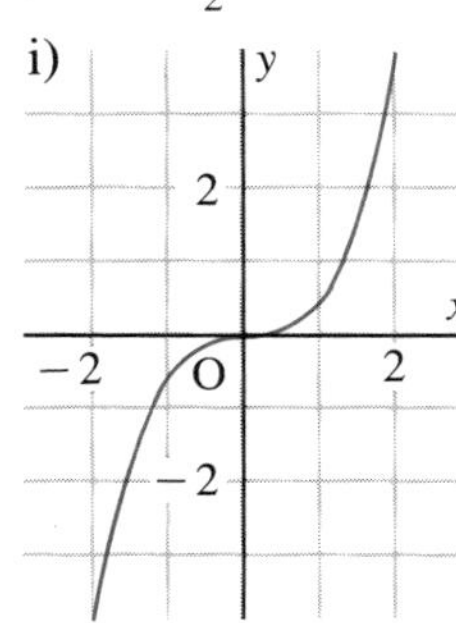

ii)

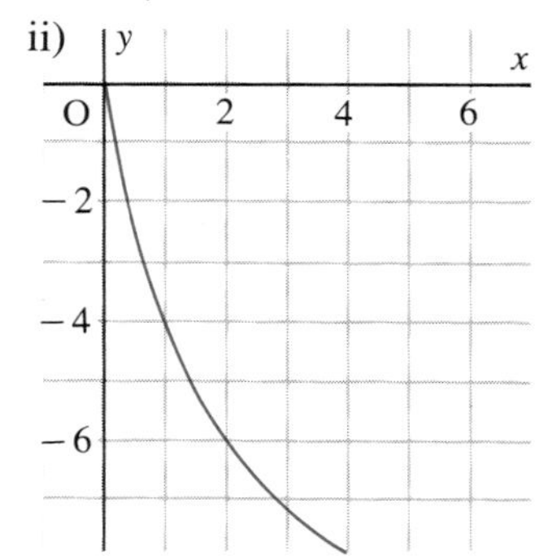

iii)

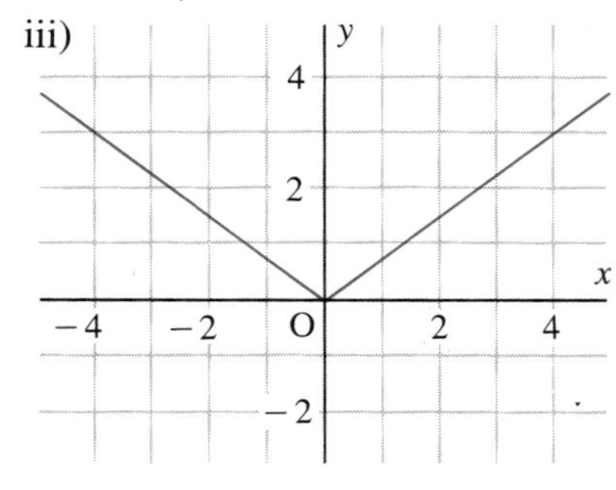

iv)

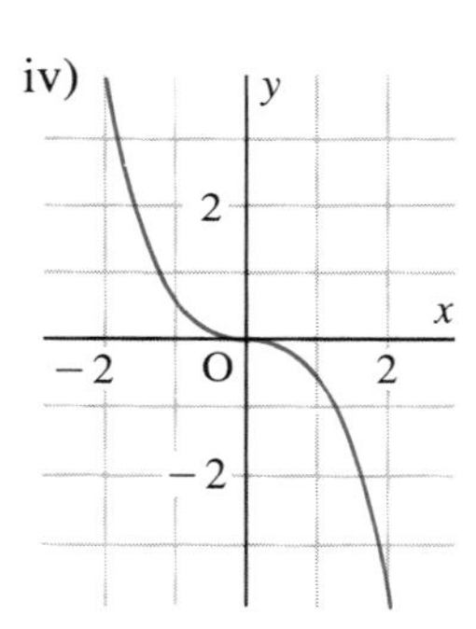

v)

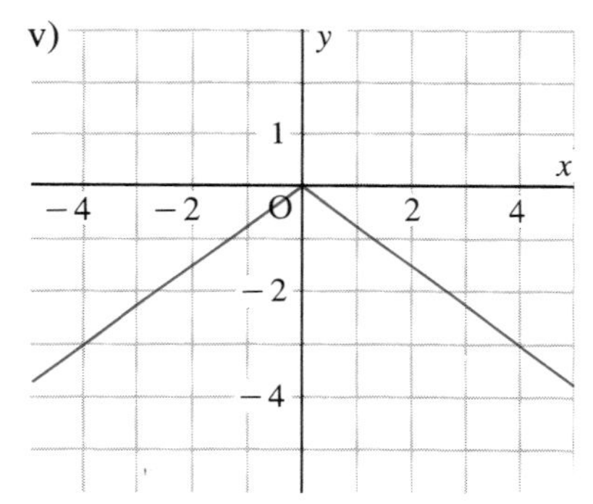

vi)

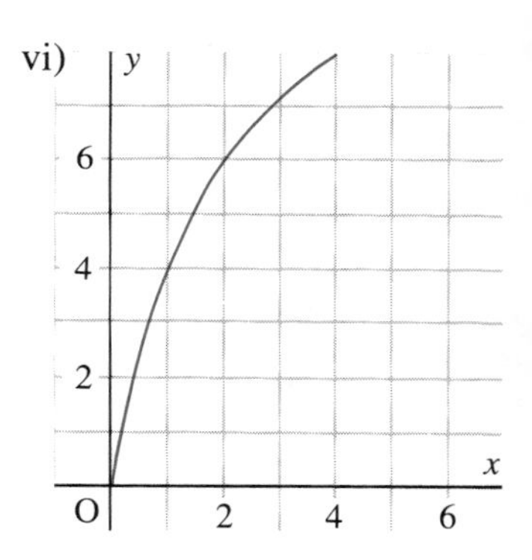

8. Sketch a graph of each function.

a) $y = -2x^2$ b) $y = \frac{1}{2}x^3$ c) $y = 3\sqrt{x}$

d) $y = -2\sqrt{x}$ e) $y = 2|x|$ f) $y = 2\sqrt{9 - x^2}$

9. Sketch a graph of each function.

a) $y = -2\sqrt{x} + 3$ b) $y = 2\sqrt{x} - 3$

c) $y = \frac{1}{3}x^2 - 2$ d) $y = -3\sqrt{16 - x^2} + 4$

e) $y = -\frac{1}{4}x^3 - 5$ f) $y = -\frac{3}{2}|x| + 2$

10. Sketch a graph of each function.

a) $y = 2(x - 1)^2 + 3$ b) $y = \frac{1}{2}|x - 4| + 3$

c) $y = \frac{1}{2}(x + 2)^3 - 1$ d) $y = \frac{1}{2}\sqrt{x + 3} - 2$

e) $y = 2\sqrt{x + 3} - 2$ f) $y = \frac{1}{2}\sqrt{9 - (x - 2)^2} + 4$

11. Sketch a graph of each function.
    a) $y = 2 \sin \theta$ b) $y = \frac{1}{2} \sin \theta$ c) $y = 3 \cos \theta$ d) $y = -\frac{1}{2} \cos \theta$

12. Sketch a graph of each function.
    a) $y = 3 \sin (\theta + 45°) - 1$ b) $y = -2 \cos (\theta - 30°) + 3$
    c) $y = 2 \sin (\theta - 60°) + 2$ d) $y = \frac{1}{2} \cos (\theta + 45°) - 2$

13. In a study of wind speeds near a large city, it was found that wind speed increases with height above the ground. If v metres per second represents the wind speed at height h metres, the equations expressing v as a function of h are:
    i) In the downtown core: $v = 0.5\sqrt{h}, \quad 0 \leqslant h \leqslant 500$
    ii) In the suburbs: $v = 0.6\sqrt{h}, \quad 0 \leqslant h \leqslant 350$
    iii) In nearby rural areas: $v = 0.7\sqrt{h}, \quad 0 \leqslant h \leqslant 200$.
    a) Sketch the graphs of these functions on the same grid.
    b) What are the domain and the range of each function?

Ⓒ

14. a) Copy the graph of $y = f(x)$. On the same grid, sketch the graphs of $y = 2f(x)$, $y = \frac{1}{2}f(x)$, $y = -f(x)$, $y = -2f(x)$, and $y = -\frac{1}{2}f(x)$.
    b) The equation of the function given in part a) is $y = \frac{5}{x^2 + 1}$. Write the equations of the images.

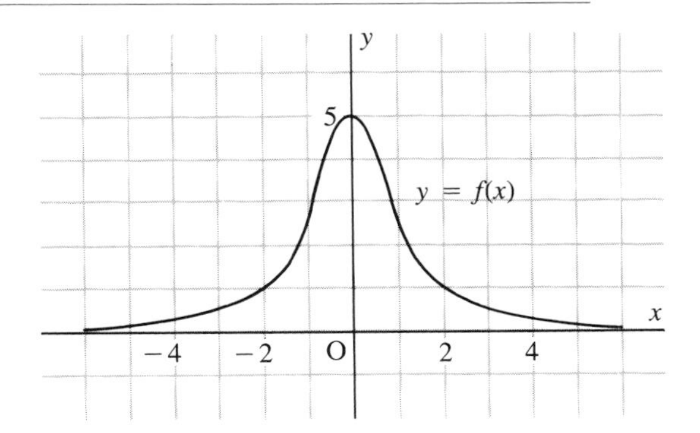

15. a) Sketch graphs of these functions on the same grid.
    $y = |x|$
    $y = 2|x| - 6$
    $y = 2|x - 3|$
    b) What transformations relate $y = 2|x| - 6$ to $y = |x|$?
    c) What transformations relate $y = 2|x - 3|$ to $y = |x|$?

16. a) Sketch graphs of these functions on the same grid.
    $y = x^2$
    $y = 2x^2 - 10$
    $y = 2(x - 5)^2$
    b) What transformations relate $y = 2x^2 - 10$ to $y = x^2$?
    c) What transformations relate $y = 2(x - 5)^2$ to $y = x^2$?

9-5 GRAPHING $y = f(kx)$

In $y = f(x)$, if x is replaced with kx, we obtain $y = f(kx)$. To investigate the effect of this on the graph of a function such as $y = (x - 3)^2$, we give different values to k in $y = (kx - 3)^2$, and graph the resulting functions.

Positive values of k

If $k = 1$, the equation is $y = (x - 3)^2$.

If $k = 2$, the equation is $y = (2x - 3)^2$.

If we were to graph this function using a table of values, we would start with values of x, multiply them by 2, subtract 3, and then square the results. To give the same y-coordinates as in $y = (x - 3)^2$, the values of x must be one-half of those in $y = (x - 3)^2$. That is, the x-coordinates of all points on the graph of $y = (2x - 3)^2$ are *one-half* of those in $y = (x - 3)^2$. Hence, the graph of $y = (2x - 3)^2$ (below left) is *compressed* horizontally relative to the graph of $y = (x - 3)^2$.

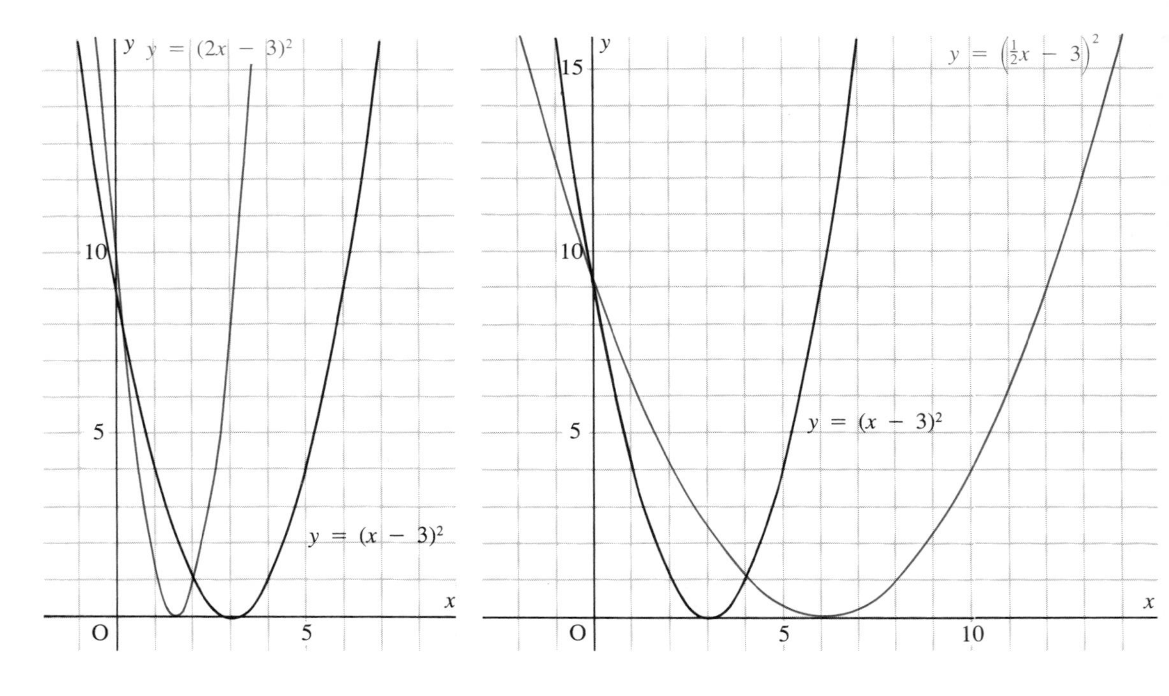

Similarly, if $k = \frac{1}{2}$, the equation is $y = \left(\frac{1}{2}x - 3\right)^2$. To give the same y-coordinates as in $y = (x - 3)^2$, the values of x must be *two times* those in $y = (x - 3)^2$. Hence, the graph of $y = \left(\frac{1}{2}x - 3\right)^2$ (above right) is *expanded* horizontally relative to the graph of $y = (x - 3)^2$.

Negative values of k

If $k = -1$, the equation is $y = (-x - 3)^2$.

If we were to graph this function using a table of values, we would multiply values of x by -1, subtract 3, and then square the results. To give the same y-coordinates as in $y = (x - 3)^2$, the values of x must be the opposites of those in $y = (x - 3)^2$. Hence, the graph of $y = (-x - 3)^2$ (below left) is the image of the graph of $y = (x - 3)^2$ under a reflection in the y-axis.

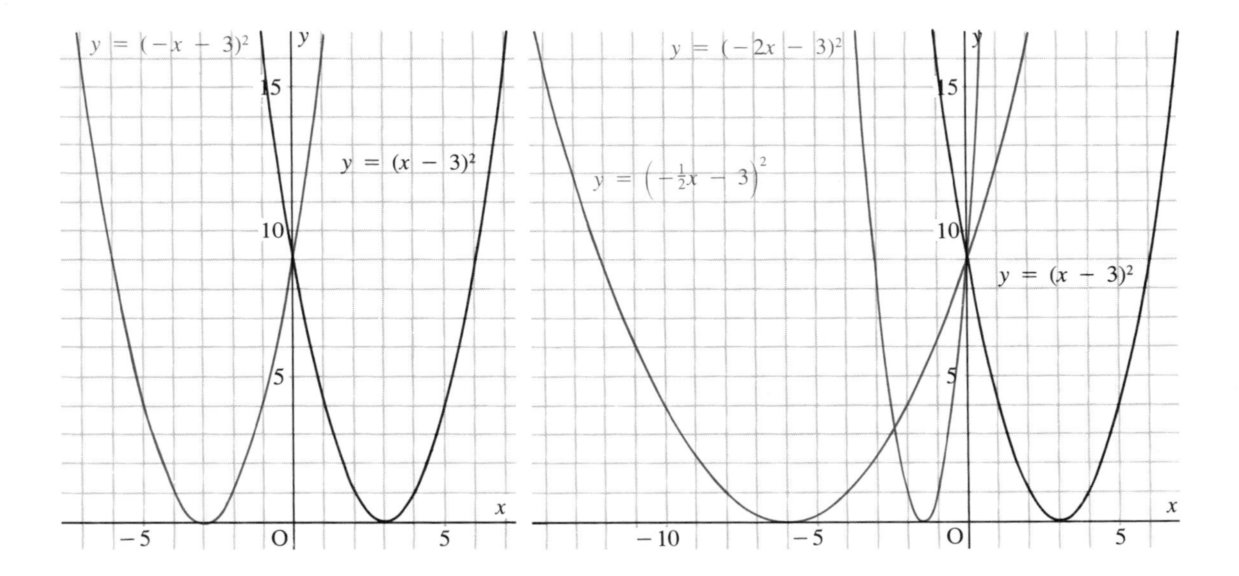

Similarly, if $k = -2$, the equation is $y = (-2x - 3)^2$. The graph of this function (above right) is the image of the graph of $y = (2x - 3)^2$ under a reflection in the y-axis.

And, if $k = -\frac{1}{2}$, the equation is $y = \left(-\frac{1}{2}x - 3\right)^2$, whose graph (above right) is the image of the graph of $y = \left(\frac{1}{2}x - 3\right)^2$ under a reflection in the y-axis.

In general, multiplying the variable x in the equation of any function $y = f(x)$ by a constant causes a horizontal expansion or compression of its graph. If the absolute value of the constant is greater than 1, the graph is compressed horizontally. If the absolute value of the constant is between 0 and 1, the graph is expanded horizontally. If the constant is negative, the graph is reflected in the y-axis.

The graph of $y = f(kx)$ is related to that of $y = f(x)$ by a horizontal compression (if $|k| > 1$) or expansion (if $0 < |k| < 1$). If $k < 0$, there is a reflection in the y-axis.

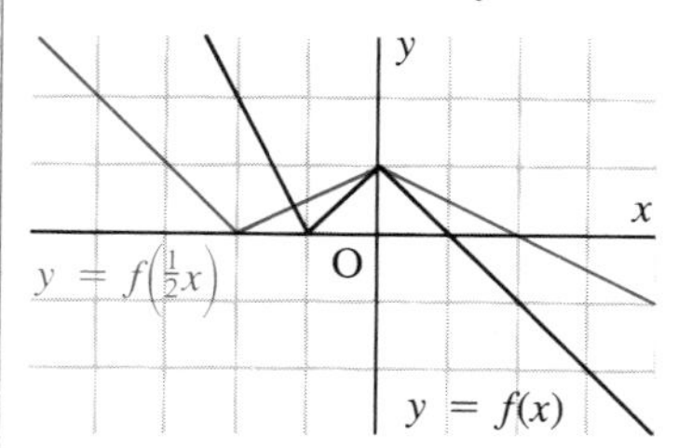

All horizontal distances are doubled.

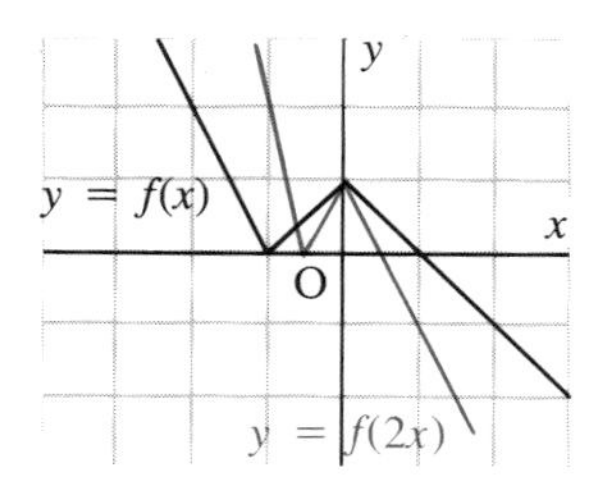

All horizontal distances are halved.

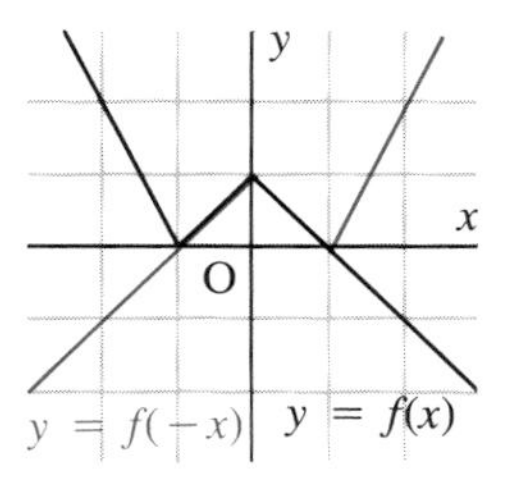

The graph is reflected in the y-axis.

We can use this property to sketch the graphs of certain functions without making a table of values.

Example. Sketch the graph of each function.

a) $y = \sqrt{25 - (2x)^2}$ b) $y = \sqrt{25 - \left(\frac{1}{2}x\right)^2}$

Solution. In each case, start with the graph of $y = \sqrt{25 - x^2}$.

a) In $y = \sqrt{25 - (2x)^2}$, the coefficient of x is greater than 1. The graph of $y = \sqrt{25 - x^2}$ is compressed horizontally by a factor of $\frac{1}{2}$.

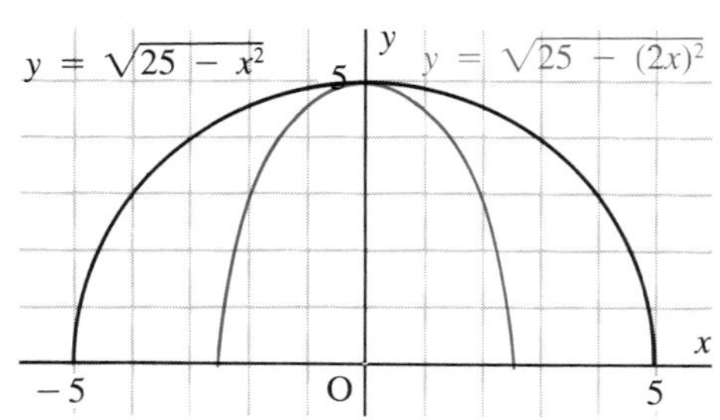

b) In $y = \sqrt{25 - \left(\frac{1}{2}x\right)^2}$, the coefficient of x is less than 1. The graph of $y = \sqrt{25 - x^2}$ is expanded horizontally by a factor of 2.

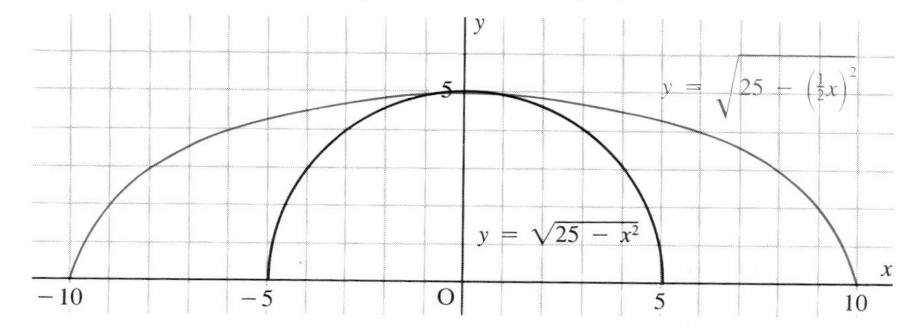

EXERCISES 9-5

Ⓐ

1. a) The graph in color (below left) is compressed horizontally by a factor of $\frac{1}{2}$ relative to the graph of $y = |x - 4|$. What is the equation of the graph?

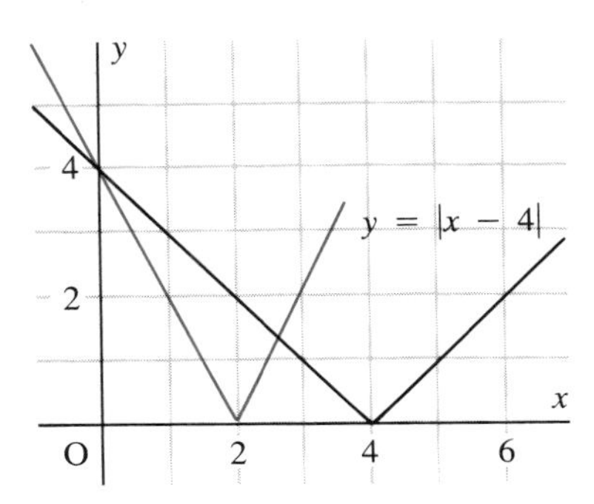

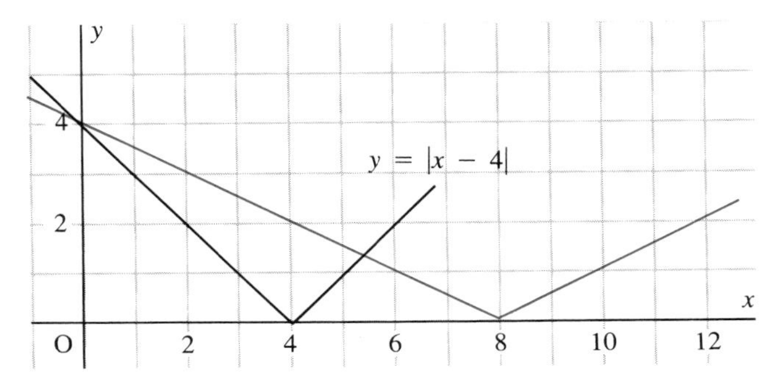

b) The graph in color (above right) is expanded horizontally by a factor of 2 relative to the graph of $y = |x - 4|$. What is the equation of the graph?

2. The graph shows the function $y = (x - 6)^2$.

a) Copy the graph, and graph these functions on the same grid.

$y = (2x - 6)^2$

$y = \left(\frac{1}{2}x - 6\right)^2$

$y = (-x - 6)^2$

$y = (-2x - 6)^2$

$y = \left(-\frac{1}{2}x - 6\right)^2$

b) Describe the effect on the graph of $y = (ax - 6)^2$ as a varies.

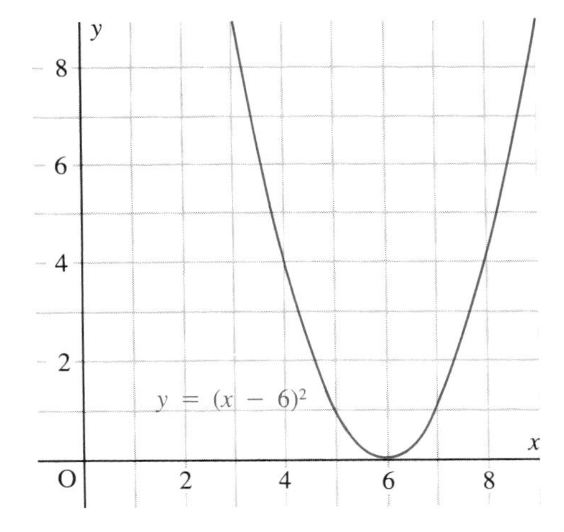

Ⓑ

3. Sketch each set of graphs on the same grid.

a) $y = \sqrt{x}$ $\quad y = \sqrt{2x}$ $\quad y = \sqrt{3x}$

b) $y = x^3$ $\quad y = (2x)^3$ $\quad y = (3x)^3$

c) $y = \sqrt{16 - x^2}$ $\quad y = \sqrt{16 - (2x)^2}$ $\quad y = \sqrt{16 - (3x)^2}$

4. Sketch each set of graphs on the same grid.

a) $y = \sqrt{-x}$ $\quad y = \sqrt{-2x}$ $\quad y = \sqrt{-3x}$

b) $y = (-x)^3$ $\quad y = (-2x)^3$ $\quad y = (-3x)^3$

c) $y = \sqrt{16 - (-x)^2}$ $\quad y = \sqrt{16 - (-2x)^2}$ $\quad y = \sqrt{16 - (-3x)^2}$

5. Sketch each set of graphs on the same grid.

   a) $y = x^2$ $y = \left(\frac{1}{3}x\right)^2$ $y = \left(\frac{1}{4}x\right)^2$ $y = (2x)^2$

   b) $y = x^3$ $y = \left(\frac{1}{2}x\right)^3$ $y = (2x)^3$ $y = \left(\frac{1}{3}x\right)^3$

   c) $y = \sqrt{x}$ $y = \sqrt{3x}$ $y = \sqrt{\frac{1}{2}x}$ $y = \sqrt{\frac{1}{3}x}$

6. Sketch each set of graphs on the same grid.

   a) $y = x^2$ $y = (-2x)^2$ $y = \left(-\frac{1}{2}x\right)^2$ $y = \left(-\frac{1}{3}x\right)^2$

   b) $y = x^3$ $y = (-2x)^3$ $y = \left(-\frac{1}{2}x\right)^3$ $y = \left(-\frac{1}{3}x\right)^3$

7. Sketch each set of graphs on the same grid.

   a) $y = \sin \theta$ $y = \sin 2\theta$ $y = \sin \frac{1}{2}\theta$ $y = \sin 3\theta$

   b) $y = \cos \theta$ $y = \cos \frac{1}{2}\theta$ $y = \cos \frac{1}{3}\theta$ $y = \cos 2\theta$

8. a) Graph the function $y = x^2$.
   b) Find the equation of the image of $y = x^2$ when it is:
      i) compressed horizontally by a factor of $\frac{1}{2}$
      ii) expanded vertically by a factor of 4.
   c) Compare the results in part b). Explain how it is possible that the same image graph can be obtained by the two different transformations.
   d) Give an example of a graph whose images would not be the same under the two transformations in part b).

Ⓒ

9. a) Copy the graph of $y = f(x)$. On the same grid, sketch the graphs of $y = f(2x)$, $y = f\left(\frac{1}{2}x\right)$, $y = f(-x)$, $y = f(-2x)$, and $y = f\left(-\frac{1}{2}x\right)$.

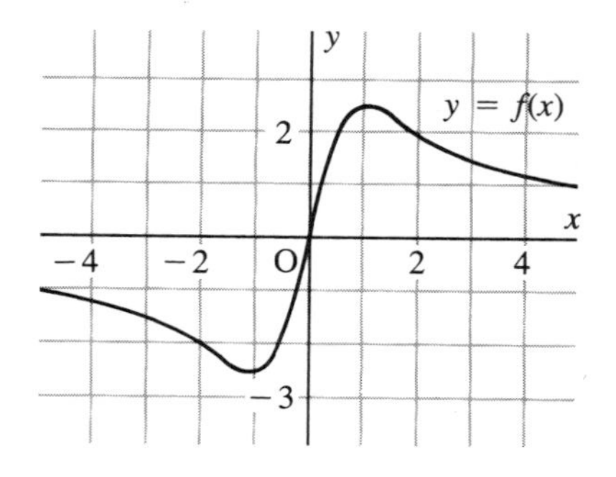

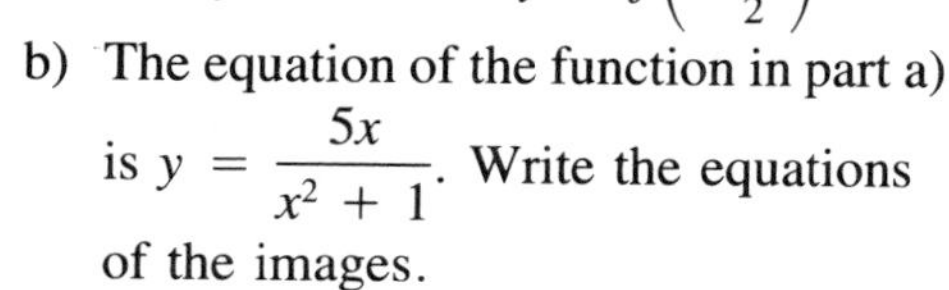
   b) The equation of the function in part a) is $y = \frac{5x}{x^2 + 1}$. Write the equations of the images.

10. a) Sketch graphs of these functions on the same grid. $y = |x|$ and $y = |2x|$
    b) Describe two different transformations that relate $y = |x|$ to $y = |2x|$.

9-6 COMBINING HORIZONTAL TRANSLATIONS AND EXPANSIONS OR COMPRESSIONS

In preceding sections we found that when the graph of a function such as $y = x^2$ is translated horizontally, there is a corresponding change in the equation. We replace x with $x - p$, where the constant p indicates the direction and magnitude of the translation. The equation then has the form $y = (x - p)^2$.

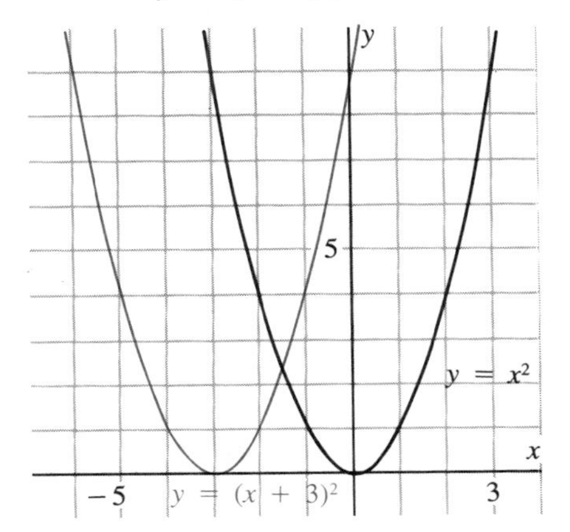

The curve is translated 3 units left. Replace x with $x + 3$.

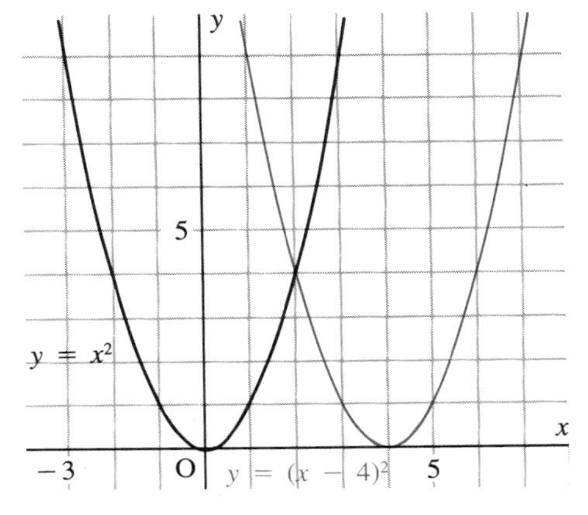

The curve is translated 4 units right. Replace x with $x - 4$.

Similarly, when the graph of $y = x^2$ is expanded or compressed horizontally, the equation changes in a different way. We replace x with kx, where the constant k determines whether there is an expansion or a compression. The equation then has the form $y = (kx)^2$.

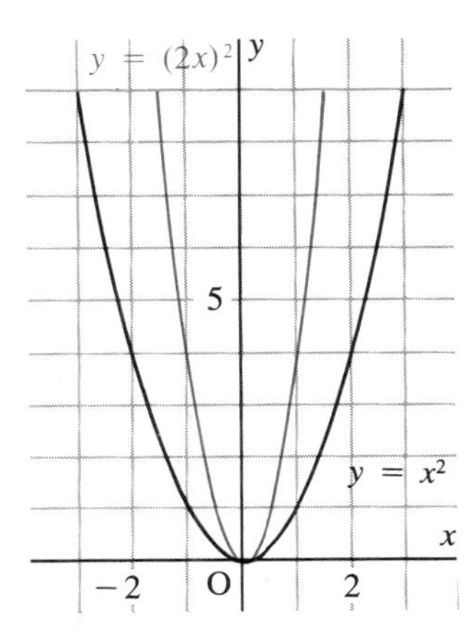

The curve is compressed horizontally by a factor of $\frac{1}{2}$. Replace x with $2x$.

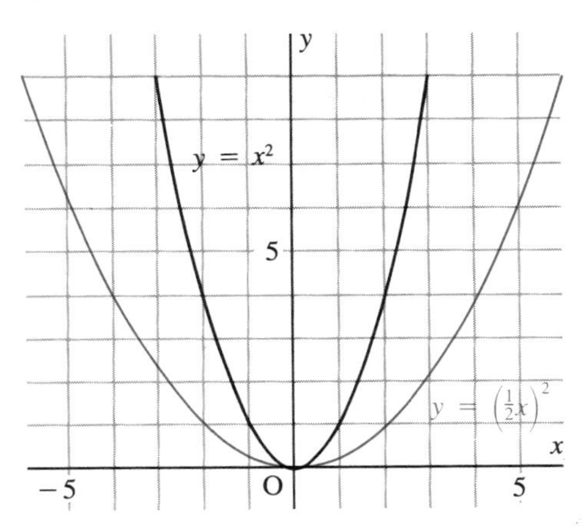

The curve is expanded horizontally by a factor of 2. Replace x with $\frac{1}{2}x$.

We now consider the effect of these transformations when they are applied together. The result depends on the order in which the transformations are performed.

Translation followed by a Compression or an Expansion

Suppose the graph of the function $y = x^2$ is translated 8 units to the right. To find the new equation, replace x with $x - 8$. The equation becomes $y = (x - 8)^2$.

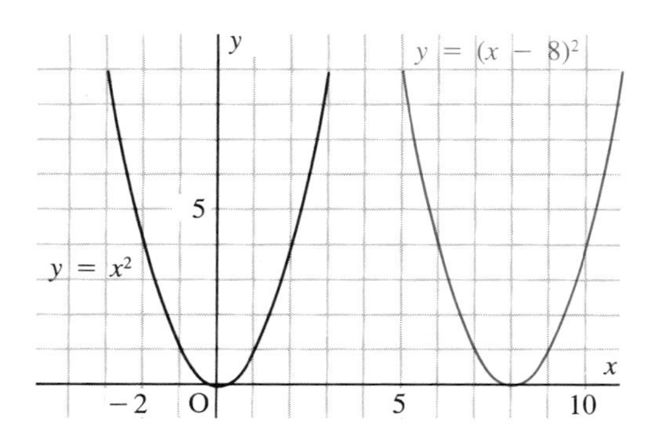

Suppose the resulting graph is compressed horizontally such that all horizontal coordinates are halved. To find the new equation, replace x with $2x$. The equation becomes $y = (2x - 8)^2$.

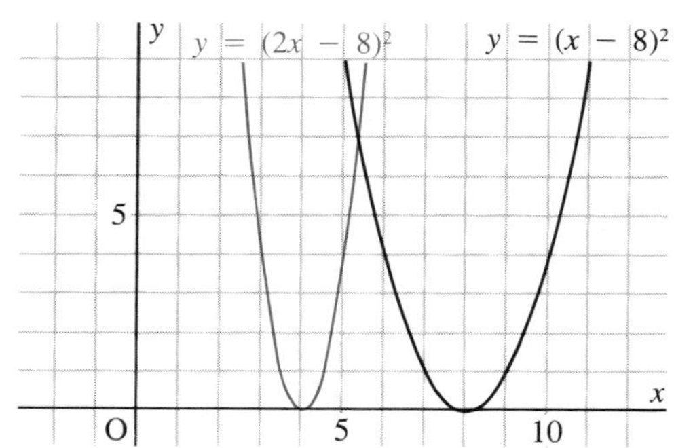

Similar results will be found for other functions.

> The graph of $y = f(kx - p)$ is related to that of $y = f(x)$ by a horizontal translation followed by a horizontal expansion or compression.

Example 1. Sketch the graph of $y = \sqrt{3x + 6}$.

Solution. *Step 1.* Sketch the graph of $y = \sqrt{x}$. Translate this graph 6 units to the left. The result is the graph of $y = \sqrt{x + 6}$.

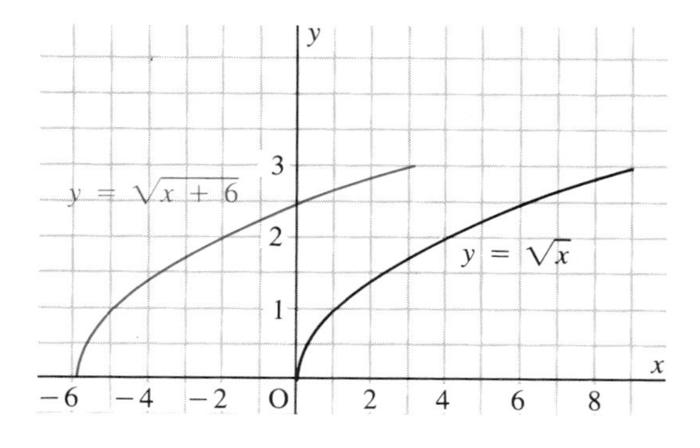

Step 2. Compress the graph of $y = \sqrt{x + 6}$ by a factor of $\frac{1}{3}$ horizontally. The result is the graph of $y = \sqrt{3x + 6}$.

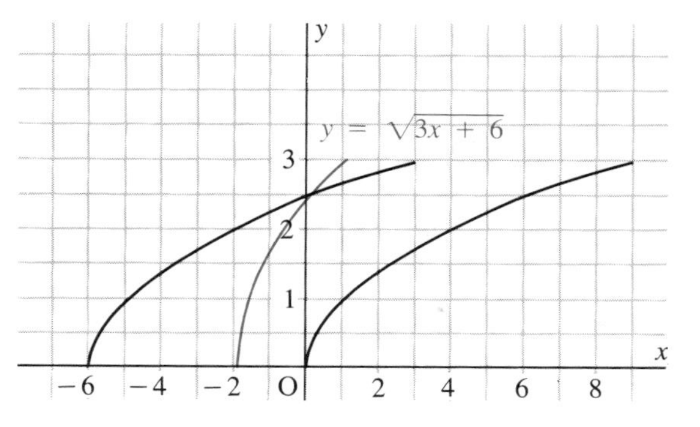

Compression or Expansion followed by a Translation

Suppose the graph of the function $y = x^2$ is compressed horizontally such that all horizontal coordinates are halved. To find the new equation, replace x with $2x$. The equation becomes $y = (2x)^2$.

Suppose the resulting graph is translated 8 units to the right. To find the new equation, replace x with $x - 8$. The equation becomes $y = [2(x - 8)]^2$.

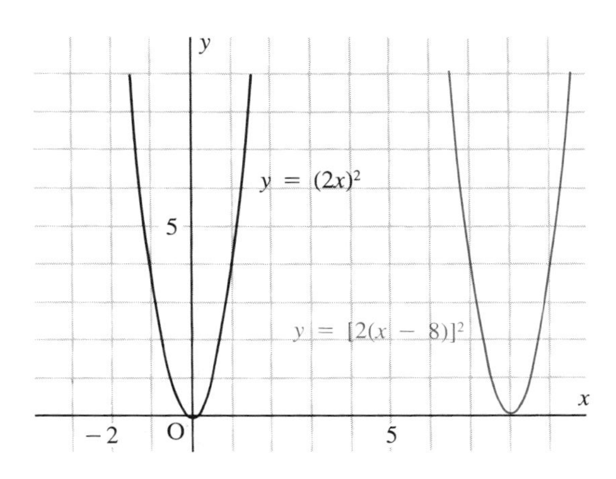

Similar results will be found for other functions.

> The graph of $y = f[k(x - p)]$ is related to that of $y = f(x)$ by a horizontal expansion or compression followed by a horizontal translation.

Example 2. Sketch the graph of $y = \sqrt{3(x + 6)}$.

Solution. *Step 1*. Sketch the graph of $y = \sqrt{x}$. Compress this graph by a factor of $\frac{1}{3}$ horizontally. The result is the graph of $y = \sqrt{3x}$.

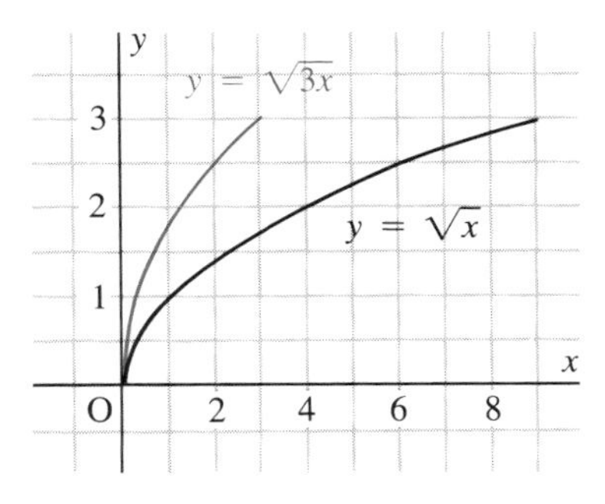

Step 2. Translate the graph of $y = \sqrt{3x}$ six units to the left. The result is the graph of $y = \sqrt{3(x + 6)}$.

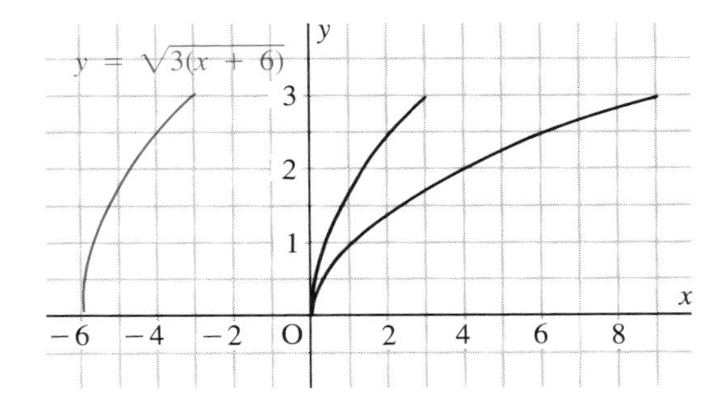

EXERCISES 9-6

Ⓑ

1. Sketch each set of graphs on the same grid.
   a) $y = x^2$ $y = (x + 6)^2$ $y = (2x + 6)^2$
   b) $y = \sqrt{x}$ $y = \sqrt{x - 5}$ $y = \sqrt{2x - 5}$
   c) $y = x^3$ $y = (x - 3)^3$ $y = (2x - 3)^3$

2. Sketch each set of graphs on the same grid.
   a) $y = x^2$ $y = (2x)^2$ $y = [2(x + 6)]^2$
   b) $y = \sqrt{x}$ $y = \sqrt{2x}$ $y = \sqrt{2(x - 5)}$
   c) $y = x^3$ $y = (2x)^3$ $y = [2(x - 3)]^3$

3. Sketch a graph of each function.
   a) $y = \left(\frac{1}{2}x + 6\right)^2$ b) $y = \sqrt{\frac{1}{2}x - 5}$ c) $y = \left(\frac{1}{2}x - 3\right)^3$

4. Sketch a graph of each function.
   a) $y = \left[\frac{1}{2}(x + 6)\right]^2$ b) $y = \sqrt{\frac{1}{2}(x - 5)}$ c) $y = \left[\frac{1}{2}(x - 3)\right]^3$

5. Sketch a graph of each function.
   a) $y = (-2x + 6)^2$ b) $y = \sqrt{-2x - 5}$ c) $y = (-2x - 3)^3$

6. Sketch a graph of each function.
   a) $y = [-2(x + 6)]^2$ b) $y = \sqrt{-2(x - 5)}$ c) $y = [-2(x - 3)]^3$

Ⓒ

7. Sketch a graph of each function.
   a) $y = (3x - 2)^2$ b) $y = \sqrt{-3x + 2}$ c) $y = |2x - 1|$
   d) $y = \sqrt{16 - (2x - 1)^2}$ e) $y = \left(\frac{1}{2}x - 3\right)^3$ f) $y = \left|\frac{1}{3}x + 2\right|$

8. Sketch a graph of each function.
   a) $y = \sqrt{\frac{1}{4}(x - 2)}$ b) $y = \left(\frac{1}{2}x + 2\right)^3$ c) $y = [-3(x + 4)]^2$
   d) $y = |3x - 5|$ e) $y = \sqrt{25 - \left(-\frac{1}{2}x - 3\right)^2}$ f) $y = [-2(x + 1)]^3$

9. Sketch a graph of each function.
   a) $y = \sin (2\theta - 45°)$ b) $y = \sin 2(\theta - 45°)$
   c) $y = \cos \left(\frac{1}{2}\theta + 30°\right)$ d) $y = \cos \frac{1}{2}(\theta + 30°)$

INVESTIGATE

Suppose a graph of the function $y = f(x)$ is given. Then if k and p are constants, the graphs of $y = f(kx - p)$ and $y = f[k(x - p)]$ are related by a horizontal translation. Investigate how the values of k and p determine how far apart they are.

MATHEMATICS AROUND US

Other Kinds of Functions

There are many other kinds of functions in addition to those described in this chapter. A few of these are illustrated here.

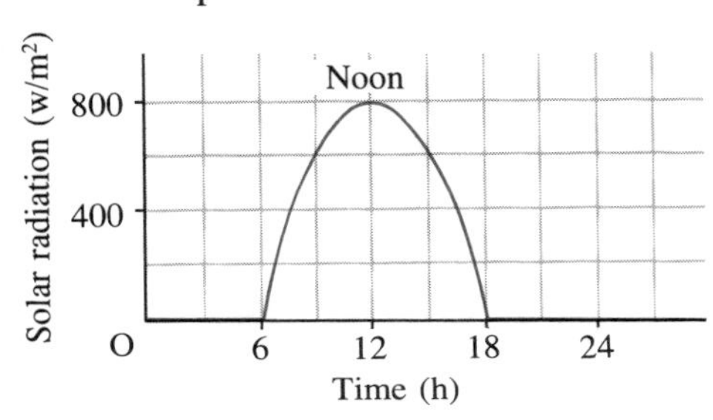

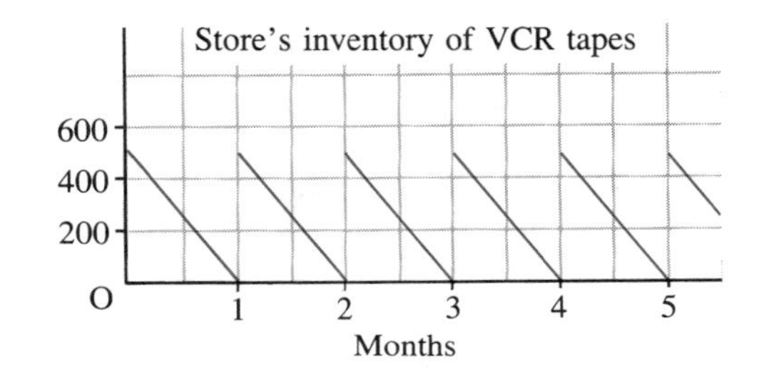

1. This graph shows the daily pattern of solar radiation on a clear day in the spring or fall, when the sun rises at 6 A.M. and sets at 6 P.M.
   a) How would the graph differ if it were drawn for:
      i) a day in the summer
      ii) a day in the winter?
   b) Draw a similar graph in which the horizontal axis represents three consecutive days.

2. At the end of each month a store buys 500 VCR tapes to replace those sold during the month. How would the graph showing the store's inventory differ if:
   a) the 500 tapes bought each month were sold out after the first 3 weeks of the next month
   b) the store sold only 400 tapes each month?

- Most of the babies born this year can expect to live at least 75 years. A few should survive to age 100 or more.
- A corn plant matures in about 100 days to a mass of about 80 g. Growth is most rapid in the second and third months.
- Wind speed usually increases rapidly with height in the first few metres above the ground. Above 20 m or so, the speed is about 5 m/s, and changes little for the next few hundred metres.

3. Graphs illustrating the three situations described above are shown below.
   a) Identify the graph which corresponds to each situation.
   b) Draw each graph, including appropriate scales and titles on the axes.
   c) In what ways do all three graphs differ from the graphs above?

i)

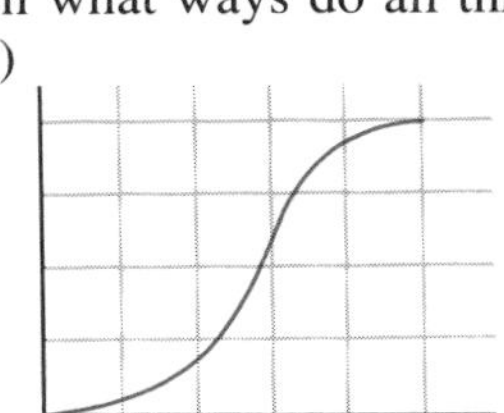

ii)

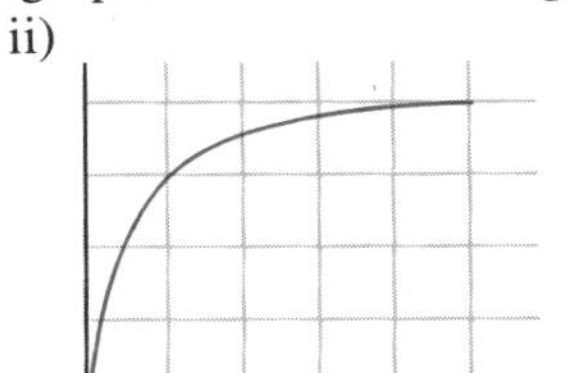

iii)

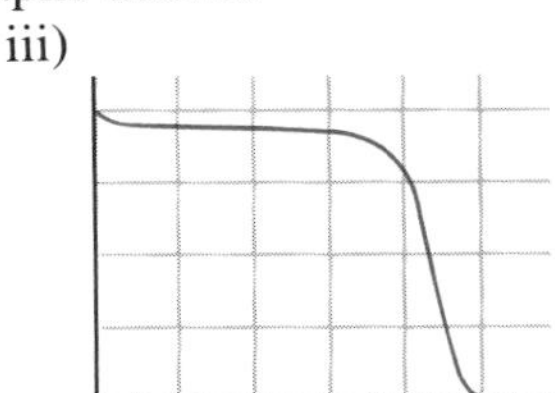

9-7 THE RECIPROCAL OF A FUNCTION, $y = \frac{1}{f(x)}$

The transformations we have studied in this and the preceding chapter have involved translations, reflections, expansions, and compressions of the graphs of functions. These are only a few examples of the many different transformations that can be applied to functions.

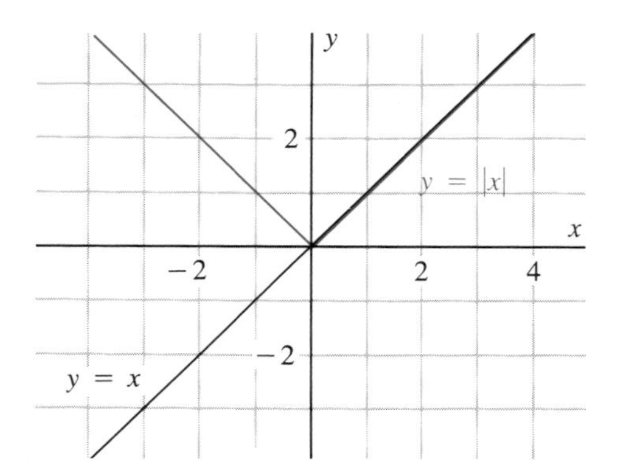

You already know one example of another kind of transformation — in *Section 9-1* we studied an example of an absolute-value function. For example, if the graph of the function $y = x$ is given, then it can be transformed to the function $y = |x|$ by reflecting in the x-axis all points on the graph which are below the x-axis.

Another example of a transformation of a function is the reciprocal of a function. Before we investigate the reciprocal of a function, recall that the reciprocal of a number x is the number $\frac{1}{x}$, provided that $x \neq 0$.

We can draw the graph of the reciprocal function $y = \frac{1}{x}$ by using a table of values.

x	$\frac{1}{x}$
−4	−0.25
−2	−0.5
−1	−1
−0.5	−2
−0.25	−4
0	undefined
0.25	4
0.5	2
1	1
2	0.5
4	0.25

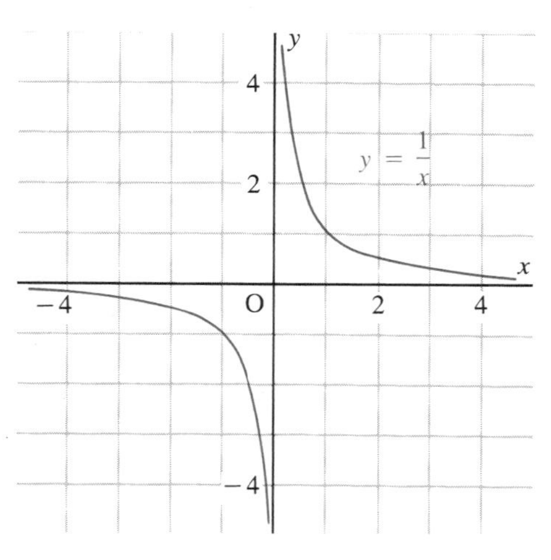

The graph of the reciprocal function $y = \frac{1}{x}$ consists of two separate parts, or branches, and is called a *rectangular hyperbola*. Hyperbolas occur in navigation, the design of telescopes, and the orbits of certain comets.

Given the function $y = f(x)$, we define the reciprocal of $f(x)$ to be the function $y = \frac{1}{f(x)}$. For example, given the function $y = x - 2$, the corresponding reciprocal function is $y = \frac{1}{x-2}$, $x \neq 2$. To discover how the given function and its reciprocal are related, we graph them using a table of values.

x	$x - 2$	$\frac{1}{x-2}$
−2	−4	−0.25
−1	−3	−0.33
0	−2	−0.5
1	−1	−1
1.5	−0.5	−2
2	0	undefined
2.5	0.5	2
3	1	1
4	2	0.5
5	3	0.33
6	4	0.25

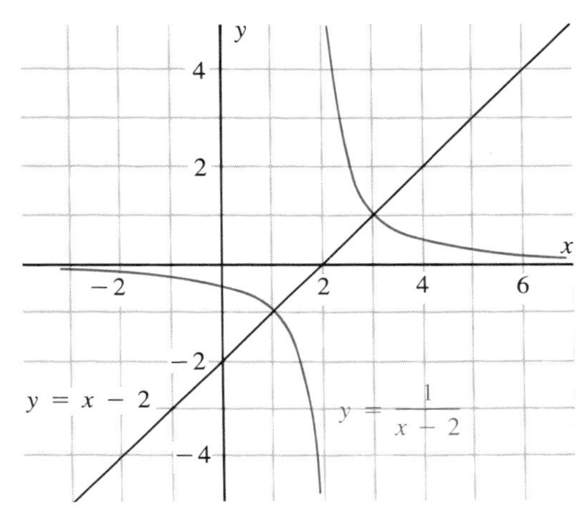

The graph of $y = \frac{1}{x-2}$ can also be obtained by translating the graph of $y = \frac{1}{x}$ two units to the right.

The table of values and the graph illustrate the following properties of reciprocals.

Properties of Reciprocals

- The reciprocal of 0 is undefined.
- The reciprocal of a positive number is positive.
  If the number is very close to 0, the reciprocal is very large.
  If the number is close to 1, the reciprocal is also close to 1.
  If the number is very large, the reciprocal is very close to 0.
- The reciprocal of a negative number is negative.
  If the number is very close to 0, the absolute value of its reciprocal is very large.
  If the number is close to −1, the reciprocal is also close to −1.
  If the absolute value of the number is very large, the reciprocal is very close to 0.

We can use these properties to sketch the graph of the reciprocal of a given function without making a table of values.

Example 1. Sketch a graph of the function $y = \dfrac{1}{x^2 - 4}$.

Solution. *Step 1*. Graph $y = x^2 - 4$ by translating the graph of $y = x^2$ four units down.

Step 2. Locate some points on the graph having y-coordinates with absolute value greater than 1. For each point, estimate the location of the corresponding point on the graph of the reciprocal function. These points will be closer to the x-axis than the points on the original graph.

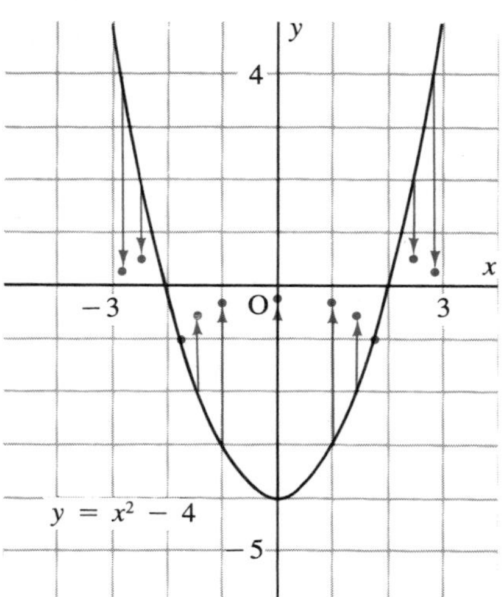

Step 3. Locate some points on the graph having y-coordinates with absolute value less than 1. For each point, estimate the location of the corresponding point on the graph of the reciprocal function. These will be farther from the x-axis than the points on the original graph.

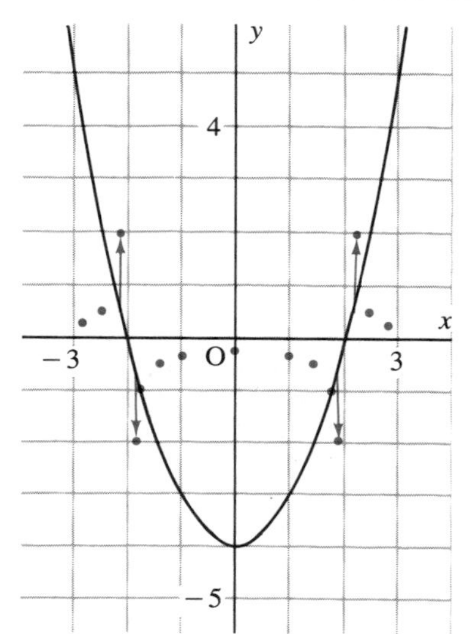

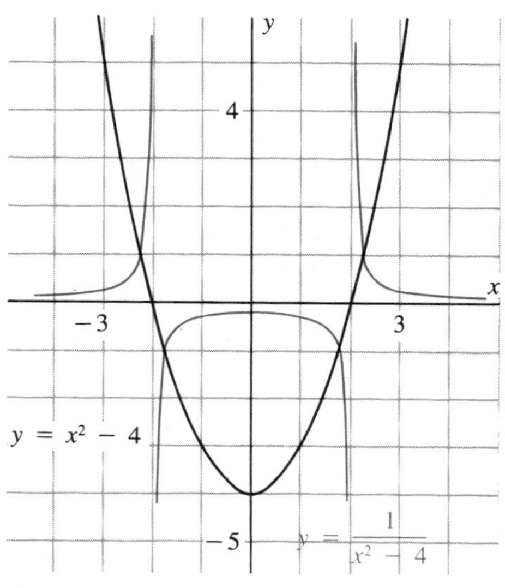

Step 4. Draw a smooth curve through the plotted points. This curve has three distinct branches, separated by values of x for which $x^2 - 4$ has a value of 0.

EXERCISES 9-7

1. Given the function $y = f(x)$, write the equation of the corresponding reciprocal function $y = \frac{1}{f(x)}$.
   a) $y = 3x - 7$
   b) $y = 5x^2 - 2x + 7$
   c) $y = (x - 2)^3 - 1$
   d) $y = \sqrt{x + 1}$
   e) $y = |3(x + 1)|$
   f) $y = \sqrt{16 - (x + 2)^2}$

2. Copy the graph of each function $y = f(x)$, and draw the graph of $y = \frac{1}{f(x)}$ on the same grid.

a)

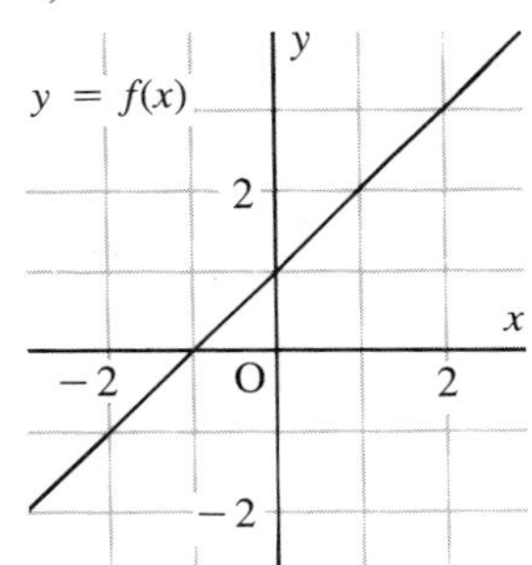

b)

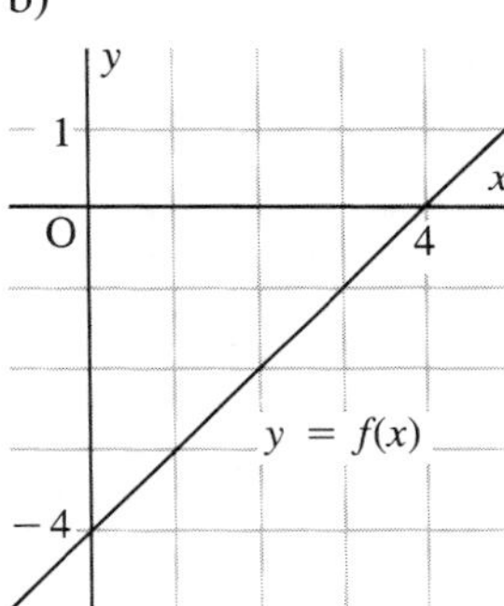

c)

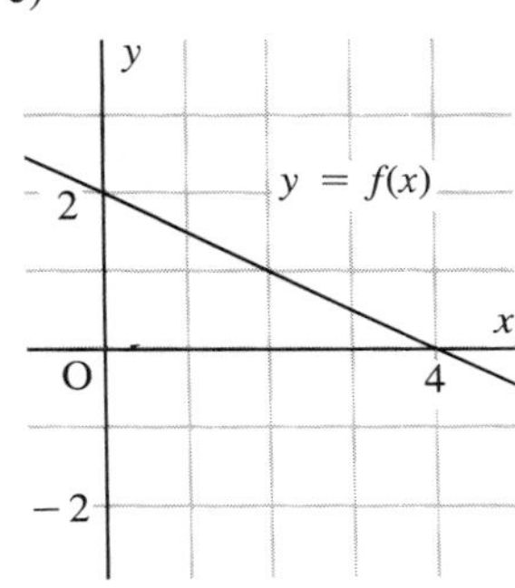

d)

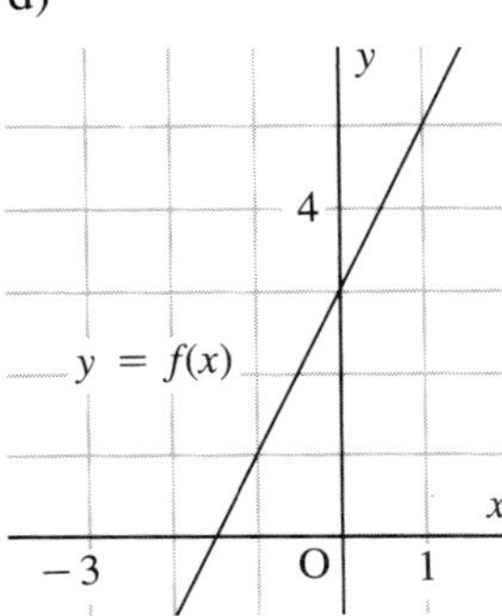

e)

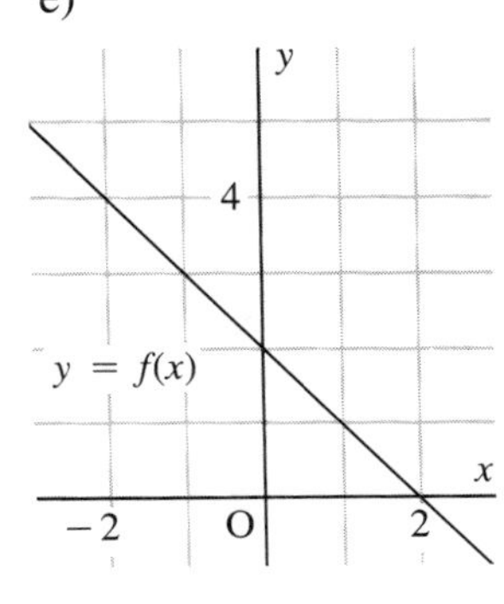

f)

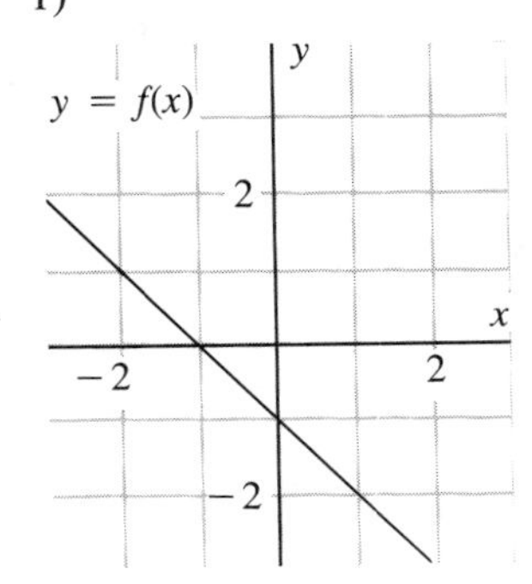

3. Draw each pair of graphs on the same grid.
   a) $y = x + 2 \quad y = \frac{1}{x + 2}$
   b) $y = x - 5 \quad y = \frac{1}{x - 5}$
   c) $y = 2x + 3 \quad y = \frac{1}{2x + 3}$
   d) $y = \frac{1}{2}x - 1 \quad y = \frac{1}{\frac{1}{2}x - 1}$
   e) $y = -x \quad y = \frac{1}{-x}$
   f) $y = -x + 4 \quad y = \frac{1}{-x + 4}$

Ⓑ

4. Graph each function $y = f(x)$. Then graph $y = \frac{1}{f(x)}$ on the same grid.

   a) $y = x^2$ b) $y = x^2 - 9$ c) $y = x^2 - 16$
   d) $y = x^2 + 5$ e) $y = (x - 2)^2$ f) $y = (x + 3)^2$

5. Graph each function. Then state its domain and range.

   a) $y = \dfrac{1}{2x + 6}$ b) $y = \dfrac{1}{\frac{1}{2}x + 3}$ c) $y = \dfrac{1}{3 - x}$

   d) $y = \dfrac{1}{x^2 - 25}$ e) $y = \dfrac{1}{x^2 - 10}$ f) $y = \dfrac{1}{(x - 5)^2}$

6. For each function in *Exercise 4*, for which real values of x does $\frac{1}{f(x)} = f(x)$?

Ⓒ

7. Graph each function. Then state its domain and range.

   a) $y = \dfrac{1}{|x|}$ b) $y = \dfrac{1}{|x| + 1}$ c) $y = \dfrac{1}{|x| - 1}$

   d) $y = \dfrac{1}{\sqrt{x}}$ e) $y = \dfrac{1}{\sqrt{x} + 1}$ f) $y = \dfrac{1}{\sqrt{x} - 1}$

   g) $y = \dfrac{1}{x^2}$ h) $y = \dfrac{1}{x^2 + 1}$ i) $y = \dfrac{1}{x^2 - 1}$

8. Graph each function.

   a) $y = \dfrac{1}{(x - 3)^2 + 5}$ b) $y = \dfrac{1}{\sqrt{\frac{1}{2}x + 5} - 3}$ c) $y = \dfrac{1}{\frac{1}{2}(x - 2)^3 + 2}$

   d) $y = \dfrac{1}{(x + 2)^2 - 2}$ e) $y = \dfrac{1}{\left[\frac{1}{2}(x + 2)\right]^2 - 4}$ f) $y = \dfrac{1}{\left|\frac{1}{2}x + 4\right| - 5}$

INVESTIGATE

Assume that a function $y = f(x)$ is given.

a) Describe how the domain of $y = \dfrac{1}{f(x)}$ is related to the domain of $y = f(x)$.

b) Describe how the range of $y = \dfrac{1}{f(x)}$ is related to the range of $y = f(x)$.

9-8 RECIPROCAL TRIGONOMETRIC FUNCTIONS

In Chapter 8 we studied the graphs of the sine and cosine functions. To graph the remaining trigonometric functions, we use the properties of reciprocal functions.

Cosecant and Secant Functions

The cosecant and secant functions are defined to be the reciprocals of the sine and cosine functions respectively.

Let P(x,y) be any point on a circle with radius r, corresponding to an angle θ in standard position. Then,

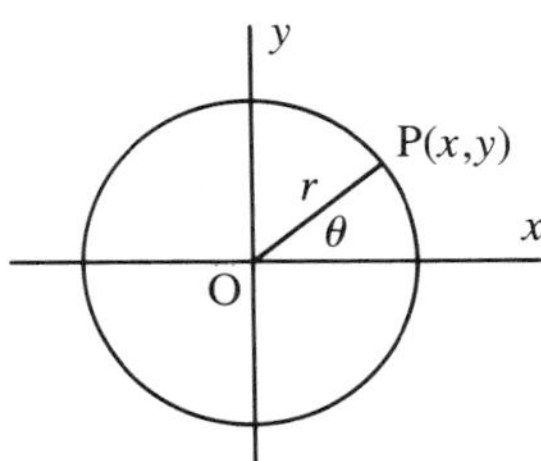

$$\csc\theta = \frac{1}{\sin\theta} = \frac{r}{y},\quad y \neq 0 \qquad \sec\theta = \frac{1}{\cos\theta} = \frac{r}{x},\quad x \neq 0$$

There are no cosecant or secant keys on a scientific calculator. These are not necessary, since you can easily find the sine or cosine of an angle and then take its reciprocal.

Example 1. Use a scientific calculator to find each value to five decimal places.
a) csc 230° b) sec 4.38

Solution. a) Find the sine of 230°, then take its reciprocal. With the calculator in *degree mode*,
key in: 230 [sin] [1/x] to display −1.3054073
To five decimal places, csc 230° = −1.305 41

b) Find the cosine of 4.38 radians, and take its reciprocal. With the calculator in *radian mode*,
key in: 4.38 [cos] [1/x] to display −3.064644
To five decimal places, sec 4.38 = −3.064 64

Cosecant and secant functions can be graphed using a table of values. A more efficient method is to graph the corresponding sine or cosine function, and use it to graph the reciprocal function. We use the properties of reciprocals given in *Section 9-7*.

Example 2. Graph the function $y = \csc\theta$ over two cycles.

Solution. *Step 1*. Graph the function $y = \sin\theta$, and draw vertical dotted lines through the points where the graph intersects the θ-axis. At these points, $\sin\theta = 0$, and hence $\csc\theta$ is not defined.

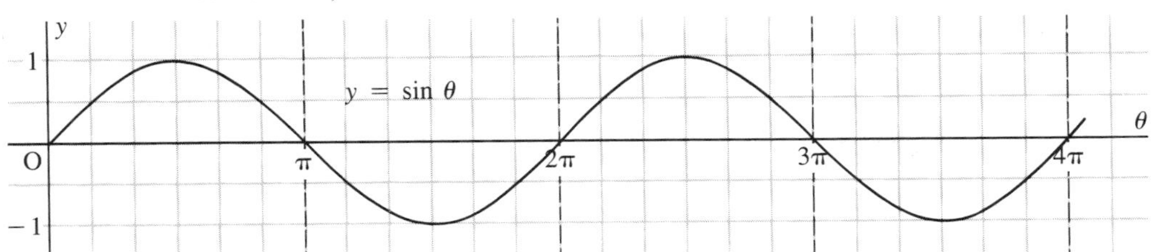

Step 2. Consider values of θ from 0 to π. Since $\sin 0 = 0$, $\csc 0$ is not defined. From the graph, we can see that as θ increases from 0 to $\frac{\pi}{2}$ and then to π, $\sin \theta$ is positive and increases from 0 to 1, and then decreases to 0. Hence, $\csc \theta$ is positive and decreases to 1 and then increases. Since $\sin \pi = 0$, $\csc \pi$ is not defined.

When θ is close to 0 or close to π, $\csc \theta$ is very large.

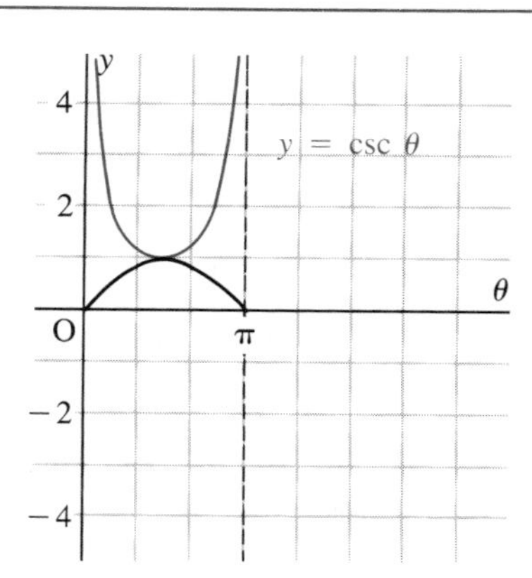

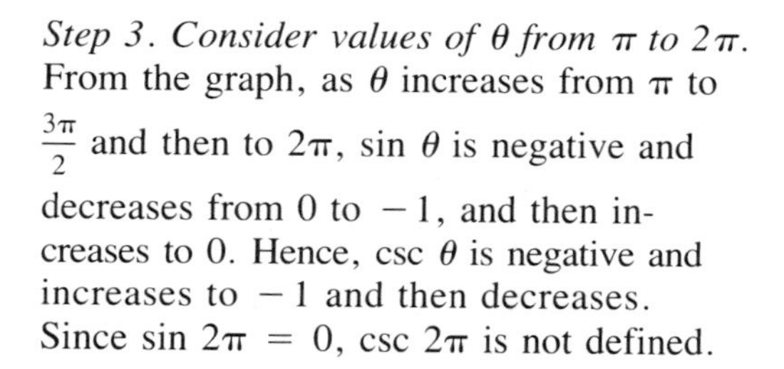

Step 3. Consider values of θ from π to 2π. From the graph, as θ increases from π to $\frac{3\pi}{2}$ and then to 2π, $\sin \theta$ is negative and decreases from 0 to -1, and then increases to 0. Hence, $\csc \theta$ is negative and increases to -1 and then decreases. Since $\sin 2\pi = 0$, $\csc 2\pi$ is not defined.

When θ is close to π or close to 2π, $\csc \theta$ is negative, but has a very large absolute value.

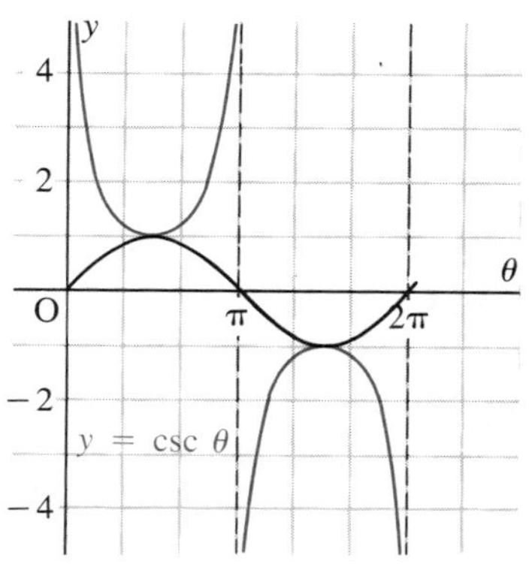

Step 4. This completes one cycle. Other cycles can be graphed similarly.

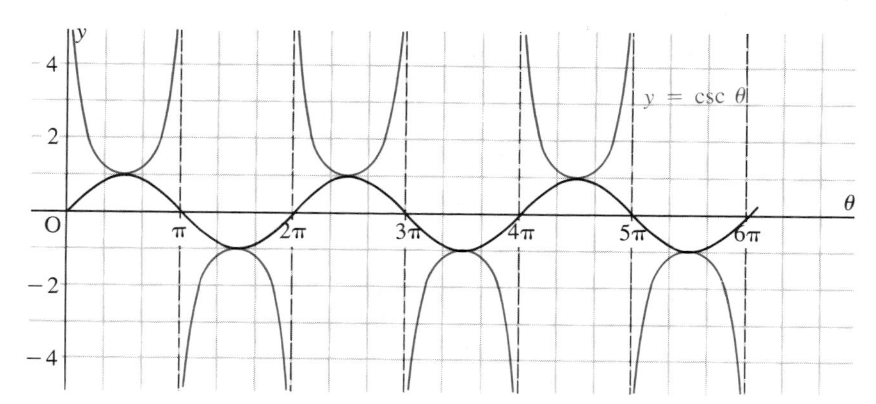

The reciprocal function of any sinusoidal function can be graphed in a similar way.

Tangent and Cotangent Functions

Let $P(x,y)$ be any point on a circle with radius r, corresponding to an angle θ in standard position. Then,

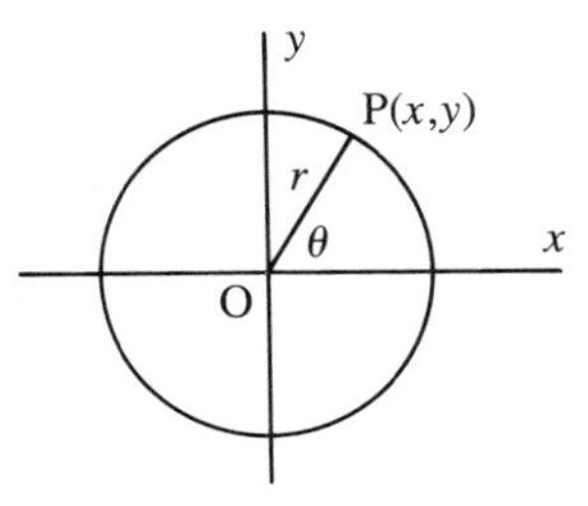

$\tan\theta = \frac{y}{x}$, $x \neq 0$ $\qquad$ $\cot\theta = \frac{x}{y}$, $y \neq 0$

The cotangent function is the reciprocal of the tangent function, and conversely.

There is no cotangent key on a scientific calculator, since you can find the tangent of an angle and then take its reciprocal.

Example 3. Use a scientific calculator to find each value to five decimal places.

a) $\cot 295°$ $\qquad$ b) $\cot(-1.5)$

Solution. a) Find the tangent of 295°, and then take its reciprocal. With the calculator in degree mode,
key in: 295 [tan] [1/x] to display -0.4663077
To five decimal places, $\cot 295° = -0.466\ 31$

b) Find the tangent of -1.5, and then take its reciprocal. With the calculator in radian mode,
key in: 1.5 [+/−] [tan] [1/x] to display -0.0709148
To five decimal places, $\cot(-1.5) = -0.070\ 91$

Tangent and cotangent functions can be graphed using a table of values. A more efficient method is to consider how the function values change as θ increases.

Example 4. Graph the function $y = \tan\theta$ over four cycles.

Solution. *Step 1. Consider values of θ from 0 to $\frac{\pi}{2}$.*

When $\theta = 0$, $y = 0$ and $x = r$, so $\tan 0 = \frac{0}{r}$, or 0. Thus, (0,0) is a point on the graph. As θ increases from 0 to $\frac{\pi}{4}$, y increases and x decreases. Hence, $\tan\theta$ increases.

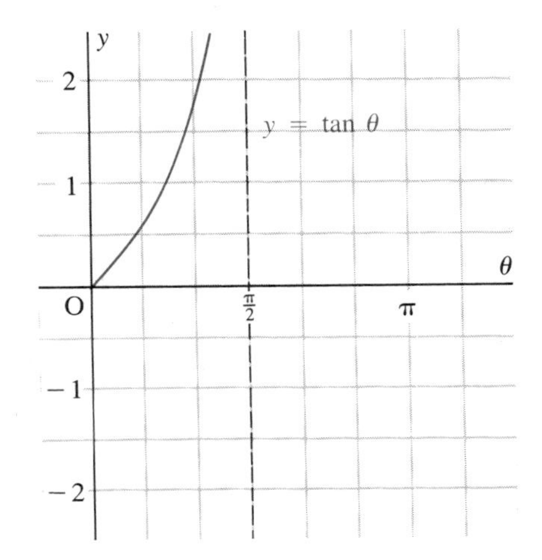

When $\theta = \frac{\pi}{4}$, x and y are equal, so $\tan\frac{\pi}{4} = 1$. Hence, $\left(\frac{\pi}{4},1\right)$ is a point on the graph. As θ increases further, $\tan\theta$ continues to increase.

When $\theta = \frac{\pi}{2}$, $y = r$ and $x = 0$.

Hence, $\tan\frac{\pi}{2}$ is undefined. When θ is close to $\frac{\pi}{2}$, $\tan\theta$ is very large.

Step 2. Consider values of θ from $\frac{\pi}{2}$ to π.

When θ is close to $\frac{\pi}{2}$, y is very large and positive. But x is negative, and has a small absolute value. Hence, $\tan\theta$ is negative and has a very large absolute value. As θ increases, y decreases and the absolute value of x increases.
Since $\tan\theta$ is negative, $\tan\theta$ increases.

When $\theta = \frac{3\pi}{4}$, x and y differ only in sign, so $\tan\frac{3\pi}{4} = -1$. As θ increases further, $\tan\theta$ continues to increase.

When $\theta = \pi$, $y = 0$ and $x = -r$.
Hence, $\tan\pi = 0$

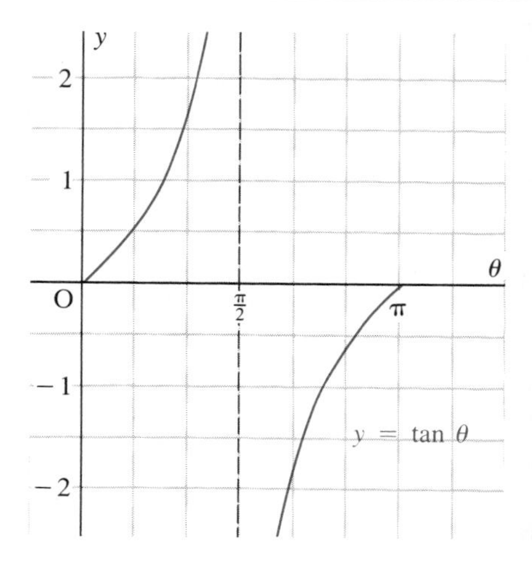

Step 3. This completes one cycle. Other cycles can be graphed similarly.

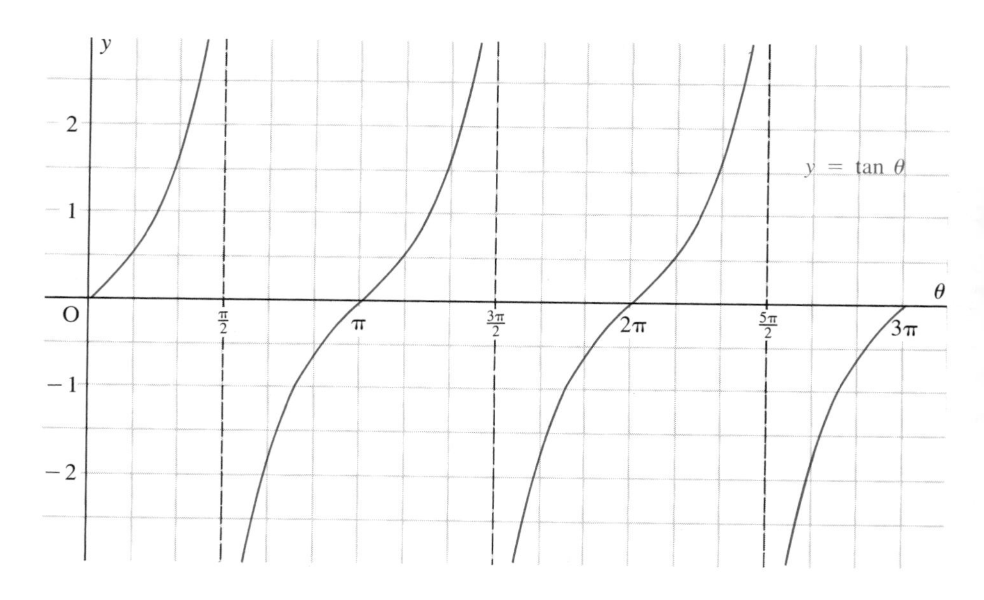

From the graph, we see that the tangent function has no amplitude, because there are no maximum or minimum points. The period of the tangent function is π.

The cotangent function can be graphed in a similar way. Or, since it is the reciprocal of the tangent function, it can be graphed using properties of reciprocals.

EXERCISES 9-8

Ⓐ

1. Compare the graphs of $y = \sin\theta$ and $y = \csc\theta$. In what ways are they different?

2. Use a scientific calculator in degree mode. Find each value to three decimal places.
   a) csc 110° b) csc 256° c) sec 95° d) sec 272°
   e) tan 123° f) tan 269° g) cot 184° h) cot 355°

3. Use a scientific calculator in radian mode. Find each value to three decimal places.
   a) csc 1.75 b) csc 3.22 c) sec 2.16 d) sec 6.75
   e) tan 2.5 f) tan (−1.65) g) cot 6.25 h) cot (−2.47)

Ⓑ

4. Graph each function for $-2\pi \leqslant \theta \leqslant 2\pi$.
   a) $y = \csc\theta$ b) $y = \sec\theta$ c) $y = \tan\theta$ d) $y = \cot\theta$

5. a) Make a list of the properties of the functions $y = \csc\theta$ and $y = \sec\theta$ which is similar to the one on page 324 for $y = \sin\theta$ and $y = \cos\theta$.
   b) Make a similar list for the functions $y = \tan\theta$ and $y = \cot\theta$.

6. Compare the graphs of $y = \tan\theta$ and $y = \cot\theta$. In what ways are they similar? In what ways are they different?

7. Graph each function, and state its period and phase shift.
   a) $y = 2\csc\left(\theta - \frac{\pi}{3}\right)$ b) $y = 3\sec(\theta + \pi)$
   c) $y = 2\csc 2\pi\frac{(\theta - 1)}{3} + 5$ d) $y = 4\sec 2\pi\frac{(\theta + 3)}{6} + 4$
   e) $y = \tan\left(\theta - \frac{\pi}{4}\right)$ f) $y = \cot\left(\theta + \frac{\pi}{2}\right)$
   g) $y = \tan\pi(\theta - 3)$ h) $y = \cot\pi(\theta + 2)$

Ⓒ

8. One factor which affects daily temperatures is the distance sunlight must pass through the atmosphere before it reaches the Earth. To express this amount of atmosphere, the term *air mass* has been coined. Air mass 1 is the distance sunlight must pass through the atmosphere to reach sea level when the sun is directly overhead. Air mass 2 is two times air mass 1; air mass 3 is 3 times air mass 1, and so on.
   a) Write an equation which expresses the air mass a as a function of the angle of inclination of the sun, θ.
   b) Graph the function in part a).

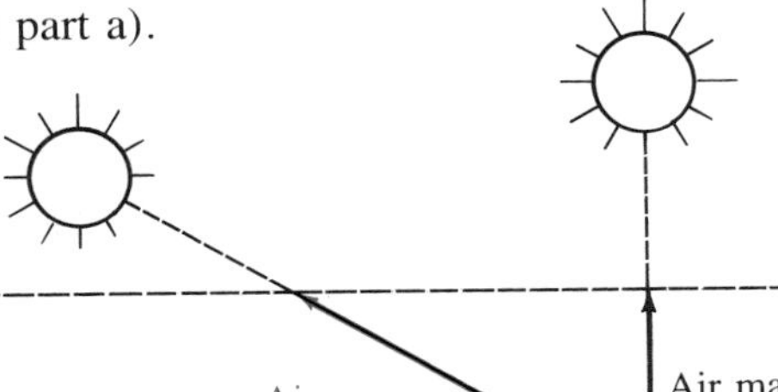

9. One energy-saving idea is to design houses with recessed windows on the side facing the sun. Sunlight will enter the window in winter when the sun's angle is low, but it will be blocked in the summer when its angle is much higher. The highest angle of elevation of the sun occurs at noon in mid-June, when the angle of elevation, in degrees, is $23.5 + l$, where l is the latitude of the location.
   a) Assume that the window shown is designed to block the sun's rays when it is at its highest elevation in the summer. Express the depth d metres of the recess as a function of the latitude l.
   b) Draw a graph of d against l.
   c) Determine the value of d for your latitude.

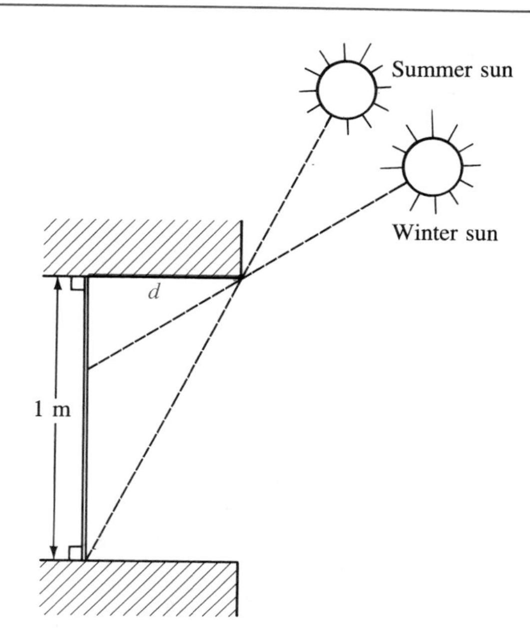

10. A police cruiser is parked such that the beacon on its roof is 3 m from a brick wall. As the beacon rotates, a spot of light moves along the wall. Assuming that the beacon makes one complete rotation in 2 s, find an equation which expresses the distance d metres as a function of time.

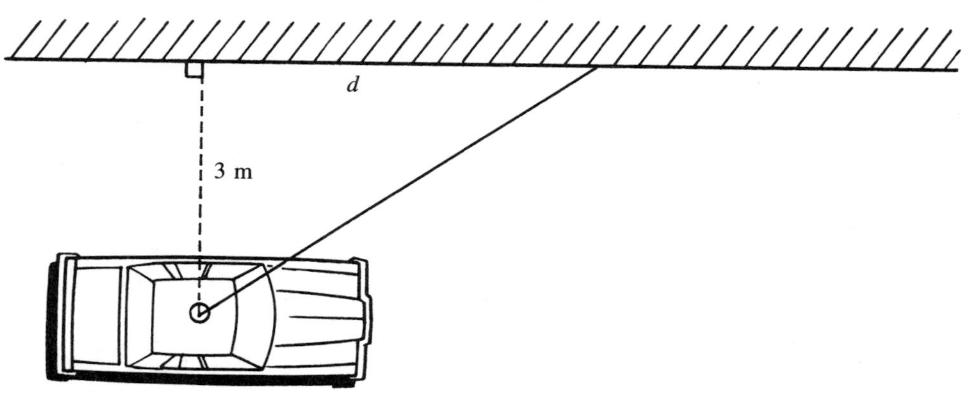

11. Assume that a 100 m building is on the equator. On June 21 each year the sun rises at 6 A.M. in the east and sets at 6 P.M. in the west.
   a) Find an equation which could be used to calculate the length of the building's shadow at any time of the day.
   b) Draw a graph showing the length of the shadow as a function of time for the day.

9-9 TRIGONOMETRIC IDENTITIES

Let P(x,y) be any point on a circle of radius r, corresponding to an angle θ in standard position. Recall that the six trigonometric functions are defined as follows.

$$\sin \theta = \frac{y}{r} \qquad \cos \theta = \frac{x}{r} \qquad \tan \theta = \frac{y}{x},\ x \neq 0$$

$$\csc \theta = \frac{r}{y},\ y \neq 0 \qquad \sec \theta = \frac{r}{x},\ x \neq 0 \qquad \cot \theta = \frac{x}{y},\ y \neq 0$$

where $r = \sqrt{x^2 + y^2}$

These definitions apply for any angle θ in any quadrant.

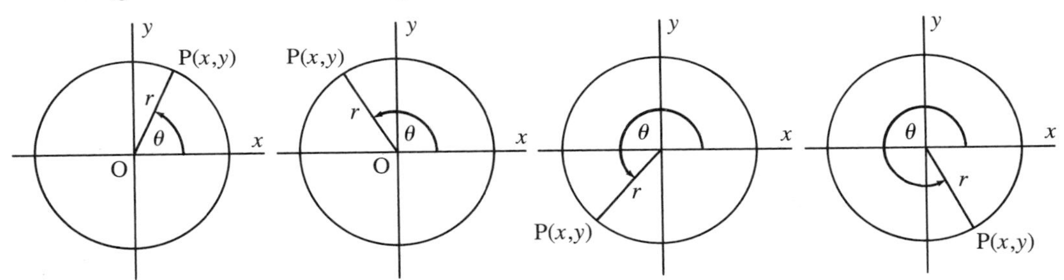

Since the definitions involve only three quantities x, y, and r, and since $r^2 = x^2 + y^2$, the trigonometric functions are related in a wide variety of different ways. For example, the following identities are direct consequences of the definitions.

Reciprocal Identities

$$\csc \theta = \frac{1}{\sin \theta} \qquad \sec \theta = \frac{1}{\cos \theta} \qquad \cot \theta = \frac{1}{\tan \theta}$$

Quotient Identities

$$\frac{\sin \theta}{\cos \theta} = \tan \theta \qquad \frac{\cos \theta}{\sin \theta} = \cot \theta$$

Equations such as those above are called *identities*. They are satisfied for all values of the variable for which they are defined. The reciprocal and quotient identities can be used to prove other identities, such as those in the following example.

Example 1. Prove each identity.

a) $\sec\theta\,(1 + \cos\theta) = 1 + \sec\theta$

b) $\sec\theta = \tan\theta\csc\theta$

Solution. a) $\sec\theta\,(1 + \cos\theta) = 1 + \sec\theta$

Left side	Reason
$\sec\theta\,(1 + \cos\theta)$	
$= \sec\theta + \sec\theta\cos\theta$	Expanding
$= \sec\theta + 1$	Reciprocal identity
$=$ Right side	

Since the left side simplifies to the right side, the identity is correct.

b) $\sec\theta = \tan\theta\csc\theta$

Left side	Reason
$\sec\theta$	
$= \dfrac{1}{\cos\theta}$	Reciprocal identity

Right side	Reason
$\tan\theta\csc\theta$	
$= \dfrac{\sin\theta}{\cos\theta} \times \dfrac{1}{\sin\theta}$	Quotient and reciprocal identities
$= \dfrac{1}{\cos\theta}$	

Since both sides simplify to the same expression, the identity is correct.

Observe the methods used in *Example 1* to prove the identities. We use the reciprocal and quotient identities, along with algebraic simplification, to show that one side of the identity is equal to the other side, or that both sides of the identity are equal to the same expression.

The reciprocal and quotient identities are rather like theorems in geometry, because they are used to prove other identities.

Another useful set of identities is called the *Pythagorean identities* because the identities are established by applying the Pythagorean Theorem to △PON in the diagram shown.

$x^2 + y^2 = r^2$

Divide both sides by r^2.

$$\frac{x^2}{r^2} + \frac{y^2}{r^2} = 1$$

$(\cos\theta)^2 + (\sin\theta)^2 = 1$

An expression such as $(\cos\theta)^2$ occurs so frequently that it is abbreviated as $\cos^2\theta$. Similarly, $(\sin\theta)^2$ is written as $\sin^2\theta$. Hence, we obtain the identity

$\cos^2\theta + \sin^2\theta = 1.$

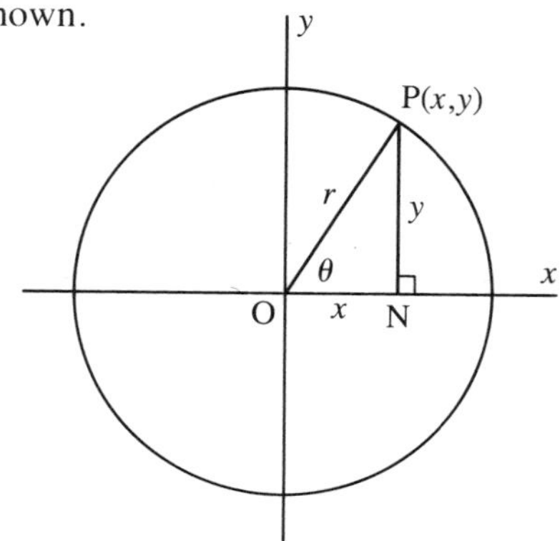

We can obtain two additional Pythagorean identities from the equation $x^2 + y^2 = r^2$.

Divide both sides by x^2.

$$1 + \frac{y^2}{x^2} = \frac{r^2}{x^2}$$
$$1 + (\tan\theta)^2 = (\sec\theta)^2$$
$$1 + \tan^2\theta = \sec^2\theta$$

Divide both sides by y^2.

$$\frac{x^2}{y^2} + 1 = \frac{r^2}{y^2}$$
$$(\cot\theta)^2 + 1 = (\csc\theta)^2$$
$$\cot^2\theta + 1 = \csc^2\theta$$

Pythagorean Identities

$\sin^2\theta + \cos^2\theta = 1 \qquad 1 + \tan^2\theta = \sec^2\theta \qquad 1 + \cot^2\theta = \csc^2\theta$

Example 2. Prove the identity $1 - \cos^2\theta = \cos^2\theta\tan^2\theta$.

Solution.

Left side	Reason
$1 - \cos^2\theta$	
$= \sin^2\theta$	Pythagorean identity

Right side	Reason
$\cos^2\theta\tan^2\theta$	
$= \cos^2\theta \times \dfrac{\sin^2\theta}{\cos^2\theta}$	Quotient identity
$= \sin^2\theta$	

Since both sides simplify to the same expression, the identity is correct.

Example 3. a) Prove the identity $\dfrac{\sin\theta}{1 + \cos\theta} = \dfrac{1 - \cos\theta}{\sin\theta}$.

b) Predict a similar identity for the expression $\dfrac{\cos\theta}{1 + \sin\theta}$, and prove that it is correct.

Solution. a)

Left side	Reason
$\dfrac{\sin\theta}{1 + \cos\theta}$	
$= \dfrac{\sin\theta}{1 + \cos\theta} \times \dfrac{1 - \cos\theta}{1 - \cos\theta}$	Multiplying by 1
$= \dfrac{\sin\theta(1 - \cos\theta)}{1 - \cos^2\theta}$	
$= \dfrac{\sin\theta(1 - \cos\theta)}{\sin^2\theta}$	Pythagorean identity
$= \dfrac{1 - \cos\theta}{\sin\theta}$	Dividing numerator and denominator by $\sin\theta$
= Right side	

Since the left side simplifies to the right side, the identity is correct.

b) The pattern of the terms $\sin\theta$ and $\cos\theta$ in part a) suggests that a similar identity might be:

$$\frac{\cos\theta}{1+\sin\theta} = \frac{1-\sin\theta}{\cos\theta}.$$

We can prove this identity in a similar way.

Another way to prove this identity (and the one in part a)) is to start with the Pythagorean identity $\sin^2\theta + \cos^2\theta = 1$ and perform the same operation to both sides. That is, we may write

$$\sin^2\theta + \cos^2\theta = 1$$

$$\cos^2\theta = 1 - \sin^2\theta$$

$$\cos^2\theta = (1 - \sin\theta)(1 + \sin\theta)$$

Hence, $\dfrac{\cos\theta}{1+\sin\theta} = \dfrac{1-\sin\theta}{\cos\theta}$

EXERCISES 9-9

(A)

1. Prove each identity.
   a) $\tan\theta\cos\theta = \sin\theta$
   b) $\cot\theta\sec\theta = \csc\theta$
   c) $\sin\theta\cot\theta = \cos\theta$
   d) $\tan\theta\csc\theta = \sec\theta$
   e) $\sin\theta = \dfrac{\tan\theta}{\sec\theta}$
   f) $\dfrac{\cot\theta}{\csc\theta} = \cos\theta$

2. Prove each identity.
   a) $\csc\theta\,(1 + \sin\theta) = 1 + \csc\theta$
   b) $\sin\theta\,(1 + \csc\theta) = 1 + \sin\theta$
   c) $\cos\theta\,(\sec\theta - 1) = 1 - \cos\theta$
   d) $\sin\theta\sec\theta\cot\theta = 1$
   e) $\dfrac{1-\tan\theta}{1-\cot\theta} = -\tan\theta$
   f) $\cot\theta = \dfrac{1+\cot\theta}{1+\tan\theta}$

(B)

3. Prove each identity.
   a) $\sin\theta\tan\theta + \sec\theta = \dfrac{\sin^2\theta + 1}{\cos\theta}$
   b) $\dfrac{1+\cos\theta}{1-\cos\theta} = \dfrac{1+\sec\theta}{\sec\theta - 1}$
   c) $\dfrac{1+\sin\theta}{1-\sin\theta} = \dfrac{\csc\theta + 1}{\csc\theta - 1}$
   d) $\dfrac{1+\tan\theta}{1+\cot\theta} = \dfrac{1-\tan\theta}{\cot\theta - 1}$
   e) $\dfrac{1+\sin\theta}{1+\csc\theta} = \sin\theta$
   f) $\dfrac{\sin\theta + \tan\theta}{\cos\theta + 1} = \tan\theta$

4. Prove each identity.
   a) $\sin^2\theta\cot^2\theta = 1 - \sin^2\theta$
   b) $\csc^2\theta - 1 = \csc^2\theta\cos^2\theta$
   c) $\sin^2\theta = \dfrac{\tan^2\theta}{1+\tan^2\theta}$
   d) $\dfrac{\sin\theta + \cos\theta\cot\theta}{\cot\theta} = \sec\theta$
   e) $\sin\theta\cos\theta\tan\theta = 1 - \cos^2\theta$
   f) $\dfrac{\cos\theta}{1+\sin\theta} + \dfrac{\cos\theta}{1-\sin\theta} = 2\sec\theta$

5. a) Prove this identity. $\dfrac{\sin\theta + \cos\theta}{\csc\theta + \sec\theta} = \sin\theta\cos\theta$

   b) Predict a similar identity for the expression $\dfrac{\sin\theta + \tan\theta}{\csc\theta + \cot\theta}$, and prove that it is correct.

   c) Establish another identity like those in parts a) and b).

6. a) Prove this identity. $\dfrac{\tan\theta}{\sec\theta + 1} = \dfrac{\sec\theta - 1}{\tan\theta}$

   b) Predict a similar identity for the expression $\dfrac{\cot\theta}{\csc\theta + 1}$, and prove that it is correct.

7. a) Prove this identity. $\dfrac{1}{1 + \sin\theta} + \dfrac{1}{1 - \sin\theta} = 2\sec^2\theta$

   b) Establish a similar identity for this expression. $\dfrac{1}{1 + \cos\theta} + \dfrac{1}{1 - \cos\theta}$

8. a) Prove this identity. $\tan^2\theta\,(1 + \cot^2\theta) = \sec^2\theta$

   b) Predict a similar identity for the expression $\cot^2\theta\,(1 + \tan^2\theta)$, and prove that it is correct.

9. a) Prove each identity.

   i) $(1 - \cos^2\theta)(1 + \tan^2\theta) = \tan^2\theta$ ii) $(1 - \sin^2\theta)(1 + \cot^2\theta) = \cot^2\theta$

   b) Establish another identity like those in part a).

10. Prove each identity.

    a) $\tan\theta + \cot\theta = \sec\theta\csc\theta$
    b) $\sec^2\theta + \csc^2\theta = \sec^2\theta\csc^2\theta$
    c) $\sec^2\theta + \csc^2\theta = (\tan\theta + \cot\theta)^2$
    d) $\sin^2\theta = \cos\theta\,(\sec\theta - \cos\theta)$

11. Let P be any point on the unit circle, and construct the tangent to the circle at P. Let the tangent intersect the x-axis at A and the y-axis at B.

    a) Show that:

    i) $PN = \sin\theta$ ii) $ON = \cos\theta$
    iii) $OB = \csc\theta$ iv) $OA = \sec\theta$
    v) $AP = \tan\theta$ vi) $BP = \cot\theta$.

    b) Use the results of part a) and similar triangles on the diagram to illustrate these identities.

    i) $1 + \tan^2\theta = \sec^2\theta$
    ii) $\sin^2\theta = \cos\theta\,(\sec\theta - \cos\theta)$
    iii) $\tan\theta\cot\theta = 1$

    c) What other identities can you find that can be illustrated by this diagram?

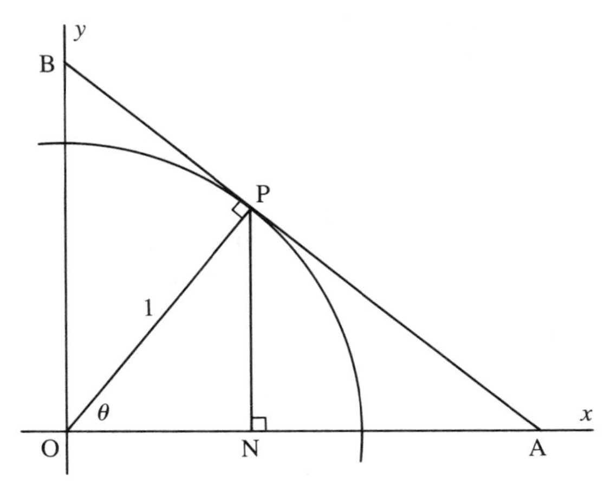

Ⓒ

12. In *Exercise 7*, identities for $\frac{1}{1 + f(x)} + \frac{1}{1 - f(x)}$, where $f(x) = \sin x$ and $f(x) = \cos x$, were established. Establish similar identities where $f(x)$ represents each of the other four trigonometric functions.

13. Establish an identity which involves all six trigonometric functions.

14. Prove each identity.
    a) $\frac{1}{1 + \cos\theta} = \csc^2\theta - \frac{\cot\theta}{\sin\theta}$
    b) $\tan\theta + \tan^3\theta = \frac{\sec^2\theta}{\cot\theta}$
    c) $\frac{1 + \csc\theta}{\cot\theta} - \sec\theta = \tan\theta$
    d) $\frac{(1 - \cos^2\theta)(\sec^2\theta - 1)}{\cos^2\theta} = \tan^4\theta$

15. Let $P(x,y)$ be any point on a circle of radius r, corresponding to an angle θ in standard position. Let A and C be the points shown on the diagram.
    a) Express the lengths AP and CP as functions of r and θ.
    b) Check the results of part a) when $\theta = 0°$, $90°$, $180°$, and $270°$.

16. Solve for x. $\sin x - \tan x = 0$, $0 \leqslant x \leqslant 2\pi$

17. Prove that the following expressions are *not* identities.
    a) $\sin 2\theta = 2\sin\theta$ b) $\cos 2\theta = 2\cos\theta$ c) $\tan 2\theta = 2\tan\theta$

INVESTIGATE

Identities for $\sin 2\theta$, $\cos 2\theta$, and $\tan 2\theta$ can be established using the diagram of the unit circle shown. Since $\triangle$ONP is a right triangle with hypotenuse 1 unit, then ON $= \cos 2\theta$ and PN $= \sin 2\theta$. Similarly, since $\triangle$MCO is a right triangle with hypotenuse 1 unit, then CM $= \cos\theta$ and MO $= \sin\theta$.

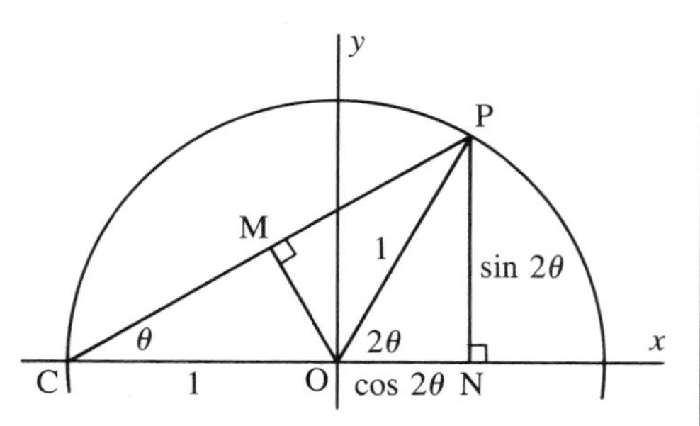

1. If $\angle$MCO $= \theta$, explain why $\angle$PON $= 2\theta$.

2. Write two different expressions for the length of CP. Use the results to establish an identity for $\cos 2\theta$ in terms of $\cos\theta$.

3. Use the results of *Question 2* to establish identities for $\sin 2\theta$ and $\tan 2\theta$ in terms of functions of θ.

1. Classify each function as linear, quadratic, square root, cubic, absolute value or semicircle.

a)

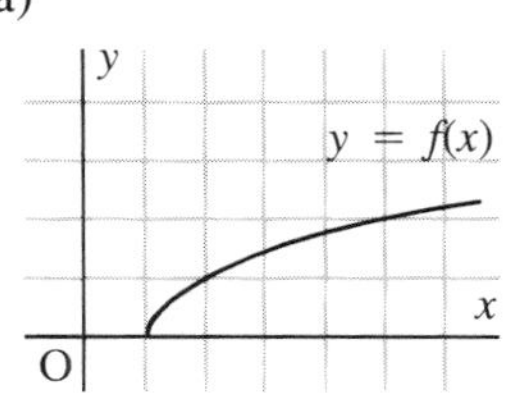

b)

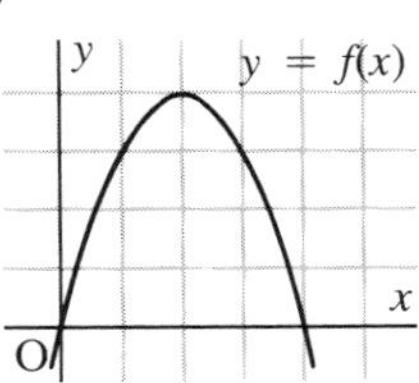

c)

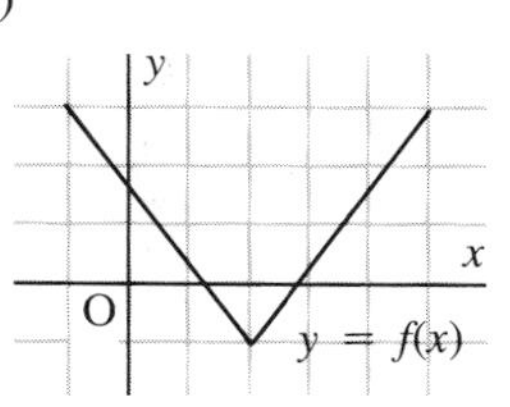

2. The volume V of a spherical balloon radius r is given by $V = \frac{4}{3}\pi r^3$. By how much does the volume change if the radius changes from 4 cm to:
a) 5 cm b) 8 cm c) 10 cm?

3. When a diver jumps off the board, her height h metres above the water after t seconds is given by the formula $h = -4.9t^2 + 8.8t + 3.0$.
a) Graph the function for $0 \leqslant t \leqslant 2.5$.
b) How high is the board above the water?
c) Write the function which gives the diver's height above the board instead of her height above the water.
d) Graph the function in part c) on the same grid as the function in part a).

4. Write each function in the form $y = f(x) + q$ and sketch its graph.
a) $y = (x - 2)(x + 2)$ b) $y = (x - 2)(x^2 + 2x + 4)$

5. Graph each set of functions on the same grid.
a) $y = x^2$ $y = (x - 3)^2$ $y = 2(x - 3)^2$
b) $y = \sqrt{x}$ $y = \sqrt{x - 2}$ $y = \sqrt{x - 2} + 4$
c) $y = x^3$ $y = -(x - 2)^3$ $y = -\frac{1}{2}(x - 2)^3 - 3$
d) $y = |x|$ $y = |x - 5|$ $y = 2|x - 5| + 1$

6. Graph each pair of functions on the same grid.
a) $y = \left(-\frac{1}{2}x + 4\right)^2$ $y = \left[-\frac{1}{2}(x + 4)\right]^2$
b) $y = \sqrt{-2x - 2}$ $y = \sqrt{-2(x - 2)}$
c) $y = \left(-\frac{1}{2}x - 1\right)^3$ $y = \left[-\frac{1}{2}(x - 1)\right]^3$

7. Graph each function.
a) $y = \dfrac{1}{x - 3}$ b) $y = \dfrac{1}{|x| + 2}$ c) $y = \dfrac{1}{(x + 1)^2}$

8. Prove each identity.
a) $\sec\theta\,(1 + \sin\theta) = \tan\theta\,(1 + \csc\theta)$ b) $\csc\theta - \dfrac{\cot\theta}{\sec\theta} = \sin\theta$
c) $\cos^2\theta = \sin\theta\,(\csc\theta - \sin\theta)$ d) $\sec^2\theta - 1 = (\sin\theta\sec\theta)^2$

Cumulative Review, Chapters 7-9

1. Find each ratio to 3 decimal places.
   a) $\cos 127°$ b) $\cot 245°$ c) $\sec 74°$ d) $\csc 287°$
   e) $\tan 2.35$ f) $\cos 3.81$ g) $\sin \frac{5\pi}{12}$ h) $\sec \frac{9\pi}{4}$

2. Solve for θ to the nearest degree, $0° \leqslant \theta \leqslant 360°$.
   a) $\tan \theta = 2.574$ b) $\csc \theta = -1.715$ c) $\cos \theta = 0.492$
   d) $\cot \theta = -0.815$ e) $\sin \theta = -0.728$ f) $\sec \theta = -8.175$

3. a) State the values of the other five trigonometric ratios for each obtuse angle θ.
   b) Find each value of θ in radians to 2 decimal places.
   c) State two angles that are coterminal with θ.
      i) $\sin \theta = \frac{7}{25}$ ii) $\tan \theta = -\frac{5}{8}$ iii) $\sec \theta = -\frac{9}{4}$

4. Solve $\triangle PQR$, if $\angle Q = 90°$ and:
   a) $PQ = 11$, $QR = 8$ b) $QR = 26$, $\angle P = 28°$.

5. Solve $\triangle XYZ$ if:
   a) $XY = 7$, $YZ = 5$, and $\angle Y = 110°$ b) $x = 3.7$, $y = 4.1$, and $\angle X = 58°$.

6. In $\triangle ABC$, AD is the altitude from A to BC. If $\angle B = 48°$, $\angle C = 32°$, and $BC = 12.8$ m, find the length of AD.

7. Solve for θ to the nearest degree, $0° \leqslant \theta \leqslant 360°$.
   a) $4 \tan \theta - 5 = 0$ b) $6 \sin^2\theta - \sin \theta - 2 = 0$ c) $3 \sec^2\theta + 2 \sec \theta = 5$

8. Find the amplitude, the period, the phase shift and the vertical displacement, then sketch the graph of each function.
   a) $y = 2 \sin 3(\theta - 30°)$ b) $y = \cos 2\pi \frac{(t - 2)}{3} + 2$
   c) $y = 3 \sin 2\left(\theta + \frac{\pi}{4}\right) - 1$ d) $y = 2 \sin 2\pi \frac{(t - 1)}{12} + 3$

9. The depth of water h metres at a seaside resort is given by the formula $h = 2.1 \sin 2\pi \frac{(t - 3.7)}{12.4} + 5.2$ where t is the time of day.
   a) Calculate the depth of water at: i) 7:30 A.M. ii) 3:15 P.M.
   b) When is high tide?

10. Sketch the graph of each function.
    a) $y = |x - 2| - 3$ b) $y = -\frac{1}{2}(x + 3)^2 + 2$ c) $y = -\sqrt{x - 1} - 2$
    d) $y = \frac{1}{x - 3}$ e) $y = \sqrt{25 - (x + 2)^2}$ f) $y = 2(x + 3)^3 + 2$

11. Prove each identity.
    a) $\frac{\sin \theta \cos \theta}{\cot \theta} = 1 - \cos^2\theta$ b) $1 + (\cos \theta + \sin \theta)(\cos \theta - \sin \theta) = \frac{2}{\sec^2\theta}$
    c) $\csc^2\theta + \sec^2\theta = \sec^2\theta \csc^2\theta$ d) $\frac{\cos \theta + \sin \theta \tan \theta}{\tan \theta} = \csc \theta$

10 Exponential Functions

In 1947 an investor bought Van Gogh's painting *Irises* for \$84 000. In 1987 she sold it for \$49 million. What annual rate of interest corresponds to an investment of \$84 000 which grows to \$49 million in 40 years? (See Section 10-4 *Example 2*.)

10-1 INTRODUCTION TO EXPONENTIAL FUNCTIONS

Exponents were originally introduced into mathematics as a shorthand for repeated multiplication. Repeated multiplication occurs frequently in applications involving growth and decay.

Compound Interest

Compound interest provides a simple example of *exponential growth*. Suppose you make a long-term investment of \$500 at a fixed interest rate of 8% per annum compounded annually. We can calculate the value of your investment at the end of each year.

Value in dollars of the investment after

year 1: $500(1.08) = 540$

year 2: $500(1.08)(1.08) = 500(1.08)^2$, or 583.20

year 3: $500(1.08)(1.08)(1.08) = 500(1.08)^3$, or 629.86

$\vdots \qquad \vdots$

year n: $500(1.08)^n$

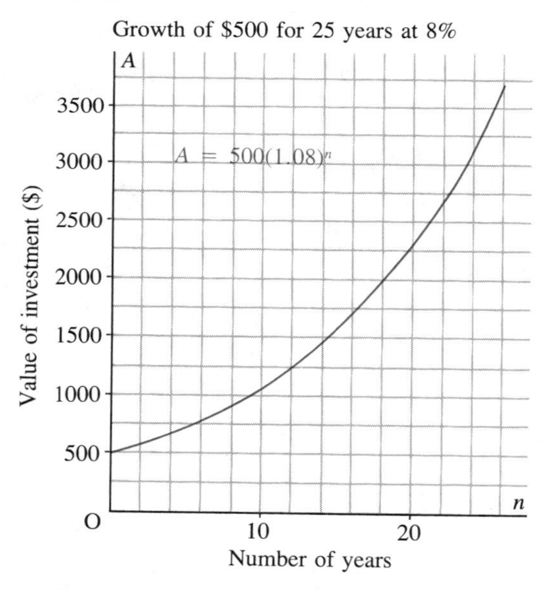

Hence, the value of an investment A dollars can be expressed as a function of the number of years n by this equation.

$$A = 500(1.08)^n$$

In this equation, n is a natural number since it indicates how many factors of 1.08 there are in the expression. Using values of n from 1 to 25, we obtain values of A and draw the graph shown. The fact that we can draw a smooth curve through the plotted points on the graph suggests that an expression such as $(1.08)^n$ can be defined for values of n that are not natural numbers. We will see how to do this in the next section.

Growth of Populations

In 1987 the world population reached 5 billion, and was increasing at the rate of approximately 1.6% per year. If we assume that this rate of growth is maintained, we can write an equation expressing the predicted population P billion as a function of the number of years n since 1987.

$$P \doteq 5(1.016)^n$$

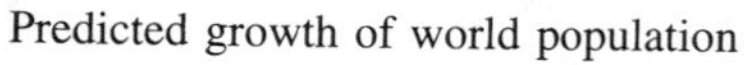

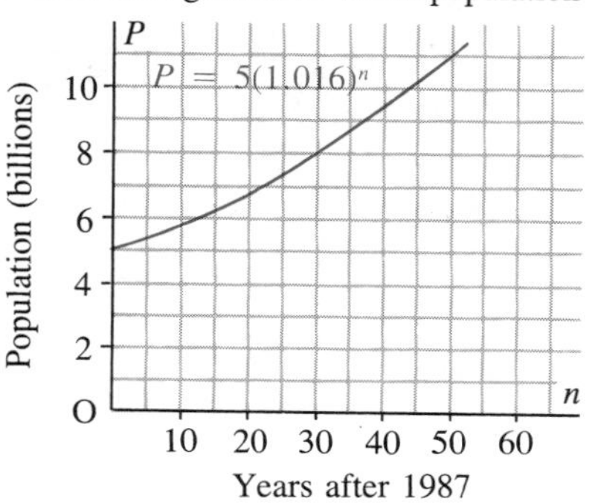

The graph on the facing page shows this equation plotted for values of n from 0 to 50 corresponding to the years from 1987 to 2037. In this equation, n is also a natural number, but since the graph represents as many as 50 values of n, the graph is drawn as a smooth curve.

A Bouncing Ball

A bouncing ball provides a simple example of *exponential decay*. In this picture, on each bounce the ball rises to 70% of the height from which it fell. Suppose that the ball originally fell from a height of 2.00 m. We can calculate the height to which the ball rises on each successive bounce.

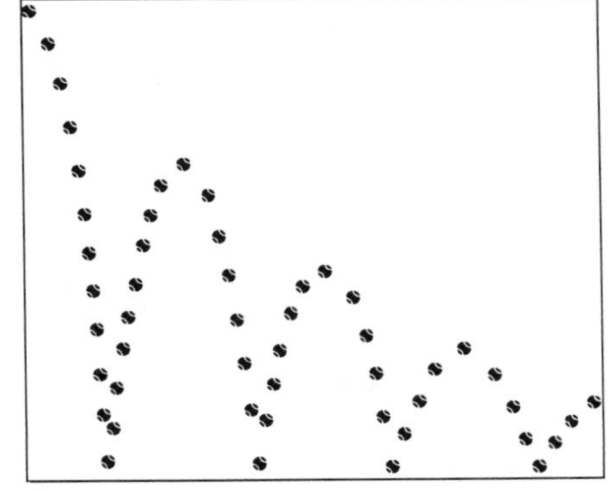

Height in metres of the ball after

bounce 1: $2.00(0.7) = 1.4$

bounce 2: $2.00(0.7)(0.7) = 2.0(0.7)^2$, or 0.98

bounce 3: $2.00(0.7)(0.7)(0.7) = 2.0(0.7)^3$, or 0.69

. .

. .

. .

bounce n: $2.00(0.7)^n$

Hence, the height h metres can be expressed as a function of the number of bounces n by this equation.

$$h = 2.00(0.7)^n$$

The graph shows the values of n for $0 \leq n \leq 10$. Since it is not meaningful to have a fractional number of bounces, the points are not joined by a smooth curve.

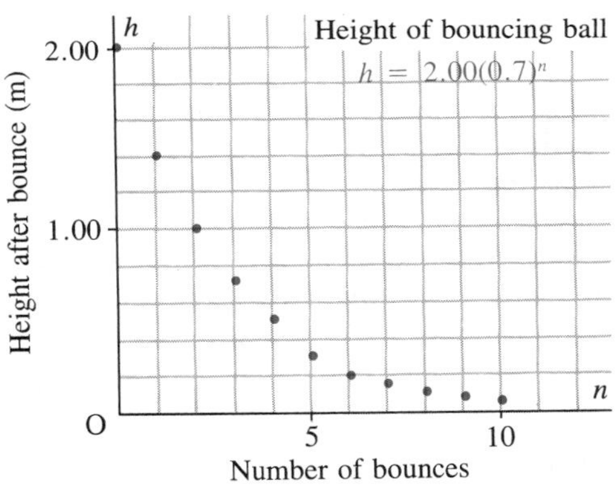

Light Penetration Under Water

For every metre a diver descends below the surface, the light intensity is reduced by 2.5%. Hence, the percent P of surface light present can be expressed as a function of the depth d metres by this equation.

$$P = 100(1 - 0.025)^d$$

$$\text{or} \quad P = 100(0.975)^d$$

The graph shows P as a function of d for $0 \leq d \leq 100$. Although d is understood to represent a natural number in the expression above, we have drawn a smooth curve to indicate light intensity at all depths to 100 m, including those depths that are not whole numbers of metres.

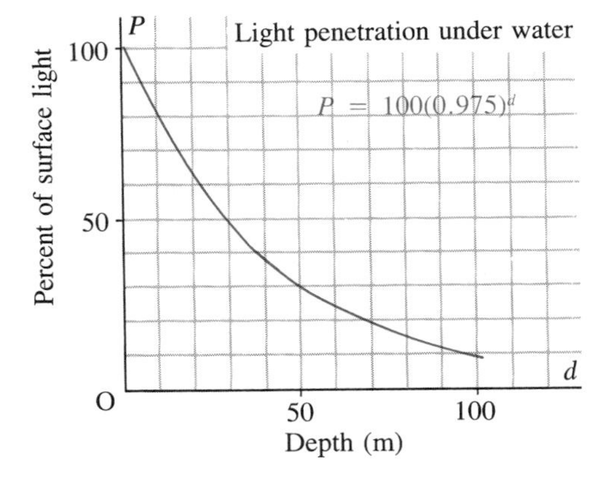

Summary
Consider the similarities in the equations of the above examples.

Exponential Growth

$A = 500(1.08)^n$

- 500: Initial amount
- 1.08: Growth factor (greater than 1)

$P = 5(1.016)^n$

- 5: Initial population

Exponential Decay

$h = 2.00(0.7)^n$

- 2.00: Initial height
- 0.7: Decay factor (less than 1)

$P = 100(0.975)^d$

- 100: Initial intensity

In each equation, the variable in the expression on the right side appears in an exponent. Functions whose defining equations have this property are called exponential functions.

> An *exponential function* has an equation which can be written in the form $y = ca^x$, where c and a are constants, and $a > 0$.

Note the following properties of the variable x, and the constants a and c.

- In this section, x is understood to represent a natural number, since it represents the number of times the constant a occurs as a factor. This restriction will be removed in the next section.
- Since all the applications of exponential functions are ones in which the base is positive, we will assume that $a > 0$.
- The constant c is any real number, though in most applications we shall encounter this number is usually positive also.

In the following example an exponential function is defined by a statement describing how variables are related.

Example. In favorable breeding conditions, a colony of insects can multiply 10-fold every 3 weeks. If there are now 500 insects in the colony, express the number of insects N as a function of the elapsed time w weeks.

Solution. "Multiply 10-fold every 3 weeks" means that every time 3 weeks elapse, there are 10 times as many insects as before.
Number of insects after:
3 weeks: $500(10)$
6 weeks: $500(10)^2$
9 weeks: $500(10)^3$

Each exponent is $\frac{1}{3}$ of the number of weeks.

. .
. .
. .

w weeks: $500(10)^{\frac{w}{3}}$
Hence, $N = 500(10)^{\frac{w}{3}}$

EXERCISES 10-1

Note: Exercises 1 to 8 refer to the above examples.

Ⓑ

1. Use the graph on page 426 to estimate how many years it takes, at 8%, for the original investment:
   a) to double in value
   b) to triple in value.

2. Describe how the graph would differ if:
   a) the interest rate were
      i) greater than 8%
      ii) less than 8%;
   b) the original investment were
      i) greater than $500
      ii) less than $500.

3. Use the graph on page 426 to estimate the number of years required for the population of the world to double.

4. Describe how the population graph would differ for a country such as:
   a) Mexico which has a growth rate of approximately 3.5%
   b) Japan which has a growth rate of approximately 1.1%.

5. Use the graph on page 427 to estimate how many bounces are needed before the ball bounces to only 10% of the original height from which it was dropped.

6. Describe how both the graph and the equation on page 427 would differ for a ball which is:
   a) more resilient, and bounces higher than the one shown
   b) less resilient, and does not bounce as high as the one shown.

7. Use the graph on page 427 to estimate the depth where the light intensity is only 50% of that at the surface.

8. The depth to which light penetrates under water depends on the color of the light. The graph was drawn for yellow light. How would the graph differ for:
   a) red light which penetrates about 20% as far as yellow light
   b) blue light which penetrates about 4 times as far as yellow light?

9. At current growth rates, the population of Mexico is doubling about every 20 years. The population in 1985 was 80 million. Write an expression for the population P million as an exponential function of the time n years since 1985.

10. There are now 300 insects in a colony. The population of the colony doubles every 5 days. Express the population P of the colony as an exponential function of the elapsed time d days.

11. Most cars have a plastic container which holds fluid for cleaning the windshield. Throughout the winter, a motorist used 100% pure solvent in the container. One day in the spring, when the container was half full of solvent, she topped up the container with water. From then on throughout the summer, whenever the container was half full, she topped it up with water. Write an equation that expresses the concentration C of the solvent in the container as an exponential function of the number of times n it was topped up with water.

12. Paint is removed from a paint brush by swirling it in mineral spirits and then shaking the brush on a newspaper. This operation is repeated several times, using clean mineral spirits. Each operation removes 75% of the paint from the brush. Write an equation which expresses the percent P of paint in the brush as an exponential function of the number of operations n.

13. For an 8-week period during the summer, the average mass of the plants in a cornfield increased by 40% every week. At the beginning of the 8-week period the average mass of the plants was 28 g.
    a) Write an equation that expresses the average mass of the plants as an exponential function of the elapsed time in weeks.
    b) What was the average mass of the plants after 8 weeks?

14. A bamboo plant is 0.7 m long. Every day for the next 3 weeks, the length of the plant increases by 9%. How long is the plant after 3 weeks?

15. Several layers of glass are stacked together, as shown. Each layer reduces the light passing through it by 5%. Write an expression for the percent P of light that passes through n panes of glass.

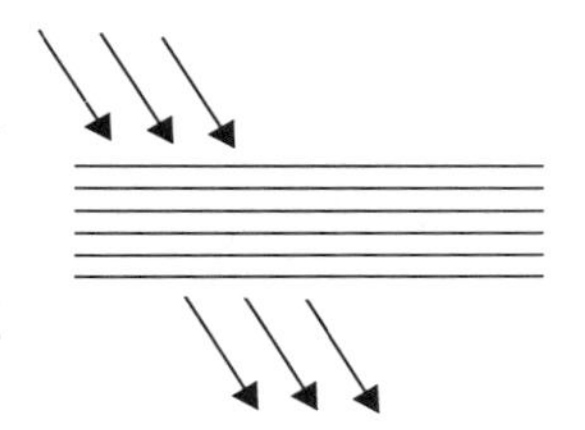

Ⓒ

16. A winery establishes an outdoor solera consisting of four tiers of oak barrels. About $\frac{1}{3}$ of the wine in the first (bottom) tier is removed every six months. Then, wine from the second tier is transferred to the bottom level to fill up the barrels. This process is repeated level by level until the youngest wine is eventually added to the top tier. By never emptying the barrels completely, some wine dating back to the origin of the solera will always remain. Write an equation which expresses the fraction of the bottom tier containing original wine as a function of the number of months since the solera was established.

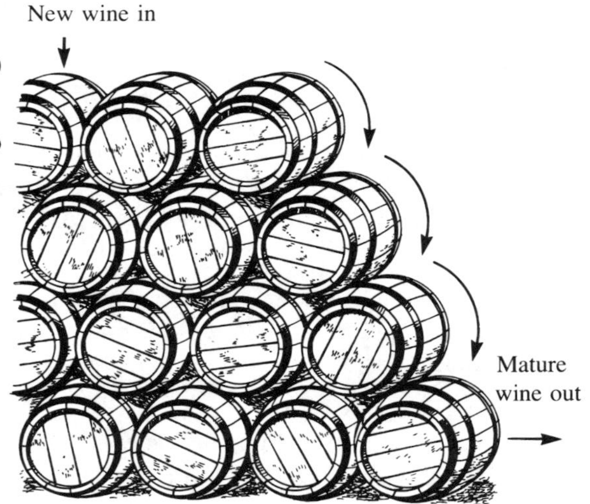

17. Rick borrows \$1000 from a relative at 10% per annum compounded annually. At the end of each year he repays 50% of the amount outstanding, including interest.
    a) Write the balance B dollars of the loan at the end of each year as an exponential function of the number of years.
    b) When the balance is reduced to approximately \$50, Rick repays the loan in full. How many years does this take?

10-2 DEFINING INTEGRAL AND RATIONAL EXPONENTS

By counting the bacteria in a culture, scientists can learn how bacteria grow under controlled conditions. The growth of a certain bacteria is shown in the table. The number of bacteria doubles every hour, over several hours. The table also shows the number of bacteria that would have been present when $t = -1, -2$, and -3.

Time t hours	**Number of bacteria** N
-3	125
-2	250
-1	500
0	1 000
1	2 000
2	4 000
3	8 000
4	16 000

The number of bacteria N is an exponential function of the time t hours. We can represent this function by the equation

$N = 1000(2)^t$ . . . ①

with the graph shown below.

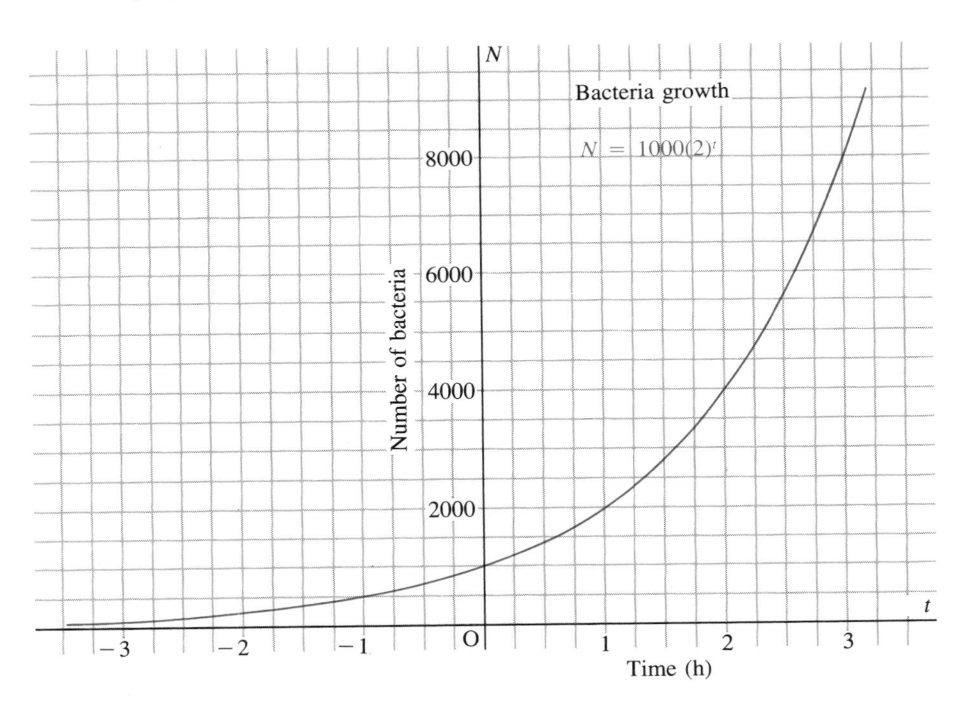

Defining Integral Exponents

Since there were 1000 bacteria when $t = 0$, we can use equation ① to determine a meaning for 2^0. Substitute 1000 for N and 0 for t in ①.

$$1000 = 1000(2)^0$$

Hence, 2^0 should be defined as follows.

$$2^0 = 1$$

Since there would have been 500 bacteria when $t = -1$, we can use equation ① to determine a meaning for 2^{-1}. Substitute 500 for N and -1 for t in ①.

$$500 = 1000(2)^{-1}$$

Hence, 2^{-1} should be defined as follows.

$$2^{-1} = \frac{1}{2}$$

Similarly, we can obtain the following definitions for 2^{-2} and 2^{-3}.

$$2^{-2} = \frac{1}{2^2}$$

$$2^{-3} = \frac{1}{2^3}$$

The graph on the previous page exemplifies a difficulty we usually encounter when we graph exponential functions. Values of N for $t = 4, 5, 6, \ldots$, cannot be plotted with the scale shown because too much vertical space would be required. Conversely, for negative values of t, for example, $t = -4, -5, -6, \ldots$, the values of N are so small that the scale makes it difficult to plot them.

An exponent indicates repeated multiplication only when it is a natural number. The above discussion suggests how to extend the definition of an exponent to include exponents that are not natural numbers. We define a^0 to be 1, and a^{-n} to be the reciprocal of a^n.

Definition of Integral Exponents

$a^0 = 1$ where $a \neq 0$ $\qquad$ $a^{-n} = \dfrac{1}{a^n}$ where $n \in N$, $a \neq 0$

Defining Rational Exponents

We can extend the table of values to include values of t between those already in the table. This requires us to define 2^t if t is a rational number.

We define:

$$2^{\frac{1}{2}} = \sqrt{2} \qquad 2^{\frac{3}{2}} = (\sqrt{2})^3$$

$$2^{-\frac{1}{2}} = \frac{1}{\sqrt{2}} \qquad 2^{-\frac{3}{2}} = \frac{1}{(\sqrt{2})^3}$$

If we substitute $\frac{1}{2}, \frac{3}{2}, -\frac{1}{2}, -\frac{3}{2}$ for t in equation ① and use these definitions we obtain this extended table of values. Each value of N is rounded to the nearest whole number.

Check that the new values of N are consistent with the graph.

Time t hours	Number of bacteria N
−2	250
−1.5	354
−1	500
−0.5	707
0	1000
0.5	1414
1	2000
1.5	2828
2	4000

N doubles when t increases by one hour.

N increases by a factor of $2^{\frac{1}{2}}$ whenever t increases by $\frac{1}{2}$ hour.

The reason for the choice of $\sqrt{2}$ for the definition of $2^{\frac{1}{2}}$ is that it is the factor that corresponds to a doubling of the number of bacteria when applied twice in succession. For example, the number of bacteria after:

$\frac{1}{2}$ hour: $1000(\sqrt{2}) \doteq 1414$
1 hour: $1000(\sqrt{2})(\sqrt{2}) = 1000(\sqrt{2})^2$, or 2000
Hence, each value of N in this table is $\sqrt{2}$ times the previous value.

Observe also that the pattern of doubling every hour is preserved with the intermediate times. For example, there are 1414 bacteria after $\frac{1}{2}$ hour and 2828 bacteria after $1\frac{1}{2}$ hours.

These examples suggest that $a^{\frac{m}{n}}$ should be defined as the mth power of the nth root of a, and $a^{-\frac{m}{n}}$ as its reciprocal.

Definition of Rational Exponents

$$a^{\frac{m}{n}} = (\sqrt[n]{a})^m \quad \text{and} \quad a^{-\frac{m}{n}} = \frac{1}{a^{\frac{m}{n}}} = \frac{1}{(\sqrt[n]{a})^m} \quad \text{where } m, n \in \mathrm{N},\ a > 0$$

With this definition of rational exponents we can approximate the number of bacteria at any time.

Example 1. How many bacteria would be in the culture when:
a) $t = 10$ min b) $t = 1$ h 40 min?

Solution. a) 10 min $= \frac{1}{6}$ hour

Substitute $\frac{1}{6}$ for t in equation ①.

$N = 1000(2)^{\frac{1}{6}}$
$= 1000(\sqrt[6]{2})$

Use your calculator.
Key in: 2 [$\sqrt[x]{y}$] 6 [×] 1000 [=] to display 1122.4620
Hence, there should be about 1122 bacteria after 10 min.

b) 1 h 40 min $= 1\frac{2}{3}$ hours, or $\frac{5}{3}$ hours

$N = 1000(2)^{\frac{5}{3}}$
$= 1000(\sqrt[3]{2})^5$

Key in: 2 [$\sqrt[x]{y}$] 3 [y^x] 5 [×] 1000 [=] to display 3174.8021
Hence, there should be about 3175 bacteria after 1 h 40 min.

On some calculators, the keying sequence for the [$\sqrt[x]{y}$] key may differ from that in *Example 1*. For example, in part a) the sequence may be 6 [$\sqrt[x]{y}$] 2 [×] 1000 [=].

Example 2. Evaluate each expression without using a calculator.

a) $(0.75)^{-2}$ b) $9^{1.5}$ c) $8^{-\frac{2}{3}}$

Solution.

a) $(0.75)^{-2} = \left(\frac{3}{4}\right)^{-2}$
$= \frac{1}{\left(\frac{3}{4}\right)^{2}}$
$= \frac{16}{9}$

b) $9^{1.5} = 9^{\frac{3}{2}}$
$= (\sqrt{9})^3$
$= 27$

c) $8^{-\frac{2}{3}} = \frac{1}{8^{\frac{2}{3}}}$
$= \frac{1}{(\sqrt[3]{8})^2}$
$= \frac{1}{4}$

We can use the $\boxed{y^x}$ key of a calculator to evaluate any expression of the form a^x where $a > 0$ and x is a rational number expressed as a terminating decimal. We can also use the definition of a rational exponent to explain the meaning of the result.

Example 3. a) Evaluate $3.2^{2.57}$ to the nearest thousandth.

b) Explain the meaning of the result.

Solution. a) Key in: 3.2 $\boxed{y^x}$ 2.57 $\boxed{=}$ to display 19.871719

Hence, to the nearest thousandth, $3.2^{2.57} \doteq 19.872$

b) To explain the meaning of the result, write the exponent 2.57 in fractional form.

$2.57 = \frac{257}{100}$

Hence, $3.2^{2.57} = 3.2^{\frac{257}{100}}$
$= (\sqrt[100]{3.2})^{257}$

Hence, $(\sqrt[100]{3.2})^{257} \doteq 19.872$

Exponential functions occur in the study of nuclear fallout. This refers to the contamination of the atmosphere and the ground from radioactive particles released in a nuclear accident or explosion. The harmful effects arise when these particles decay into other particles and release radiation. Each radioactive substance decays with a characteristic *halflife*. This is the time required for one-half of the material to decay.

Example 4. In a nuclear test explosion, some strontium-90 is released. This substance has a halflife of 28 years.

a) Draw a graph showing the percent of strontium-90 remaining up to 140 years.

b) Express the percent P of strontium-90 remaining as a function of:

i) the number of halflives elapsed, n

ii) the number of years elapsed, t.

c) What percent of strontium-90 remains after 50 years?

Solution. a) Make a table of values for time intervals of 1 halflife. Plot the percent remaining against the time in years.

Halflives (n)	0	1	2	3	4	5
Years (t)	0	28	56	84	112	140
Percent remaining (P)	100	50	25	12.5	6.25	3.13

b) i) After each halflife, the percent remaining is halved. Hence, the percent remaining after n halflives have elapsed is:

$$P = 100\left(\frac{1}{2}\right)^n \quad \ldots \text{①}$$

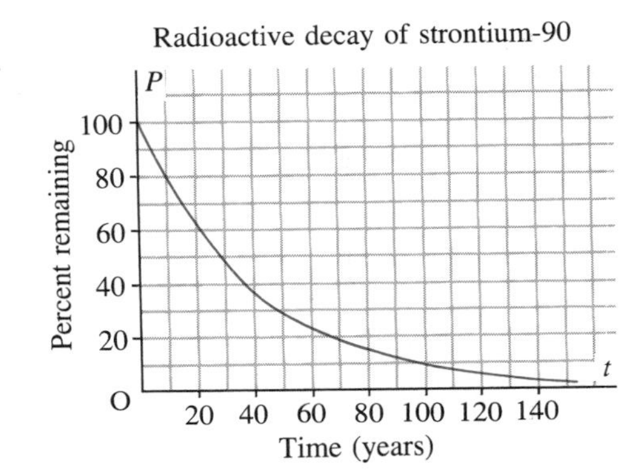

ii) Since $t = 28n$, we can write equation ① in terms of t.

Substitute $\frac{t}{28}$ for n.

$$P = 100\left(\frac{1}{2}\right)^{\frac{t}{28}} \quad \ldots \text{②}$$

c) Substitute 50 for t in equation ②.

$$P = 100\left(\frac{1}{2}\right)^{\frac{50}{28}}$$

Key in:
0.5 [y^x] [(] 50 [÷] 28 [)] [×] 100 [=] to display 29.003235.
Hence, about 29% of the strontium-90 remains after 50 years.

EXERCISES 10-2

Ⓐ

1. Evaluate.

a) 7^0 b) 5^{-1} c) $\left(\frac{2}{5}\right)^3$ d) 2^{-3} e) 4^{-2} f) $\left(\frac{4}{9}\right)^0$

g) $\left(\frac{1}{2}\right)^{-2}$ h) $\left(\frac{3}{2}\right)^{-4}$ i) 8^{-2} j) $\left(\frac{5}{3}\right)^{-2}$ k) 3^4 l) $\left(\frac{3}{4}\right)^{-3}$

2. Evaluate.

a) $27^{\frac{1}{3}}$ b) 3^{-2} c) $(0.4)^{-1}$ d) $25^{\frac{1}{2}}$ e) $(0.008)^{-\frac{1}{3}}$ f) $16^{-\frac{1}{4}}$

g) 10^{-3} h) $64^{\frac{1}{6}}$ i) $\left(\frac{25}{49}\right)^{-\frac{1}{2}}$ j) $81^{-\frac{1}{2}}$ k) $(0.125)^{-\frac{1}{3}}$ l) $32^{\frac{1}{5}}$

3. Evaluate.

a) $36^{-\frac{3}{2}}$ b) $27^{\frac{2}{3}}$ c) $(0.125)^{-\frac{2}{3}}$ d) $16^{-\frac{5}{4}}$ e) $9^{-\frac{5}{2}}$ f) $(2.25)^{\frac{3}{2}}$

g) $(0.6)^{-3}$ h) $100^{-\frac{3}{2}}$ i) $\left(\frac{8}{125}\right)^{\frac{2}{3}}$ j) $(0.36)^{-\frac{3}{2}}$ k) $64^{\frac{5}{6}}$ l) $81^{-\frac{3}{4}}$

4. Evaluate.

a) $4^{2.5}$ b) $25^{-1.5}$ c) $81^{-1.25}$ d) $400^{1.5}$

e) $32^{0.6}$ f) $\left(\frac{1}{16}\right)^{-0.75}$ g) $\left(\frac{27}{49}\right)^{0}$ h) $(6.25)^{-2.5}$

i) $(0.0625)^{-\frac{1}{4}}$ j) $\left(\frac{32}{243}\right)^{0.8}$ k) $\left(\frac{9}{4}\right)^{-1.5}$ l) $(5.25)^{0}$

5. Evaluate to the nearest thousandth.

a) $2.1^{1.6}$ b) $3.7^{2.14}$ c) $7.4^{0.85}$ d) $16^{0.75}$ e) $4.5^{3.19}$ f) $1.9^{1.9}$

g) $1.37^{4.72}$ h) $12.4^{0.22}$ i) $81^{1.25}$ j) $1.73^{2.65}$ k) $2.18^{3.41}$ l) $4.75^{1.68}$

6. Evaluate to the nearest hundredth.

a) $1.4^{-2.2}$ b) $2.8^{-1.7}$ c) $4.65^{2.75}$ d) $0.52^{-3.61}$ e) $3.82^{-1.44}$ f) $1.75^{-0.64}$

g) $0.27^{-4.8}$ h) $2.35^{-1.88}$ i) $4.25^{0.72}$ j) $5.12^{-1.65}$ k) $0.82^{-5.11}$ l) $1.37^{-1.69}$

(B)

7. Simplify.

a) $3^2 - 16^{\frac{1}{2}}$ b) $2^5 - 5^2$ c) $3^{-2} + 2^{-3}$

d) $2^{-4} - 4^{-2}$ e) $3^3 - \left(\frac{1}{2}\right)^{-4}$ f) $12^0 - 4^{-\frac{1}{2}}$

8. Simplify.

a) $(8^{\frac{2}{3}})(16^{\frac{3}{2}})$ b) $4^{\frac{1}{2}} + \left(\frac{1}{2}\right)^4$ c) $\left(\frac{4}{9}\right)^{-\frac{3}{2}} \div \left(\frac{16}{25}\right)^{-\frac{1}{2}}$

d) $3^{-4} + 4^{-3}$ e) $(3^2 + 2^3) \div 8^{\frac{5}{3}}$ f) $(4^{-\frac{3}{2}} + 27^{-\frac{2}{3}}) \div 16^{-\frac{3}{4}}$

9. A colony of insects doubles in size every 6 days. If there are now 2000 insects in the colony, how many

a) will there be in: i) 12 days ii) 21 days iii) 3 days;

b) were there: i) 6 days ago ii) 3 days ago iii) 10 days ago?

10. The halflives of two products of a nuclear explosion are shown. For each substance

Substance	Halflife
Iodine-131	8.1 days
Cesium-144	282 days

a) Draw a graph showing the percent remaining during the first five halflives.

b) Express the percent remaining as a function of:

i) the number of halflives elapsed, n ii) the number of days elapsed, t.

c) What percent of the substance remains after:

i) one week ii) 30 days iii) one year?

11. Another product of a nuclear explosion is plutonium-239, which has a halflife of 24 000 years. What percent of plutonium-239 remains after:
    a) 100 years b) 1000 years c) 10 000 years d) 100 000 years?

12. Polonium-210 is a radioactive element with a halflife of 20 weeks. From a sample of 25 g, how much would remain after:
    a) 30 weeks b) 14 weeks c) 1 year d) 511 days?

13. During the twentieth century, the population of Canada has been growing at the rate of approximately 1.85% per annum. The population in 1981 was 24.3 million.
    a) Write an equation representing the population P million as a function of the time t years relative to 1981.
    b) Use this equation to approximate the population in 1971.

14. In 1940, a large computer could perform about 100 operations per second. Since then, the speed of computers has multiplied 10-fold about every 7 years.
    a) Express the number of operations per second N as an exponential function of the time t years since 1940.
    b) About how many operations per second could computers perform in 1986?

Ⓒ

15. Use your calculator to evaluate to the nearest thousandth.
    a) 3^{π} b) π^{π} c) $10^{\sqrt{2}}$ d) $(\sqrt{2})^{\sqrt{3}}$
    e) $4^{-\pi}$ f) $7^{-\sqrt{2}}$ g) $2^{\sqrt{\pi}}$ h) $2^{\sqrt{2}} + 2^{-\sqrt{2}}$

16. a) Evaluate each power.
    i) 2^2 ii) $(0.5)^2$ iii) 2^{-2} iv) $(0.5)^{-2}$
    v) $4^{\frac{1}{2}}$ vi) $(0.25)^{\frac{1}{2}}$ vii) $4^{-\frac{1}{2}}$ viii) $(0.25)^{-\frac{1}{2}}$
    b) Using the results of part a) as a guide, make a conjecture about how you can tell, given the values of x and y ($y > 0$), if:
    i) $y^x > 1$ ii) $0 < y^x < 1$.

Powers with Negative Bases

Some powers with negative bases can be defined as real numbers, such as $(-3)^2 = 9$ and $(-8)^{\frac{1}{3}} = \sqrt[3]{-8}$, or -2, but others cannot, such as $(-4)^{\frac{1}{2}}$.

1. Evaluate those expressions which can be defined as real numbers. For those that cannot be defined, explain why not.
   a) $(-3)^{\frac{1}{5}}$ b) $(-3)^{\frac{1}{4}}$ c) $(-3)^{\frac{1}{25}}$ d) $(-3)^{\frac{7}{10}}$
   e) $(-3)^{0.4}$ f) $(-3)^{0.75}$ g) $(-3)^{0.16}$ h) $(-3)^{1.12}$

2. Let a represent any negative base. Explain how you can tell whether or not each power can be defined as a real number.
   a) $a^{\frac{m}{n}}$, where m and n are integers, $n \neq 0$
   b) a^x, where x is a rational number expressed as a terminating decimal

10-3 THE LAWS OF EXPONENTS

The definition of a positive integral exponent, as indicating repeated multiplication, leads to the following *laws of exponents*, where m and n are positive integers.

Law 1. $a^m \times a^n = a^{m+n}$

Law 2. $\dfrac{a^m}{a^n} = a^{m-n}$ $(m > n, a \neq 0)$

Law 3. $(a^m)^n = a^{mn}$

Law 4. $(ab)^n = a^n b^n$

Law 5. $\left(\dfrac{a}{b}\right)^n = \dfrac{a^n}{b^n}$ $(b \neq 0)$

We now investigate whether the definitions given in *Section 10-2* for integral, rational, and real exponents are consistent with these laws. If they are, then we can drop the restriction that m and n are positive integers (and that $m > n$ in Law 2) in the exponent laws.

In the previous section, we defined $a^0 = 1$ $(a \neq 0)$ and $a^{-n} = \dfrac{1}{a^n}$ $(n \in \text{N}, a \neq 0)$. We can check that these definitions are consistent with the exponent laws. Here are some examples.

If $m = 2$ and $n = 0$,

Law 1 becomes

$$\text{L.S.} = a^2 \times a^0 = a^2(1) = a^2 \qquad \text{R.S.} = a^{2+0} = a^2$$

(correct)

Law 2 becomes

$$\text{L.S.} = \frac{a^2}{a^0} = \frac{a^2}{1} = a^2 \qquad \text{R.S.} = a^{2-0} = a^2$$

(correct)

If $m = 0$ and $n = 3$,

Law 2 becomes

$$\text{L.S.} = \frac{a^0}{a^3} = \frac{1}{a^3} \qquad \text{R.S.} = a^{0-3} = a^{-3} = \frac{1}{a^3}$$

(correct)

If $m = 2$ and $n = 3$,

Law 2 becomes

$$\text{L.S.} = \frac{a^2}{a^3} = \frac{1}{a} \qquad \text{R.S.} = a^{2-3} = a^{-1} = \frac{1}{a}$$

(correct)

In the previous section, we defined $a^{\frac{m}{n}} = (\sqrt[n]{a})^m$ and $a^{-\frac{m}{n}} = \dfrac{1}{(\sqrt[n]{a})^m}$ $(m, n \in \text{N}, a > 0)$. We can check that these definitions are consistent with the laws of exponents.

For example, if $m = \frac{2}{3}$ and n $= \frac{1}{3}$, Law 1 becomes

$$\begin{aligned} \text{L.S.} &= a^{\frac{2}{3}} \times a^{\frac{1}{3}} \\ &= (\sqrt[3]{a})^2(\sqrt[3]{a}) \\ &= (\sqrt[3]{a})^3 \\ &= a \end{aligned} \qquad \begin{aligned} \text{R.S.} &= a^{\frac{2}{3}+\frac{1}{3}} \\ &= a^1 \\ &= a \end{aligned}$$

(correct)

Examples such as these suggest that the laws of exponents can be extended to include integral and rational exponents, as defined in *Section 10-2*. This can be proved using general methods which are similar to the examples above. In fact, the definition of an exponent and the laws of exponents can even be extended to include irrational exponents such as π and $\sqrt{2}$. We will not check this, but the truth of the laws for rational exponents provides a degree of validity. Hence, we will accept that the exponent laws can be extended to include exponents which are real numbers.

Laws of Exponents for Real Exponents
If m and n are any real numbers, then

1. $a^m \times a^n = a^{m+n}$
2. $\dfrac{a^m}{a^n} = a^{m-n} \qquad (a \neq 0)$
3. $(a^m)^n = a^{mn}$
4. $(ab)^n = a^n b^n$
5. $\left(\dfrac{a}{b}\right)^n = \dfrac{a^n}{b^n} \qquad (b \neq 0)$

The laws of exponents are useful for simplifying expressions involving exponents.

Example 1. Simplify each expression.

a) $\dfrac{a^2b^{-1}}{a^{-3}b}$ b) $\left(\dfrac{a^{\frac{1}{2}}}{b^{-2}}\right)^{\frac{2}{3}}$ c) $\left(\dfrac{x}{y^2}\right)^{\frac{1}{2}}(xy^2)^{-\frac{1}{2}}$

Solution. a) $\dfrac{a^2b^{-1}}{a^{-3}b} = a^{2-(-3)}b^{-1-1}$

$= a^5b^{-2}$, or $\dfrac{a^5}{b^2}$

b) $\left(\dfrac{a^{\frac{1}{2}}}{b^{-2}}\right)^{\frac{2}{3}} = (a^{\frac{1}{2}}b^2)^{\frac{2}{3}}$

$= a^{\frac{1}{3}}b^{\frac{4}{3}}$

c) $\left(\dfrac{x}{y^2}\right)^{\frac{1}{2}}(xy^2)^{-\frac{1}{2}} = (xy^{-2})^{\frac{1}{2}}(xy^2)^{-\frac{1}{2}}$

$= x^{\frac{1}{2}}y^{-1}x^{-\frac{1}{2}}y^{-1}$

$= x^0y^{-2}$

$= \dfrac{1}{y^2}$

Example 2. If $x = 4$ and $y = \frac{1}{9}$, evaluate this expression. $(x^2y^{-\frac{1}{2}})^{-2}(x^{-3}y)^{-\frac{1}{2}}$

Solution. Simplify the expression before substituting.

$$(x^2y^{-\frac{1}{2}})^{-2}(x^{-3}y)^{-\frac{1}{2}} = (x^{-4}y^1)(x^{\frac{3}{2}}y^{-\frac{1}{2}})$$
$$= x^{-\frac{5}{2}}y^{\frac{1}{2}}$$

Substitute.
$$= 4^{-\frac{5}{2}}\left(\frac{1}{9}\right)^{\frac{1}{2}}$$
$$= \frac{1}{(\sqrt{4})^5}\left(\frac{1}{3}\right)$$
$$= \left(\frac{1}{32}\right)\left(\frac{1}{3}\right)$$
$$= \frac{1}{96}$$

EXERCISES 10-3

Ⓐ

1. Simplify.

a) $m^2 \times m^{-8}$ b) $\frac{x^{-4}}{x^{-9}}$ c) $-15a^{-3} \times 3a^{10}$

d) $\frac{42s^4}{-3s^{-11}}$ e) $-3m^4 \times 12m^{-6} \times \frac{1}{4}m^7$ f) $\frac{(16n^{-2})(12n^{-3})}{15n^{-6}}$

2. Simplify.

a) $x^{\frac{2}{3}} \times x^{-\frac{5}{3}}$ b) $\frac{s^{-\frac{3}{4}}}{s^{-\frac{1}{2}}}$ c) $\frac{-12m^{-\frac{8}{5}}}{4m^{\frac{2}{5}}}$

d) $\frac{18a^{\frac{2}{5}}}{-6a^{-\frac{1}{5}}}$ e) $n^{\frac{3}{4}} \times n^{-\frac{3}{5}} \times n^{\frac{2}{3}}$ f) $\frac{-5x^{-\frac{1}{2}} \times 8x^{-\frac{3}{4}}}{10x^{-2}}$

Ⓑ

3. Simplify.

a) $\frac{-28a^2b^{-5}}{4a^{-7}b^3}$ b) $4m^{-3}n^9 \times 5m^{-4}n^{-6}$ c) $\frac{12x^{-2}y^4 \times 15x^7y^{-11}}{20x^{-4}y^5}$

d) $\frac{6a^3b^{-7}c^0 \times 18a^{-5}b^2}{-9a^{-5}b^{-1}c^4}$ e) $\frac{(14m^{-3}n)(-15m^4n^{-2})}{-21mn^{-5}}$ f) $\frac{(24x^3z^{-4})(-35x^{-7}z^3)}{(-8x^5z^0)(-14x^{-5}z^{-6})}$

4. Simplify.

a) $\frac{-12a^{-\frac{1}{3}}b}{3a^{-\frac{1}{3}}b^{\frac{2}{3}}}$ b) $\frac{-25m^{\frac{3}{4}}n^{-\frac{1}{2}}}{-10m^{-\frac{1}{4}}n^{\frac{1}{2}}}$ c) $\left(\frac{x^{\frac{2}{3}}}{y^{-\frac{1}{2}}}\right)^{\frac{6}{5}}$

d) $\left(\frac{a^2}{b^{\frac{1}{3}}}\right)^{\frac{3}{4}}(a^2b^{-1})^{-3}$ e) $\left(\frac{m^{\frac{3}{4}}n^{\frac{4}{3}}}{m^2}\right)^{\frac{2}{3}}$ f) $\frac{(a^{-5}b^3)^{\frac{1}{2}}}{a^{-\frac{3}{2}}b^{-\frac{1}{2}}}$

5. Simplify.

a) $\dfrac{-21m^{\frac{5}{6}}n^{-\frac{1}{3}}}{7m^{\frac{1}{2}}n^{\frac{1}{6}}}$ b) $-7a^{\frac{2}{3}}b^{-\frac{1}{2}} \times 6a^{-\frac{1}{2}}b^{\frac{2}{3}}$

c) $\dfrac{-8x^{-\frac{4}{3}}y^{\frac{1}{2}} \times 6x^{-\frac{3}{4}}y^{-\frac{2}{3}}}{24x^{-\frac{5}{6}}y^{-\frac{1}{6}}}$ d) $\dfrac{(9a^{-\frac{1}{3}}b^{-\frac{4}{5}}c^{-\frac{4}{5}})(-4a^{-\frac{1}{2}}b^{\frac{3}{5}}c^{0})}{-18a^{\frac{1}{6}}b^{-\frac{1}{2}}c^{-\frac{1}{3}}}$

e) $\dfrac{(13a^{-\frac{3}{4}}c^{-\frac{1}{2}})(-6a^{-\frac{1}{2}}c^{-\frac{3}{2}})}{(-21c^{\frac{1}{4}})(-39a^{-\frac{3}{2}}c^{\frac{3}{4}})}$ f) $\dfrac{(25x^{\frac{1}{4}}z^{\frac{1}{2}})(-16x^{-\frac{3}{4}}z^{\frac{3}{2}})}{(-6x^{-\frac{1}{4}}z^{-\frac{1}{2}})(-15x^{\frac{3}{2}}z^{\frac{3}{4}})}$

6. If $a = \frac{1}{8}$ and $b = 4$, evaluate each expression.

a) $a^{-1}b^{\frac{1}{2}}$ b) $(a^{-2}b^{\frac{1}{2}})(a^{\frac{1}{3}}b^{\frac{3}{2}})^{-1}$

c) $(a^{\frac{4}{3}}b^{-\frac{3}{2}})^{3}(a^{-2}b^{\frac{5}{2}})$ d) $(a^{\frac{2}{3}}b^{-2})^{2}(a^{-\frac{2}{3}}b^{-1})^{-3}$

7. If $x = \frac{4}{9}$ and $y = 27$, evaluate each expression.

a) $-x^{2}y^{\frac{2}{3}}$ b) $(3x^{-1}y^{\frac{1}{3}})(-4x^{\frac{3}{2}})^{-2}$

c) $\dfrac{6x^{-\frac{3}{2}}y^{-\frac{2}{3}}}{16x^{-\frac{5}{2}}y^{-\frac{4}{3}}}$ d) $\dfrac{-16x^{-\frac{5}{2}}y^{\frac{4}{3}}}{-9x^{-\frac{1}{2}}y^{-\frac{1}{3}}}$

8. If $x = 2a^{4}$, $y = a^{3}$, and $z = \frac{1}{2}a^{2}$, write each expression as an exponential function of a.

a) $(xyz)^{\frac{1}{2}}$ b) $xy^{-2}z^{-1}$ c) $(3x^{2}yz)^{3}$

9. If $p = 3x$, $q = \frac{2}{3}x^{2}$, and $r = x^{5}$, write each expression as an exponential function of x.

a) $p^{2}qr$ b) $p^{-1}q^{2}r^{-3}$ c) $(9p^{-2}q^{2}r^{-1})^{-1}$

10. Simplify.

a) $\dfrac{(x^{2a})(x^{-5a})}{x^{-3a}}$ b) $\dfrac{(s^{2n})(s^{-n})}{(s^{-3n})(s^{-4n})}$ c) $\dfrac{(a^{x-1})(a^{x+1})}{a^{2x-1}}$

d) $\dfrac{(m^{-ac})(m^{-ab})}{m^{-bc}}$ e) $\dfrac{(x^{-3})^{a}(x^{a})^{2}}{x^{a-2}}$ f) $\dfrac{(a^{2x-y})(a^{x-y})}{(3a^{x+y})^{2}}$

11. Simplify.

a) $\dfrac{(x^{\frac{a}{4}})(x^{-\frac{a}{3}})}{x^{\frac{a}{12}}}$ b) $\dfrac{(m^{-\frac{n}{2}})(n^{-\frac{m}{4}})}{(m^{\frac{n}{3}})(n^{\frac{m}{2}})}$ c) $\dfrac{(a^{-\frac{x}{2}})^{3}(a^{-\frac{x}{3}})^{4}}{(a^{\frac{x}{4}})^{2}}$

d) $\dfrac{(c^{\frac{x}{3}})^{-2}(c^{\frac{x}{2}})^{-3}}{(c^{2})^{\frac{x}{3}}(c^{3})^{\frac{x}{2}}}$ e) $\dfrac{(x^{\frac{c}{2}})^{\frac{1}{3}}(y^{\frac{c}{4}})^{\frac{1}{2}}}{(y^{\frac{c}{3}})^{\frac{3}{2}}(x^{-\frac{c}{3}})^{\frac{1}{2}}}$ f) $\dfrac{(h^{-\frac{a}{4}})^{-\frac{1}{2}}(k^{-\frac{a}{3}})^{2}}{(h^{-\frac{a}{2}})^{\frac{1}{3}}(k^{\frac{2a}{3}})^{-1}}$

Ⓒ

12. Write as a single power.

a) $3(5)^{\frac{1}{3}} + 2(5)^{\frac{1}{3}}$ b) $(2^{x})^{2} + 2^{2x}$ c) $3(4)^{x} + 2^{2x}$

MATHEMATICS AROUND US

The Loudness of Sounds

The range of sounds detectable by the human ear is enormous. A rock group can be *10 trillion* times as loud as a leaf rustling in a breeze. The loudness of sounds is measured in units called *decibels* (dB).

> Every increase of 10 dB corresponds to a 10-fold increase in loudness.

For example, the increase from the hum of a refrigerator to an air conditioner is 20 dB. This is 2 increases of 10 dB, so the increase in loudness is $(10)^2$, or 100. Hence, an air conditioner is 100 times as loud as a refrigerator.

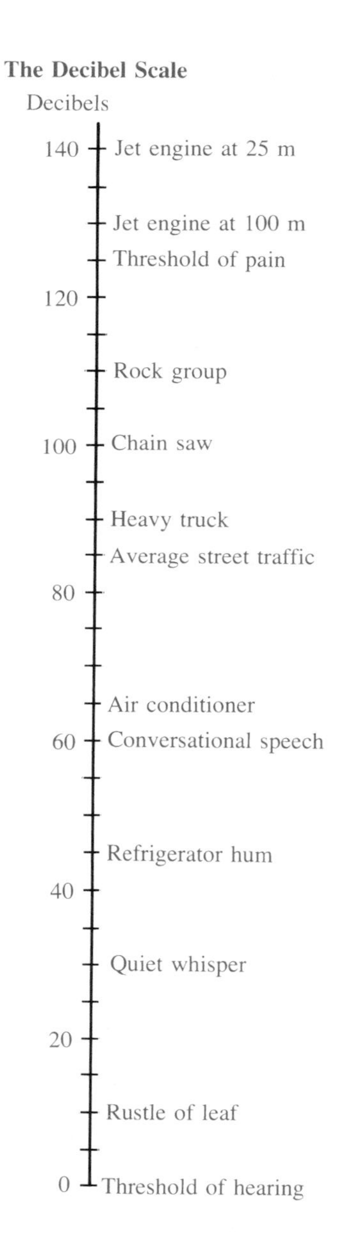

QUESTIONS

1. a) How many times as loud as conversational speech is a chain saw?
   b) How many times as loud as a quiet whisper is a chain saw?
2. Let L_1 and L_2 represent the loudnesses of sounds of S_1 decibels and S_2 decibels respectively. Show that
   $$\frac{L_2}{L_1} = 10^{0.1(S_2 - S_1)}$$
   Use this equation in the questions below.
3. How many times as loud as:
   a) an air conditioner is a heavy truck
   b) a refrigerator hum is average street traffic
   c) average street traffic is a jet at 100 m?
4. It was once reported that the loudness level of a heavy snore is 69 dB. How many times is this as loud as:
   a) conversational speech
   b) a quiet whisper?

Composers use these symbols to indicate the levels of loudness for playing their music.

pp	pianissimo (very soft)
p	piano (soft)
mp	mezzopiano (moderately soft)
mf	mezzoforte (moderately loud)
f	forte (loud)
ff	fortissimo (very loud)

But do performers actually play in such a way that the differences between six levels of loudness can be detected? It has been determined that, during a performance, the level of loudness must change by at least 5 dB before most people can detect it. Several musicians were asked to play their instruments at each of the six loudness levels indicated above. The difference in loudness between the softest notes and the loudest notes was measured. These are the results.

Bassoon 10 dB Flute 20 dB Trumpet 36 dB Clarinet 45 dB

5. a) For which instruments could the six loudness levels have been detected?
   b) At how many levels of loudness could each instrument have been played?

6. The use of earplugs can reduce the noise level by as much as 25 dB. How many times less intense would a sound be if earplugs were worn?

7. In a noise reduction study, the noise caused by a train was compared at two locations A and B. It was found that the forest reduced high frequency sounds by as much as 20 dB, but low frequency sounds were reduced by 4 dB or less. By what factor did the forest reduce:

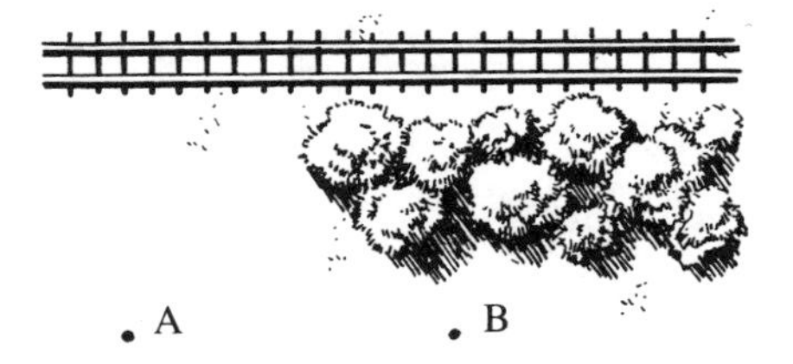

   a) high frequency sounds b) low frequency sounds?

8. A person's hearing can be permanently damaged by listening to very loud sounds for prolonged periods of time. An 8 h exposure to a 90 dB sound is considered acceptable. For every 5 dB increase in loudness, the acceptable exposure time is reduced by one-half.
   a) Derive an equation expressing the acceptable exposure time t hours as an exponential function of the loudness level d decibels.
   b) What is the acceptable exposure time for:
      i) a rock group playing at 100 dB? ii) a jet engine at 130 dB? 140 dB?

THE MATHEMATICAL MIND

Doubling the Cube

It is said that around 427 B.C. in ancient Greece, a plague was responsible for the death of more than a quarter of the Athenian population. A special delegation was sent to the oracle of Apollo at Delos to inquire how the plague should be averted. The oracle instructed that they must double the size of Apollo's cubical altar. The Athenians thought that they could do this by doubling each dimension of the altar, but in doing so, they were not able to curb the plague. Since each dimension was doubled, they had in fact multiplied the volume of the altar by $2 \times 2 \times 2$, or 8.

According to the legend, this faulty mathematics on the part of the Athenians led the Greek geometers to study the problem of doubling the volume of a given cube while keeping its cubic shape. The first progress in the solution of this problem was given by Hippocrates. He reduced the problem to that of constructing lengths x and y such that $\frac{r}{x} = \frac{x}{y} = \frac{y}{2r}$, where r is the given length of an edge of the cubical altar. From these equations he deduced that $x^3 = 2r^3$. Hence, x is the edge length of a cube having twice the volume of the cube with edge length r.

For 2000 years mathematicians tried to construct a segment of length x using straightedge and compasses, but none succeeded. This construction was proved to be impossible by the mathematicians of the nineteenth century.

QUESTIONS

1. a) Show that $x^3 = 2r^3$ can be deduced from the equations $\frac{r}{x} = \frac{x}{y} = \frac{y}{2r}$.
   b) Solve the equation for x.
   c) Find a similar equation for y, and solve it.

2. In his attempt to solve the problem of doubling the cube, Plato used this diagram. Show that if the figure were constructed such that DE $= r$ and CE $= 2r$, then BE would be the segment whose length is the edge length of the cubical altar to be constructed.

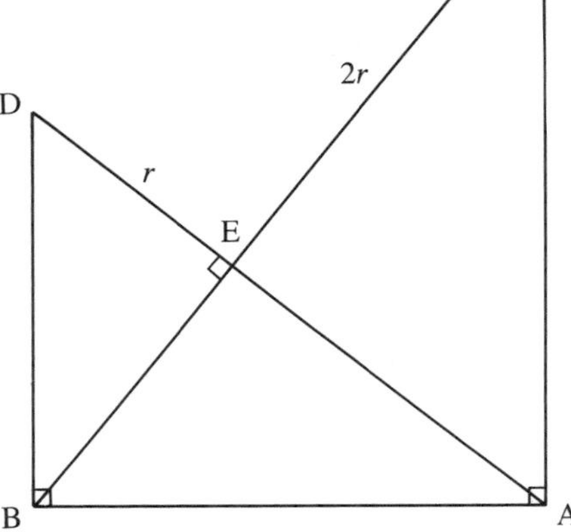

10-4 APPLICATIONS OF EXPONENTIAL FUNCTIONS

In the previous three sections we considered exponential functions with defining equations of the form $y = ca^x$, where $a > 0$. If we are given any three of the quantities, c, a, x, and y, we should be able to calculate the fourth one. This idea is illustrated in the following examples.

Example 1. What amount of money would grow to $1000 in 5 years if it is invested at 9% per annum compounded annually?

Solution. Let the amount of money be P dollars. Then,

$$P(1.09)^5 = 1000$$

$$P = \frac{1000}{(1.09)^5}$$

$$= 1000(1.09)^{-5}$$

Key in: 1.09 [y^x] 5 [+/−] [×] 1000 [=] to display 649.93139

$$P \doteq 649.931\ 39$$

Hence, $649.93 would grow to $1000 in 5 years at 9% per annum.

Solving for the Base

Solving an equation of the form $y = ca^x$ for the base a amounts to taking a root of both sides. We illustrate this in the next example.

Example 2. In 1947 an investor bought Van Gogh's painting *Irises* for $84 000. In 1987 she sold it for $49 million. What annual rate of interest corresponds to an investment of $84 000 which grows to $49 million in 40 years?

Solution. Let i represent the rate of interest. Then,

$$84\ 000(1 + i)^{40} = 49\ 000\ 000$$

$$(1 + i)^{40} = \frac{49\ 000}{84}$$

Take the 40th root of each side.

$$1 + i = \left(\frac{49\ 000}{84}\right)^{\frac{1}{40}}$$

Key in: 49000 [÷] 84 [=] [y^x] 40 [$1/x$] [=] to display 1.1725947

$$1 + i \doteq 1.172\ 594\ 7$$

$$i \doteq 0.172\ 594\ 7$$

The annual rate of interest is approximately 17.3%.

Solving for the Exponent

In many applications of exponential functions it is necessary to solve an equation of the form $y = ca^x$ for the exponent x.

Example 3. Suppose you invest $200 at 8% per annum compounded annually. How many years would it take for your investment to grow to $300?

Solution. Let n represent the number of years. Then,

$$200(1.08)^n = 300$$

$$(1.08)^n = 1.5$$

At the moment, the only way we can solve this equation is by *systematic trial*. Using a calculator we find the following values of $(1.08)^n$.

n	2	4	5	6
$(1.08)^n$	1.1664	1.360 489 0	1.469 328 1	1.586 874 3

We see that \$200 earning interest at 8% per annum will grow to \$300 in a little more than 5 years.

Example 4. The percent P of surface light present under water is expressed as a function of the depth d metres by the equation $P = 100(0.975)^d$. At what depth is only 50% of the surface light present?

Solution. Substitute 50 for P in the equation $P = 100(0.975)^d$.

$$50 = 100(0.975)^d$$

$$(0.975)^d = 0.5$$

Solve by systematic trial.

d	10	20	25	27	28
$(0.975)^d$	0.776 330	0.602 687 7	0.531 025 5	0.504 806 1	0.492 186 0

We see that only 50% of the surface light is present at a depth of approximately 27 m.

In the next chapter, we will develop a more efficient and more accurate method of solving exponential equations such as those in *Examples 3* and *4*.

EXERCISES 10-4

(A)

1. How much should you invest at 7% per annum compounded annually so that \$5000 will be available in 4 years?

2. A colony of bees increases by 25% every three months. How many bees should Raiman start with if he wishes to have 10 000 bees in 18 months?

3. The town of Springfield is growing at a rate of 6.5% per annum. How many people are there in Springfield now, if there will be 15 000 in 4.5 years?

4. A colony of insects doubles every 10 days. If the colony has 850 insects now, how many were there 3 days ago?

(B)

5. In 1950 the world population was approximately 2.5 billion. The population doubled to 5 billion in 1987. What was the average annual growth rate of the world population from 1950 to 1987?

6. The 50¢ Bluenose is one of Canada's most famous postage stamps. In 1930 it could be bought at the post office for 50¢. In 1987 a superb copy was sold at an auction for \$500. What annual rate of interest corresponds to an investment of 50¢ in 1930 which grows to \$500 in 1987?

7. In 1626 Manhattan Island was sold for $24. If that money had been invested at 8% per annum compounded annually, what would it have amounted to today?

8. A culture has 750 bacteria. The number of bacteria doubles every 5 h. How many bacteria are in the culture after 12 h?

9. Suppose you invest $200 at 9% per annum compounded annually. How many years would it take for your investment to grow to $500?

10. Mary invests $2500 at 11% per annum compounded annually. How many years will it take for her investment to double in value?

11. If the population of a colony of bacteria doubles every 30 min, how long would it take for the population to triple?

12. Jacques bought a new car for $15 000. Each year the value of the car depreciates to 70% of its value the previous year. In how many years will the car be worth only $500?

Ⓒ

13. Prove that if the growth rate is constant, the time required for a population to double is independent of the population size.

14. A pan of water is brought to a boil and then removed from the heat. Every 5 min thereafter the difference between the temperature of the water and room temperature is reduced by 50%.
    a) Room temperature is 20°C. Express the temperature of the water as a function of the time since it was removed from the heat.
    b) How many minutes does it take for the temperature of the water to reach 30°C?

15. A cup of coffee contains approximately 100 mg of caffeine. When you drink the coffee, the caffeine is absorbed into the bloodstream, and is eventually metabolized by the body. Every 5 h the amount of caffeine in the bloodstream is reduced by 50%.
    a) Write an equation which expresses the amount of caffeine c milligrams in the bloodstream as an exponential function of the elapsed time t hours since drinking one cup of coffee.
    b) How many hours does it take for the amount of caffeine to be reduced to:
    i) 10 mg ii) 1 mg?

16. For every metre a diver descends under water, the intensity of three colors of light is reduced as shown.
    a) For each color, write an equation which expresses the percent P of surface light as a function of the depth d metres.
    b) For each color, determine the depth at which about half the light has disappeared.
    c) Let us agree that, for all practical purposes, the light has disappeared when the intensity is only 1% of that at the surface. At what depth would this occur for each color?

Color	**Percent Reduction** per metre
Red	35%
Green	5%
Blue	2.5%

MATHEMATICS AROUND US

Carbon Dating

In 1950 the Nobel Prize in chemistry went to Dr. W.F. Libby who had developed a method of dating organic matter, known as *carbon dating*. All living matter contains traces of radioactive carbon-14. When an organism dies, the carbon-14 decays with a halflife of about 5760 years. Hence, the age of an ancient specimen can be determined by measuring the radioactivity of the carbon-14 it contains, and comparing it with that of living matter. The table shows the percent remaining at various times after an organism dies.

Time		Percent remaining P
Halflives n	Years t	
0	0	100
1	5 760	50
2	11 520	25
3	17 280	12.5
4	23 040	6.25
5	28 800	3.125

The percent P remaining after n halflives have elapsed is expressed as a function of n by the equation $P = 100(0.5)^n$. Since $t = 5760n$, we can write this equation in terms of t.

$$P = 100(0.5)^{\frac{t}{5760}}$$

We can use this equation to approximate the age of a specimen if we know the radioactivity of its carbon-14 relative to living matter.

QUESTIONS

1. The Dead Sea Scrolls are about 2000 years old. What percent radioactivity should be expected from a sample taken from the Dead Sea Scrolls?
2. Charred remains found in Lascaux Cave in France are about 15.3% radioactive. About how old might the famous paintings in this cave be?
3. Determine the approximate age of each specimen, given its radioactivity relative to living matter.
   a) charred bread found at Pompeii 79.6%
   b) wood in First Dynasty tombs 68.9%
   c) charcoal found at Stonehenge 62.0%
   d) specimen from the end of the last ice age 24.0%
   e) skin of a Siberian mammoth 2.2%
4. Illustrate the above results on a graph.

10-5 USING EXPONENTIAL FUNCTIONS TO MAKE COMPARISONS

Occasionally we see statements such as this, in magazines and newspapers.

> In favorable breeding conditions, the population of a swarm of desert locusts can multiply 10-fold in 20 days.

This information is not sufficient to calculate the population of a swarm of locusts, since an initial population figure is not given. But we can still use the statement to compare the populations of a swarm at two different times.

Example 1. Use the information above to compare the population of a swarm of locusts after 30 days with its population after 20 days.

Solution. Let P_0 represent the population of a swarm at $t = 0$. Then we can use the fact that the population is multiplied 10-fold in 20 days to express the population P as an exponential function of the time t days.

$$P = P_0(10)^{\frac{t}{20}}$$

or

$$P = P_0(10)^{0.05t} \quad \ldots ①$$

Let P_{20} and P_{30} represent the populations after 20 and 30 days respectively. Then, using equation ①, we obtain

$$\begin{aligned} P_{20} &= P_0(10)^{0.05(20)} \\ &= P_0(10) \quad \ldots ② \\ P_{30} &= P_0(10)^{0.05(30)} \\ &= P_0(10)^{1.5} \quad \ldots ③ \end{aligned}$$

Since we do not know the value of P_0, we cannot calculate P_{20} or P_{30}. But we can find their ratio by dividing equation ③ by equation ②.

$$\begin{aligned} \frac{P_{30}}{P_{20}} &= \frac{P_0(10)^{1.5}}{P_0(10)} \\ &= 10^{0.5} \\ &\doteq 3.162\ 277\ 7 \end{aligned}$$

A swarm is about 3.2 times as large after 30 days as it was after 20 days.

Calculations such as those in *Example 1* are used in many applications. A common example is a scale for comparing the intensities of earthquakes, which was devised by Charles Richter about 50 years ago. The intensity of an earthquake is measured by the amount of ground motion as recorded on a seismometer.

When we use the Richter scale, we do not need to know the actual intensities, or seismometer readings. The scale is used simply to compare the intensities of two earthquakes using the following rule.

> Each increase of 1 unit in magnitude on the Richter scale represents a 10-fold increase in intensity as measured on a seismometer.

Consider, for example, the Italy earthquake of 1976 which had a magnitude of 6.5 on the Richter scale. Notice that the Guatemala earthquake the same year had a magnitude of 7.5, which is exactly 1 unit greater. This means that the second earthquake was *10 times* as intense as the first. Similarly, the Alaska earthquake in 1964 was 10 × 10, or *100 times* as intense as the 1976 Italy earthquake, and 10 × 10 × 10, or *1000 times* as intense as the 1983 earthquake in Colombia. But, how do we compare the intensities of earthquakes such as the Alaska earthquake in 1964 and the Turkey earthquake in 1966, whose magnitudes do not differ by a whole number?

The Richter Scale

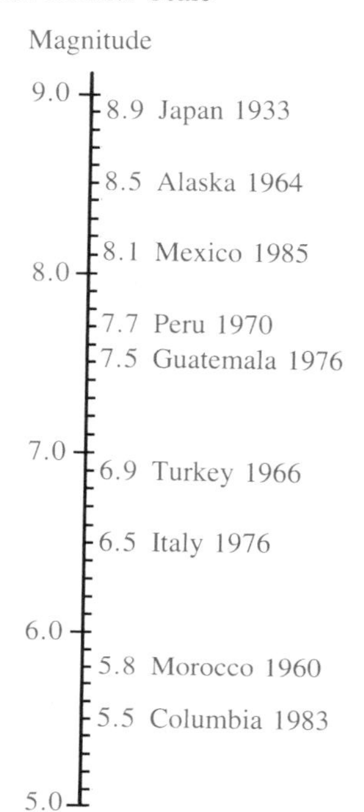

Example 2. Use the information above to compare the intensity of the 1964 Alaska earthquake with the intensity of the 1966 Turkey earthquake.

Solution. Let I_0 represent the intensity of an earthquake with a magnitude of 0 on the Richter scale. Then we can use the fact that the intensity is multiplied 10-fold for each increase in 1 unit of magnitude to express the intensity I as an exponential function of the magnitude M.

$$I = I_0(10)^M \quad \ldots ①$$

Let I_A and I_T represent the intensities of the Alaska and Turkey earthquakes respectively. Then, using equation ①, we obtain

$$I_A = I_0(10)^{8.5} \quad \ldots ②$$
$$I_T = I_0(10)^{6.9} \quad \ldots ③$$

Since we do not know the value of I_0, we cannot calculate I_A or I_T. But we can find their ratio by dividing equation ② by equation ③.

$$\begin{aligned} \frac{I_A}{I_T} &= \frac{I_0(10)^{8.5}}{I_0(10)^{6.9}} \\ &= 10^{8.5-6.9} \\ &= 10^{1.6} \\ &\doteq 39.810\ 717 \end{aligned}$$

The Alaska earthquake was about 40 times as intense as the Turkey earthquake.

EXERCISES 10-5

(A)

1. The population of a swarm of insects can multiply 5-fold in 4 weeks. Let P_0 represent the population at time $t = 0$.
   a) Write expressions to represent the population after:
      i) 4 weeks ii) 6 weeks.
   b) How many times as great is the population after 6 weeks as it was after 4 weeks?

2. The population of a nest of ants can multiply 3-fold in 5 weeks. After 8 weeks, how many times as great is the population as it was after 5 weeks?

3. The population of a colony of bacteria can double in 25 min. After one hour, how many times as great is the population as it was after 25 min?

(B)

4. On July 26, 1986, an earthquake with magnitude 5.5 hit California. The next day a second earthquake with magnitude 6.2 hit the same region. How many times as intense as the first earthquake was the second earthquake?

5. In 1985/86, three earthquakes hit Mexico City. How many times as intense as:
   a) the second earthquake was the first
   b) the third earthquake was the second
   c) the third earthquake was the first?

Mexico City Earthquakes	
Date	**Magnitude**
Sept. 19, 1985	8.1
Sept. 21, 1985	7.5
April 30, 1986	7.0

6. For every increase of 1 unit in magnitude of an earthquake, there is a 31-fold increase in the amount of energy released. Use the scale on page 450.
   a) How many times as much energy was released by:
      i) the 1976 Guatemala earthquake as by the 1976 Italy earthquake
      ii) the 1964 Alaska earthquake as by the 1976 Italy earthquake?
   b) Let E_1 and E_2 represent the energies released by earthquakes of magnitudes M_1 and M_2 respectively. Derive an equation which expresses the ratio of the energies $\frac{E_2}{E_1}$ as an exponential function of the difference in magnitudes $M_2 - M_1$.
   c) How many times as much energy was released by the 1933 Japan earthquake as by the 1983 Colombia earthquake?

7. The Italy earthquake in 1976 (see scale) released approximately 10^{14} J (joules) of energy. How much energy was released by these earthquakes?
   a) Guatemala 1976 b) Alaska 1964 c) Japan 1933

8. It has been observed that for every decrease of 1 unit in magnitude, earthquakes are about 6 or 7 times as frequent. In a given year, how should the number of earthquakes with magnitudes between 4.0 and 4.9 compare with the number of earthquakes with magnitudes between:
   a) 5.0 and 5.9 b) 6.0 and 6.9 c) 7.0 and 7.9?

Ⓒ

9. If the temperature is constant, the pressure of the Earth's atmosphere decreases by 5% for every 300 m increase in altitude.
   a) Let P_1 and P_2 represent the pressures at altitudes h_1 and h_2 respectively. Derive an equation which expresses the ratio $\frac{P_2}{P_1}$ as an exponential function of the difference in altitudes $h_2 - h_1$.
   b) A jet gains 1000 m in altitude. By what percent did the atmospheric pressure decrease?

10. One of the most remarkable technological trends ever recorded is the growth of the number of components on a silicon chip. Since 1970, the number of components on each chip has quadrupled every three years. It is expected that this level should persist until the early 1990s.
    a) Let N_1 and N_2 represent the numbers of components on a chip in the years t_1 and t_2 respectively. Derive an equation which expresses the ratio $\frac{N_2}{N_1}$ as an exponential function of the time difference $t_2 - t_1$.
    b) How did the number of components on a chip in 1985 compare with the number in: i) 1980 ii) 1975 iii) 1970?

11. A magazine article reported that the area on a silicon chip required for a given function has been shrinking by a factor of 2 every 18 months.
    a) Let A_1 and A_2 represent the areas required at times t_1 and t_2 respectively. Derive an equation which expresses the ratio $\frac{A_2}{A_1}$ as an exponential function of the time difference $t_2 - t_1$.
    b) How did the area required in January 1982 compare with that in:
    i) January 1979 ii) September 1985 iii) May 1987?

INVESTIGATE

There are two possible meanings for an expression such as 3^{3^3}, depending on the order in which the exponents are calculated.

$3^{(3^3)} = 3^{27}$ $\quad (3^3)^3 = 27^3$

One might think that the operations would be performed in order from left to right, as they are in an expression such as $12 - 5 + 2$. But expressions involving repeated exponents are exceptions to the rules for the order of operations. By convention, expressions such as 3^{3^3} are evaluated starting at the top. Hence, the accepted definition for 3^{3^3} is $3^{(3^3)}$.

a) Investigate how your calculator interprets an expression such as 3^{3^3} by keying in: 3 [yˣ] 3 [yˣ] 3 [=].

b) Investigate how a computer interprets an expression such as 3^{3^3} by entering this BASIC instruction and then pressing [RETURN]. PRINT 3∧3∧3

10-6 GRAPHING EXPONENTIAL FUNCTIONS

Some of the properties of exponential functions that we have studied can be illustrated on a graph. For example, we can graph the function $y = 2^x$ using a table of values.

$y = 2^x$

x	y
-3	0.13
-2.5	0.18
-2	0.25
-1.5	0.35
-1	0.50
-0.5	0.71
0	1.00
0.5	1.41
1	2.00
1.5	2.83
2	4.00
2.5	5.66
3	8.00

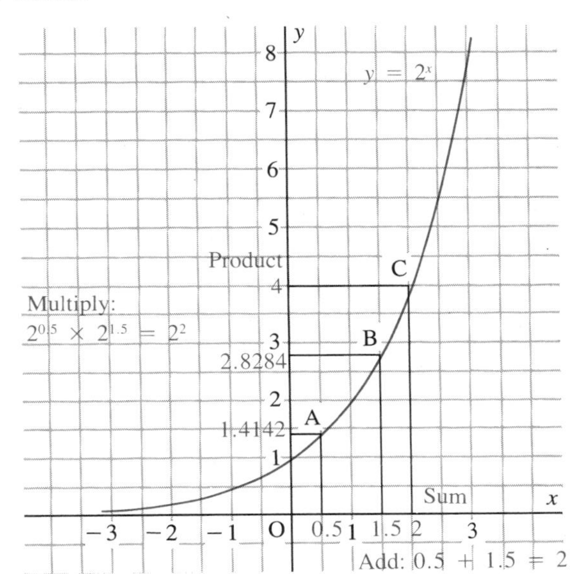

We can use the graph to illustrate the following properties of the function $y = 2^x$.

y-intercept
Substitute $x = 0$ in $y = 2^x$.
$y = 2^0$
$= 1$
The y-intercept is 1.

x-intercept
Substitute $y = 0$ in $y = 2^x$.
$0 = 2^x$
This equation has no real solution since $2^x > 0$ for all real values of x. Hence, there is no x-intercept.

Domain
Since we can define 2^x for all real values of x, the domain is the set of all real numbers.

Range
Since we can find a value for x for all positive real values of y, the range is the set of all positive real numbers.

Law of Exponents
Select any two points on the curve, such as $A(0.5, 2^{0.5})$ and $B(1.5, 2^{1.5})$.
Add their x-coordinates.
$0.5 + 1.5 = 2$
Multiply their y-coordinates.
$(2^{0.5})(2^{1.5}) = 2^2$
The results are the coordinates of another point $C(2, 2^2)$ on the graph. Is this true for any two points on the graph?

We can graph other exponential functions using tables of values, but it is more efficient to sketch the graphs by considering how they are related to the graph of $y = 2^x$, which we have already drawn.

Example 1. Sketch these functions on the same grid.

a) $y = 2^x$ b) $y = 1.5^x$ c) $y = 1^x$ d) $y = 0.5^x$

Solution. All four graphs pass through the point (0,1).

a) The graph of $y = 2^x$ is shown.

b) If $x > 0$, then $1.5^x < 2^x$. Hence, in the first quadrant, the graph of $y = 1.5^x$ lies below that of $y = 2^x$. To judge how far below, use a test point. Substitute $x = 2$ into $y = 1.5^x$ to get $y = 2.25$. Hence, the point (2,2.25) lies on the graph.
Conversely, if $x < 0$, then $1.5^x > 2^x$. Hence, in the second quadrant, the graph of $y = 1.5^x$ lies above that of $y = 2^x$. To judge how far above, use a test point. Substitute $x = -2$ into $y = 1.5^x$ to get $y \doteq 0.44$. Hence, $(-2,0.44)$ lies on the graph.

c) Since $1^x = 1$ for all values of x, the graph of $y = 1^x$ is a horizontal line 1 unit above the x-axis.

d) If $x > 0$, 0.5^x is less than 1. Also, as x increases, 0.5^x becomes closer and closer to 0. If $x < 0$, 0.5^x becomes larger and larger, without limit.

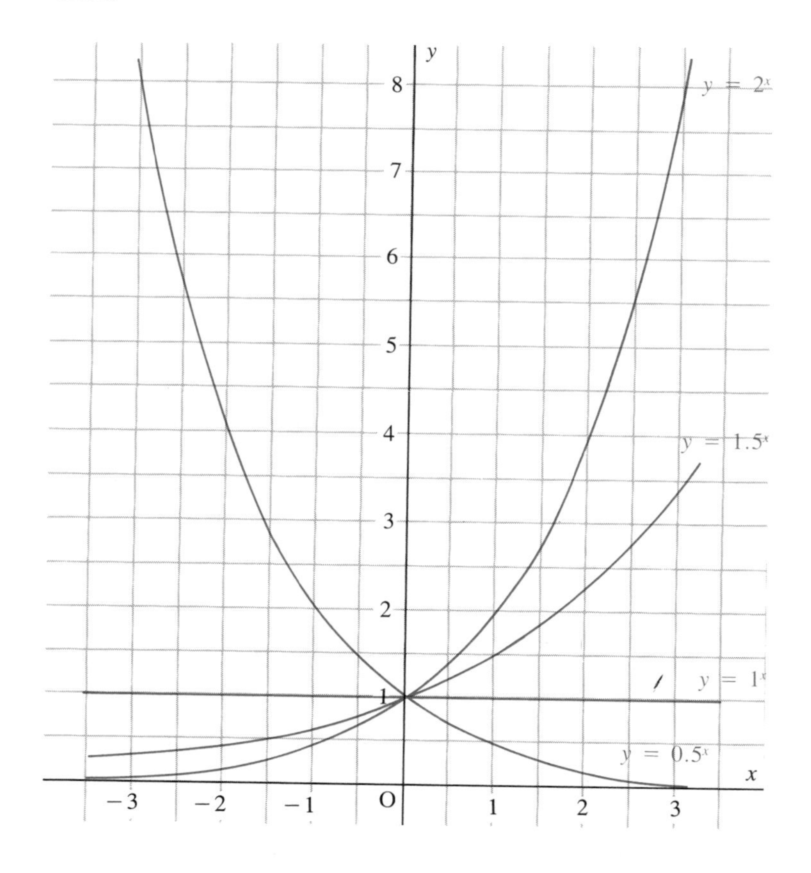

Example 1 illustrates properties of the exponential function $y = a^x$.

Properties of the function $y = a^x$
y-intercept: 1
x-intercept: none
Domain: all real numbers
Range: all positive real numbers

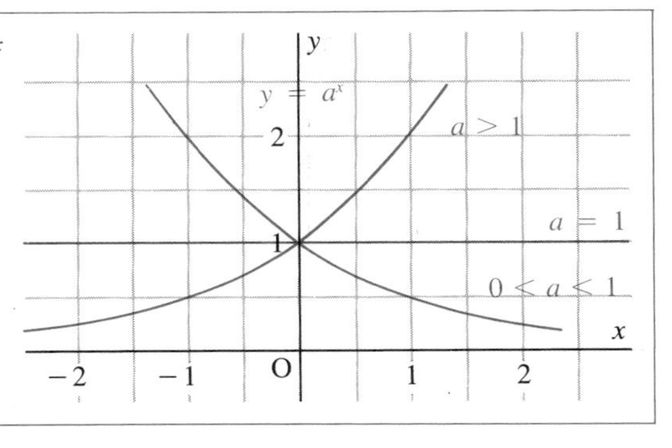

Example 2. Prove that if (x_1,y_1) and (x_2,y_2) are points on the graph of $y = a^x$, then $(x_1 + x_2,y_1y_2)$ is also a point on the graph.

Solution. Since (x_1,y_1) is on the graph of $y = a^x$, its coordinates satisfy the equation.

Hence, $\quad y_1 = a^{x_1} \ldots$ ①

Similarly, $\quad y_2 = a^{x_2} \ldots$ ②

Multiply equations ① and ②, and use the law of exponents.

$$\begin{aligned} y_1y_2 &= (a^{x_1})(a^{x_2}) \\ &= a^{x_1+x_2} \end{aligned}$$

Hence, the coordinates of the point $(x_1 + x_2,y_1y_2)$ also satisfy the equation $y = a^x$. That is, $(x_1 + x_2,y_1y_2)$ is also a point on the graph.

The result of *Example 2* is a consequence of the law of exponents for multiplication. Adding the x-coordinates of points on the graph of $y = a^x$ corresponds to multiplying their y-coordinates.

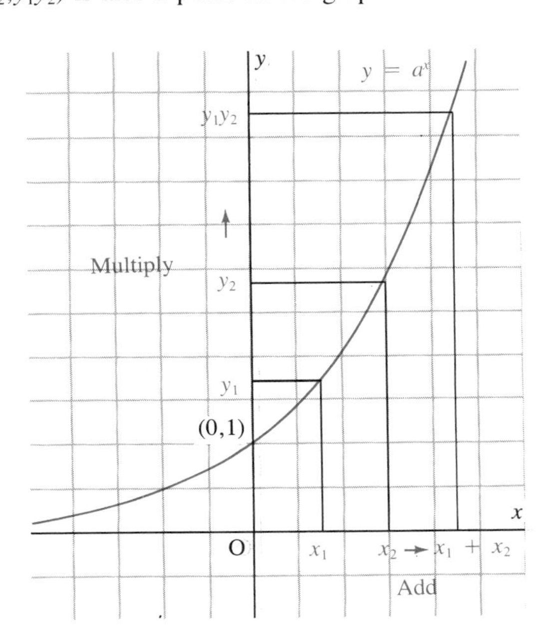

EXERCISES 10-6

Ⓐ

1. Identify the graph which best represents each function.

   a) $y = 3^x$ b) $y = 10^x$ c) $y = \left(\frac{3}{4}\right)^x$ d) $y = \left(\frac{1}{4}\right)^x$

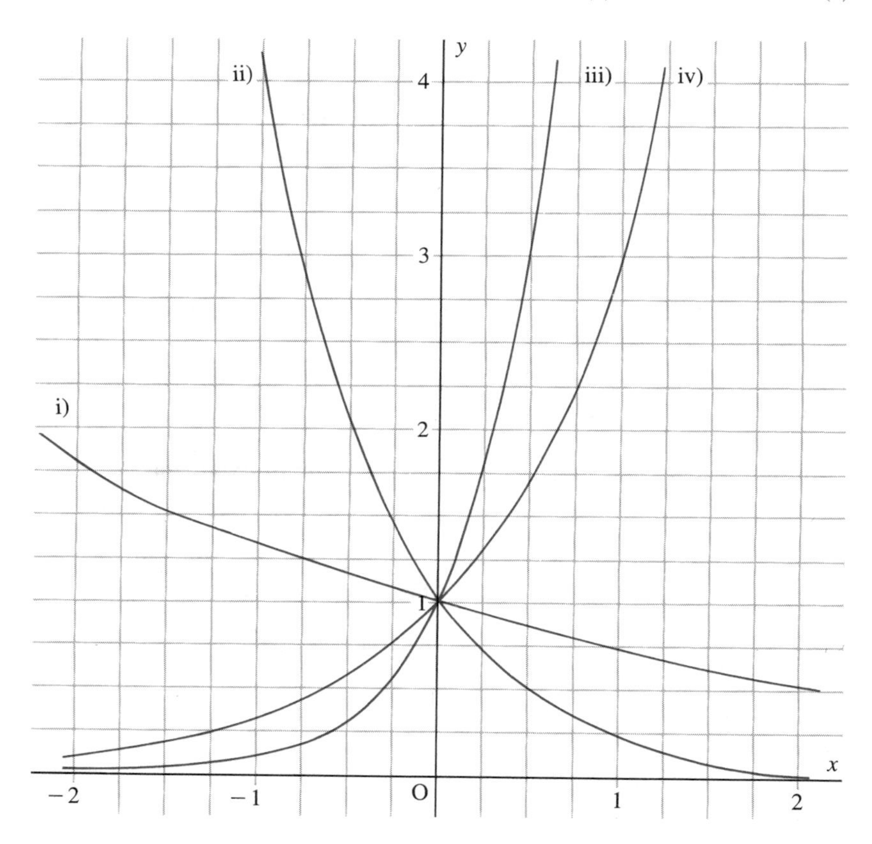

2. Describe how the graph of $y = a^x$ varies as a varies.

Ⓑ

3. a) Make tables of values and graph these functions on the same grid.

   $y = 3^x$ for $-2 \leqslant x \leqslant 2$ $y = \left(\frac{1}{3}\right)^x$ for $-2 \leqslant x \leqslant 2$

   b) On the same grid as in part a), sketch the graph of each function.

   $y = 4^x$ $y = 2^x$ $y = \left(\frac{1}{2}\right)^x$ $y = \left(\frac{1}{4}\right)^x$

4. Draw the graphs of these functions on the same grid.

   $y = 2^x$ $y = 5^x$ $y = 10^x$ $y = \left(\frac{1}{2}\right)^x$ $y = \left(\frac{1}{5}\right)^x$ $y = \left(\frac{1}{10}\right)^x$

5. Find each value of a if the graph of $y = a^x$ passes through each point.
   a) A(3,216) b) B(5,32) c) C(3,512) d) D(4,256)
   e) E(−2,64) f) $F\left(-3,\frac{1}{216}\right)$ g) G(3,343) h) $H\left(\frac{1}{3},3\right)$

6. Prove that if $f(x) = a^x$, then $f(x)f(y) = f(x + y)$.

7. a) Prove that if (x_1,y_1) and (x_2,y_2) are two points on the graph of $y = a^x$, then both $(x_1 + x_2, y_1y_2)$ and $\left(x_1 - x_2, \frac{y_1}{y_2}\right)$ are points on the graph.
   b) Prove that if (x_1,y_1) is a point on the graph of $y = a^x$, then both $(2x_1, y_1^2)$ and $\left(-x_1, \frac{1}{y_1}\right)$ are points on the graph.

8. a) Graph the function $y = 2^x$.
   b) On the same grid as in part a), sketch the graph of each function.
      i) $y = 2^x - 1$ ii) $y = 2^{x-1}$ iii) $y = 2^{x+1}$
      iv) $y = 2^{0.5x}$ v) $y = 2^{2x}$ vi) $y = 2^{-x}$

(C)

9. If $a > 0$, for what values of a and x is each statement true?
   a) $a^x = 1$ b) $a^x > 1$ c) $0 < a^x < 1$

10. a) Graph the function $y = 2^x$ for $-3 \leq x \leq 3$.
    b) By expressing 5 as a power of 2, show that the graph of $y = 5^x$ is a horizontal compression of the graph of $y = 2^x$.
    c) Similarly, show that the graph of $y = 1.5^x$ is a horizontal expansion of the graph of $y = 2^x$.
    d) Use the results of parts b) and c) to graph the functions $y = 5^x$ and $y = 1.5^x$ on the same grid as in part a).

11. Explain why the graphs of all exponential functions can be regarded as transformations of the graph of $y = 2^x$.

12. Graph each function.
    a) $y = 2^{|x|}$ b) $y = x(2^x)$ c) $y = x^x$

INVESTIGATE

Find out what the [log] key on your calculator does. For example, key in: 2 [log] and observe the result. Try this with a wide variety of numbers other than 2, such as those below. Look for patterns in the results.

- Numbers selected at random, for example, 3, 65, 239, 4772
- Powers of 10, for example, 10, 100, 1000, 10 000, 1, 0.1, 0.01, 0.001
- Multiples of 10, for example, 20, 200, 2000, 30, 300, 3000
- Zero and negative numbers, for example, 0, −2, −3, −10

Write a report of your findings.

Review Exercises

1. a) If \$1000 is invested in an account which pays 9.5% interest compounded annually, write an expression which gives the amount A after n years.
   b) How much will accumulate in 6 years?

2. When light passes through ice, its intensity is reduced by 4% for every centimetre of thickness. Write an expression which gives the percent P of light which penetrates x centimetres of ice.

3. Evaluate.

   a) $8^{-\frac{2}{3}}$ b) $27^{\frac{1}{3}}$ c) $32^{\frac{3}{5}}$ d) $\left(\frac{1}{125}\right)^{-\frac{2}{3}}$

   e) $(2.25)^{1.5}$ f) $\left(\frac{16}{81}\right)^{-0.75}$ g) $(0.0144)^0$ h) $(0.0016)^{1.25}$

4. Evaluate to the nearest hundredth.
   a) $2.6^{1.7}$ b) $5.14^{2.31}$ c) $14.7^{-1.61}$ d) $0.475^{-0.79}$

5. A bacteria culture doubles in size every 8 h. If there are now 1000 bacteria in the culture, how many:
   a) will there be in i) 16 h ii) 44 h
   b) were there i) 24 h ago ii) 1.5 days ago?

6. Simplify.

   a) $\dfrac{-15x^{-3}y^2 \times 8x^5y^3}{-24x^{-1}y^7}$ b) $\dfrac{18m^2n^{-5} \times (-5m^{-4}n^2)}{-15m^3n^{-4} \times 12m^{-7}n^0}$

   c) $(2a^2b)^{-3}(5ab^{-2})^2$ d) $(x^{\frac{1}{2}}y^{-\frac{2}{3}})^3 \times \left(\frac{3}{5}x^{-\frac{3}{4}}y^{\frac{1}{3}}\right)^2$

   e) $\dfrac{21a^{-\frac{3}{4}}b^{\frac{2}{3}}}{-35a^{-\frac{1}{2}}b}$ f) $\dfrac{6m^{\frac{1}{4}}n^{-\frac{1}{3}} \times 35m^{-\frac{3}{4}}n^{\frac{1}{2}}}{14m^{\frac{1}{2}}n^{\frac{5}{6}} \times 10m^{\frac{3}{2}}n^{-\frac{1}{2}}}$

7. If $x = 3a^2$, $y = a^4$, and $z = 2a^{-3}$, write each expression as an exponential function of a.

   a) $\left(\frac{1}{8}x^2yz\right)^{\frac{1}{2}}$ b) $x^{-1}y^{\frac{3}{2}}z^{-2}$

8. Simplify.

   a) $\dfrac{(x^{3a})(x^{-5a})}{x^{-2a}}$ b) $\dfrac{(m^{3x+y})(2m^{x-2y})}{(3m^{-2x+3y})}$ c) $\dfrac{(a^{\frac{x}{4}})(b^{\frac{2x}{3}})^3}{(a^{\frac{3x}{2}})^{-\frac{1}{2}}(b^{\frac{3x}{4}})^2}$

9. How much must be invested at 7.5% interest compounded annually, so that there will be \$5600 in 12 years?

10. There are 5400 red ants in a particular colony. If there were 1200 ants in the colony 8 months ago, what is the monthly rate of growth?

11. A diamond ring worth \$12 500 increases in value by 12% per year. In how many years will it be worth \$50 000?

11 Logarithmic Functions

In April 1986 there was a major nuclear accident at the Chernobyl power plant in the Soviet Union. Quantities of radioactive iodine-131 were released into the atmosphere. How long did it take for the level of radiation to reduce to 1% of the level immediately after the accident? (See Section 11-3 *Example 5*.)

11-1 COMMON LOGARITHMS

In *Section 10-4* we encountered problems such as these.

In how many years will an investment double in value at 8% per annum compounded annually?

The answer to this question is the solution of this equation.

$$2 = 1(1.08)^n$$

or $(1.08)^n = 2$

At what depth under water is the light level 10% of the light level at the surface?

The answer to this question is the solution of this equation.

$$10 = 100(0.975)^d$$

or $(0.975)^d = 0.1$

In these equations the variable appears in an exponent. Such equations are called *exponential equations*, and they can be solved to any degree of accuracy by systematic trial. However, exponential equations occur so frequently in applications that mathematicians have developed a more direct method of solution. This method involves logarithms. After defining a logarithm and introducing some of its properties, we will show how the above equations can be solved using logarithms.

In a preceding investigation you may have discovered that the [log] key of a calculator gives exponents for powers of 10.

Key in: 100 [log] to display 2.
2 is the exponent that 100 has when it is expressed as a power of 10.
Since $100 = 10^2$
we write $\log 100 = 2$

Key in: 0.001 [log] to display -3.
-3 is the exponent that 0.001 has when it is expressed as a power of 10.
Since $0.001 = 10^{-3}$
we write $\log 0.001 = -3$

These logarithms are called *common logarithms* since they are the exponents of numbers written as powers with base 10. In a later section we will study logarithms with bases other than 10.

Definition of a Logarithm

- $\log x$ is the exponent that x would have if it were written as a power with base 10.
- $\log x = y$ means that $x = 10^y$.

Since $10^y > 0$ for all real values of y, then $x > 0$. Hence, $\log x$ is defined as a real number only when $x > 0$.

Example 1. Use the definition of a logarithm to evaluate each expression. Check the result with your calculator.

a) $\log 100\,000$ b) $\log 0.01$ c) $\log \sqrt{10}$ d) $\log 1$

Solution.

a) Since $100\,000 = 10^5$, then $\log 100\,000 = 5$
Key in: 100 000 [log] to display 5

b) Since $0.01 = 10^{-2}$, then $\log 0.01 = -2$
Key in: 0.01 [log] to display -2

c) Since $\sqrt{10} = 10^{0.5}$, then $\log \sqrt{10} = 0.5$
Key in: 10 [√] [log] to display 0.5

d) Since $1 = 10^0$, then $\log 1 = 0$
Key in: 1 [log] to display 0

We can use the [log] key of a calculator to find approximations to the logarithm of any positive number. Hence, we can write any positive number as a power of 10.

Example 2. Use your calculator to evaluate each logarithm. Then write the result in exponential form, and check with the calculator.

a) log 7 b) log 500 c) log 0.4

Solution. a) Key in: 7 [log] to display 0.8450980
Hence, $\log 7 \doteq 0.845\,098$
This means that $10^{0.845098} \doteq 7$
To check, key in: 10 [y^x] 0.845098 [=] to display 6.9999993

b) Key in: 500 [log] to display 2.6989700
Hence, $\log 500 \doteq 2.698\,97$
This means that $10^{2.69897} \doteq 500$
To check, key in: 10 [y^x] 2.69897 [=] to display 499.99999

c) Key in: 0.4 [log] to display −0.3979400
Hence, $\log 0.4 \doteq -0.397\,94$
This means that $10^{-0.39794} \doteq 0.4$
To check, key in: 10 [y^x] 0.39794 [+/−] [=] to display 0.4000000

Since $\log x$ is defined as a real number only when $x > 0$, you will get an error message if you attempt to find the logarithm of 0, or of a negative number.

Key in: 0 [log] and observe the result.
$\log 0 = y$ means $10^y = 0$, which is impossible.

Key in: 2 [+/−] [log] and observe the result.
$\log(-2) = y$ means $10^y = -2$, which is impossible.

Example 3. Simplify each expression.

a) $\log 10^x$ b) $10^{\log x}$

Solution. a) $\log 10^x$ is the exponent that 10^x would have if it were written as a power of 10. But, 10^x *is* written as a power of 10, and has exponent x. Hence, $\log 10^x = x$

b) $10^{\log x}$ is 10 raised to the exponent that x would have if x were written as a power of 10. Hence, $10^{\log x} = x$

Example 3 shows that taking a common logarithm of a number and raising the number to a power of 10 are inverse operations, just as squaring a number and taking the square root of the number are inverse operations. If your calculator has a [10^x] key, you can illustrate this by entering any positive number and then pressing the [log] key and the [10^x] key in either order.

Key in: 4.5 [log] [10^x] to display 4.5
Key in: 4.5 [10^x] [log] to display 4.5

Summary

- A logarithm is an exponent.
- $\log x = y$ means that $x = 10^y$, $x > 0$.
- $\log x$ is defined only when $x > 0$.
- $\log 10^x = x$ and $10^{\log x} = x$

EXERCISES 11-1

Ⓐ

1. Use the definition to evaluate each logarithm.
   a) $\log 100$ b) $\log 1000$ c) $\log 1\ 000\ 000$ d) $\log 10$
   e) $\log 0.1$ f) $\log 0.001$ g) $\log 1$ h) $\log \sqrt[3]{10}$
   i) $\log 10^5$ j) $\log 10^{\frac{1}{5}}$ k) $\log 10^{\frac{2}{3}}$ l) $\log 10^n$

2. Use your calculator to evaluate each logarithm to 4 decimal places. Then write each result in exponential form, and check it with the calculator.
   a) $\log 5$ b) $\log 18$ c) $\log 62.4$ d) $\log 4877$
   e) $\log 0.25$ f) $\log 0.8$ g) $\log 0.02$ h) $\log 0.006$

3. On February 23, 1987, the Canadian astronomer Ian Shelton discovered a supernova, or exploding star, from an observatory in Chile. State the common logarithm of each number.
   a) The supernova was more than 100 000 light years from the Earth.
   b) One light year is approximately 10^{15} m.
   c) Throughout recorded history only about 10 supernovas have been visible to the unaided eye.
   d) At its brightest, a supernova is about 10^9 times as bright as a star like the sun.
   e) A supernova liberates about 10^{30} times as much energy as would be unleashed by the detonation of all the nuclear weapons on the Earth.

4. On a single optical disk, an amount of data equivalent to all the text appearing in 15 years of daily newspapers can be recorded. State the common logarithm of each number.
   a) More than 10^{12} bytes of data are recorded on each disk.
   b) To avoid errors, a laser beam is focused within 10^{-7} m of dead centre for each pit on the surface of the disk.
   c) The error rate for a typical disk is 10^{-12}.

Ⓑ

5. Write in exponential form.
   a) $\log 10\ 000 = 4$ b) $\log 10 = 1$ c) $\log 0.01 = -2$

6. Write in logarithmic form.
   a) $10^3 = 1000$ b) $10^0 = 1$ c) $10^{-3} = 0.001$

7. The centillion is defined as the 100th power of 1 000 000. What is the common logarithm of one centillion?

8. Solve each equation.
   a) $\log x = 2$ b) $\log x = 5$ c) $\log x = -3$
   d) $\log x = 0$ e) $\log x = 1$ f) $\log \log x = 1$

9. a) Simplify each expression.
   i) $\log 10^4$ ii) $\log 10^5$ iii) $\log 10^{-3}$
   iv) $\log 10^{0.5}$ v) $\log 10^{2.4}$ vi) $\log 10^{-1.5}$
   b) Based on the results of part a), state a general result.

10. a) Simplify each expression.
   i) $10^{\log 100}$ ii) $10^{\log 1000}$ iii) $10^{\log 0.01}$
   iv) $10^{\log 20}$ v) $10^{\log 500}$ vi) $10^{\log 0.2}$
   b) Based on the results of part a), state a general result.

11. a) Use your calculator to evaluate each logarithm.
   i) $\log 2$ ii) $\log 20$ iii) $\log 200$ iv) $\log 2000$
   v) $\log 0.2$ vi) $\log 0.02$ vii) $\log 0.002$ viii) $\log 0.0002$
   b) Account for the pattern in the results.

INVESTIGATE

You can use your calculator to find an approximation to the common logarithm of a number *without* using the [log] key. The method depends on trying to find a power of that number which is close to a power of 10.

For example, to find an approximation to log 2, try different powers of 2 such as 2^6, 2^7, and 2^8. Notice that $2^{10} = 1024$, which is approximately 10^3. Hence, we may write:

$$2^{10} \doteq 10^3$$

Take the 10th root of both sides.

$$2 \doteq 10^{\frac{3}{10}}$$

Hence, $\log 2 \doteq \frac{3}{10}$, or 0.3

a) Use this method to construct a table of approximations to the logarithms of the integers from 2 to 9.
b) Compare the results with the actual values obtained using the [log] key. Which of the approximations is the most accurate?
c) Compare your approximations for log 2, log 4, and log 8. How are they related? Can you explain this relationship?
d) Repeat part c) for log 3 and log 9.

11-2 THE LAWS OF LOGARITHMS FOR MULTIPLICATION AND DIVISION (BASE 10)

A logarithm is an exponent. Hence, it should be possible to write the laws of exponents in logarithmic form.

Consider an example of the law of exponents for multiplication, such as $10^2 \times 10^3 = 10^5$. Since $\log 10^2 = 2$, $\log 10^3 = 3$, and $\log 10^5 = 5$, we can write this equation as:

$\log 10^2 + \log 10^3 = \log 10^5$

or $\quad \log 10^5 = \log 10^2 + \log 10^3$

This example suggests that a possible law of logarithms for multiplication might be $\log xy = \log x + \log y$. This equation states that the exponent that xy would have if it were expressed as a power of 10 is equal to the sum of the exponents that x and y would have if they were expressed as powers of 10. We now prove this law.

Theorem **Law of Logarithms for Multiplication (Base 10)**

If x and y are any positive real numbers, then $\log xy = \log x + \log y$.

Given: Two real numbers x and y

Required to Prove: $\log xy = \log x + \log y$

Proof: Let $\log x = M$ and $\log y = N$

$$x = 10^M \qquad y = 10^N$$

Hence, $xy = (10^M)(10^N)$

$$= 10^{M+N}$$

Therefore, $\log xy = \log (10^{M+N})$

$$= M + N$$

$$= \log x + \log y$$

Corollary **Law of Logarithms for Division (Base 10)**

If x and y are any positive real numbers, then $\log \left(\frac{x}{y}\right) = \log x - \log y$.

Example 1. a) Write log 6 as:

i) a sum of two logarithms ii) a difference of two logarithms.

b) Check the results of part a) with a calculator.

Solution. a) i) Since $6 = 2 \times 3$, then by the law of logarithms for multiplication, $\log 6 = \log 2 + \log 3$

ii) Since $6 = 12 \div 2$, then by the law of logarithms for division, $\log 6 = \log 12 - \log 2$

b) i) Key in: 6 [log] to display 0.7781512

Key in: 2 [log] [+] 3 [log] [=] to display 0.7781512

ii) Key in: 12 [log] [−] 2 [log] [=] to display 0.7781512

In *Example 1*, log 6 can be expressed as a sum or a difference of logarithms in infinitely many other ways, such as:

$\log 6 = \log 1.5 + \log 4$ $\quad \log 6 = \log 18 - \log 3$

$\log 6 = \log 10 + \log 0.6$ $\quad \log 6 = \log 60 - \log 10$

Check these results with your calculator.

Example 2. Write each expression as a single logarithm, and check with a calculator.

a) $\log 5 + \log 4$ b) $\log 21 - \log 3$

Solution. a) $\log 5 + \log 4 = \log (5 \times 4)$

$= \log 20$

Key in: 5 [log] [+] 4 [log] [=] to display 1.3010300

Key in: 20 [log] to display 1.3010300

b) $\log 21 - \log 3 = \log \left(\frac{21}{3}\right)$

$= \log 7$

Key in: 21 [log] [−] 3 [log] [=] to display 0.8450980

Key in: 7 [log] to display 0.8450980

Example 3. Given that $\log 5 \doteq 0.698\,97$, find an approximation for each logarithm.

a) $\log 50$ b) $\log 500$ c) $\log 0.5$ d) $\log 0.05$

Solution. a) $\log 50 = \log 10 + \log 5$

$\doteq 1 + 0.698\,97$

$\doteq 1.698\,97$

b) $\log 500 = \log 100 + \log 5$

$\doteq 2 + 0.698\,97$

$\doteq 2.698\,97$

c) $\log 0.5 = \log 5 - \log 10$

$\doteq 0.698\,97 - 1$

$\doteq -0.301\,03$

d) $\log 0.05 = \log 5 - \log 100$

$\doteq 0.698\,97 - 2$

$\doteq -1.301\,03$

Check the results of *Example 3* with your calculator.

Laws of Logarithms for Multiplication and Division (Base 10)

$\log xy = \log x + \log y \qquad x,y > 0$

$\log \left(\frac{x}{y}\right) = \log x - \log y \qquad x,y > 0$

These laws are the laws of exponents for multiplication and division of powers (with base 10) restated in logarithmic form. They allow us to expand logarithms of products and quotients, and to write sums and differences of logarithms as single logarithms.

Example 4. Write $\log \left(\frac{3a}{2b}\right)$ in terms of $\log a$ and $\log b$.

Solution.

$$\begin{aligned}\log \left(\frac{3a}{2b}\right) &= \log (3a) - \log (2b)\\ &= \log 3 + \log a - \log 2 - \log b\\ &= \log 3 - \log 2 + \log a - \log b\\ &= \log \left(\frac{3}{2}\right) + \log a - \log b\\ &= \log 1.5 + \log a - \log b\end{aligned}$$

If desired, the term log 1.5 in the solution of *Example 4* can be evaluated with a calculator, and the result can be approximated as 0.176 091 3 + log a − log b.

Write as a single logarithm. $\log a + \log b - \log c$

Solution. $\log a + \log b - \log c = \log ab - \log c$

$$= \log\left(\frac{ab}{c}\right)$$

EXERCISES 11-2

(A)

1. Write as a single logarithm, and check with your calculator.
   a) log 6 + log 7 b) log 24 − log 6 c) log 3 + log 8
   d) log 35 − log 5 e) log 12 + log 7 f) log 42 − log 3
   g) log 64 − log 2 h) log 1 − log 2 i) log 17 + log 8

2. Write as a sum of logarithms, and check with your calculator.
   a) log 10 b) log 21 c) log 28 d) log 36
   e) log 9 f) log 44 g) log 57 h) log 121

3. Write as a difference of logarithms, and check with your calculator.
   a) log 5 b) log 8 c) log 12 d) log 13
   e) log 10 f) log 21 g) log 17 h) log 40

4. Write as a single logarithm, and check with your calculator.
   a) log 2 + log 3 + log 5 b) log 3 + log 4 + log 7
   c) log 5 + log 8 − log 4 d) log 6 + log 3 + log 5
   e) log 12 − log 4 + log 7 f) log 7 + log 8 − log 2

(B)

5. Given log 3 ≐ 0.477 12, find an approximation for each logarithm.
   a) log 30 b) log 3000 c) log 0.3 d) log 0.003

6. If log 70 ≐ 1.8451, find an approximation for each logarithm.
   a) log 7 b) log 700 c) log 0.07
   d) log 0.7 e) log 700 000 f) log 0.007

7. Write in terms of log a and log b.
   a) $\log\left(\frac{2a}{3b}\right)$ b) $\log\left(\frac{7a}{2b}\right)$ c) $\log\left(\frac{5b}{2a}\right)$ d) $\log\left(\frac{12a}{5b}\right)$

8. Write as a single logarithm.
   a) $\log x + \log y - \log z$
   b) $\log m - (\log n + \log p)$
   c) $\log a + \log b - \log c - \log d$
   d) $\log a + \log (a + b) - \log (a - b)$
   e) $\log (m + 3) + \log (m + 7)$
   f) $\log (2x - y) + \log (3x + 2y) - \log (x + y)$

9. Write as a single logarithm. For what values of the variable is each expression not defined?
   a) $\log(x + 3) - \log(x - 1)$
   b) $\log(2x - 7) - \log(x + 3)$
   c) $-\log(a - 2) + \log(a + 2)$
   d) $\log(8a + 15) - \log(2a + 3)$

10. If $\log 2 = x$ and $\log 3 = y$, write each logarithm as an expression in x and y.
    a) $\log 6$
    b) $\log 1.5$
    c) $\log 60$
    d) $\log 12$
    e) $\log 18$
    f) $\log 36$
    g) $\log 3.6$
    h) $\log\left(\frac{1}{6}\right)$

11. Prove the corollary on page 464 using:
    a) a method similar to the one used to prove the theorem
    b) the result of the theorem.

12. Assume that x and y are natural numbers, and $x > y$. How many solutions does each equation have?
    a) $\log 24 = \log x + \log y$
    b) $\log 24 = \log x - \log y$

13. Prove the law of logarithms for three factors. $\log xyz = \log x + \log y + \log z$

Ⓒ

14. Prove each identity, and state the value(s) of x for which the identity is true.
    a) $\log(x - 1) + \log(x - 2) = \log(x^2 - 3x + 2)$
    b) $\log x + \log(x + 3) = \log(x^2 + 3x)$
    c) $\log(x - 5) + \log(x + 5) = \log(x^2 - 25)$

15. Solve and check.
    a) $\log(x + 2) + \log(x - 1) = 1$
    b) $\log(3x + 2) + \log(x - 1) = 2$
    c) $2\log(x - 1) = 2 + \log 100$

16. Express y as a function of x. What is the domain?
    a) $\log 3 + \log y = \log(x + 2) - \log x$
    b) $\log y - 2 + \log x - \log(x + 1) = 0$
    c) $\log 4y = x + \log 4$

17. a) By writing $x = 10^{\log x}$, $y = 10^{\log y}$, and $xy = 10^{\log xy}$, prove the law of logarithms for multiplication.
    b) Use this method to prove the law of logarithms for division.

INVESTIGATE

1. Use your calculator to evaluate each logarithm and account for the pattern in the results. $\log 2$, $\log 4$, $\log 8$, $\log 16$

2. Repeat *Question 1*, but round the results to 5 decimal places. Do you see another pattern? Extend the pattern by evaluating these logarithms to 5 decimal places. $\log 32$, $\log 64$, $\log 128$, $\log 256$, ...
   What is the first power of 2 for which the pattern in the rounded values breaks down?

MATHEMATICS AROUND US

Orders of Magnitude

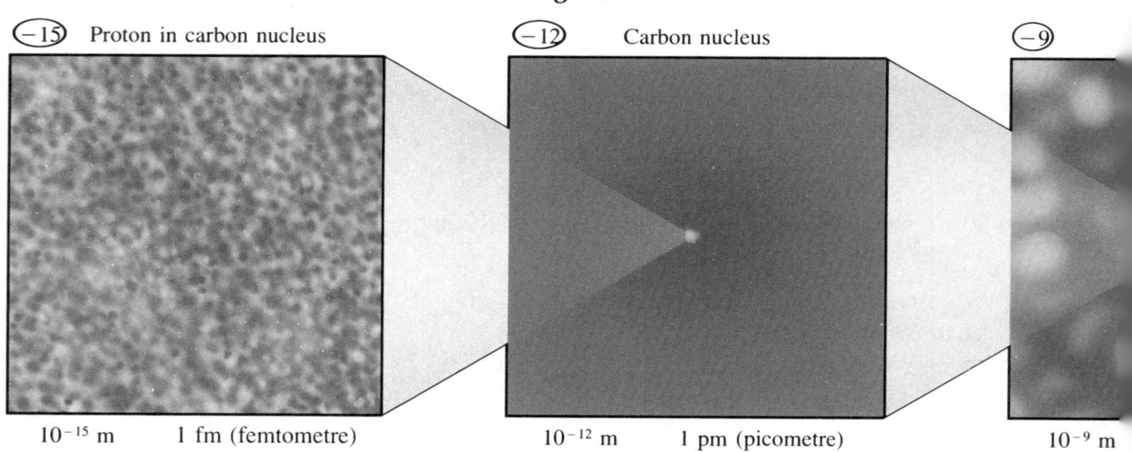

Scientists have always wanted to extend our range of observation of the world around us, from the microscopic scale to the astronomic scale. What might we see if we could take an imaginary journey along a straight line beginning at the nucleus of an atom and ending at the farthermost reaches of outer space?

The first illustration shows part of the nucleus of a carbon atom. As we get farther and farther away, greater and greater distances are brought into view. The steps we take in this journey are not regular steps, but rather, each step is 1000 times as great as the previous one.

Hence, the dimensions of each illustration represent a distance 1000 times as long as the one before it. And, each illustration shows a 1000× enlargement of a small portion at the centre of the next one. Although it can be seen in only the first illustration, the nucleus of the carbon atom where we started the journey is at the centre of all of them.

The journey covers four pages in this book. Study the illustrations on all four pages before you begin the questions.

QUESTIONS

1. Notice the circled number in the upper left corner of each illustration.
   a) How is this number related to the distance represented by the illustration?
   b) As you move from one illustration to the next, compare the change in the circled number with the change in the distance represented by the illustration.
2. A factor of 10 is called one *order of magnitude*. Hence, a factor of 100, or 10×10, represents two orders of magnitude. How many orders of magnitude are represented by the change from:
   a) any illustration to the next
   b) the first illustration to the last?

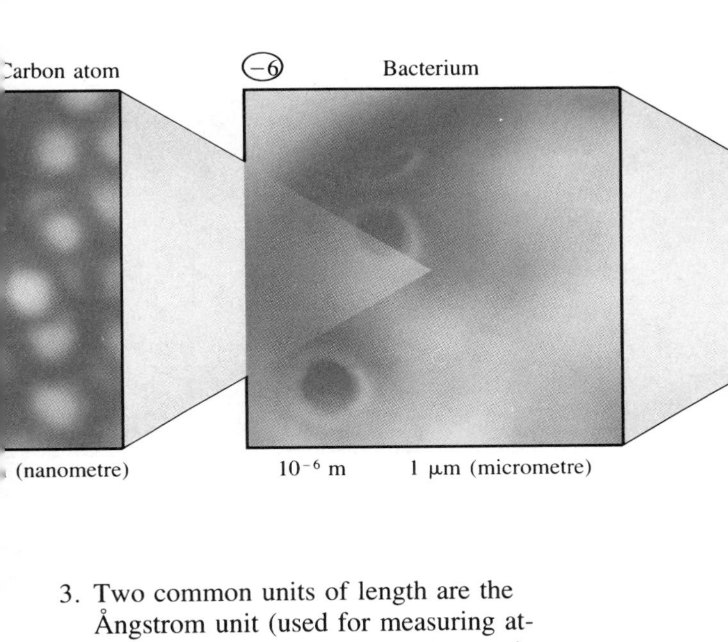

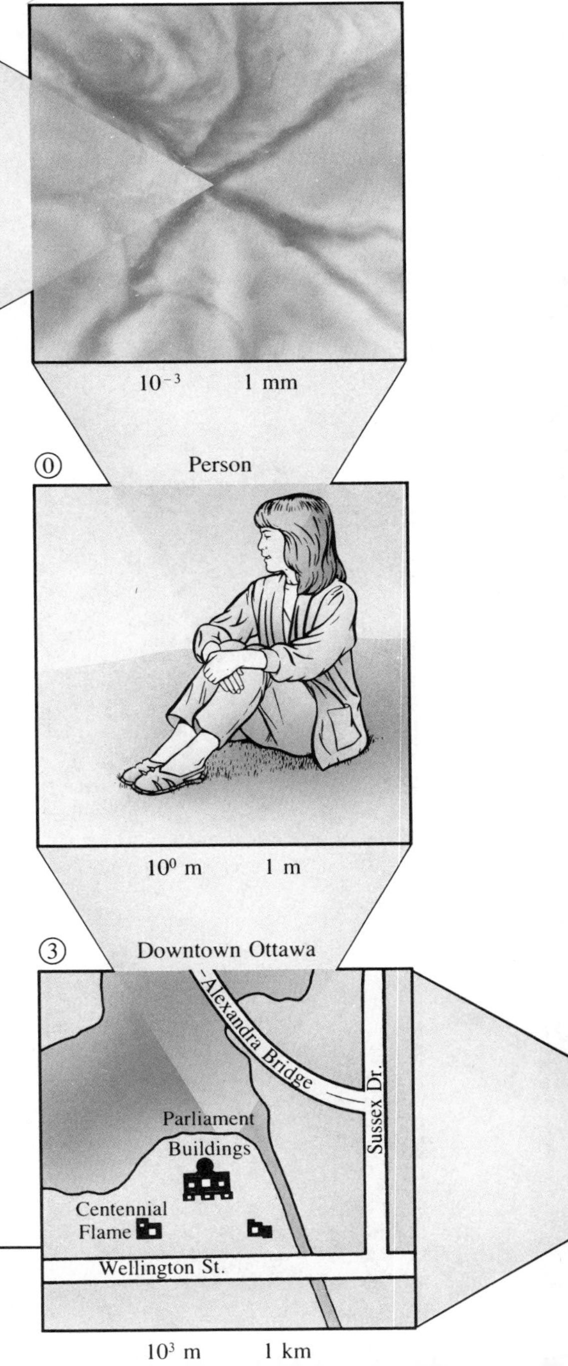

3. Two common units of length are the Ångstrom unit (used for measuring atoms) and the fermi (used for measuring nuclear particles).

1 Ångstrom unit	10^{-10} m
1 fermi	10^{-15} m

   a) How many orders of magnitude is the Ångstrom unit greater than the fermi?
   b) Name two other units of length that differ by the same order of magnitude.

4. The double-helix strands of a DNA molecule are approximately 2×10^{-9} m apart. If the twisted molecule were stretched out, its length would be 7 orders of magnitude greater. How long is the molecule?

5. What common interval of time is approximately 4 orders of magnitude longer than one minute?

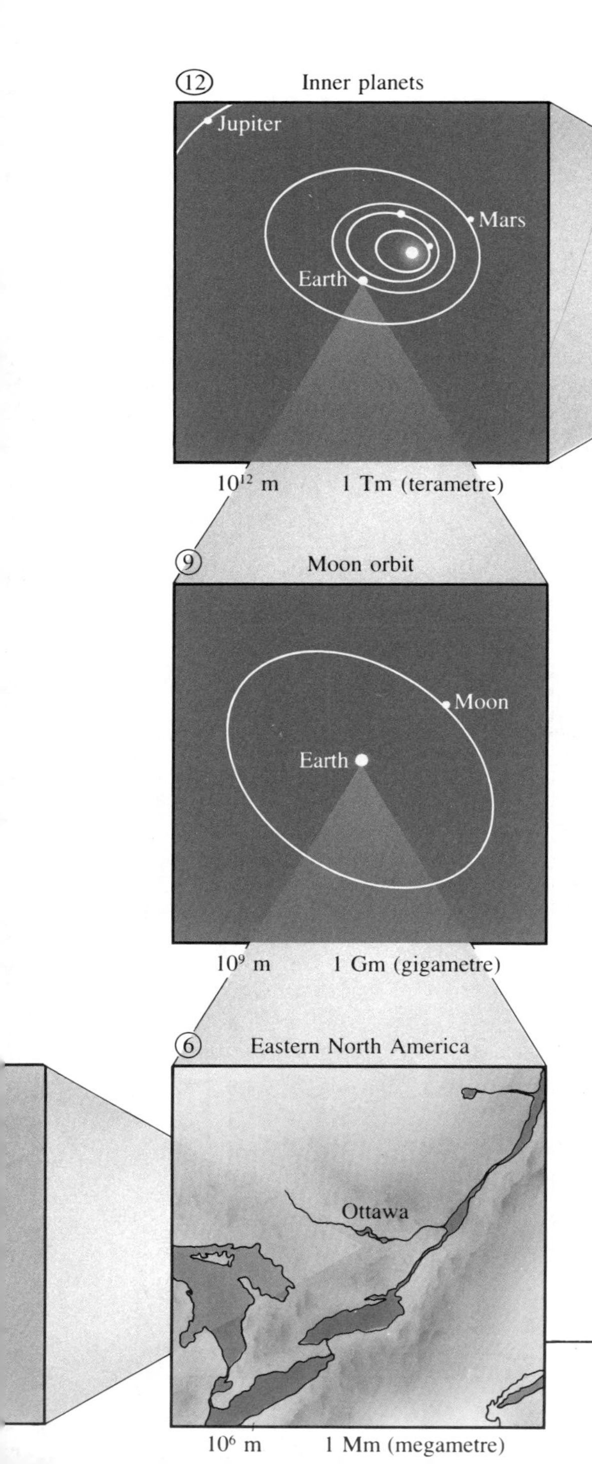

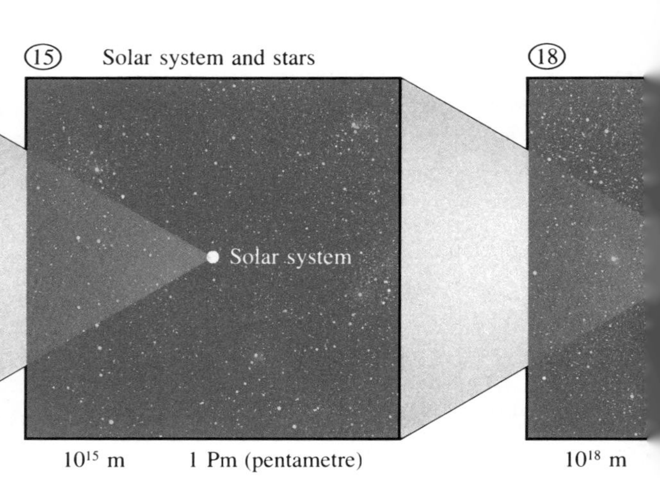

	Diameter (m)
Sun	1.4×10^9
Earth	1.3×10^7
Moon	3.5×10^6

Order of magnitude is a relative term, and refers to a comparison of two numbers using powers of 10. For example, the diameter of the sun is approximately 100, or 10^2 times the diameter of the Earth. We say that the diameter of the sun is approximately 2 orders of magnitude greater than that of the Earth. This statement means that:

$$\frac{\text{diameter of sun}}{\text{diameter of Earth}} \doteq 10^2$$

or, $\log\left(\frac{\text{diameter of sun}}{\text{diameter of Earth}}\right) \doteq 2$

Hence, the difference in their orders of magnitude is the logarithm of their quotient. This example suggests the following definition.

Definition: If a and b are any two positive numbers, the difference in their orders of magnitude is $\log\left(\frac{a}{b}\right)$.

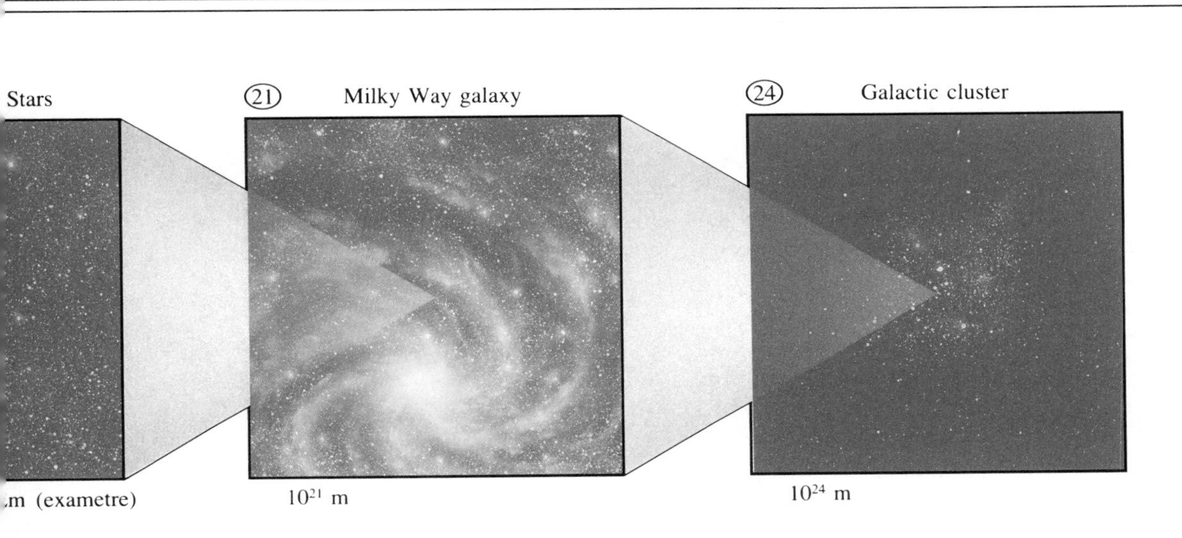

6. Show that the diameter of the sun is approximately 2.6 orders of magnitude greater than that of the moon.

7. Two common units of length are the astronomical unit (used for measuring planetary distances) and the light year (used for measuring stellar and galactic distances).

1 astronomical unit	1.5×10^{11} m
1 light year	9.5×10^{15} m

How many orders of magnitude is the light year greater than the astronomical unit?

8. The planets Neptune and Pluto are approximately 5×10^{12} m from the Earth. How many orders of magnitude greater than this are these distances?
   a) The nearest star, Proxima Centauri, 4×10^{18} m from Earth
   b) The centre of the Milky Way Galaxy, 6.7×10^{20} m from Earth
   c) A chain of galaxies 7×10^{24} m from Earth

9. In 1989, the space probe *Voyager II* will photograph the planet Neptune, about 5×10^{12} m from the Earth. The *Space Telescope* will be able to examine objects 13.4 orders of magnitude farther than this. What is the limit of observation of the Space Telescope?

10. The limit of the known universe is about 2.3 orders of magnitude greater than the distance represented by the last illustration above. How many metres is this?

11. Now that we have finished our journey from the nucleus of the carbon atom to outer space, suppose we reverse our direction and take the return trip back to the nucleus of the carbon atom where we started. What percent of the remaining distance would we cover from one illustration to the next?

11-3 THE LAWS OF LOGARITHMS FOR POWERS AND ROOTS (BASE 10)

The law of logarithms for products may be applied when the factors are equal. For example, if $x = y$, then the law:

$$\log xy = \log x + \log y \quad \text{may be written}$$

$$\log (x)(x) = \log x + \log x$$

or

$$\log (x^2) = 2 \log x$$

This example suggests that a possible law of logarithms for powers might be $\log (x^n) = n \log x$. This equation states that the exponent that x^n would have if it were expressed as a power of 10 is n times the exponent that x would have if it were expressed as a power of 10. We now prove this law.

Theorem **Law of Logarithms for Powers (Base 10)**
If x and n are real numbers, and $x > 0$, then $\log (x^n) = n \log x$

Given: Two real numbers x and n, where $x > 0$
Required to Prove: $\log (x^n) = n \log x$
Proof: Let $\log x = M$

$$x = 10^M$$

Hence, $x^n = (10^M)^n$

$$= 10^{nM}$$

Therefore, $\log (x^n) = \log (10^{nM})$

$$= nM$$

$$= n \log x$$

Corollary **Law of Logarithms for Roots (Base 10)**

If x and n are real numbers, and $x > 0$, then $\log \sqrt[n]{x} = \frac{1}{n} \log x$

Example 1. a) i) Write log 125 as a product of a whole number and a logarithm.
ii) Write 4 log 3 as a single logarithm.
b) Check the results of part a) with a calculator.

Solution. a) i) Since $125 = 5^3$, then $\log 125 = \log (5^3)$

$$= 3 \log 5$$

ii) $4 \log 3 = \log (3^4)$, or $\log 81$

b) i) Key in: 125 [log] to display 2.0969100
Key in: 5 [log] [×] 3 [=] to display 2.0969100
ii) Key in: 3 [log] [×] 4 [=] to display 1.9084850
Key in: 3 [y^x] 4 [=] [log] to display 1.9084850

Example 2. Given that $\log 2 \doteq 0.301\ 03$, find an approximation for each logarithm.
a) $\log 8$
b) $\log \sqrt[3]{2}$

Solution. a) $\log 8 = \log (2^3)$
$= 3 \log 2$
$\doteq 3(0.301\ 03)$
$\doteq 0.903\ 09$

b) $\log \sqrt[3]{2} = \log (2^{\frac{1}{3}})$
$= \frac{1}{3} \log 2$
$\doteq \frac{1}{3}(0.301\ 03)$
$\doteq 0.100\ 34$

Check the results of *Example 2* with your calculator.

Laws of Logarithms for Powers and Roots (Base 10)

$\log (x^n) = n \log x \qquad x > 0$

$\log \sqrt[n]{x} = \frac{1}{n} \log x \qquad x > 0$

An important application of the laws of logarithms is to the problem of expressing any positive number as a power of any other positive number (except 1).

Example 3. Express 19 as a power of 2 and check with a calculator.

Solution. Let $19 = 2^x$

Take the logarithm of each side.

$\log 19 = \log (2^x)$

$\log 19 = x \log 2$

Hence, $x = \dfrac{\log 19}{\log 2}$

Key in: 19 [log] [÷] 2 [log] [=] to display 4.2479275

Therefore, $19 \doteq 2^{4.2479275}$

To check, key in: 2 [y^x] 4.2479275 [=] to display 19.000000

Recall that in *Section 11-1* we mentioned that logarithms can be used to solve exponential equations, in which the variable appears as an exponent. Such an equation occurred in *Example 3*. As the solution of *Example 3* indicates, we can solve an exponential equation by taking the logarithm of each side and using the law of logarithms. We can now solve applied problems such as those at the beginning of *Section 11-1*.

Example 4. a) In how many years will an investment double in value at 8% per annum compounded annually?

b) At what depth under water is the light level 10% of the light level at the surface?

Solution. a) The answer is the solution of this equation.

$2 = 1(1.08)^n$

or $(1.08)^n = 2$

Take the logarithm of each side.

$n \log 1.08 = \log 2$

$n = \dfrac{\log 2}{\log 1.08}$

Key in: 2 [log] [÷] 1.08 [log] [=] to display 9.0064683
Hence, $n \doteq 9$
The investment will double in approximately 9 years.

b) The answer is the solution of this equation.

$$10 = 100(0.975)^d$$
$$\text{or } (0.975)^d = 0.1$$

Take the logarithm of each side.

$$d \log 0.975 = \log 0.1$$
$$d = \frac{\log 0.1}{\log 0.975}$$

Key in: 0.1 [log] [÷] 0.975 [log] [=] to display 90.947253
Hence, $d \doteq 91$
At a depth of about 91 m, approximately 10% of surface light is present.

Exponential equations frequently arise in applications involving exponential growth and decay.

Example 5. In April 1986 there was a major nuclear accident at the Chernobyl power plant in the Soviet Union. The atmosphere was contaminated with quantities of radioactive iodine-131, which has a half life of 8.1 days. How long did it take for the level of radiation to reduce to 1% of the level immediately after the accident?

Solution. Let P represent the percent of the original radiation that was present after t days. Then, since the halflife is 8.1 days,

$$P = 100\left(\frac{1}{2}\right)^{\frac{t}{8.1}}$$

Substitute 1 for P and solve for t by taking the logarithm of each side.

$$1 = 100(0.5)^{\frac{t}{8.1}}$$

$$\log 1 = \log 100 + \frac{t}{8.1}\log 0.5$$

$$0 = 2 + \frac{t}{8.1}\log 0.5$$

$$t = -\frac{16.2}{\log 0.5}$$

Key in: 0.5 [log] [1/x] [×] 16.2 [+/−] [=] to display 53.815235
Hence, $t \doteq 54$
It took about 54 days for the level of radiation to reduce to 1% of the level immediately after the accident.

Another application of the laws of logarithms is to the problem of finding approximations to very large powers.

Example 6. In 1952, Raphael M. Robinson used a SWAC computer to prove that $2^{3217} - 1$ is a prime number.

a) Write an approximation to this number in scientific notation.

b) How many digits does this number have?

Solution. a) The number 2^{3217} is so large that we can ignore the subtraction of 1 from it.

$$\text{Let } 2^{3217} = 10^x$$

Take the logarithm of each side.

$$\log (2^{3217}) = \log (10^x)$$
$$3217 \log 2 = x$$

Key in: 2 [log] [×] 3217 [=] to display 968.4135

$$\text{Therefore, } 2^{3217} \doteq 10^{968.4135}$$
$$\doteq 10^{0.4135} \times 10^{968}$$

Key in: 10 [y^x] 0.4135 [=] to display 2.5911944

Hence, $2^{3217} - 1 \doteq 2.591\,194\,4 \times 10^{968}$

b) Since 10^{968} has 969 digits, then $2^{3217} - 1$ has 969 digits.

Example 7. a) Write $\log (10x^2)$ in terms of $\log x$.

b) Write as a single logarithm. $\log a + 3 \log b - \frac{1}{2} \log c$

Solution. a)

$$\log (10x^2) = \log 10 + \log (x^2)$$
$$= 1 + 2 \log x$$

b)

$$\log a + 3 \log b - \frac{1}{2} \log c = \log a + \log (b^3) - \log \sqrt{c}$$
$$= \log \left(\frac{ab^3}{\sqrt{c}}\right), \text{ or } \log (ab^3c^{-\frac{1}{2}})$$

EXERCISES 11-3

Ⓐ

1. Write as a product of a whole number and a logarithm, and check with your calculator.

   a) $\log 9$ b) $\log 25$ c) $\log 8$ d) $\log 27$
   e) $\log 1000$ f) $\log 32$ g) $\log 343$ h) $\log 128$

2. Write as a single logarithm, and check with your calculator.

   a) $2 \log 6$ b) $3 \log 4$ c) $2 \log 9$ d) $2 \log 7$
   e) $5 \log 3$ f) $4 \log 2$ g) $3 \log 6$ h) $5 \log 10$

3. Given that $\log 3 \doteq 0.477\,12$, find an approximation for each logarithm.

   a) $\log 9$ b) $\log 81$ c) $\log \sqrt{3}$ d) $\log \sqrt[5]{3}$

4. Given that $\log 5 \doteq 0.698\,97$, find an approximation for each logarithm.

   a) $\log 625$ b) $\log \sqrt[3]{5}$ c) $\log 0.2$ d) $\log 0.04$

(B)

5. Express.
   a) 7 as a power of 3
   b) 5 as a power of 2
   c) 29 as a power of 2
   d) 77 as a power of 8
   e) 3 as a power of 0.5
   f) 0.45 as a power of 6

6. Solve to the nearest thousandth.
   a) $2^x = 11$
   b) $3^x = 17$
   c) $6^x = 5$
   d) $5^{x-1} = 9$
   e) $2^{x+3} = 6$
   f) $5^{1+x} = 2^{1-x}$

7. Solve.
   a) $3^x = 2$
   b) $4^x = 5$
   c) $7^{-x} = 3$
   d) $3^{1-x} = 5$
   e) $\left(\frac{1}{8}\right)^x = 25$
   f) $5^{3x} = 41$

8. Write each expression in terms of $\log x$.
   a) $\log \sqrt{x}$
   b) $\log \sqrt{10}x$
   c) $\log \sqrt{10x}$
   d) $\log 10x$
   e) $\log 10\sqrt{x}$

9. Write as a single logarithm.
   a) $2 \log a + 5 \log b$
   b) $3 \log x + \frac{1}{2} \log y$
   c) $2 \log m + \log n - 5 \log p$
   d) $\frac{1}{2} \log x - 2 \log y - \log z$
   e) $3 \log a + \frac{1}{2} \log b - \frac{5}{4} \log c$
   f) $10 \log a - 3 \log b + \frac{1}{2} \log c - \log d$

10. When strontium-90 decays, the percent P remaining is expressed as a function of the time t years by the equation $P \doteq 100(2)^{-0.0357t}$. (See *Example 4*, page 434.) How long is it until the percent remaining is: a) 10% b) 1%?

11. The halflives of iodine-131 and cesium-144 were given in *Exercise 11*, page 436. How long is it until the percent remaining of each substance is: a) 10% b) 0.1%?

12. In a steel mill, red-hot slabs of steel are pressed many times between heavy rollers. The drawings show two stages in rolling a slab.

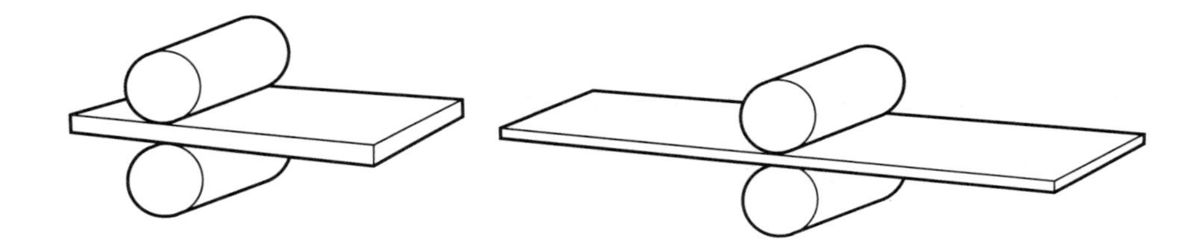

A slab is 2.00 m long and 0.120 m thick. On each pass through the rollers, its length increases by 20%.
   a) Write the equation which expresses the length L metres of the slab as an exponential function of the number of passes n through the rollers.
   b) How many passes are needed to increase the length of the slab to 50 m?

13. a) For the slab in *Exercise 12*, by what factor does the thickness of the slab decrease on each pass through the rollers? Assume the width is constant.
    b) Write an equation which expresses the thickness t metres of the slab as an exponential function of the number of passes n through the rollers.
    c) How many passes are needed to reduce the thickness of the slab to 0.001 m?
    d) How long would the slab be when its thickness is 0.001 m?

14. x and y are two positive numbers. How are $\log x$ and $\log y$ related if:
    a) $y = 10x$ b) $y = \frac{1}{x}$ c) $y = x^2$
    d) $y = \sqrt{x}$ e) $y = 10\sqrt{x}$ f) $y = \sqrt{10x}$?

15. a) What is the first digit in 2^{1000}?
    b) How many digits are there in 2^{1000}?
    c) What is the last digit in 2^{1000}?

16. The table shows some large prime numbers that were discovered using computers. How many digits does each prime number have?

	Prime Number	Year	Computer
a)	$2^{11213} - 1$	1963	ILLIAC-II
b)	$2^{21701} - 1$	1978	CDC-CYBER-174
c)	$2^{132049} - 1$	1983	CRAY-1
d)	$2^{216091} - 1$	1985	CRAY-1

17. In 1938 the physicist Sir Arthur Eddington calculated that the number of particles in the universe is 33×2^{259}. He called this number the *cosmical number*.
    a) Write the cosmical number in scientific notation.
    b) How many digits are there in this number?

18. How many digits are there in the number 9^{9^9}?

19. In 1951 the UNIVAC computer performed approximately 1000 arithmetic operations per second. Since then, the speed of computers has doubled, on the average, about every 2 years.
    a) Express the number of operations per second N as an exponential function of the time n years since 1951.
    b) Predict when computers will be able to perform a billion operations per second. What assumption are you making?

20. After every 10 pages of printing, the ribbon in a dot matrix printer loses about 0.5% of its ink.
    a) What percent of the ink is left in the ribbon after printing:
       i) 100 pages ii) 1000 pages?
    b) Write an equation which expresses the percent P of ink left in the ribbon as a function of the number n of pages printed.
    c) Approximately how many pages can be printed before the ink content is reduced to 75% of its original content?

21. On each bounce a ball rises to 70% of the height from which it fell. Let us agree that, for all practical purposes, the ball stops bouncing when the height to which it rises is only 0.1% of the height from which it was dropped originally. How many bounces will this take?

22. Prove the corollary on page 472 using:
    a) a method similar to the one used to prove the theorem
    b) the result of the theorem.

23. Prior to *Example 3* in this section it was stated that any positive number can be expressed as a power of any other positive number, except 1. Give two reasons why the number 1 is excepted.

24. a) Evaluate each expression without using a calculator.
    i) 2^5 ii) $(-2)^5$ iii) $\sqrt[5]{32}$ iv) $\sqrt[5]{-32}$
    b) Attempt to evaluate each expression in part a) using the $\boxed{y^x}$ key on your calculator. Which expressions result in error messages?
    c) If there was an error message, the chips in your calculator may be programmed to evaluate powers using the law of logarithms $\log (x^n) = n \log x$. How does this account for the results in part b)?

Ⓒ

25. Solve each equation.
    a) $7(2)^{-x} = 5^{2x+3}$ b) $3(4)^x = 13^{3x-1}$ c) $3^x = 4^{x-1}$ d) $10^{2-x} = 4(7)^x$

26. The population of town A is double that of town B, but it is decreasing at the rate of 5% per year. The population of town B is increasing at the rate of 5% per year.
    a) In how many years will the population of town B be double that of town A?
    b) At the end of this time, how will the population of town B compare with the initial population of town A?

27. The total amount of arable land in the world is about 3.2×10^9 ha. At current population rates, about 0.4 ha of land is required to grow food for each person in the world.
    a) Assuming a 1987 world population of 5 billion and a constant growth rate of 1.5%, determine the year when the demand for arable land exceeds the supply.
    b) Compare the effect of each comment on the result of part a).
        i) doubling the productivity of the land so that only 0.2 ha is required to grow food for each person
        ii) reducing the growth rate by one-half, to 0.75%
        iii) doubling the productivity of the land *and* reducing the growth rate by 50%

28. If n is a natural number, find the least value of n such that:
    a) $1.1^n > 10^9$ b) $1.01^n > 10^9$ c) $1.001^n > 10^9$
    d) 1.001^n exceeds the capacity of your calculator's display.

29. Let N be any positive number, no matter how large. Prove that no matter how small the positive number x is, it is always possible to find a value of n such that $(1 + x)^n > N$.

MATHEMATICS AROUND US

The Perception of Sensations

How good are you at distinguishing weight? If you hold an object in each hand, can you tell which is heavier? It has been determined that the mass of an object must be increased by $\frac{1}{50}$ for most people to be able to notice the difference in the weight of the object.

For example, one of the weights for a balance scale has a mass of 100 g. An increase of $\frac{1}{50}$ results in a mass of $100\left(1 + \frac{1}{50}\right)$ g, or 102 g. Hence, most people notice the difference between the weights of masses of 100 g and 102 g. We can apply these increases in succession to produce a sequence of masses. Most people would just be able to tell the difference between the weight of each mass and the next.

$100\left(1 + \frac{1}{50}\right)^2 \text{ g} = 104.04 \text{ g}$ $\quad 100\left(1 + \frac{1}{50}\right)^3 \text{ g} \doteq 106.12 \text{ g}$

$100\left(1 + \frac{1}{50}\right)^4 \text{ g} \doteq 108.24 \text{ g} \ldots$

QUESTIONS

1. Another weight for a balance scale has a mass of 200 g. How many weights, each slightly heavier than the previous one, could be placed between weights with masses of 100 g and 200 g such that most people would just be able to tell the difference between each weight and the next?

The table shows the fractional increase which is just enough so that most people would notice a difference for certain sensations. Use the data in the table to answer Questions 2 and 3.

Sensation	Fraction
Distinguishing weights	$\frac{1}{50}$
Brightness	$\frac{1}{60}$
Taste, saline	$\frac{1}{5}$

2. Suppose one light is twice as bright as another. How many lights, each slightly brighter than the previous one, could be placed between them such that most people would just be able to tell the difference in brightness between each light and the next?
3. Suppose one food is twice as salty as another. How many foods, each slightly saltier than the previous one, could be placed between them such that most people would just be able to tell the difference in saltiness between each food and the next?

11-4 INTRODUCTION TO LOGARITHMIC FUNCTIONS

Many examples of exponential functions were given in the previous chapter. Associated with each of these functions there is a corresponding function whose equation we can obtain by solving for the variable in the exponent.

Growth of Populations

In 1987 the world population reached 5 billion. At the time, the population was increasing at the rate of approximately 1.6% per year. If the rate of growth remains constant, then the population P billion is expressed as an exponential function of the number of years n relative to 1987 by this equation.

$$P = 5(1.016)^n \quad \ldots \text{①}$$

Suppose we ask in how many years will the population reach P billion? We express the number of years n as a function of P by solving equation ① for n. Hence, we take the logarithm of each side.

$$\log P = \log 5 + n \log 1.016$$

Solve for n.

$$n \log 1.016 = \log P - \log 5$$

$$n = \frac{\log\left(\frac{P}{5}\right)}{\log 1.016}$$

The coefficient of the expression on the right side is $\frac{1}{\log 1.016}$.

Key in: 1.016 [log] [1/x] to display 145.05982

Hence, the equation for n becomes

$$n \doteq 145 \log\left(\frac{P}{5}\right) \quad \ldots \text{②}$$

Equation ② expresses the number of years n as a logarithmic function of the population P. The graph shows the values of n for $3 \leqslant P \leqslant 10$. Compare this graph with the one on page 426.

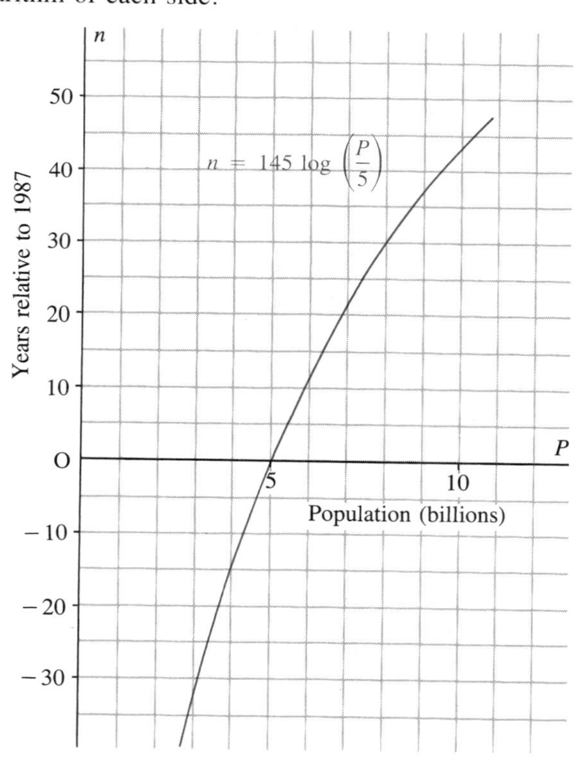

In this example, notice that n is not defined if P is 0, or if P is negative. This is reasonable, since the population P must be a positive number. Hence, the domain of the function is the set of positive integers.

Light Penetration Under Water

For every metre a diver descends below the surface, the light intensity is reduced by 2.5%. The percent P of surface light present is expressed as an exponential function of the depth d metres by this equation.

$$P = 100(0.975)^d \ldots ①$$

Suppose we ask at what depth is the light intensity P%? We express d as a function of P by solving equation ① for d. Take the logarithm of each side.

$\log P = \log 100 + d \log 0.975$

Solve for d.

$$d = \frac{\log\left(\frac{P}{100}\right)}{\log 0.975}$$

$$d \doteq -90.9 \log\left(\frac{P}{100}\right) \ldots ②$$

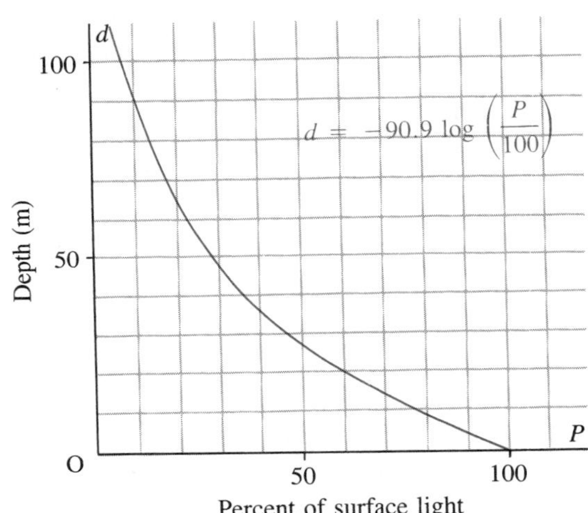

Equation ② expresses the depth d metres as a logarithmic function of the light intensity P. The graph shows the values of d for $0 < P \leq 100$. Compare this graph with the one on page 427.

Acid Rain

Acid rain has become a major environmental problem. The acidity of rainwater is measured on a special scale called a *pH scale*. Each 1 unit decrease in pH represents a 10-fold *increase* in acidity. For example, the pH of vinegar is 2 units less than that of tomatoes. Hence, vinegar is 10^2, or 100 times more acidic than tomatoes.

Let A represent the acid content of a substance with a pH of P. Then, since each increase of 1 unit in P represents a 10-fold decrease in A,

$$A = A_0(0.1)^P \ldots ①$$

where A_0 represents the acid content of a substance with pH 0.
To express P as a function of A, solve equation ① for P.

$$\log A = \log A_0 + P \log 0.1$$

$$P \log 0.1 = \log A - \log A_0$$

$$P = \frac{\log\left(\frac{A}{A_0}\right)}{\log 0.1}$$

or $$P = -\log\left(\frac{A}{A_0}\right) \ldots ②$$

Equation ② expresses the pH of a substance as a logarithmic function of its acid content.

Summary

Consider the similarities in the equations of the above examples.

$n \doteq 145 \log\left(\frac{P}{5}\right)$ — 5: Initial population

$d \doteq -90.9 \log\left(\frac{P}{100}\right)$ — 100: Initial intensity

$P = -\log\left(\frac{A}{A_0}\right)$ — A_0: Acid content when $P = 0$

In each equation the expression on the right side involves the logarithm of the variable. Also, each coefficient is the reciprocal of the logarithm of the base of the corresponding exponential function.

> A *logarithmic function* has an equation which can be written in the form $y = k \log\left(\frac{x}{c}\right)$ where k and c are constants, and $c > 0$.

In the equation for pH, $P = -\log\left(\frac{A}{A_0}\right)$, notice that the value of A_0 is not given. Despite this, we can still use this equation to obtain useful information. This involves a comparison of the acid content, or pH of two substances.

Example 1. A lake in the Muskoka region of Ontario has a pH of 4.0. How many times as acidic as clean rain water, which has a pH of 5.6, is the water in this lake?

Solution. Use the equation developed above. $P = -\log\left(\frac{A}{A_0}\right)$

Let P_1 and A_1 represent the pH and acid content of clean rain water, and let P_2 and A_2 represent the pH and acid content of the lake. Then,

$$P_1 = -\log\left(\frac{A_1}{A_0}\right)$$

$$P_2 = -\log\left(\frac{A_2}{A_0}\right)$$

Subtract and then use the law of logarithms for division.

$$\begin{aligned} P_1 - P_2 &= -\log\left(\frac{A_1}{A_0}\right) + \log\left(\frac{A_2}{A_0}\right) \\ &= \log\left(\frac{A_2}{A_0}\right) - \log\left(\frac{A_1}{A_0}\right) \\ &= \log\left(\frac{A_2}{A_1}\right) \end{aligned}$$

Substitute 5.6 for P_1 and 4.0 for P_2.

$$5.6 - 4.0 = \log\left(\frac{A_2}{A_1}\right)$$

$$1.6 = \log\left(\frac{A_2}{A_1}\right)$$

By the definition of a logarithm

$$\frac{A_2}{A_1} = 10^{1.6}$$
$$\doteq 39.8$$

Hence, the lake is about 40 times as acidic as clean rain water.

Example 2. Given the exponential function $f(x) = 10^x$
a) Determine the inverse function $y = f^{-1}(x)$.
b) Graph $y = f(x)$ and $y = f^{-1}(x)$ on the same grid.

Solution. a) Recall that to obtain the inverse of a function from its equation, we interchange x and y in the equation and solve for y. Hence, to find the inverse of $y = 10^x$:
Step 1. Interchange x and y. $x = 10^y$
Step 2. Solve for y. $y = \log x$
Hence, the inverse of the exponential function $f(x) = 10^x$ is the logarithmic function $f^{-1}(x) = \log x$.

b) We graph $f(x) = 10^x$ using a table of values. Recall that we can graph the inverse by reflecting the graph of $y = 10^x$ in the line $y = x$. This is equivalent to interchanging the ordered pairs in the table of values for $y = f(x)$.

$y = 10^x$

x	y
−2	0.01
−1.5	0.03
−1	0.10
−0.5	0.32
−0.2	0.63
0	1.00
0.1	1.26
0.2	1.58
0.3	2.00

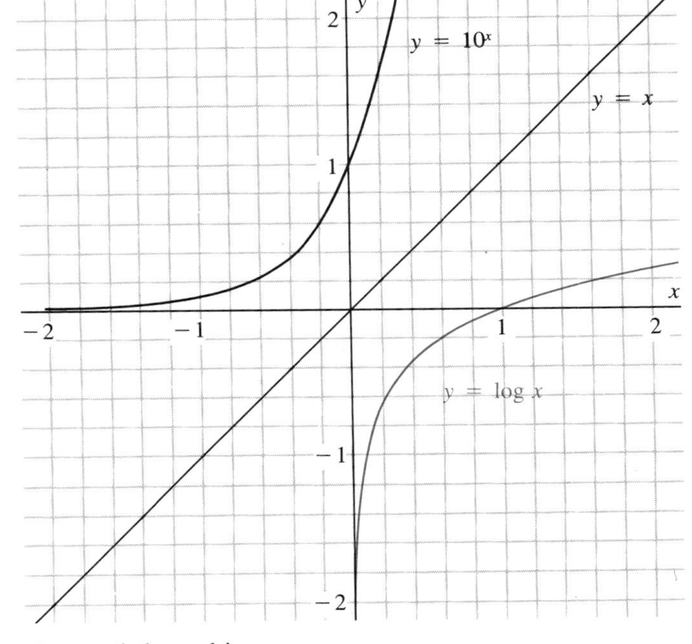

Recall that in *Section 11-1* we observed that taking a common logarithm of a number and raising the number to a power of 10 are inverse operations. This is consistent with *Example 2* above, which shows that the logarithmic function $y = \log x$ can be defined as the inverse of the exponential function $y = 10^x$.

EXERCISES 11-4

1. Solve each equation for x, thus expressing x as a logarithmic function of y.
   a) $y = 5(2)^x$ b) $y = 1.3(10)^x$ c) $y = 8.2(1.03)^x$
   d) $y = 6.4\left(\frac{1}{2}\right)^x$ e) $y = 3.5(2.7)^x$ f) $y = 2.75\left(\frac{2}{3}\right)^x$

2. Find the values of x for the given y values. Give the answers to 3 decimal places where necessary.
   a) $y = 3(2)^x$ and $y = 12; 48; 3072$ b) $y = 7(3)^x$ and $y = 189; 75; 462$
   c) $y = 2(5)^x$ and $y = 0.08; 12; 32$ d) $y = 5(7)^x$ and $y = 5; 275; 675$

3. An investment of \$500 at 8% per annum compounded annually grows to A dollars in n years. In Chapter 10, page 426, we showed that an equation expressing the amount A dollars as an exponential function of the time n years is $A = 500(1.08)^n$.
   a) Solve this equation for n, thus expressing n as a logarithmic function of A.
   b) Calculate the value of n for each value of A and interpret the result.
      i) $A = 1250$ ii) $A = 350$
   c) Graph the function in part a) for $0 < A \leqslant 1250$. Compare your graph with the one on page 426.
   d) State the domain and the range of the function.

4. A ball is dropped from a height of 2.00 m. On each bounce the ball rises to 70% of the height from which it fell. In Chapter 10, page 427, we showed that an equation expressing the bounce height h metres as an exponential function of the number of bounces n is $h = 2.00(0.7)^n$.
   a) Solve this equation for n, thus expressing n as a logarithmic function of h.
   b) Calculate the value of n for each value of h and interpret the result.
      i) 0.7 m ii) 0.12 m
   c) Graph the function in part a) for $0 < h \leqslant 2.00$. Compare your graph with the one on page 427.
   d) What is the range of the function?

5. a) The population of the town of Elmira was 6800 in 1987. If the population is growing at the rate of 1.8% per annum, write an equation expressing the population P as a function of n, the number of years relative to 1987.
   b) Solve this equation for n.
   c) Find the value of n if P is: i) 9200 ii) 5500.
   d) Graph the functions in parts a) and b). How are these functions related?

6. On bright sunny days, the amount of bromine in a municipal swimming pool decreases by 10% each hour. If there was 145 g of bromine in the pool at noon on a sunny day, when would the pool contain: a) 102 g b) 85 g c) 200 g?

7. Between 1956 and 1976 the annual average pH of precipitation at Sault Ste. Marie, Ontario, dropped from 5.6 to 4.3. How many times as acidic as the precipitation in 1956 was the precipitation in 1976?

8. In the spring, the pH of a stream dropped from 6.5 to 5.5 during a 3-week period in April.
   a) How many times as acidic did the stream become?
   b) Why would this happen in April?
   c) The mean pH of Lake Huron is 8.2. How many times as acidic was the stream:
      i) before the 3-week period ii) after the 3-week period?

9. When the pH of the water in a lake falls below 4.7, nearly all species of fish in the lake are deformed or killed. How many times as acidic as clean rainwater, which has a pH of 5.6, is such a lake?

10. Given the exponential function $f(x) = 3^x$, graph $y = f(x)$ and $y = f^{-1}(x)$ on the same grid.

11. Graph each function and its inverse on the same grid.
    a) $y = 2^x$ b) $y = \left(\frac{2}{3}\right)^x$

Ⓒ

12. In astronomy, the brightnesses of stars are compared using a scale of magnitudes defined by a logarithmic function. If a star has brightness b, then its *magnitude* m is defined by this equation.
    $m = -2.5 \log\left(\frac{b}{b_0}\right)$, where b_0 is the brightness of a star with magnitude 0.
    a) Write this equation in exponential form.
    b) If the magnitude increases by 2.5 units, by what factor does the brightness change? Does it increase or decrease?
    c) i) How many times as bright as the North Star is Vega?
       ii) How many times as bright as Vega is Sirius?
       iii) How many times as bright as the North Star is Sirius?

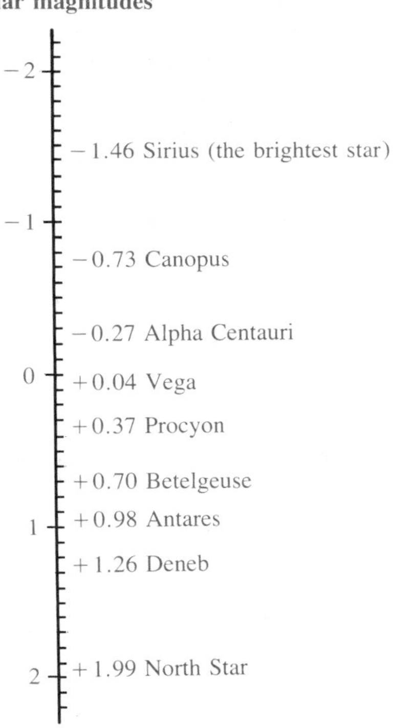

Magnitudes in the Solar System	
Sun	−26.8
Full moon	−12.7
Venus	−4.4*
Uranus	+5.5
Pluto	+15

*maximum brightness

13. Refer to *Exercise 12*. How many times as bright as:
a) the full moon is the sun b) Venus is the sun c) Pluto is Uranus?

14. In 1987, the Canadian astronomer Ian Shelton became the first person to observe an exploding star, or supernova, in our galaxy since the invention of the telescope four hundred years ago. Supernova 1987A, as it is now called, increased in brightness at least 200 times in the first day, and almost 1000 times in the first two days. What change occurred in its magnitude:

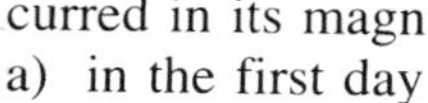

a) in the first day
b) in the first two days?

15. Our star, the sun, appears billions of times brighter than the other stars because it is relatively near to us. Hence, astronomers are interested in comparing the brightnesses of stars if they could all be viewed from the same distance. The *luminosity* of a star refers to its brightness at a distance of 32.6 light years. By allowing for the sun's magnitude, and its distance from us, astronomers have established the following formula for the luminosity L of a star relative to the sun.
$\log L = 0.4(5 \log d - m) - 1.1$,
where m is the magnitude of the star, and d is its distance in light years.
a) How many times as luminous as the sun are the stars in the table?
b) The distance to the sun is 1.55×10^{-5} light years. Check that the luminosity of the sun, as defined by the above equation, is 1.

Some Stellar Distances

Star	**Distance** (light years)
Sirius	8.7
Vega	26.5
North Star	680
Deneb	1600

INVESTIGATE

At the beginning of this section, the equation $n \doteq 145 \log \left(\frac{P}{5}\right)$ was derived to represent the number of years for the world population to grow to P billion, assuming a constant growth rate of 1.6% per year. Notice that the coefficient 145 is the reciprocal of the logarithm of the base of the corresponding exponential function; that is, $\frac{1}{\log 1.016} \doteq 145$. This suggests that the form of the equation of the logarithmic function will be simpler if the base of the corresponding exponential function is 10, for then that coefficient will be 1, since $\log 10 = 1$.

Investigate whether this is true by first changing the base of the corresponding exponential function, $P = 5(1.016)^n$, to base 10, and then solving for n to obtain the corresponding logarithmic function.

11-5 DEFINING AND GRAPHING LOGARITHMIC FUNCTIONS

In *Example 2* of the preceding section we saw that the logarithmic function $y = \log x$ can be defined as the inverse of the exponential function $y = 10^x$. This suggests that other logarithmic functions can be defined as inverses of exponential functions with bases other than 10. In fact, for each choice of base for the exponential function $y = a^x$, $a > 0$, there is an associated logarithmic function. Hence, we define the function $y = \log_a x$, $a > 0$, as follows.

> The logarithmic function $y = \log_a x$ $(a > 0,\ a \neq 1)$ is the inverse of the exponential function $y = a^x$.

We say, "y equals log to the base a of x".

Recall that we can graph the inverse of any function by reflecting its graph in the line $y = x$. This is equivalent to interchanging the ordered pairs in the table of values of the function. For example, the graph below shows the function $y = 2^x$ and its inverse $y = \log_2 x$. Compare this graph with the one on page 483.

$y = 2^x$

x	y
−3	0.13
−2	0.25
−1	0.50
−0.5	0.71
0	1.00
0.5	1.41
1	2.00
1.5	2.83
2	4.00

$y = \log_2 x$

x	y
0.13	−3
0.25	−2
0.50	−1
0.71	−0.5
1.00	0
1.41	0.5
2.00	1
2.83	1.5
4.00	2

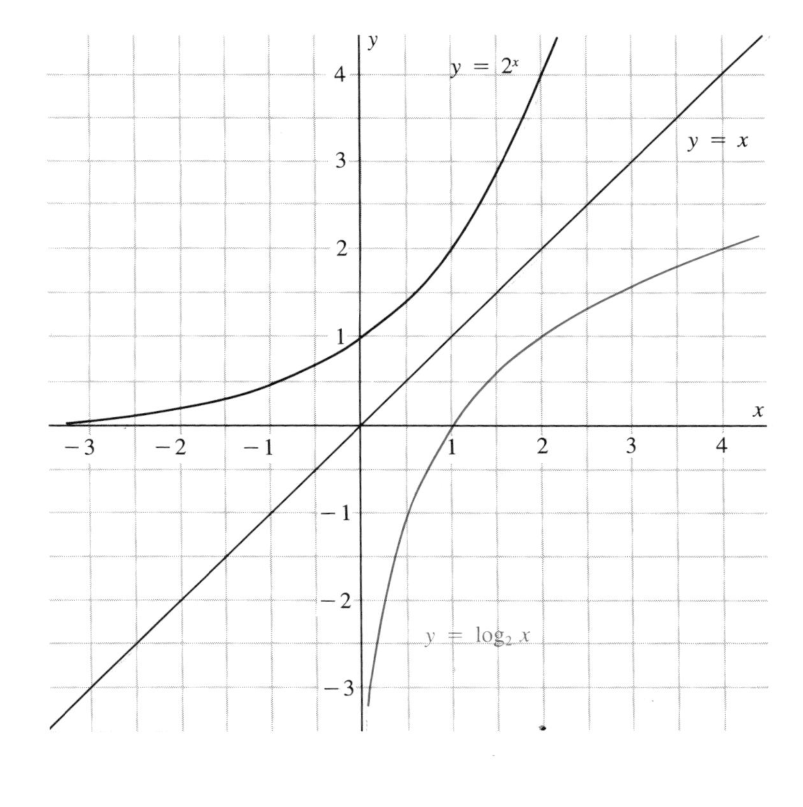

The graph illustrates the following properties of the function $y = \log_2 x$. These properties are consequences of the corresponding properties of $y = 2^x$.

y-intercept
There is no y-intercept since the function $y = 2^x$ has no x-intercept.

x-intercept
The x-intercept is 1, since the y-intercept of $y = 2^x$ is 1. Hence, $\log_2 1 = 0$

Domain
The domain of $y = \log_2 x$ is the set of positive real numbers, since this is the range of $y = 2^x$.

Range
The range of $y = \log_2 x$ is the set of all real numbers, since this is the domain of $y = 2^x$.

If any exponential function is given, we can sketch its graph. The graph of the inverse is then the graph of the corresponding logarithmic function.

Example. a) Sketch the graph of the exponential function $y = \left(\frac{1}{3}\right)^x$.

b) Sketch the graph of the inverse of the function in part a) on the same grid.

c) Write the equation of the inverse function.

Solution. a) $y = \left(\frac{1}{3}\right)^x$

When x is very large and positive, y is very small and positive.
When $x = 0$, $y = 1$
When x is negative and has a large absolute value, y is very large.

b) Reflect $y = \left(\frac{1}{3}\right)^x$ in the line $y = x$. The image is $y = \log_{\frac{1}{3}} x$.

c) The equation of the inverse function is $y = \log_{\frac{1}{3}} x$.

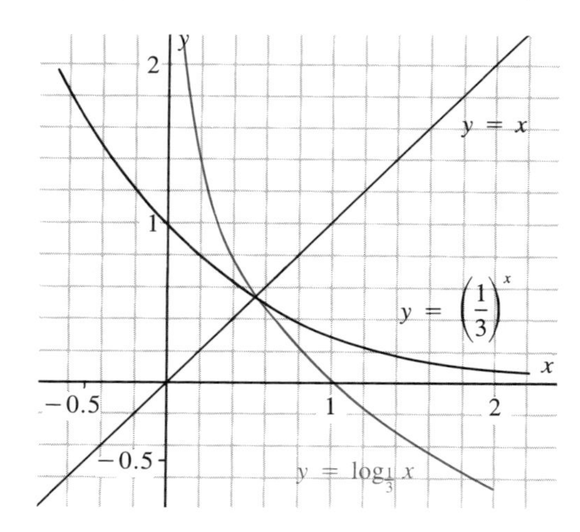

The graphs in the above examples illustrate properties of the logarithmic function $y = \log_a x$.

Properties of the function $y = \log_a x$
y-intercept: none
x-intercept: 1
Domain: all positive real numbers
Range: all real numbers

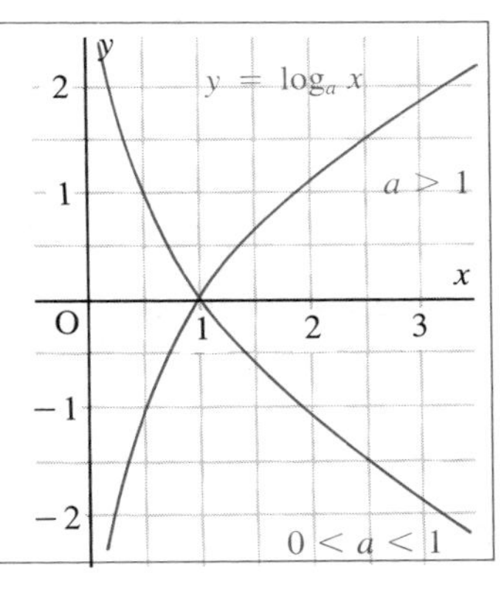

EXERCISES 11-5

Ⓐ

1. Write the inverse of each exponential function.
   a) $y = 10^x$ b) $y = 3^x$ c) $y = 7^x$
   d) $y = (0.4)^x$ e) $y = \left(\frac{3}{2}\right)^x$ f) $y = 15^x$

2. Write the inverse of each logarithmic function.
   a) $y = \log x$ b) $y = \log_2 x$ c) $y = \log_6 x$
   d) $y = \log_{\frac{1}{2}} x$ e) $y = \log_{\frac{5}{4}} x$ f) $y = \log_{21} x$

Ⓑ

3. Copy each graph and sketch the graph of the inverse of the given function on the same grid. Then write the equation of the inverse function.

a)

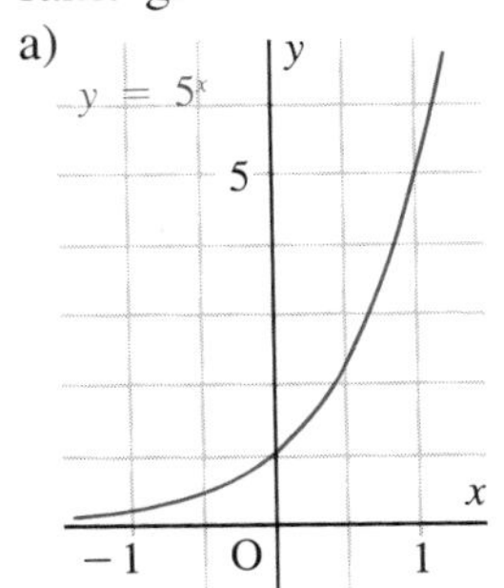

b)

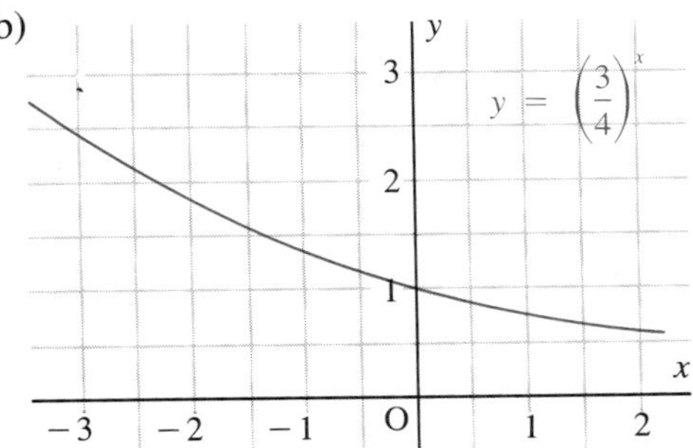

c)

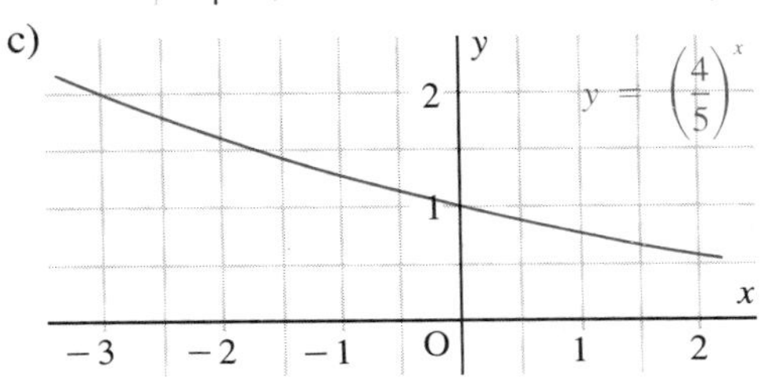

d)

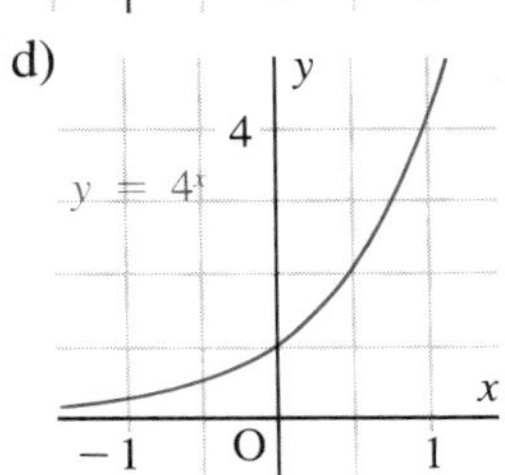

4. a) Sketch the graph of the exponential function $y = 3^x$.
   b) Sketch the graph of the inverse of the function in part a) on the same grid.
   c) Write the equation of the inverse function.

5. Repeat *Exercise 4*, starting with the function $y = \left(\frac{1}{2}\right)^x$

6. Graph each function.

   a) $y = \log_4 x$ b) $y = \log_6 x$ c) $y = \log_{\frac{1}{2}} x$

   d) $y = \log_{0.8} x$ e) $y = \log_{1.5} x$ f) $y = \log_{\frac{2}{5}} x$

7. Prove that if $f(x) = \log_a x$, then $f(xy) = f(x) + f(y)$.

Ⓒ

8. In the *Example*, the graphs of $y = \left(\frac{1}{3}\right)^x$, $y = \log_{\frac{1}{3}} x$, and $y = x$ are shown.
   Determine the coordinates of their point of intersection to 3 decimal places.

9. Given the exponential function $f(x) = a^x$ and its inverse $f^{-1}(x) = \log_a x$, where $a > 0$
   a) For what values of a do the graphs of $y = f(x)$ and $y = f^{-1}(x)$ intersect?
   b) Find out as much as you can about the point of intersection of the graphs in part a).

Changing the Base of Logarithms

We can solve an equation such as $a^x = y$ in two ways.

- Using base a logarithms
  $x = \log_a y$
- Using base 10 logarithms
  $x \log a = \log y$
  $x = \dfrac{\log y}{\log a}$

Since the results must be equal, we have the following formula.

$$\log_a y = \frac{\log y}{\log a}$$

This formula can be used to change from base 10 logarithms to base a logarithms without having to solve an exponential equation each time.

1. Use the formula and your calculator to find an approximation to each logarithm.
   a) $\log_3 4$ b) $\log_3 6$ c) $\log_3 40$ d) $\log_3 225$

2. If a and b represent two different bases, prove that $\log_a y = \dfrac{\log_b y}{\log_b a}$.

11-6 LOGARITHMS AS EXPONENTS

Recall that to find the inverse of a function from its equation, we interchange x and y in the equation and solve for y. Hence, to find the inverse of $y = a^x$:

Step 1. Interchange x and y. $\quad x = a^y \ldots$ ①

Step 2. Solve for y. We can do this using common logarithms, but it is preferable to use the definition on page 487. According to the definition, the inverse is $y = \log_a x \ldots$ ②

Hence, this is the equation that results when equation ① is solved for y.

Comparing equations ① and ②, we see that

$$\underbrace{\log_a}_{\text{base}} x = \underbrace{y}_{\text{exponent}} \quad \text{means that} \quad x = a^y,\ x > 0.$$

Hence, $\log_a x$ is an exponent. It is the exponent that x would have if it were written in power form with base a ($a > 0$, $a \neq 1$). If the base is omitted, it is understood to be base 10.

Example 1. Evaluate each logarithm.

a) $\log_5 25$ b) $\log_7 \sqrt{7}$ c) $\log_{\frac{1}{3}} 9$ d) $\log_a a$

Solution. a) Since $25 = 5^2$, then $\log_5 25 = 2$

b) Since $\sqrt{7} = 7^{\frac{1}{2}}$, then $\log_7 \sqrt{7} = \frac{1}{2}$

c) Write 9 as a power of $\frac{1}{3}$. Since $\left(\frac{1}{3}\right)^2 = \frac{1}{9}$, then $\left(\frac{1}{3}\right)^{-2} = 9$

Hence, $\log_{\frac{1}{3}} 9 = -2$

d) Since $a = a^1$, then $\log_a a = 1$

Since any positive number can be expressed as a power of any other positive number (except 1), we can find approximations to the logarithm of any positive number to any positive base (except 1).

Example 2. Find $\log_5 9$ to the nearest thousandth.

Solution. To find $\log_5 9$ means to find the exponent that 9 would have if it were expressed as a power of 5.

Let $9 = 5^x$

Take the logarithm of each side to base 10.

$\log 9 = \log (5^x)$

$\log 9 = x \log 5$

$$x = \frac{\log 9}{\log 5}$$

Key in: 9 [log] [÷] 5 [log] [=] to display 1.3652124

Hence, $x \doteq 1.365\,212\,4$

To the nearest thousandth, $9 \doteq 5^{1.365}$

Therefore, $\log_5 9 \doteq 1.365$

Example 2 illustrates why a calculator does not have [log] keys for many different bases. Logarithms to any base can be found by converting to base 10 and then using the [log] key.

Example 3. Simplify each expression.

a) $\log_a a^x$ b) $a^{\log_a x}$

Solution. a) $\log_a a^x$ is the exponent that a^x would have if it were written as a power of a. This exponent is x. Hence, $\log_a a^x = x$

b) $a^{\log_a x}$ is a raised to the exponent that x would have if x were written as a power of a. Hence, $a^{\log_a x} = x$

Summary

- $\log_a x = y$ means that $x = a^y$, where $a > 0$, $a \neq 1$, and $x > 0$
- $\log_a a^x = x$ and $a^{\log_a x} = x$
- $\log_a a = 1$

Example 4. Write each expression in exponential form.

a) $\log_2 16 = 4$ b) $\log_2 0.5 = -1$

Solution. a) $\log_2 16 = 4$

$16 = 2^4$

b) $\log_2 0.5 = -1$

$0.5 = 2^{-1}$

Example 5. Write each expression in logarithmic form.

a) $3^5 = 243$ b) $a^b = c$

Solution. a) $3^5 = 243$

$5 = \log_3 243$

b) $a^b = c$

$b = \log_a c$

Example 6. If $\log_8 5 = m$ and $\log_4 3 = n$, find an expression for $\log_2 15$ in terms of m and n.

Solution. Since $\log_8 5 = m$, then $8^m = 5$ . . . ①

Since $\log_4 3 = n$, then $4^n = 3$ . . . ②

Let $\log_2 15 = x$, so that $2^x = 15$.

Since $15 = 5 \times 3$, we can use equations ① and ②.

$$\begin{aligned} 2^x &= 5 \times 3 \\ &= 8^m \times 4^n \\ &= 2^{3m} \times 2^{2n} \\ &= 2^{3m + 2n} \end{aligned}$$

Hence, $x = 3m + 2n$, or $\log_2 15 = 3m + 2n$

EXERCISES 11-6

Ⓐ

1. Write in exponential form.

a) $\log_2 8 = 3$ b) $\log_2 32 = 5$ c) $\log_2 \left(\frac{1}{4}\right) = -2$

d) $\log_5 625 = 4$ e) $\log_3 9 = 2$ f) $\log_9 3 = \frac{1}{2}$

2. Evaluate each logarithm.

a) $\log_2 16$ b) $\log_2 4$ c) $\log_3 27$ d) $\log_5 25$

e) $\log_5 \left(\frac{1}{5}\right)$ f) $\log_7 7$ g) $\log_3 1$ h) $\log_3 3^4$

3. Evaluate each logarithm.

a) $\log_5 \sqrt{5}$ b) $\log_{\frac{1}{2}} \left(\frac{1}{16}\right)$ c) $\log_{\frac{3}{2}} \left(\frac{9}{4}\right)$ d) $\log_{\sqrt{3}} 9$

e) $\log_{\frac{1}{2}} 8$ f) $\log_{\frac{2}{5}} \left(\frac{25}{4}\right)$ g) $\log_3 (\sqrt{3})^3$ h) $\log_{\sqrt{5}} 125$

4. In geography, sediments are classified by particle size, as shown.
   a) Write the logarithm to base 2 of each number.
   b) Write the logarithm to base 4 of each number.

Type of sediment	Size (mm)
Boulder	256
Cobble	64
Pebble	4
Granule	2
Sand	$\frac{1}{16}$
Silt	$\frac{1}{256}$

5. Simplify each expression.

a) $\log_2 2^5$ b) $\log_7 7^{13}$ c) $\log_{0.4} (0.4)^9$

d) $3^{\log_3 7}$ e) $14^{\log_{14} 5}$ f) $0.23^{\log_{0.23} 11}$

6. Write in logarithmic form.

a) $6^2 = 36$ b) $4^{-2} = \frac{1}{16}$ c) $3^5 = 243$

d) $7^3 = 343$ e) $8^{\frac{1}{3}} = 2$ f) $2^0 = 1$

Ⓑ

7. Write in logarithmic form.

a) $5^{-2} = 0.04$ b) $4^{-\frac{1}{2}} = \frac{1}{2}$ c) $\left(\frac{1}{2}\right)^2 = \frac{1}{4}$

d) $\left(\frac{2}{3}\right)^{-1} = \frac{3}{2}$ e) $\left(\frac{1}{9}\right)^2 = \frac{1}{81}$ f) $x^y = z$

8. Write in exponential form.

a) $\log_{20} 400 = 2$ b) $\log_7 \left(\frac{1}{49}\right) = -2$ c) $\log_8 4 = \frac{2}{3}$

d) $\log_6 36^2 = 4$ e) $\log_{0.5} 8 = -3$ f) $\log_r s = t$

9. Evaluate each logarithm to the nearest thousandth.
   a) $\log_3 5$ b) $\log_7 4$ c) $\log_2 50$ d) $\log_5 12$ e) $\log_4 27$ f) $\log_{16} 8$

10. Evaluate each logarithm to the nearest thousandth.
   a) $\log_{2.5} 6$ b) $\log_5 9.3$ c) $\log_{\frac{1}{2}} \left(\frac{1}{3}\right)$
   d) $\log_{2.57} 3.68$ e) $\log_{\frac{3}{2}} 19.76$ f) $\log_{4.9} 35.27$

11. If $\log_8 3 = x$ and $\log_4 7 = y$, find an expression in terms of x and y for:
   a) $\log_2 21$ b) $\log_2 63$.

12. If $\log_9 4 = a$ and $\log_{27} 5 = b$, find an expression in terms of a and b for:
   a) $\log_3 20$ b) $\log_3 80$ c) $\log_{\sqrt{3}} 100$ d) $\log_{\sqrt{3}} 40$.

13. Solve for x.
   a) $\log_2 x = 9$ b) $\log_4 1 = x$ c) $\log_x 16 = 2$
   d) $\log_x 125 = -3$ e) $\log_3 x = -4$ f) $\log_{\sqrt{2}} 32 = x$

14. Given that $f(x) = x - \log_2 x$ and $g(x) = 2^x$, find: a) $f(g(x))$ b) $g(f(x))$.

15. If a telephone network is designed to carry N telephone calls simultaneously, then the number of switches needed per call must be at least $\log_2 N$. If the network can carry 10 000 calls simultaneously, how many switches would be needed:
   a) for one call b) for 10 000 simultaneous calls?

Ⓒ

16. a) Evaluate each logarithm. i) $\log_2 8$ and $\log_8 2$ ii) $\log_5 25$ and $\log_{25} 5$
   b) On the basis of the results of part a), make a conjecture about how $\log_a b$ and $\log_b a$ are related, where $a, b > 0$. Prove your conjecture.

17. a) Evaluate each logarithm.
   i) $\log_2 4$ ii) $\log_{\frac{1}{2}} 4$ iii) $\log_4 2$ iv) $\log_{\frac{1}{4}} 2$
   v) $\log_2 \left(\frac{1}{4}\right)$ vi) $\log_{\frac{1}{2}} \left(\frac{1}{4}\right)$ vii) $\log_4 \left(\frac{1}{2}\right)$ viii) $\log_{\frac{1}{4}} \left(\frac{1}{2}\right)$
   b) Using the results of part a) as a guide, make a conjecture about how you can tell, given the values of x and y, if:
   i) $\log_y x > 0$ ii) $\log_y x < 0$ iii) $\log_y x > 1$
   iv) $\log_y x < -1$ v) $0 < \log_y x < 1$ vi) $-1 < \log_y x < 0$.
   c) Illustrate the results of part b) on a grid.
   d) Compare the results in parts a), b), and c) with *Exercise 16*, page 437.

18. Let a and b be any two positive numbers. Prove that for all positive values of x, $\log_b x$ is directly proportional to $\log_a x$.

INVESTIGATE

Your calculator should have a key marked [ln]. This key calculates logarithms of numbers to a base different from 10. Find the base of these logarithms as accurately as you can.

MATHEMATICS AROUND US

The Logarithmic Spiral

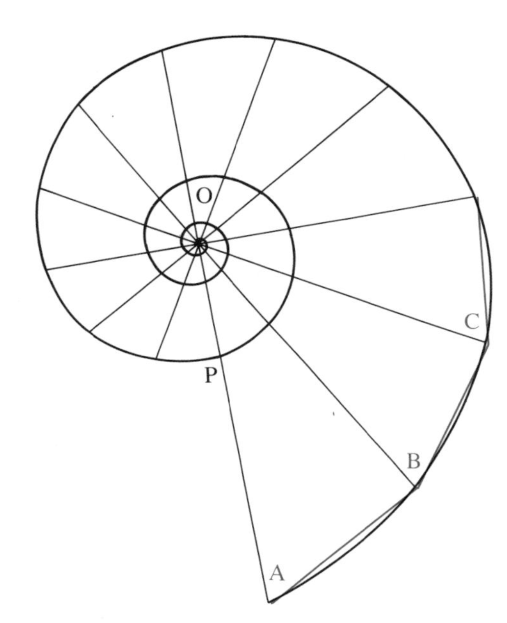

Some living creatures exhibit exponential growth in their dimensions. A well-known example is the chambered nautilus of the Indian and Pacific Oceans. As it grows, the shell extends continuously, generating a natural spiral.

QUESTIONS

1. The diagram shows a series of equally-spaced radii drawn from the centre of the spiral. The radii are spaced every 30°.
   a) Measure and record the length of each radius, starting with OP and proceeding clockwise around the spiral.
   b) Verify that the length of the radius L centimetres satisfies the equation $L = 1.5(1.0034)^{\theta}$, where θ degrees is the angle of rotation measured clockwise starting at OP.

2. a) Measure the angles represented by $A, B, C, \ldots$, on the diagram.
   b) Prove that if the length of the radius is an exponential function of the angle of rotation, then the angles $A, B, C, \ldots$, are all equal.

3. a) Suggest why the spiral is called a *logarithmic spiral*.
   b) The spiral is also referred to as an *equiangular spiral*. Suggest why.

11-7 THE LAWS OF LOGARITHMS (BASE a)

In *Sections 11-2* and *11-3* we developed the laws of logarithms for logarithms with base 10. The restriction to base 10 is not necessary, and the laws can be extended to logarithms with any positive base (except 1).

For example, an equation such as $2^3 \times 2^4 = 2^7$ can be written in logarithmic form as $\log_2 8 + \log_2 16 = \log_2 128$. This equation states that the sum of the exponents that 8 and 16 have when expressed as powers of 2 is equal to the exponent that 128 has when expressed as a power of 2.

> **Theorem Law of Logarithms for Multiplication (Base a)**
> If x and y are positive real numbers, then
> $\log_a xy = \log_a x + \log_a y \qquad a > 0, a \neq 1$

Given: Two positive real numbers x and y
Required to Prove: $\log_a xy = \log_a x + \log_a y \qquad a > 0, a \neq 1$
Proof: Let $\log_a x = M$ and $\log_a y = N$

$$x = a^M \qquad y = a^N$$

Hence, $xy = (a^M)(a^N)$
$= a^{M+N}$

Therefore, $\log_a xy = \log_a (a^{M+N})$
$= M + N$
$= \log_a x + \log_a y$

> **Corollary Law of Logarithms for Division (Base a)**
> If x and y are positive real numbers, then
> $\log_a \left(\frac{x}{y}\right) = \log_a x - \log_a y \qquad a > 0, a \neq 1$

Example 1. Write $\log_2 15$ as:
a) a sum of two logarithms b) a difference of two logarithms.

Solution. a) Since $15 = 5 \times 3$, then $\log_2 15 = \log_2 5 + \log_2 3$
b) Since $15 = 30 \div 2$, then $\log_2 15 = \log_2 30 - \log_2 2$

What other answers can you find for *Example 1*?

Example 2. Write each expression as a single logarithm and simplify it.
a) $\log_3 6 + \log_3 1.5$ b) $\log_5 50 - \log_5 0.4$

Solution. a) $\log_3 6 + \log_3 1.5 = \log_3 (6 \times 1.5)$
$= \log_3 9$
$= 2$

b) $\log_5 50 - \log_5 0.4 = \log_5 \left(\frac{50}{0.4}\right)$
$= \log_5 125$
$= 3$

Theorem **Law of Logarithms for Powers (Base a)**
If x and n are real numbers, and $x > 0$, then
$\log_a (x^n) = n \log_a x \qquad a > 0, a \neq 1$

Given: Two real numbers x and n, where $x > 0$
Required to Prove: $\log_a (x^n) = n \log_a x$
Proof: Let $\log_a x = M$

$$x = a^M$$

Hence, $x^n = (a^M)^n$
$= a^{nM}$

Therefore, $\log_a (x^n) = \log_a (a^{nM})$
$= nM$
$= n \log_a x$

Corollary **Law of Logarithms for Roots (Base a)**
If x and n are real numbers, and $x > 0$, then
$\log_a \sqrt[n]{x} = \frac{1}{n} \log_a x \qquad a > 0, a \neq 1$

Example 3. a) Write $\log_5 16$ as a product of a whole number and a logarithm.
b) Write as a single logarithm. i) $2 \log_6 5$ ii) $\frac{1}{3} \log_4 125$

Solution. a) Since $16 = 2^4$, then $\log_5 16 = \log_5 (2^4)$
$= 4 \log_5 2$

b) i) $2 \log_6 5 = \log_6 (5^2)$
$= \log_6 25$

ii) $\frac{1}{3} \log_4 125 = \log_4 (\sqrt[3]{125})$
$= \log_4 5$

Example 4. Given that $\log_2 7 \doteq 2.8074$, find an approximation for each logarithm.

a) $\log_2 14$ b) $\log_2 49$ c) $\log_2 \left(\frac{4}{7}\right)$ d) $\log_2 \sqrt[3]{7}$

Solution. a) $\log_2 14 = \log_2 (7 \times 2)$
$= \log_2 7 + \log_2 2$
$\doteq 2.8074 + 1$
$\doteq 3.8074$

b) $\log_2 49 = \log_2 (7^2)$
$= 2 \log_2 7$
$\doteq 2(2.8074)$
$\doteq 5.6148$

c) $\log_2 \left(\frac{4}{7}\right) = \log_2 4 - \log_2 7$
$\doteq 2 - 2.8074$
$\doteq -0.8074$

d) $\log_2 \sqrt[3]{7} = \frac{1}{3} \log_2 7$
$\doteq \frac{1}{3} (2.8074)$
$\doteq 0.9358$

Laws of Logarithms (Base a) $a > 0, a \neq 1$

- Multiplication $\log_a xy = \log_a x + \log_a y$ $x, y > 0$
- Division $\log_a \left(\frac{x}{y}\right) = \log_a x - \log_a y$ $x, y > 0$
- Powers $\log_a (x^n) = n \log_a x$ $x > 0$
- Roots $\log_a \sqrt[n]{x} = \frac{1}{n} \log_a x$ $x > 0$

Example 5. Prove that if (x_1, y_1) and (x_2, y_2) are points on the graph of $y = \log_a x$, then $(x_1x_2, y_1 + y_2)$ is also a point on the graph.

Solution. Since (x_1, y_1) is on the graph of $y = \log_a x$, its coordinates satisfy the equation.

Hence, $y_1 = \log_a x_1 \ldots$ ①

Similarly, $y_2 = \log_a x_2 \ldots$ ②

Add equations ① and ②, and use the law of logarithms.

$$\begin{aligned} y_1 + y_2 &= \log_a x_1 + \log_a x_2 \\ &= \log_a (x_1x_2) \end{aligned}$$

Hence, the coordinates of the point $(x_1x_2, y_1 + y_2)$ also satisfy the equation $y = \log_a x$. That is, $(x_1x_2, y_1 + y_2)$ is also a point on the graph.

The result of *Example 5* is a consequence of the law of logarithms for multiplication. Multiplying the x-coordinates of points on the graph of $y = \log_a x$ corresponds to adding their y-coordinates. Compare this example with *Example 2*, page 455.

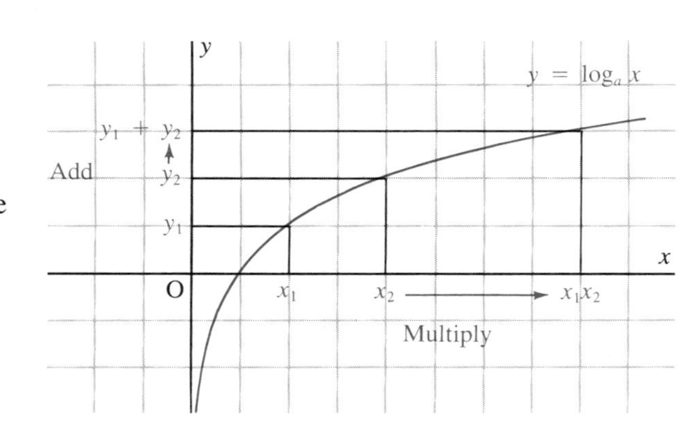

We can solve equations involving logarithms by using the laws of logarithms and the definition of a logarithm.

Example 6. Solve each equation, and check.

a) $2 \log x = \log 8 + \log 2$ b) $\log_8 (2 - x) + \log_8 (4 - x) = 1$

Solution. a)

$$\begin{aligned} 2 \log x &= \log 8 + \log 2 \\ \log x^2 &= \log 16 \\ \text{Hence, } x^2 &= 16 \\ x &= \pm 4 \end{aligned}$$

To check, substitute each value of x into the original equation.

When $x = 4$,
L.S. $= 2 \log 4$ $\quad$ R.S. $= \log 8 + \log 2$
$= \log 16$ $\quad$ $= \log 16$
4 is a root.
When $x = -4$, the left side is not defined since $\log x$ is defined only when $x > 0$. Hence, -4 is an extraneous root.

b) $\log_8 (2 - x) + \log_8 (4 - x) = 1$
Simplify the left side using the law of logarithms for multiplication.
$$\log_8 (2 - x)(4 - x) = 1$$
Use the definition of a logarithm.
$$(2 - x)(4 - x) = 8^1$$
$$8 - 6x + x^2 = 8$$
$$-6x + x^2 = 0$$
$$x = 0 \text{ or } x = 6$$
When $x = 0$,
L.S. $= \log_8 2 + \log_8 4$ $\quad$ R.S. $= 1$
$= \log_8 8$
$= 1$
0 is a root.
When $x = 6$, the left side is not defined. Hence, 6 is an extraneous root.

In *Example 6b* we may ask, if 6 is an extraneous root, then where did it come from? The key to the answer is the quadratic equation $(2 - x)(4 - x) = 8$ which occurred in the solution. This equation may also be written as $(x - 2)(x - 4) = 8$ without changing the two roots. But then the associated logarithmic equation would be $\log_8 (x - 2) + \log_8 (x - 4) = 1$. Hence, if this equation were solved using the method of *Example 6b* the same two roots 0 and 6 would result, but this time 6 would be the root and 0 would be extraneous.

EXERCISES 11-7

(A)

1. Write each expression as a single logarithm, and simplify it.
   a) $\log_6 9 + \log_6 4$ b) $\log_5 15 - \log_5 3$ c) $\log_4 2 + \log_4 32$
   d) $\log_2 48 - \log_2 6$ e) $\log_3 54 - \log_3 2$ f) $\log_3 9 + \log_3 9$

2. Write as a sum of logarithms.
   a) $\log_3 20$ b) $\log_7 45$ c) $\log_5 90$ d) $\log_{12} 6$ e) $\log_8 75$ f) $\log_{20} 39$

3. Write as a difference of logarithms.
   a) $\log_4 11$ b) $\log_3 12$ c) $\log_9 5$ d) $\log_6 7$ e) $\log_{11} 21$ f) $\log_2 13$

4. Write each expression as a single logarithm and simplify it.
   a) $\log_6 4 + \log_6 3 + \log_6 3$ b) $\log_4 8 + \log_4 6 + \log_4 \left(\frac{4}{3}\right)$
   c) $\log_3 18 + \log_3 5 - \log_3 10$ d) $\log_2 20 - \log_2 5 + \log_2 8$
   e) $\log_5 50 + \log_5 10 - \log_5 4$ f) $\log_3 45 - \log_3 5 + \log_3 3$

5. a) Simplify.
   i) $\log_2 (8 \times 16)$ ii) $\log_3 (27 \times 81)$ iii) $\log_5 (625 \times 25)$
   b) Simplify.
   i) $\log_2 \left(\frac{32}{4}\right)$ ii) $\log_3 \left(\frac{27}{3}\right)$ iii) $\log_5 \left(\frac{125}{25}\right)$
6. Write each logarithm as a product of a whole number and a logarithm.
   a) $\log_3 8$ b) $\log_5 36$ c) $\log_2 27$ d) $\log_6 32$ e) $\log_{12} 81$ f) $\log_4 125$
7. Write as a single logarithm.
   a) $3 \log_2 5$ b) $2 \log_7 4$ c) $6 \log_3 8$
   d) $5 \log_{12} 4$ e) $15 \log_2 3$ f) $2 \log_5 9$

B

8. Write as a single logarithm and simplify it.
   a) $\log_4 48 + \log_4 \left(\frac{2}{3}\right) + \log_4 8$ b) $\log_8 24 + \log_8 4 - \log_8 3$
   c) $\log_9 36 + \log_9 18 - \log_9 24$ d) $\log_4 20 - \log_4 5 + \log_4 8$
9. Write as a single logarithm and simplify it.
   a) $\log_3 \sqrt{45} - \log_3 \sqrt{5}$ b) $\log_2 \sqrt{5} - \log_2 \sqrt{40}$
   c) $\log_5 \sqrt{10} + \log_5 \sqrt{\frac{25}{2}}$ d) $\log_4 \sqrt{40} + \log_4 \sqrt{48} - \log_4 \sqrt{15}$
10. Simplify.
    a) $\log_2 24 - \log_2 \left(\frac{3}{4}\right)$ b) $\log_2 20 + \log_2 0.4$
    c) $\log_8 48 + \log_8 4 - \log_8 3$ d) $\log_{21} 7 + \log_{21} 9 + \log_{21} \left(\frac{1}{3}\right)$
11. Given $\log_2 5 \doteq 2.3219$, find an approximation for each logarithm.
    a) $\log_2 20$ b) $\log_2 25$ c) $\log_2 2.5$ d) $\log_2 \sqrt{5}$
12. Given $\log_3 10 \doteq 2.0959$, find an approximation for each logarithm.
    a) $\log_3 1000$ b) $\log_3 30$ c) $\log_3 \sqrt{0.3}$ d) $\log_3 \left(\frac{100}{9}\right)$
13. Express y as a function of x. What is the domain?
    a) $\log_2 xy = 3 \log_2 x$
    b) $\log_5 y = 2 \log_5 (x + 1) + \log_5 (x - 1)$
    c) $\log_3 (y - 3) = 1 + 2 \log_3 (x + 3)$
14. Use your calculator to evaluate each expression.
    a) i) $\log_2 3000$ ii) $\log_2 300$ iii) $\log_2 30$ iv) $\log_2 3$
    v) $\log_2 0.3$ vi) $\log_2 0.03$ vii) $\log_2 0.003$ viii) $\log_2 0.0003$
    b) Can you find a pattern in the results of part a)? Account for the pattern.
15. Prove that if (x_1,y_1) and (x_2,y_2) are two points on the graph of $y = \log_a x$, then $\left(\frac{x_1}{x_2}, y_1 - y_2\right)$ is also a point on the graph.

16. Prove that if (x_1,y_1) is a point on the graph of $y = \log_a x$, then $(x_1^2, 2y_1)$ and $\left(\frac{1}{x_1}, -y_1\right)$ are also points on the graph.

17. If $\log_3 2 = x$, simplify each logarithm.
    a) $\log_3 8$ b) $\log_3 24$ c) $\log_3 \sqrt{2}$ d) $\log_3 6\sqrt{2}$

18. If $\log_2 5 = x$, simplify each logarithm.
    a) $\log_2 20$ b) $\log_2 100$ c) $\log_2 10\sqrt{5}$ d) $\log_2 \left(\frac{\sqrt[3]{5}}{2}\right)$

19. Given that $\log_2 x = 5$, evaluate each logarithm.
    a) $\log_2 2x$ b) $\log_2 \left(\frac{x}{2}\right)$ c) $\log_2 (x^2)$ d) $\log_2 (4x^2)$

20. Given that $\log_3 x = 2$ and $\log_3 y = 5$, evaluate each logarithm.
    a) $\log_3 xy$ b) $\log_3 (9x^2y)$ c) $\log_3 \left(\frac{3x^2}{y}\right)$ d) $\log_3 (27x^{-2}y)$

21. Solve and check.
    a) $2 \log x = \log 32 + \log 2$
    b) $2 \log x = \log 3 + \log 27$
    c) $\log_4 (x + 2) + \log_4 (x - 1) = 1$
    d) $\log_2 (x - 5) + \log_2 (x - 2) = 2$
    e) $\log_2 x + \log_2 (x + 2) = 3$
    f) $\log_6 (x - 1) + \log_6 (x + 4) = 2$

22. Solve and check.
    a) $2 \log m + 3 \log m = 10$
    b) $\log_3 x^2 - \log_3 2x = 2$
    c) $\log_3 s + \log_3 (s - 2) = 1$
    d) $\log (x - 2) + \log (x + 1) = 1$
    e) $\log_7 (x + 4) + \log_7 (x - 2) = 1$
    f) $\log_2 (2m + 4) - \log_2 (m - 1) = 3$

Ⓒ

23. Solve each equation to the nearest thousandth.
    a) $\log_2 x + \log_4 x = 5$
    b) $\log_5 x + \log_{10} x = 5$

24. Prove.
    a) $(\log_a b)(\log_b x) = \log_a x$
    b) $(\log_a b)(\log_b c)(\log_c x) = \log_a x$

25. Let a represent any positive number other than 1. Prove that:
    a) if $(x + 1)^2 = 4x$, then $\log_a \left(\frac{x+1}{2}\right) = \frac{1}{2} \log_a x$
    b) if $(x + y)^2 = 4xy$, then $\log_a \left(\frac{x+y}{2}\right) = \frac{1}{2} (\log_a x + \log_a y)$.

26. Determine how $\log_a x$ and $\log_x a$ are related.

27. a) Show that: i) $\frac{1}{\log_3 10} + \frac{1}{\log_4 10} = \frac{1}{\log_{12} 10}$ ii) $\frac{1}{\log_3 x} + \frac{1}{\log_4 x} = \frac{1}{\log_{12} x}$.
    b) Using the results of part a) as a guide, state a general result and prove it.

THE MATHEMATICAL MIND

Natural Logarithms

Logarithms were introduced into mathematics almost four hundred years ago by the Scotsman, John Napier. The invention was enthusiastically hailed throughout Europe as a great breakthrough in computation. This was because logarithms can be used to reduce multiplication and division to the simpler operations of addition and subtraction. For example, the law of logarithms, $\log xy = \log x + \log y$, can be applied to multiply two numbers x and y by adding their logarithms. In the past, extensive tables of logarithms were prepared for this purpose. Of course, modern technology has rendered this method of computation obsolete.

Originally, Napier's logarithms had a certain base which was different from 10. These logarithms are called *natural logarithms*.

You can evaluate natural logarithms using the [ln] key on your calculator. For example, key in: 3 [ln] to display 1.0986123. We write $\ln 3 \doteq 1.098\ 612\ 3$, and we say "lawn 3 is approximately 1.098 612 3". To explain what this means, we need to know the base of the logarithms. The base of the natural logarithms is always represented by the letter e.

You can use your calculator to find the value of e.
Key in: 1 [e^x] or 1 [INV] [ln] to display 2.7182818.
Hence, $e \doteq 2.718\ 281\ 8$
Therefore, $\ln 3 \doteq 1.098\ 612\ 3$ means that $e^{1.0986123} \doteq 3$, where $e \doteq 2.718\ 281\ 8$.

Natural logarithms are a particular case of logarithms to base a, which were studied earlier in this chapter. Hence, natural logarithms have all the properties of logarithms to base a. This means that we can use natural logarithms to solve problems like those solved earlier.

For example, to solve the equation $e^x = 3.5$ for x, take the natural logarithm of both sides, and write $x \ln e = \ln 3.5$. Since $\ln e = 1$, then $x = \ln 3.5$. Key in: 3.5 [ln] to display 1.2527630. Hence, $x \doteq 1.252\ 763$.

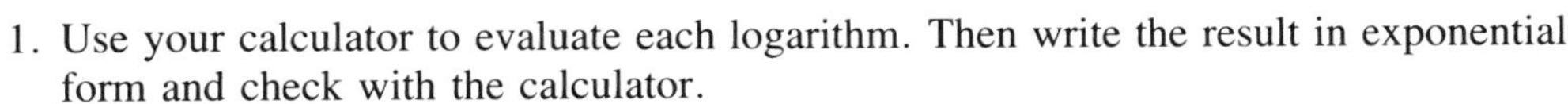

QUESTIONS

1. Use your calculator to evaluate each logarithm. Then write the result in exponential form and check with the calculator.
   a) ln 2 b) ln 4 c) ln 30 d) ln 100
   e) ln 8750 f) ln 0.5 g) ln 0.1 h) ln 0.000 44

2. Solve for x.
   a) $e^x = 5$ b) $e^x = 15$ c) $e^x = 53.9$ d) $e^x = 266$
   e) $e^x = 1$ f) $e^x = 0.25$ g) $e^x = 0.092$ h) $e^x = 0.0003$

3. Solve for x.
   a) $\ln x = 1$ b) $\ln x = 1.6$ c) $\ln x = 3$ d) $\ln x = 4.5$
   e) $\ln x = 0.33$ f) $\ln x = -1$ g) $\ln x = -1.4$ h) $\ln x = -2.2$

4. Write as a single logarithm, and check with your calculator.
   a) $\ln 5 + \ln 3$ b) $\ln 2 + \ln 10$ c) $2 \ln 6$
   d) $\ln 18 - \ln 2$ e) $\ln 21 - \ln 3$ f) $\frac{1}{2} \ln 25$

5. a) Simplify each expression.
      i) $\ln e$ ii) $\ln e^2$ iii) $\ln e^{-3}$ iv) $\ln e^{0.2}$
   b) Based on the results of part a), state a general result.

6. About 200 years ago, at age 15, Carl Friedrich Gauss noticed that the number of primes less than a given natural number n can be approximated by $\frac{n}{\ln n}$.
   Use this expression to approximate the number of primes less than:
   a) 10 b) 100 c) 1000 d) 10^6 e) 10^9.

7. Although it has never been proved, mathematicians have observed that the number of twin primes less than a given number n is approximately equal to $\frac{2n}{(\ln n)^2}$. Use this result to approximate the number of twin primes less than:
   a) 10 b) 100 c) 1000 d) 10^6 e) 10^9.

8. It has been proved that the average spacing of the prime numbers near a given natural number n is approximately equal to $\ln n$. For example, the six prime numbers closest to 50, and the successive differences between them are:

   41 43 47 53 59 61
   2 4 6 6 2

   The average spacing is $\frac{2 + 4 + 6 + 6 + 2}{5} = 4$.
   a) Find ln 50, and compare it with the above result.
   b) Check that the average spacing of the six primes closest to:
      i) 100 is approximately ln 100 ii) 150 is approximately ln 150.

MATHEMATICS AROUND US

Applications of Natural Logarithms

In the applications of exponential and logarithmic functions studied in *Chapters 10* and *11*, many different bases were used. For example, in compound interest applications the base depended on the interest rate. In other applications we used bases 2, $\frac{1}{2}$, and 10. It would simplify matters to use the same base every time, and mathematicians have found that there is an advantage to using base e.

For example, consider population growth. In 1987 the world population reached 5 billion, and was increasing at about 1.6% per annum. Hence, an equation expressing the population P billion as a function of time t years relative to 1987 is

$$P = 5(1.016)^t \ldots ①$$

Let's investigate what would happen if we express this equation with base e instead of base 10. To do this, we must write 1.016 as a power of e.

Let $1.016 = e^k$. Then, by definition, $k = \ln 1.016$
Key in: 1.016 [ln] to display 0.0158733
To two significant figures, $k \doteq 0.016$
Hence, $1.016 \doteq e^{0.016}$, and equation ① can be written as follows.

$$P = 5e^{0.016t}$$

Initial population — Growth rate

Look at that! The constant in the exponent is 0.016, which is the growth rate. We now see an advantage of using base e. When an exponential function is expressed with base e, the constant in the exponent is the rate of growth. e is the only number with this property. Hence, it is the natural base to use in problems involving exponential growth and decay.

There is another advantage. Notice that the value of k obtained was not exactly 0.016. This slight discrepancy is caused by the way in which e is defined in higher mathematics. The definition assumes that the population grows continuously, and that the new members are not added all at once at the end of the year. In this case, the growth rate is called *instantaneous*. In the above example, the instantaneous rate of growth is 0.015 873 3, whereas the annual rate is 0.016. In some applications the difference may not be significant. Since a rigorous development of instantaneous rates of growth requires calculus, we will ignore its effect.

Example 1. In 1986 the population of Canada was 25.5 million, and was growing at the rate of approximately 1.0% per annum.

a) Write an equation for the population P million after t years.

b) Assuming that the growth rate remains constant, use the equation to determine:

i) the predicted population in the year 2000

ii) the number of years required for the population to reach 40 million.

Solution. a) The equation is $P = 25.5e^{0.01t}$.

b) i) The year 2000 is 14 years later than 1986. Hence, substitute 14 for t.

$$P = 25.5e^{0.01(14)}$$
$$= 25.5e^{0.14}$$
$$\doteq 29.331\ 982$$

The population will be approximately 29.3 million in the year 2000.

ii) Substitute 40 for P.

$$40 = 25.5e^{0.01t}$$

To solve for t, take the natural logarithm of each side.

$$\ln 40 = \ln 25.5 + 0.01t$$
$$t = \frac{\ln 40 - \ln 25.5}{0.01}$$
$$\doteq 45.020\ 100$$

The population will reach 40 million 45 years after 1986, or in the year 2031.

Example 2. In 1987 the world population reached 5 billion. According to United Nations forecasts, the population will reach 6.1 billion in the year 2001. Calculate the average annual rate of growth from 1987 to 2001.

Solution. Let $P = P_0e^{kt}$

Substitute 5 for P_0, 6.1 for P, and 14 for t.

$$6.1 = 5e^{14k}$$

Take the natural logarithm of each side.

$$\ln 6.1 = \ln 5 + 14k$$
$$k = \frac{\ln 6.1 - \ln 5}{14}$$
$$\doteq 0.014\ 203\ 6$$

Hence, the average annual rate of growth is about 1.42%.

The conventions of writing $\log x$ to mean the logarithm to base 10 of x, and $\ln x$ to mean the logarithm to base e of x are by no means universal. In higher mathematics, natural logarithms are usually the only logarithms that are used, and $\log x$ often refers to the natural logarithm of x. Also, many computer languages use LOG(X) for the natural logarithm function.

QUESTIONS

1. Each equation represents the population P million of a country t years after 1985. State the 1985 population and the growth rate for each country.
   a) Italy $P = 57e^{0.007t}$
   b) Kenya $P = 20e^{0.030t}$
   c) Costa Rica $P = 2.6e^{0.038t}$

2. In 1985 the population of India was 770 million, and was growing at approximately 1.6% per annum.
   a) Write an equation for the population P million after t years, using an exponential function with base e.
   b) Assuming that the growth rate is constant, determine:
      i) the predicted population in 1995
      ii) when the population will reach 1 billion
      iii) when the population was 500 million.

3. When uranium-238 decays, the percent P remaining after t years is given by the equation $P = 100e^{-1.53 \times 10^{-10}t}$.
   a) What percent remains after 10 million years?
   b) Determine the halflife of uranium-238.

4. The altitude of an aircraft can be determined by measuring the air pressure. In the stratosphere (between 12 000 m and 30 000 m) the pressure P kilopascals is expressed as an exponential function of the altitude h metres by the equation $P = 130e^{-0.000155h}$.
   a) What is the altitude if the pressure is 8.5 kPa; 2.5 kPa?
   b) What is the pressure at an altitude of 20 000 m?
   c) Solve the equation for h to obtain an equation expressing the altitude as a logarithmic function of the pressure.

5. A rule of thumb which is used to approximate the time required for an investment to double in value is to divide 70 by the interest rate. For example, if the interest rate is 8%, then an investment will double in approximately $\frac{70}{8}$, or 9 years. Explain why the rule of thumb works.

1. Evaluate.
   a) $\log 100\,000$ b) $\log 0.001$ c) $\log \sqrt[3]{10}$ d) $\log_2 8$
2. Evaluate to 4 decimal places.
   a) $\log 6$ b) $\log 7.4$ c) $\log 19$ d) $\log 27.1$
3. Write in exponential form.
   a) $\log 1000 = 3$ b) $\log \sqrt{10} = \frac{1}{2}$ c) $\log_3 81 = 4$
4. Write in logarithmic form.
   a) $10^4 = 10\,000$ b) $10^{-3} = 0.001$ c) $5^4 = 625$
5. Solve for x.
   a) $\log x = 2$ b) $\log x = -5$ c) $\log_x 64 = 2$
   d) $\log_3 x = 3$ e) $\log_5 0.04 = x$ f) $\log_2 x = 5$
6. Simplify.
   a) $\log 10^5$ b) $\log 10^{3.1}$ c) $\log 10^{-1.5}$ d) $\log_3 3^7$ e) $\log_{11} 121$
7. Simplify.
   a) $10^{\log 7}$ b) $10^{\log 2.8}$ c) $10^{\log 0.09}$ d) $6^{\log_6 2}$ e) $17^{\log_{17} 11}$
8. Write as a single logarithm.
   a) $\log 7 + \log 4 - \log 5$ b) $\log_5 142 - \log_5 19 - \log_5 3$
   c) $\log p - \log q + \log r$ d) $\log (2a - 3) + \log (a + 5)$
   e) $2 \log_4 m + 5 \log_4 n - 3 \log_4 p$ f) $\frac{2}{3} \log_a x - \frac{1}{4} \log_a y - \log_a z$
9. If $\log 6 = m$ and $\log 5 = n$, write each logarithm as an expression in m and n.
   a) $\log 30$ b) $\log 1.2$ c) $\log 7.2$ d) $\log 0.24$
10. Given that $\log 7 \doteq 0.8451$ find an approximation for each logarithm.
    a) $\log 7^{\frac{1}{2}}$ b) $\log 343$ c) $\log \sqrt[3]{7}$ d) $\log \left(\frac{1}{49}\right)$
11. Express.
    a) 8 as a power of 3 b) 24 as a power of 6
    c) 12 as a power of 1.3 d) 0.78 as a power of 2
12. Solve for x. Give the answers to 4 decimal places.
    a) $5^x = 9$ b) $14^x = 8$ c) $3^{2x-1} = 25$ d) $4^{5-x} = 45$
    e) $7^{3-x} = 4$ f) $8^{5x-2} = 69$ g) $2^{1-x} = 9^{x+1}$ h) $5^{3x+1} = 12^{x+4}$
13. m and n are two positive numbers. How are $\log m$ and $\log n$ related if:
    a) $m = 100n$ b) $m = n^3$ c) $m = \sqrt{10n}$ d) $m = \frac{1}{\sqrt{n}}$?
14. Express x as a logarithmic function of y.
    a) $y = 2^x$ b) $y = 3(5)^x$ c) $y = 2.7(8)^x$

15. Evaluate.

a) $\log 10\,000$ b) $\log_2 16$ c) $\log_3 243$ d) $\log_2 \left(\frac{1}{8}\right)$

e) $\log_{\frac{1}{3}} 27$ f) $\log_{\sqrt{2}} 32$ g) $\log_5 0.008$ h) $\log_7 343$

16. Evaluate to the nearest thousandth.

a) $\log_2 7$ b) $\log_{12} 8$ c) $\log_{3.5} 19.1$ d) $\log_{\frac{1}{4}} 0.65$

e) $\log_5 42$ f) $\log_{2.1} 78$ g) $\log_{1.8} 27.3$ h) $\log_{0.4} 0.21$

17. Solve for x.

a) $\log_5 x = -3$ b) $\log_{17} 1 = x$ c) $\log_x 64 = -3$

18. Simplify.

a) $\log_6 90 + \log_6 12 - \log_6 5$ b) $\log_3 24 - \log_3 16 + \log_3 6\sqrt{3}$

c) $\log_8 16 + \log_8 5 - \log_8 2.5$ d) $\log_5 8 - \log_5 40 - \log_5 50 + \log_5 10$

19. If $\log_3 4 \doteq 1.2619$ find an approximation for each logarithm.

a) $\log_3 12$ b) $\log_3 64$ c) $\log_3 \left(\frac{16}{3}\right)$ d) $\log_3 2$

20. Solve and check.

a) $3 \log x = \log 512 - \log 8$ b) $\log_2 x + \log_2 (x - 3) = 2$

c) $\log_{\sqrt{2}} (x - 2) + \log_{\sqrt{2}} (x + 1) = 4$ d) $\log_6 (x + 3) + \log_6 (x - 2) = 1$

21. Graph each function and its inverse on the same grid.

a) $y = 3^x$ b) $y = \log_5 x$ c) $y = \log_{\frac{1}{3}} x$

22. The halflife of a radioactive substance is 23 days. How long is it until the percent remaining is:

a) 10% b) 3% ?

23. a) An air filter loses about 0.3% of its effectiveness each day. What is its effectiveness after 145 days as a percent of its initial effectiveness?

b) The filter should be replaced when its effectiveness has decreased to 20% of its initial value. After how long should it be replaced?

24. If the population of a city is 178 500 and it is growing at the rate of 2.1% per annum, in how many years will the population be 210 000?

25. The pH of water in a small lake in northern Quebec has dropped from 5.4 to 4.8 in the last three years. How many times as acidic as it was three years ago, is the lake now?

26. If a coil spring is stretched 1.5 m beyond its resting point and then released it will return to a point which is 90% of the previous distance from the resting point. How many vibrations are required before the spring moves less than 10 cm from its resting point?

12 Second-Degree Relations

Some bridges have curved arches like this one. If the type of the arch is known, and if the height and the width at its base are known, how can the height be determined at other points under the arch? (See Section 12-5 *Example 2*.)

12-1 INTRODUCTION TO SECOND-DEGREE RELATIONS

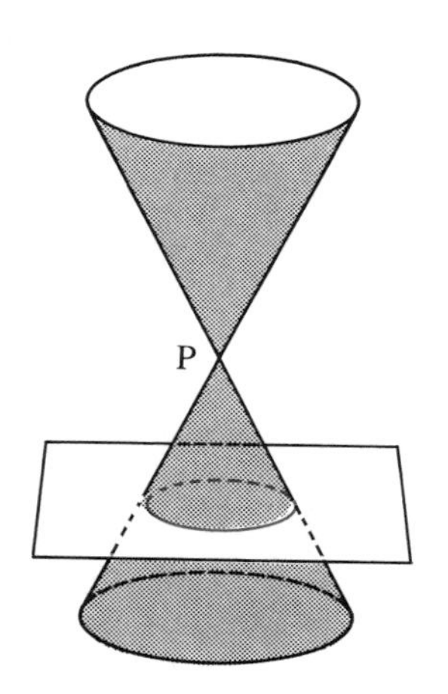

The ancient Greeks defined a cone as the surface generated when a line is rotated about a fixed point P on the line. Notice that the cone has two symmetric parts on either side of P.

The curves that result when a plane intersects a cone are called *conic sections*, or *conics*. The Greeks discovered many properties of conics, but they were not interested in practical applications. In the seventeenth century, Isaac Newton proved that the orbit of a body revolving around another in accordance with the law of gravitation is a conic.

When a plane intersects a cone, the angle of inclination of the plane with respect to the cone determines the shape of the curve that results.

The Circle

In the drawing above, the plane is parallel to the base of the cone. In this case the curve of intersection is a *circle*. Hence, a circle is a conic.

The orbits of satellites and planets are nearly circular. The spectacular photographs we see of a total solar eclipse are caused by the fact that both the sun and the moon appear to us as circular discs of about the same size.

Although the conics are defined as sections of a cone, they also occur as the graphs of certain equations in x and y.

Example 1. Graph the relation $x^2 + y^2 = 16$.

Solution. We could use a table of values to draw the graph. A more efficient method is to observe that the equation expresses the condition that the distance from a point $P(x,y)$ to $O(0,0)$ be 4 units. Hence, the graph is a circle, with centre (0,0) and radius 4.

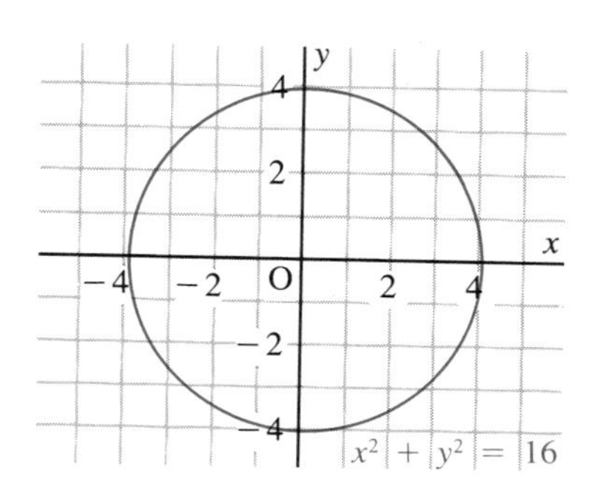

The Ellipse

If the intersecting plane is inclined to the base of the cone as shown, an *ellipse* results. As the angle of the intersecting plane increases, the shape of the ellipse changes from circular to long and elongated.

Satellites, planets, and some comets travel in elliptical orbits. Halley's comet, which returns to the sun approximately every 76 years, has a very long elliptical orbit.

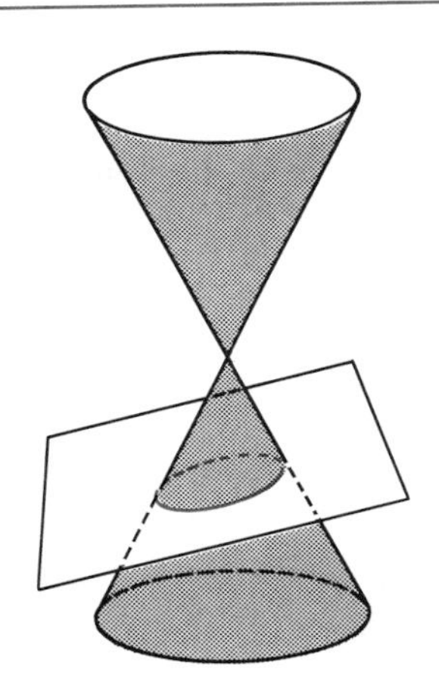

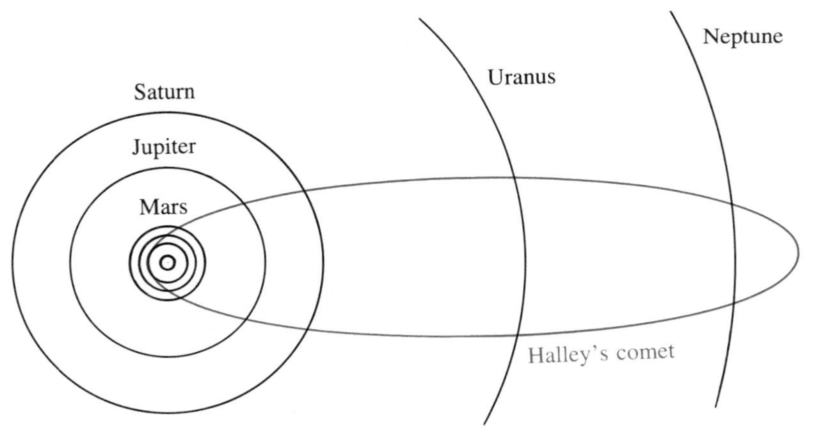

Example 2. Graph the relation $4x^2 + 9y^2 = 36$ using a table of values.

Solution. To prepare a table of values, we first solve the equation for y.

$$4x^2 + 9y^2 = 36$$
$$9y^2 = 36 - 4x^2$$
$$y = \frac{\pm\sqrt{36 - 4x^2}}{3}$$

x	y
0	±2.00
0.5	±1.97
1.0	±1.89
1.5	±1.73
2.0	±1.49
2.5	±1.11
3.0	0

x	y
0	±2.00
−0.5	±1.97
−1.0	±1.89
−1.5	±1.73
−2.0	±1.49
−2.5	±1.11
−3.0	0

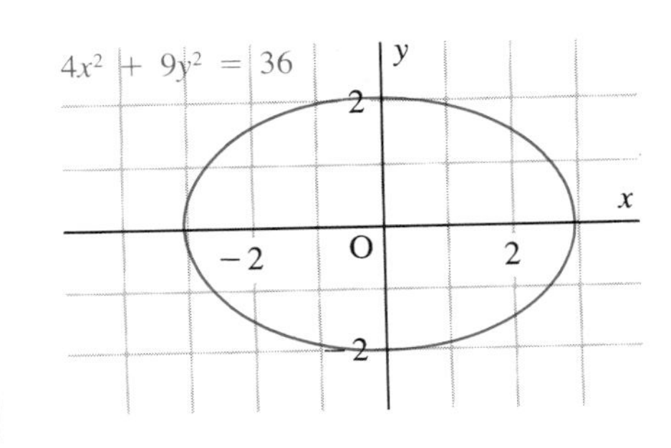

The Parabola

In this diagram, the intersecting plane is parallel to the line AB on the cone. The resulting curve is a *parabola*. Hence, a parabola is a conic.

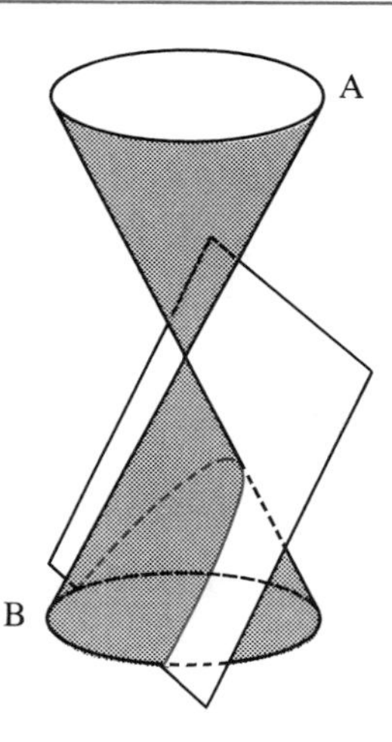

Parabolas have many applications in astronomy. The mirrors in some telescopes have surfaces whose cross sections are parabolas. Many comets have orbits which extend far beyond the outermost planets. In the vicinity of the sun, these orbits are nearly parabolic. Also, as the photograph below suggests, a parabolic shape is sometimes formed by the coma and dust tail of a comet.

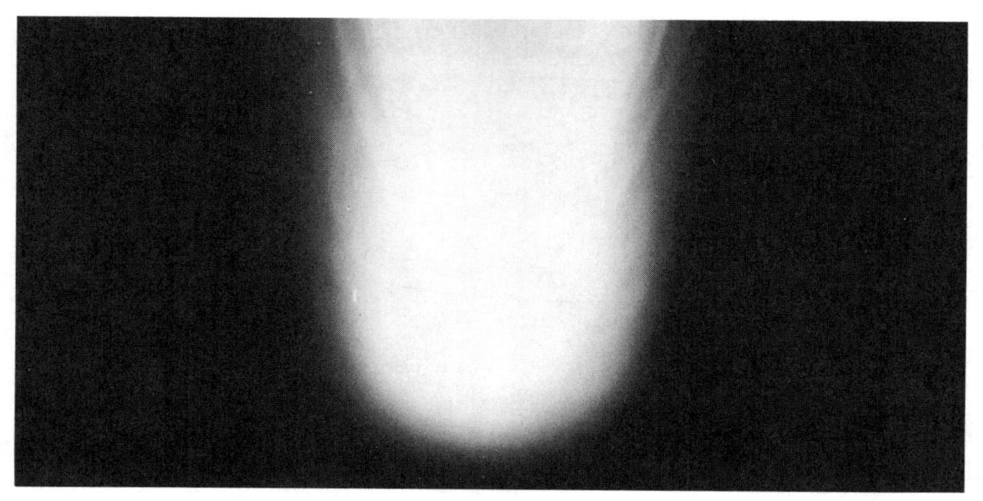

Example 3. Graph the relation $x^2 - 4y = 0$.

Solution. We could use a table of values to draw the graph. A more efficient method is to solve the equation for y and use our knowledge of the transformations of functions.

$$x^2 - 4y = 0$$

$$y = \frac{1}{4}x^2$$

The graph is a parabola with vertex (0,0), axis of symmetry the y-axis, and opens up. It is a vertical compression of the parabola $y = x^2$.

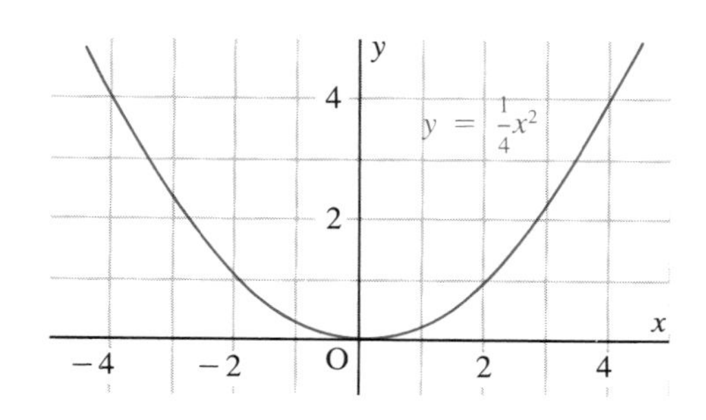

The Hyperbola

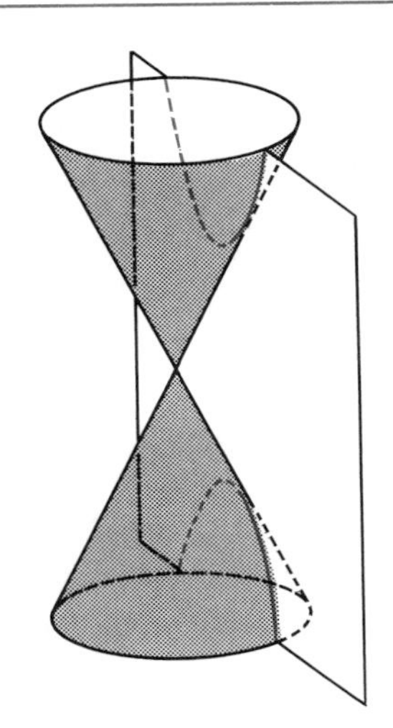

If the plane intersects the cone as shown, the resulting curve is called a *hyperbola*. Note that a hyperbola intersects both parts of the cone. Hence, a hyperbola has two distinct parts, or branches.

Some comets travel along paths which are slightly hyperbolic. As a result, they only appear once near the sun, and do not return. If a star passes another star, each is deflected along a hyperbolic path by the other. Another example of a hyperbolic path is provided by the Voyager 2 space probe which was launched to the outer planets in August, 1977. The diagram shows Voyager's path as it passed by Uranus in January, 1986.

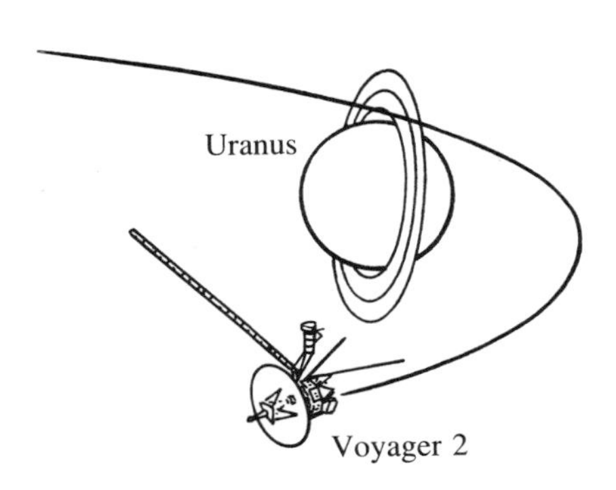

Example 4. Graph the relation $x^2 - y^2 = 4$ using a table of values.

Solution. To prepare a table of values, we first solve the equation for y.

$$x^2 - y^2 = 4$$
$$y^2 = x^2 - 4$$
$$y = \pm\sqrt{x^2 - 4}$$

x	y
2	0
3	± 2.24
4	± 3.46
5	± 4.58
6	± 5.66

x	y
-2	0
-3	± 2.24
-4	± 3.46
-5	± 4.58
-6	± 5.66

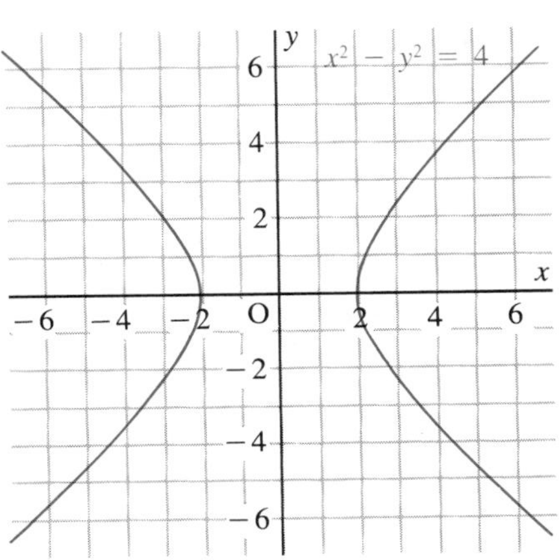

Each equation in the above examples has terms of the second degree in x or y. Any relation whose defining equation contains terms of the second degree, but no terms of higher degree, is called a *second-degree relation*.

These are second-degree relations.
$x^2 + 9y^2 = 18$
$2x^2 + xy - 2x = 14$

These are not second-degree relations.
$y = x^3$
$x^2 + 2xy^2 + 3y = 6$

In this chapter we will develop techniques for graphing certain second-degree relations without making tables of values.

EXERCISES 12-1

1. Which of these are second-degree relations?
   a) $x^2 - y^2 = 9$
   b) $2x^3 + y^3 = 24$
   c) $3x^2 + 2y^2 = 12$
   d) $x^2 + 3x^2y = 6$
   e) $x^2 - 2y^2 + x - y = 7$
   f) $xy = 12$

(B)

2. Graph each relation and identify the curve.
   a) $x^2 + y^2 = 9$
   b) $4x^2 + y^2 = 16$
   c) $4x^2 - y^2 = 16$
   d) $y = \frac{x^2}{8}$
   e) $4x^2 + 25y^2 = 100$
   f) $4x^2 - 25y^2 = 100$

3. a) Graph each relation.
   i) $x^2 + y^2 = 0$ ii) $x^2 - y^2 = 0$ iii) $(x - y)^2 = 0$
   b) Explain how the graphs of the relations in part a) could result when a plane intersects a cone.

4. A jet breaking the sound barrier creates a shock wave which has the shape of a cone. Describe the shape of the shock wave on the ground if the jet is:
   a) flying parallel to the ground
   b) gaining altitude
   c) losing altitude.

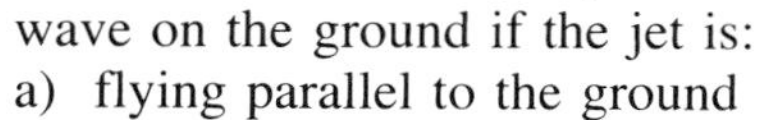

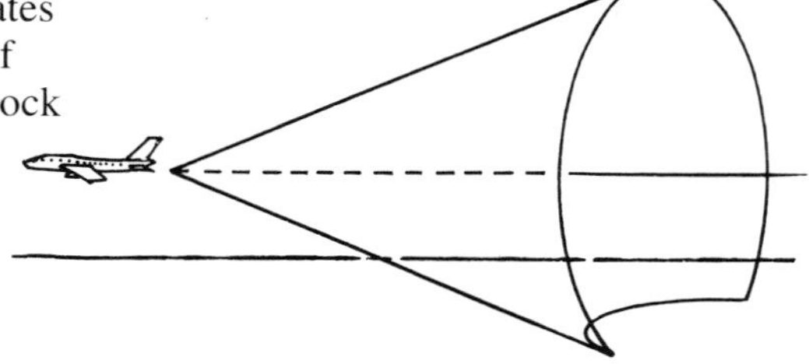

INVESTIGATE

Models of the Conics

You can make models of the conics using styrofoam cones, which can be obtained from a craft store. Cut some styrofoam cones with a fine-toothed saw to create a circle, an ellipse, a parabola, and a hyperbola. Paint the surfaces.

Can you make four cuts in one cone to show a circle, an ellipse, a parabola, and a hyperbola?

12-2 THE PARABOLA

When major league baseball games are televised, a parabolic reflector microphone is often used to pick up the voices of the players and umpires. A cross section of the microphone has the shape of a parabola.

When the axis of symmetry of a parabola is the y-axis, and the vertex is the origin, the parabola has an equation of the form $y = ax^2$, where a is a constant.

Example 1. A parabola has vertex (0,0) and axis of symmetry the y-axis.
a) Find the equation of the parabola if it passes through the point A(4,12).
b) Find the value of y_1 if B(3,y_1) is on the parabola.

Solution. a) Let the equation of the parabola be $y = ax^2$. Since A(4,12) is a point on the parabola, its coordinates satisfy the equation. Substitute 4 for x and 12 for y in $y = ax^2$.

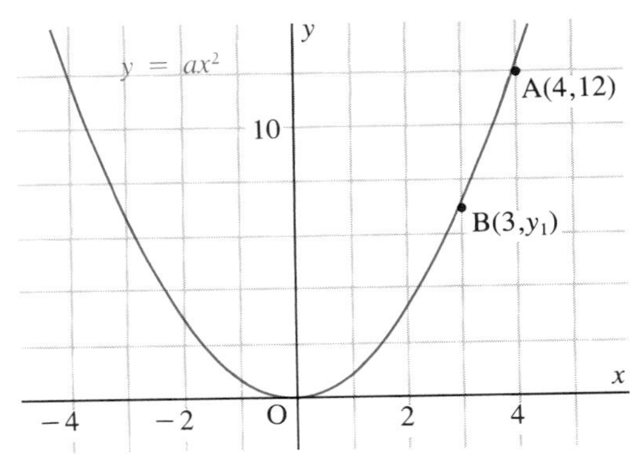

$y = ax^2$
$12 = a(4)^2$
$a = \frac{3}{4}$

The equation of the parabola is $y = 0.75x^2$.

b) Substitute 3 for x and y_1 for y in $y = 0.75x^2$.
$y_1 = 0.75(3)^2$
$= 6.75$

Hence, if B(3,y_1) is on the parabola, $y_1 = 6.75$.

In *Example 1* we used the following fundamental property of any relation which can be defined by an equation.

Property of Equations of Relations
- The coordinates of every point on the graph of a relation satisfy the equation of the relation.
- Every point whose coordinates satisfy the equation of a relation is on the graph of the relation.

Parabolas arise in many applications involving construction and design. In such applications we often use the above property.

Example 2. A bridge over a river is supported by a parabolic arch which is 40 m wide at water level. The maximum height of the arch is 16 m.

a) Write an equation to represent the arch.

b) How high is the arch at a point 10 m from the centre?

Solution. a) Use a coordinate system as shown.

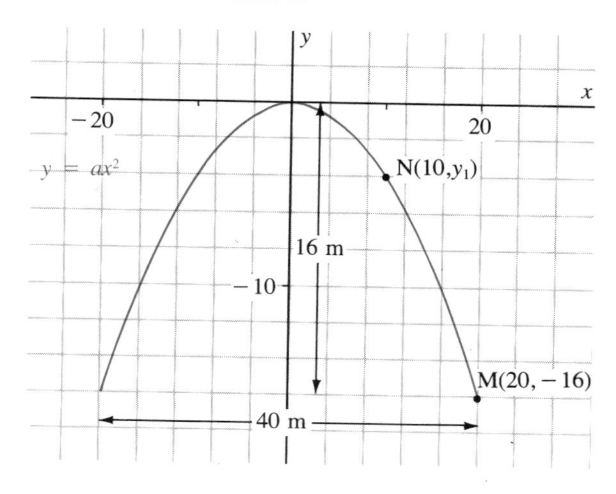

Let the equation of the arch be $y = ax^2$.
From the given information, and the diagram, the point M(20, −16) is on the parabola. Hence, these coordinates satisfy the equation.
Substitute 20 for x and −16 for y in $y = ax^2$.

$-16 = a(20)^2$

$-16 = 400a$

$a = -\frac{16}{400}$

$= -0.04$

The equation of the parabola is $y = -0.04x^2$.

b) Let N(10,y_1) represent a point on the arch which is 10 m from the centre. Then these coordinates satisfy the equation.
Substitute 10 for x and y_1 for y in $y = -0.04x^2$.

$y_1 = -0.04(10)^2$

$= -4$

A point 10 m from the centre is 4 m below the highest point, and therefore 12 m above the water level. Hence, the arch is 12 m high at a point 10 m from the centre.

EXERCISES 12-2

(A)

1. Determine if each point is on the parabola defined by $y = 3x^2$.
   a) (−1,3) b) (3,9) c) (−2,−12) d) (−2,12)

2. Sketch the parabola defined by each equation.
   a) $y = x^2$ b) $y = 0.5x^2$ c) $y = -0.5x^2$ d) $y = -2x^2$

(B)

3. Sketch the parabolas defined by these equations on the same grid.
   a) $x^2 - 2y = 0$ b) $x^2 + 2y = 0$ c) $x^2 - 4y = 0$ d) $x^2 + 3y = 0$

4. A parabola has vertex (0,0) and axis of symmetry the y-axis. Find the equation of the parabola if it passes through each point.
   a) (2,8) b) (4,6) c) $(-4,10)$ d) $(4,-2)$
   e) (8,20) f) (10,12) g) $(-6,5)$ h) $(7,-3)$

5. A parabola has vertex (0,0) and axis of symmetry the y-axis.
   a) Find the equation of the parabola if it passes through each point.
      i) (8,8) ii) (5,5) iii) $(-3,-3)$ iv) $(-7,-7)$
   b) What conclusion can you make about the equation of a parabola if it passes through a point whose x- and y-coordinates are equal?

6. The cables of a suspension bridge hang in a curve which approximates a parabola. The road bed passes through the vertex. If the supporting towers are 720 m apart and 60 m high, find:
   a) an equation of the parabola
   b) the height of the cables at a point 30 m from the vertex.

7. A stone thrown horizontally from a bridge 25 m above a river splashes in the water 40 m from the base of the bridge. If the stone falls in a parabolic path, find its equation relative to the position from which it was thrown.

8. The supporting structure for the roof of a curling rink has parabolic arches anchored at ground level. If the arches are 15.3 m high, and span 70 m, find:
   a) an equation of the parabola
   b) the height of the arches at a point 10 m from the centre.

9. Find the coordinates of the vertex of the parabola defined by each equation.
   a) $y = x^2 - 8x + 20$ b) $y = 3x^2 - 18x + 2$

10. The parabola defined by $y = 2x^2$ is translated 3 units to the right and 2 units down. What is the equation of the image parabola?

11. A rectangle has a perimeter of 50 cm, and a length of x centimetres.
    a) Write the area A square centimetres as a function of the length.
    b) Draw a graph of the function in part a).

Ⓒ

12. Sketch the parabola defined by each equation.
    a) $x = y^2$ b) $x = 0.5y^2$ c) $x = -0.5y^2$ d) $x = -2y^2$

13. $P(x_1,y_1)$ is any point on the parabola defined by $y = 0.25x^2$. $D(x_1,-1)$ is the corresponding point below P, on the line defined by $y = -1$. If F is the point (0,1), prove that PF = PD for any position of P on the parabola.

14. a) $P(x_1,y_1)$ is any point on the parabola defined by $4py = x^2$. $D(x_1,-p)$ is the point where a vertical line through P intersects the line defined by $y = -p$. If F is the point $(0,p)$, prove that PF = PD.
    b) Conversely, let P be a point which is equidistant from $F(0,p)$ and the line defined by $y = -p$. Prove that P lies on the parabola defined by $4py = x^2$.

12-3 THE CIRCLE

Many farms in western North America use an automated centre-pivot irrigation system. A long pipe sprays water as it rotates about the centre. Distinctive circular traces are left by the wheels, and, since the end of the pipe is always the same distance from the centre, the area watered forms a circle.

When a circle is plotted on a grid, its equation has a distinctive form. The simplest case occurs when the centre is the origin.

Example 1. A circle has centre (0,0) and radius 5 units.

a) Find the equation of the circle.

b) Find the value of y_1 if $(-2,y_1)$ is on the circle.

Solution. a) Let $P(x,y)$ be any point on the circle. Since OP is a radius, its length is 5 units. Since $\triangle$OPN is right-angled,

$$x^2 + y^2 = 5^2$$
$$x^2 + y^2 = 25$$

The equation of the circle is $x^2 + y^2 = 25$.

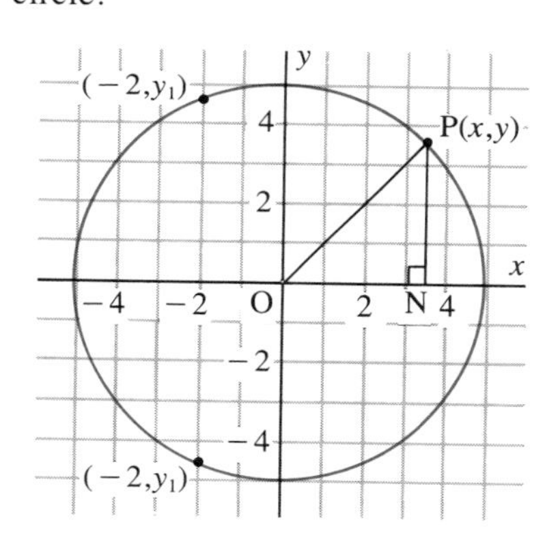

b) Substitute -2 for x and y_1 for y in the equation.

$$x^2 + y^2 = 25$$
$$(-2)^2 + y_1^2 = 25$$
$$y_1^2 = 21$$
$$y_1 = \pm\sqrt{21}$$

Hence, if $(-2,y_1)$ is on the circle, $y_1 = \pm\sqrt{21}$.

In *Example 1*, we obtained the equation $x^2 + y^2 = 25$. If we were to graph this equation using a table of values, the ordered pairs would have the property that their squares add to 25.

Using the method of *Example 1*, we can write the equation of any circle with centre (0,0) and a given radius.

Standard Equation of a Circle with Centre (0,0)

The equation of a circle with centre (0,0) and radius r is $x^2 + y^2 = r^2$.

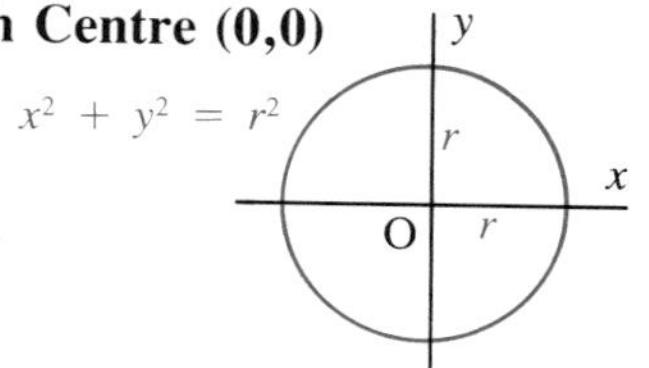

In *Chapters 8* and *9* we transformed the graphs of functions by expanding or compressing the graphs vertically and horizontally, and by translating them relative to the axes. We can transform graphs of relations in the same way. As we might expect, the changes in the equations are similar to those we found with functions.

The first step is to translate the graph of the circle defined by $x^2 + y^2 = r^2$ so that the centre is not at the origin. We will investigate expansions and compressions in the next section.

Graphing $(x - p)^2 + (y - q)^2 = r^2$

Compare these two equations.

$$x^2 + y^2 = 25 \quad \ldots ①$$
$$(x - 6)^2 + (y + 3)^2 = 25 \quad \ldots ②$$

Each equation states that the sum of the squares of two numbers is 25. In equation ①, these numbers are the coordinates of the points on the circle with centre (0,0) and radius 5. In equation ②, to give the same numbers whose squares add to 25 as in equation ①, the values of x must be 6 *greater* than those in equation ①, and the values of y must be 3 *less* than those in equation ①. Every point whose coordinates satisfy equation ② must be 6 units to the *right* of, and 3 units *below*, the corresponding point whose coordinates satisfy equation ①. Hence, equation ② represents a circle with centre (6, −3) and radius 5.

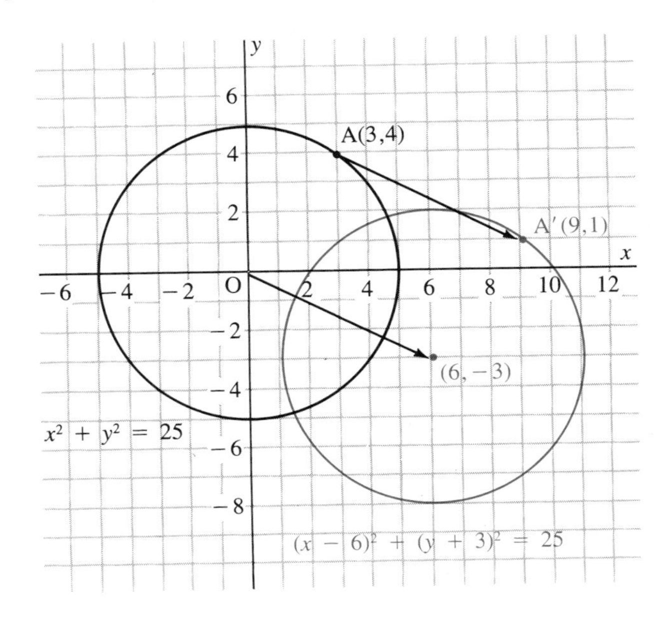

In general, adding constants to the variables x and y in the equation of the circle defined by $x^2 + y^2 = r^2$ causes horizontal and vertical translations of its graph.

Standard Equation of a Circle with Centre (p,q)

The equation of a circle with centre (p,q) and radius r is $(x - p)^2 + (y - q)^2 = r^2$.

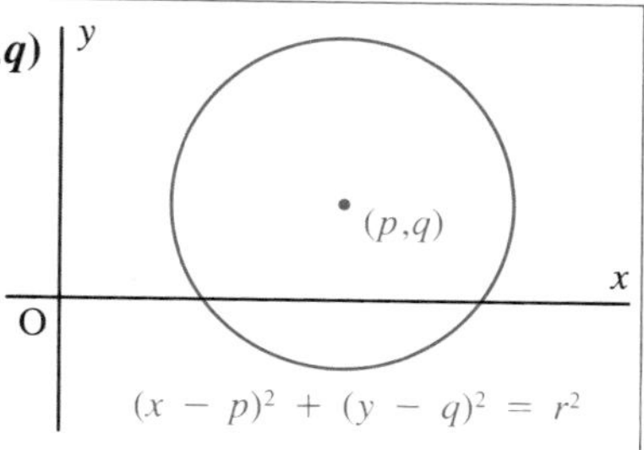

Example 2. Given the equation $(x + 3)^2 + (y - 5)^2 = 20$

a) State the radius and the coordinates of the centre of the circle defined by this equation.

b) Identify the transformation which maps the graph of the circle defined by $x^2 + y^2 = 20$ to the graph defined by $(x + 3)^2 + (y - 5)^2 = 20$, and illustrate on a diagram.

Solution. a) The radius is $\sqrt{20}$, or $2\sqrt{5}$. The centre is $(-3,5)$.

b) The graph defined by $(x + 3)^2 + (y - 5)^2 = 20$ is the image of the circle defined by $x^2 + y^2 = 20$ under a translation of 3 units to the left and 5 units up.

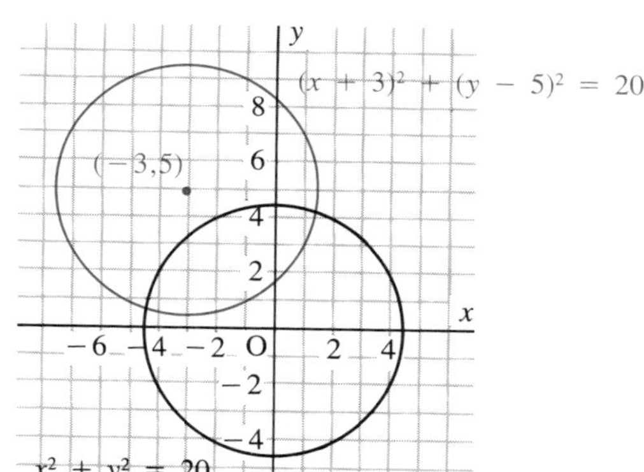

In *Example 2*, the left side of the equation of the circle could be expanded and the equation written as $x^2 + y^2 + 6x - 10y + 14 = 0$. When the equation is written in this form, the radius and the coordinates of the centre cannot be seen in the equation. But we can determine the radius and the coordinates of the centre by completing the square.

Example 3. A circle has the equation $x^2 + y^2 - 6x + 14y + 10 = 0$. Determine the radius and the coordinates of the centre.

Solution. We collect the terms containing x, and the terms containing y, and then use the method of completing the square.

$$x^2 + y^2 - 6x + 14y + 10 = 0$$
$$x^2 - 6x + y^2 + 14y + 10 = 0$$

Add the squares of $\frac{1}{2}(-6)$ and $\frac{1}{2}(14)$ to both sides.

$$(x^2 - 6x + 9) + (y^2 + 14y + 49) + 10 = 9 + 49$$
$$(x - 3)^2 + (y + 7)^2 = 48$$

The radius is $\sqrt{48}$, or $4\sqrt{3}$, and the centre is $(3,-7)$.

EXERCISES 12-3

Ⓐ

1. Determine if each point is on the circle defined by $x^2 + y^2 = 85$.
   a) $(9, -2)$ b) $(-5,8)$ c) $(-7,-6)$ d) $(4,8)$

2. State the radius and the coordinates of the centre of the circle defined by each equation.
   a) $x^2 + y^2 = 64$
   b) $x^2 + y^2 = 12$
   c) $(x - 3)^2 + (y + 4)^2 = 81$
   d) $(x + 2)^2 + (y - 1)^2 = 5$
   e) $(x + 4)^2 + y^2 = 15$
   f) $x^2 + (y - 6)^2 = 48$

3. Write the equation of the circle with each given centre and radius.
   a) $(0,0)$, 3 b) $(0,0)$, 7 c) $(5,3)$, 4 d) $(-2,6)$, 5
   e) $(4,0)$, 6 f) $(0,-3)$, 9 g) $(0,0)$, $\sqrt{5}$ h) $(3,-5)$, $\sqrt{10}$

Ⓑ

4. Sketch the circles defined by these equations on the same grid.
   a) $x^2 + y^2 = 9$
   b) $(x - 4)^2 + y^2 = 9$
   c) $x^2 + (y - 5)^2 = 9$
   d) $(x - 4)^2 + (y - 5)^2 = 9$

5. Identify the transformation which maps the circle defined by $x^2 + y^2 = 25$ to the graph defined by each equation.
   a) $(x - 3)^2 + y^2 = 25$
   b) $x^2 + (y + 2)^2 = 25$
   c) $(x - 3)^2 + (y + 2)^2 = 25$

6. Identify the transformation which maps the circle defined by $x^2 + y^2 = 10$ to the graph defined by each equation.
   a) $x^2 + (y - 4)^2 = 10$
   b) $(x + 1)^2 + y^2 = 10$
   c) $(x + 1)^2 + (y - 4)^2 = 10$

7. A circle has centre $(0,0)$ and radius 6 units.
   a) Find the equation of the circle.
   b) Find the value of y_1 if $(4,y_1)$ is on the circle.

8. A circle has centre $(3,2)$ and radius 5 units.
   a) Find the value of x_1 if $(x_1,3)$ is on the circle.
   b) Find the value of y_1 if $(2,y_1)$ is on the circle.

9. Determine the coordinates of the centre, and the radius of the circle defined by each equation.
   a) $x^2 + y^2 - 10x + 4y + 20 = 0$
   b) $x^2 + y^2 - 6x - 2y - 15 = 0$
   c) $x^2 + y^2 + 8x - 12y + 1 = 0$
   d) $x^2 + y^2 + x + y - 4 = 0$

Ⓒ

10. The boundary of a region which can be watered by a rotating sprinkler is defined by the equation $x^2 + y^2 - 10x + 8y = 6$. A second sprinkler waters a region defined by $x^2 + y^2 + 4x - 6y = 9$. Is any part of the lawn watered by both sprinklers?

12-4 THE ELLIPSE

A spotlight is often used in skating shows. The light rays form a cone of light which illuminates an elliptical region on the ice.

We can obtain an ellipse graphically by starting with a circle, and expanding it horizontally or vertically. We can also expand it by different amounts both horizontally and vertically. And, if we know the equation of the circle, we can use our knowledge of transformations to find the equation of the ellipse.

Compare these two equations.

$$x^2 + y^2 = 1 \qquad \ldots \text{①}$$

$$\left(\frac{x}{3}\right)^2 + y^2 = 1 \qquad \ldots \text{②}$$

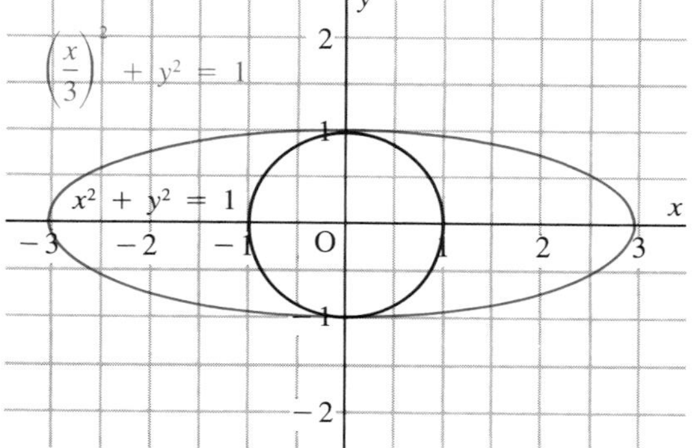

Each equation states that the sum of the squares of two numbers is 1. In equation ①, these numbers are the coordinates of points on a unit circle. In equation ②, to give the same numbers whose squares add to 1 as in equation ①, the values of x must be 3 *times* those in equation ①. Every point whose coordinates satisfy equation ② is 3 times as far from the y-axis as the corresponding point whose coordinates satisfy equation ①. Hence, the graph of equation ② is *expanded horizontally* by a factor of 3 relative to the graph of equation ①. Equation ② represents an ellipse with x-intercepts 3 and -3, and with y-intercepts 1 and -1.

Consider this equation.

$$x^2 + \left(\frac{y}{2}\right)^2 = 1 \qquad \ldots \text{③}$$

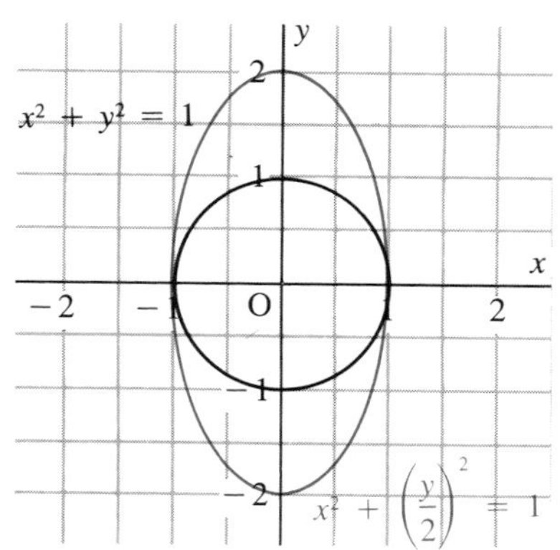

To give the same numbers whose squares add to 1 as in equation ①, the values of y must be 2 *times* those in equation ①. Every point whose coordinates satisfy equation ③ is 2 times as far from the x-axis as the corresponding point whose coordinates satisfy equation ①. Hence, the graph of equation ③ is *expanded vertically* by a factor of 2 relative to the graph of equation ①. Equation ③ represents an ellipse with x-intercepts 1 and -1, and with y-intercepts 2 and -2.

Consider this equation.

$$\left(\frac{x}{3}\right)^2 + \left(\frac{y}{2}\right)^2 = 1 \quad \ldots ④$$

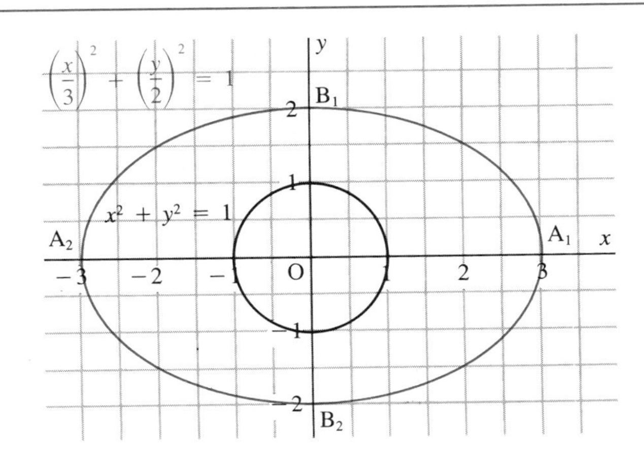

The graph of equation ④ is *expanded horizontally* by a factor of 3 and *expanded vertically* by a factor of 2 relative to the graph of equation ①. Equation ④ represents an ellipse with x-intercepts 3 and -3, and with y-intercepts 2 and -2. The equation is usually written as $\frac{x^2}{9} + \frac{y^2}{4} = 1$.

(0,0) is called the *centre* of the ellipse. The line segment A_1A_2 is called the *major axis*. The line segment B_1B_2 is called the *minor axis*. Points $A_1(3,0)$ and $A_2(-3,0)$ are called the *vertices*; these are the endpoints of the major axis.

For any ellipse, the length of the major axis is represented by $2a$, and the length of the minor axis is represented by $2b$. Since the major axis is longer than the minor axis, this means that $a > b > 0$. As the examples on the facing page show, the major axis can be on either the x-axis or the y-axis. Hence, when we write the standard equation of an ellipse, we must distinguish between these two cases.

Standard Equations of an Ellipse with Centre (0,0)

The equation of an ellipse with centre (0,0) and major axis on the x-axis is $\frac{x^2}{a^2} + \frac{y^2}{b^2} = 1$, where $a > b$.

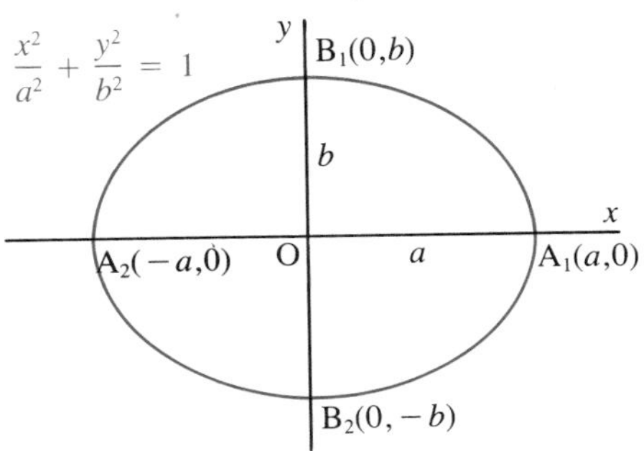

Length of major axis: $2a$
Length of minor axis: $2b$
Vertices: $(a,0)$ and $(-a,0)$

The equation of an ellipse with centre (0,0) and major axis on the y-axis is $\frac{x^2}{b^2} + \frac{y^2}{a^2} = 1$, where $a > b$.

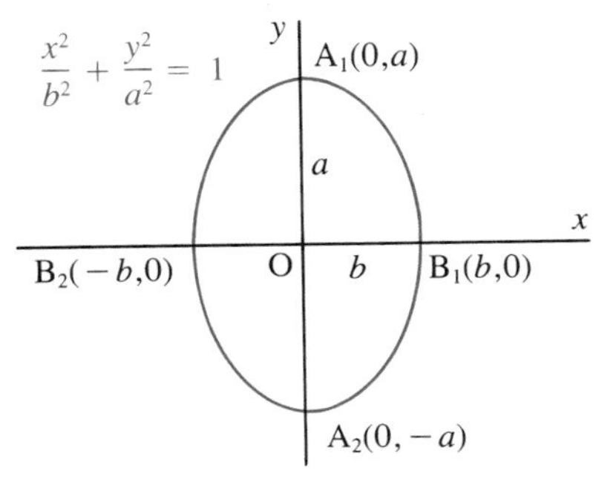

Length of major axis: $2a$
Length of minor axis: $2b$
Vertices: $(0,a)$ and $(0,-a)$

We can always tell whether the major axis is on the x-axis or the y-axis from the standard equation. If the larger denominator occurs in the term containing x, the major axis is on the x-axis; if it occurs in the term containing y, the major axis is on the y-axis.

Example 1. Given the equation $4x^2 + 25y^2 = 100$

a) Show that this equation represents an ellipse. Determine the lengths of the major and minor axes, and the coordinates of the vertices.

b) Identify the transformation which maps the circle defined by $x^2 + y^2 = 1$ to the ellipse.

c) Graph the ellipse.

Solution. a) Since the standard equation has 1 on the right side, we divide both sides of the equation by 100.

$$\frac{4x^2}{100} + \frac{25y^2}{100} = 1$$

$$\frac{x^2}{25} + \frac{y^2}{4} = 1$$

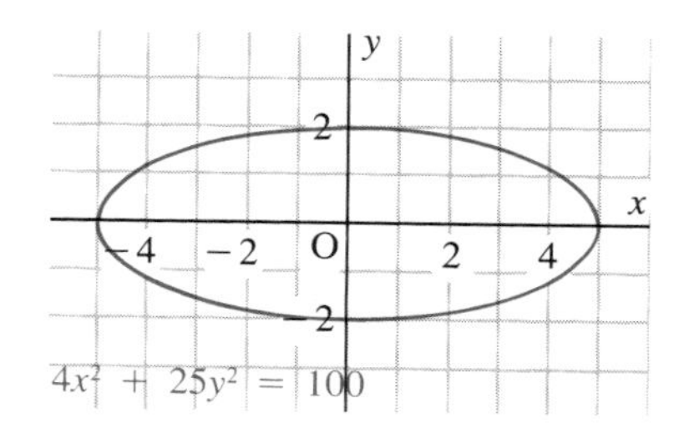

Hence, the equation represents an ellipse.

For this equation, $a = 5$ and $b = 2$
The major axis has length $2a$, or 10.
The minor axis has length $2b$, or 4.
Since the larger denominator occurs under x^2, the major axis lies on the x-axis. The coordinates of the vertices are (5,0) and (−5,0).

b) The ellipse is the image of the circle defined by $x^2 + y^2 = 1$ under an expansion by a factor of 5 horizontally and a factor of 2 vertically.

Example 2. An ellipse has centre (0,0) and one vertex A(0,6).

a) **Find the equation of the ellipse if it passes through the point R(4,2).**

b) Find the value of x_1 if $S(x_1,4)$ is on the ellipse.

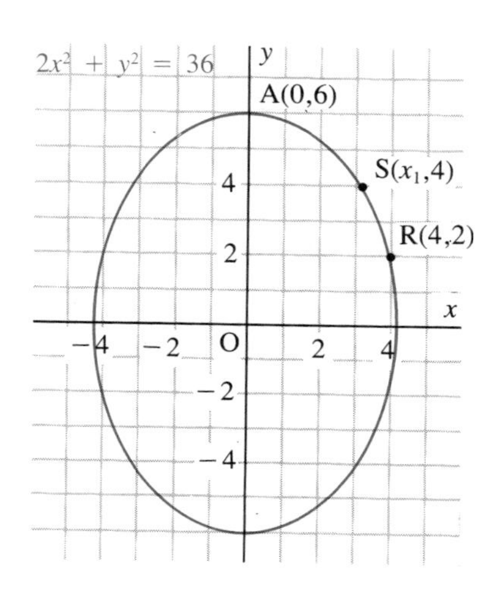

Solution. a) Since one vertex is A(0,6), then $a = 6$.
Since the vertices are on the y-axis, let the equation of the ellipse be $\frac{x^2}{b^2} + \frac{y^2}{36} = 1$.

Since R(4,2) is a point on the ellipse, its coordinates satisfy the equation.

$$\frac{16}{b^2} + \frac{1}{9} = 1$$

$$\frac{16}{b^2} = \frac{8}{9}$$

$$b^2 = 18$$

The equation of the ellipse is $\frac{x^2}{18} + \frac{y^2}{36} = 1$, which can be written in a different form by multiplying both sides by 36. The result is $2x^2 + y^2 = 36$.

b) Substitute x_1 for x and 4 for y in the equation.

$$2x_1^2 + 16 = 36$$

$$x_1^2 = 10$$

$$x_1 = \pm\sqrt{10}$$

Hence, if $S(x_1,4)$ is on the ellipse, $x_1 = \pm\sqrt{10}$.

In *Example 2* we wrote the equation of the ellipse in the form $Ax^2 + By^2 = C$. Any equation in this form represents an ellipse with centre (0,0) and vertices on a coordinate axis. Whether the major axis is on the x-axis or the y-axis depends on the relative magnitudes of the coefficients.

Example 3. A pool has the shape of an ellipse. The major axis has length 10 m and the minor axis has length 6 m.

a) Write an equation of the ellipse.

b) Find the width of the pool at a point on the major axis which is 2 m from the centre.

Solution. a) Let the equation of the ellipse be $\frac{x^2}{a^2} + \frac{y^2}{b^2} = 1$.

Since the major axis has length 10 m and the minor axis has length 6 m, then $2a = 10$ and $2b = 6$.

Hence, $a = 5$ and $b = 3$

The equation of the ellipse is

$$\frac{x^2}{25} + \frac{y^2}{9} = 1$$

or $$9x^2 + 25y^2 = 225$$

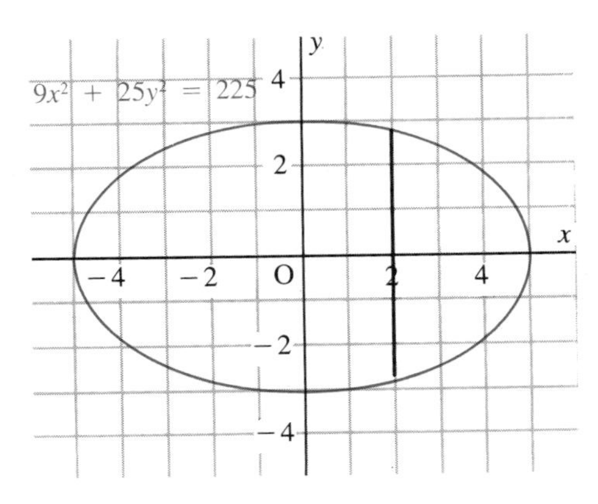

b) To find the width of the pool at a point on the major axis which is 2 m from the centre, substitute 2 for x in the equation.

$$\begin{aligned} 9(2)^2 + 25y^2 &= 225 \\ 36 + 25y^2 &= 225 \\ 25y^2 &= 189 \\ y &= \frac{\pm\sqrt{189}}{5} \\ &\doteq \pm 2.75 \end{aligned}$$

Hence, the points (2,2.75) and (2, −2.75) are on the ellipse. The required width is the distance between these points, which is 2(2.75 m), or 5.50 m.

EXERCISES 12-4

Ⓐ

1. Determine if each point is on the ellipse defined by $x^2 + 4y^2 = 20$.
   a) (4,1) b) (−2,2) c) (0, −5) d) $(0,\sqrt{5})$

2. State the coordinates of the centre, the coordinates of the vertices, and the lengths of the major and minor axes of the ellipse defined by each equation.
   a) $\frac{x^2}{16} + \frac{y^2}{9} = 1$ b) $\frac{x^2}{36} + \frac{y^2}{25} = 1$ c) $\frac{x^2}{4} + \frac{y^2}{9} = 1$
   d) $\frac{x^2}{16} + \frac{y^2}{49} = 1$ e) $\frac{x^2}{64} + \frac{y^2}{16} = 1$ f) $\frac{x^2}{9} + \frac{y^2}{25} = 1$

Ⓑ

3. An ellipse has centre (0,0) and major axis on the x-axis. Write the equation of the ellipse if:
   a) $a = 5$ and $b = 3$
   b) $a = 8$ and $b = 6$
   c) $a = 4$ and $b = 1$
   d) the x-intercepts are ± 7 and the y-intercepts are ± 3
   e) the major axis has length 10 and the minor axis has length 6
   f) one vertex is $A_1(6,0)$ and one y-intercept is 2.

4. For each ellipse whose equation is given below
   i) Write the standard equation.
   ii) Determine the lengths of the major and minor axes, and the coordinates of the vertices.
   iii) Graph the ellipse.
   a) $4x^2 + 9y^2 = 36$ b) $x^2 + 4y^2 = 16$ c) $16x^2 + 9y^2 = 144$
   d) $25x^2 + 16y^2 = 400$ e) $9x^2 + y^2 = 9$ f) $2x^2 + 3y^2 = 6$

5. Sketch the ellipse defined by each equation. Then identify the transformation which maps the circle defined by $x^2 + y^2 = 1$ to the ellipse.

a) $\frac{x^2}{16} + \frac{y^2}{36} = 1$ b) $\frac{x^2}{49} + \frac{y^2}{25} = 1$ c) $\frac{x^2}{9} + \frac{y^2}{6} = 1$

d) $x^2 + 3y^2 = 12$ e) $4x^2 + y^2 = 20$ f) $3x^2 + 4y^2 = 36$

6. An ellipse has centre (0,0) and one vertex A(10,0).
   a) Find the equation of the ellipse if it passes through R(6,4).
   b) Find the value of x_1 if $S(x_1,3)$ is on the ellipse.
   c) Find the value of y_1 if $T(5,y_1)$ is on the ellipse.

7. A retractable dome on a sports stadium has the shape of an ellipse. Its height is 25 m and it spans 60 m.
   a) Write an equation of the ellipse.
   b) Calculate the height of the dome at a point on the major axis which is 20 m from the centre.

8. A tunnel is built under a river for a road 12 m wide with a 2 m sidewalk on either side. The top of the tunnel is semi-elliptical. A local bylaw stipulates that there must be a clearance of at least 3.6 m at all points on the road. If the smallest possible ellipse is used, find the clearance at the centre of the road.

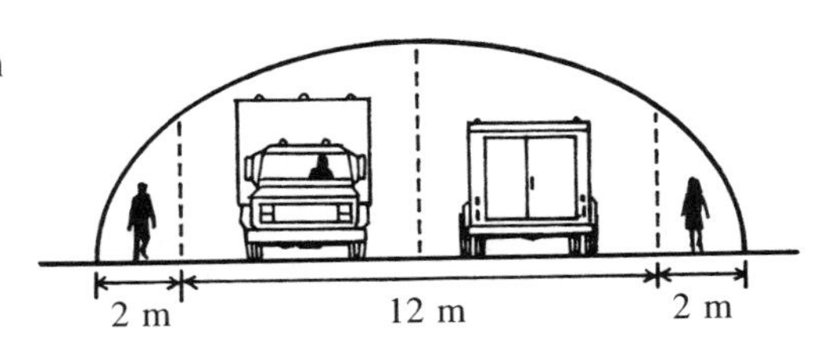

Ⓒ

9. Describe how the graph of the ellipse $\frac{x^2}{a^2} + \frac{y^2}{b^2} = 1$ changes if:

a) b is kept constant and a varies b) a is kept constant and b varies.

10. Given the equation $Ax^2 + By^2 + C = 0$, what conditions must be satisfied by A, B, and C if this equation represents an ellipse with major axis on:
   a) the x-axis b) the y-axis?

11. Draw a diagram to represent the ellipse defined by $\frac{x^2}{a^2} + \frac{y^2}{b^2} = 1$. Let P be any point on this ellipse.
   a) On the same grid, draw the circle defined by $x^2 + y^2 = a^2$. Draw a vertical line through P to intersect this circle at Q and the x-axis at R. Prove that $\frac{\text{PR}}{\text{QR}} = \frac{b}{a}$.
   b) On the same grid, draw the circle defined by $x^2 + y^2 = b^2$. Draw a horizontal line through P to intersect this circle at S and the y-axis at T. Prove that $\frac{\text{PT}}{\text{ST}} = \frac{a}{b}$.

Constructing an Ellipse

To construct an ellipse, follow these steps. You will need a piece of corrugated cardboard, some string, some tape, and two paper fasteners.

Step 1.
Tape a piece of paper to the cardboard, and push the paper fasteners through it, about 6 cm apart. Tie the string into a loop about 16 cm long.

Step 2.
Place the loop around the paper fasteners. Use a pencil to keep the string taut.

Step 3.
Keeping the string taut, move the pencil to trace out an ellipse.

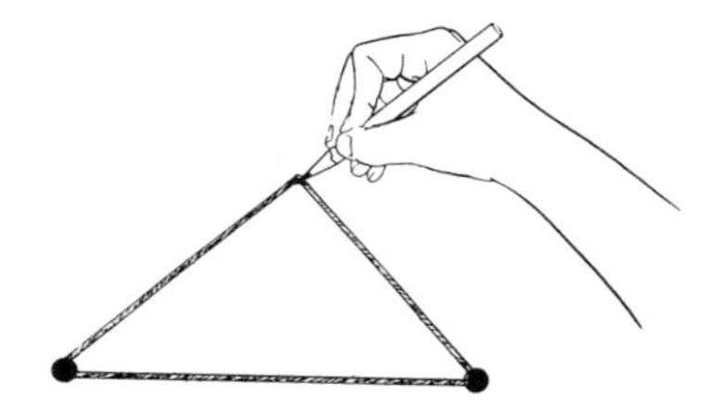

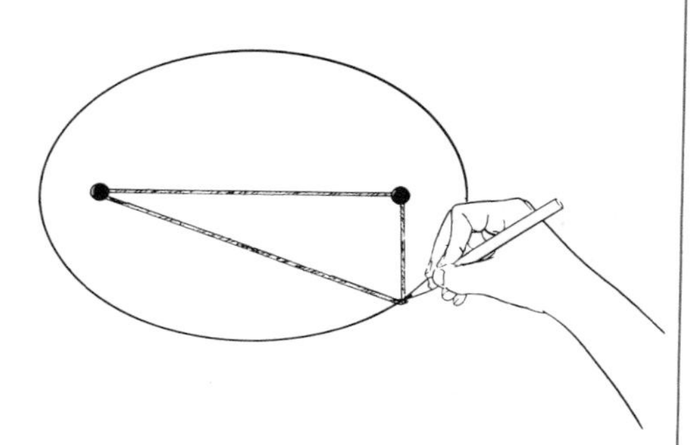

1. Construct an ellipse by following the above steps.
2. Explain how this construction illustrates the following definition of an ellipse.

   An *ellipse* is a set of points P such that the sum of the distances from P to two fixed points is constant. The two fixed points are called the *foci* of the ellipse.
3. For the ellipse you constructed, mark the foci F_1 and F_2.
   a) Mark any point P on the ellipse. Measure PF_1 and PF_2, and calculate the sum $PF_1 + PF_2$. Repeat for other points P on the ellipse.
   b) Locate the vertices A_1 and A_2. How does the length of A_1A_2 compare with the sum $PF_1 + PF_2$ for any point P on the ellipse?
4. Use the above definition to show that, for any point P on an ellipse, the sum $PF_1 + PF_2$ is always equal to the length of the major axis.
5. Investigate the effect on the shape of the ellipse of changing the length of the loop of string, or changing the distance between the paper fasteners.

Using the Constant Sum Definition to Develop the Equation of an Ellipse

In *Section 12-4* we obtained an ellipse by expanding a circle horizontally and vertically by different factors. But the definition of an ellipse given on the facing page is different from that used in *Section 12-4*. Hence, we should be able to develop the equation of an ellipse from the new definition.

For example, let F_1 and F_2 be the points (3,0) and (−3,0) respectively. Then, using the definition on the facing page, a set of points P such that the sum of the distances from P to F_1 and to F_2 is constant is an ellipse. Let us assume that the constant sum is 10 units. Then we can find the equation of the ellipse as follows.

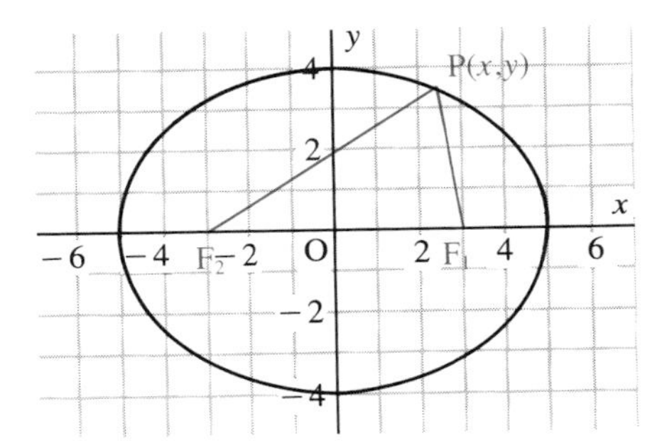

Let $P(x,y)$ be any point on the ellipse.

$$PF_1 + PF_2 = 10$$

$$\sqrt{(x-3)^2 + y^2} + \sqrt{(x+3)^2 + y^2} = 10$$

Isolate one of the radicals and square both sides.

$$\sqrt{(x-3)^2 + y^2} = 10 - \sqrt{(x+3)^2 + y^2}$$

$$\left(\sqrt{(x-3)^2 + y^2}\right)^2 = \left(10 - \sqrt{(x+3)^2 + y^2}\right)^2$$

$$(x-3)^2 + y^2 = 100 - 20\sqrt{(x+3)^2 + y^2} + (x+3)^2 + y^2$$

$$x^2 - 6x + 9 + y^2 = 100 - 20\sqrt{(x+3)^2 + y^2} + x^2 + 6x + 9 + y^2$$

Isolate the radical and square both sides again.

$$20\sqrt{(x+3)^2 + y^2} = 100 + 12x$$

$$5\sqrt{(x+3)^2 + y^2} = 25 + 3x$$

$$25(x^2 + 6x + 9 + y^2) = 625 + 150x + 9x^2$$

This equation simplifies to

$$16x^2 + 25y^2 = 400$$

or

$$\frac{x^2}{25} + \frac{y^2}{16} = 1$$

1. Let F_1 and F_2 be the points (2,0) and (−2,0) respectively. Find the equation of the ellipse defined by points P such that the sum of the distances from P to F_1 and to F_2 is 6 units.
2. Let F_1 and F_2 be the points $(c,0)$ and $(-c,0)$ respectively. Find the equation of the ellipse defined by points P such that the sum of the distances from P to F_1 and to F_2 is $2a$ units.

MATHEMATICS AROUND US

Inverse Variation

Police often identify speeders on a highway by measuring, from the air, the time it takes a car to cover a marked portion of the road. The table shows how the speed of a car is related to the time it takes to travel 0.5 km.

Time t (s)	Speed v (km/h)
20	90
40	45
60	30
80	22.5
100	18

The table shows that when t is doubled, v is divided by 2; when t is tripled, v is divided by 3, and so on. That is, the product of v and t is constant. We say that v *varies inversely* as t, and write $vt = k$, or $v = \frac{k}{t}$, where k is a constant. From the table, we can verify that $vt = 1800$ for all values of v and t.

If we plot the data, the resulting curve is part of a *rectangular hyperbola*. The equation of this hyperbola is $vt = 1800$.

The graph shows only one branch of the hyperbola. Another branch, corresponding to negative values of v and t, could be plotted in the third quadrant, but this would not be appropriate for distances and speeds, which are positive.

We can use the equation or the graph to find the speed of the car for times other than those given in the table. For example, if the time is measured as 23 s, then the speed of the car is found by substituting 23 for v in $vt = 1800$. Solving for v, we find $v \doteq 78$. Hence, a car which takes 23 s to complete the marked portion of the road is travelling at about 78 km/h.

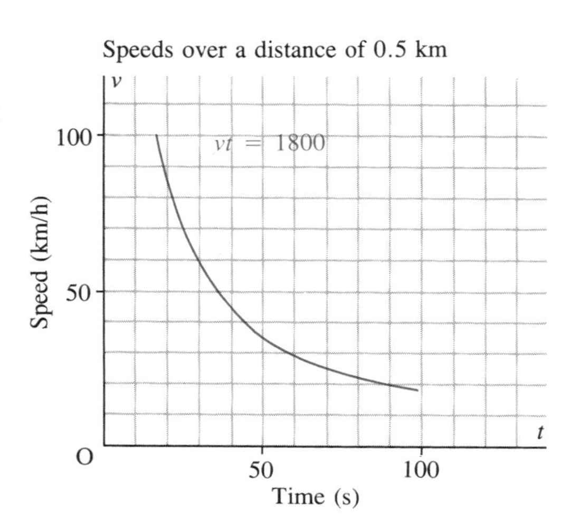

QUESTIONS

1. Make a table of values and sketch the rectangular hyperbola represented by each equation on the same grid. Show both branches of each hyperbola.
   a) $xy = 24$ b) $xy = 12$ c) $xy = 6$ d) $xy = 1$

2. If y varies inversely as x, find the equation relating x and y, then copy and complete the tables.

a)

x	4	8	12	16	24
y	12				

b)

x	10	12	15	20	30
y	6				

3. y varies inversely as x and when $x = 9$, $y = 4$.
   a) Find an equation relating x and y.
   b) Find: i) y when $x = 12$ ii) x when $y = 2$.
   c) Graph the relation between x and y.

4. The time it takes to complete a bike-a-thon course varies inversely as the cyclist's average speed. At an average speed of 15 km/h it takes 3.2 h to complete the course.
   a) How long does it take to complete the course at: i) 12 km/h ii) 20 km/h?
   b) If the course is completed in 2 h, what is the average speed?
   c) Graph the relation between the time to complete the course and the average speed.

5. The number of hours required to construct a motion-picture set varies inversely as the number of workers. If the set can be constructed in 3 days by 20 workers, how many days would 12 workers require?

6. The number of years required for an investment to double varies inversely as the interest rate. At 8% per annum compound interest, an investment will double in about 9 years. Find an equation expressing the time n years for an investment to double as a function of the interest rate r percent.

7. Each rectangle in a set of rectangles has an area of 360 cm^2.
   a) Graph the relation between the length and the width of the rectangles.
   b) Graph the relation between the length and the perimeter.
   c) Does the length vary inversely as: i) the width ii) the perimeter?

8. The intensity of illumination of a screen varies inversely as the square of its distance from a projector. When the distance is 4 m, the intensity is 10 units.
   a) Find an equation relating the intensity I units to the distance d metres.
   b) If a graph of the relation between I and d were drawn, explain why the curve would not be a rectangular hyperbola.
   c) Explain how a graph of the relation could be drawn such that the curve would be a rectangular hyperbola.

12-5 THE RECTANGULAR HYPERBOLA

In *Section 12-3* we saw that an equation such as $x^2 + y^2 = 9$ represents a circle. A similar equation is $x^2 - y^2 = 9$. Since the squared terms are subtracted, this equation cannot represent a circle. But it is a second-degree equation, and it represents a conic.

Example 1. Graph the relation $x^2 - y^2 = 9$, and identify the conic it represents.

Solution. First, solve the equation for y.

$$x^2 - y^2 = 9$$
$$y^2 = x^2 - 9$$
$$y = \pm\sqrt{x^2 - 9}$$

We could graph the relation by making a table of values. But a more efficient method is to consider how the values of y are related to the values of x.

Since $x^2 - 9$ occurs under the radical sign, then $x^2 - 9 \geqslant 0$. Hence, values of y are defined only when $x \geqslant 3$ or when $x \leqslant -3$.

If $x = \pm 3$, then $y = \pm\sqrt{(\pm 3)^2 - 9}$

$$= 0$$

Hence, (3,0) and (−3,0) are on the graph.

For each value of $x > 3$, or $x < -3$, there are two values of y, one positive and the other negative. If $|x|$ is large, then x^2 is very large compared with 9, and so

$$y = \pm\sqrt{x^2 - 9}$$
$$\doteq \pm\sqrt{x^2}$$
$$\doteq x \text{ or } -x$$

Hence, the graph comes closer to the lines defined by $y = x$ and $y = -x$. The graph is a hyperbola.

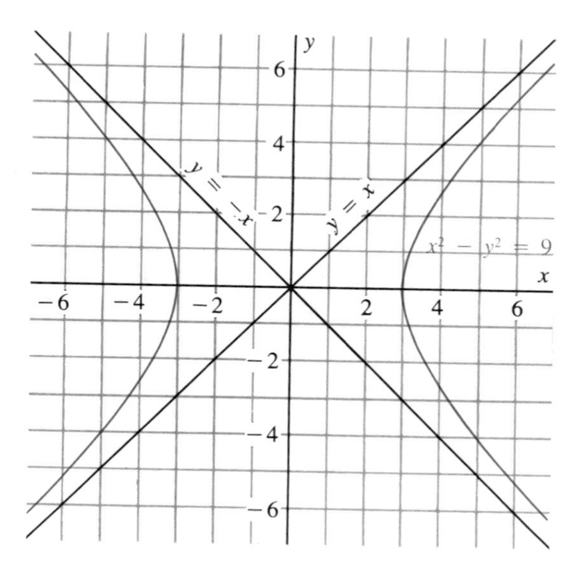

In *Example 1* the point (0,0) is called the *centre* of the hyperbola. The points (3,0) and (−3,0) are called the *vertices*. The lines defined by $y = x$ and $y = -x$ are called the *asymptotes*. Since the asymptotes are perpendicular, we say that the hyperbola is *rectangular*.

The above example suggests that any equation of the form $x^2 - y^2 = a^2$ represents a rectangular hyperbola with centre (0,0) and vertices on the x-axis. A rectangular hyperbola with vertices on the y-axis will have a different form of equation. To discover this form, we can interchange x and y in the equation of the hyperbola in *Example 1*. This has the effect of reversing the coordinates of the points which satisfy the equation. Hence, the graph of the relation is reflected in the line defined by $y = x$.

If we interchange x and y in $x^2 - y^2 = 9$, we obtain $y^2 - x^2 = 9$.

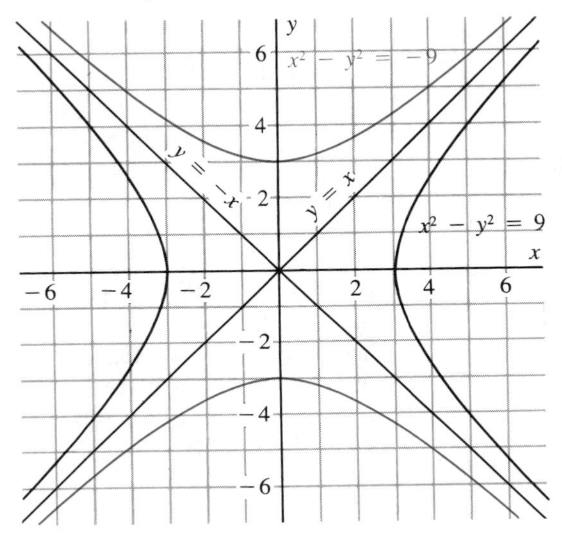

It is customary to write this equation as $x^2 - y^2 = -9$. The graph of this relation is shown. It was obtained by reflecting the graph of *Example 1* in the line defined by $y = x$.

Using the methods of the above examples, we can write the equation of any rectangular hyperbola with centre (0,0) and vertices on the coordinate axes. The form of the equation depends on whether the vertices are on the x-axis or the y-axis.

Standard Equations of a Rectangular Hyperbola with Centre (0,0)

The equation of a rectangular hyperbola with centre (0,0) and vertices on the x-axis is $x^2 - y^2 = a^2$.

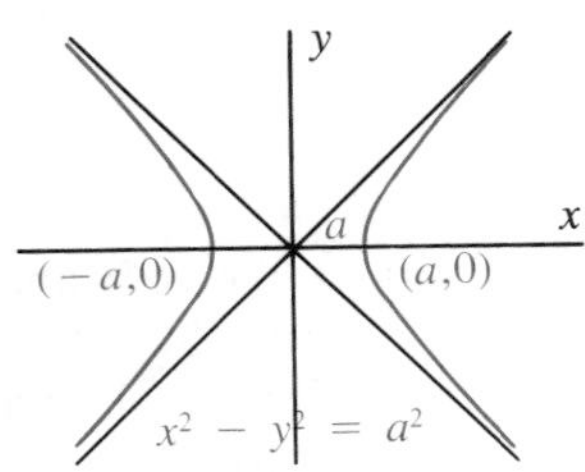

Vertices: $(a,0)$ and $(-a,0)$
Asymptotes: $y = x$ and $y = -x$

The equation of a rectangular hyperbola with centre (0,0) and vertices on the y-axis is $x^2 - y^2 = -a^2$.

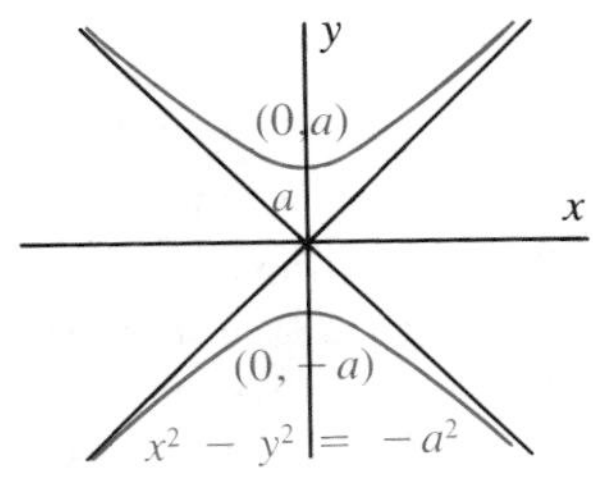

Vertices: $(0,a)$ and $(0,-a)$
Asymptotes: $y = x$ and $y = -x$

We can always tell whether the vertices are on the x-axis or the y-axis from the standard equation. If the constant term on the right side is positive, the vertices are on the x-axis; if it is negative, the vertices are on the y-axis.

Example 2. The arch of a bridge has the shape of a rectangular hyperbola. The base is 120 m wide, and the vertex is 30 m above the base.

a) Find an equation of the hyperbola.

b) Find the height of the arch at a point 25 m from the centre.

Solution. a) Let the equation of the hyperbola be $x^2 - y^2 = -a^2$. The coordinates of vertex A_2 are $(0, -a)$. Let P be a point 60 m to the right of A_2 and 30 m below A_2. Hence, the coordinates of P are $(60, -a - 30)$. Since P is on the hyperbola, its coordinates satisfy the equation. Substitute 60 for x and $-a - 30$ for y in $x^2 - y^2 = -a^2$.

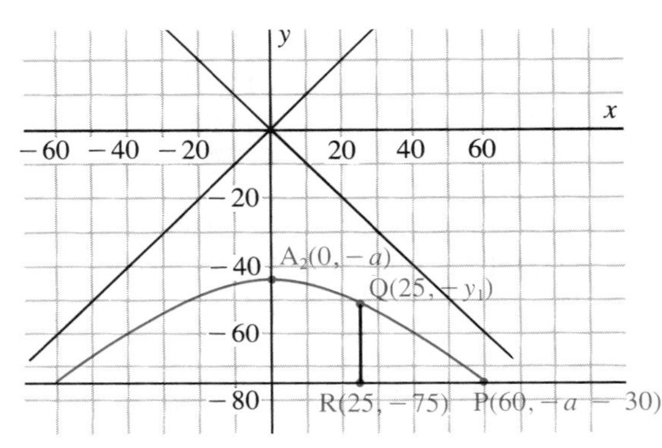

$$\begin{aligned} 3600 - (-a - 30)^2 &= -a^2 \\ 3600 - (a^2 + 60a + 900) &= -a^2 \\ a &= \frac{2700}{60} \\ &= 45 \end{aligned}$$

Hence, the equation of the hyperbola is $x^2 - y^2 = -45^2$, or $x^2 - y^2 = -2025$.

b) Let $Q(25, -y_1)$ represent a point on the arch 25 m from the centre. Then these coordinates satisfy the equation. Substitute 25 for x and y_1 for y.

$$\begin{aligned} x^2 - y^2 &= -2025 \\ 625 - y_1^2 &= -2025 \\ y_1^2 &= 2650 \\ y_1 &= \sqrt{2650} \\ &\doteq 51.5 \end{aligned}$$

The coordinates of Q are $(25, -51.5)$. From part a), the coordinates of P are $(60, -75)$. Hence, the coordinates of R are $(25, -75)$, and the length of segment QR is $75 - 51.5$, or 23.5. Hence, the arch is 23.5 m high at a point which is 25 m from the centre.

EXERCISES 12-5

(A)

1. Determine if each point is on the rectangular hyperbola defined by $x^2 - y^2 = 15$.
   a) $(-4,1)$ b) $(7,8)$ c) $(8,7)$ d) $(0,\sqrt{15})$

2. State the coordinates of the centre, the coordinates of the vertices, and the equations of the asymptotes of the rectangular hyperbola defined by each equation.
   a) $x^2 - y^2 = 25$ b) $x^2 - y^2 = 64$ c) $x^2 - y^2 = -81$
   d) $x^2 - y^2 = 2$ e) $x^2 - y^2 = -5$ f) $x^2 - y^2 = -20$

3. The coordinates of one vertex of a rectangular hyperbola are given. If the centre is (0,0), write an equation of the rectangular hyperbola.
   a) $(7,0)$ b) $(0,4)$ c) $(0,-6)$ d) $(-10,0)$

(B)

4. Sketch the rectangular hyperbolas defined by these equations on the same grid.
   a) $x^2 - y^2 = 4$ b) $x^2 - y^2 = 16$ c) $x^2 - y^2 = 36$
   d) $x^2 - y^2 = -4$ e) $x^2 - y^2 = -16$ f) $x^2 - y^2 = -36$

5. When a square is cut from another square as shown, the area of the remaining portion is 144 cm^2.
   a) Find the relation between x and y.
   b) Graph the relation.

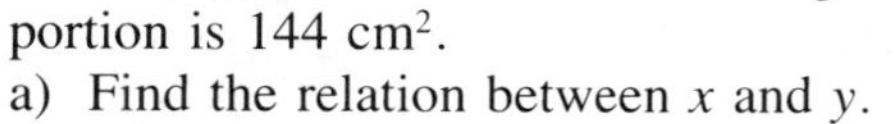

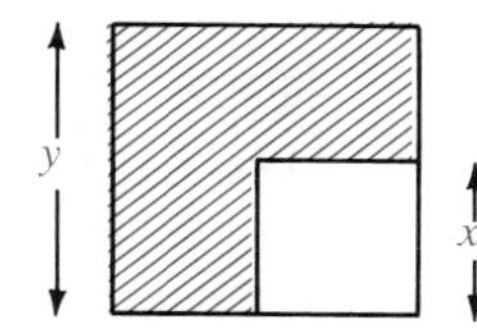

6. A rectangular hyperbola has centre (0,0) and vertices on the x-axis.
   a) Find an equation of the hyperbola if it passes through (8,2).
   b) Find the value of x_1 if $(x_1,14)$ is on the hyperbola.

7. A rectangular hyperbola has centre (0,0) and vertices on the y-axis.
   a) Find an equation of the hyperbola if it passes through $(7,-8)$.
   b) Find the value of y_1 if $(1,y_1)$ is on the hyperbola.

8. A bridge over a river is supported by a hyperbolic arch which is 200 m wide at the base. The maximum height of the arch is 50 m.
   a) Write an equation to represent the arch.
   b) How high is the arch at a point 30 m from the centre?

(C)

9. Given the equation $Ax^2 + By^2 + C = 0$, what conditions must be satisfied by A, B, and C if this equation represents a rectangular hyperbola with vertices on:
   a) the x-axis b) the y-axis?

10. $P(x_1,y_1)$ is a point on the right branch of the rectangular hyperbola defined by $x^2 - y^2 = 4$. $D(\sqrt{2},y_1)$ is the corresponding point to the left of P on the line defined by $x = \sqrt{2}$.
    a) If F is the point $(2\sqrt{2},0)$ prove that $PF = \sqrt{2}PD$ for any position of P on the right branch of the hyperbola.
    b) Obtain a similar result if P is a point on the left branch.

12-6 THE HYPERBOLA: PART ONE

The *Saddledome* was built for the figure skating and hockey events of the 1988 Olympic Winter Games in Calgary, and it is used by the Calgary Flames hockey team. Horizontal cross-sections of its saddle-shaped roof are hyperbolas.

Not all hyperbolas are rectangular hyperbolas. We can obtain any hyperbola by expanding a rectangular hyperbola horizontally or vertically. We can also expand it by different amounts both horizontally and vertically. And, if we know the equation of the rectangular hyperbola, we can find the equation of the image hyperbola.

Compare these two equations.

$$x^2 - y^2 = 1 \quad \ldots ①$$

$$\left(\frac{x}{3}\right)^2 - y^2 = 1 \quad \ldots ②$$

Each equation states that the difference of the squares of two numbers is 1. In equation ①, these numbers are the coordinates of points on a rectangular hyperbola. In equation ②, to give the same numbers whose squares differ by 1 as in equation ①, the values of x must be 3 *times* those in equation ①. Every point whose coordinates satisfy equation ② is 3 times as far from the y-axis as the corresponding point whose coordinates satisfy equation ①. Hence, the graph of equation ② is *expanded horizontally* by a factor of 3 relative to the graph of equation ①. Equation ② represents a hyperbola with x-intercepts 3 and -3. There are no y-intercepts.

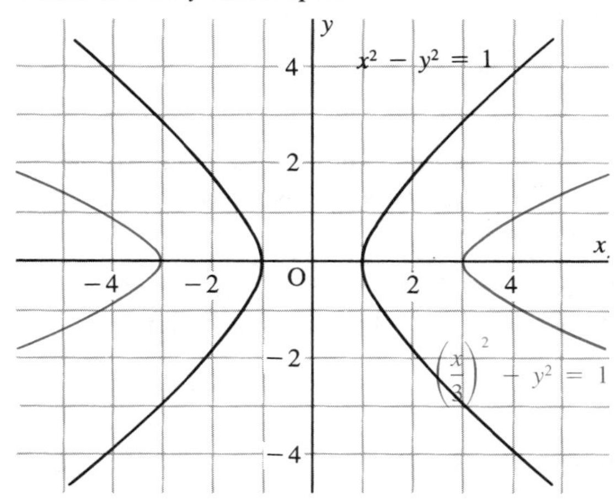

Consider this equation.

$$x^2 - \left(\frac{y}{2}\right)^2 = 1 \quad \ldots ③$$

To give the same numbers whose squares differ by 1 as in equation ①, the values of y must be 2 *times* those in equation ①. Every point whose coordinates satisfy equation ③ is 2 times as far from the x-axis as the corresponding point whose coordinates satisfy equation ①. Hence, the graph of equation ③ is *expanded vertically* by a factor of 2 relative to the graph of equation ①. Equation ③ represents a hyperbola with x-intercepts 1 and -1. There are no y-intercepts.

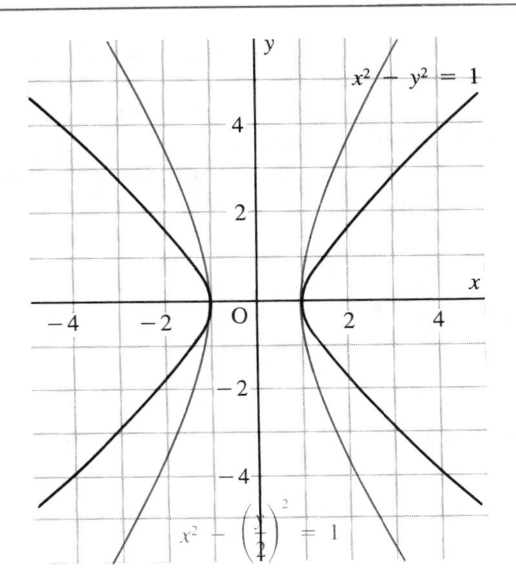

Consider this equation.

$$\left(\frac{x}{3}\right)^2 - \left(\frac{y}{2}\right)^2 = 1 \quad \ldots ④$$

The graph of equation ④ is *expanded horizontally* by a factor of 3 and *expanded vertically* by a factor of 2 relative to the graph of equation ①. Equation ④ represents a hyperbola with x-intercepts 3 and -3. There are no y-intercepts. The equation is usually written as $\frac{x^2}{9} - \frac{y^2}{4} = 1$.

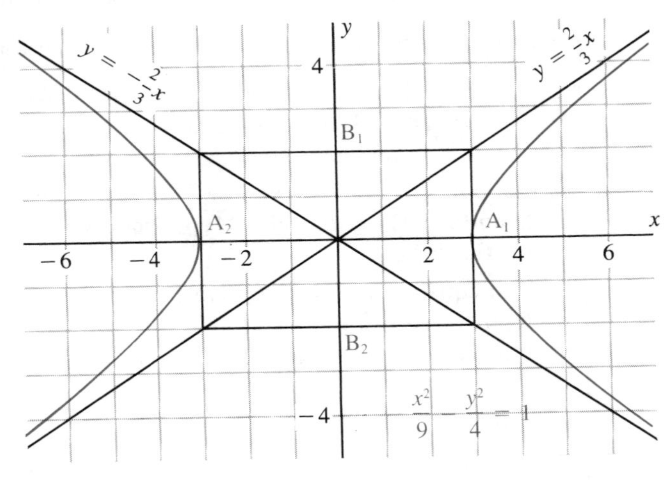

(0,0) is called the *centre* of the hyperbola.
The line segment A_1A_2 is called the *transverse axis*.
Points $A_1(3,0)$ and $A_2(-3,0)$ are called the *vertices*; these are the endpoints of the transverse axis.
Since there was a vertical expansion by a factor of 2, we indicate the points $B_1(0,2)$ and $B_2(0,-2)$ on the y-axis. The line segment B_1B_2 is called the *conjugate axis*.

The diagram shows a rectangle centred at the origin, whose sides have lengths equal to the lengths of the transverse and conjugate axes. The points A_1, A_2, B_1, and B_2 are the midpoints of the sides of this rectangle. The hyperbola lies between the lines containing its diagonals. As $|x|$ increases, the hyperbola comes closer to these lines. We can see why by solving the equation for y.

$$\frac{y^2}{4} = \frac{x^2}{9} - 1$$

$$\frac{y^2}{4} = \frac{x^2 - 9}{9}$$

$$y = \pm\frac{2}{3}\sqrt{x^2 - 9}$$

If $|x|$ is large, then x^2 is very large compared with 9. Hence,

$$y \doteq \pm\frac{2}{3}\sqrt{x^2}$$

$$\doteq \pm\frac{2}{3}x$$

The lines defined by $y = \frac{2}{3}x$ and $y = -\frac{2}{3}x$ are called the *asymptotes* of the hyperbola.

For any hyperbola, the length of the transverse axis is represented by $2a$, and the length of the conjugate axis is represented by $2b$. As the above examples suggest, an equation of the form $\frac{x^2}{a^2} - \frac{y^2}{b^2} = 1$ represents a hyperbola with transverse axis on the x-axis, for all positive values of a and b. Hence, there is no restriction that a be greater than b, as there was for the ellipse.

Standard Equation of a Hyperbola with Centre (0,0) and Transverse Axis on the x-axis

The equation of a hyperbola with centre (0,0) and transverse axis on the x-axis is $\frac{x^2}{a^2} - \frac{y^2}{b^2} = 1$.

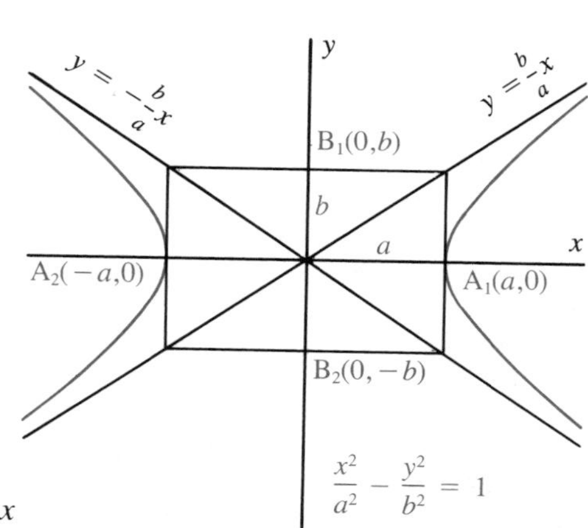

Length of transverse axis: $2a$
Length of conjugate axis: $2b$
Vertices: $(a,0)$ and $(-a,0)$
Asymptotes: $y = \frac{b}{a}x$ and $y = -\frac{b}{a}x$

Example. Given the equation $9x^2 - 16y^2 = 144$

a) Show that this equation represents a hyperbola. Determine the lengths of the transverse and conjugate axes, and the coordinates of the vertices.
b) Write the equations of the asymptotes.
c) Identify the transformation which maps the rectangular hyperbola defined by $x^2 - y^2 = 1$ to the hyperbola.
d) Graph the hyperbola.

Solution. a) The standard equation has 1 on the right side. Hence, we divide both sides of the equation by 144.

$$\frac{9x^2}{144} - \frac{16y^2}{144} = 1$$

$$\frac{x^2}{16} - \frac{y^2}{9} = 1$$

Hence, the equation represents a hyperbola.

For this equation, $a = 4$ and $b = 3$
Length of transverse axis: $2a = 8$
Length of conjugate axis: $2b = 6$
Vertices: $(4,0)$ and $(-4,0)$

b) The equations of the asymptotes are $y = \frac{3}{4}x$ and $y = -\frac{3}{4}x$.

c) The hyperbola is the image of the rectangular hyperbola defined by $x^2 - y^2 = 1$ under an expansion by a factor of 4 horizontally and a factor of 3 vertically.

d) To graph the hyperbola, locate the vertices and draw a rectangle centred at the origin, with length 8 units and width 6 units. Next, draw the asymptotes, which are the diagonals of this rectangle. Then sketch the hyperbola.

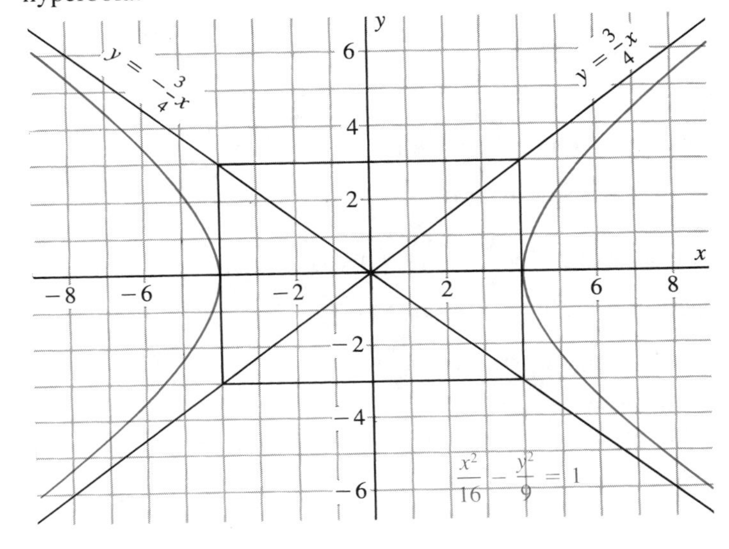

EXERCISES 12-6

Ⓐ

1. Determine if each point is on the hyperbola defined by $3x^2 - 2y^2 = 10$.
   a) $(-2,1)$ b) $(5,6)$ c) $(6,-7)$ d) $(0,\sqrt{5})$

2. State the coordinates of the centre, the coordinates of the vertices, and the lengths of the transverse and conjugate axes of the hyperbola defined by each equation.
   a) $\frac{x^2}{4} - \frac{y^2}{16} = 1$ b) $\frac{x^2}{25} - \frac{y^2}{9} = 1$ c) $\frac{x^2}{81} - \frac{y^2}{49} = 1$

Ⓑ

3. A hyperbola has centre $(0,0)$ and transverse axis on the x-axis. Write the equation of the hyperbola if:
   a) $a = 6$ and $b = 3$
   b) $a = 3$ and $b = 2$
   c) $a = 4$ and $b = 7$
   d) the transverse axis has length 10 and the conjugate axis has length 14
   e) one vertex is A(2,0) and one asymptote is defined by $y = 2x$
   f) one x-intercept is 7 and one asymptote is defined by $y = -x$.

4. For each hyperbola whose equation is given below
   i) Write the standard equation.
   ii) Find the lengths of the transverse and conjugate axes, the coordinates of the vertices, and the equations of the asymptotes.
   iii) Graph the hyperbola.
   a) $9x^2 - 4y^2 = 36$ b) $x^2 - 9y^2 = 36$ c) $25x^2 - 9y^2 = 225$
   d) $4x^2 - y^2 = 16$ e) $x^2 - 3y^2 = 12$ f) $4x^2 - 5y^2 = 20$

5. Sketch the hyperbola defined by each equation. Then identify the transformation which maps the rectangular hyperbola defined by $x^2 - y^2 = 1$ to the hyperbola.
   a) $\frac{x^2}{36} - \frac{y^2}{16} = 1$ b) $\frac{x^2}{81} - \frac{y^2}{25} = 1$ c) $\frac{x^2}{49} - \frac{y^2}{64} = 1$
   d) $3x^2 - y^2 = 18$ e) $x^2 - 4y^2 = 8$ f) $5x^2 - 4y^2 = 40$

Ⓒ

6. Describe how the graph of the hyperbola defined by $\frac{x^2}{a^2} - \frac{y^2}{b^2} = 1$ changes if:
   a) b is kept constant and a varies b) a is kept constant and b varies.

7. Since the ellipse defined by $\frac{x^2}{b^2} + \frac{y^2}{a^2} = 1$ has its major axis on the y-axis, one might think that the hyperbola defined by $\frac{x^2}{b^2} - \frac{y^2}{a^2} = 1$ has its transverse axis on the y-axis. Investigate whether this is true.

8. Given the equation $Ax^2 + By^2 + C = 0$, what conditions must be satisfied by A, B, and C if this equation represents a hyperbola with transverse axis on the x-axis?

12-7 THE HYPERBOLA: PART TWO

In the preceding section we found that when the rectangular hyperbola defined by $x^2 - y^2 = 1$ is expanded horizontally and vertically, the equation of the image has the form $\frac{x^2}{a^2} - \frac{y^2}{b^2} = 1$. The image is a hyperbola with transverse axis on the x-axis. Similar results occur for the rectangular hyperbola defined by $x^2 - y^2 = -1$. The image is a hyperbola with transverse axis on the y-axis.

Example 1. The rectangular hyperbola defined by $x^2 - y^2 = -1$ is expanded horizontally by a factor of 2 and vertically by a factor of 3.

a) Graph the image hyperbola.
b) Find the equation of the image hyperbola.
c) For the image hyperbola, state the coordinates of the vertices, the lengths of the transverse and conjugate axes, and the equations of the asymptotes.

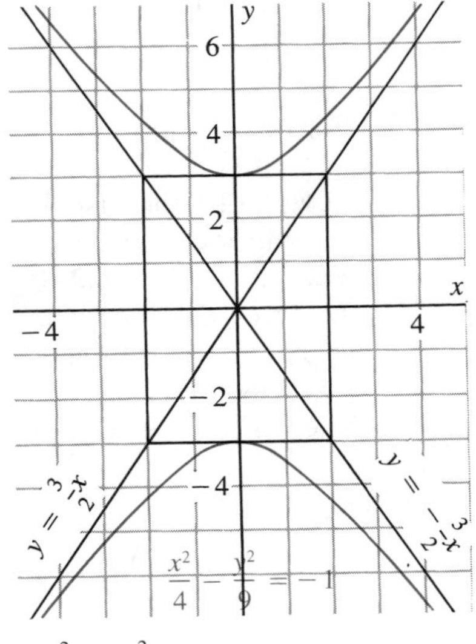

Solution. b) The equation of the image is

$$\left(\frac{x}{2}\right)^2 - \left(\frac{y}{3}\right)^2 = -1,$$

or $\frac{x^2}{4} - \frac{y^2}{9} = -1$.

c) For this hyperbola,
$a = 3$ and $b = 2$
Length of transverse axis:
$2a = 6$
Length of conjugate axis:
$2b = 4$
Vertices: $(0,3)$ and $(0,-3)$
Asymptotes:
$y = \frac{3}{2}x$ and $y = -\frac{3}{2}x$

As *Example 1* suggests, an equation of the form $\frac{x^2}{b^2} - \frac{y^2}{a^2} = -1$ represents a hyperbola with transverse axis on the y-axis, for all positive values of a and b. There is no restriction that a be greater than b, as there was for the ellipse.

We can always tell whether the transverse axis of the hyperbola is on the x-axis or the y-axis from the standard equation. If there is a 1 on the right side, the transverse axis is on the x-axis; if there is a -1 on the right side, the transverse axis is on the y-axis. In either case, the value of a occurs in the term on the left side that has the same sign as the constant term.

Standard Equation of a Hyperbola with Centre (0,0) and Transverse Axis on the y-axis

The equation of a hyperbola with centre (0,0) and transverse axis on the y-axis is $\frac{x^2}{b^2} - \frac{y^2}{a^2} = -1$.

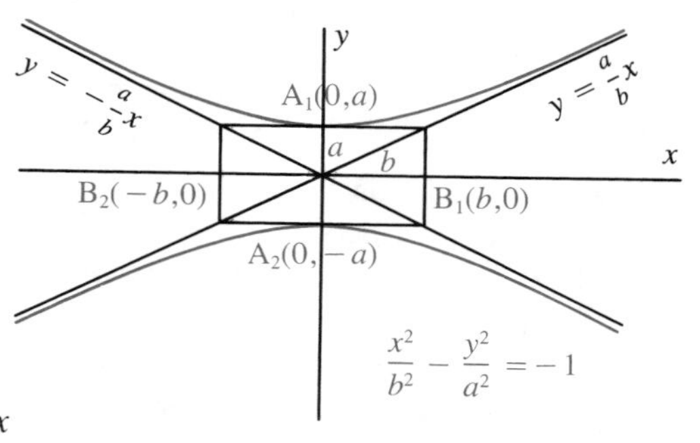

Length of transverse axis: $2a$
Length of conjugate axis: $2b$
Vertices: $(0,a)$ and $(0,-a)$

Asymptotes: $y = \frac{a}{b}x$ and $y = -\frac{a}{b}x$

Example 2. Graph the hyperbola defined by the equation $x^2 - 2y^2 = -8$.

Solution. Divide both sides of the equation by 8.

$$\frac{x^2}{8} - \frac{y^2}{4} = -1$$

For this equation, $a^2 = 4$ and $b^2 = 8$
$a = 2 \qquad b = 2\sqrt{2}$

Length of transverse axis: $2a = 4$
Length of conjugate axis: $2b = 4\sqrt{2}$
Vertices: $(0,2)$ and $(0,-2)$

To graph the hyperbola, locate the vertices and draw a rectangle, centred at the origin, with length $4\sqrt{2}$ units and width 4 units.
Draw the diagonals, and extend them to form the asymptotes.
Then sketch the hyperbola.

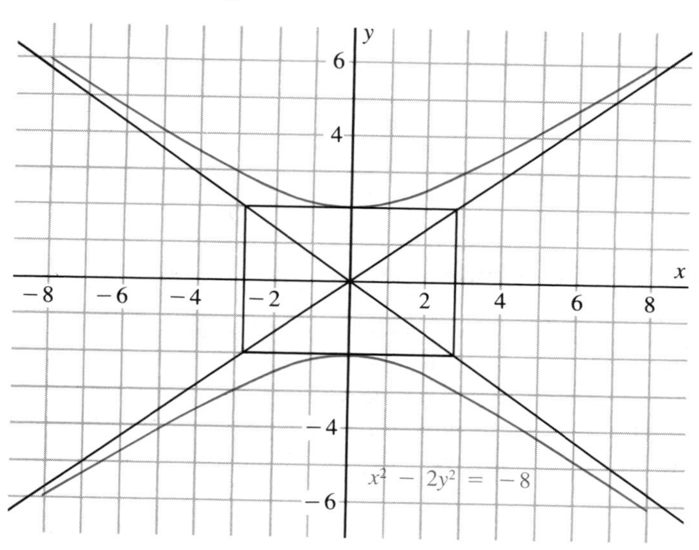

EXERCISES 12-7

(A)

1. Determine if each point is on the hyperbola defined by $7x^2 - 3y^2 = -20$.
   a) $(-1,3)$ b) $(2,-4)$ c) $(5,8)$ d) $(-7,-11)$

2. State the coordinates of the centre, the coordinates of the vertices, and the lengths of the transverse and conjugate axes of the hyperbola defined by each equation.
   a) $\frac{x^2}{16} - \frac{y^2}{9} = -1$ b) $\frac{x^2}{4} - \frac{y^2}{25} = -1$ c) $\frac{x^2}{64} - \frac{y^2}{36} = -1$

(B)

3. A hyperbola has centre (0,0) and transverse axis on the y-axis. Write the equation of the hyperbola if:
   a) $a = 3$ and $b = 4$
   b) $a = 7$ and $b = 2$
   c) $a = 3$ and $b = 9$
   d) the transverse axis has length 10 and the conjugate axis has length 12
   e) one vertex is A(0,3) and one asymptote is defined by $y = 2x$.

4. For each hyperbola whose equation is given below
   i) Write the standard equation.
   ii) Find the lengths of the transverse and conjugate axes, the coordinates of the vertices, and the equations of the asymptotes.
   iii) Graph the hyperbola.
   a) $4x^2 - 9y^2 = -36$ b) $x^2 - 4y^2 = -16$ c) $16x^2 - 25y^2 = -400$
   d) $4x^2 - y^2 = -100$ e) $x^2 - 2y^2 = -50$ f) $3x^2 - 4y^2 = -24$

5. Sketch the hyperbola defined by each equation. Then identify the transformation which maps the rectangular hyperbola defined by $x^2 - y^2 = -1$ to the hyperbola.
   a) $\frac{x^2}{49} - \frac{y^2}{25} = -1$ b) $\frac{x^2}{16} - \frac{y^2}{81} = -1$ c) $\frac{x^2}{9} - \frac{y^2}{49} = -1$
   d) $3x^2 - y^2 = -27$ e) $x^2 - 6y^2 = -36$ f) $8x^2 - 6y^2 = -48$

(C)

6. Describe how the graph of the hyperbola defined by $\frac{x^2}{b^2} - \frac{y^2}{a^2} = -1$ changes if:
   a) b is kept constant and a varies b) a is kept constant and b varies.

7. Given the equation $Ax^2 + By^2 + C = 0$, what conditions must be satisfied by A, B, and C if this equation represents a hyperbola with transverse axis on the y-axis?

8. Two hyperbolas are called *conjugate hyperbolas* if the transverse axis of one is the conjugate axis of the other.
   a) Give an example of the equations of two conjugate hyperbolas.
   b) If the equation of a hyperbola is given in standard form, how can you find the equation of the conjugate hyperbola?

Constructing a Hyperbola

To construct a hyperbola, follow these steps. You will need a piece of corrugated cardboard, some string, some tape and two paper fasteners.

Step 1.
Tape a piece of paper to the cardboard, and push the paper fasteners through it, about 10 cm apart. Make a knotted loop in the string to hold a pencil.

Step 2.
Pass the string around the paper fasteners as shown. Hold the ends of the string together, and keep the string taut with the pencil.

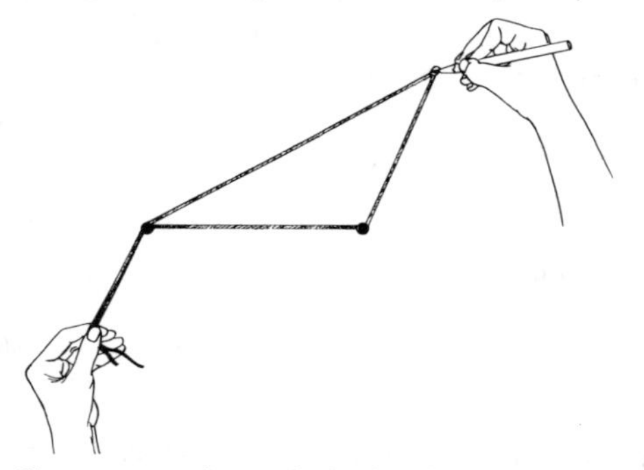

Step 3.
Keeping the string taut, move the pencil to trace out a hyperbola; repeat by reversing the position of the string to form the other branch of the hyperbola.

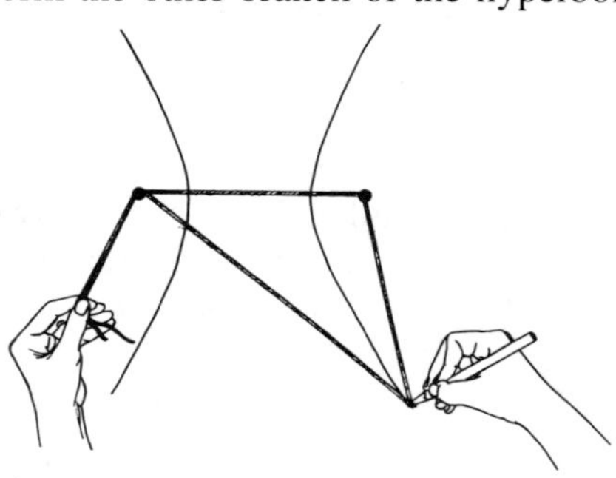

1. Construct a hyperbola by following the above steps.
2. Explain how this construction illustrates the following definition of a hyperbola.

   A *hyperbola* is a set of points P such that the difference of the distances from P to two fixed points is constant. The two fixed points are called the *foci* of the hyperbola.
3. For the hyperbola you constructed, mark the foci F_1 and F_2.
   a) Mark any point P on the hyperbola. Measure PF_1 and PF_2, and calculate the difference $|PF_1 - PF_2|$. Repeat for other points P on the hyperbola.
   b) Locate the vertices A_1 and A_2. How does the length of A_1A_2 compare with the difference $|PF_1 - PF_2|$ for any point P on the hyperbola?
4. Use the above definition to show that, for any point P on a hyperbola, the difference $|PF_1 - PF_2|$ is always equal to the length of the transverse axis.
5. Investigate the effect on the shape of the hyperbola of changing the distance between the paper fasteners.

Using the Constant Difference Definition to Develop the Equation of a Hyperbola

In *Sections 12-6* and *12-7* we obtained hyperbolas by expanding a rectangular hyperbola horizontally and vertically by different factors. But the definition of a hyperbola given on the facing page is different from that used in *Sections 12-6* and *12-7*. Hence, we should be able to develop the equation of a hyperbola from the new definition.

For example, let F_1 and F_2 be the points (5,0) and (−5,0) respectively. Then, using the definition on the facing page, a set of points P such that the difference of the distances from P to F_1 and to F_2 is constant is a hyperbola. Let us assume that the constant difference is 8 units. Then we can find the equation of the hyperbola as follows.

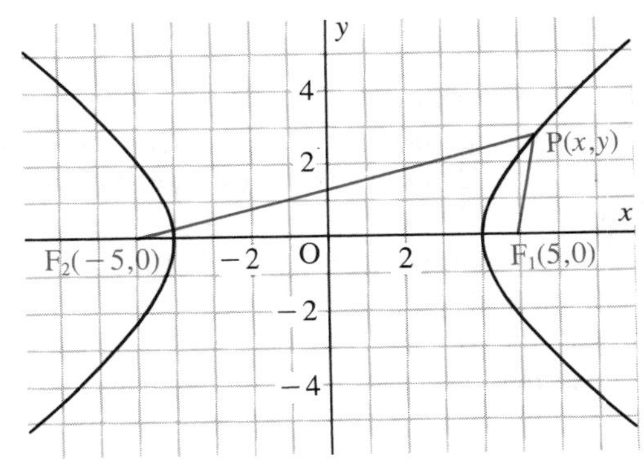

Let P(*x*,*y*) be any point on the hyperbola.

$$PF_1 - PF_2 = \pm 8$$

$$\sqrt{(x-5)^2+y^2} - \sqrt{(x+5)^2+y^2} = \pm 8$$

Isolate one of the radicals and square both sides.

$$\sqrt{(x-5)^2+y^2} = \pm 8 + \sqrt{(x+5)^2+y^2}$$

$$\left(\sqrt{(x-5)^2+y^2}\right)^2 = \left(\pm 8 + \sqrt{(x+5)^2+y^2}\right)^2$$

$$(x-5)^2+y^2 = 64 \pm 16\sqrt{(x+5)^2+y^2} + (x+5)^2 + y^2$$

$$x^2 - 10x + 25 + y^2 = 64 \pm 16\sqrt{(x+5)^2+y^2} + x^2 + 10x + 25 + y^2$$

Isolate the radical and square both sides again.

$$-20x - 64 = \pm 16\sqrt{(x+5)^2+y^2}$$

$$-5x - 16 = \pm 4\sqrt{(x+5)^2+y^2}$$

$$25x^2 + 160x + 256 = 16(x^2 + 10x + 25 + y^2)$$

This equation simplifies to

$$9x^2 - 16y^2 = 144$$

or

$$\frac{x^2}{16} - \frac{y^2}{9} = 1$$

1. Let F_1 and F_2 be the points (6,0) and (−6,0) respectively. Find the equation of the hyperbola defined by points P such that the difference of the distances from P to F_1 and to F_2 is 4 units.

2. Let F_1 and F_2 be the points $(c,0)$ and $(-c,0)$ respectively. Find the equation of the hyperbola defined by points P such that the difference of the distances from P to F_1 and to F_2 is $2a$ units.

MATHEMATICS AROUND US

Reflector Property of the Parabola

We have all seen dish antennas for receiving TV signals from satellites. These antennas have parabolic cross sections. When the antenna is aimed at a satellite, the signals entering the antenna are reflected to the receiver, which is placed at the focus of the antenna.

Every parabola has a *focus*, which is a particular point on the axis of symmetry. The position of the focus can be defined as follows.

For any parabola, the *focus* is the point on the axis of symmetry which is half as far from the vertex as it is from the parabola, measured along a line perpendicular to the axis of symmetry. For example, in the diagram, FV = p, and FL = $2p$. That is, F is half as far from V as from L. Hence, F is the focus of the parabola. Every parabola has one and only one focus.

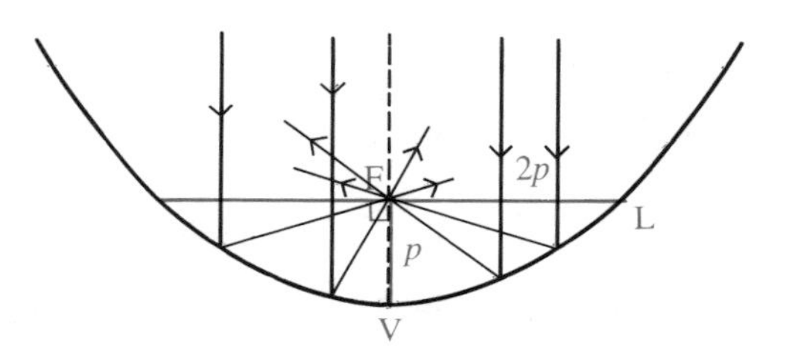

You can illustrate the reflector property of the parabola by completing the questions below.

QUESTIONS

1. a) Use a table of values to construct an accurate graph of the parabola defined by $y = \frac{1}{8}x^2$ for values of x between -8 and 8.

   b) Mark the point F(0,2) on the graph. Verify that F satisfies the above definition of the focus.

2. a) Mark any point P on the parabola you constructed in *Question 1*. Join PF, and draw a line PM parallel to the axis of symmetry. By estimation, draw a tangent to the parabola at P. Verify that PF and PM form equal angles with the tangent.

   b) Repeat part a) for other points P on the parabola.

3. Use the above definition of the focus to prove that the coordinates of the focus of the parabola defined by $y = ax^2$ are $\left(0, \frac{1}{4a}\right)$.

MATHEMATICS AROUND US

Reflector Property of the Ellipse

In the Capitol at Washington, D.C., there is a room known as the whispering gallery. In this room there are two points a considerable distance apart, where a whisper at one point can be heard at the other point. The room has an elliptical cross section. When someone standing at one of the points whispers, the curved walls reflect the sound waves and focus them at the other point, where the whisper can be clearly heard.

Every ellipse has two *foci*, which are particular points on the major axis. The positions of the foci can be defined as follows.

For any ellipse, let the centre be O, and let A_1 and A_2 be the vertices. Let the *semi-major axis* OA_1 have length a. Let B_1 and B_2 be the points at the ends of the minor axis. Then, the *foci* are the points F_1 and F_2 on A_1A_2 such that $B_1F_1 = a$ and $B_1F_2 = a$.

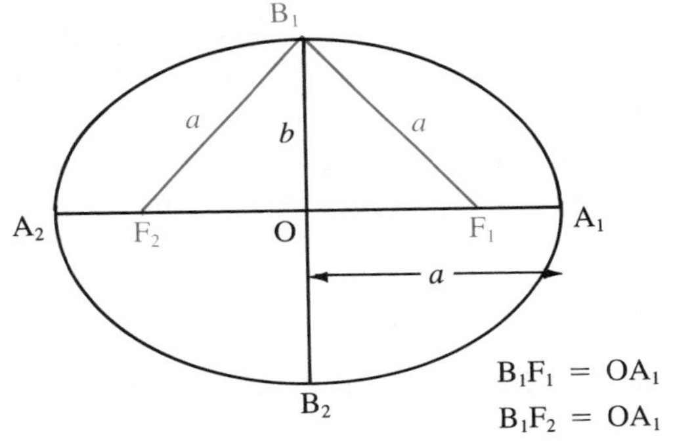

You can illustrate the reflector property of the ellipse by completing the questions below.

QUESTIONS

1. a) Use a table of values to construct an accurate graph of the ellipse defined by $\frac{x^2}{100} + \frac{y^2}{64} = 1$.
   b) Mark the points $F_1(6,0)$ and $F_2(-6,0)$ on the graph. Verify that F_1 and F_2 satisfy the above definition of the foci.
2. a) Mark any point P on the ellipse you constructed in *Question 1*. Join PF_1 and PF_2. By estimation, draw a tangent to the ellipse at P. Verify that PF_1 and PF_2 form equal angles with the tangent.
   b) Repeat part a) for other points P on the ellipse.
3. Use the above definition of the foci to find expressions for the coordinates of the foci of the ellipse defined by $\frac{x^2}{a^2} + \frac{y^2}{b^2} = 1$.

MATHEMATICS AROUND US

Reflector Property of the Hyperbola

Like the parabola and the ellipse, the hyperbola also has a reflector property. This property is sometimes employed in the design of telescopes. The *Space Telescope*, for example, contains two hyperboloidal mirrors. Light striking the primary mirror is reflected to the secondary mirror, where it is reflected back through a hole in the centre of the primary mirror to a focus behind the primary mirror.

Every hyperbola has two *foci*, which are particular points on the axis of symmetry containing the transverse axis. The positions of the foci can be defined as follows.

For any hyperbola, let the centre be O, and let A_1 and A_2 be the vertices. Let the *semi-transverse axis* OA_1 have length a. Let B_1 and B_2 be the points at the ends of the conjugate axis. Then, the *foci* are the points F_1 and F_2 on the line $\overleftrightarrow{A_1A_2}$ such that $OF_1 = OF_2 = A_1B_1$.

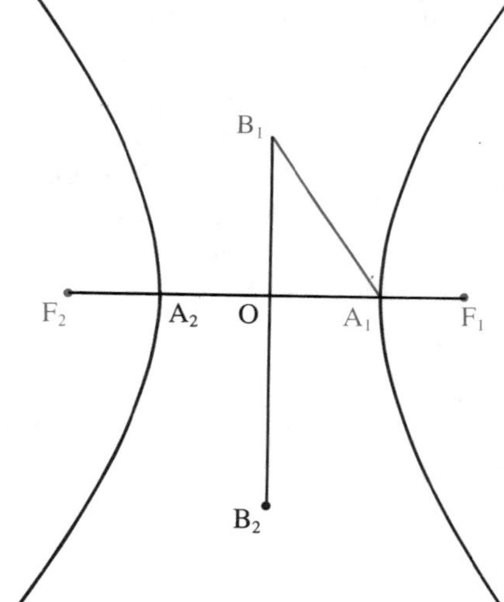

You can illustrate the reflector property of the hyperbola by completing the questions below.

QUESTIONS

1. a) Use a table of values to construct an accurate graph of the hyperbola defined by $\frac{x^2}{36} - \frac{y^2}{64} = 1$.
   b) Mark the points $F_1(10,0)$ and $F_2(-10,0)$ on the graph. Verify that F_1 and F_2 satisfy the above definition of the foci.
2. a) Mark any point P on the hyperbola you constructed in *Question 1*. Join PF_1 and PF_2. By estimation, draw a tangent to the hyperbola at P. Verify that PF_1 and PF_2 form equal angles with the tangent.
   b) Repeat part a) for other points P on the hyperbola.
3. Use the above definition of the foci to find expressions for the coordinates of the foci of the hyperbola defined by $\frac{x^2}{a^2} - \frac{y^2}{b^2} = 1$.

1. Graph each relation and identify the curve.
   a) $\frac{x^2}{16} + \frac{y^2}{9} = 1$ b) $x^2 = 4y$ c) $x^2 + y^2 = 25$
   d) $x^2 - y^2 = 9$ e) $4x^2 + 4y^2 = 49$ f) $9x^2 - 16y^2 = -144$

2. Determine if the given point is on the given conic. Identify the conic.
   a) $(-2,-20)$; $y = 5x^2$ b) $(-4,7)$; $x^2 + y^2 = 65$
   c) $(-7,2)$; $\frac{x^2}{25} - \frac{y^2}{4} = 1$ d) $(2,-\sqrt{2})$; $4x^2 + 9y^2 = 36$

3. Find the equation of a parabola with vertex (0,0) and axis of symmetry the y-axis if it passes through: a) (4,2) b) $(-4,-24)$.

4. Find the equation of a circle with:
   a) centre $(5,-2)$, radius 2 b) centre (0,3), radius $3\sqrt{2}$.

5. A rectangular hyperbola with centre (0,0) and vertices on the y-axis passes through $(6,-9)$. Is $(-2,7)$ on the hyperbola?

6. For each conic, state the coordinates of its vertices and the lengths of its axes.
   a) $\frac{x^2}{25} + \frac{y^2}{4} = 1$ b) $\frac{x^2}{9} - \frac{y^2}{16} = 1$ c) $9x^2 + 4y^2 = 36$

7. Find the centre and the radius of each circle.
   a) $4x^2 + 4y^2 = 25$ b) $x^2 + y^2 - 4x + 6y - 12 = 0$

8. State the equation of an ellipse with centre (0,0) and major axis on the x-axis if:
   a) the major axis has length 20 and the minor axis has length $4\sqrt{3}$.
   b) one vertex is $(-5,0)$, and it passes through $\left(-4,\frac{9}{5}\right)$.

9. State the equation of a hyperbola with centre (0,0) and transverse axis on the y-axis if:
   a) one vertex is $(0,-7)$, and the conjugate axis has length 12
   b) the transverse axis has length 10 and an asymptote is $y = 3x$.

10. Sketch each conic.
    a) $2x^2 + 8y = 0$ b) $3x^2 + 3y^2 = 48$ c) $4x^2 - 25y^2 = 100$

11. A stone thrown horizontally from a bridge 25 m above the river splashes in the water 40 m from the base of the bridge. If the stone falls in a parabolic path, find its equation.

12. One of the supports in a retractable roof of a sports complex is semi-elliptical. If it is 25 m high and spans 60 m, find its equation.

13. The base of a bridge arch is 80 m wide and 25 m high. Find its equation if the arch is in the shape of a rectangular hyperbola.

14. The arch of a bridge is semi-elliptical. The base is 30 m wide and 9 m below the vertex of the arch. How far below the vertex of the arch is a point 10 m from the centre line of the arch?

Cumulative Review, Chapters 10-12

1. If a principal P dollars is invested in an account which pays $r\%$ interest per annum compounded semi-annually, then the amount A dollars in the account after n years is given by this formula.

$$A = P\left(1 + \frac{r}{200}\right)^{2n}$$

Find the amount of each investment.
   a) \$1000 at 8% compounded semi-annually for 3 years
   b) \$5000 at 9.5% compounded semi-annually for 6 years
   c) \$4250 at 12.5% compounded semi-annually for 7.5 years

2. Evaluate.
   a) $9^{\frac{3}{2}}$ b) $(64)^{\frac{1}{3}}$ c) $125^{-\frac{2}{3}}$ d) $(2.75)^0$
   e) $(0.0625)^{\frac{3}{4}}$ f) $\left(\frac{27}{64}\right)^{\frac{2}{3}}$ g) $\left(\frac{25}{4}\right)^{\frac{1}{2}}$ h) $(5.76)^{\frac{1}{2}}$

3. Simplify.
   a) $\dfrac{12x^3y^{-2} \times 5x^{-7}y^5}{15xy^{-3}}$ b) $\dfrac{-18m^{-4}n^{-2} \times 15m^2n^{-7}}{-10m^2n^{-3} \times 6m^9n^{-4}}$
   c) $\dfrac{2a^{3x+y} \times 3a^{x-3y}}{-4a^{-x+5y}}$ d) $\dfrac{8x^{2a}y^{a-b} \times 3x^a y^{-2b}}{2x^{-3a}y^{2a+b}}$

4. Evaluate to the nearest thousandth.
   a) $5.7^{3.1}$ b) $12.8^{-1.7}$ c) $127^{0.68}$ d) $\log 68$
   e) $\log_8 256$ f) $\log_{\sqrt{5}} 0.04$ g) $\log_{2.3} 17.6$ h) $\log_{0.4} 2.13$

5. Solve.
   a) $\log x = -2$ b) $\log_x 27 = \frac{3}{2}$ c) $\log_4 x = \frac{7}{2}$
   d) $3^x = 12$ e) $5^{x+3} = 83$ f) $7^{x-3} = 3^{x+1}$

6. Express as a single logarithm.
   a) $\log 12 + \log 8 - \log 16$
   b) $\log_4 (x + 5) + \log_4 (2x - 3) - \log_4 (x + 4)$

7. If $\log 12 = x$ and $\log 4 = y$, write each logarithm in terms of x and y.
   a) $\log 3$ b) $\log 0.75$ c) $\log 480$ d) $\log\left(\frac{16}{3}\right)$

8. If $\log 11 \doteq 1.0414$, find an approximation for each logarithm.
   a) $\log 121$ b) $\log \sqrt{11}$ c) $\log 110$ d) $\log\left(\frac{1}{11}\right)$

9. Solve and check.
   a) $\log_3 x + \log_3 (x + 24) = 4$
   b) $\log_{\sqrt{7}} (x + 4) + \log_{\sqrt{7}} (x - 2) = 2$

10. a) Prove that if $(x + 1)^2 = 4x$, then $\log\left(\frac{x + 1}{2}\right) = \frac{1}{2}\log x$.

 b) Prove that if $(x + y)^2 = 4xy$, then $\log\left(\frac{x + y}{2}\right) = \frac{1}{2}(\log x + \log y)$.

11. A swarm of locusts doubles every 3 weeks. If there are 4500 locusts now, how many:
 a) will there be in i) 12 weeks ii) 25 weeks
 b) were there i) 6 weeks ago ii) 10 weeks ago?

12. A car selling for \$22 950 depreciates at the rate of 25% per year. How old is the car when it is worth \$10 000?

13. The intensity of light in a solution decreases at the rate of 4% for each metre of depth. What depth is required to reduce the intensity to 50%?

14. Sketch the graph of each relation.
 a) $3x^2 = 2y$
 b) $\frac{x^2}{16} - \frac{y^2}{9} = -1$
 c) $\frac{x^2}{25} + \frac{y^2}{16} = 1$
 d) $x^2 - y^2 = 9$
 e) $25x^2 - 16y^2 = -400$
 f) $81x^2 + 4y^2 = 324$

15. Find the centre and the radius of each circle.
 a) $x^2 - 10x + y^2 + 6y + 30 = 0$
 b) $x^2 + y^2 + 4x - 8y = 16$
 c) $x^2 + y^2 + 10x - 2y + 17 = 0$

16. For each conic, state the coordinates of the vertices and the lengths of the axes.
 a) $\frac{x^2}{100} + \frac{y^2}{49} = 1$
 b) $\frac{x^2}{64} - \frac{y^2}{25} = -1$
 c) $36x^2 - 25y^2 = 900$

17. Find the equation of a parabola with vertex (0,0) and axis of symmetry the y-axis if it passes through $(-3, -1.5)$.

18. Find the equation of an ellipse with centre (0,0) and major axis on the y-axis if one vertex is (0,7) and the minor axis has length 8.

19. Find the equations of a hyperbola and its asymptotes, if it is centred at (0,0), has its vertices on the x-axis and has a conjugate axis of length 10 and a transverse axis of length $4\sqrt{5}$.

20. A railroad bridge is supported by a semi-elliptical arch which is 60 m wide at the base and 18 m high.
 a) Find the equation of the ellipse.
 b) How far from the centre line of the arch is a point 6 m above ground level?

Answers

Chapter 1

Exercises 1-1, page 6

1. a) Function **2. a)** Domain: February to October; range, about 75.5¢ to 80.2¢
b) Domain: 0 km to 50 km; range: 20°C to 29°C

3. a), c) Functions

4. a) R; R **b)** R; $\{y \mid y \geqslant 0, y \in R\}$
c) $\{x \mid x \geqslant -1, x \in R\}$; $\{y \mid y \geqslant 0, y \in R\}$
d), f) Not functions **e)** R; $\{y \mid y > 0, y \in R\}$

5. a), b) R; R
c) $\{x \mid x \leqslant 1, x \in R\}$;$\{y \mid y \geqslant 0, y \in R\}$
d) $\{x \mid x \neq 0, x \in R\}$; $\{y \mid y \neq 0, y \in R\}$
e) $\{x \mid x \neq \pm 1, x \in R\}$; $\{y \mid y \neq 0, y \in R\}$
f) $\{x \mid x \neq \pm 2, x \in R\}$;
$\{y \mid y \leqslant 0 \text{ or } y > 1, y \in R\}$

7. a) i) 100 kPa **ii)** 85 kPa **iii)** 80 kPa **iv)** 40 kPa **v)** 28 kPa **b)** 6.5 km
c) Domain: 0 km to 14 km, range: 23 kPa to 100 kPa **8. a)** 560 km, 360 km, 272 km, 240 km
b) Domain: 0.025 m² to 0.6 m²; range: 28 km/h to 100 km/h **c)** Domain would not change: the highest and lowest values of the range would increase.

10. a) Hammer-fist strike **i)** 2.5 m/s, 5 m/s **ii)** 12 m/s Forward karate punch **i)** 3.8 m/s, 5.1 m/s **ii)** 6.8 m/s **b)** Speed decreases because it's after the punch; speed increasing before the strike.

Exercises 1-2, page 11

1. a) 4 **b)** 7 **c)** 3 **d)** 4 **e)** 7 **f)** 12

2. a) −1 **b)** 5 **c)** 11 **d)** 1 **e)** −11 **f)** 2

3. a) −17, 18, −4.5 **b)** 4, 11, −4.75
c) 6, 20, −0.25

4. a) −3, 2, −2 **b)** 4, −2, −1

5. a) 30 **b)** 24 **c)** 0 **d)** 10 **e)** 2 **f)** 1.25

6. a) −5 **b)** −8 **c)** −20 **d)** −6
e) −50 **f)** −8

7. a) i) 1 **ii)** 2 **iii)** 3 **b) i)** 9 **ii)** 90 **iii)** 900

8. a) $2a + 1$ **b)** $6a + 1$ **c)** $3 + 2y$
d) $2x + 3$ **e)** $3 - y$ **f)** $1 + y$
g) $4 - z$ **h)** $6 - 2x$ **i)** $4x + 2$
j) $15 - 5n$ **k)** $-6x - 3$ **l)** $2a - 6$

9. a) R; R **b)** R; $\{y \mid y \geqslant 0, y \in R\}$
c) $\{x \mid x \geqslant 0; x \in R\}$, $\{y \mid y \geqslant 0, y \in R\}$

10. a) −4 **b)** −7 **c)** 8 **d)** 6 **e)** 6 **f)** 3

11. a) $\dfrac{2x+1}{2x-1}, x \neq \dfrac{1}{2}$ **b)** $\dfrac{x-1}{x+1}, x \neq -1$
c) $\dfrac{1+x}{1-x}, x \neq 1$ **d)** $\dfrac{1+x}{1-x}, x \neq 1$
e) $\dfrac{x+2}{x}, x \neq 0$ **f)** $\dfrac{-x}{x-2}, x \neq 2$
g) $\dfrac{x+1}{x}, x \neq 0$ **h)** $\dfrac{x-1}{x}, x \neq 0$

12. a) $\dfrac{2}{3}$ **b)** −2 **c)** 2 **d)** 1 **e)** $\dfrac{1}{4}$

13. a) $\dfrac{5}{3}$ **b)** 2 **c)** $\dfrac{1}{3}$ **d)** 0 **e)** No solution

14. a) i) 6 **ii)** 14 **iii)** 14 **b) i)** 1, 10, 100,1000, etc. **ii)** 2, 11, 20, 200, 101, 110, etc. **c) i), ii)** Infinite number

16. a) i) 0 **ii)** 2 **iii)** 1 **iv)** 2 **b) i)** 30 **ii)** 210

17. b) i) 4, 6, 8, 10, 12, etc. **ii)** 3, 5, 7, 9, etc.

18. a) i) 1, 4, 9, 16 **ii)** 1, 4, 9, 16 **b)** $f(x) = x^2$

20. Answers may vary, for example, 2^x, 2^y

Exercises 1-3, page 15

1. a) $\{(-3,9), (-2,7), (-1,5), (0,3), (1,1), (2,-1), (3,-3)\}$ **b)** $\{(5,3), (10,4), (15,5), (20,6), (25,7), (30,8), (35,9)\}$ **c)** $\{(-3,10), (-2,5), (-1,2), (0,1), (1,2), (2,5), (3,10)\}$

2. a) x: 1, 2, 3, 4, 5; y: 3, 5, 7, 9, 11
b) x: −2, −1, 0, 1, 2, 3; y: 10, 5, 2, 1
c) x: 2, 3, 4, 5, 6, 7; y: 1, 8, 4, 2, 5

3. a) x: −3, −2, −1, 0, 1, 2, 3; y: 15, 10, 5, 0, 5, 10, 15
b) x: −3, −2, −1, 0, 1, 2, 3; y: 17, 7, 1, −1
c) x: −3, −2, −1, 0, 1, 2, 3; f(x): 1, 6, 9, 10
d) x: −3, −2, −1, 0, 1, 2, 3; g(x): 6, 2, 0, 12

4. a) $f: x \to 5x$ **b)** $f: x \to 2x^2 - 1$
c) $f: x \to 10 - x^2$ **d)** $f: x \to x^2 + x$

5. a)

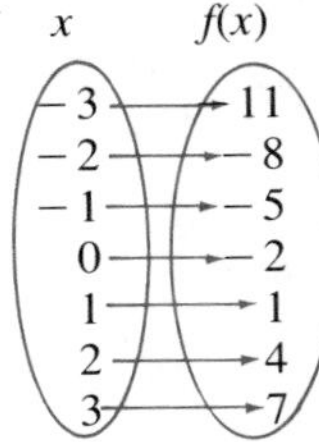

b)

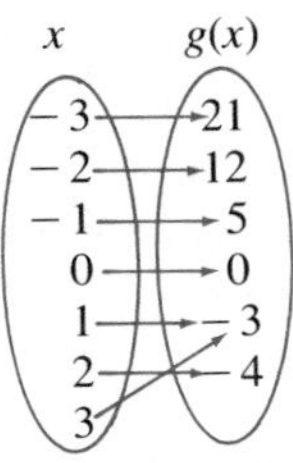

c)

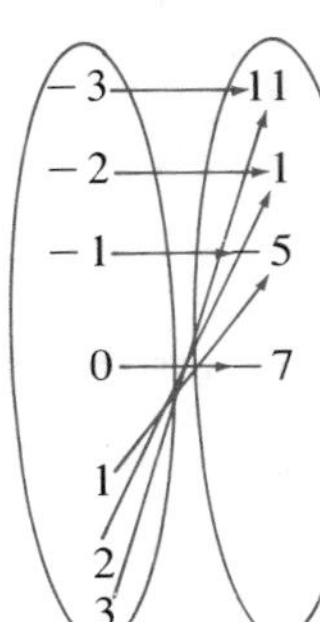

d) u $f(u)$: $-3 \to \frac{1}{2}$; $-2 \to 1$; $1 \to \frac{1}{2}$; $2 \to \frac{1}{3}$; $3 \to \frac{1}{4}$

6. a) and **b)** represent functions.

7. If no number in the domain has 2 arrows starting at it. **8.** Mapping diagrams may vary.

a) $f: x \to \frac{2}{3}x - 6$ **b)** $f: x \to 2^x - 1$

c) $f: x \to \frac{x^2}{x - 1}, x \neq 1$

d) $g: x \to \frac{\sqrt{2x - 3}}{x}, x \neq 0$

Exercises 1-4, page 20

1. a) 7 **b)** 22 **c)** 10 **d)** 21 **2. a)** $6x + 4$ **b)** $6x + 3$ **3. a)** 5 **b)** 10 **c)** 4 **d)** 17 **4. a)** $2x^2 + 2$ **b)** $4x^2 + 1$

5. a) $-6x + 19; -6x - 3$
b) $4x^2 + 14x + 6; 2x^2 + 10x + 1$
c) $32x^2 - 100x + 78; -8x^2 + 12x + 3$

6. a) $3x^2 + 12x + 11; 3x^2 + 1$
b) $12x^2 - 12x + 2; 3 - 6x^2$
c) $3x^4 - 1; 9x^4 - 6x^2 + 1$
d) $3x^4 + 6x^3 + 3x^2 - 1; 9x^4 - 3x^2$
e) $12x^4 - 36x^3 + 27x^2 - 1; 18x^4 - 21x^2 + 5$
f) $\frac{3}{x^2} - 1; \frac{1}{3x^2 - 1}$ **7.** $A = \frac{\pi d^2}{4}$ **8.** $\frac{\pi d^3}{6}$

9. a) -11 **b)** -8 **c)** 5 **d)** 16

10. a) $1 - 6x$ **b)** $4 - 6x$ **c)** $4x - 3$ **d)** $9x - 2$

11. a) 4 **b)** 30 **c)** -1 **d)** 0

12. a) $4 - x - x^2$ **b)** $20 - 9x + x^2$ **c)** x **d)** $x^4 + 2x^3 + 2x^2 + x$

13. a) $\sqrt{4 - 2x}; 4 - 2\sqrt{x}; \sqrt[4]{x}; 4x - 4$
b) $\sqrt{2 + 6x}; 1 + 3\sqrt{2x}; \sqrt{2\sqrt{2x}}; 9x + 4$
c) $\frac{x^2 - 1}{x^2}; \frac{x^2}{(x + 1)^2} - 1; \frac{x}{2x + 1}; x^4 - 2x^2$
d) $2^{3x-4}; 3(2^x) - 4; 2^{2^x}; 9x - 16$

14. $A = \frac{P^2}{16}$ **15.** $A = \frac{d^2}{2}$ **17. b)** No

18. $T = 0.05t + 20$ **19. a)** $0, -6$ **b)** -1

20. a) $f(k(x))$ **b)** $g(e(x))$ **c)** $f(e(x))$ **d)** $k(e(x))$ or $e(k(x))$ **21.** Answers may vary, for example,
a) $f(x) = x^2; g(x) = x^3 + 1; f(g(x))$
b) $f(x) = x^2 + 3x + 4; g(x) = x - 4; f(g(x))$
c) $f(x) = \sqrt{x}; g(x) = 3x - 2; f(g(x))$
d) $f(x) = \frac{1}{x}; g(x) = x + 3; f(g(x))$

22. a) $\sqrt{x} - 3$ **b)** $\{x \mid x \geqslant 0, x \in R\}$
c) $\{y \mid y \geqslant -3, y \in R\}$ **d)** $\sqrt{x - 3}$
e) $\{x \mid x \geqslant 3, x \in R\}$ **f)** $\{y \mid y \geqslant 0, y \in R\}$

23. a) x **b)** R **c)** R **d)** $\sqrt{x^2}$ **e)** R **f)** $\{y \mid y \geqslant 0, y \in R\}$

24. a) $\frac{x - 1}{x}, x \neq 0$ **b)** $-\frac{1}{x}, x \neq 0$

25. a) i) $4x + 3$ **ii)** $8x + 7$ **iii)** $16x + 15$
b) i) $32x + 31$ **ii)** $2^n x + 2^n - 1$

26. a) i) $\frac{x}{2x + 1}, x \neq -\frac{1}{2}$ **ii)** $\frac{x}{3x + 1}, x \neq -\frac{1}{3}$
iii) $\frac{x}{4x + 1}, x \neq -\frac{1}{4}$ **b) i)** $\frac{x}{5x + 1}, x \neq -\frac{1}{5}$
ii) $\frac{x}{nx + 1}, x \neq -\frac{1}{n}$ **27.** $d(a - 1) = b(c - 1)$

Mathematics Around Us, page 22

1. 4.5, 18 **2.** 4 km **3.** The graph would be stretched vertically by a factor of 4.

Exercises 1-5, page 27

1. a), b) Yes **c)** No **2. a)** $y = \frac{x - 5}{2}$, yes

b) $y = \pm\sqrt{\frac{4 + x}{3}}$, no **c)** $y = \frac{10 - 2x}{5}$, yes

d) $y = \pm\frac{\sqrt{x + 1}}{2}$, no **e)** $f^{-1}(x) = \frac{3}{1 - x}$, yes

f) $f^{-1}(x) = \dfrac{4x - 3}{2}$, yes

4. a) $f^{-1}(x) = \dfrac{x - 3}{2}$; R; R

b) $y = \pm\sqrt{\dfrac{x + 3}{2}}$; not a function

c) $h^{-1}(x) = \dfrac{1}{x} - 1$; $\{x \mid x \neq 0, x \in R\}$; $\{y \mid y \neq -1, y \in R\}$

d) $y = -1 \pm \sqrt{x}$; not a function

e) $g^{-1}(x) = \dfrac{1}{x - 1}$; $\{x \mid x \neq 1, x \in R\}$; $\{y \mid y \neq 0, y \in R\}$

f) $y = x^2 + 2$; $\{x \mid x \geqslant 0, x \in R\}$; $\{y \mid y \geqslant 2, y \in R\}$

5. Answers may vary. Typical answers are:
a) $y = x^2 - 2, x \geqslant 0$
b) $y = 2(x + 1)^2 - 3, x \geqslant -1$
c) $y = -x^2 + 5, x \geqslant 0$
d) $y = -\frac{1}{2}x^2 + 2, x \geqslant 0$
e) $y = (x - 1)^2 - 1, x \geqslant 1$
f) $y = -(x - 3)^2 + 4, x \geqslant 3$

6. a) $f^{-1}(x) = \dfrac{x - 1}{x}, x \neq 0$

b) $f^{-1}(x) = \dfrac{2x + 2}{1 - x}, x \neq 1$

c) $y = \pm\sqrt{\dfrac{4x}{x - 2}}, x \neq 2$

d) $y = \pm\sqrt{\dfrac{1 - 4x}{3x}}, x \neq 0$

7. a) Yes **b)** No **c)** Yes **d)** Yes

8. a) $\dfrac{x - 5}{2}$ **b)** x **c)** x

9. a) $\dfrac{1 + x}{1 - x}$ **b)** x **c)** x **10.** The line $y = x$

12. Yes, except $y = k$, whose inverse is $x = k$, which is not a function.

13. Yes, the inverse of the inverse is the original function.

14. a) $x \geqslant -1$ or $x \leqslant -1$ **b)** $x \geqslant 0$ or $x \leqslant 0$
c) $x \geqslant -\dfrac{3}{2}$ or $x \leqslant -\dfrac{3}{2}$

Exercises 1-6, page 33

1. a) $3x - 2$ **b)** $x^2 + 2x - 1$
c) $2x^2 - 3x + 2$ **d)** $5x^2 - 8x + 5$

2. a) $4x + 1$ **b)** $6x + 2$ **c)** $4x$
d) $-5x^2 - 24x + 5$

5. a) $y = 2x + 1$ **d)** R

6. a) $y = x + 3$ **d)** R

7. a) Storage cost + manufacturing cost = total cost
b) Expenses + profit = income

13. a) Income − expenses = profit **b)** Total car sales − domestic car sales = foreign car sales

15. b) i) $0 < x < 2$ **ii)** $0 < x < 1.3$
iii) $0 < x < 1.1$

The Mathematical Mind, page 37

2. $f(x) = \begin{cases} x + 2, & x < -2 \\ x^2, & -2 \leqslant x \leqslant 2 \\ x + 2, & x \geqslant 2 \end{cases}$

3. Answers may vary, for example: page 6, Exercise 2: page 10, Examples 3 and 4.

4. Answers may vary, for example,

$f(x) = \begin{cases} 1, & \text{if } x \text{ is rational} \\ -1, & \text{if } x \text{ is irrational} \end{cases}$

Review Exercises, page 38

1. a) R; R
b) R; $\{y \mid y \geqslant -3, y \in R\}$
c) $\{x \mid x \neq 0, x \in R\}$; $\{y \mid y \neq 1, y \in R\}$

2. a) $y = \frac{3}{2}x - \frac{1}{2}$; R; R
b) $y = 2 + \sqrt{x + 3}$; $\{x \mid x \geqslant -3; x \in R\}$; R
c) $y = \dfrac{3}{x - 1}$; $\{x \mid x \neq 1, x \in R\}$; $\{y \mid y \neq 0, y \in R\}$

3. a) -17 **b)** $10a - 2$
c) $5x + 3$ **d)** $15n - 12$

4. a) -2 **b)** -2 **c)** $1 - 6x^2$ **d)** $x^2 - 6$
e) $19 - 6x - 3x^2$ **f)** $9x^2 - 30x + 19$
g) $x^2 - 4x + 3$ **h)** $x^2 + 5x - 9$

5. a) $\frac{1}{2}, 2$ **b)** $-\frac{3}{2}, 4$ **c)** $-\frac{3}{4}, 2$

6. a) 2 **b)** $\dfrac{a + 2}{a - 2}, a \neq 2$ **c)** $\dfrac{3x - 1}{x - 1}, x \neq 1$
d) $\dfrac{x + 1}{x - 1}, x \neq 1$

7. a) i) **ii)**

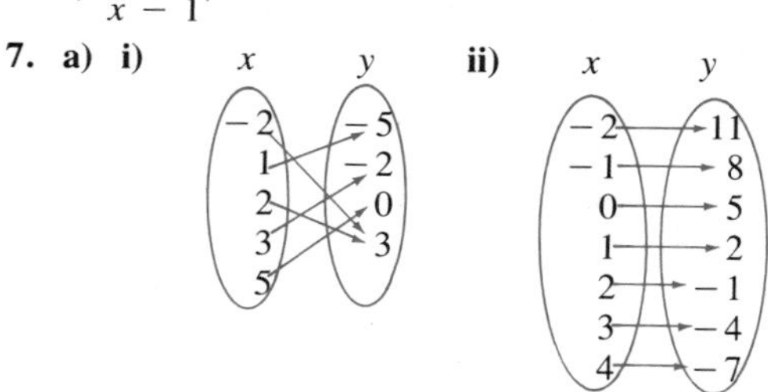

iii)

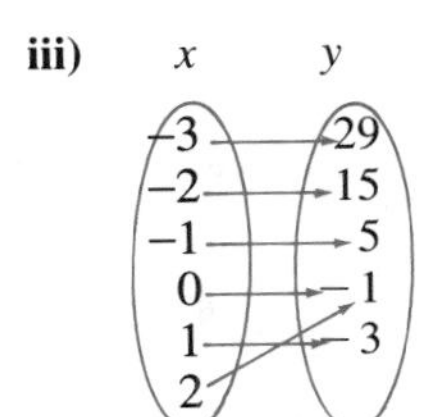

8. a) 11 **b)** −9 **c)** 35 **d)** −7
e) $6x - 1$ **f)** $\frac{2x - 3}{3}$ **g)** $\frac{2x - 7}{3}$
h) $\frac{3x + 3}{2}$ **9. a)** $2x^2 - 6x + 9$
b) $4x^2 + 14x + 12$ **c)** $4x + 15$
d) $x^4 - 6x^3 + 10x^2 - 3x$ **e)** $\frac{x^2 - 3x - 3}{2}$
f) $\frac{x^2 - 16x + 63}{4}$ **g)** x **h)** $\frac{x - 15}{4}$

10. a) $y = -3x + 7$; yes **b)** $y^2 = 2.5x + 0.5$; no
c) $y = \frac{2x + 1}{x - 3}$; yes

Chapter 2

Exercises 2-1, page 42

1. a) $x + 17$ **b)** −15 **c)** $14x + 3y$
d) $10p - 34q$ **e)** $3x^2 - 8xy + 7y^2$
f) $2x^3 + 3x^2 + x$

2. a) $4x^2 - 39x + 29$ **b)** $4 - 7x - x^2$
c) $11a - 9b - 8c$ **d)** $-7n^3 - 4n^2 + 8n$

3. a) $x^2 - x - 12$ **b)** $n^2 - 2n - 63$
c) $x^2 - 16x + 64$ **d)** $6x^2 + x - 15$
e) $8a^2 - 2ab - 3b^2$ **f)** $2x^2 - xy - 15y^2$
g) $6x^2 - 38x + 56$ **h)** $3x^2 + 3xy - 18y^2$
i) $9x^3 - 12x^2y + 4xy^2$

4. a) $x^2 - 17x + 49$ **b)** $10 + 8x - x^2$
c) $3a^2 - 26ab + 16b^2$ **d)** $-20xy - 34y^2$

5. a) $-a^2 - a - 6$ **b)** $10x^2 - 15y^2$
c) $14x^2 - 30xy - 23y^2$
d) $-6x^2 - 68xy + 45y^2$

6. a) $13x^4 - 24x^2 + 13$ **b)** $21y^4 - 21$
c) $-3x^3 - 3x^2$ **d)** $-14x^4 - 24x^2y^2 - 9y^4$

7. a) $x^2 + 2xy - 8x - 6y + 15$
b) $3n^3 + 5n^2 + n + 6$
c) $3x^2 + 8xy + 10xz + 4y^2 + 8yz + 3z^2$
d) $x^3 - 7x + 6$ **e)** $2x^3 - 14x^2 + 30x - 18$
f) $x^3 + 3x^2y + 3xy^2 + y^3$

8. a) $4x$ cm **b)** $(x^2 + 10x)$ cm^2

9. a) $2\pi x$ cm **b)** $\pi(x^2 + 20x)$ cm^2

10. a) $(x^3 + 130x^2 + 5600x)$ cm^3
b) $(6x^2 + 520x)$ cm^2

11. a) $4\pi(x^2 + 12x)$ cm^2
b) $\frac{4\pi}{3}(108x + 18x^2 + x^3)$ cm^3

12. a) $2\pi(13x + 4y + x^2 + xy)$ cm^2
b) $\pi(16y + 40x + 8xy + 5x^2 + x^2y)$ cm^3

13. a) $\frac{3a^2}{4}$ **b)** $\frac{a^2}{3}$

14. a) $\frac{1}{8}$ **b)** $\frac{1}{12}$ **c)** $\frac{5}{24}$

15. a) i) $x^2 + (a + b)x + ab$
ii) $x^3 + (a + b + c)x^2 + (ab + ac + bc)x + abc$
b) $x^4 + (a + b + c + d)x^3 +$
$(ab + ac + ad + bc + bd + cd)x^2 +$
$(abc + abd + acd + bcd)x$

16. a) $x^3 + 6x^2 + 11x + 6$ **b)** $x^3 + 6x^2 - x - 30$
c) $x^4 + 10x^3 + 35x^2 + 50x + 24$
d) $x^4 + 3x^3 - 21x^2 - 43x + 60$

Investigate, page 43

1.

×	x	y	z
x	x^2	xy	xz
y	xy	y^2	yz
z	xz	yz	z^2

$x^2 + y^2 + z^2 + 2xy + 2xz + 2yz$

2. Square each term, then multiply the terms together in pairs and double them. Add the results.

3. a) $x^2 + y^2 + 2xy + 10x + 10y + 25$
b) $a^2 + b^2 - 2ab + 6a - 6b + 9$
c) $p^2 + q^2 - 2pq - 8p + 8q + 16$
d) $4x^2 + y^2 - 4xy + 12x - 6y + 9$
e) $9m^2 + 4n^2 - 12mn - 30m + 20n + 25$
f) $16a^2 + 25b^2 + 9c^2 + 40ab - 30bc - 24ac$

Exercises 2-2, page 46

1. a) $(x + 1)(x + 2)$ **b)** $(x - 3)(x - 2)$
c) $(3x + 1)(x + 2)$ **d)** $(2x + 1)(x + 1)$
e) $(2x - 3)(x - 2)$ **f)** $(3x - 2)(2x - 5)$

2. a) $(x + 3)(x - 2)$ **b)** $(3x - 4)(x - 1)$
c) $(2x + 5)(x + 2)$ **d)** $(2x + 5)(x - 3)$
e) $(2x + 3)(2x - 7)$ **f)** $(4x - 5)(x - 3)$

3. a) $(5x + 1)(x + 2)$ **b)** $(7y - 1)(y - 3)$
c) $(3x + 5)(x + 5)$ **d)** $(3 + 2a)(2 + 5a)$
e) $(2u - 5)(3u + 2)$ **f)** $(2x - 3)(3x - 2)$

4. a) $3(2x - 1)(x + 1)$ **b)** $(3m + 2)(2m - 7)$
c) $4(1 - 2a)(1 + 5a)$ **d)** $5(2x - 3)(3x + 4)$
e) $2(4 - 3x)(5 - x)$ **f)** $(5y + 4)(2y + 3)$

5. a) $(x + 2y)(x + 4y)$ **b)** $3(2x + y)(x - 5y)$
c) $(3mn + 2)(mn + 3)$ **d)** $(16h - 25k)(h + k)$
e) $2(7t - 5s)(t + s)$

f) $2(3xy - 5)(xy - 2)$

6. a) $(3p + 2q)(p - 7q)$ **b)** $(2a - b)(a + 8b)$
c) $(7a + b)(3a - 4b)$ **d)** $2(5x - 3y)(2x - 3y)$
e) $-(6p - 5q)(2p + 3q)$ **f)** $(5x + 2y)(2x + 3y)$

7. a) $(3x^2 + 2)^2$ **b)** $(3x^2 + 4)(2x^2 - 3)$
c) $2(3m^2 - n^2)(m^2 + n^2)$
d) $(5x^2y^2 + 2)(2x^2y^2 - 5)$
e) $3(2a^2 - 3b^2)(a^2 + 2b^2)$
f) $5(2x^2 - 3)(x^2 + 4)$

8. a) $-2(3p^2 + 4q^2)(2p^2 - 5q^2)$
b) $-(2y^2 - x^2)(2y^2 - 7x^2)$
c) $-(3a^2 + 4b^2)(a^2 + b^2)$
d) $(5a^2 - 2b^2)(5a^2 - 3b^2)$
e) $-3(7x^2 + 3y^2)(x^2 + 2y^2)$
f) $-(3x^2 + 4y^2)(5x^2 - 6y^2)$

9. a) $(x + 1)(2x - 1)(4x + 3)$
b) $(a - 3b)(a + 2b)(a - 2b)(a + b)$
c) $(2x + 1)(3x - 2y)(x - 2y)$

10. a) $(ax - m)(bx + n)$ **b)** $(ax + 2y)(3x + by)$
c) $(mnx^2 - a)(nx^2 - 3a)$
d) $2(2ax - by)(3bx + 2ay)$

11. a) $x^2(x - y^2)(x + 3y^2)$
b) $2m^2(2m^2 - 3n^2)(m^2 + 2n^2)$
c) $a(ax^2 + by^2)(bx^2 - ay^2)$
d) $(3m^2x - 2n)(n^2x + 4m)$

Exercises 2-3, page 48

1. a) $(b - a)(b + a)$ **b)** $(1 - 3b)(1 + 3b)$
c) $(9x - 5)(9x + 5)$ **d)** $(7x - y)(7x + y)$
e) $(2m + 3)(2m - 3)$ **f)** $(4p - 7)(4p + 7)$

2. a) $(x + y)^2$ **b)** $(3e + 1)^2$ **c)** $(2x - 5)^2$
d) $(2m + 3)^2$ **e)** $(3x - 4)^2$ **f)** $(5x - 2)^2$

3. a) $(x - y)(a + b)$ **b)** $(a - b)(x - y)$
c) $(x - y)(c + d)$ **d)** $(x + 1)(x^2 + 1)$
e) $(2x + 3)(y + 2)$ **f)** $(2b + 1)(3a - 5)$

4. a) $(mp + 10a)(mp - 10a)$
b) $3(1 - 4x)(1 + 4x)$
c) $(ax + by)(ax - by)$
d) $(x + y + w)(x + y - w)$
e) $(y^2 + 9)(y - 3)(y + 3)$
f) $(4x^2 + 25y^2)(2x + 5y)(2x - 5y)$
g) $(7p - 3c)^2$ **h)** $(1 - 10y^2z^2)^2$ **i)** $d^3(a + 1)^2$
j) $3(2m - 3)^2$ **k)** $2a(3a + 1)^2$
l) $x^2(5x - 2y^2)^2$

5. a) $(2x - 1 + y)(2x - 1 - y)$
b) $(3m - 5n + 1)(3m + 5n - 1)$
c) $(2a - 3)(2a + 3 - b)$
d) $(x - 3y)(x + 3y + 1)$
e) $(x - a)(1 + x - a)$
f) $(2x + y + 1)(2x + y - 1)$
g) $(a - c - b)(a - c + b)$
h) $(5x + 2)(5x + 2 - y)$

6. a) $(x - 1)(a + b + c)$
b) $(x - b + c)(x - b - c)$
c) $(x + 1)(x^2 - 3)$ **d)** $(y - 2)(2y^2 + 5)$
e) $(m - n + 3)(m + n - 3)$
f) $(3x - 5)(2y - 3x + 5)$
g) $(17x - 19y)(-7x - 11y)$ **h)** $d(1 - r)^2$

7. 121, 169; 49, 1

8. b) $(x^2 - x + 1)(x^2 + x + 1)$

9. a) $(x^2 - 3x + 5)(x^2 + 3x + 5)$
b) $(x^2 - x - 1)(x^2 + x - 1)$
c) $(x^2 - 2x + 2)(x^2 + 2x + 2)$
d) $(x^2 - xy + y^2)(x^2 + xy + y^2)$

Computer Power, page 50

1. a) $((5x + 2)x - 7)x + 8$; 8, 42, 140, 332, 648
b) $((2x - 5)x + 3)x - 9$; -9, -7, 9, 51, 131
c) $((6x + 1)x - 4)x + 12$; 15, 56, 171, 396, 767
d) $(((2x + 3)x - 5)x + 6)x - 11$; -5, 37, 205, 637, 1519

2. a) 24, 39, 56, 75, 96, 119, 144, 171, 200, 231
b) 7 **c) i)** 3 **ii)** 9 **iii)** 12

3. d) Linear function

Exercises 2-4, page 54

1. a) $x + 4$, R 2 **b)** $x - 1$, R 3
c) $c - 2$, R 4 **d)** $n - 16$, R 86

2. a) $x^2 - 2x + 4$, R -3
b) $m^2 - 3m - 7$, R -24
c) $3s^2 - s - 2$, R -2
d) $2x^2 - 5x - 12$

3. $x^3 - 2x^2 - 7x + 10$

4. $x^3 - x^2 - 11x + 12$

5. a) $2x + 3$, R -4 **b)** $3x + 8$, R 11
c) $5u - 3$, R 10 **d)** $3x - 6$, R 21
e) $4x + 3$, R 20 **f)** $3m - 2$, R -1

6. a) $c^2 + 4c + 3$, R -7
b) $x^2 - 6x - 11$, R 15
c) $1 + n - 2n^2$ **d)** $x^2 - 2x - 8$, R -4
e) $5a^2 + 8a + 3$, R 6
f) $m^2 + 3m - 10$, R -54

7. a) $x^2 - x - 2$, R 1 **b)** $-a^2 - 5a + 14$, R 2
c) $-3m^2 + 13m + 10$, R -3
d) $2s^2 - s - 6$

8. a) $(x - 3)(x - 4)$ **b)** $(3x + 1)(x - 1)$
c) $-(x + 1)^2$ **d)** $(5x - 2)(x + 5)$
e) $(2x + 3)(8x + 3)$ **f)** $(2x + 1)(-5x + 3)$

9. a) $x - 2$ **b)** $y - 3$, R $13y + 6$
c) $2a^2 - a + 3$, R 8 **d)** $3t^2 + 2t + 1$

10. a) $x^2 + 5x + 6$ **b)** $m^2 - 2m - 3$
c) $3x^2 - x - 10$, R -2 **d)** $a^2 - 4a - 12$, R 7

11. a) $(x - 3y)(x + 3y)$ **b)** $-(x + 4y)(x + 2y)$
c) $-(8a + 3b)(a - 3b)$
d) $-(3m + n)(m - 3n)$

12. a) $x^2 - 3$ **b)** $2a^2 + 3$ **c)** $3m^2 + 2$
d) $2x^2 + 3$ **13.** $(4x + 3)(x + 5)$

14. $(2a + 3)(3a - 2)$ **15. a)** $x^2 - x + 1$
b) $-5 - 2a + 3a^2$ **c)** $s^2 - 2s + 3$

16. a) $x^2 - x + 1$ **b)** $a^4 + a^3 + a^2 + a + 1$
c) $s^2 - st + t^2$ **d)** $m^2 - 2mn + 2n^2$

17. $-21, -3$ **18.** -8 **19.** $x^2 + bx + c$

20. a) $x^2 + (b + c)x + bc$
b i) $x^2 + (a + c)x + ac$
ii) $x^2 + (a + b)x + ab$

Investigate, page 55

1. a) 2 **b)** 2 **c)** 10, -70 **d)** When $f(x)$ is divided by $x - a$, the remainder is $f(a)$.

Exercises 2-5, page 58

1. a) $a^2 - 2a - 13 = (a + 3)(a - 5) + 2$
b) $x^3 + x^2 + x + 11 = (x + 2)(x^2 - x + 3) + 5$
c) $2p^3 + 5p^2 - 2p - 3$
$= (p + 1)(2p^2 + 3p - 5) + 2$
d) $2s^3 - 7s^2 + 16s - 22$
$= (2s - 3)(s^2 - 2s + 5) - 7$

2. a) 3 **b)** 14 **c)** 43 **d)** 11 **e)** 18
f) 19 **3. a)** -4 **b)** 11 **c)** 0 **d)** 16
e) 21 **f)** -43 **4. a)** 4 **b)** 44 **c)** 27
d) 7 **e)** 37 **f)** -1

5. a) 0 **b)** -6 **c)** 8 **d)** 1 **e)** 0 **f)** 2

6. a) 9 **b)** -9 **c)** 18 **d)** 43 **e)** 0
f) -16 **7. a)** 4 **b)** 2 **c)** 3

8. 3, -1 **9.** 1 **10. a)** 4 **b)** 3 **c)** 6

12. a) 11 **b)** -4 **c)** 5 **d)** $-\frac{3}{2}$

13. a) i), ii) No **iii)** Yes **b)** $7x - 5$

14. a) 1 **b)** $x + 10$ **c)** $x^2 - 2$

15. a) $f\left(-\frac{b}{a}\right)$ **b)** $\left(\frac{f(a) - f(b)}{a - b}\right)x + \frac{af(b) - bf(a)}{a - b}$

Exercises 2-6, page 63

4. 0 **5.** $x - 5$ **6.** a, b, d **7.** a, c, d **8.** b

9. a) $x^3 + 7x^2 + 7x - 15$
b) $x^3 - 5x^2 - 17x + 21$

10. $(y + 1)(y - 2)(y + 3)$ **11.** a, c **12.** c, d

13. a) Yes **b)** Yes **c)** No

14. a) $(a - 2)(a - 1)(a - 3)$
b) $(a + 2)(a - 2)(a + 3)$
c) $(x + 3)(x + 2)(x - 1)$

15. a) Yes **b)** No **c)** Yes **d)** No **e)** Yes
f) Yes **16. a)** $x - 1$ **b)** $x + 1$ **c)** $y + 1$
d) $x - 3$ **e)** $y - 2$ **f)** $x + 1$

17. b) $x - 4$ **18. b)** $2x - 1$

19. a) $(x - 1)(x - 3)(x - 4)$
b) $x^3 - 3x^2 + 3x - 1$; $x^3 - 3x + 2$

20. a) $(x - 1)(x + 2)(x + 4)$
b) $(x + 1)(x + 3)(x + 5)$
c) $(x + 1)(x - 4)(x + 5)$
d) $(x + 1)(x + 2)(x - 3)$
e) $(x - 1)^2(5x + 3)$ **f)** $(x - 2)(x^2 - 7x + 3)$
g) $(x + 1)(x + 2)(x + 5)$
h) $(x + 2)(x - 3)(2x + 1)$

21. a) $(x - 3)(x^2 - 5x + 2)$ **b)** $(x + 2)^2(x - 7)$
c) $(x + 1)(x - 4)(x + 9)$
d) $(x + 2)(x + 4)(x - 6)$
e) $(x + 1)(x - 2)(3x + 5)$
f) $(x - 2)(2x + 1)(5x - 3)$
g) $(x + 2)(x + 5)(x - 7)$
h) $(x - 3)(x + 4)(3x + 1)$

22. a) 11 **b)** -8 **c)** -4 **23.** Yes **24.** Yes
25. Yes **26. a)** 1, 5, -4 **b)** -2, 3, 7
c) 1, -3, $-\frac{1}{6}$ **d)** -2, 5, $-\frac{2}{5}$

Computer Power, page 66

1. a) $(x + 6)(x + 5)(x - 4)$
b) $(x + 25)(x - 4)(x - 10)$
c) $(x + 7)(x - 6)(2x - 3)$
d) $(x - 10)(x + 4)^2$
e) $(x + 6)(x - 5)^2$ **f)** $(x + 20)(x^2 - 3x + 5)$

Exercises 2-7, page 67

1. a) $(x + 2)(x^2 - 2x + 4)$
b) $(x + 3)(x^2 - 3x + 9)$
c) $(x - 5)(x^2 + 5x + 25)$
d) $(p - d)(p^2 + pd + d^2)$
e) $\left(x + \frac{1}{2}\right)\left(x^2 - \frac{1}{2}x + \frac{1}{4}\right)$

2. a) $(4x + 5)(16x^2 - 20x + 25)$
b) $(5x - 6y)(25x^2 + 30xy + 36y^2)$
c) $(3 - ab)(9 + 3ab + a^2b^2)$
d) $(x + 1)(x^2 + 8x + 19)$
e) $(y - 9)(y^2 + 12y + 111)$ **f)** $4(3x^2 + 4)$
g) $5(x - 2)(x^2 + 2x + 4)$
h) $2(x + 2y)(x^2 - 2xy + 4y^2)$
i) $m(c + 10)(c^2 - 10c + 100)$

j) $x(x + 1)(x^2 - x + 1)$
k) $3y(1 - 2y)(1 + 2y + 4y^2)$
l) $2(2x + 3)(4x^2 + 10x + 7)$

3. a) $(x - y)(x^2 + xy + y^2)(x^6 + x^3y^3 + y^6)$
b) $\left(\frac{1}{x} + \frac{4}{y}\right)\left(\frac{1}{x^2} - \frac{4}{xy} + \frac{16}{y^2}\right)$
c) $(x - y + 3)(x^2 + y^2 - 3y + xy + 3)$

5. a) $(x - y)(x + y)(x^4 + x^2y^2 + y^4)$
b) $(x - y)(x + y)(x^2 + xy + y^2)(x^2 - xy + y^2)$

Exercises 2-8, page 70

1. a) 9 b) 15 c) -14 d) 20 e) -150 f) -200 g) 0.4 h) 0.2

2. a) -2 b) -22 c) 2 d) -2 e) 1 f) 6 g) 20 h) 0.2 **3.** a) 6 b) -12 c) 6 d) $-\frac{1}{3}$ e) 1 f) -1

4. a) 37 b) 125 c) 121 d) 36 e) 136 f) 75 g) -847 h) 144

5. a) $6|x|$ b) $5m$ c) $-3|a|$ d) $2xy^2$ e) $-2xy^2$ f) $-2a^2|b^3|$ g) $3x^2y$ h) $2|m|n^2$

6. a) $11|x|y^2$ b) $3m^2n^3$ c) $-3a^2b$ d) $4x^2|y^3|$ e) $2pq^2r$ f) $-2m^3n^5$ g) $-3x^2|y^3|$ h) $-5a^2b^4c^3$ **7.** $4\sqrt{x}$ cm

8. a) $5x^4|y^3|$ b) $2|m||n^3|$ c) $3a^4b^2c^6$ d) $-2x^2|y|$ e) $-2m^2n^3$ f) $15|x^3||y^5|z^8$ g) $-3|m||n^3|p^2$ h) $10a^2b^5c^7$ i) $3x^2yz$

9. a) $2\sqrt{5}$ b) $3\sqrt{5}$ c) $4\sqrt{5}$ d) $3\sqrt{7}$ e) $2\sqrt{14}$ f) $6\sqrt{3}$

10. a) $\sqrt[4]{81}$ b) The even number roots
c) Roots which are multiplies of 3

11. $6x^{\frac{2}{3}}$ **12.** $4\sqrt{3}, 2\sqrt{12}; 3\sqrt{8}, 6\sqrt{2}$

13. a) $3\sqrt{3}, \sqrt{30}, 4\sqrt{2}$ b) $6\sqrt{2}, 5\sqrt{3}, 4\sqrt{5}$
c) $4\sqrt{6}, 7\sqrt{2}, 6\sqrt{3}, 4\sqrt{7}$
d) $2\sqrt[3]{12}, 3\sqrt[3]{4}, 4\sqrt[3]{2}, 3\sqrt[3]{5}$

14. 240 cm^2 **15.** $a(1 + \sqrt{10})$

16. a) $\sqrt{14} : 3$ b) $\sqrt{14} : 2$ c) $\sqrt{14} : 1$

17. a) $\sqrt{l^2 + w^2 + h^2} : l$ b) $\sqrt{l^2 + w^2 + h^2} : w$
c) $\sqrt{l^2 + w^2 + h^2} : h$

18. a) $\sqrt[3]{65}$ b) $\sqrt{10}$ c) $\sqrt[3]{15}$

19. a) $a^2b = c^2d, b > 0, d > 0$
b) $a^2b < c^2d, b > 0, d > 0$
c) $a^2b > c^2d, b > 0, d > 0$

Investigate, page 71

1. The square root of a number is greater than the number if the number is less than 1.

2. The cube root of a number is greater than the square root if the number is less than 1.

Review Exercises, page 72

1. a) $-2x^2 + 26xy$ b) $16a^2 - 14ab + 30ac$ c) $x^2 + 22xy - x$ d) $10m^2 - 22m$

2. a) $2x^2 + 6xy - 3x + 21y - 35$
b) $4m^3 + 8m^2 - 5mn - 3m - 10n + 6$
c) $3x^2 - 10y^2 - 3z^2 + xy + 17yz - 8xz$
d) $-5x^2 + 6x + 8$
e) $6x^3 + 5x^2 - 12x + 4$
f) $48x^3 - 112x^2 + 12x - 72$

3. a) $(x - 3)(x - 8)$ b) $(2m - 5)(m + 3)$
c) $(3x + 4y)(x - 2y)$ d) $(3x - 5y)^2$
e) $(2a + 3b)(5a + 3b)$ f) $(3x - 5y)(2x + 3y)$

4. a) $(8x + 7y)(8x - 7y)$
b) $5x^2(4x + 3y)(4x - 3y)$
c) $3(5a - 2)(2a - 3)$
d) $2x(4x - 3y)(x + 2y)$
e) $(2x + 1)(2x^2 - x + 3)$
f) $(2x + 3y + 5)(2x + 3y - 5)$

5. a) $(2a - 3)(a - 3)$ b) $(x + 2)(2x - 5)$
c) $(3x - 2y)(2x - y)$
d) $16x^2 - 16x - 1$, R 10

6. a) 5 b) -3 c) 5 **7.** 2 **8.** b, c, d

9. a) $(x - 2)(x + 2)(x + 3)$
b) $(x + 1)(x + 1)(x - 2)$
c) $(x - 1)(x + 2)(x + 4)$
d) $(x + 1)(x - 3)(x + 3)$ **10.** -16

11. a) $(2x - 3)(4x^2 + 6x + 9)$
b) $(4m + 5n)(16m^2 - 20mn + 25n^2)$
c) $2(3x^2 + 2y)(9x^4 - 6x^2y + 4y^2)$
d) $5y(1 - 2y)(1 + 2y + 4y^2)$
e) $(5a + 1)(67a^2 - 11a + 1)$
f) $3(3p - 10q)(9p^2 + 30pq + 100q^2)$

12. a) 15 b) -51 c) $12|m|$ d) $4x^2y^3$

13. a) $2\sqrt{10}, 3\sqrt{5}, 4\sqrt{3}, 5\sqrt{2}$
b) $3\sqrt[3]{6}, 2\sqrt[3]{21}, 4\sqrt[3]{3}, 5\sqrt[3]{2}$

Chapter 3

Exercises 3-1, page 76

1. a) -7 b) 14 c) -12 d) 11

2. a) -1 b) -1.3 c) 8 d) 4.5 e) 3 f) -6

3. a) $\frac{c - b}{a}$ b) $ac - ab$ c) $\frac{bd - bc}{a}$
d) $\frac{cd - b}{a}$ e) $\frac{bde - bc}{ad}$ f) $\frac{cd - b}{ac}$

4. a) $n = \frac{100\,000}{A - 200}$ b) i) 500 ii) 1000 iii) 2000 iv) 4000 **5.** $h = \frac{A}{2\pi R} - R$

6. a) $a = \frac{2A}{h} - b$ **b)** $b = \frac{2A}{h} - a$
c) $h = \frac{2A}{a + b}$

7. a) -21 **b)** 8 **c)** 2 **d)** 0.2 **e)** $\frac{1}{3}$
f) No solution **g)** 2 **h)** -4

8. a) -14 **b)** -1 **c)** -3 **d)** $\frac{6}{11}$
e) $\frac{ec - de + b}{a}$ **f)** $\frac{db + bce}{ae}$

9. a) -14 **b)** $\frac{20}{21}$ **c)** -0.6 **d)** 3 **e)** 21
f) -1 **10.** $n = \frac{360°}{180° - x}$

11. a) $m_1 = \frac{Fd^2}{Gm_2}$ **b)** $p = \frac{fq}{q - f}$ **c)** $v = u + at$
d) $R = \frac{nE - nrC}{C}$ **e)** $s = \frac{2ut + gt^2}{2}$
f) $h = \frac{A}{2\pi r} - \frac{r}{2}$ **12.** 10 L

Exercises 3-2, page 80

1. a) ± 2.74 **b)** ± 5.66 **c)** ± 2.24
d) ± 6.93 **e)** ± 2.26 **f)** ± 3.92

2. a) 2, 7 **b)** 5, -3 **c)** 3, 11 **d)** $-4, -8$
e) 2, -9 **f)** $-6, -9$

3. a) $-2.5, -3$ **b)** $-\frac{1}{3}, \frac{7}{4}$ **c)** $\frac{2}{3}, \frac{3}{2}$
d) $-1.5, -4$ **e)** $-0.8, 3$ **f)** $-\frac{1}{4}, \frac{7}{3}$

4. a) $-\frac{1}{2}, \frac{3}{2}$ **b)** $-0.5, -3$ **c)** 5, -1.5
d) 0.75, -0.8 **e)** ± 5 **f)** $-\frac{2}{3}, 3$

5. a) $x^2 - 10x + 21 = 0$ **b)** $x^2 - 5x - 36 = 0$
c) $3x^2 + 13x - 10 = 0$
d) $8x^2 + 10x + 3 = 0$
e) $2x^2 + 13x - 24 = 0$
f) $15x^2 + 11x - 12 = 0$

6. a) $c = \sqrt{\frac{E}{m}}$ **b)** $v = \sqrt{\frac{2E}{m}}$
c) $u = \sqrt{v^2 - 2as}$ **d)** $R = r + \sqrt{s^2 - h^2}$
e) $d = \sqrt{\frac{G\, m_1 m_2}{F}}$ **f)** $r = \sqrt{\frac{V}{\pi h}}$

7. a) $-11, 2$ **b)** $-\frac{5}{3}, 3$ **c)** 0, 5
d) $-\frac{5}{7}, -2$ **e)** $\frac{3}{4}, 1$ **f)** 4

8. a) i) 2.56 m **ii)** 5.76 m **b)** $v = \sqrt{\frac{L}{0.64}}$
c) i) 4.0 m/s **ii)** 4.8 m/s **d) i)** Quadrupled
ii) Increased by a factor 9

9. a) y **b)** $-5y, 2y$ **c)** $-3y, -17y$
d) $-\frac{3}{2}y, -4y$ **e)** $\frac{5}{3}y, 2y$ **f)** $-\frac{4}{3}y, \frac{3}{2}y$

10. a) $s = \sqrt{\frac{d}{0.05}}$ **b) i)** 4.5 m/s **ii)** 6.3 m/s
iii) 10.0 m/s **c) i)** Increased by a factor $\sqrt{2}$
ii) Increased by a factor $\sqrt{3}$

11. a) 2827 m^3 **b)** $r = \sqrt{\frac{3V}{\pi h}}$ **c) i)** 95 m
ii) 82 m **12.** $4\sqrt{3}$

13. 3 cm, 5 cm; two different triangles can be drawn from the given information

14. $4\sqrt{3}$ cm **15.** About 0.94 cm

16. $y = r(\sqrt{1 + 0.01x} - 1)$

17. i) 986 N **ii)** 983 N **iii)** 989 N
b) i) 345 km **ii)** 2640 km

Mathematics Around Us, page 83

1. 0.44 s **2.** 96 cm **3.** 81 cm **4.** 379 km/h

Exercises 3-3, page 87

1. a) $\frac{2}{3}, 1$ **b)** $-\frac{1}{5}, -1$ **c)** $\frac{3 \pm \sqrt{11}}{2}$
d) 3, 3 **e)** $\frac{13 \pm \sqrt{89}}{4}$ **f)** $-0.5, 1.5$

2. a) $-\frac{2}{3}, \frac{3}{4}$ **b)** $\frac{7 \pm \sqrt{109}}{30}$ **c)** $\frac{17 \pm \sqrt{241}}{8}$
d) $\frac{2}{3}, -\frac{1}{2}$ **e)** $-\frac{5}{3}, -1$ **f)** $-1.5, 5$

3. a) $\frac{-7 \pm \sqrt{97}}{2}$ **b)** $4 \pm \sqrt{2}$ **c)** $\frac{-5 \pm \sqrt{13}}{6}$
d) 1.25, 1 **e)** $\frac{-5 \pm \sqrt{23}i}{4}$ **f)** $\frac{-2 \pm \sqrt{6}i}{5}$

4. a) $\frac{-5 \pm \sqrt{10}}{2}$ **b)** $-1.5, -3.5$

c) $\frac{-5 \pm \sqrt{15}}{2}$ d) $-2.5, -2.5$
e) $\frac{-5 \pm \sqrt{5}i}{2}$ f) $\frac{-5 \pm \sqrt{10}i}{2}$

5. a) $1 - 2i$ **b)** $5 + 3i$ **c)** $1 - 4i$
d) $-2 - i$ **e)** $-i$

6. a) 1 **b)** 73 **c)** -39 **d)** 0 **e)** 121
f) -68 **7. a)** a, b, and e **b)** d **c)** c and f

8. a), b), d) 2 different real roots **e)** 2 equal real roots **c), f)** 2 complex roots

9. a) $-1, 0.2$ **b)** $\frac{4 \pm \sqrt{6}}{2}$ **c)** $\frac{-5 \pm \sqrt{13}}{6}$
d) $\frac{-7 \pm \sqrt{31}i}{8}$ **e)** $2, \frac{2}{3}$ **f)** $\frac{2 \pm \sqrt{6}i}{2}$

10. a) $3 - 4i$; $x^2 - 6x + 25 = 0$
b) $1 + 2i$; $x^2 - 2x + 5 = 0$
c) $2 - 7i$; $x^2 - 4x + 53 = 0$
d) $2 - 3i$; $x^2 - 4x + 13 = 0$
e) $-1 - i$; $x^2 + 2x + 2 = 0$

11. a) $-4 \pm \sqrt{15}$ **b)** $-0.8, -1$
c) $\frac{-6 \pm \sqrt{37}}{2}$ **d)** $2 + \sqrt{2}i$ **e)** $-\frac{2}{3}, -\frac{2}{3}$
f) $8 \pm \sqrt{102}$

12. a) $5, -3.5$ **b)** $\frac{2 \pm \sqrt{14}i}{3}$ **c)** $\frac{11 \pm \sqrt{185}}{2}$
d) $0.8, 2$ **e)** $\frac{1 \pm \sqrt{217}}{4}$ **f)** $1 \pm i$

13. a) $x^2 - 5x - 14 = 0$
b) $15x^2 + 19x + 6 = 0$
c) $x^2 - 4x - 1 = 0$ **d)** $x^2 - 6x + 10 = 0$
e) $4x^2 - 12x - 15 = 0$
f) $16x^2 - 16x + 13 = 0$

14. a) $\pm 4\sqrt{6}$ **b)** -1.6 **c)** 9 **d)** $6 \pm 2\sqrt{10}$

15. a) $m \geqslant 6\sqrt{2}, m \leqslant -6\sqrt{2}$ **b)** $m \leqslant 0.9$
c) $m \geqslant -\frac{9}{8}$ **d)** $m \geqslant 2\sqrt{3}, m \leqslant -2\sqrt{3}$

16. a) 10.25% **b)** 17.26% **17.** 4.5 cm

18. a) 629.757 184 3 or -635.157 184 3
b) 3461.401 917 or -3466.801 917

19. a) $(3\sqrt{5} - 3)$ cm **b)** $(27\sqrt{5} - 45)$ cm^2

20. a) 1413 km **b)** 455 km

21. a) $\pm 13, \pm 8, \pm 7$ **b)** $\pm 7, \pm 2$
c) 0, 4, 10, 18, . . . **22. a)** $b^2 = 4ac$
b), c) $2b^2 = 9ac$ **d)** $nmb^2 = ac(m + n)^2$

23. a) The left side is always positive and hence cannot equal 0. **b)** $\pm i$

24. No **25. b)** $\frac{2n + 1}{n}$

Exercises 3-4, page 92

1. a) 1.7 **b)** 2.3 **c)** $-2.7, -1.1, 0.5, 3.3$
d) $-2.9, -1.4, 0, 1.4, 2.9$ **2. a)** $0, \pm 3.2$
b) 3.6, 2 **c)** $-2, -1.5, 3.7$ **d)** 4

3. a) $-3.5, -0.7, 4.2$ **b)** 2.3 **c)** $\pm 1.2, \pm 3.7$
d) $-2.3, 3.2$ **4. a)** 1.6 **b)** 3.5
c) $-3.3, -0.6, 1.2, 2.7$ **d)** $-2.1, 3.2$

5. There could be 2 negative roots which are approximately equal, or there could be no real roots. **9.** About 4.5 s

10. a) i) $x^3 - 12x + 10 = 0$
ii) $x^3 - 12x + 20 = 0$, $x^3 - 12x - 20 = 0$
b) i) $-16 < k < 16$ **ii)** $k = \pm 16$
iii) $k > 16$; $k < -16$

11. a)

n	1	2	3	4	5	6
$n^3 + n^2$	2	12	36	80	150	252

n	7	8	9	10
$n^3 + n^2$	392	576	810	1100

b) 7 **c)** No

12. About 7.9 cm by 5.3 cm by 11.8 cm

Exercises 3-5, page 96

1. a) $0, 2, -5$ **b)** $0, -\frac{3}{2}, 4$ **c)** $0, -3, -7$
d) $0, -\frac{7}{3}, \frac{3}{2}$ **e)** $0, \pm 2$ **f)** $0, -2, -3$

2. a) 0 **b) i)** $-\frac{1}{2}, 3$ **ii)** $\pm\frac{3}{2}$ **iii)** $\frac{5}{2}, 3$
iv) $0, -\frac{2}{3}, -4$ **v)** $0, \pm\frac{5}{3}$ **vi)** 3, 4

3. a) $2, \pm\sqrt{3}i$ **b)** $-5, \pm 3$ **c)** $-2, \frac{1}{2}, 3$
d) $\pm 2, \frac{2}{3}$ **4. a)** $-2, 3, -4$ **b)** $1, \pm 3i$
c) $1, 2, -\frac{3}{2}$ **d)** $-\frac{1}{2}, \pm\frac{3}{2}$

5. a) $2, -1 \pm 2i$ **b)** $\pm 3, 2$
c) $-1, \frac{-4 \pm \sqrt{6}}{2}$ **d)** $\frac{2}{3}, \pm 5i$

6. a) $-2, -3, -4$ **b)** $-4, -5, -6$

7. a) 3 **b)** -5

8. 10 cm by 6 cm by 1 cm or $\left(\frac{9-\sqrt{21}}{2}\right)$ cm by $(3+\sqrt{21})$ cm by $(\sqrt{21}-1)$ cm

9. $\pm 22, \pm 23$

10. a) $x^3 - 8x^2 + 17x - 10 = 0$
b) $x^3 - 3x^2 - 3x + 1 = 0$
c) $2x^4 - x^3 - 19x^2 + 9x + 9 = 0$
d) $4x^3 - 8x^2 - 23x - 11 = 0$
e) $x^3 - 7x^2 + 17x - 15 = 0$
f) $x^4 + 2x^3 - x - 2 = 0$

11. a) 13; 5, $-\frac{1}{2}$ **b)** -104; $\pm\frac{2}{5}$, -2
c) 20; $\frac{9 \pm \sqrt{57}}{6}$ **d)** 23; $-\frac{1}{3}$, $3 \pm \sqrt{2}$

12. a) $\pm 1, \pm 2$ **b)** $2, -1 \pm i$

13. a) 1, 5, 14, 30 **b)** 24

Computer Power, page 99

1. 0.694 593, 3.064 178 **2. a)** 1.1409
b) 1.5897 **c)** 2.2790

3. a) $-4.2916, -0.4283, 2.7180$
b) $-2.0205, 0.0636, 1.9364, 4.0204$
c) -2.4233 **4.** 88.7 m

The Mathematical Mind, page 100

1. a) 0.327 480 0 **b)** $-0.673\ 593\ 1$
c) $-0.568\ 946\ 4$

Exercises 3-6, page 103

1. a) ± 5 **b)** ± 2 **c)** 0 **d)** No solution

2. a) $-5, 9$ **b)** $-1, -7$ **c)** $4, -6$ **d)** 7
e) $2, -\frac{2}{3}$ **f)** No solution **g)** $9, -7$
h) $11, -1$ **i)** $3, -\frac{5}{3}$

3. a) 1 **b)** No solution **c)** $-1, 7$ **d)** $\frac{1}{2}$
e) No solution **f)** $\frac{1}{3}, \frac{1}{5}$ **4. a)** 1 **b)** $\frac{1}{2}$
c) 1 **d)** $\frac{1}{12}$ **e)** No solution **f)** $0, \frac{1}{2}$

5. a) $3, -5$ **b)** $1, -5$ **c)** $3.5, -1.5$ **d)** $\frac{4}{3}, \frac{12}{23}$
e) No solution **f)** $-1.5, 4.5$

6. a) No solution **b)** 4 **c)** No solution **d)** 3

7. a) ± 2 **b)** $1, -5$ **c)** $0, -2$
d) No solution **e), f)** All real numbers

8. a) $14, -3$ **b)** $\frac{1}{4}, \frac{1}{6}$ **c)** $5, -1$
d) $\{x \mid 1 \leq x \leq 3, x \in R\}$ **9. a)** ± 4 **b)** $\frac{1}{2}$
c) No solution **d)** All real numbers

10. a) 0, 5 **b)** $\{x \mid 1 \leq x \leq 4, x \in R\}$
c) No solution

Exercises 3-7, page 105

1. a) $\{x \mid -3 < x < 3\}$ **b)** $\{x \mid x > 4 \text{ or } x < -4\}$
c) $\{x \mid -6 \leq x \leq 6\}$ **d)** $\{x \mid -3 < x < 7\}$
e) $\left\{x \mid x \geq \frac{8}{5} \text{ or } \leq -\frac{8}{5}\right\}$ **f)** $\{x \mid -10 \leq x \leq 8\}$

2. a) $\{x \mid -3 \leq x \leq 5\}$ **b)** $\{x \mid x > 6 \text{ or } x < -8\}$
c) $\{x \mid -5 < x < 4\}$ **d)** $\left\{x \mid -\frac{4}{3} < x < 2\right\}$
e) $\{x \mid x \geq 7 \text{ or } x \leq -13\}$
f) $\{x \mid x \geq 3 \text{ or } x \leq -2.5\}$

3. a) R **b)** $\{x \mid -1 \leq x \leq 6\}$
c) $\left\{x \mid x > \frac{1}{5} \text{ or } x < -1\right\}$ **d)** $\left\{x \mid \frac{1}{4} < x < \frac{3}{2}\right\}$
e) No solution **f)** $\left\{x \mid x < \frac{1}{2}\right\}$

4. a) $\{x \mid -5 < x < 4\}$ **b)** $\{x \mid -6 \leq x \leq 2\}$
c) $\{x \mid x > 6 \text{ or } x < -1.5\}$ **d)** $\{x \mid x > 1\}$
e) No solution **f)** $\left\{x \mid x > \frac{1}{2}\right\}$

5. a) $\left\{x \mid x \geq 2 \text{ or } x \leq -\frac{8}{7}\right\}$
b) $\{x \mid -1 < x < 5\}$ **c)** R
d) $\{x \mid x > 1\}$ **e)** $\{x \mid x = 2\}$
f) No solution

6. a) $\{x \mid -2 < x < 3\}$ **b)** $\left\{x \mid -\frac{17}{5} \leq x \leq 19\right\}$
c) No solution **d)** $\{x \mid -1 \leq x \leq 1\}$

7. a) $\{x \mid x < 5\}$ **b)** $\{x \mid x > 8 \text{ or } x < -8\}$
c) $\left\{x \mid x > -\frac{7}{3} \text{ or } x < -13\right\}$ **d)** No solution

8. a) $5 - x + \frac{1}{x-2}$ **b)** $2 < x \leq 3.7808$

9. Answers may vary. Typical inequalities are:
a) $|x - 2| > x - 2$ **b)** $|x| > 0$
c) $|x - 1| < 2$ **d)** $|x - 1| > 2$

10. Answers may vary. Typical inequalities are:
a) $|x - 3| \geqslant 3 - x$ **b)** $|x - 2| \leqslant 2$
c) $|x - 2| > 2$ **d)** $|x - 2| > 0$

11. Answers may vary. Typical inequalities are:
a) $|2 - 3x| < 3x - 4$ **b)** $|x + 1| > x - 1$
c) $|6 - 3x| \leqslant x - 2$

Exercises 3-8, page 110

1. a) 16 **b)** 9 **c)** 16 **d)** 6.25 **e)** 1 **f)** 9 **2. a)** 23 **b)** 53 **c)** 37 **d)** 4 **e)** 4 **f)** $\frac{10}{3}$ **3. a)** $\frac{49}{18}$ **b)** $\frac{14}{5}$ **c)** No solution **d)** $\frac{19}{4}$ **e)** 3 **f)** 4

4. a, c, e **5.** $a = \sqrt{d^2 - b^2}$ **6. a)** 1 **b)** $\frac{19}{5}$ **c)** 1.5 **d)** No solution **e)** $-\frac{1}{3}$ **f)** -4

7. a) 6 **b)** 9 **c)** 9 **d)** 1 **e)** 3 **f)** 11
8. a) 1 **b)** 7 **c)** 1 **d)** 3 **e)** 7 **f)** 5
9. a) 4, 5 **b)** 1, -11 **c)** 8, -4 **d)** 9 **e)** 6 **f)** 7

10. a) $d = \left(\frac{v + 7}{8.2}\right)^2$ **b) i)** 67 m **ii)** 140 m **iii)** 240 m **c) i)** 51 km/h **ii)** 75 km/h **iii)** 93 km/h

11. a) $l = \frac{T^2 g}{4\pi^2}$ **b)** $a = \frac{v^2 - u^2}{2s}$ **c)** $W = \frac{2gE}{V^2}$ **d)** $c = \frac{vm}{\sqrt{m^2 - M^2}}$ **e)** $k = \frac{F}{m(v^2 + u^2)}$ **f)** $E = \frac{h^2 - 2ae^2m}{2a^2m}$

12. $h = \sqrt{\left(\frac{A}{\pi r} - r\right)^2 - r^2}$

13. 20 cm, 21 cm, 29 cm **14.** 9, 16

15. $h = \frac{2r \pm \sqrt{4r^2 - c^2}}{2}$

16. a) $h = r$ **b)** $c \leqslant 2r$ **17.** c, d, e

Review Exercises, page 112

1. a) -1.25 **b)** -2 **c)** $-\frac{1}{16}$ **d)** 5

2. a) ± 2.3 **b)** 5, -1.5 **c)** $-\frac{2}{3}, -\frac{5}{2}$ **d)** 9, $-\frac{1}{2}$ **3. a)** $-1 \pm \sqrt{5}$ **b)** $\frac{5 \pm \sqrt{13}}{6}$ **c)** $\frac{5 \pm \sqrt{57}}{4}$ **d)** $1 \pm \sqrt{2}i$ **e)** $\frac{-3 \pm \sqrt{11}i}{4}$ **f)** $\frac{-3 \pm \sqrt{31}i}{10}$

4. a) $3x^2 - 7x - 20 = 0$ **b)** $6x^2 + 13x + 6 = 0$ **c)** $3x^2 + x = 0$

5. a) $r = \pm\sqrt{\frac{3V}{\pi h}}$ **b)** $t = \pm\sqrt{\frac{d + 20}{4.9}}$ **c)** $v = \frac{t^2 + 9s^2}{18s^2}$ **6.** $6 \pm 4\sqrt{6}$

7. a) 2 different real roots **b)** 2 complex roots **c)** 2 equal real roots **8. a)** $x^2 - 6x + 13 = 0$ **b)** $x^2 - 10x + 34 = 0$ **c)** $x^2 + 8x + 25 = 0$

9. a) $\frac{1 \pm \sqrt{15}i}{2}$ **b)** $-1, -3, -6, 2$

10. a) $-2\sqrt{14} < p < 2\sqrt{14}$ **b)** $p < -\frac{9}{40}$ **c)** $p < -2$ **11. a)** -2.9 **b)** 0, ± 3

12. a) 1, ± 2 **b)** -1, 2, 3 **c)** -2, $\frac{3 \pm \sqrt{3}i}{2}$ **d)** 1, 2, ± 2 **13. a)** ± 4 **b)** 8, -2 **c)** 2, -6 **14. a)** $\{x \mid -3 \leqslant x \leqslant 4\}$ **b)** $\left\{x \mid x < \frac{1}{3}\right\}$ **c)** $\left\{x \mid \frac{1}{8} < x < \frac{3}{2}\right\}$

15. a) 6 **b)** 5 **c)** No solution

Cumulative Review, Chapters 1-3, page 113

1. a) i) -8, 7, 1.6 **ii)** R; R **iii)** $y = \frac{x + 2}{3}$ **b) i)** 15, 10, 0.28 **ii)** R; $\left\{y \mid y \geqslant -\frac{1}{8}, y \in \mathrm{R}\right\}$ **iii)** $y = \frac{\pm\sqrt{8x + 1} + 3}{4}$ **c) i)** $-2, -\frac{1}{3}, \frac{2}{3}$ **ii)** $\{x \mid x \neq 0, x \in \mathrm{R}\}$, $\{y \mid y \neq -1, y \in \mathrm{R}\}$ **iii)** $y = \frac{2}{x + 1}$

2. a) $4k^2 - 6k + 1$ **b)** $4k^2 + 6k + 1$ **c)** $-z^2 + 3z - 1$ **d)** $x^2 + x - 1$ **e)** $4x^2 - 10x + 5$ **f)** $\frac{1}{x^2} - \frac{3}{x} + 1$

3. $2x^2 + 12x + 13 \neq 2x^2 + 8$

4. a) 0.5, 2 **b)** -1.5, 4 **c)** -0.75, 2

5. a) x y **b)** x y **c)** x y

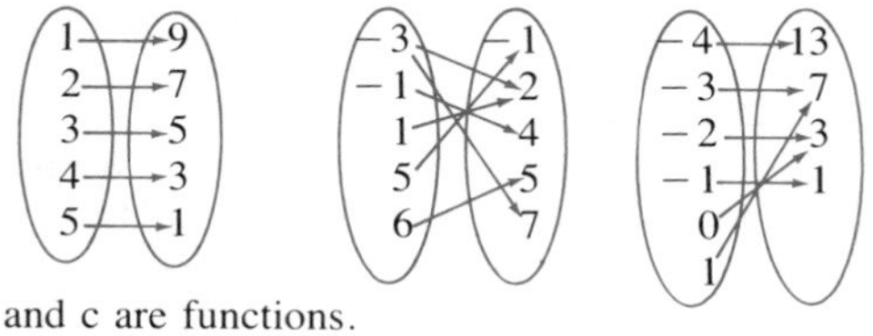

a and c are functions.

6. a) $4x^2 + 14x + 12$ **b)** $4x + 15$ **c)** $\frac{x - 15}{4}$

d) $2x^2 - 6x + 9$

7. a) i) $\frac{6x - 5}{2}$ **ii)** $2\sqrt{\frac{x + 3}{x - 2}}$

iii) $6\sqrt{x + 1} - 1$ **iv)** $2\sqrt{3x}$

b) i) R; R

ii) $\{x \mid x \geqslant -1, x \in R\}$; $\{y \mid y \geqslant 0, y \in R\}$

iii) $\{x \mid x \geqslant -1, x \in R\}$, $\{y \mid y \geqslant -1, y \in R\}$

iv) $\{x \mid x \geqslant 0, x \in R\}$, $\{y \mid y \geqslant 0, y \in R\}$

9. $d = \sqrt{2w^2 - 10w + 25}$

10. a) $x + 24y$ **b)** $-9m^2 - 31mn$

c) $-2x^2 - 18xy + 31x$

d) $10a^2 + 29ab - 21b^2$ **e)** $x^2 - 10x + 10$

f) $-28m^2 + 38mn + 18m - 15n - n^2 - 6$

11. a) $3x(5x - 2y + 7)$ **b)** $(x - 14)(x - 3)$

c) $(2x + 3y)(5x - 4y)$

d) $(3m - 2)(m^2 - 5m + 3)$

e) $3x(x + 2y)(5x - 3y)$

f) $4(5p - 3q)(5p + 3q)$

12. a) $(x + 4y + 3)(x + 4y - 3)$

b) $(4x - 2y + 3)(4x + 2y - 3)$

c) $(5x - 2y + 5z)(-x + 10y - z)$

d) $(a - 1 - x - y)(a - 1 + x + y)$

e) $(3x - 1)(2x - 1)(x - 2)$

f) $(3x + y + 2)^2$

13. $2m + 1, m - 6$ **14.** $-3x^3 - x^2 + 2x + 5$

15. a) -6 **b)** $18a^2 + 15a - 4$

c) $128x^2 - 120x + 21$

16. a) $(x + 1)^2(x + 2)$ **b)** $(x - 1)(x^2 + 3x + 3)$

c) $(3x + 5y)(9x^2 - 15xy + 25y^2)$

d) $(2x + 1)(2x - 1)(x + 2)$

17. a) $\frac{1}{2}$ **b)** $\frac{9}{7}$ **c)** $\frac{7}{3}, -2$ **d)** $\frac{-2 \pm 3\sqrt{2}}{2}$

e) $-\frac{3}{5}, -1$ **f)** $-\frac{1}{2}, 3$ **18. a)** $\frac{5 \pm \sqrt{7}i}{4}$

b) $0, \frac{3 \pm \sqrt{23}i}{8}$ **c)** $-1, -2, 3$ **d)** $\frac{3}{2}, \pm 2$

e) 1, 3, 2, 2 **f)** $-\frac{5}{3}, 3$

19. a) $t = \pm\sqrt{\frac{2(s - 3u)}{a}}$ **b)** $n = \frac{(m + 1)^2 - 20}{12}$

20. a) 2 equal real roots **b)** 2 different real roots **c)** 2 complex roots

21. a) $4x^2 + 5x - 6 = 0$ **b)** $x^2 + 4x + 13 = 0$

22. a) $k = \pm 2\sqrt{6}$ **b)** $k < -\frac{25}{8}$

23. a) 4, -3 **b)** No solution **c)** 2, -10 **d)** No solution

24. a) 9 **b)** 6 **c)** 4 **d)** $\frac{6 - \sqrt{11}}{2}$

Chapter 4

Exercises 4-1, page 119

1. B **2. a)** 6 **b)** 8 **3.** $\angle A = \angle D$; $\angle B = \angle E$; $\angle C = \angle F$; AB = DE; BC = EF; AC = DF **4.** 0, 1, or infinitely many

5. Yes **6. a)** Infinite number **b)** 1

7. i) f **ii)** d **iii)** e **iv)** g **v)** b **vi)** a **vii)** c

13. a) Yes **b)** Yes **c)** Yes **d)** Yes

Exercises 4-2, page 124

6. a) 110°, 20° **b)** 45°, 22.5° **c)** 120°, 65°

7. i) a) Subtract x from 180° **b)** $x + y = 180°$

ii) a) Subtract 90° from x **b)** $y = x - 90°$

iii) a) Subtract x from 90° **b)** $x + y = 90°$

8. a), b), c) $x + y + z = 180°$

17. $(n - 2)180°$

Exercises 4-3, page 131

1. a) AC = DF; BC = EF **b)** QP = SU; RP = TU **c)** IJ = LM; IK = LN

2. a) $\angle P = \angle U$ **b)** $\angle Y = \angle U$

c) $\angle M = \angle G$ or $\angle L = \angle F$

3. a) $\triangle ABC \cong \triangle EDC$, ASA

b) $\triangle PQS \cong \triangle RSQ$, SSS or AAS or SAS

c) $\triangle ADE \cong \triangle EFC$, AAS

4. a) 23° **b)** 118°, 62°, 118° **c)** 45°, 45°

d) 65°, 65°, 50° **e)** 30°, 60° **f)** 76°, 52°, 76°

5. a) 36°, 36° **b)** 60°, 30° **c)** 55°

Exercises 4-4, page 138

4. a) $\angle A = \angle B$; $\angle C = \angle D$; ITT

b) $\angle PTS = \angle QTR$, $\angle PTQ = \angle STR$; OAT,

other answers possible
c) $\angle YXW = \angle YWX$, $\angle WYZ = \angle WZY$; ITT

5. a) Yes **b)** 9 m **c)** 12 m **6.** 5 cm

Exercises 4-5, page 149

1. a) 110° **b)** 75° **c)** 140° **d)** 25°
2. a) 360° **b)** 180° **c)** 360°
3. a), b), f) Yes **c), d), e)** No

Exercises 4-6, page 153

1. a) $\angle N$ **b)** $\angle R$ **c)** $\angle W$
2. a) EF **b)** KL **c)** JH
5. a) $0 < x < 45°$ **b)** $40° < x < 180°$
c) $135° < x < 180°$

Mathematics Project, page 156

1. a) $y = 90° - x; \{x \mid 0° < x < 90°\}$
b) $y = 270° - x; \{x \mid 90° < x < 180°\}$
c) $y = 180° - 2x; \{x \mid 0° < x < 90°\}$
d) $y = x - 60°; \{x \mid 60° < x < 180°\}$
e) $y = 3x; \{x \mid 0° < x < 45°\}$
f) $y = 90° + \frac{x}{2}; \{x \mid 0° < x < 180°\}$

2. a) 0°, 40°, 180°, 320°, 360°

Exercises 4-7, page 160

5. a), b), c), d) true

Exercises 4-8, page 165

1. a) BD ∥ FE, DE ∥ AF **b)** SR ∥ TU ∥ PQ; PS ∥ QR
c) AB ∥ CD; AC ∥ BD
3. a) Infinite number **b)** 1 **5.** Yes

Exercises 4-9, page 169

4. a) i) C **ii)** B **iii)** CD **iv)** BD
5. a) i) B **ii)** A **iii)** P **iv)** BP
11. a) i) U **ii)** T **iii)** SU **iv)** ST **b)** 90°

Review Exercises, page 172

2. a) 35°, 25° **b)** 30°, 50° **c)** 30°, 60°

Exercises 5-1, page 177

1. i) a) $\angle A = \angle D$, $\angle B = \angle E$, $\angle C = \angle F$
b) $\frac{AB}{DE} = \frac{BC}{EF} = \frac{AC}{DF}$
ii) a) $\angle P = \angle T$, $\angle Q = \angle W$, $\angle R = \angle V$, $\angle S = \angle U$ **b)** $\frac{PQ}{TW} = \frac{QR}{WV} = \frac{RS}{VU} = \frac{PS}{TU}$
iii) a) $\angle K = \angle G$, $\angle L = \angle H$, $\angle M = \angle J$
b) $\frac{KL}{GH} = \frac{LM}{HJ} = \frac{KM}{GJ}$ **3. a)** Yes **b)** No

4. 0.5625 : 1 **5. a)** 14, 105°, 42 **b)** 35, 30, 80°
6. a) 1.5 **b)** 0.6 **7. a)** 425.25 cm^2
b) 266.76 cm^2
8. a) 9.6 cm, 13.5 cm, 8.4 cm **b)** 2.56 cm, 3.6 cm, 2.24 cm **c)** 4.48 cm, 6.3 cm, 3.92 cm
9. a) 3.75 m by 2.7 m, 10.125 m^2
b) 1.5 m by 1.08 m, 1.62 m^2
10. a) 2 **b)** 1.6 **c)** $\frac{1}{3}$ **11.** 1.2 m^2
13. a) 7:11 **b) i)** 3.5 cm **ii)** 8.6 cm
14. 12, 13.3, 17.1, 28, 18.7, 14.3, 100°, 110°

Exercises 5-2, page 185

1. a) SAS ~ **b)** AA~
2. i) a) $\triangle JKL \sim \triangle MNP$, SSS~
b) $\frac{JK}{MN} = \frac{KL}{NP} = \frac{JL}{MP}$
ii) a) $\triangle DGH \sim \triangle DEF$, AA~
b) $\frac{DG}{DE} = \frac{GH}{EF} = \frac{DH}{DF}$
3. a) 16.3, 11.9 **b)** 9, 13.3
4. i) a) $\triangle QPR \sim \triangle STR$, AA~ **b)** 13.1, 17.5
ii) a) $\triangle DGH \sim \triangle DEF$, AA~ **b)** 9, 15.4
iii) a) $\triangle XWY \sim \triangle WZY \sim \triangle XZW$, AA~
b) 9.6, 18.7 **5.** $\triangle ABC \sim \triangle DAC \sim \triangle DBA \sim \triangle EBD \sim \triangle EDA$, AA ~ **7. a)** 20, 18
b) 0.9, 0.3 **c)** $1.\overline{6}$, $3.\overline{3}$ **8.** 2.5
9. i) a) $\triangle ABC \sim \triangle EDC$, AA~ **b)** 35, 15
ii) a) $\triangle PQR \sim \triangle PST$, AA~ **b)** 14, 10.7
iii) a) $\triangle EFD \sim \triangle EDC$, AA~ **b)** 20, 12.6
10. a) 10.5 m, 3 m, 4.5 m, 2.1 m, 4.5 m, 4.5 m,
b) 39.4 m^2
11. $\frac{bx(h - x)}{h}$ cm^2 **12.** 13.7 cm
13. a) 3.50 m, 1.75 m **b)** 3.85 m by 2.80 m
14. 14.0 m

Mathematics Around Us, page 189

1. a) $\frac{1}{9000}$ **b)** 3.321 km **c)** 8.9 cm by 2.8 cm
2. $GD = \frac{xh}{f}$ **3.** $RF = \frac{kf}{h}$
4. a) $\frac{9}{10\,000}$ **b)** 306 m **5.** $\frac{1}{1056}$ to $\frac{1}{1167}$
6. 0.125 km^2 **7. a)** 100 m^2 **b)** 0.1435 km^2

Exercises 5-3, page 195

2. a) 10 **b)** 12 **c)** 15 **3. a), b)** Yes **c)** No **4. a)** 4 **b)** 15 cm **5. a)** 4 **b)** 4 cm **6. a), c), d), e)** Yes **b), f)** No
7. a) 225 cm^2 **b)** 324 cm^2 **c)** 576 cm^2 **d)** 144 cm^2 **8. a)** 1:2 **b)** 1:5 **c)** 3:4 **d)** 4:5 **9. a)** 18 cm^2 **b)** 50 cm^2 **c)** 30.5 cm^2 **d)** 131.25 cm^2 **10.** 8 cm, 16.8 cm **12. i) a)** 10 cm **b)** 20 cm **c)** 15 cm **d)** 12.5 cm **ii) a)** 24 cm **b)** 48 cm **c)** 36 cm **d)** 30 cm **14. a)** 5 **b)** 6 cm **15. a)** SAS~ **b)** 27 cm **c)** 2689 cm^2 **16.** 1:9 **17. a)** $1 : \sqrt{2}$ **b)** $1 : (\sqrt{2} - 1)$ **18.** Quad XPRM = Quad RQZN = $(2\sqrt{2} - 2.5)k$; △PRN = Quad MYQR = $(3 - 2\sqrt{2})k$

Exercises 5-4, page 201

1. a) ± 4 **b)** ± 6 **c)** ± 8 **d)** ± 9 **e)** ± 12 **f)** ± 20
2. a) $\pm 2\sqrt{15}$ **b)** $\pm 4\sqrt{15}$ **c)** $\pm 6a\sqrt{2}$ **d)** $\pm m$ **e)** $\pm 15x\sqrt{5y}$ **f)** $\pm 12\sqrt{st}$
3. a) 36 **b)** −75 **c)** 18 **d)** 20 **e)** −6 **f)** −90 **4.** 2, 8
5. 48, 3 or −48, −3 **6.** 1.2×10^{-5} cm
7. About 124.0 t **8. a)** 12 **b)** 4.6 **c)** 12.8
9. a) PS **b)** QP **c)** TS **d)** PR **e)** PS **f)** QS
10. a) 2, 4.5 or 8, 8.9 **b)** 3, 10.4 **c)** 11.8, 7.5
11. 5 cm, 10 cm, 20 cm
12. \$14 940, \$19 920, \$26 560
13. a) 21 cm **b)** 63 cm^2

Exercises 5-5, page 205

1. 21 m **2.** 3.63 cm **3.** 17 m **4.** 22.1 m
5. 11 m **6.** 20.2 cm **7.** 6.48 m beyond the net
8. 6660 km **9. a)** $1.\dot{3}$ cm **b)** $\frac{xz}{x + z}$ **c)** No
10. a) 21.1 m, 15.8 m, 10.5 m **b)** 16.7 m, 21.7 m
11. 30 cm by 16 cm, 60 cm by 32 cm, 90 cm by 48 cm, 120 cm by 64 cm
12. a) 0.60 m by 0.32 m, 0.77 m by 0.41 m **b)** 2.25 m
13. a) 30 Ω **b)** 20 Ω **c)** About 43 Ω **15.** $l > 2w$
16. a) 3620 km/h **b)** 3.2 min
17. $\frac{\pi R^2 x^3}{3h^2}$ **18.** $\frac{2}{\sqrt{5}}$ km

Review Exercises, page 208

1. a) 27, 28, 116° **b)** 14.4, 20, 7.2
2. a) 14.4 cm **b)** 0.9 cm
3. △KLM ~ △PNR, SSS~ **4.** 9.4 m **5. a)** 5 **b)** 6 m **6. a)** 4 **b)** 16 cm **7.** 2.3 cm

Exercises 6-1, page 212

1. The centre **2.** $2R$ **4. b)** Yes
6. Infinite number **7. a)** 6 **b)** 1
8. a) Infinite number **b)** 2 **9.** 2 **10.** 3 cm
11. a) 51 cm **b)** About 68 cm **c)** About 31 cm

Exercises 6-2, page 215

1. a) 9.8 **b)** 5.7 **c)** 6
2. a) 45° **b)** 2.2 **c)** 4.5
3. About 6 cm **4. a)** 8 **b)** 2.1 **c)** 4.1
7. 34 cm **8.** About 77 m **9.** 10 cm
15. $\frac{d^2 + R^2 - r^2}{2d}$; $\frac{d^2 - R^2 + r^2}{2d}$ **16.** $\frac{3\sqrt{3}R^2}{2}$

Exercises 6-3, page 221

1. a) ∠D, ∠E, ∠F, ∠G, ∠H **b)** ∠D, ∠F **c)** Typical answers are: ∠D, ∠G **d)** ∠H **e)** ∠AOB **2. a)** 90° **b)** 180° **3. a)** 30° **b)** 55° **c)** 20°
4. a) 90°, 50°, 40° **b)** 28°, 62°, 90° **c)** 45°, 90°, 45° **5.** 120°, 30° **6.** 105°, 105°
7. $\frac{\sqrt{5}}{2}$ cm **17.** 24 cm **20.** 2.1

Exercises 6-4, page 226

1. They are collinear. **2. c)** Answers may vary. ∠FEB = ∠FCB; ∠EFC = ∠EBC
3. Answers may vary. ∠PQS = ∠PRS; ∠SQR = ∠SPR; ∠RPQ = ∠RSQ; ∠QSP = ∠QRP; ∠QTR = ∠PTS
4. A circle

Exercises 6-5, page 229

1. a) 105° **b)** 35° **c)** 45°
2. a) 50°, 60° **b)** 20°, 60° **c)** 115°, 20°

Exercises 6-6, page 234

1. a) 7 **b)** 18° **c)** 130° **2. a)** 30°, 60° **b)** 40°, 25° **11.** 21 cm **12. c)** $\frac{2rR}{\sqrt{r^2 + R^2}}$
16. a) 3 cm

Exercises 6-7, page 239

1. a) 30° **b)** 75° **c)** 60° **2. a)** 70°, 70° **b)** 115°, 115° **c)** 70°, 70° **3. a)** 60° **b)** 60° **c)** 7 cm

Exercises 6-8, page 244

1. a) 9 **b)** 13 **c)** $5\sqrt{2}$ **2. a)** 6 **b)** 4 **c)** 6 **3.** 3 cm, 2 cm **4.** $12\sqrt{2}$ cm **5.** 16 m **7.** 20 cm **9. a)** 576 cm² **b)** 48 cm **10.** 5.4 cm

Exercises 6-9, page 249

1. a) $\frac{\pi}{6}$ **b)** $\frac{\pi}{4}$ **c)** $\frac{\pi}{3}$ **d)** $\frac{\pi}{2}$ **e)** $\frac{2\pi}{3}$ **f)** $\frac{3\pi}{4}$ **g)** $\frac{5\pi}{6}$ **h)** π **i)** $\frac{7\pi}{6}$ **j)** $\frac{5\pi}{4}$ **k)** $\frac{4\pi}{3}$ **l)** $\frac{3\pi}{2}$ **m)** $\frac{5\pi}{3}$ **n)** $\frac{7\pi}{4}$ **o)** $\frac{11\pi}{6}$ **p)** 2π **q)** $\frac{13\pi}{6}$ **r)** $\frac{9\pi}{4}$

2. a) 90° **b)** 135° **c)** −120° **d)** 210° **e)** 45° **f)** −270° **g)** 315° **h)** 360° **i)** −300° **j)** 225° **k)** 30° **l)** −330°

3. a) 1.75 **b)** 3.93 **c)** 1.00 **d)** −2.18 **e)** $1.31x$ **f)** 0.33 **g)** −1.13 **h)** $0.43x$ **i)** 2.62 **j)** 0.52 **k)** 1.00 **l)** $-1.57x$

4. a) 114.6° **b)** −286.5° **c)** 183.3° **d)** 103.1° **e)** −40.1° **f)** $80.2\theta°$ **g)** 383.9° **h)** $-360x°$

5. a) 10 cm **b)** 15 cm **c)** 9 cm **d)** 30.5 cm **e)** 21 cm **f)** 3 cm

6. a) 28.3 cm **b)** 15.7 cm **c)** 22.0 cm **d)** 34.6 cm **e)** 50.3 cm **f)** 37.7 cm **g)** 64.9 cm **h)** 41.9 cm

7. a) i) 157 cm² **ii)** 419 cm² **b) i)** 113 cm² **ii)** 283 cm² **c) i)** 818 cm² **ii)** 1309 cm²

8. a) i) 15 m **ii)** 26 m **b) i)** 47 cm **ii)** 353 cm **c) i)** 509 mm **ii)** 1131 mm

9. a) 2π **b)** π **c)** $\frac{\pi}{2}$ **10.** 627 cm²

11. 15 m **12.** 51 cm **13.** 90 cm² **14.** 20 cm

15. a) $\frac{\pi R^2}{n}$ **b)** $\frac{360°}{n}$ **c)** $\frac{2\pi R}{n}$ **d)** $\frac{2\pi}{n}$

16. a) $\frac{\pi}{30}$ **b)** $\frac{\pi}{360}$ **c)** 12 **17.** $\frac{\pi x}{50}$

18. a) About 0.0172 **b)** 2 560 000 km

19. a) About 87 rad/s **b)** $\frac{500x}{9d}$ rad/s

20. a) i) $R\sqrt{2}$ **ii)** $\frac{\pi R}{2}$ **b)** $\frac{\pi}{2\sqrt{2}}$ **c)** $\frac{R^2(\pi - 2)}{4}$ **d)** $\frac{R\sqrt{2}}{2}$

Review Exercises, page 252

1. a) 24 **b)** $2\sqrt{6}$ **c)** $\sqrt{41}$ **2.** Obtuse

8. a) $\frac{\pi}{2}$ **b)** $\frac{\pi}{3}$

Cumulative Review, Chapters 4-6, page 253

2. i) a) Subtract x from 180° **b)** $y = 180° - x$
ii) a) Subtract x from 90° **b)** $y = 90° - x$
iii) a) Double x **b)** $y = 2x$

7. ∠ABC = ∠DBA = ∠DAC; ∠BAC = ∠BDA = ∠ADC; ∠BCA = ∠BAD = ∠ACD; $\frac{AB}{DB} = \frac{BC}{BA} = \frac{AC}{DA}$; $\frac{AB}{DA} = \frac{BC}{AC} = \frac{AC}{DC}$; $\frac{DB}{DA} = \frac{BA}{AC} = \frac{DA}{DC}$

10. 9.2 m **11.** 3.1 cm **16.** 25 cm

Chapter 7

Exercises 7-1, page 258

1. a) 0.27 **b)** 0.70 **c)** 1.73 **d)** 3.73
2. a) 27° **b)** 45° **c)** 58° **d)** 68°
3. a) 0.424 **b)** 1.072 **c)** 1.881 **d)** 0.123 **e)** 0.781 **f)** 7.115 **g)** 1.235 **h)** 0.306 **i)** 2.747 **j)** 28.6 **4. a)** 40° **b)** 65° **c)** 28° **d)** 57° **e)** 79° **f)** 5° **g)** 19° **h)** 33° **i)** 85° **j)** 67° **5. a)** 15°, 0.3 **b)** 30°, 0.6 **c)** 42°, 0.9 **6. a)** 0.087 **b)** 0.700 **c)** 1.732 **d)** 5.671
7. 34.3°, 0.682; 53.7°, 1.364 **8.** 0.943, 43.3°
9. 2.778, 70.2° **10.** 11°, 3° **11.** 24°
12. a) 3.84 m **b)** 1.68 m

Exercises 7-2, page 262

1. a) 0.5000 **b)** 0.2079 **c)** 0.6157 **d)** 0.2756 **e)** 0.8829 **f)** 0.6428 **g)** 0.9903 **h)** 0.9877 **i)** 0.8572 **j)** 0.7986 **2. a) i)** 12° **ii)** 26° **iii)** 48° **iv)** 65° **v)** 84° **b) i)** 78° **ii)** 64° **iii)** 42° **iv)** 25° **v)** 6° **3. a)** $\frac{28}{53}, \frac{45}{53}, \frac{28}{45}$ **b)** $\frac{8}{10}, \frac{6}{10}, \frac{8}{6}$ **c)** $\frac{5}{13}, \frac{12}{13}, \frac{5}{12}$ **d)** $\frac{20}{29}, \frac{21}{29}, \frac{20}{21}$

e) $\frac{8}{17}, \frac{15}{17}, \frac{8}{15}$ **f)** $\frac{3.6}{3.9}, \frac{1.5}{3.9}, \frac{3.6}{1.5}$

4. a) $\sin P = \frac{9}{41}, \cos P = \frac{40}{41}, \tan P = \frac{9}{40}$
b) 12.7°, 77.3° **5.** 9.6° **6.** 72.7°
7. 47.8° **8. a)** 7.1° **b)** 0.6, 32.0°
9. 25.8° **10. a)** 1223 m **b)** 10°

11. a) $\frac{1}{2}$ **b)** $\frac{\sqrt{3}}{2}$ **c)** $\frac{1}{\sqrt{3}}$

12. a) $\sin A = \frac{a}{b}, \cos A = \frac{c}{b}, \tan A = \frac{a}{c}$
b) $\sin C = \frac{c}{b}, \cos C = \frac{a}{b}, \tan C = \frac{c}{a}$;
$\sin A = \cos C; \cos A = \sin C; \tan A = \frac{1}{\tan C}$

13. 36.9°, 53.1° **14.** $\frac{2}{3} l^3 (\cos \theta)^2 \sin \theta$

Exercises 7-3, page 266

1. a) AB = 24, ∠A = 36.9°, ∠C = 53.1°
b) DE = 33.2, ∠D = 50.3°, ∠F = 39.7°
c) ∠H = 35°, GK = 12.6, HK = 22.0
d) ∠M = 58°, LM = 38.7, MN = 73.1
e) PR = 34.2, ∠P = 37.9°, ∠R = 52.1°
f) ∠S = 50°, SU = 23.1, UT = 27.6
2. a) YZ = 25.5, ∠X = 46.7°, ∠Z = 43.3°
b) ∠Z = 63°, YZ = 8.2, XZ = 18.0
c) XY = 49.3, ∠X = 14.8°, ∠Z = 75.2°
d) ∠X = 38°, XY = 56.7, YZ = 44.3
e) ∠Z = 26°, XY = 15.6, XZ = 35.6
f) XZ = 49.2, ∠Z = 66.0°, ∠X = 24.0°

3. a) $\cos \theta = \frac{15}{17}, \tan \theta = \frac{8}{15}$
b) $\sin \theta = \frac{24}{25}, \tan \theta = \frac{24}{7}$
c) $\sin \theta = \frac{20}{29}, \cos \theta = \frac{21}{29}$
d) $\cos \theta = \frac{\sqrt{799}}{32}, \tan \theta = \frac{15}{\sqrt{799}}$
e) $\sin \theta = \frac{\sqrt{168}}{23}, \tan \theta = \frac{\sqrt{168}}{19}$
f) $\sin \theta = \frac{43}{\sqrt{14\,393}}, \cos \theta = \frac{112}{\sqrt{14\,393}}$

4. a) $\cos \theta = \frac{\sqrt{q^2 - p^2}}{q}, \tan \theta = \frac{p}{\sqrt{q^2 - p^2}}$
b) $\sin \theta = \frac{2\sqrt{a+1}}{a+2}, \tan \theta = \frac{2\sqrt{a+1}}{a}$
c) $\sin \theta = \frac{x-y}{\sqrt{2x^2 + 2y^2}}, \cos \theta = \frac{x+y}{\sqrt{2x^2 + 2y^2}}$

5. a) 60 m **b)** 66 m **6. a)** 21.0 m
b) 4.5 m **7.** 62° **8. a)** 34° **b)** 37°
9. 7.2 cm **10. a)** 24.6 m **b)** 4.3 m **c)** 5.67
11. 151.7 m, 168.2 m **12. a) i)** 45.0° **ii)** 80.3°
iii) 110.3° **iv)** 136.8° **b)** 16 **13.** 8.9 cm

Exercises 7-4, page 270

1. a) 3.420 **b)** 1.804 **c)** 2.281 **d)** 0.158
e) 1.836 **f)** 1.058 **g)** 5.145 **h)** 1.012
i) 0.754 **j)** 1.589 **k)** 1.086 **l)** 1.006
2. a) sin 25° = 0.423, csc 25° = 2.366;
cos 25° = 0.906, sec 25° = 1.103;
tan 25° = 0.466, cot 25° = 2.145
b) sin 50° = 0.766; csc 50° = 1.305;
cos 50° = 0.643, sec 50° = 1.556,
tan 50° = 1.192, cot 50° = 0.839
c) sin 75° = 0.966, csc 75° = 1.035;
cos 75° = 0.259, sec 75° = 3.864;
tan 75° = 3.732, cot 75° = 0.268
d) sin 30° = 0.500, csc 30° = 2.000;
cos 30° = 0.866, sec 30° = 1.155;
tan 30° = 0.577, cot 30° = 1.732
e) sin 45° = cos 45° = 0.707;
csc 45° = sec 45° = 1.414;
tan 45° = cot 45° = 1.000
f) sin 60° = 0.866,
csc 60° = 1.155; cos 60° = 0.500,
sec 60° = 2.000; tan 60° = 1.732,
cot 60° = 0.577 **3. a)** 38° **b)** 56°
c) 19° **d)** 61° **e)** 41° **f)** 50° **g)** 15°
h) 74° **i)** 23° **j)** 67° **k)** 12° **l)** 52°

4. a), b) $\sin A = \cos B = \frac{a}{c}; \cos A = \sin B = \frac{b}{c}$;
$\tan A = \cot B = \frac{a}{b}; \csc A = \sec B = \frac{c}{a}$;
$\sec A = \csc B = \frac{c}{b}; \cot A = \tan B = \frac{b}{a}$
5. sin A = cos B, cos A = sin B, tan A = cot B,
csc A = sec B, sec A = csc B, cot A = tan B
6. a) AB = 16.1, ∠A = 43.0°; ∠C = 47.0°
b) ∠N = 33°, PM = 26.1, PN = 40.3
c) ∠S = 57°, VS = 22.4, TS = 41.1

7. a) $\sin \theta = \frac{q}{p}, \cos \theta = \frac{\sqrt{p^2 - q^2}}{p}$,
$\tan \theta = \frac{q}{\sqrt{p^2 - q^2}}, \sec \theta = \frac{p}{\sqrt{p^2 - q^2}}$,
$\cot \theta = \frac{\sqrt{p^2 - q^2}}{q}$ **b)** $\sin \phi = \frac{2\sqrt{x}}{x+1}$,
$\cos \phi = \frac{x-1}{x+1}, \tan \phi = \frac{2\sqrt{x}}{x-1}, \csc \phi = \frac{x+1}{2\sqrt{x}}$,

$\cot\phi = \dfrac{x-1}{2\sqrt{x}}$ **c)** $\sin\alpha = \dfrac{a+1}{\sqrt{5a^2+2a+1}}$,

$\cos\alpha = \dfrac{2a}{\sqrt{5a^2+2a+1}}$, $\tan\alpha = \dfrac{a+1}{2a}$,

$\csc\alpha = \dfrac{\sqrt{5a^2+2a+1}}{a+1}$,

$\sec\alpha = \dfrac{\sqrt{5a^2+2a+1}}{2a}$

8. a) 31 cm **b)** 7.85 m **c)** 196.23 m **d)** 9613 m

Exercises 7-5, page 272

1. About 36 cm **2.** 37° **3.** 66° **4. a)** 9.3 m **b)** 3.6 m **5. a)** 25 cm **b)** 4 cm **6. a)** 76 m **b)** 2 h 42 min **7.** 34.2 m **8. a)** 6367 km **b)** 40 003 km **9.** 75.83° **10. a) i)** 108 m **ii)** 70.5 m **iii)** 62.4 m **b)** 64° **c) i)** 5.6 m **ii)** 6.7 m **iii)** 7.0 m **11.** 56°, 79° **12. a) i)** 260 m **ii)** 62 m **iii)** 87 m **iv)** 1139 m **b)** 9:52 A.M. and 2:08 P.M. **c)** 7 h and 59 min **13.** 32°

Exercises 7-6, page 278

1. a) $\frac{1}{2}$ **b)** $\frac{1}{2}$ **c)** $\frac{2}{\sqrt{3}}$ **d)** 1 **e)** $\frac{2}{\sqrt{3}}$ **f)** $\sqrt{3}$ **g)** $\frac{1}{\sqrt{2}}$ **h)** $\frac{1}{\sqrt{3}}$ **i)** $\frac{1}{\sqrt{2}}$ **j)** $\frac{1}{\sqrt{3}}$ **k)** $\sqrt{2}$ **l)** $\sqrt{2}$ **2. a)** 2 **b)** $\sqrt{3}$ **c)** 0 **d)** ∞ **e)** $\frac{\sqrt{3}}{2}$ **f)** 1 **g)** ∞ **h)** 1 **i)** 2 **j)** ∞ **k)** ∞ **l)** 1 **3. a)** 45° **b)** 0° **c)** 60° **d)** 60° **e)** 30° **f)** 45° **g)** 0° **h)** 45° **i)** 60° **j)** 45° **k)** 0° **l)** 0° **4. a)** 45° **b)** 60° **c)** 90° **d)** 45° **e)** 90° **f)** 30° **g)** 90° **h)** 30° **i)** 30° **j)** 60° **k)** 0° **l)** 0° **5.** $3\sqrt{2}$ km **6.** 19.4 m **7. a)** 8.8 m, 6.2 m **b)** 7.2 m, 3.6 m **c)** 12.4 m, 10.7 m **8.** 39.7 m

9. $10\sqrt{3}$ cm **10. a)** $x = \frac{s}{\sqrt{2}}$ **b)** $y = \frac{s}{\sqrt{3}}$; $z = \sqrt{\frac{2}{3}}s$ **11.** $\sqrt{3}l$ **12.** 2:1

13. $x = \frac{\sqrt{7}s}{3}$ **14. a)** $\frac{1}{1+\sqrt{2}}$ **b)** $\frac{1}{\sqrt{4+2\sqrt{2}}}$ **c)** $\frac{1+\sqrt{2}}{\sqrt{4+2\sqrt{2}}}$

15. a) $A = \frac{nx^2}{4}\cot\left(\frac{180°}{n}\right)$ **b) i)** $A = x^2$ **ii)** $A = \frac{3\sqrt{3}x^2}{2}$ **iii)** $\frac{\sqrt{3}x^2}{4}$ **16.** $\frac{10\sqrt{3}}{3}$ cm

17. $4\pi : 3\sqrt{3}$ **18.** 10 cm **19.** $30(2+\sqrt{3})$ cm **20.** $10(\sqrt{3}+4)$ m **21.** $5(3+\sqrt{3})$ m **22. a)** BF = CD = $\sqrt{3}$, AD = $\sqrt{3}+1$, AE = $\sqrt{3}-1$, ED = $2\sqrt{2}$, EF = FD = 2

b) i) $\frac{\sqrt{3}-1}{2\sqrt{2}}$ **ii)** $\frac{\sqrt{3}+1}{2\sqrt{2}}$ **iii)** $\frac{\sqrt{3}-1}{\sqrt{3}+1}$ **iv)** $\frac{\sqrt{3}+1}{2\sqrt{2}}$ **v)** $\frac{\sqrt{3}-1}{2\sqrt{2}}$ **vi)** $\frac{\sqrt{3}+1}{\sqrt{3}-1}$

Exercises 7-7, page 283

1. a) 0.990 **b)** −2.356 **c)** −0.559 **d)** −1.006 **e)** 3.072 **f)** −1.327

2. a) $\sin\theta = \frac{12}{13}$, $\cos\theta = -\frac{5}{13}$, $\tan\theta = -\frac{12}{5}$, $\csc\theta = \frac{13}{12}$, $\sec\theta = -\frac{13}{5}$, $\cot\theta = -\frac{5}{12}$

b) $\sin\theta = \frac{3}{5}$, $\cos\theta = -\frac{4}{5}$, $\tan\theta = -\frac{3}{4}$, $\csc\theta = \frac{5}{3}$, $\sec\theta = -\frac{5}{4}$, $\cot\theta = -\frac{4}{3}$

c) $\sin\theta = \frac{8}{17}$, $\cos\theta = -\frac{15}{17}$, $\tan\theta = -\frac{8}{15}$, $\csc\theta = \frac{17}{8}$, $\sec\theta = -\frac{17}{15}$, $\cot\theta = -\frac{15}{8}$

3. a) $-\frac{1}{2}$ **b)** $\frac{1}{2}$ **c)** −1 **d)** 2 **e)** $-\sqrt{2}$ **f)** $\frac{1}{\sqrt{2}}$ **g)** $-\sqrt{3}$ **h)** $-\frac{1}{\sqrt{3}}$ **i)** $\frac{\sqrt{3}}{2}$ **j)** $-\sqrt{3}$ **k)** $\sqrt{2}$ **l)** −2 **4. a)** −0.34 **b)** −0.09 **c)** 1.49 **d)** −3.08 **e)** 0.62 **f)** −0.18 **g)** −2.37 **h)** −0.84 **i)** 3.86 **j)** −0.77 **k)** −1.00 **l)** 0.98

5. a) $-\frac{15}{8}$, $-\frac{17}{8}$ **b)** $-\frac{24}{25}$, $\frac{25}{7}$ **c)** $\frac{12}{13}$, $-\frac{5}{12}$ **d)** $-\frac{20}{29}$, $\frac{29}{21}$ **e)** $\frac{9}{41}$, $-\frac{40}{9}$ **f)** $-\frac{4}{3}$, $-\frac{5}{3}$

6. a) 135° **b)** 120° **c)** 120° **d)** 135° **e)** 150° **f)** 150° **g)** 135° **h)** 120° **i)** 150° **j)** 150° **k)** 135° **l)** 135° **7. a)** 115° **b)** 125° **c)** 105° **d)** 145° **e)** 145° **f)** 112° **g)** 152° **h)** 102° **i)** 97° **j)** 113° **k)** 141° **l)** 172°

8. a) $-\frac{\sqrt{13}}{2}$, 124° **b)** $-\frac{3}{\sqrt{58}}$, 113°

c) $-\frac{2}{\sqrt{77}}$, 103° **d)** −2, 117°
e) $\frac{\sqrt{10}}{3}$, 108° **f)** $\frac{28}{53}$, 148°

9. a) $\sin(180° + \theta) = -\frac{y}{r}$; $\csc(180° + \theta) = -\frac{r}{y}$
$\cos(180° + \theta) = -\frac{x}{r}$; $\sec(180° + \theta) = -\frac{r}{x}$
$\tan(180° + \theta) = \frac{y}{x}$; $\cot(180° + \theta) = \frac{x}{y}$
b) $\sin(360° - \theta) = -\frac{y}{r}$; $\csc(360° - \theta) = -\frac{r}{y}$
$\cos(360° - \theta) = \frac{x}{r}$; $\sec(360° - \theta) = \frac{r}{x}$
$\tan(360° - \theta) = -\frac{y}{x}$; $\cot(360° - \theta) = -\frac{x}{y}$

10. a) $-\frac{1}{\sqrt{2}}$ **b)** $-\frac{1}{2}$ **c)** $\sqrt{3}$ **d)** −1
e) $-\sqrt{3}$ **f)** $\sqrt{2}$ **g)** −1 **h)** −2 **i)** 1

11. a) 65°, 115° **b)** 128°, 232° **c)** 100°, 280°
d) 200°, 340° **e)** 55°, 305° **f)** 25°, 205°
g) 145°, 325° **h)** 150°, 210° **i)** 255°, 285°
j) 115°, 245° **k)** 75°, 105° **l)** 160°, 340°

12. a) sin 0° = 0; cos 0° = 1; tan 0° = 0; sec 0° = 1; cot 0°, csc 0° are undefined
b) sin 90° = 1; cos 90° = 0; csc 90° = 1; sec 90°, tan 90° are undefined; cot 90° = 0
c) sin 180° = 0; cos 180° = −1; tan 180° = 0; csc 180°, cot 180° are undefined; sec 180° = −1
d) sin 270° = −1, cos 270° = 0, tan 270°, sec 270° are undefined, csc 270° = −1, cot 270° = 0 **e)** sin 360° = 0; cos 360° = 1; tan 360° = 0, csc 360°, cot 360° are undefined, sec 360° = 1

Exercises 7-8, page 288

1. a) 8.6 **b)** 14.3 **c)** 15.6 **2. a)** 4.0
b) 23.6 **c)** 33.7 **d)** 8.0 **e)** 14.1
3. a) 129.1° **b)** 26.4° **c)** 53.6°
4. a) i) 25.2° **ii)** 121.6° **b) i)** 20.0°
ii) 121.0° **c) i)** 13.4° **ii)** 148.4°
d) i) 31.9° **ii)** 90° **e) i)** 41.6° **ii)** 87.6°
f) i) 12.5° **ii)** 108.9° **5. a)** 4.4 **b)** 48
c) 29.3 **6.** 4.7 m **7.** 6.0 km
8. 6.4 cm, 9.4 cm **9.** 35° **10.** 16°
11. 9.6 cm **12. a)** 195 cm^2 **b)** 91 cm^2
c) 210 cm^2 **13. a)** $r\sqrt{2 - \sqrt{3}}$ **b)** r
c) $r\sqrt{2}$ **d)** $r\sqrt{3}$ **e)** $r\sqrt{2 + \sqrt{3}}$ **f)** $2r$
14. a) $3\sqrt{2 - \sqrt{3}}$ cm **b)** $3\sqrt{2 + \sqrt{3}}$ cm
15. a) $\sqrt{2 + \sqrt{3}}$ cm **b)** 0.25 cm^2
16. a) $\sqrt{5}$ cm, $\sqrt{5}$ cm **b)** $2\sqrt{13}$ cm, $\sqrt{73}$ cm
18. $\sqrt[3]{2}$, $\sqrt[3]{4}$

Exercises 7-9, page 296

1. a) 22.2 **b)** 18.0 **c)** 15.9 **2. a)** 36.4°
b) 38.7° **c)** 140.6° **3. a)** 10.6 **b)** 22.2
c) 27.7 **d)** 15.3 **e)** 15.1
4. a) ∠Q = 46.4°, ∠R = 28.6°, r = 5.9
b) ∠R = 49.2°, ∠P = 67.8°, p = 20.8
c) ∠R = 46.4°, ∠Q = 21.6°, q = 12.7
d) ∠P = 40.7°, ∠Q = 61.3°, q = 37.7
5. a) ∠B = 45.8°, ∠C = 99.2°, c = 20.7 or ∠B = 134.2°, ∠C = 10.8°, c = 3.9
b) ∠C = 75.5°, ∠A = 49.5°, a = 10.2 or ∠C = 104.5°, ∠A = 20.5°, a = 4.7
c) c = 27.3, ∠B = 42.9°, ∠A = 59.1°
d) ∠C = 55.2°, ∠A = 82.8°, a = 32.6 or ∠C = 124.8°, ∠A = 13.2°, a = 7.5
e) a = 28.5, ∠C = 45.0°, ∠B = 96.0°
f) ∠A = 23.5°, ∠C = 32.5°, c = 17.5
6. a) ∠Y = 58°, y = 30.3, z = 27.4
b) x = 21.0, ∠Y = 46.4°, ∠Z = 87.2°
c) ∠X = 69.5°, ∠Z = 56.5°, z = 19.6 or ∠X = 110.5°, ∠Z = 15.5°, z = 6.3
d) z = 7.3, ∠X = 69.2°, ∠Y = 49.8°
7. 54.3 m **8.** 31.6 km, 22.8 km **9. a)** 21 m
b) 8 m **10. a)** 191 m, 256 m or 929 m, 693 m **b)** 151 m or 546 m **11.** 122 m
12. a) 1.9 **b)** 2.7 **13.** $20\left(1 + \frac{1}{\sqrt{3}}\right)$
14. ∠O = 104.8°, ∠Y = ∠H = 37.6° **15.** 10 cm

Computer Power, page 300

1. a) b = 37.4, ∠A = 22.4°, ∠C = 31.6°
b) ∠A = 107.6°, ∠B = 45.6°, ∠C = 26.7°
c) ∠C = 70°, a = 14.4, b = 21
d) ∠A = 111.1°, ∠C = 51.6°, a = 21.8 or ∠A = 34.3°, ∠C = 128.4°, a = 13.2
e) ∠A = 60°, a = 15.5, c = 13.3
f) ∠A = 40.5°, ∠B = 71.7°, b = 60.7
2. 3475 km **3.** 325 091 000 km
4. 4.12×10^{13} km

Review Exercises, page 302

1. a) 0.819 **b)** 0.510 **c)** 6.392 **d)** 1.327
e) 0.423 **f)** 2.669 **g)** −0.900 **h)** 0.978
i) 1.004 **j)** −0.306 **k)** −0.777
l) −1.015 **2. a)** 74° **b)** 28° **c)** 27°
d) 28°, 152° **e)** 19°, 161° **f)** 66°
3. sin: **a)** 0 **b)** $\frac{1}{2}$ **c)** $\frac{1}{\sqrt{2}}$ **d)** $\frac{\sqrt{3}}{2}$
e) 1 **f)** $\frac{\sqrt{3}}{2}$ **g)** $\frac{1}{\sqrt{2}}$ **h)** $\frac{1}{2}$ **i)** 0;

csc: **a), i)** Undefined **b)** 2 **c)** $\sqrt{2}$
d) $\frac{2}{\sqrt{3}}$ **e)** 1 **f)** $\frac{2}{\sqrt{3}}$ **g)** $\sqrt{2}$ **h)** 2;

cos: **a)** 1 **b)** $\frac{\sqrt{3}}{2}$ **c)** $\frac{1}{\sqrt{2}}$ **d)** $\frac{1}{2}$
e) 0 **f)** $-\frac{1}{2}$ **g)** $-\frac{1}{\sqrt{2}}$ **h)** $-\frac{\sqrt{3}}{2}$
i) -1;

sec: **a)** 1 **b)** $\frac{2}{\sqrt{3}}$ **c)** $\sqrt{2}$ **d)** 2
e) Undefined **f)** -2 **g)** $-\sqrt{2}$ **h)** $-\frac{2}{\sqrt{3}}$
i) -1; tan: **a)** 0 **b)** $\frac{1}{\sqrt{3}}$ **c)** 1 **d)** $\sqrt{3}$
e) Undefined **f)** $-\sqrt{3}$ **g)** -1 **h)** $-\frac{1}{\sqrt{3}}$
i) 0; cot: **a), i)** Undefined **b)** $\sqrt{3}$ **c)** 1
d) $\frac{1}{\sqrt{3}}$ **e)** 0 **f)** $-\frac{1}{\sqrt{3}}$ **g)** -1
h) $-\sqrt{3}$

4. a) $\sin\theta = \frac{15}{17}$; $\csc\theta = \frac{17}{15}$; $\sec\theta = \frac{17}{8}$;
$\tan\theta = \frac{15}{8}$; $\cot\theta = \frac{8}{15}$
b) $\sin\theta = \frac{12}{13}$; $\csc\theta = \frac{13}{12}$; $\cos\theta = \frac{5}{13}$;
$\sec\theta = \frac{13}{5}$; $\cot\theta = \frac{5}{12}$ **c)** $\sin\theta = \frac{8\sqrt{5}}{21}$;
$\csc\theta = \frac{21}{8\sqrt{5}}$; $\cos\theta = \frac{11}{21}$; $\tan\theta = \frac{8\sqrt{5}}{11}$;
$\cot\theta = \frac{11}{8\sqrt{5}}$ **d)** $\csc\theta = \frac{9}{5}$; $\cos\theta = \frac{2\sqrt{14}}{9}$;
$\sec\theta = \frac{9}{2\sqrt{14}}$; $\tan\theta = \frac{5}{2\sqrt{14}}$; $\cot\theta = \frac{2\sqrt{14}}{5}$

5. a) $\csc\theta = \frac{b}{a}$; $\cos\theta = \frac{\sqrt{b^2 - a^2}}{b}$;
$\sec\theta = \frac{b}{\sqrt{b^2 - a^2}}$; $\tan\theta = \frac{a}{\sqrt{b^2 - a^2}}$;
$\cot\theta = \frac{\sqrt{b^2 - a^2}}{a}$
b) $\sin\theta = \frac{p}{\sqrt{2p^2 + 2pq + q^2}}$;
$\csc\theta = \frac{\sqrt{2p^2 + 2pq + q^2}}{p}$;
$\cos\theta = \frac{p + q}{\sqrt{2p^2 + 2pq + q^2}}$;
$\sec\theta = \frac{\sqrt{2p^2 + 2pq + q^2}}{p + q}$; $\cot\theta = \frac{p + q}{p}$
c) $\sin\theta = \frac{\sqrt{3m^2 - 10m - 8}}{2m - 1}$;
$\csc\theta = \frac{2m - 1}{\sqrt{3m^2 - 10m - 8}}$; $\cos\theta = \frac{m + 3}{2m - 1}$;
$\tan\theta = \frac{\sqrt{3m^2 - 10m - 8}}{m + 3}$;
$\cot\theta = \frac{m + 3}{\sqrt{3m^2 - 10m - 8}}$

6. a) AC = 31.0, ∠A = 61°, ∠C = 29°
b) AB = 15, ∠C = 56°, ∠A = 34°
c) BC = 13.6, AC = 44.2, ∠A = 18°
d) ∠C = 55°, AB = 9.8, BC = 6.9

7. a) q = 11.8, ∠P = 64.0°, ∠R = 41.0°
b) ∠Q = 44.7°, ∠P = 83.3°, p = 35.3
c) ∠R = 37.0°, q = 50.3, r = 31.3
d) ∠Q = 113.7°, ∠R = 36.8°, ∠P = 29.6°
e) ∠R = 64.0°, ∠P = 59.0°, p = 42.9 or ∠R = 116.0°, ∠P = 7.0°, p = 6.1
f) r = 14.4, ∠P = 32.0°, ∠Q = 115.0°

8. 6.6° **9.** 35.4 m **10. a)** 987 m **b)** 51°
11. 85.6 m **12.** 52.1° **13.** 4.2 km
14. a) 21.8 m **b)** 5.8 m **15.** 18.6 km

Chapter 8

Section 8-1, page 304

Estimates may vary.

1. a) i) 17:00 h **ii)** 20:00 h **iii)** 17:00 h
b) Approximate dates: **i)** May 20, July 23
ii) April 12, Aug. 30 **iii)** Mar. 13, Sept. 29
iv) Feb. 20, Oct. 24 **3.** 10 to 11 years

4. Typical answers: **a)** 173 m, 58 m **b)** 6 h

7. 5 s **9.** Sunsets: 1 year; sunspots; 10.5 years; volume and pressure of blood: 0.8 s; volume of air: 5 s **10.** 15 **11.** Sunspots

Exercises 8-2, page 310

1. a) 180°, π **b)** 450°, $\frac{5\pi}{2}$ **c)** $-90°$, $-\frac{\pi}{2}$
d) $-270°$, $-\frac{3\pi}{2}$ **3.** Typical answers:
a) 410°, −310° **b)** 480°, −240°
c) 525°, −195° **d)** 600°, −120°
e) $\frac{5\pi}{2}$, $-\frac{3\pi}{2}$ **f)** $\frac{9\pi}{4}$, $-\frac{7\pi}{4}$ **g)** $\frac{8\pi}{3}$, $-\frac{4\pi}{3}$
h) $\frac{7\pi}{2}$, $-\frac{\pi}{2}$ **4.** Typical answers:

a) $420°, -300°$ **b)** $150°, -570°$
c) $\frac{13\pi}{4}, -\frac{3\pi}{4}$ **d)** $\frac{3\pi}{2}, -\frac{5\pi}{2}$

5. Typical answers: **a)** $3\pi, -\pi$ **b)** $\frac{5\pi}{2}, -\frac{3\pi}{2}$
c) $\frac{5\pi}{3}, -\frac{7\pi}{3}$ **d)** $0, -4\pi$ **6. a)** 1
b) First **7. a)** 1; second **b)** 1; fourth
c) 2; second **d)** 2; fourth **9. a)** 1
b) First **10. a)** 0; between second and third
b) 0; between third and fourth
c) 1; between fourth and first
d) 1; between first and second

12. a) $45° + 360°n$ **b)** $150° + 360°n$
c) $240° + 360°n$ **d)** $-30° + 360°n$
e) $\pi + 2\pi n$ **f)** $-\frac{\pi}{4} + 2\pi n$
g) $\frac{5\pi}{2} + 2\pi n$ **h)** $1 + 2\pi n$

14. b) R; $\{y \mid 0 \leq y < 2\pi, y \in R\}$

Exercises 8-3, page 314

1. a) 0.8000, 0.6000, 1.3333
b) 0.8000, −0.6000, −1.3333
c) −0.7071, −0.7071, 1.000
d) −0.9231, 0.3846, −2.4000

2. a) 0.1961, −0.9806, −0.2000
b) −0.8944, −0.4472, −2.000
c) −0.3162, 0.9487, −0.3333
d) 0.8944, −0.4472, −2.000 **3. a)** 0.766
b) −0.819 **c)** −1.192 **d)** −0.342
e) −0.174 **f)** −0.574 **g)** −0.231
h) −0.995 **4. a)** 0.389 **b)** 0.825
c) 3.010 **d)** 0.974 **e)** −0.990 **f)** 1.587
g) −0.779 **h)** −0.781

5. b) −0.6, 0.8, −0.75

6. b) 0.894, −0.447, −2.000

7. a) $-\frac{5}{13}, \frac{12}{13}, -\frac{5}{12}$ **b)** $-\frac{1}{\sqrt{5}}, -\frac{2}{\sqrt{5}}, \frac{1}{2}$
c) $\frac{1}{\sqrt{10}}, -\frac{3}{\sqrt{10}}, -\frac{1}{3}$ **d)** $-\frac{4}{5}, -\frac{3}{5}, \frac{4}{3}$
e) $-\frac{1}{\sqrt{10}}, \frac{3}{\sqrt{10}}, -\frac{1}{3}$ **f)** $\frac{9}{\sqrt{85}}, \frac{2}{\sqrt{85}}, 4.5$
g) 1, 0, undefined **h)** 0, −1, 0

8. a) 0.819 15 **b)** Typical answers: 485°, 845°, −235°

9. a) −0.766 04
b) Typical answers: 580°, 940°, −140°

10. a) 0.95
b) Typical answers: 7.53, 13.82, −5.03

11. a) 80.71
b) Typical answers: 10.98, 17.27, −1.58

12. b) P(3,2) **c)** $\sin\theta = \frac{2}{\sqrt{13}}, \cos\theta = \frac{3}{\sqrt{13}}$

13. b) P(−2,5) **c)** $\sin\theta = \frac{5}{\sqrt{29}}, \cos\theta = -\frac{2}{\sqrt{29}}$

14. b) P(−1,2) **c)** $\cos\theta = -\frac{1}{\sqrt{5}}, \tan\theta = -2$

15. a) $\sin\theta = \frac{12}{13}, \tan\theta = -2.4$
b) $\cos\theta = -\frac{\sqrt{15}}{4}, \tan\theta = \frac{1}{\sqrt{15}}$
c) $\sin\theta = -\frac{3}{\sqrt{13}}, \cos\theta = -\frac{2}{\sqrt{13}}$
d) $\cos\theta = \frac{\sqrt{7}}{4}, \tan\theta = -\frac{3}{\sqrt{7}}$

16. a) Typical answers: 30°, 150°, 390°
b) An infinite number

Exercises 8-4, page 319

1. a) 20° **b)** 84° **c)** 26° **d)** 32° **e)** 65°
f) 64° **2. a)** 0.96 **b)** 0.72 **c)** 0.60
d) 1.46 **e)** 0.26 **f)** 1.26

3. a) 49°, 131° **b)** 84°, 276° **c)** 8°, 172°
d) 69°, 291° **e)** 42°, 138° **f)** 9°, 351°

4. a) 1.12, 5.17 **b)** 0.75, 2.39 **c)** 0.47, 5.81
d) 0.27, 2.87 **e)** 1.21, 4.35 **f)** 1.21, 5.07

5. a) 223°, 317° **b)** 101°, 259° **c)** 195°, 345°

6. a) 0.60, 5.68 **b)** 4.61, 1.68 **c)** 4.08, 5.35

8. 252° **9. a)** 256° **b)** 307° **c)** 304°
d) 117° **10. a)** 14°, 166° **b)** 132°, 228°
c) 52°, 308° **d)** 26°, 154°, 230°, 310°
e) 19°, 30°, 150°, 161° **f)** 71°, 289°

11. a) 1.74, 4.54 **b)** 0.34, 2.80 **c)** 1.29, 5.00
d) 3.53, 5.89 **e)** 0.73, 2.41 **f)** 0.72, 5.56

12. a) 24.3°, 65.7° **b)** 20.7° **c)** 9.7°, 80.3°
d) 37.8°, 60.0° **14. a)** 34°, 214°
b) 106°, 286° **c)** 27°, 45°, 207°, 225°
d) 57°, 139°, 237°, 319° **15. a)** 8.9°, 68.9°
b) 79.1° **c)** 29.5° **d)** 56.3°
e) 13.3°, 67.5° **f)** 31.7°, 35.8°

16. a) 1020° **b)** 1868°

Exercises 8-5, page 325

2. a) $\cos\theta = 1, 0.5, 0, -0.5, -1$
b) $\cos\theta = -0.5, 0, 0.5, 1$

5. a) $y = 1$ when $\theta = 90°$ and $-270°$
b) $y = -1$ when $\theta = 270°$ and $-90°$
c) $\{y \mid -1 \leq y \leq 1\}$ **d)** 0
e) 0, ±180°, ±360°

6. a) $y = 1$ when $\theta = 0°$ and ±360°
b) $y = -1$ when $\theta = \pm 180°$
c) $\{y \mid -1 \leq y \leq 1\}$ **d)** 1 **e)** ±90°, ±270°

9. a) $\tan\theta = 0, 0.6, 1, 1.7$, undefined
b) $\tan\theta = -1.7, -1, -0.6, 0$ **11. c)** Odd

Exercises 8-6, page 330

3. a) $y = \sin\theta + 0.5; 0.5; 1.5; -0.5; 0.5$
b) $y = \cos\theta - 1; -1; 0; -2; 0$
4. a) i) 6, 4, 5 **ii)** 6, 4, 6 **iii)** $-1, -3, -1$
b) i) R; $\{y \mid 4 \leqslant y \leqslant 6\}$ **ii)** R; $\{y \mid 4 \leqslant y \leqslant 6\}$
iii) R; $\{y \mid -3 \leqslant y \leqslant -1\}$
5. a) $y = \sin\theta + 1$ **b)** $y = \sin\theta - 1$
c) $y = \sin\theta + 1.5$ **d)** $y = \sin\theta - \sqrt{2}$
6. a) $y = \cos\theta - 1$ **b)** $y = \cos\theta + 2$
c) $y = \cos\theta - 2.5$ **d)** $y = \cos\theta + 2.5$
7. a) $y = q + 1$ when $\theta = -270°, 90°, \ldots$
b) $y = q - 1$ when $\theta = -90°, 270°, \ldots$
8. a) $y = q + 1$ when $\theta = 0°, \pm 360°, \ldots$
b) $y = q - 1$ when $\theta = \pm 180°, \ldots$
9. $y = \sin\theta + 1$ or $y = \sin\theta - 1$; 2

Exercises 8-7, page 337

3. Typical answers: **a)** $\frac{\pi}{3}, y = \sin\left(\theta - \frac{\pi}{3}\right)$;
$-\frac{5\pi}{3}, y = \sin\left(\theta + \frac{5\pi}{3}\right)$
b) $-\frac{\pi}{6}, y = \sin\left(\theta + \frac{\pi}{6}\right)$;
$\frac{11\pi}{6}, y = \sin\left(\theta - \frac{11\pi}{6}\right)$

4. Typical answers: **a)** $\frac{5\pi}{6}, y = \cos\left(\theta - \frac{5\pi}{6}\right)$;
$-\frac{7\pi}{6}, y = \cos\left(\theta + \frac{7\pi}{6}\right)$
b) $\frac{\pi}{3}, y = \cos\left(\theta - \frac{\pi}{3}\right)$;
$-\frac{5\pi}{3}, y = \cos\left(\theta + \frac{5\pi}{3}\right)$

6. a) R; $\{y \mid 2 \leqslant y \leqslant 4\}$ **b)** R; $\{y \mid 0 \leqslant y \leqslant 2\}$
c) R; $\{y \mid -2 \leqslant y \leqslant 0\}$ **d)** R; $\{y \mid 1 \leqslant y \leqslant 3\}$

8. Typical answers: **a)** $y = \sin\left(\theta - \frac{\pi}{6}\right)$
b) $y = \sin\left(\theta - \frac{5\pi}{6}\right)$ **c)** $y = \sin(\theta + \pi)$
d) $y = \sin\left(\theta + \frac{7\pi}{12}\right)$ **9.** Typical answers:

a) $y = \cos\left(\theta + \frac{3\pi}{4}\right)$ **b)** $y = \cos\left(\theta - \frac{\pi}{6}\right)$
c) $y = \cos\left(\theta - \frac{11\pi}{6}\right)$
d) $y = \cos\left(\theta + \frac{7\pi}{4}\right)$ **10.** Typical answer: $\frac{3\pi}{4}$

11. Typical answer: $\frac{2\pi}{3}$

12. a) $y = q + 1$ when $\theta = \frac{\pi}{2} + p; -\frac{3\pi}{2} + p; \ldots$
b) $y = q - 1$ when $\theta = \frac{3\pi}{2} + p; -\frac{\pi}{2} + p; \ldots$

13. a) $y = q + 1$ when $\theta = p; \pm 2\pi + p; \ldots$
b) $y = q - 1$ when $\theta = \pm\pi + p; \ldots$

14. Typical answer: $y = \sin\left(\theta + \frac{\pi}{2}\right) + 2$

15. Typical answer: $y = \cos(\theta + \pi) - 4$

Exercises 8-8, page 342

2. a) $y = 1.5\sin\theta$ **b)** $y = 2.5\sin\theta$
c) $y = 0.5\cos\theta$ **4. a)** $y = 2\sin\theta$
b) $y = 3\sin\theta$ **c)** $y = 2\sin\theta$
d) $y = 2\sin\theta$ **5. a)** $y = 3\cos\theta$
b) $y = \sqrt{2}\cos\theta$ **c)** $y = 2\cos\theta$
d) $y = 2\cos\theta$ **6. b) i)** $2, \frac{\pi}{3}$
ii) $3, -\frac{\pi}{4}$ **iii)** $2, \frac{\pi}{6}$ **iv)** $4, -\frac{2\pi}{3}$
c) i) R; $\{y \mid -2 \leqslant y \leqslant 2\}$
ii) R; $\{y \mid -3 \leqslant y \leqslant 3\}$
iii) R; $\{y \mid 0 \leqslant y \leqslant 4\}$
iv) R; $\{y \mid -6 \leqslant y \leqslant 2\}$
7. $y = \sin\left(\theta + \frac{\pi}{4}\right)$ **8.** $y = 4\cos\left(\theta + \frac{\pi}{6}\right)$

9. $y = 4\sin\left(\theta - \frac{\pi}{6}\right); y = 4\cos\theta$

11. a) 4 **b)** 0.2 **c)** 9

12. a) i) $y = a + q$ when $\theta = p + \frac{\pi}{2}; p - \frac{3\pi}{2}; \ldots$
ii) $y = -a + q$ when $\theta = p + \frac{3\pi}{2}; p - \frac{\pi}{2}; \ldots$
b) i) $y = a + q$ when $\theta = p; \pm 2\pi + p; \ldots$
ii) $y = -a + q$ when $\theta = \pm\pi + p; \ldots$

Exercises 8-9, page 348

2. a) $y = \sin 3\theta$ **b)** $y = \sin 6\theta$ **c)** $y = \cos \frac{1}{2}\theta$ **3. a)** 2; π **b)** 3; 4π **c)** 4; π **d)** 4; 4π **e)** 5; π **f)** 3; $\frac{2\pi}{3}$

4. a) 5; $\frac{2\pi}{3}$; π **b)** 2; $\frac{\pi}{2}$; $-\frac{\pi}{2}$ **c)** 2.5; $\frac{\pi}{3}$; $\frac{2\pi}{3}$ **d)** 0.5; $\frac{2\pi}{5}$; $-\frac{5\pi}{4}$ **5. a)** 1; π; $\frac{\pi}{3}$ **b)** 2; $\frac{2\pi}{3}$; $\frac{\pi}{2}$ **c)** 4; 4π; $-\pi$ **d)** 0.5; 4π; $\frac{5\pi}{4}$

6. a) $y = \sin 2\theta$ **b)** $y = \sin \theta$ **c)** $y = \sin 2\theta$ **d)** $y = \sin 2\theta$ **7. a)** $y = \cos \frac{1}{2}\theta$ **b)** $y = \cos 4\theta$ **c)** $y = \cos 1.5\theta$ **d)** $y = \cos 1.5\theta$ **8.** $\frac{\pi}{4}$ **9.** $\frac{\pi}{12}$

14. a) $\frac{2\pi}{3}$ **b)** 4π **c)** π

The Mathematical Mind, page 351

1. a) 6 **b)** 120 **c)** 5040 **d)** 40 320 **e)** 362 880 **f)** 3 628 800

2. $\sin x = x - \frac{x^3}{6} + \frac{x^5}{120} - \frac{x^7}{5040} + \frac{x^9}{362\,880} - \frac{x^{11}}{39\,916\,800}$;
$\cos x = 1 - \frac{x^2}{2} + \frac{x^4}{24} - \frac{x^6}{720} + \frac{x^8}{40\,320} - \frac{x^{10}}{3\,628\,800}$

4. a) 3 **b)** 4 **c)** 5

Exercises 8-10, page 355

1. a) i) 2 **ii)** 2π
iii) Typical answer: $\frac{\pi}{4}$ for cosine function
iv) $y = 5$ when $\theta = \frac{\pi}{4}, \frac{9\pi}{4}, \ldots$
v) $y = 1$ when $\theta = \frac{5\pi}{4}, \ldots$
vi) 3 **b) i)** 3 **ii)** π
iii) Typical answer: $\frac{\pi}{2}$ for sine function
iv) $y = 6$ when $\theta = -\frac{\pi}{4}, \frac{3\pi}{4}, \frac{7\pi}{4}, \ldots$
v) $y = 0$ when $\theta = \frac{\pi}{4}, \frac{5\pi}{4}, \ldots$
vi) 3 **c) i)** 5 **ii)** 2π
iii) Typical answer: $\frac{\pi}{6}$ for cosine function
iv) $y = 20$ when $\theta = \frac{\pi}{6}, \frac{13\pi}{6}, \ldots$
v) $y = 10$ when $\theta = \frac{7\pi}{6}, \frac{19\pi}{6}, \ldots$ **vi)** 15

2. Typical answers: **a)** $y = 2\cos\left(\theta - \frac{\pi}{4}\right) + 3$
b) $y = 3\sin 2\left(\theta - \frac{\pi}{2}\right) + 3$
c) $y = 5\cos\left(\theta - \frac{\pi}{6}\right) + 15$ **3. a)** 60°; 180° **b)** 4; 2 **4. a)** $\frac{\pi}{4}$; π **b)** 3; 3

5. a) $\frac{\pi}{2}$; $\frac{2\pi}{3}$ **b)** $-180°$; 90° **c)** $-\frac{\pi}{6}$; π **d)** 30°; 120° **8. a)** $\frac{\pi}{2}$; π **b)** $\frac{\pi}{3}$; $\frac{2\pi}{3}$ **c)** $\frac{\pi}{3}$; $\frac{2\pi}{3}$ **d)** $-\frac{\pi}{4}$; $\frac{\pi}{2}$

10. a and c **11.** a and b
12. a) Typical answers: 0, $\pm\pi$, $\pm 2\pi$, $\pm 3\pi$
b) $n\pi$ where n is an integer
13. a) Typical answers:
$-\frac{3\pi}{4}, -\frac{\pi}{4}, \frac{\pi}{4}, \frac{3\pi}{4}, \frac{5\pi}{4}, \frac{7\pi}{4}, \frac{9\pi}{4}$
b) $\frac{n\pi}{2} + \frac{\pi}{4}$ where n is an integer

15. a) 0; 1 **16. a)** 0; 1 **b)** 0; 4 **c)** 0; 4

Exercises 8-11, page 362

1. a) 3; 5; 1; 4 **b)** 2; 4; 5; 6
2. a) 2; 12; typical answer: 2; 3
b) 6; 4; typical answer: 0; 8
c) 10; 40; typical answer: -5; 20
3. a) $y = 2\sin\frac{2\pi(t-2)}{12} + 3$
b) $y = 6\cos\frac{2\pi t}{4} + 8$
c) $y = 10\cos\frac{2\pi(t+5)}{40} + 20$
4. a) $y = \sin \pi t$ **b)** $y = \cos \pi t$ **c)** $y = \cos\frac{\pi t}{2}$ **d)** $y = \sin\frac{\pi t}{2}$
5. a) $y = 5\cos 2\pi(t-9) + 4$
b) $y = 12\cos 4\pi(t+3) + 1.5$
c) $y = 2.4\cos\frac{2\pi(t-19)}{27} + 15.1$

8. a) $y = 5$ when $t = -5, -2, 1, 4$;
$y = 1$ when $t = -3.5, -0.5, 2.5$
b) $y = 0$ when $t = -0.75, 4.25$;
$y = -8$ when $t = -3.25, 1.75$
c) $y = 8$ when $t = -4.25, -1.25, 1.75, 4.75$;
$y = 4$ when $t = -2.75, 0.25, 3.25$
d) $y = 7$ when $t = -3, 3$; $y = -3$ when $t = 0$

9. a) $y = 6 \sin \frac{2\pi(t - 9)}{5} + 17$

b) $y = 4.3 \sin \frac{2\pi(t - 4.7)}{3.9} + 12.9$

10. Typical answer: $y = 2000 \sin \frac{\pi t}{5} + 3000$

11. b) Typical answer: $y = 80 \sin \frac{\pi t}{5}$

12. a) i) 40 cm **ii)** 0 cm **iii)** 0.05 s

b) 72 000 **13. a)** $y = 0.5 \sin \frac{\pi t}{50}$;

$y = 0.5 \sin \frac{\pi t}{25}$; $y = 0.5 \sin \frac{3\pi t}{50}$;

$y = 0.5 \sin \frac{2\pi t}{25}$ **14.** b and c

Exercises 8-12, page 369

1. a) About 4.0 m; 1.7 m
b) 4.9 m at 7:06 A.M. and 7:30 P.M.
2. About 2.3 m

3. a) $y = 4 \cos \frac{2\pi(t - 8.00)}{12.4}$ **b)** About 2.1 m

4. a) $y = 4.6 \cos \frac{2\pi(t - 4.50)}{12.4} + 5$

b) 1.2 m, 7.7 m

5. a) $y = 1.4 \cos \frac{2\pi(t - 4.50)}{12.4} + 5$

b) 3.9 m, 5.8 m

6. b) Typical answer:

$y = 0.4 \cos \frac{2\pi(t - 0.6)}{1.2} + 0.5$ or

$y = 0.4 \sin \frac{2\pi(t - 0.3)}{1.2} + 0.5$ **c) i)** 0.50 m

ii) About 0.85 m **iii)** 0.10 m

7. b) Typical answer: $h = 25 \cos \frac{2\pi(t - 25)}{50} + 26$

c) i) 18 m **ii)** 46 m **iii)** 18 m **iv)** 18 m

8. b) Typical answer: $y = 16.5 \cos \frac{2\pi t}{5} + 29$

c) i) 45.5 cm **ii)** 15.7 cm **iii)** 15.7 cm

9. a) Typical answer:

$t = 2.5 \cos \frac{2\pi(n - 172)}{365} + 17.7$

b) i) 7:34 P.M. **ii)** 8:10 P.M. **iii)** 5:50 P.M.
iv) 3:20 P.M.

10. a) Typical answer: $t = 2 \cos \frac{2\pi(n - 172)}{365} + 18.3$

b) i) 5:19 P.M. **ii)** 7:05 P.M. **iii)** 7:58 P.M.
iv) 4:53 P.M. **11. a)** 5:28 A.M.

12. a) Typical answer:

$d = 2.5 \cos \frac{2\pi(n - 172)}{365} + 149.7$

b) i) 148.8 million km **ii)** 151.3 million km
iii) 150.5 million km

15. b) Feb. 16 and Oct. 23 **16. a)** 6:56 A.M.
b) 9:02 A.M.

Review Exercises, page 372

1. Typical answers: **a)** 425°, −295°
b) 495°, −225° **c)** 560°, −160°

d) 270°, −90° **e)** $\frac{7\pi}{3}, -\frac{5\pi}{3}$ **f)** $\frac{13\pi}{4}, -\frac{3\pi}{4}$

g) $\frac{11\pi}{6}, -\frac{13\pi}{6}$ **h)** $\frac{2\pi}{3}, -\frac{4\pi}{3}$

2. a) 0.906, 0.423, 2.145
b) 0.707, −0.707, −1.000
c) −0.342, −0.940, 0.364
d) −1.000, 0, undefined
e) 0.866, 0.500, 1.732
f) −0.707, −0.707, 1.000
g) −0.500, 0.866, −0.577
h) 0.866, −0.500, −1.732

3. a) 0.914, 0.406, 2.250
b) −0.882, 0.471, −1.875
c) 0.868, −0.496, −1.75
d) −0.640, −0.768, 0.833

4. a) 66.0°, 1.153 **b)** 298.1°, 5.202
c) 119.7°, 2.090 **d)** 219.8°, 3.836

5. a) 47°, 133° **b)** 113°, 293° **c)** 101°, 281°

6. a) 1.30, 4.98 **b)** 0.82, 3.96 **c)** 5.80, 3.63

7. a) 222°, 318° **b)** 74°, 254°
c) 14°, 42°, 138°, 166° **d)** 67°, 93°
e) 48°, 132°, 228°, 312° **f)** 193°, 347°

8. a) $\sin \theta$: 1 at −270°, 90°; $\cos \theta$: 1 at 0°, ± 360°
b) $\sin \theta$: −1 at −90°, 270°; $\cos \theta$: −1 at ± 180°
c) $\sin \theta$: y-intercept 0, θ-intercepts ± 360°, ± 180°, 0°;
$\cos \theta$: y-intercept 1, θ-intercepts ± 270°, ± 90°

9. a) 3; π; 45°; −4 **b)** 2; $\frac{2\pi}{5}$; $-\frac{\pi}{3}$; 1

c) 4; $\frac{2\pi}{3}$; $-\frac{\pi}{6}$; −5

12. a) $h = 16\cos\dfrac{2\pi(t - 24)}{48} + 17$
 b) 12.9 m, 32.9 m

Chapter 9

Exercises 9-1, page 377

1. a) Square root b) Quadratic c) Cubic d) Semicircle e) Linear f) Absolute value
2. a) Quadratic b) Square root c) Linear d) Quadratic e) Cubic
3. b) i), ii), iii) R; $\{y \mid y \geq 0\}$
4. a), b) $y = \sqrt{2}x$, linear
 c), d) $y = (\sqrt{2} - 1)x$
5. a) $h = \dfrac{2}{3}s$ b) $x = \dfrac{\sqrt{13}}{3}s$ 6. $x = \dfrac{2}{\sqrt{3}}s$
7. a) i) Increases by a factor 8
 ii) Increases by a factor 27
 iii) Increases by a factor 64 b) ii
8. a) i) Sirius is about 772% of the sun
 ii) Antares is about 13% of the sun b) ii
9. a) 2 b) 3 c) 4 d) $\dfrac{1}{2}$ e) -1 f) 1
11. $r = \dfrac{(\sqrt{2} - 1)R}{\sqrt{2} + 1}$

The Mathematical Mind, page 381

1. Shortest route is: Goderich—Clinton—Mitchell—Listowel—Wingham—Harriston—Walkerton—Kincardine—Amberley—Goderich (286 km); Items packed: {360 g, 350 g, 290 g}, {280 g, 260 g, 250 g, 210 g}, {290 g, 230 g, 210 g, 140 g, 130 g}
2. Typical answer: 3 pieces cut into 145 cm, 88 cm, 59 cm; 2 pieces cut into 59 cm, 74 cm, 74 cm, 44 cm, 44 cm; 1 piece cut into 59 cm, 74 cm, 74 cm, 88 cm
3. a) 100; 2500; 10 000; 90 000; 1024; 1.126×10^{15}; 1.268×10^{30}; 2.037×10^{90}
 b) 1000; 125 000; 1 000 000; 27 000 000; 57.7; 637 621 500; 4.066×10^{17}, 6.720×10^{52}
 c) 10^{10}; 9.766×10^{16}; 10^{20}; 5.905×10^{24}; 2.594; 117.4; 13 781; 2.617×10^{12}

Exercises 9-2, page 383

2. a) ii b) iii c) i 3. a) i) $y = x^2 - 2$ ii) $y = x^2$ iii) $y = x^2 + 1$
 b) i) $y = \sqrt{x} + 2$ ii) $y = \sqrt{x}$ iii) $y = \sqrt{x} - 1$ c) i) $y = |x| + 2$ ii) $y = |x|$ iii) $y = |x| - 3$ 5. a) ii
 b) iii c) v 8. b) $y = \dfrac{5x^2}{x^2 + 1} + 2$; $y = \dfrac{5x^2}{x^2 + 1} - 2$

Exercises 9-3, page 388

3. a) ii b) iii c) i 4. a) iii b) ii c) i 5. a) $y = (x - 3)^2$ b) $y = (x + 2)^2$
 c) $y = (x - 5)^2$ d) $y = |x + 1|$
 e) $y = |x - 4|$ f) $y = |x + 3|$
6. b) i) $y = (x - 5)^2$ ii) $y = x^2 - 2$
 iii) $y = (x - 5)^2 - 2$ 7. b) i) $y = (x + 3)^3$
 ii) $y = x^3 + 2$ iii) $y = (x + 3)^3 + 2$
8. a) i b) iv c) vi
13. a) $V = 0.0003(d - 10)^2$
14. b) $y = \dfrac{5\sqrt{x - 3}}{(x - 3)^2 + 1}$; $y = \dfrac{5\sqrt{x + 5}}{(x + 5)^2 + 1}$
16. b) i) $(x - 3)^2 + y^2 = 25$
 ii) $x^2 + (y - 2)^2 = 25$
 iii) $(x + 2)^2 + (y + 4)^2 = 25$
 iv) $(x - 1)^2 + (y - 5)^2 = 25$
17. a) $y^2 - x - 2 = 0$ b) $(y + 3)^2 - x = 0$
 c) $(y - 4)^2 - x + 3 = 0$
 d) $(y + 2)^2 - x - 4 = 0$

Exercises 9-4, page 393

2. a) ii b) i c) iii
4. b) $\{l \mid l \geq 0\}$; $\{T \mid T \geq 0\}$
5. b) i) $y = 2x^2$ ii) $y = x^2 - 3$
 iii) $y = (x + 4)^2$ iv) $y = 2(x + 4)^2 - 3$
6. b) i) $y = \dfrac{1}{3}\sqrt{16 - x^2}$
 ii) $y = \sqrt{16 - (x - 4)^2}$
 iii) $y = \sqrt{16 - x^2} + 1$
 iv) $y = \dfrac{1}{3}\sqrt{16 - (x - 4)^2} + 1$
7. a) ii b) vi c) i d) iv e) iii f) v
13. b) i) $\{h \mid 0 \leq h \leq 500\}$; $\{v \mid 0 \leq v \leq 11.2\}$
 ii) $\{h \mid 0 \leq h \leq 350\}$; $\{v \mid 0 \leq v \leq 11.2\}$
 iii) $\{h \mid 0 \leq h \leq 200\}$; $\{v \mid 0 \leq v \leq 9.9\}$
14. b) $y = \dfrac{10}{x^2 + 1}$; $y = \dfrac{2.5}{x^2 + 1}$; $y = \dfrac{-5}{x^2 + 1}$; $y = \dfrac{-10}{x^2 + 1}$; $y = \dfrac{-2.5}{x^2 + 1}$

15. b) An expansion of factor 2 in the y-direction followed by a translation of 6 units down
c) A translation of 3 units to the right followed by an expansion of factor 2 in the y-direction
16. b) An expansion of factor 2 in the y-direction followed by a translation of 10 units down
c) A translation of 5 units to the right followed by an expansion of factor 2 in the y-direction

Exercises 9-5, page 399

1. a) $y = |2x - 4|$ **b)** $y = \left|\frac{1}{2}x - 4\right|$

8. b) i) $y = (2x)^2$ **ii)** $y = (2x)^2$

9. b) $y = \frac{10x}{4x^2 + 1}$; $y = \frac{2.5x}{0.25x^2 + 1}$;
$y = \frac{-5x}{x^2 + 1}$; $y = \frac{-10x}{4x^2 + 1}$; $y = \frac{-2.5x}{0.25x^2 + 1}$

10. b) A horizontal compression by a factor $\frac{1}{2}$; a vertical expansion by a factor 2

Mathematics Around Us, page 405

3. a) i) Growth of corn plant **ii)** Wind speed **iii)** Survival rate

Exercises 9-7, page 409

1. a) $y = \frac{1}{3x - 7}$ **b)** $y = \frac{1}{5x^2 - 2x + 7}$
c) $y = \frac{1}{(x - 2)^3 - 1}$ **d)** $y = \frac{1}{\sqrt{x + 1}}$
e) $y = \frac{1}{|3(x + 1)|}$ **f)** $y = \frac{1}{\sqrt{16 - (x + 2)^2}}$
5. a) $\{x \mid x \neq -3\}$; $\{y \mid y \neq 0\}$
b) $\{x \mid x \neq -6\}$; $\{y \mid y \neq 0\}$
c) $\{x \mid x \neq 3\}$; $\{y \mid y \neq 0\}$
d) $\{x \mid x \neq \pm 5\}$; $\{y \mid y \neq 0\}$
e) $\{x \mid x \neq \pm\sqrt{10}\}$; $\{y \mid y \neq 0\}$
f) $\{x \mid x \neq 5\}$; $\{y \mid y \neq 0\}$
6. a) ± 1 **b)** $\pm\sqrt{10}, \pm\sqrt{8}$
c) $\pm\sqrt{17}, \pm\sqrt{15}$ **d)** No solution **e)** 3, 1
f) $-4, -2$ **7. a)** $\{x \mid x \neq 0\}$; $\{y \mid y > 0\}$
b) R; $\{y \mid 0 < y \leq 1\}$
c) $\{x \mid x \neq \pm 1\}$; $\{y \mid y > 0 \text{ or } y \leq -1\}$
d) $\{x \mid x > 0\}$; $\{y \mid y > 0\}$
e) $\{x \mid x \geq 0\}$; $\{y \mid 0 < y \leq 1\}$
f) $\{x \mid x \neq 1, x > 0\}$; $\{y \mid y > 0 \text{ or } y \leq -1\}$
g) $\{x \mid x \neq 0\}$; $\{y \mid y > 0\}$
h) R; $\{y \mid 0 < y \leq 1\}$
i) $\{x \mid x \neq \pm 1\}$; $\{y \mid y > 0 \text{ or } y \leq -1\}$

Exercises 9-8, page 415

2. a) 1.064 **b)** -1.031 **c)** -11.474
d) 28.654 **e)** -1.540 **f)** 57.290
g) 14.301 **h)** -11.430 **3. a)** 1.016
b) -12.767 **c)** -1.800 **d)** 1.120
e) -0.747 **f)** 12.599 **g)** -30.123
h) 1.258 **7. a)** $2\pi; \frac{\pi}{3}$ **b)** $2\pi; -\pi$
c) 3; 1 **d)** 6; -3 **e)** $\pi; \frac{\pi}{4}$ **f)** $\pi; -\frac{\pi}{2}$
g) 1; 3 **h)** 1; -2 **8. a)** $a = \csc\theta$
9. a) $d = \cot(23.5 + l)$ **10.** $d = 3\tan\pi t$
11. $y = 100\cot\frac{\pi(t - 6)}{12}$

Exercises 9-9, page 420

5. b) $\frac{\sin\theta + \tan\theta}{\csc\theta + \cot\theta} = \sin\theta\tan\theta$
6. b) $\frac{\cot\theta}{\csc\theta + 1} = \frac{\csc\theta - 1}{\cot\theta}$
7. b) $\frac{1}{1 + \cos\theta} + \frac{1}{1 - \cos\theta} = 2\csc^2\theta$
8. b) $\cot^2\theta(1 + \tan^2\theta) = \csc^2\theta$
15. a) $r\sqrt{2 - 2\cos\theta}$; $r\sqrt{2 + 2\cos\theta}$
16. $0, \pi, 2\pi$

Review Exercises, page 423

1. a) Square root **b)** Quadratic **c)** Absolute value **d)** Cubic **2. a)** $\frac{244\pi}{3}$ cm³
b) $\frac{1792\pi}{3}$ cm³ **c)** 1248π cm³
3. b) 3.0 m **c)** $h = -4.9t^2 + 8.8t$
4. a) $y = x^2 - 4$ **b)** $y = x^3 - 8$

Cumulative Review, Chapters 7-9, page 424

1. a) -0.602 **b)** 0.466 **c)** 3.628
d) -1.046 **e)** -1.012 **f)** -0.785
g) 0.966 **h)** 1.414
2. a) 69°, 249° **b)** 216°, 324° **c)** 61°, 299°
d) 129°, 309° **e)** 227°, 313° **f)** 97°, 263°
3. i) a) $\cos\theta = -\frac{24}{25}$; $\tan\theta = -\frac{7}{24}$;
$\csc\theta = \frac{25}{7}$; $\sec\theta = -\frac{25}{24}$; $\cot\theta = -\frac{24}{7}$
b) 2.86 **c)** -3.43, 9.14
ii) a) $\sin\theta = \frac{5}{\sqrt{89}}$; $\cos\theta = -\frac{8}{\sqrt{89}}$;

$\csc\theta = \frac{\sqrt{89}}{5}$; $\sec\theta = -\frac{\sqrt{89}}{8}$; $\cot\theta = -\frac{8}{5}$
b) 2.58 **c)** 8.87, −3.70
iii) a) $\sin\theta = \frac{\sqrt{65}}{9}$; $\cos\theta = -\frac{4}{9}$;
$\tan\theta = -\frac{\sqrt{65}}{4}$; $\csc\theta = \frac{9}{\sqrt{65}}$;
$\cot\theta = -\frac{4}{\sqrt{65}}$ **b)** 2.03 **c)** 8.31, −4.25

4. a) $q = 13.6$; $\angle R = 54°$; $\angle P = 36°$
b) $\angle R = 62°$; $r = 48.9$; $q = 55.4$
5. a) $y = 9.9$; $\angle Z = 42°$; $\angle X = 28°$
b) $\angle Y = 70°$; $\angle Z = 52°$; $z = 3.4$
6. 5.1 m **7. a)** 51°, 231°
b) 42°, 138°, 210°, 330°
c) 0°, 127°, 233°, 360°
8. a) 2, 120°, 30°, 0 **b)** 1, 3, 2, 2
c) 3, π, $-\frac{\pi}{4}$, −1 **d)** 2, 12, 1, 3
9. a) i) 7.2 m **ii)** 4.3 m
b) i) 6:48 A.M., 7:12 P.M.

Chapter 10

Exercises 10-1, page 429

1. a) About 9 years **b)** About 14 years
3. About 45 years **5.** About 6 bounces
7. About 27 m **9.** $P = 80(2)^{\frac{n}{20}}$
10. $P = 300(2)^{\frac{d}{5}}$ **11.** $C = 100(0.5)^n$
12. $P = 100(0.25)^n$ **13. a)** $m = 28(1.4)^n$
b) 413 g **14.** About 4.3 m
15. $P = 100(0.95)^n$ **16.** $F = \left(\frac{2}{3}\right)^{\frac{n}{6}}$
17. a) $B = 1000(0.55)^n$ **b)** 5 years

Exercises 10-2, page 435

1. a) 1 **b)** $\frac{1}{5}$ **c)** $\frac{8}{125}$ **d)** $\frac{1}{8}$ **e)** $\frac{1}{16}$
f) 1 **g)** 4 **h)** $\frac{16}{81}$ **i)** $\frac{1}{64}$ **j)** $\frac{9}{25}$
k) 81 **l)** $\frac{64}{27}$ **2. a)** 3 **b)** $\frac{1}{9}$ **c)** 2.5
d) 5 **e)** 5 **f)** $\frac{1}{2}$ **g)** $\frac{1}{1000}$ **h)** 2 **i)** $\frac{7}{5}$
j) $\frac{1}{9}$ **k)** 0.5 **l)** 2 **3. a)** $\frac{1}{216}$ **b)** 9
c) 4 **d)** $\frac{1}{32}$ **e)** $\frac{1}{243}$ **f)** $\frac{27}{8}$ **g)** $\frac{125}{27}$
h) $\frac{1}{1000}$ **i)** $\frac{4}{25}$ **j)** $\frac{125}{27}$ **k)** 32 **l)** $\frac{1}{27}$
4. a) 32 **b)** $\frac{1}{125}$ **c)** $\frac{1}{243}$ **d)** 8000 **e)** 8
f) 8 **g)** 1 **h)** $\frac{32}{3125}$ **i)** 2 **j)** $\frac{16}{81}$
k) $\frac{8}{27}$ **l)** 1 **5. a)** 3.278 **b)** 16.442
c) 5.481 **d)** 8.000 **e)** 121.268 **f)** 3.386
g) 4.419 **h)** 1.740 **i)** 243.000 **j)** 4.274
k) 14.261 **l)** 13.704 **6. a)** 0.48
b) 0.17 **c)** 68.47 **d)** 10.60 **e)** 0.15
f) 0.70 **g)** 536.36 **h)** 0.20 **i)** 2.83
j) 0.07 **k)** 2.76 **l)** 0.59 **7. a)** 5
b) 7 **c)** $\frac{17}{72}$ **d)** 0 **e)** 11 **f)** $\frac{1}{2}$
8. a) 256 **b)** $\frac{33}{16}$ **c)** 2.7 **d)** $\frac{145}{5184}$ **e)** $\frac{17}{32}$
f) $\frac{17}{9}$ **9. a) i)** 8000 **ii)** 22 627
iii) 2828 **b) i)** 1000 **ii)** 1414 **iii)** 630
10. For iodine − 131 **b) i)** $P = 100(0.5)^n$
ii) $P = 100(0.5)^{\frac{t}{8.1}}$ **c) i)** 55% **ii)** 7.7%
iii) 2.7×10^{-12}% For cesium − 144
b) i) $P = 100(0.5)^n$ **ii)** $P = 100(0.5)^{\frac{t}{282}}$
c) i) 98% **ii)** 93% **iii)** 41%
11. a) 99.7% **b)** 97.2% **c)** 74.9% **d)** 5.6%
12. a) 8.8 g **b)** 15 g **c)** 4.1 g **d)** 2.0 g
13. a) $P = 24.3(1.0185)^t$ **b)** 20.2 million
14. a) $N = 100(10)^{\frac{t}{7}}$ **b)** 3.7×10^8
15. a) 31.544 **b)** 36.462 **c)** 25.955
d) 1.823 **e)** 0.013 **f)** 0.064 **g)** 3.416
h) 3.040 **16. a) i)** 4 **ii)** 0.25 **iii)** 0.25
iv) 4 **v)** 2 **vi)** 0.5 **vii)** 0.5 **viii)** 2

Investigate, page 437

1. a) −1.245 730 9 **c)** −1.044 924 3
e) 1.551 845 6 **g)** 1.192 173 3
h) 3.442 754 9

Exercises 10-3, page 440

1. a) m^{-6} **b)** x^5 **c)** $-45a^7$ **d)** $-14s^{15}$
e) $-9m^5$ **f)** $\frac{64n}{5}$ **2. a)** x^{-1} **b)** $s^{-\frac{1}{4}}$
c) $-3m^{-2}$ **d)** $-3a^{\frac{3}{5}}$ **e)** $n^{\frac{49}{60}}$ **f)** $-4x^{\frac{3}{4}}$
3. a) $-7a^9b^{-8}$ **b)** $20m^{-7}n^3$ **c)** $9x^9y^{-12}$
d) $12a^3b^{-4}c^{-4}$ **e)** $10n^4$ **f)** $\frac{15x^{-4}z^5}{2}$

4. a) $-4b^{\frac{1}{3}}$ **b)** $\frac{5mn^{-1}}{2}$ **c)** $x^{\frac{4}{5}}y^{\frac{3}{5}}$ **d)** $a^{-\frac{9}{2}}b^{\frac{11}{4}}$
e) $m^{-\frac{5}{6}}n^{\frac{8}{9}}$ **f)** $a^{-1}b^2$ **5. a)** $-3m^{\frac{1}{3}}n^{-\frac{1}{2}}$
b) $-42a^{\frac{1}{6}}b^{\frac{1}{6}}$ **c)** $-2x^{-\frac{5}{4}}$ **d)** $2a^{-1}b^{\frac{3}{10}}c^{-\frac{7}{15}}$
e) $-\frac{2a^{\frac{1}{4}}c^{-3}}{21}$ **f)** $-\frac{40x^{-\frac{7}{4}}z^{\frac{7}{4}}}{9}$ **6. a)** 16
b) 32 **c)** $\frac{1}{1024}$ **d)** $\frac{1}{4096}$ **7. a)** $-\frac{16}{9}$
b) $\frac{59\ 049}{4096}$ **c)** 1.5 **d)** 2187 **8. a)** $a^{\frac{9}{2}}$
b) $4a^{-4}$ **c)** $216a^{39}$ **9. a)** $6x^9$ **b)** $\frac{4x^{-12}}{27}$
c) $\frac{9x^3}{4}$ **10. a)** 1 **b)** s^{8n} **c)** a
d) $m^{bc-ac-ab}$ **e)** x^{-2a+2} **f)** $\frac{a^{x-4y}}{9}$
11. a) $x^{-\frac{a}{6}}$ **b)** $m^{-\frac{5n}{6}}n^{-\frac{3m}{4}}$ **c)** $a^{-\frac{10x}{3}}$ **d)** $c^{-\frac{13x}{3}}$
e) $x^{\frac{c}{3}}y^{-\frac{3c}{8}}$ **f)** $h^{\frac{7a}{24}}$ **12. a)** $5^{\frac{4}{3}}$ **b)** 2^{2x+1}
c) 2^{2x+2}

Mathematics Around Us, page 442

1. a) 10 000 **b)** 10 000 000 **3. a)** 316
b) 10 000 **c)** 31 623 **4. a)** 8 **b)** 7943
5. a) Trumpet, clarinet
b) Bassoon, 3; flute; 5; trumpet, clarinet, 6
6. 316 **7. a)** 100 **b)** 2.5
8. a) $t = 8(0.5)^{\frac{d-90}{5}}$ **b) i)** 2 h **ii)** 2 min, 28s

The Mathematical Mind, page 444

1. b) $x = r\sqrt[3]{2}$ **c)** $y = r\sqrt[3]{4}$

Exercises 10-4, page 446

1. \$3814.48 **2.** 2620 **3.** 11 300 **4.** 690
5. About 1.9% **6.** About 12.9%
7. In 1988, about \$3 × 10^{13} **8.** 3960
9. Between 10 and 11 years
10. Between 6 and 7 years **11.** 48 min
12. Between 9 and 10 years
14. a) $T = 80(0.5)^{\frac{t}{5}} + 20$ **b)** 15 min
15. a) $c = 100(0.5)^{\frac{t}{5}}$
b) i) 16.6 h **ii)** 33.2 h
16. a) $P = 100(0.65)^d$; $P = 100(0.95)^d$;
$P = 100(0.975)^d$ **b)** 1.6 m; 13.5 m; 27.4 m
c) 10.7 m; 89.8 m; 181.9 m

Mathematics Around Us, page 448

1. About 78.6% **2.** 15 600 years
3. a) About 1900 years **b)** About 3100 years
c) About 4000 years **d)** About 11 900 years
e) About 31 700 years

Exercises 10-5, page 451

1. a) i) $P_4 = P_0(5)$ **ii)** $P_6 = P_0(5)^{1.5}$
b) About 2.2 **2.** About 1.9 **3.** About 2.6
4. 5 **5. a)** About 4 **b)** About 3
c) About 13 **6. a) i)** 31 **ii)** 961
b) $\frac{E_2}{E_1} = 31^{M_2-M_1}$ **c)** About 117 660
7. a) 3.1×10^{15} J **b)** 9.6×10^{16} J
c) 3.8×10^{17} J **8. a)** 6 or 7 times as frequent
b) 36 to 49 times as frequent **c)** 216 to 343 times as frequent **9. a)** $\frac{P_2}{P_1} = (0.95)^{\frac{h_2-h_1}{300}}$
b) About 15.7% **10. a)** $\frac{N_2}{N_1} = 4^{\frac{t_2-t_1}{3}}$
b) i) 10 times as many **ii)** 102 times as many
iii) 1024 times as many **11. a)** $\frac{A_2}{A_1} = (0.5)^{\frac{t_2-t_1}{18}}$
b) i) $\frac{1}{4}$ the area **ii)** 5.4 times the area
iii) 11.8 times the area

Exercises 10-6, page 456

1. a) iv **b)** iii **c)** i **d)** ii
3. a)

x	-2	-1	0	1	2
3^x	0.11	0.33	1	3	9
$\left(\frac{1}{3}\right)^x$	9	3	1	0.33	0.11

5. a) 6 **b)** 2 **c)** 8 **d)** 4 **e)** $\frac{1}{8}$ **f)** 6
g) 7 **h)** 27
9. a) $a \in R$, $x = 0$ or $a = 1$, $x \in R$
b) $a > 1$, $x > 0$ or $0 < a < 1$, $x < 0$
c) $0 < a < 1$, $x > 0$ or $a > 1$, $x < 0$

Review Exercises, page 458

1. a) $A = 1000(1.095)^n$ **b)** \$1723.79
2. $P = 100(0.96)^x$
3. a) $\frac{1}{4}$ **b)** 3 **c)** 8 **d)** 25 **e)** 3.375
f) 3.375 **g)** 1 **h)** 0.000 32
4. a) 5.08 **b)** 43.89 **c)** 0.01 **d)** 1.80
5. a) i) 4000 **ii)** 45 255 **b) i)** 125 **ii)** 44
6. a) $5x^3y^{-2}$ **b)** $\frac{m^2n}{2}$ **c)** $\frac{25a^{-4}b^{-7}}{8}$ **d)** $\frac{9y^{-\frac{4}{3}}}{25}$
e) $-\frac{3a^{-\frac{1}{4}}b^{-\frac{1}{3}}}{5}$ **f)** $\frac{3m^{-\frac{5}{2}}n^{-\frac{1}{6}}}{2}$

7. a) $1.5a^{\frac{5}{2}}$ **b)** $\frac{a^{10}}{12}$

8. a) 1 **b)** $\frac{2m^{6x - 4y}}{3}$ **c)** $a^x b^{\frac{x}{2}}$

9. \$2351.18 **10.** About 20.7%

11. About 12.25 years

Chapter 11

Exercises 11-1, page 462

1. a) 2 **b)** 3 **c)** 6 **d)** 1 **e)** -1 **f)** -3 **g)** 0 **h)** $\frac{1}{3}$ **i)** 5 **j)** $\frac{1}{5}$ **k)** $\frac{2}{3}$ **l)** n **2. a)** $10^{0.6990}$ **b)** $10^{1.2553}$ **c)** $10^{1.7952}$ **d)** $10^{3.6882}$ **e)** $10^{-0.6021}$ **f)** $10^{-0.0969}$ **g)** $10^{-1.6990}$ **h)** $10^{-2.2218}$ **3. a)** 5 **b)** 15 **c)** 1 **d)** 9 **e)** 30 **4. a)** 12 **b)** -7 **c)** -12 **5. a)** $10\ 000 = 10^4$ **b)** $10 = 10^1$ **c)** $0.01 = 10^{-2}$ **6. a)** $\log 1000 = 3$ **b)** $\log 1 = 0$ **c)** $\log 0.001 = -3$ **7.** 600

8. a) 100 **b)** 100 000 **c)** 0.001 **d)** 1 **e)** 10 **f)** 10^{10} **9. a) i)** 4 **ii)** 5 **iii)** -3 **iv)** 0.5 **v)** 2.4 **vi)** -1.5 **b)** $\log 10^n = n$ **10. a) i)** 100 **ii)** 1000 **iii)** 0.01 **iv)** 20 **v)** 500 **vi)** 0.2 **b)** $10^{\log x} = x$ **11. a) i)** 0.301 03 **ii)** 1.301 03 **iii)** 2.301 03 **iv)** 3.301 03 **v)** $-0.698\ 97$ **vi)** $-1.698\ 97$ **vii)** $-2.698\ 97$ **viii)** $-3.698\ 97$

Investigate, page 463

a)

n	Approx. based on		Actual Value
2	0.3	2^{10}	0.301
3	0.476	3^{21}	0.477
4	0.6	4^5	0.602
5	0.7	5^{10}	0.699
6	0.778	6^9	0.778
7	0.846	7^{13}	0.845
8	0.9	8^{10}	0.903
9	0.952	9^{21}	0.954

b) log 6 **c), d)** The values increase by a factor of 2.

Exercises 11-2, page 466

1. a) log 42 **b)** log 4 **c)** log 24 **d)** log 7 **e)** log 84 **f)** log 14 **g)** log 32 **h)** log 0.5 **i)** log 136

2. Answers may vary. Typical answers:
a) log 2 + log 5 **b)** log 3 + log 7 **c)** log 4 + log 7 **d)** log 3 + log 12 **e)** log 3 + log 3 **f)** log 4 + log 11 **g)** log 3 + log 19 **h)** log 11 + log 11

3. Answers may vary. Typical answers:
a) log 10 − log 2 **b)** log 16 − log 2 **c)** log 24 − log 2 **d)** log 26 − log 2 **e)** log 20 − log 2 **f)** log 42 − log 2 **g)** log 34 − log 2 **h)** log 80 − log 2

4. a) log 30 **b)** log 84 **c)** log 10 **d)** log 90 **e)** log 21 **f)** log 28 **5. a)** 1.477 12 **b)** 3.477 12 **c)** $-0.522\ 88$ **d)** $-2.522\ 88$

6. a) 0.8451 **b)** 2.8451 **c)** -1.1549 **d)** -0.1549 **e)** 5.8451 **f)** -2.1549

7. a) $\log\left(\frac{2}{3}\right) + \log a - \log b$

b) $\log 3.5 + \log a - \log b$
c) $\log 2.5 + \log b - \log a$
d) $\log 2.4 + \log a - \log b$

8. a) $\log\left(\frac{xy}{z}\right)$ **b)** $\log\left(\frac{m}{np}\right)$ **c)** $\log\left(\frac{ab}{cd}\right)$

d) $\log\left(\frac{a^2 + ab}{a - b}\right)$ **e)** $\log(m^2 + 10m + 21)$

f) $\log\left(\frac{6x^2 + xy - 2y^2}{x + y}\right)$

9. a) $\log\left(\frac{x + 3}{x - 1}\right), x \neq 1$

b) $\log\left(\frac{2x - 7}{x + 3}\right), x \neq -3$

c) $\log\left(\frac{a + 2}{a - 2}\right), a \neq 2$

d) $\log\left(\frac{8a + 15}{2a + 3}\right), a \neq -1.5$

10. a) $x + y$ **b)** $y - x$ **c)** $1 + x + y$ **d)** $2x + y$ **e)** $x + 2y$ **f)** $2x + 2y$ **g)** $2x + 2y - 1$ **h)** $-x - y$ **12. a)** 4 **b)** Infinite number **14. a)** $x > 2$ **b)** $x > 0$ **c)** $x > 5$ **15. a)** 3 **b)** 6 **c)** 101

16. a) $y = \frac{x + 2}{3x}$; $\{x \mid x > 0, x \in R\}$

b) $y = 100 + \frac{100}{x}$; $\{x \mid x > 0, x \in R\}$

c) $y = 10^x$; R

Investigate, page 467

2. 0.301 03; 0.602 06; 0.903 09; 1.204 12; 1.505 15; 1.806 18; 2.107 21; 2.408 24; 2^{34}

Mathematics Around Us, page 468

1. a) It's the logarithm of the distance in metres.
b) The number increases by 3, the distance is 10^3 times as great. **2. a)** 3 **b)** 39 **3. a)** 5
b) km and cm **4.** 2 cm **5.** 1 week
7. 4.8 **8. a)** 6 **b)** 8 **c)** 12
9. 1.3×10^{26} m **10.** 2.0×10^{26} m **11.** 99.9%

Exercises 11-3, page 475

1. a) 2 log 3 **b)** 2 log 5 **c)** 3 log 2
d) 3 log 3 **e)** 3 log 10 **f)** 5 log 2
g) 3 log 7 **h)** 7 log 2 **2. a)** log 36
b) log 64 **c)** log 81 **d)** log 49
e) log 243 **f)** log 16 **g)** log 216
h) log 100 000 **3. a)** 0.954 24
b) 1.908 48 **c)** 0.238 56 **d)** 0.095 42
4. a) 2.795 88 **b)** 0.232 99 **c)** −0.698 97
d) −1.397 94 **5. a)** $3^{1.7712437}$ **b)** $2^{2.3219281}$
c) $2^{4.8579809}$ **d)** $8^{2.0889288}$ **e)** $0.5^{-1.5849625}$
f) $6^{-0.4456556}$ **6. a)** 3.459 **b)** 2.579
c) 0.898 **d)** 2.365 **e)** −0.415
f) −0.398 **7. a)** 0.630 929 8
b) 1.160 964 **c)** −0.564 575
d) −0.464 973 5 **e)** −1.547 952 1
f) 0.769 124 **8. a)** $\frac{1}{2}\log x$ **b)** $\frac{1}{2} + \log x$
c) $\frac{1}{2} + \frac{1}{2}\log x$ **d)** $1 + \log x$ **e)** $1 + \frac{1}{2}\log x$
9. a) $\log (a^2b^5)$ **b)** $\log (x^3y^{\frac{1}{2}})$ **c)** $\log \left(\frac{m^2n}{p^5}\right)$
d) $\log \left(\frac{x^{\frac{1}{2}}}{y^2z}\right)$ **e)** $\log \left(\frac{a^3b^{\frac{1}{2}}}{c^{\frac{5}{4}}}\right)$ **f)** $\log \left(\frac{a^{10}c^{\frac{1}{2}}}{b^3d}\right)$
10. a) 93 years **b)** 186 years
11. Iodine − 131: **a)** 27 days
b) 80.7 days Cesium − 144: **a)** 937 days
b) 2810 days **12. a)** $L = 2.00(1.2)^n$ **b)** 18
13. a) $\frac{5}{6}$ **b)** $t = 0.120\left(\frac{5}{6}\right)^n$ **c)** 26 **d)** 229 m
14. a) $\log y = 1 + \log x$ **b)** $\log y = -\log x$
c) $\log y = 2\log x$ **d)** $\log y = \frac{1}{2}\log x$
e) $\log y = 1 + \frac{1}{2}\log x$
f) $\log y = \frac{1}{2} + \frac{1}{2}\log x$ **15. a)** 1 **b)** 302
c) 6 **16. a)** 3376 **b)** 6533 **c)** 39 751
d) 65 050 **17. a)** $3.056\ 912 \times 10^{79}$ **b)** 80
18. 369 693 100 **19. a)** $N = 1000(2)^{\frac{n}{2}}$ **b)** 1991
20. a) i) 95% **ii)** 61% **b)** $P = 100(0.995)^{\frac{n}{10}}$
c) 574 pages **21.** 19 **24. a) i)** 32
ii) −32 **iii)** 2 **iv)** −2
25. a) −0.736 806 4 **b)** 0.580 729 2
c) 4.818 841 7 **d)** 0.757 650 8
26. a) About 14 years **b)** 1.7% less
27. a) 2018 **b) i)** 2065 **ii)** 2050
iii) 2142 will be the year when demand exceeds supply **28. a)** 218 **b)** 2083 **c)** 20 734

Mathematics Around Us, page 479

1. 35 **2.** 41 **3.** 3

Exercises 11-4, page 484

1. a) $x \doteq 3.3\log\left(\frac{y}{5}\right)$ **b)** $x = \log\left(\frac{y}{1.3}\right)$
c) $x \doteq 78\log\left(\frac{y}{8.2}\right)$ **d)** $x \doteq -3.3\log\left(\frac{y}{6.4}\right)$
e) $x \doteq 2.3\log\left(\frac{y}{3.5}\right)$ **f)** $x \doteq -5.7\log\left(\frac{y}{2.75}\right)$
2. a) 2; 4; 10 **b)** 3; 2.159; 3.814
c) −2; 1.113; 1.723 **d)** 0; 2.059; 2.521
3. a) $n \doteq 30\log\left(\frac{A}{500}\right)$
b) i) 11.9 years; \$500 will amount to \$1250 in nearly 12 years
ii) −4.6 years; \$350 invested about 4.6 years ago will amount to \$500 now
d) $\{A \mid A > 0, A \in \mathrm{R}\}$; R
4. a) $n \doteq -6.5\log\left(\frac{h}{2}\right)$
b) i) 3; after 3 bounces, the height is about 0.7 m
ii) 8; after 8 bounces, the height is about 0.12 m
d) N **5. a)** $P = 6800(1.018)^n$
b) $n \doteq 129\log\left(\frac{P}{6800}\right)$ **c) i)** 17 **ii)** −12
d) They are inverses of each other.
6. a) 3:20 P.M. **b)** 5:04 P.M. **c)** 8:57 A.M.
7. 20 **8. a)** 10 **c) i)** 50 **ii)** 501 **9.** 8
12. a) $b = b_0(10)^{-\frac{m}{2.5}}$
b) Decreases by a factor of 10 **c) i)** 6 **ii)** 4
iii) 24 **13. a)** 436 516 **b)** 9.12×10^8
c) 6310
14. a) Decreased by 5.75 **b)** Decreased by 7.5
15. a) Sirius: 23; Vega: 54; North Star: 5875; Deneb: 63 715

Exercises 11-5, page 489

1. a) $y = \log x$ **b)** $y = \log_3 x$ **c)** $y = \log_7$. **d)** $y = \log_{0.4} x$ **e)** $y = \log_{\frac{3}{2}} x$ **f)** $y = \log_{15} x$ **2. a)** $y = 10^x$ **b)** $y = 2^x$ **c)** $y = 6^x$ **d)** $y = \left(\frac{1}{2}\right)^x$ **e)** $y = \left(\frac{5}{4}\right)^x$ **f)** $y = 21^x$ **3. a)** $y = \log_5 x$ **b)** $y = \log_{\frac{3}{4}} x$ **c)** $y = \log_{\frac{4}{5}} x$ **d)** $y = \log_4 x$
4. c) $y = \log_3 x$ **5. c)** $y = \log_{\frac{1}{2}} x$
8. (0.548, 0.548) **9. a)** $0 < a < 1$

Investigate, page 490

1. a) 1.261 859 5 **b)** 1.630 929 8 **c)** 3.357 762 8 **d)** 4.929 947 0

Exercises 11-6, page 493

1. a) $8 = 2^3$ **b)** $32 = 2^5$ **c)** $\frac{1}{4} = 2^{-2}$ **d)** $625 = 5^4$ **e)** $9 = 3^2$ **f)** $3 = 9^{\frac{1}{2}}$
2. a) 4 **b)** 2 **c)** 3 **d)** 2 **e)** -1 **f)** 1 **g)** 0 **h)** 4 **3. a)** $\frac{1}{2}$ **b)** 4 **c)** 2 **d)** 4 **e)** -3 **f)** -2 **g)** 1.5 **h)** 6
4. a) 8; 6; 2; 1; -4, -8 **b)** 4; 3; 1; 0.5; -2, -4
5. a) 5 **b)** 13 **c)** 9 **d)** 7 **e)** 5 **f)** 11
6. a) $\log_6 36 = 2$ **b)** $\log_4 \left(\frac{1}{16}\right) = -2$ **c)** $\log_3 243 = 5$ **d)** $\log_7 343 = 3$ **e)** $\log_8 2 = \frac{1}{3}$ **f)** $\log_2 1 = 0$
7. a) $\log_5 0.04 = -2$ **b)** $\log_4 \left(\frac{1}{2}\right) = -\frac{1}{2}$ **c)** $\log_{\frac{1}{2}} \left(\frac{1}{4}\right) = 2$ **d)** $\log_{\frac{2}{3}} \frac{3}{2} = -1$ **e)** $\log_{\frac{1}{9}} \left(\frac{1}{81}\right) = 2$ **f)** $\log_x z = y$
8. a) $400 = 20^2$ **b)** $\frac{1}{49} = 7^{-2}$ **c)** $4 = 8^{\frac{2}{3}}$ **d)** $36^2 = 6^4$ **e)** $8 = (0.5)^{-3}$ **f)** $s = r^t$
9. a) 1.465 **b)** 0.712 **c)** 5.644 **d)** 1.544 **e)** 2.377 **f)** 0.750 **10. a)** 1.955 **b)** 1.386 **c)** 1.585 **d)** 1.380 **e)** 7.359 **f)** 2.242 **11. a)** $3x + 2y$ **b)** $6x + 2y$
12. a) $2a + 3b$ **b)** $4a + 3b$ **c)** $4a + 12b$ **d)** $6a + 6b$ **13. a)** 512 **b)** 0 **c)** 4 **d)** $\frac{1}{5}$ **e)** $\frac{1}{81}$ **f)** 10 **14. a)** $2^x - 2$ **b)** $\frac{2^x}{x}$ **15. a)** 14 **b)** 132 878 **16. a) i)** 3; $\frac{1}{3}$ **ii)** 2; $\frac{1}{2}$ **b)** $\log_a b = \frac{1}{\log_b a}$ **17. a) i)** 2 **ii)** -2 **iii)** $\frac{1}{2}$ **iv)** $-\frac{1}{2}$ **v)** -2 **vi)** 2 **vii)** $-\frac{1}{2}$ **viii)** $\frac{1}{2}$

Investigate, page 494

2.718 281 8

Exercises 11-7, page 499

1. a) 2 **b)** 1 **c)** 3 **d)** 3 **e)** 3 **f)** 4
2. Answers may vary. Typical answers: **a)** $\log_3 10 + \log_3 2$ **b)** $\log_7 5 + \log_7 9$ **c)** $\log_5 10 + \log_5 9$ **d)** $\log_{12} 2 + \log_{12} 3$ **e)** $\log_8 5 + \log_8 15$ **f)** $\log_{20} 3 + \log_{20} 13$
3. Answers may vary. Typical answers: **a)** $\log_4 22 - \log_4 2$ **b)** $\log_3 24 - \log_3 2$ **c)** $\log_9 10 - \log_9 2$ **d)** $\log_6 14 - \log_6 2$ **e)** $\log_{11} 42 - \log_{11} 2$ **f)** $\log_2 26 - \log_2 2$
4. a) 2 **b)** 3 **c)** 2 **d)** 5 **e)** 3 **f)** 3
5. a) i) 7 **ii)** 7 **iii)** 6 **b) i)** 3 **ii)** 2 **iii)** 1
6. a) $3 \log_3 2$ **b)** $2 \log_5 6$ **c)** $3 \log_2 3$ **d)** $5 \log_6 2$ **e)** $4 \log_{12} 3$ **f)** $3 \log_4 5$
7. a) $\log_2 125$ **b)** $\log_7 16$ **c)** $\log_3 262\ 144$ **d)** $\log_{12} 1024$ **e)** $\log_2 14\ 348\ 907$ **f)** $\log_5 81$
8. a) 4 **b)** $\frac{5}{3}$ **c)** 1.5 **d)** 2.5
9. a) 1 **b)** -1.5 **c)** 1.5 **d)** 1.75
10. a) 5 **b)** 3 **c)** 2 **d)** 1 **11. a)** 4.3219 **b)** 4.6438 **c)** 1.3219 **d)** 1.1610
12. a) 6.2877 **b)** 3.0959 **c)** $-0.547\ 95$ **d)** 2.1918 **13. a)** $y = x^2$; $\{x \mid x > 0, x \in R\}$ **b)** $y = (x + 1)^2(x - 1)$; $\{x \mid x > 1, x \in R\}$ **c)** $y = 3(x + 3)^2 + 3$; $\{x \mid x > -3, x \in R\}$
14. a) i) 11.550 747 **ii)** 8.228 819 **iii)** 4.906 891 **iv)** 1.584 963 **v)** $-1.736\ 966$ **vi)** $-5.058\ 894$ **vii)** $-8.380\ 822$ **viii)** $-11.702\ 750$
17. a) $3x$ **b)** $1 + 3x$ **c)** $0.5x$ **d)** $1 + 1.5x$
18. a) $2 + x$ **b)** $2 + 2x$ **c)** $1 + 1.5x$ **d)** $\frac{1}{3}x - 1$ **19. a)** 6 **b)** 4 **c)** 10 **d)** 12 **20. a)** 7 **b)** 11 **c)** 0 **d)** 4
21. a) 8 **b)** 9 **c)** 2 **d)** 6 **e)** 2 **f)** 5
22. a) 100 **b)** 18 **c)** 3 **d)** 4 **e)** 3 **f)** 2 **23. a)** 10.079 **b)** 114.036
26. $\log_a x = \frac{1}{\log_x a}$ **27. b)** $\frac{1}{\log_a x} + \frac{1}{\log_b x} = \frac{1}{\log_{ab} x}$

The Mathematical Mind, page 503

1. a) $e^{0.6931471} \doteq 2$ **b)** $e^{1.3862944} \doteq 4$ **c)** $e^{3.4011974} \doteq 30$ **d)** $e^{4.6051702} \doteq 100$ **e)** $e^{9.0768090} \doteq 8750$ **f)** $e^{-0.6931472} \doteq 0.5$ **g)** $e^{-2.3025851} \doteq 0.1$ **h)** $e^{-7.7287358} \doteq 0.000\ 44$
2. a) 1.609 437 9 **b)** 2.708 050 2 **c)** 3.987 130 5 **d)** 5.583 496 3 **e)** 0 **f)** −1.386 294 4 **g)** −2.385 966 7 **h)** −8.111 728 1 **3. a)** 2.718 281 8 **b)** 4.953 032 4 **c)** 20.085 537 **d)** 90.017 131 **e)** 1.390 968 1 **f)** 0.367 879 4 **g)** 0.246 597 0 **h)** 0.110 803 2 **4. a)** ln 15 **b)** ln 20 **c)** ln 36 **d)** ln 9 **e)** ln 7 **f)** ln 5 **5. a) i)** 1 **ii)** 2 **iii)** −3 **iv)** 0.2 **b)** $\ln e^n = n$ **6. a)** 4 **b)** 22 **c)** 145 **d)** 72 382 **e)** 48 254 942
7. a) 4 **b)** 9 **c)** 42 **d)** 10 478 **e)** 4 657 079 **8. a)** 3.912 023

Mathematics Around Us, page 506

1. a) 57 million; 0.7% **b)** 20 million; 3.0% **c)** 2.6 million; 3.8% **2. a)** $P = 770e^{0.016t}$ **b) i)** 903.6 million **ii)** 2001 **iii)** 1958
3. a) 99.8% **b)** 4.53×10^9 years
4. a) 17 600 m; 25 500 m **b)** 5.9 kPa **c)** $h \doteq -6452 \ln\left(\frac{P}{130}\right)$

Review Exercises, page 507

1. a) 5 **b)** −3 **c)** $\frac{1}{3}$ **d)** 3
2. a) 0.7782 **b)** 0.8692 **c)** 1.2788 **d)** 1.4330
3. a) $1000 = 10^3$ **b)** $\sqrt{10} = 10^{\frac{1}{2}}$ **c)** $81 = 3^4$
4. a) $\log 10\ 000 = 4$ **b)** $\log 0.001 = -3$ **c)** $\log_5 625 = 4$
5. a) 100 **b)** 0.000 01 **c)** 8 **d)** 27 **e)** −2 **f)** 32 **6. a)** 5 **b)** 3.1 **c)** −1.5 **d)** 7 **e)** 2
7. a) 7 **b)** 2.8 **c)** 0.09 **d)** 2 **e)** 11
8. a) log 5.6 **b)** $\log_5\left(\frac{142}{57}\right)$ **c)** $\log\left(\frac{pr}{q}\right)$ **d)** $\log\left(2a^2 + 7a - 15\right)$ **e)** $\log_4\left(\frac{m^2n^5}{p^3}\right)$ **f)** $\log_a\left(\frac{x^{\frac{2}{3}}}{y^{\frac{1}{4}}z}\right)$
9. a) $m + n$ **b)** $m - n$ **c)** $2m - n$ **d)** $m - 2n$ **10. a)** 0.4226 **b)** 2.5353 **c)** 0.2817 **d)** −1.6902
11. a) $3^{1.8927893}$ **b)** $6^{1.7737056}$ **c)** $1.3^{9.4712085}$ **d)** $2^{-0.358454}$
12. a) 1.3652 **b)** 0.7879 **c)** 1.9650 **d)** 2.2541 **e)** 2.2876 **f)** 0.8072 **g)** −0.5204 **h)** 3.5547
13. a) $\log m = 2 + \log n$ **b)** $\log m = 3 \log n$ **c)** $\log m = \frac{1}{2} + \frac{1}{2}\log n$ **d)** $\log m = -\frac{1}{2}\log n$
14. a) $x = \frac{\log y}{\log 2}$ **b)** $x = \frac{\log y - \log 3}{\log 5}$ **c)** $x = \frac{\log y - \log 2.7}{\log 8}$
15. a) 4 **b)** 4 **c)** 5 **d)** −3 **e)** −3 **f)** 10 **g)** −3 **h)** 3
16. a) 2.807 **b)** 0.837 **c)** 2.355 **d)** 0.311 **e)** 2.322 **f)** 5.872 **g)** 5.626 **h)** 1.703
17. a) 0.008 **b)** 0 **c)** 0.25
18. a) 3 **b)** 2.5 **c)** $\frac{5}{3}$ **d)** −2
19. a) 2.2619 **b)** 3.7857 **c)** 1.5238 **d)** 0.6310
20. a) 4 **b)** 4 **c)** 3 **d)** 3
22. a) 76 days **b)** 116 days
23. a) 64.7% **b)** 536 days
24. Nearly 8 years **25.** 4 times **26.** 26

Chapter 12

Exercises 12-1, page 514

1. a, c, e, f **2. a)** Circle **b), e)** Ellipse **c), f)** Hyperbola **d)** Parabola
4. a) Hyperbola **b)** Hyperbola, parabola or ellipse **c)** Hyperbola

Exercises 12-2, page 516

1. a), d) Yes **b), c)** No **4. a)** $y = 2x^2$ **b)** $y = \frac{3}{8}x^2$ **c)** $y = \frac{5}{8}x^2$ **d)** $y = -\frac{1}{8}x^2$ **e)** $y = \frac{5}{8}x^2$ **f)** $y = 0.12x^2$ **g)** $y = \frac{5}{36}x^2$ **h)** $y = -\frac{3}{49}x^2$ **5. a) i)** $y = \frac{1}{8}x^2$ **ii)** $y = \frac{1}{5}x^2$ **iii)** $y = -\frac{1}{3}x^2$ **iv)** $y = -\frac{1}{7}x^2$
6. a) $y = \frac{1}{2160}x^2$ **b)** 42 cm **7.** $y = -\frac{1}{64}x^2$
8. Typical answers: **a)** $y = -\frac{15.3}{1225}x^2$ **b)** 14 m

9. a) (4,4) **b)** (3,25) **10.** $y = 2(x - 3)^2 - 2$
11. a) $A = -x^2 + 25x$

Exercises 12-3, page 521

1. a), c) Yes **b), d)** No **2. a)** 8; (0,0)
b) $2\sqrt{3}$; (0,0) **c)** 9; (3, −4)
d) $\sqrt{5}$; (−2,1) **e)** $\sqrt{15}$; (−4,0)
f) $4\sqrt{3}$; (0,6) **3. a)** $x^2 + y^2 = 9$
b) $x^2 + y^2 = 49$
c) $(x - 5)^2 + (y - 3)^2 = 16$
d) $(x + 2)^2 + (y - 6)^2 = 25$
e) $(x - 4)^2 + y^2 = 36$
f) $x^2 + (y + 3)^2 = 81$ **g)** $x^2 + y^2 = 5$
h) $(x - 3)^2 + (y + 5)^2 = 10$
5. a) 3 units right **b)** 2 units down
c) 3 units right and 2 units down
6. a) 4 units up **b)** 1 unit left
c) 1 unit left and 4 units up
7. a) $x^2 + y^2 = 36$ **b)** $\pm 2\sqrt{5}$
8. a) $3 + 2\sqrt{6}$; $3 - 2\sqrt{6}$
b) $2 + 2\sqrt{6}$; $2 - 2\sqrt{6}$ **9. a)** (5, −2); 3
b) (3,1); 5 **c)** $\sqrt{51}$; (−4,6)
d) $\sqrt{4.5}$; (−0.5, −0.5) **10.** Yes

Exercises 12-4, page 526

1. a), b), d) Yes **c)** No **2.** Centre (0, 0)
a) (±4,0); 8; 6 **b)** (±6,0); 12; 10
c) (0, ±3); 6; 4 **d)** (0, ±7); 14; 8
e) (±8,0); 16; 8 **f)** (0, ±5); 10, 6
3. a) $\frac{x^2}{25} + \frac{y^2}{9} = 1$ **b)** $\frac{x^2}{64} + \frac{y^2}{36} = 1$
c) $\frac{x^2}{16} + y^2 = 1$ **d)** $\frac{x^2}{49} + \frac{y^2}{9} = 1$
e) $\frac{x^2}{25} + \frac{y^2}{9} = 1$ **f)** $\frac{x^2}{36} + \frac{y^2}{4} = 1$
4. a) i) $\frac{x^2}{9} + \frac{y^2}{4} = 1$ **ii)** 6; 4; (±3,0)
b) i) $\frac{x^2}{16} + \frac{y^2}{4} = 1$ **ii)** 8; 4; (±4,0)
c) i) $\frac{x^2}{9} + \frac{y^2}{16} = 1$ **ii)** 8; 6; (0, ±4)
d) i) $\frac{x^2}{16} + \frac{y^2}{25} = 1$ **ii)** 10; 8; (0, ±5)
e) i) $\frac{x^2 + y^2}{9} = 1$ **ii)** 6; 2; (0, ±3)
f) i) $\frac{x^2}{3} + \frac{y^2}{2} = 1$ **ii)** $2\sqrt{3}$; $2\sqrt{2}$; $(\pm\sqrt{3},0)$
5. Expansion by:
a) factor 4 horizontally and factor 6 vertically
b) factor 7 horizontally and factor 5 vertically
c) factor 3 horizontally and factor $\sqrt{6}$ vertically
d) factor $2\sqrt{3}$ horizontally and factor 2 vertically
e) factor $\sqrt{5}$ horizontally and factor $2\sqrt{5}$ vertically
f) factor $2\sqrt{3}$ horizontally and factor 3 vertically
6. a) $x^2 + 4y^2 = 100$ **b)** ±8 **c)** $\pm\frac{5\sqrt{3}}{2}$
7. a) $625x^2 + 900y^2 = 562\,500$ **b)** 19 m
8. 5.4 m
10. a) $C < 0 < A < B$ or $B < A < 0 < C$
b) $C < 0 < B < A$ or $A < B < 0 < C$

Investigate, page 528

3. b) $A_1A_2 = PF_1 + PF_2$

Investigate, page 529

1. $5x^2 + 9y^2 = 45$
2. $(a^2 - c^2)x^2 + a^2y^2 = a^2(a^2 - c^2)$

Mathematics Around Us, page 531

2. a) $xy = 48$; $y = 6, 4, 3, 2$
b) $xy = 60$; $y = 5, 4, 3, 2$ **3. a)** $xy = 36$
b) i) 3 **ii)** 18 **4. a) i)** 4 h **ii)** 2.4 h
b) 24 km/h **5.** 5 days **6.** $nr = 72$
7. a) $lw = 360$ **b)** $P = \frac{720 + 2l^2}{l}$ **c) i)** Yes
ii) No **8. a)** $Id^2 = 160$

Exercises 12-5, page 535

1. a), c) Yes **b), d)** No
2. Centre (0,0); asymptotes $y = \pm x$ **a)** (±5,0)
b) (±8,0) **c)** (0, ±9) **d)** $(\pm\sqrt{2},0)$
e) $(0, \pm\sqrt{5})$ **f)** $(0, \pm 2\sqrt{5})$
3. a) $x^2 - y^2 = 49$ **b)** $x^2 - y^2 = -16$
c) $x^2 - y^2 = -36$ **d)** $x^2 - y^2 = 100$
5. a) $x^2 - y^2 = -144$ **6. a)** $x^2 - y^2 = 60$
b) ±16 **7. a)** $x^2 - y^2 = -15$ **b)** ±4
8. a) $x^2 - y^2 = -5625$ **b)** 44 m
9. a) $B < 0$, $A = |B|$, $C < 0$ or
$A < 0$, $B = |A|$, $C > 0$
b) $B < 0$, $A = |B|$, $C > 0$ or
$A < 0$, $B = |A|$, $C < 0$

Exercises 12-6, page 540

1. a), c) Yes **b, d)** No **2.** Centre (0,0)
a) (±2,0); 4; 16 **b)** (±5,0); 10; 6
c) (±9,0); 18; 14 **3. a)** $\frac{x^2}{36} - \frac{y^2}{9} = 1$
b) $\frac{x^2}{9} - \frac{y^2}{4} = 1$ **c)** $\frac{x^2}{16} - \frac{y^2}{49} = 1$
d) $\frac{x^2}{25} - \frac{y^2}{49} = 1$ **e)** $\frac{x^2}{4} - \frac{y^2}{16} = 1$

f) $\frac{x^2}{49} - \frac{y^2}{49} = 1$ **4. a) i)** $\frac{x^2}{4} - \frac{y^2}{9} = 1$

ii) 4; 6; $(\pm 2,0)$; $y = \pm\frac{3}{2}x$ **b) i)** $\frac{x^2}{36} - \frac{y^2}{4} = 1$

ii) 12; 4; $(\pm 6,0)$; $y = \pm\frac{1}{3}x$ **c) i)** $\frac{x^2}{9} - \frac{y^2}{25} = 1$

ii) 6; 10; $(\pm 3,0)$; $y = \pm\frac{5}{3}x$ **d) i)** $\frac{x^2}{4} - \frac{y^2}{16} = 1$

ii) 4; 8; $(\pm 2,0)$; $y = \pm 2x$ **e) i)** $\frac{x^2}{12} - \frac{y^2}{4} = 1$

ii) $4\sqrt{3}$; 4; $(\pm 2\sqrt{3},0)$; $y = \pm\frac{1}{\sqrt{3}}x$

f) i) $\frac{x^2}{5} - \frac{y^2}{4} = 1$ **ii)** $2\sqrt{5}$; 4; $(\pm\sqrt{5},0)$;

$y = \pm\frac{2}{\sqrt{5}}x$

5. Expansion by:
- **a)** factor 6 horizontally and factor 4 vertically
- **b)** factor 9 horizontally and factor 5 vertically
- **c)** factor 7 horizontally and factor 8 vertically
- **d)** factor $\sqrt{6}$ horizontally and factor $3\sqrt{2}$ vertically
- **e)** factor $2\sqrt{2}$ horizontally and factor $\sqrt{2}$ vertically
- **f)** factor $2\sqrt{2}$ horizontally and factor $\sqrt{10}$ vertically

8. $A > 0, B < 0, C < 0$ or $A < 0, B > 0, C > 0$

Exercises 12-7, page 543

1. a), b), d) Yes **c)** No **2.** Centre (0,0)
a) $(0,\pm 3)$; 6; 8 **b)** $(0,\pm 5)$; 10; 4

c) $(0,\pm 6)$; 12; 16 **3. a)** $\frac{x^2}{16} - \frac{y^2}{9} = -1$

b) $\frac{x^2}{4} - \frac{y^2}{49} = -1$ **c)** $\frac{x^2}{81} - \frac{y^2}{9} = -1$

d) $\frac{x^2}{36} - \frac{y^2}{25} = -1$ **e)** $\frac{4x^2}{9} - \frac{y^2}{9} = -1$

4. a) i) $\frac{x^2}{9} - \frac{y^2}{4} = -1$ **ii)** 4; 6; $(0,\pm 2)$;

$y = \pm\frac{2}{3}x$ **b) i)** $\frac{x^2}{16} - \frac{y^2}{4} = -1$

ii) 4; 8; $(0,\pm 2)$; $y = \pm\frac{1}{2}x$

c) i) $\frac{x^2}{25} - \frac{y^2}{16} = -1$

ii) 8; 10; $(0,\pm 4)$; $y = \pm\frac{4}{5}x$

d) i) $\frac{x^2}{25} - \frac{y^2}{100} = -1$

ii) 20; 10; $(0,\pm 10)$; $y = \pm 2x$

e) i) $\frac{x^2}{50} - \frac{y^2}{25} = -1$ **ii)** 10; $10\sqrt{2}$; $(0,\pm 5)$;

$y = \pm\frac{1}{\sqrt{2}}x$ **f) i)** $\frac{x^2}{8} - \frac{y^2}{6} = -1$

ii) $2\sqrt{6}$; $4\sqrt{2}$; $(0,\pm\sqrt{6})$; $y = \pm\frac{\sqrt{3}}{2}x$

5. Expansion by:
- **a)** factor 7 horizontally and factor 5 vertically
- **b)** factor 4 horizontally and factor 9 vertically
- **c)** factor 3 horizontally and factor 7 vertically
- **d)** factor 3 horizontally and factor $3\sqrt{3}$ vertically
- **e)** factor 6 horizontally and factor $\sqrt{6}$ vertically
- **f)** factor $\sqrt{6}$ horizontally and factor $2\sqrt{2}$ vertically

7. $A > 0, B < 0, C > 0$ or $A < 0, B > 0, C < 0$

8. a) Typical answer: $\frac{x^2}{4} - \frac{y^2}{9} = 1$; $\frac{x^2}{4} - \frac{y^2}{9} = -1$
b) Change the sign of the constant term.

Investigate, page 544

3. b) $A_1A_2 = |PF_1 - PF_2|$

Investigate, page 545

1. $\frac{x^2}{4} - \frac{y^2}{32} = 1$
2. $(c^2 - a^2)x^2 - a^2y^2 = a^2(c^2 - a^2)$

Mathematics Around Us, page 547

3. $(\pm\sqrt{a^2 - b^2}, 0)$

Mathematics Around Us, page 548

3. $(\pm\sqrt{a^2 + b^2},0)$

Review Exercises, page 549

1. a) Ellipse **b)** Parabola **c),e)** Circle
d) Rectangular hyperbola **f)** Hyperbola
2. a) No; parabola **b)** Yes; circle
c) No; hyperbola **d)** No; ellipse

3. a) $y = \frac{1}{8}x^2$ **b)** $y = -1.5x^2$

4. a) $(x - 5)^2 + (y + 2)^2 = 4$
b) $x^2 + (y - 3)^2 = 18$
5. Yes **6. a)** $(\pm 5,0)$; 10; 4 **b)** $(\pm 3,0)$; 6; 8
c) $(0,\pm 3)$; 6; 4
7. a) (0,0); 2.5 **b)** $(2,-3)$; 5

8. a) $\frac{x^2}{100} + \frac{y^2}{12} = 1$ **b)** $\frac{x^2}{25} + \frac{y^2}{9} = 1$

9. a) $\frac{x^2}{49} - \frac{y^2}{144} = -1$ **b)** $\frac{9x^2}{25} - \frac{y^2}{25} = -1$

11. $y = -\frac{1}{64}x^2$ **12.** $\frac{x^2}{900} + \frac{y^2}{625} = 1$
13. $x^2 - y^2 = -380.25$ **14.** 2.3 m

Cumulative Review, page 550

1. a) \$1265.32 **b)** \$8726.06 **c)** \$10 551.71
2. a) 27 **b)** 4 **c)** $\frac{1}{25}$ **d)** 1 **e)** 0.125
f) 0.5625 **g)** 2.5 **h)** 2.4
3. a) $4x^{-2}y^6$ **b)** $\frac{9m^{-13}n^{-2}}{2}$ **c)** $-\frac{3a^{5x-7y}}{2}$
d) $12x^{6a}y^{-a-4b}$
4. a) 220.400 **b)** 0.013 **c)** 26.952
d) 1.833 **e)** 2.667 **f)** −4.000 **g)** 3.443
h) −0.8252
5. a) 0.01 **b)** 9 **c)** 128 **d)** 2.261 859 5
e) −0.254 412 **f)** 8.186 427 8
6. a) log 6 **b)** $\log\left(\frac{2x^2 + 7x - 15}{x + 4}\right)$
7. a) $x - y$ **b)** $x - 2y$ **c)** $1 + x + y$
d) $3y - x$
8. a) 2.0828 **b)** 0.5207 **c)** 2.0414
d) −1.0414
9. a) 3 **b)** 3 **11. a) i)** 72 000
ii) 1 451 429 **b) i)** 1125 **ii)** 446
12. Nearly 3 years **13.** 17 m
15. a) $(5,-3)$; 2 **b)** $(-2,4)$; 6 **c)** $(-5,1)$; 3
16. a) $(\pm 10,0)$; 20; 14 **b)** $(0,\pm 5)$; 10; 16
c) $(\pm 5,0)$; 10; 12
17. $y = -\frac{1}{6}x^2$ **18.** $\frac{x^2}{16} + \frac{y^2}{49} = 1$
19. $\frac{x^2}{20} - \frac{y^2}{25} = 1$; $y = \pm\frac{\sqrt{5}}{2}x$
20. a) $\frac{x^2}{900} + \frac{y^2}{324} = 1$ **b)** About 28 m

Index